P9-CMY-409

Scott Foresman - Addison Wesley
MIDDLE SCHOOL MATH
Course 1

Randall I. Charles John A. Dossey Steven J. Leinwand
Cathy L. Seeley Charles B. Vonder Embse

L. Carey Bolster • Janet H. Caldwell • Dwight A. Cooley • Warren D. Crown
Linda Proudfit • Alma B. Ramírez • Jeanne F. Ramos • Freddie Lee Renfro
David F. Robitaille • Jane Swafford

Teacher's Edition

Volume 2

Chapters 7–12

SF
AW
Scott Foresman
Addison Wesley

Editorial Offices: Menlo Park, California • Glenview, Illinois
Sales Offices: Reading, Massachusetts • Atlanta, Georgia • Glenview, Illinois
Carrollton, Texas • Menlo Park, California

http://www.sf.aw.com

Math

that Makes Sense...

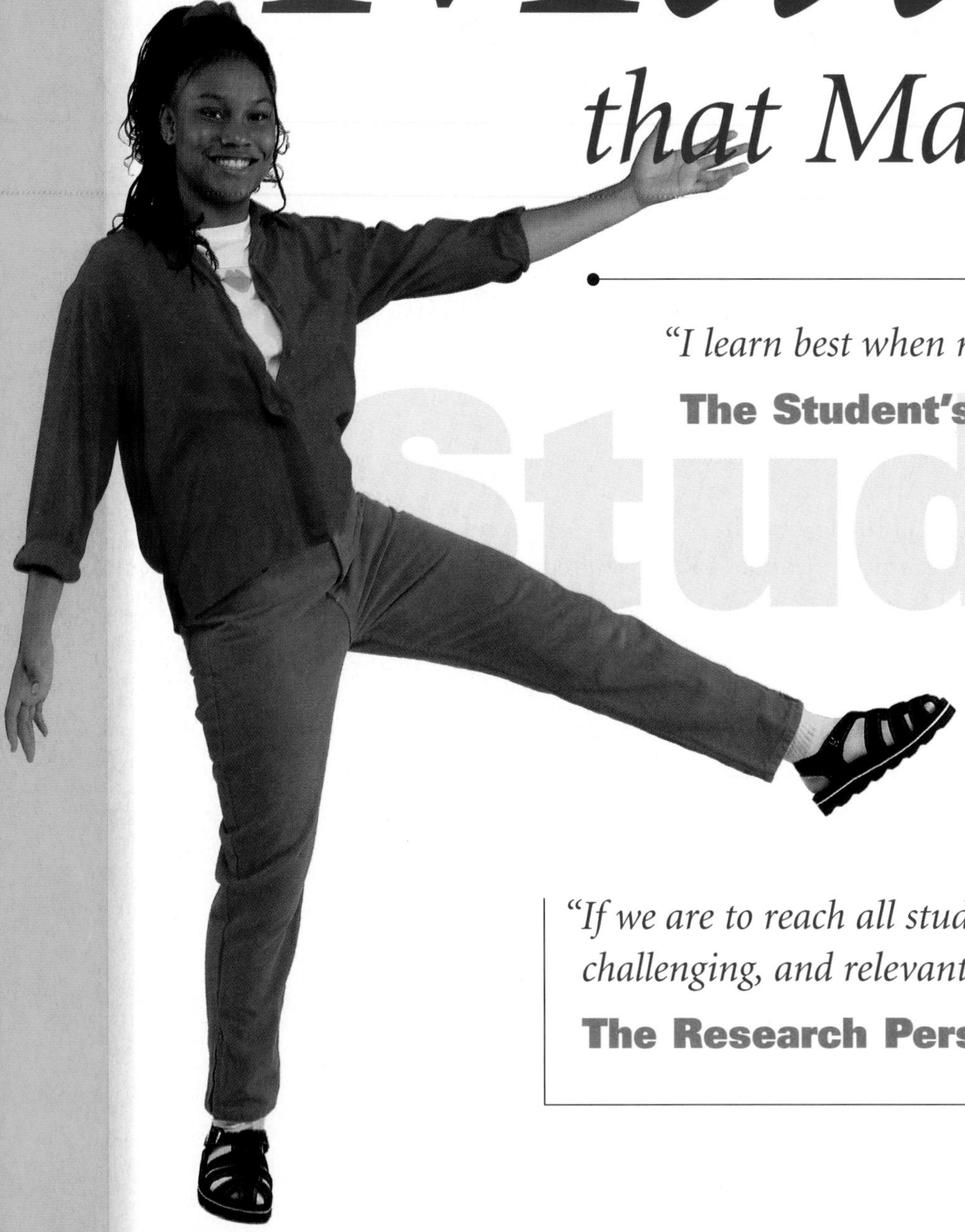

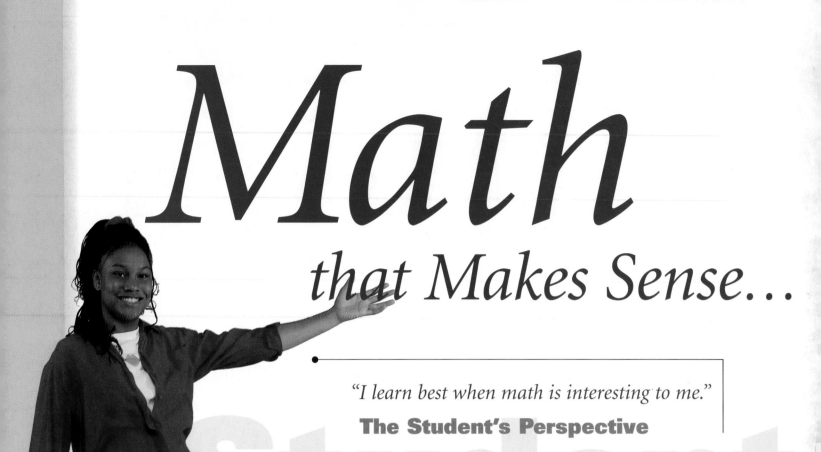

"I learn best when math is interesting to me."

The Student's Perspective

"If we are to reach all students, we must strive for meaningful, challenging, and relevant learning in the classroom."

The Research Perspective

Many of the designations used by manufacturers and sellers to distinguish their products are claimed as trademarks. When those designations appear in this book and Addison Wesley Longman was aware of a trademark claim, the designations have been printed with initial capital letters (e.g., Macintosh).

Copyright © 1998 Addison Wesley Longman, Inc.

All rights reserved. No part of this publication may be reproduced, stored in a retrieval system or transmitted, in any form or by any means, electronic, mechanical, photocopying, recording, or otherwise, without the prior written permission of the publisher.

Printed in the United States of America

ISBN 0-201-69036-5

1 2 3 4 5 6 7 8 9 10-DOW-01 00 99 98 97

Teacher

The Teacher's Perspective

*"My primary concern in teaching is to help **all** my students succeed."*

from **EVERY** *Perspective*

What kind of a math program are you looking for? What about your students? And how about mathematics education research? Can one program really satisfy *all* points of view? Through its content, features, and format, *Scott Foresman - Addison Wesley Middle School MATH* recognizes the real-life needs and concerns specific to middle school—supported by research but grounded in real classroom experience.

Welcome to a math program that excels from every perspective—especially yours!

Math that Connects to the Student's World

Middle school students have a perspective all their own. We've tapped into their world with experiences and information that grab their attention and don't let go.

Relevance

"I want to know when I'll use this."

Real, age-appropriate data
Data based on what middle school students buy, eat, study in school, and enjoy permeate every lesson.

Cool themes like *Spiders, Disasters, Food,* and *Whales*
Student-friendly topics blend learning with what kids love.

MathSURF Internet Site
MathSURF's up and so is student interest! Kids can go online to explore text content of every chapter in safe and exciting destinations around the world.

Interactive CD-ROM
Interactive lessons for every chapter provide an exciting environment for learning.

Math that Promotes High School Success

Teachers in today's middle schools need a program that prepares their students for high school math. That means rigorous content, including preparation for algebra and geometry, NTCM content and process standards—PLUS practical strategies for taking tests and problem solving.

> *"My students need to be prepared for high school math. And let's face it, how they perform is a reflection of how **I** perform!"*

Performance

The building blocks of algebra
Prepare students for success in high school math with instruction in mathematical reasoning.

Course 1—focuses on *numerical reasoning.*

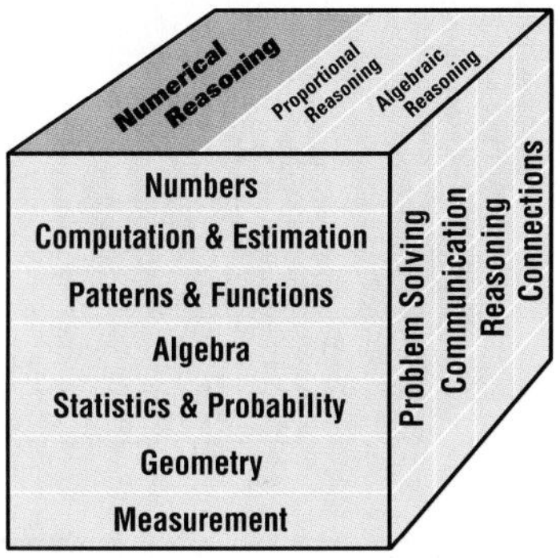

Course 2—focuses on *proportional reasoning.*

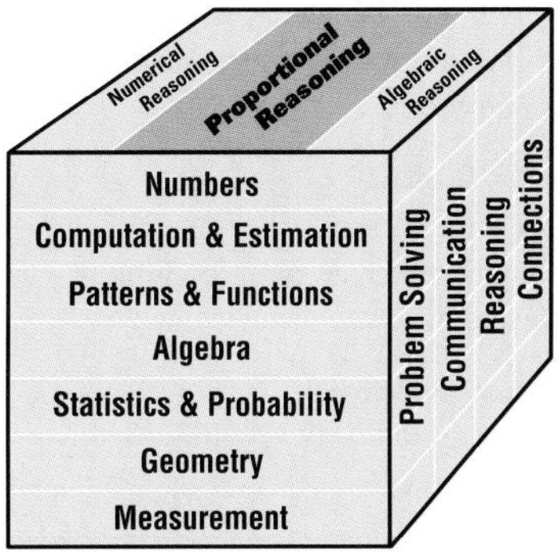

Course 3—focuses on *algebraic reasoning.*

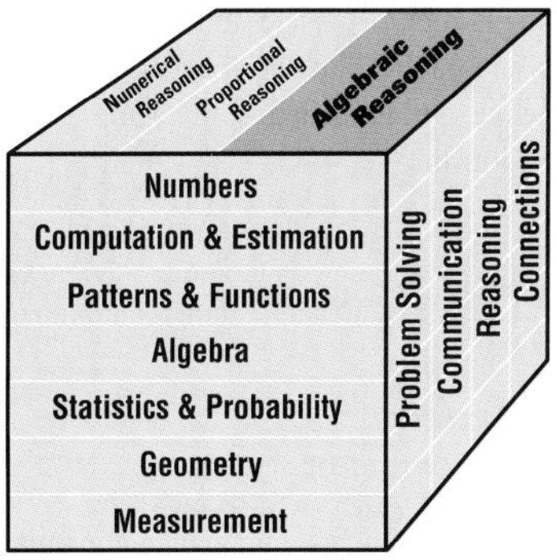

Test prep strategies
The next step in strategies! Helping students be smart about how they take standardized tests builds confidence and leads to success.

Problem solving that's no problem
Sharpen students' problem-solving skills with numerous opportunities to analyze and use the problem-solving process.

A Program that Supports Teaching Success

Teachers in today's middle schools face unique challenges—from improving student performance to adapting to each student's unique learning needs. This program is designed to help you meet those challenges. You'll find help for every teaching need—including *block scheduling* and *interdisciplinary team teaching,* PLUS *outstanding technology,* and more!

Student Edition

Colorful lessons, filled with student-oriented data, have a unique "middle school" look.

Teacher's Edition

(with Teacher's Resource Planner CD-ROM)
Two hardbound volumes, packaged with a CD-ROM Planner, provide complete lesson plans plus practical help to meet your every challenge—block scheduling, team teaching, and more.

Teacher's Resource Package

Practice Masters
Exercises reinforce content of every lesson. Also available as a workbook.

Alternative Lessons (Reteaching Masters)
Masters for every lesson offer another look at skills and concepts.

Extend Your Thinking (Enrichment Masters)
Masters enhance thinking skills and creativity in every lesson.

Problem-Solving Masters (for Guided Problem Solving)
Masters guide students step-by-step through one problem from every Student Edition exercise set. Also available as a workbook.

Assessment Sourcebook
Options to help profile students as learners. Includes multiple-choice, short-response, performance, and mixed-format chapter tests, as well as section quizzes and record forms.

Home and Community Connections
Make math a family affair! Booklet with letters in English and Spanish, also provides classroom tips, community projects, and more.

Teacher's Toolkit
Saves time with a variety of Management Resources, plus Teaching Tool Transparencies.

Technology Masters
Computer and calculator activities energize lessons with the power of technology.

Chapter Project Masters
Masters support the on-going project in each Student Edition chapter.

Interdisciplinary Team Teaching
Math across the curriculum! Masters provide an engaging 2-page interdisciplinary lesson for each section.

Resources to Customize Instruction

Print Resources

Block Scheduling Handbook
Practical suggestions let you tailor the program to various block scheduling formats.

Overhead Transparency Package
Daily Transparencies (for Problem of the Day, Review, and Quick Quiz) and Lesson Enhancement Transparencies help enliven class presentations.

Multilingual Handbook
Enhanced math glossary with examples in multiple languages provides a valuable resource for teaching. Especially useful with ESL students.

Mathematics Dictionary
Handy reference tool of middle school math terms.

Solutions Manual
Manual includes convenient solutions to Student Edition exercises.

Technology

Teacher's Resource Planner CD-ROM
The entire Teacher's Resource Package on CD-ROM! Includes an electronic planning guide which allows you to set criteria when planning lessons, customize worksheets, correlate your curriculum to specific objectives, and more!

Interactive CD-ROM
Interactive, multimedia lessons with built-in math tools help students explore concepts in enjoyable and involving ways.

MathSURF Internet Site (for Students)
Math on the Web! Provides links to other sites, project ideas, interactive surveys and more.

MathSURF Internet Site (for Teachers)
Offers exciting opportunities for in-service ideas and sharing.

MathSURF Internet Site (for Parents)
This Web site offers a variety of practical tips to parents.

TestWorks: Test and Practice CD-ROM
CD-ROM saves hours of test-prep time by generating and customizing tests and worksheets.

Manipulative Kits

Student Manipulative Kit
Quantities of angle rulers, Power Polygons, and other items help students grasp mathematics concepts on a concrete level.

Teacher's Overhead Manipulative Kit
Kit makes demonstrating concepts from an overhead projector easy and convenient.

Authors with Middle School Expertise!

Math that makes sense from every perspective—it's a commitment we've kept in all aspects of this program, including our outstanding team of authors. Their expertise in mathematics education brings to the program extensive knowledge of how middle school students learn math and how best to teach them.

Expertise

"Students learn and perform better when they are taught in ways that match their own strengths."

Charles B. Vonder Embse

Professor of Mathematics Education and Mathematics

Central Michigan University
Mt. Pleasant, Michigan

Member of NCTM Instructional Issues Advisory Committee

Member of the Advisory Board of Teachers Teaching with Technology (T^3)

Randall I. Charles

Professor, Department of Mathematics and Computer Science

San Jose State University
San Jose, California

Past Vice-President, National Council of Supervisors of Mathematics

Co-author of two NCTM publications on teaching and evaluating progress in problem solving

Jane Swafford

Professor of Mathematics

Illinois State University
Normal, Illinois

Dwight A. Cooley

Assistant Principal

Mary Louise Phillips
Elementary School
Fort Worth, Texas

Member, NCTM Board of Directors

John A. Dossey

Distinguished University
Professor of Mathematics

Illinois State University
Normal, Illinois

Past President, NCTM

Guided development of NCTM Standards

Recipient, NCTM Lifetime Achievement Award

Chairman, Conference Board of the Mathematical Sciences

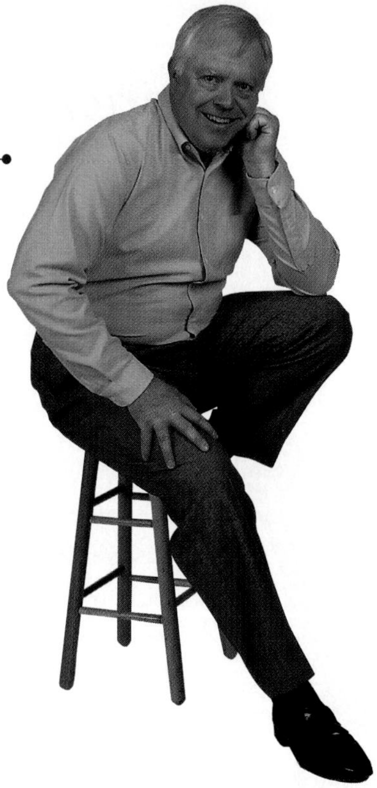

"A program that asks real-life questions provides rich possibilities for students."

Steven J. Leinwand

Mathematics Consultant

Connecticut Department
of Education
Hartford, Connecticut

Member, NCTM Board of Directors

Past President, National Council of Supervisors of Mathematics

Cathy L. Seeley

Director of Policy and Professional
Development for Texas SSI

University of Texas
Austin, Texas

Texas State Mathematics Supervisor

Writer, Curriculum and Evaluation Standards for School Mathematics

Member, NCTM Board of Directors

Turn the page, for more authors!

More Authors with Middle School Expertise!

Freddie Lee Renfro

Coordinator of Mathematics

Fort Bend Independent
School District
Sugarland, Texas

L. Carey Bolster

Director, K–12 Math Projects

Public Broadcasting Service
MATHLINE
Alexandria, Virginia

"Students construct new learning from a basis of prior knowledge and experience."

Linda Proudfit

University Professor of
Mathematics and Computer
Education

Governors State University
University Park, Illinois

Janet H. Caldwell

Professor of Mathematics

Rowan University
Glassboro, New Jersey

David F. Robitaille

Professor of Mathematics Education

University of British Columbia
Vancouver, British Columbia,
Canada

Alma Ramírez

Bilingual Mathematics and
Science Teacher

Oakland Charter Academy
Oakland, California

"To be successful in high school, students need a solid foundation in mathematical reasoning."

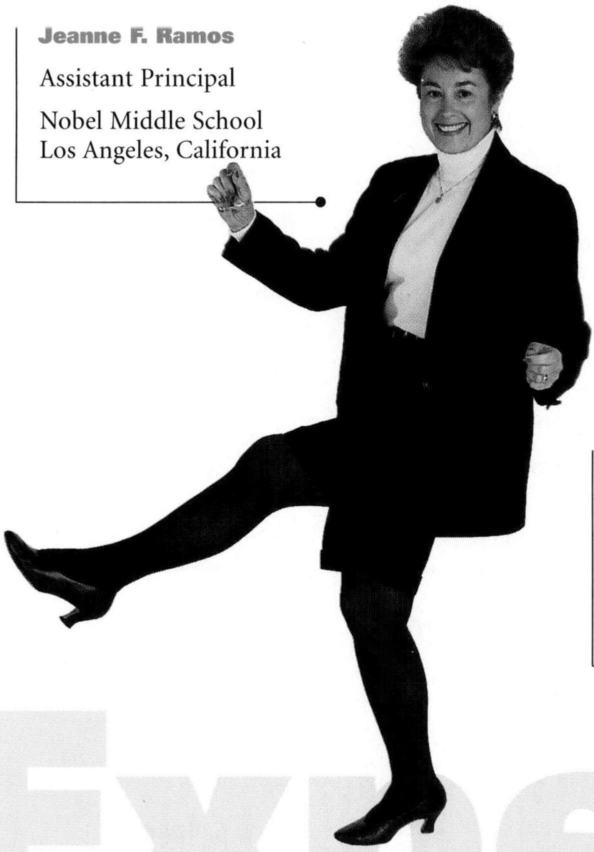

Jeanne F. Ramos

Assistant Principal

Nobel Middle School
Los Angeles, California

Warren D. Crown

Professor of Mathematics Education

Rutgers, The State University
of New Jersey
New Brunswick, New Jersey

Expertise

Contributors from Across the Country!

A Nationwide Perspective

Educators from across the country helped shape this program with valuable input about local needs and concerns.

Contributing Writers

Phillip E. Duren
California State University
Hayward, CA

Kathy A. Ross
Loyola University (LaSIP)
New Orleans, LA

Sheryl M. Yamada
Beverly Hills High School
Beverly Hills, CA

Content Reviewers

Ann Boltz
Coldwater, MI

John David Bridges
Greenville, SC

Glenn Bruckhart
Fort Collins, CO

Sharon Bourgeois Butler
Spring, TX

Carol Cameron
Seattle, WA

Steven T. Cottrell
Farmington, UT

Patricia Creel
Lawrenceville, GA

Wendi M. Cyford
New Market, MD

Scott Firkins
Owensboro, KY

Madelaine Gallin
New York, NY

Roy E. Griggs
Boise, ID

Lucy Hahn
Boise, ID

Allison Harris
Seattle, WA

Clay Hutson
Kingsport, TN

Beryl W. Jackson
Alexandria, VA

Janet Jomp
Wilson, NC

Ann P. Lawrence
Marietta, GA

Cheryl McCormack
Indianapolis, IN

Gary McCracken
Tuscaloosa, AL

Allison McNaughton
Marstons Mills, MA

Sandra A. Nagy
Mesa, AZ

Kent Novak
Greene, RI

Jeff C. Nusbaum
Rock Island, IL

Vince O'Connor
Milwaukee, WI

Mary Lynn Raith
Pittsburgh, PA

Kathleen Rieke
Zionsville, IN

Ellen G. Robertson
Norwich, NY

Nancy Rolsen
Worthington, OH

Edith Roos
Helena, MT

Lynn A. Sandro
Cedar Springs, MI

Carol Sims
Arcadia, CA

Paul E. Smith
Newburgh, IN

Donald M. Smyton
Kenmore, NY

Stella M. Turner
Indianapolis, IN

Tommie Walsh
Lubbock, TX

Terri Weaver
Houston, TX

Jacqueline Weilmuenster
Colleyville, TX

Multicultural Reviewers

Mary Margaret Capraro
Hialeah, FL

Robert Capraro
Miami, FL

Bettye Forte
Fort Worth, TX

Hector Hirigoyen
Miami, FL

James E. Hopkins
Auburn, WA

Patricia Locke
Mobridge, SD

Jimmie Rios
Fort Worth, TX

Linda Skinner
Edmond, OK

ESL Reviewers

Anna Uhl Chamot
Washington, DC

Jimmie Rios
Fort Worth, TX

Inclusion Reviewers

Lucy Blood
Amesbury, MA

Janett Borg
Monroe, UT

John David Bridges
Greenville, SC

Edith Roos
Helena, MT

Cross-Curricular Reviewers

Janett Borg
Monroe, UT

Kurt Brorson
Bethesda, MD

Geoffrey Chester
Washington, DC

Trudi Hammel Garland
Orinda, CA

M. Frank Watt Ireton
Washington, DC

Donna Krasnow
Carmel, CA

Chelcie Liu
San Francisco, CA

Edith Roos
Helena, MT

Technology Reviewers

Kurt Brorson
Bethesda, MD

Beverly W. Nichols
Overland Park, KS

Susan Rhodes
Springfield, IL

David L. Stout
Pensacola, FL

TABLE OF CONTENTS

Teacher's Edition

VOLUME 1: CHAPTERS 1–6

VOLUME 2: CHAPTERS 7–12

FROM THE AUTHORS

FROM THE AUTHORS

Dear Student,

We have designed a unique mathematics program that answers the question students your age have been asking for years about their math lessons: "When am I ever going to use this?"

In *Scott Foresman - Addison Wesley Middle School Math,* you'll learn about math in your own world and develop problem-solving techniques that will work for you in everyday life. The chapters have two or three sections, each with a useful math topic and an interesting theme. For example, you'll relate fractions to floods, algebra to the Oregon Trail, and geometry to origami.

Each section begins with an opportunity to explore new topics and make your own conjectures. Lessons are presented clearly with examples and chances to try the math yourself. Then, real kids like you and your friends say what they think about each concept and show how they understand it. And every section contains links to the World Wide Web, making your math book a dynamic link to an ever-expanding universe of knowledge.

You will soon realize how mathematics is not only useful, but also connected to you and your life as you continue to experience the real world. We trust that each of you will gain the knowledge necessary to be successful and to be everything you want to be.

Randall I. Charles *John A. Dossey* *Steven J. Leinwand*
Cathy L. Seeley *Charles B. Vonder Embse*

L. Carey Bolster *Janet H. Caldwell* *Dwight A. Cooley* *Warren D. Crown* *Linda Proudfit*
Alma B. Ramirez *Jeanne F. Ramos* *Freddie Lee Renfro* *David Robitaille* *Jane Swafford*

CHAPTER 1

Statistics—Real World Use of Whole Numbers

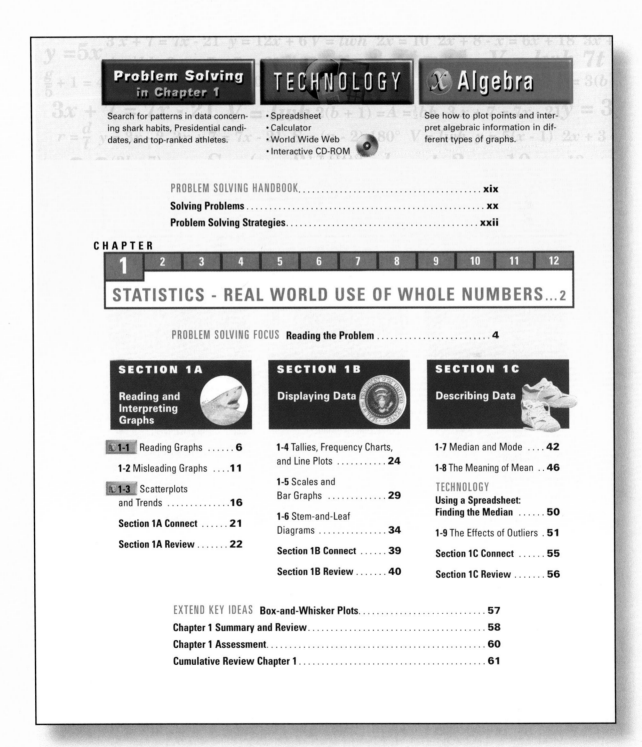

Problem Solving in Chapter 1

Search for patterns in data concerning shark habits, Presidential candidates, and top-ranked athletes.

TECHNOLOGY

- Spreadsheet
- Calculator
- World Wide Web
- Interactive CD-ROM

Algebra

See how to plot points and interpret algebraic information in different types of graphs.

CHAPTER 2

Connecting Arithmetic to Algebra

Problem Solving in Chapter 2

Present information concerning space probes, collections, and deep-sea diving to demonstrate your decision-making skills.

TECHNOLOGY

- Spreadsheet
- Calculator
- World Wide Web
- Interactive CD-ROM

x Algebra

See how to use one of the basic units of algebra — the variable.

CHAPTER 1 **2** 3 4 5 6 7 8 9 10 11 12

CHAPTER 3

Decimals

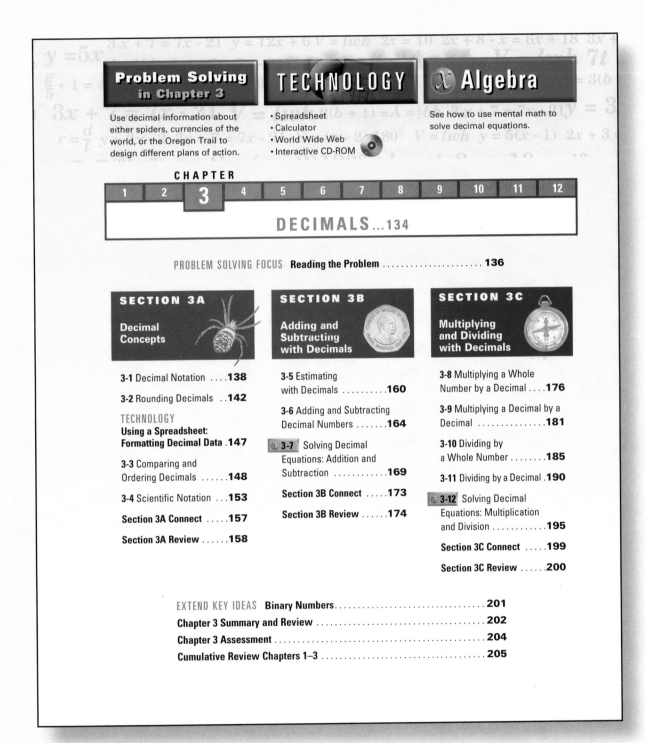

Problem Solving in Chapter 3

Use decimal information about either spiders, currencies of the world, or the Oregon Trail to design different plans of action.

TECHNOLOGY

- Spreadsheet
- Calculator
- World Wide Web
- Interactive CD-ROM

Algebra

See how to use mental math to solve decimal equations.

CHAPTER 1 2 3 4 5 6 7 8 9 10 11 12

CHAPTER 4

Measurement

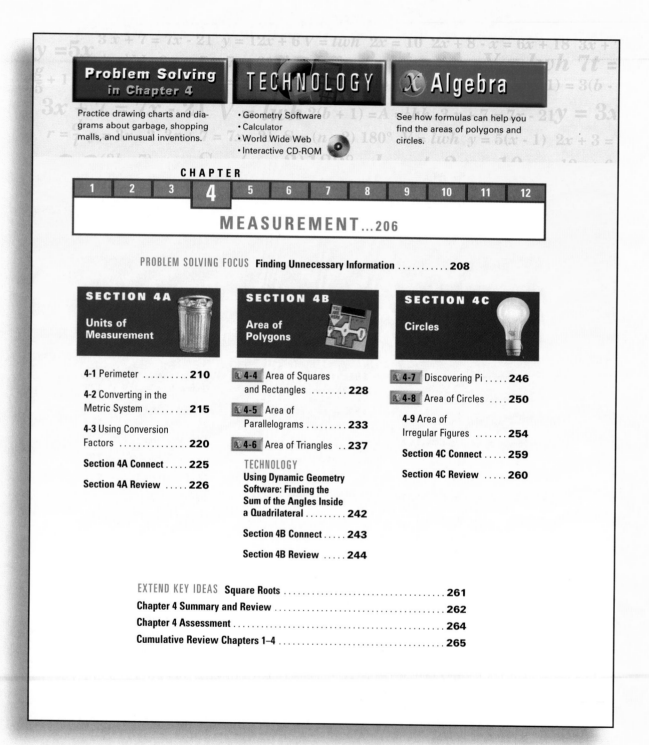

Problem Solving in Chapter 4

Practice drawing charts and diagrams about garbage, shopping malls, and unusual inventions.

TECHNOLOGY

- Geometry Software
- Calculator
- World Wide Web
- Interactive CD-ROM

Algebra

See how formulas can help you find the areas of polygons and circles.

CHAPTER 1 2 3 4 5 6 7 8 9 10 11 12

CHAPTER 5

Patterns and Number Theory

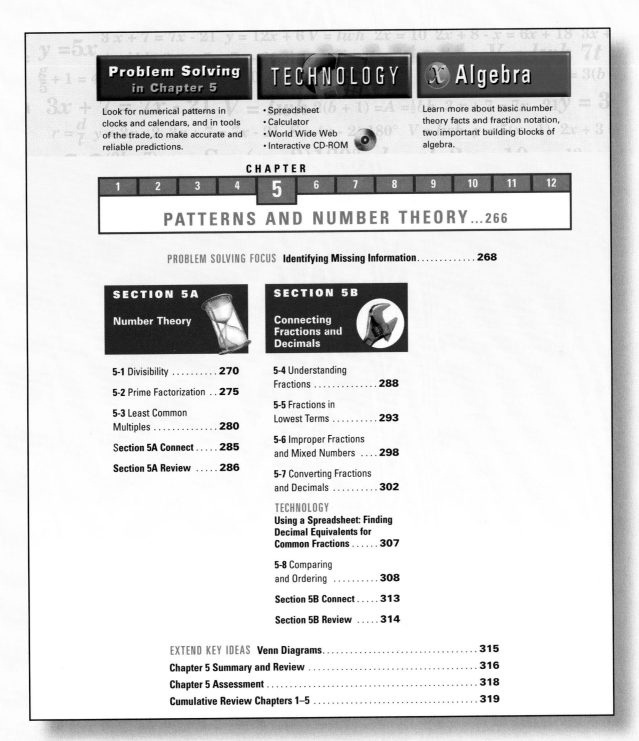

Problem Solving in Chapter 5

Look for numerical patterns in clocks and calendars, and in tools of the trade, to make accurate and reliable predictions.

TECHNOLOGY

- Spreadsheet
- Calculator
- World Wide Web
- Interactive CD-ROM

Algebra

Learn more about basic number theory facts and fraction notation, two important building blocks of algebra.

CHAPTER

1 2 3 4 **5** 6 7 8 9 10 11 12

CHAPTER 6

Adding and Subtracting Fractions

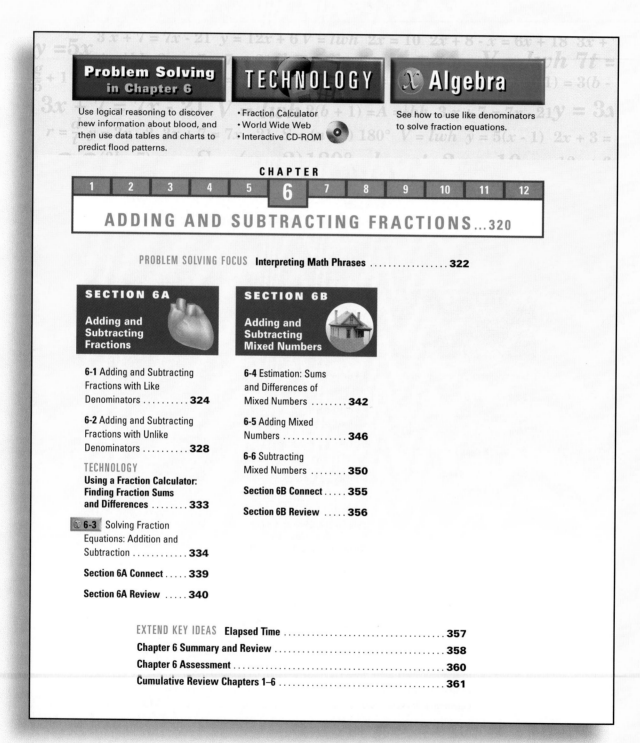

Problem Solving in Chapter 6

Use logical reasoning to discover new information about blood, and then use data tables and charts to predict flood patterns.

TECHNOLOGY

- Fraction Calculator
- World Wide Web
- Interactive CD-ROM

Algebra

See how to use like denominators to solve fraction equations.

CHAPTER 1 2 3 4 5 **6** 7 8 9 10 11 12

CHAPTER 7

Multiplying and Dividing Fractions

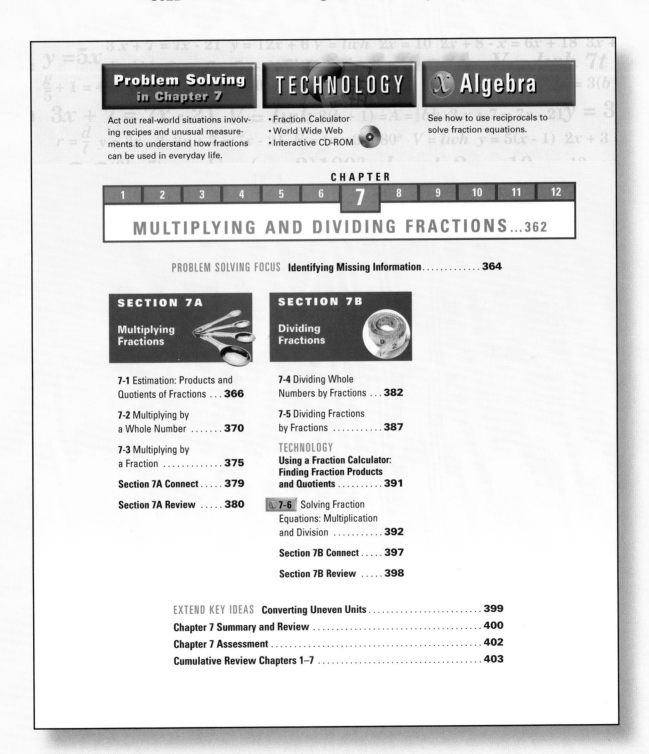

Problem Solving in Chapter 7

Act out real-world situations involving recipes and unusual measurements to understand how fractions can be used in everyday life.

TECHNOLOGY

- Fraction Calculator
- World Wide Web
- Interactive CD-ROM

Algebra

See how to use reciprocals to solve fraction equations.

CHAPTER

1 2 3 4 5 6 **7** 8 9 10 11 12

CHAPTER 8

The Geometry of Polygons

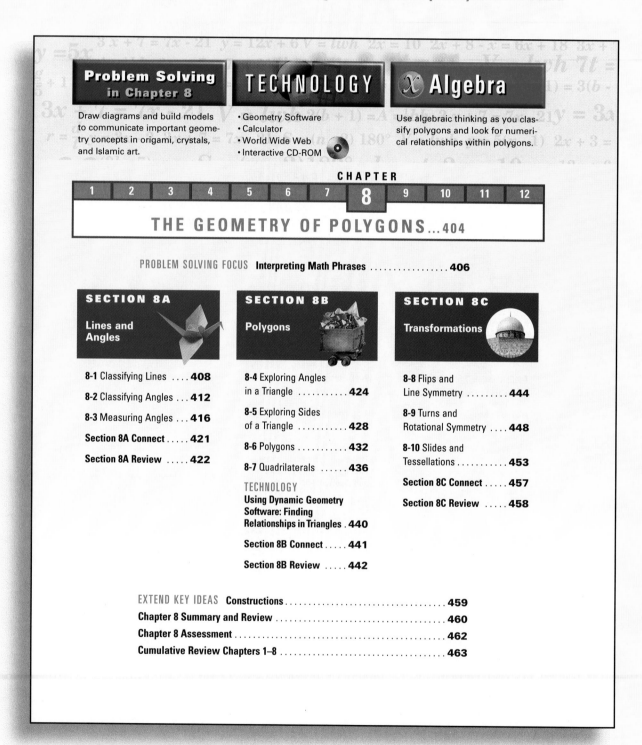

Problem Solving in Chapter 8

Draw diagrams and build models to communicate important geometry concepts in origami, crystals, and Islamic art.

TECHNOLOGY

- Geometry Software
- Calculator
- World Wide Web
- Interactive CD-ROM

Algebra

Use algebraic thinking as you classify polygons and look for numerical relationships within polygons.

CHAPTER 1 2 3 4 5 6 7 **8** 9 10 11 12

CHAPTER 9

Integers and the Coordinate Plane

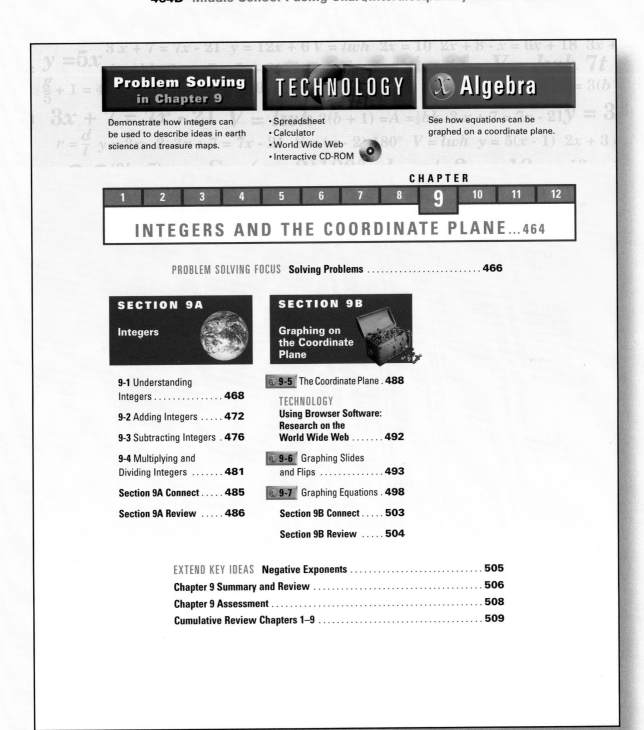

Problem Solving in Chapter 9

Demonstrate how integers can be used to describe ideas in earth science and treasure maps.

TECHNOLOGY

- Spreadsheet
- Calculator
- World Wide Web
- Interactive CD-ROM

Algebra

See how equations can be graphed on a coordinate plane.

CHAPTER 1 2 3 4 5 6 7 8 **9** 10 11 12

CHAPTER 10

Ratio, Proportion, and Percent

Problem Solving in Chapter 10

Determine how information about fire prevention, statues, and rain forests can help you make predictions and identify patterns.

TECHNOLOGY

- Spreadsheet
- Calculator
- World Wide Web
- Interactive CD-ROM

Algebra

See how proportions can be solved using algebra.

CHAPTER 1 2 3 4 5 6 7 8 9 **10** 11 12

RATIO, PROPORTION, AND PERCENT...510

CHAPTER 11

Solids and Measurement

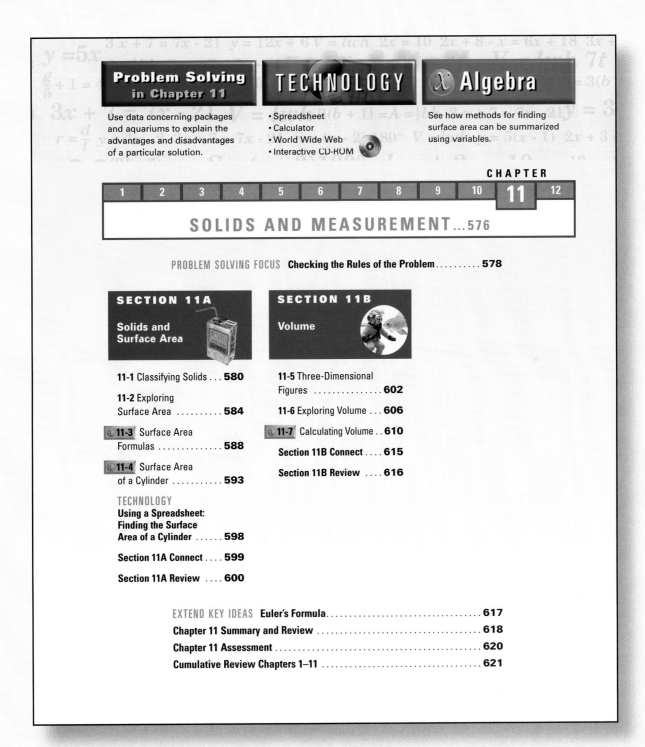

Problem Solving in Chapter 11

Use data concerning packages and aquariums to explain the advantages and disadvantages of a particular solution.

TECHNOLOGY

- Spreadsheet
- Calculator
- World Wide Web
- Interactive CD-ROM

Algebra

See how methods for finding surface area can be summarized using variables.

CHAPTER 1 2 3 4 5 6 7 8 9 10 **11** 12

SOLIDS AND MEASUREMENT ...576

CHAPTER 12

Probability

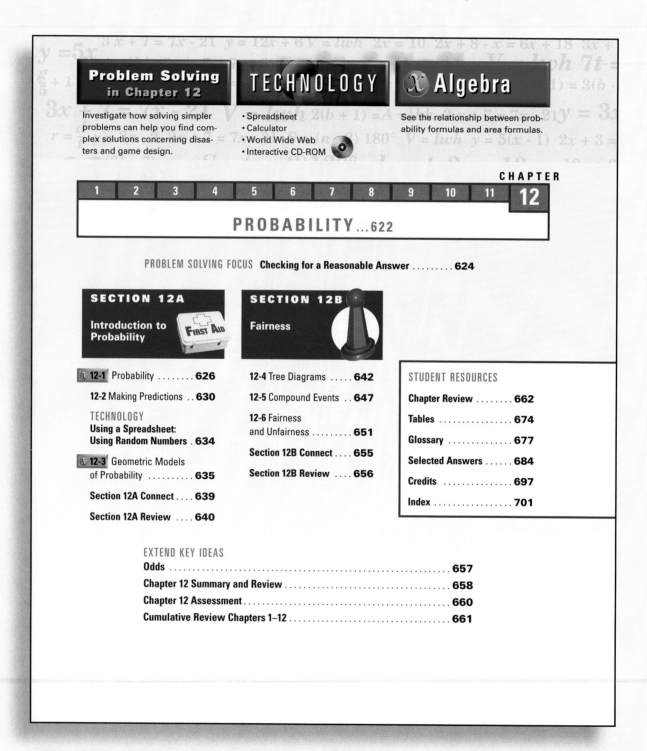

Problem Solving in Chapter 12

Investigate how solving simpler problems can help you find complex solutions concerning disasters and game design.

TECHNOLOGY

- Spreadsheet
- Calculator
- World Wide Web
- Interactive CD-ROM

Algebra

See the relationship between probability formulas and area formulas.

CHAPTER 1 2 3 4 5 6 7 8 9 10 11 **12**

Pacing Guide

The pacing suggested in the chart at the right assumes one day for most lessons, one day for end-of-section Connect and Review, and two days for end-of-chapter Summary, Review, and Assessment. The same number of days per chapter is used for the block scheduling options. For example, see page 2D.

You may need to adjust pacing to meet the needs of your students and your district curriculum.

	CHAPTER	PAGES	NUMBER OF DAYS
1	Statistics—Real World Use of Whole Numbers	2–61	15
2	Connecting Arithmetic to Algebra	62–133	19
3	Decimals	134–205	18
4	Measurement	206–265	15
5	Patterns and Number Theory	266–319	13
6	Adding and Subtracting Fractions	320–361	11
7	Multiplying and Dividing Fractions	362–403	11
8	The Geometry of Polygons	404–463	16
9	Integers and the Coordinate Plane	464–509	12
10	Ratio, Proportion, and Percent	510–575	17
11	Solids and Measurement	576–621	12
12	Probability	622–661	11
	Total Days		**170**

Materials List

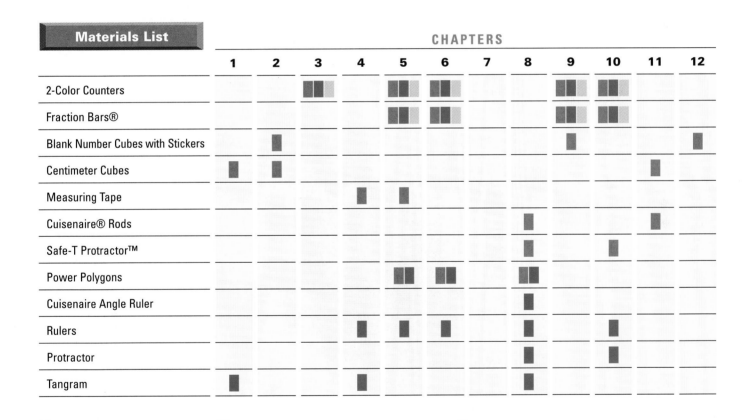

	CHAPTERS											
	1	**2**	**3**	**4**	**5**	**6**	**7**	**8**	**9**	**10**	**11**	**12**
2-Color Counters			S T O		S T O	S T O			S T O	S T O		
Fraction Bars®					S T O	S T O			S T O	S T O		
Blank Number Cubes with Stickers		S							S			S
Centimeter Cubes	S	S									S	
Measuring Tape				S	S							
Cuisenaire® Rods								S			S	
Safe-T Protractor™								S		S		
Power Polygons					S T	S T		S T				
Cuisenaire Angle Ruler								T				
Rulers				T	T	T		T		T		
Protractor								T		T		
Tangram	T			T				T				

Student Manipulative Kit (S) **Teacher's Overhead Manipulative Kit** (O) **Transparencies in Teacher's Toolkit** (T)

Chapter 7

▶ OVERVIEW

Multiplying and Dividing Fractions

Section 7A

Multiplying Fractions: Students learn to estimate products and quotients of fractions and to multiply by fractions.

Section 7B

Dividing Fractions: Students learn to divide by fractions and to solve equations by multiplying or dividing by fractions.

7-1 Estimation: Products and Quotients of Fractions

7-2 Multiplying by a Whole Number

7-3 Multiplying by a Fraction

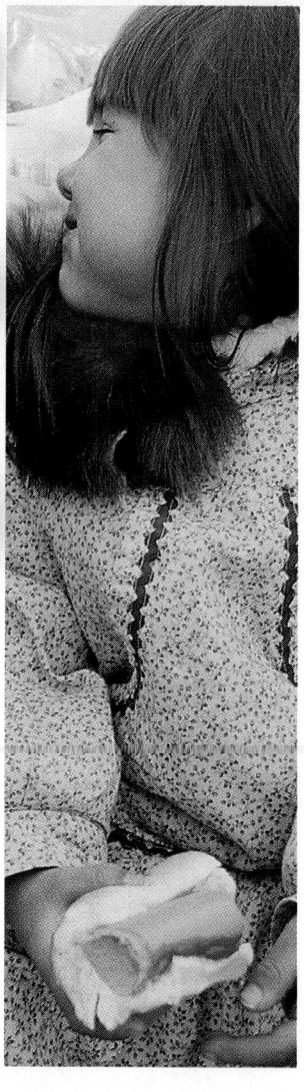

7-4 Dividing Whole Numbers by Fractions

7-5 Dividing Fractions by Fractions

7-6 Solving Fraction Equations: Multiplication and Division

Meeting NCTM Standards

Curriculum Standards

STANDARD			pages
1	**Problem Solving**	Skills and Strategies	364, 367, 371, 378, *385*, *395*, 396
		Applications	368–369, 373–374, 377–378, 379, 385–386, 389–390, 395–396, 397
		Exploration	366, 370, 375, 382, 387, 392
2	**Communication**	Oral	365, 367, 372, 377, 381, 384, 388, 394, *396*
		Written	*364*, 369, 374, 379, 386, 390, 396
		Cooperative Learning	*366*, *370*, *375*, *382*, *384*, *387*, *392*
3	**Reasoning**	Critical Thinking	369, 374, 378, 386, 390, 396
4	**Connections**	Mathematical	See Standards 6, 7, 9, 10, 13 below.
		Interdisciplinary	Arts & Literature 362; Entertainment 362; Health 373, *384*, 398; History 368, 374, *381*, 388, 395; Industry *365*, *381*, 390; Science 363, 371, *372*, 374, 377, 385; Social Studies 363, 369, 385
		Technology	391
		Cultural	362, 379, *394*
6	**Number Systems and Number Theory**		395
7	**Computation and Estimation**		366–390, *393*
9	**Algebra**		392–396
10	**Statistics**		374
13	**Measurement**		380, 381, 389, 397, 398, 399

Italic type indicates Teacher Edition reference.

Teaching Standards

Focus on Diversity

Every classroom has students from diverse backgrounds and with diverse knowledge. Teachers should pose tasks that

- are based on the range of ways that diverse students learn mathematics.
- display sensitivity to, and draw on, students' diverse background experiences and dispositions.

Assessment Standards

Focus on Learning

Projects The Learning Standard suggests that an assessment better enhances learning if it offers students activities that are relevant and mathematically worthwhile. Projects can make the skills and concepts more meaningful to students. The project in Chapter 7 asks students to

- conduct an interview.
- identify a multiplier.

TECHNOLOGY

For the Teacher

- **Teacher Resource Planner CD-ROM**
  Use the teacher planning CD-ROM to view resources available for Chapter 7. You can prepare custom lesson plans or use the default lesson plans provided.

- **World Wide Web**
  Visit **www.teacher.mathsurf.com** for links to lesson plans from teachers and other professionals, NCTM information, and other sites.

- **TestWorks**
  TestWorks provides ready-made tests and can create custom tests and practice worksheets.

For the Parent

- **World Wide Web**
  Parents can use the Web site at **www.parent.mathsurf.com.**

For the Student

- **Interactive CD-ROM**
  Lessons 7-2 and 7-3 have *Interactive CD-ROM Lessons*. The *Interactive CD-ROM Journal* and *Interactive CD-ROM Spreadsheet/Grapher Tool* are also used in Chapter 7.

- **World Wide Web**
  Use with Chapter and Section Openers;
  Students can go online to the Scott Foresman-Addison Wesley Web site at **www.mathsurf.com/6/ch7** to collect information about chapter themes.

STANDARDIZED - TEST CORRELATION

SECTION 7A

LESSON	OBJECTIVE	ITBS Form M	CTBS 4th Ed.	CAT 5th Ed.	SAT 9th Ed.	MAT 7th Ed.	Your Form
7-1	• Estimate products and quotients of fraction problems.					✘	
7-2	• Multiply whole numbers by fractions.	✘	✘	✘	✘		
7-3	• Multiply a fraction by another fraction.	✘	✘	✘	✘		

SECTION 7B

LESSON	OBJECTIVE	ITBS Form M	CTBS 4th Ed.	CAT 5th Ed.	SAT 9th Ed.	MAT 7th Ed.	Your Form
7-4	• Divide a whole number by a fraction.		✘	✘	✘		
7-5	• Divide a fraction by a fraction or a whole number.		✘	✘	✘		
7-6	• Solve multiplication and division equations containing fractions.			✘		✘	

Key: ITBS - Iowa Test of Basic Skills; CTBS - Comprehensive Test of Basic Skills; CAT - California Achievement Test; SAT - Stanford Achievement Test; MAT - Metropolitan Achievement Test

ASSESSMENT PROGRAM

Traditional Assessment

QUICK QUIZZES	SECTION REVIEW	CHAPTER REVIEW	CHAPTER ASSESSMENT FREE RESPONSE	CHAPTER ASSESSMENT MULTIPLE CHOICE	CUMULATIVE REVIEW
TE: pp. 369, 374, 378, 386, 390, 396	SE: pp. 380, 398 *Quiz 7A, 7B	SE: pp. 400–401	SE: p. 402 *Ch. 7 Tests Forms A, B, E	*Ch. 7 Tests Forms C, E	SE: p. 403 *Ch. 7 Test Form F

Alternate Assessment

INTERVIEW	JOURNAL	ONGOING	PERFORMANCE	PORTFOLIO	PROJECT	SELF
TE: p. 396	SE: pp. 369, 374, 386, 390 TE: pp. 369, 386	TE: pp. 366, 370, 375, 382, 387, 392	SE: p. 402 TE: p. 374 *Ch. 7 Tests Forms D, E	TE: p. 378	SE: pp. 378, 386 TE: p. 363	TE: p. 390

*Tests and quizzes are in *Assessment Sourcebook*. Test Form E is a mixed response test. Forms for Alternate Assessment are also available in *Assessment Sourcebook*.

TestWorks: Test and Practice Software

MIDDLE SCHOOL PACING CHART

REGULAR PACING

Day	5 classes per week
1	Chapter 7 Opener; Problem Solving Focus
2	Section **7A** Opener; Lesson **7-1**
3	Lesson **7-2**
4	Lesson **7-3**
5	**7A** Connect; **7A** Review
6	Section **7B** Opener; Lesson **7-4**
7	Lesson **7-5**; Technology
8	Lesson **7-6**
9	**7B** Connect; **7B** Review; Extend Key Ideas
10	Chapter 7 Summary and Review
11	Chapter 7 Assessment Cumulative Review, Chapters 1–7

BLOCK SCHEDULING OPTIONS

Block Scheduling for Complete Course

Chapter 7 may be presented in

- five 90-minute blocks
- eight 75-minute blocks

Each block consists of a combination of

- Chapter and Section Openers
- Explores
- Lesson Development
- Problem Solving Focus
- Technology
- Extend Key Ideas
- Connect
- Review
- Assessment

For details, see *Block Scheduling Handbook.*

Block Scheduling for Interdisciplinary Course

Each block integrates math with another subject area.

In Chapter 7, interdisciplinary topics include

- Recipes
- Measurements

Themes for Interdisciplinary Team Teaching 7A and 7B are

- Human Growth
- Newspaper Page Layouts

For details, see *Block Scheduling Handbook.*

Block Scheduling for Lab-Based Course

In each block, 30–40 minutes is devoted to lab activities including

- Explores in the Student Edition
- Connect pages in the Student Edition
- Technology options in the Student Edition
- Reteaching Activities in the Teacher Edition

For details, see *Block Scheduling Handbook.*

Block Scheduling for Course with *Connected Mathematics*

In each block, investigations from **Connected Mathematics** replace or enhance the lessons in Chapter 7.

Connected Mathematics topics for Chapter 7 can be found in

- *Bits and Pieces II*

For details, see *Block Scheduling Handbook.*

INTERDISCIPLINARY BULLETIN BOARD

Set Up

Divide a bulletin board into three sections labeled *Category, Number Endangered, and Fraction of Total.* Under *Category*, list Mammals, Birds, Reptiles and Amphibians, Fish and Shellfish, Insects. Leave space below each name.

Procedure

- Explain that some species of mammals, birds, reptiles, amphibians, fish and shellfish, and insects are endangered in the U.S.
- Assign small groups of students to each of the categories. Have them research an endangered animal in that category.
- Groups should draw a picture of an animal(s) that represents the category and display it in the first section of the board. They should record appropriate information in the other two sections.

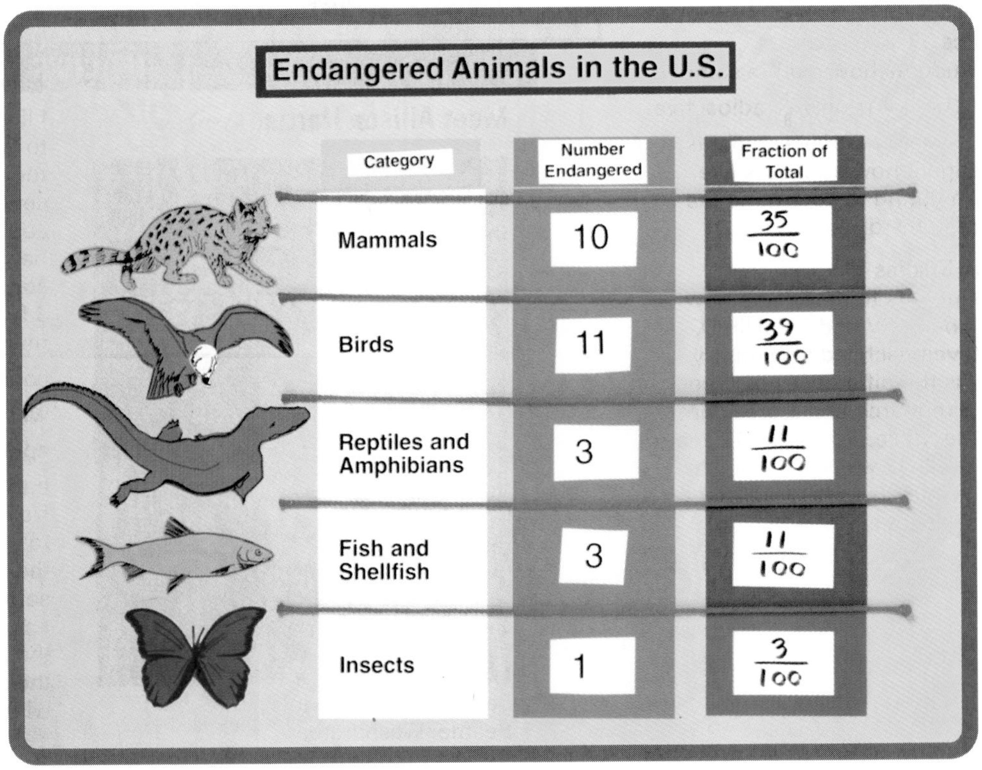

Endangered Animals in the U.S.
Category
Number Endangered
Fraction of Total
Mammals
10
35/100
Birds
11
39/100
Reptiles and Amphibians
3
11/100
Fish and Shellfish
3
11/100
Insects
1
3/100

Problem Solving Focus

Identifying Missing Information

The Point
Students focus on determining whether any additional information is needed to solve a problem.

Resources
Teaching Tool Transparency 18: Problem-Solving Guidelines

Interactive CD-ROM Journal

About the Page

Using the Problem-Solving Process
It is critical that students be able to identify missing information when trying to solve a problem. Discuss the following suggestions.

- Determine what the problem is asking.
- Organize given information.
- Identify missing information needed to complete the problem-solving process.

Ask ...
- To find out how long it takes to get somewhere, as in Problem 1, what kind of information do you need? The total distance and the distance driven each day.
- In Problem 2, did Jennie eat more shrimp than David? This cannot be determined based on the information given.
- Can you solve any of the problems with the information given? Yes, Problem 4.

Answers for Problems
1. Distance to Arches National Park.
2. How much shrimp David and Mr. Halloran had, or how much shrimp Mrs. Halloran and Jennie had.
3. How much money she had.
4. No missing information.

Journal
Ask students to write a paragraph describing their favorite trip or experience. Check that they have included all necessary and important details.

Problem Solving
Understand
Plan
Solve
Look Back

Identifying Missing Information

When you plan a project, you are often told how the finished product should look. But you may not be told all the information you will need in order to complete that product. A critical problem-solving skill is being able to determine what information you need to complete a project or answer a question.

Problem Solving Focus

Identify what additional information would be needed to solve each problem. Some of the problems may not be missing any needed information.

1. Mr. and Mrs. Halloran and their children David and Jennie are planning to drive to Arches National Park. Mrs. Halloran suggests that they drive 400 miles each day. At this rate, how long will it take them to get there?

2. The Hallorans stopped at a restaurant and everyone ordered the all-you-can-eat shrimp. Mrs. Halloran had twice as much shrimp as David. Jennie had three more pieces than Mr. Halloran. Who ate the most shrimp?

3. At the park, Jennie bought a souvenir map for $2.25, three postcards at $0.50 each, and a key ring for $1.00. How much money did she have left?

4. David had to write a 500-word report about the trip for his Language Arts class. He wrote half of the report at the park, and half of what was left on the way home. How many words did he have to write to finish the report?

364

Additional Problem

The sixth graders decided to present a play to raise money for a trip to a science museum in a nearby town. They charged $2 for adult tickets and $1.25 for student tickets. How much money did they make on the play?

1. What is the problem about? Determining the amount of money students raised by staging a play.
2. Is all the information given that you need to solve the problem? If not, what is missing? No; The number of each kind of ticket sold is missing.
3. If you had the missing information, how would you solve the problem? Multiply the number of student tickets sold by $1.25, the number of adult tickets sold by $2, and add the two amounts together.

MIDDLE SCHOOL PACING CHART

REGULAR PACING

Day	5 classes per week
1	Chapter 7 Opener; Problem Solving Focus
2	Section **7A** Opener; Lesson **7-1**
3	Lesson **7-2**
4	Lesson **7-3**
5	**7A** Connect; **7A** Review
6	Section **7B** Opener; Lesson **7-4**
7	Lesson **7-5**; Technology
8	Lesson **7-6**
9	**7B** Connect; **7B** Review; Extend Key Ideas
10	Chapter 7 Summary and Review
11	Chapter 7 Assessment Cumulative Review, Chapters 1–7

BLOCK SCHEDULING OPTIONS

Block Scheduling for
Complete Course

Chapter 7 may be presented in

- five 90-minute blocks
- eight 75-minute blocks

Each block consists of a combination of

- Chapter and Section Openers
- Explores
- Lesson Development
- Problem Solving Focus
- Technology
- Extend Key Ideas
- Connect
- Review
- Assessment

For details, see *Block Scheduling Handbook.*

Block Scheduling for
Interdisciplinary Course

Each block integrates math with another subject area.

In Chapter 7, interdisciplinary topics include

- Recipes
- Measurements

Themes for Interdisciplinary Team Teaching 7A and 7B are

- Human Growth
- Newspaper Page Layouts

For details, see *Block Scheduling Handbook.*

Block Scheduling for
Lab-Based Course

In each block, 30–40 minutes is devoted to lab activities including

- Explores in the Student Edition
- Connect pages in the Student Edition
- Technology options in the Student Edition
- Reteaching Activities in the Teacher Edition

For details, see *Block Scheduling Handbook.*

Block Scheduling for
Course with *Connected Mathematics*

In each block, investigations from **Connected Mathematics** replace or enhance the lessons in Chapter 7.

Connected Mathematics topics for Chapter 7 can be found in

- *Bits and Pieces II*

For details, see *Block Scheduling Handbook.*

INTERDISCIPLINARY BULLETIN BOARD

Set Up

Divide a bulletin board into three sections labeled *Category, Number Endangered, and Fraction of Total.* Under *Category,* list Mammals, Birds, Reptiles and Amphibians, Fish and Shellfish, Insects. Leave space below each name.

Procedure

- Explain that some species of mammals, birds, reptiles, amphibians, fish and shellfish, and insects are endangered in the U.S.
- Assign small groups of students to each of the categories. Have them research an endangered animal in that category.
- Groups should draw a picture of an animal(s) that represents the category and display it in the first section of the board. They should record appropriate information in the other two sections.

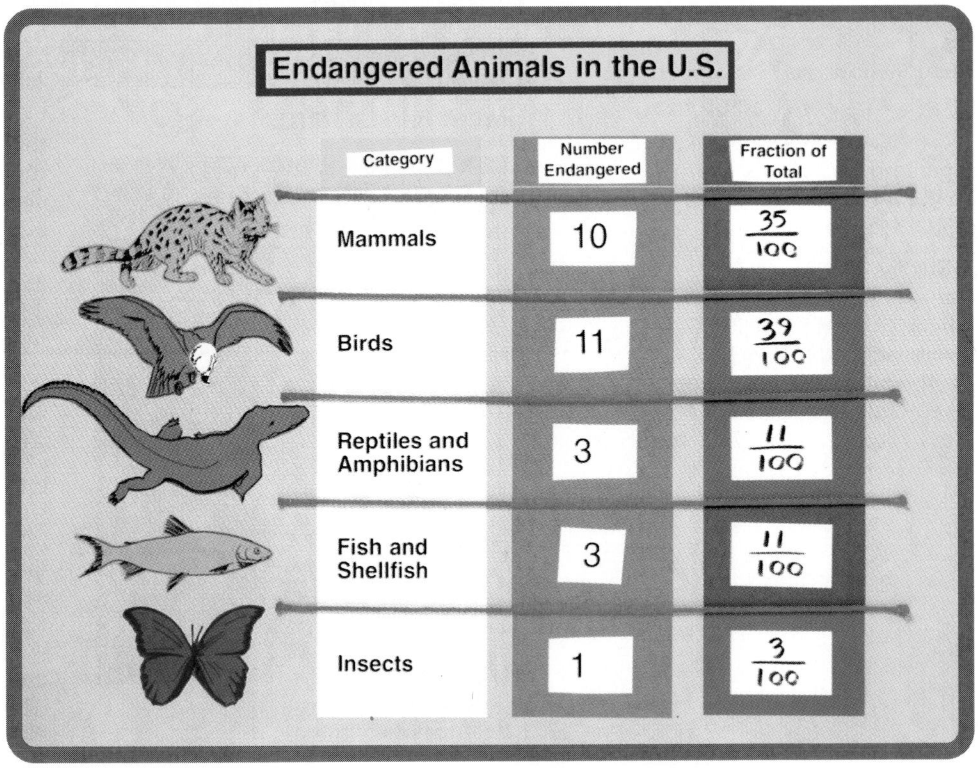

Endangered Animals in the U.S.
Category
Number Endangered
Fraction of Total
Mammals
10
35/100
Birds
11
39/100
Reptiles and Amphibians
3
11/100
Fish and Shellfish
3
11/100
Insects
1
3/100

Chapter 7

The information on these pages shows how fractions are used in real-life situations.

World Wide Web

If your class has access to the World Wide Web, you might want to use the information found at the Web site addresses given.

Extensions

The following activities do not require access to the World Wide Web.

Entertainment
Suggest that students investigate the different weight categories in weight lifting and the weights lifted at the last Olympics.

People of the World
Have students work in groups of four to find the number of people per square mile in India. Then have them compare that number with similar statistics for the United States and one other country of their choice.

Arts & Literature
Crazy Horse was an extraordinary military leader of the Oglala band of the Teton Lakota/Dakota nation. Ask students to research Crazy Horse and his times.

Science
Ask students how old the sample would be if it is only $\frac{1}{8}$ radioactive. 17,190 years old Have students investigate how scientists use carbon dating to determine the age of items discovered.

Social Studies
Ask students to determine how long Louis XIV and Franklin D. Roosevelt each led his country. Discuss the differences between how a monarch and a president assume office. Louis XIV, 72 years; Roosevelt, 12 years. The monarch is born into his or her role, whereas the President is elected.

7 Multiplying and Dividing Fractions

Entertainment Link
www.mathsurf.com/6/ch7/ent

Arts & Literature Link
www.mathsurf.com/6/ch7/arts

Entertainment

At the 1996 Centennial Olympic Games in Atlanta, Naim Suleymanoglu of Turkey won the gold medal in the 141-pound division of weightlifting by lifting 413 pounds. This was over $2\frac{3}{4}$ times his own body weight.

People of the World

One out of every 6 people in the world lives in India. With a world population of 5,423,000,000 people, there are about 900,000,000 people in India.

Arts & Literature

Upon completion, the statue of Chief Crazy Horse at Thunderhead Mountain, South Dakota, will be the largest free-standing statue in the world at 563 feet tall. The model of the statue on display is $\frac{1}{34}$ the size of the final statue.

TEACHER TALK

Meet Allison Harris

Seattle Public Schools
Seattle, Washington

I like to relate the division of fractions to what students already know about the division of whole numbers. If I present the question, "How many children could get 3 bagels each if I have a dozen bagels?" students may approach the solution by seeing that they can subtract 3 from 12 a total of 4 times. If I change my question to "How many children could get $1\frac{1}{2}$ bagels?" some students will see that the same strategy can be applied. Others will reason that $1\frac{1}{2}$ is half of 3 and construct their solution from that insight. I challenge students to draw a sketch or diagram to illustrate their thinking. Constructing intuitive solutions through sketches, diagrams, and discussions helps students justify the answers they get when they use the standard algorithm for division with fractions.

Social Studies Link
www.mathsurf.com/6/ch7/social

Science

Carbon 14 is radioactive. It takes 5,730 years for $\frac{1}{2}$ of the radioactive material to decay. If a sample has decayed so that only $\frac{1}{4}$ is radioactive, the sample is 11,460 years old.

KEY MATH IDEAS

Fraction products and quotients can be estimated by rounding fractions to the closest whole numbers.

Multiplying fractions is similar to multiplying whole numbers. To find the product, multiply the numerators and then multiply the denominators.

When you multiply by a fraction less than 1, the product is smaller than the number you started with.

When you divide by a fraction less than 1, the quotient is bigger than the number you started with.

Social Studies

Louis XIV, king of France from 1643 to 1715, had the longest documented reign of any monarch. Franklin Delano Roosevelt, U.S. President from 1933 to 1945, served as U.S. President the longest. His time as a national leader was $\frac{1}{6}$ that of Louis XIV.

CHAPTER PROJECT

Problem Solving

Understand
Plan
Solve
Look Back

In this project, you will interview senior citizens to determine how much they paid for common items when they were your age, and how those prices compare to the prices of things today. Begin by thinking about what they bought back then that you buy today.

363

PROJECT ASSESSMENT

You may choose to use this project as a performance assessment for the chapter.

Performance Assessment Key

Level 4 Full Accomplishment

Level 3 Substantial Accomplishment

Level 2 Partial Accomplishment

Level 1 Little Accomplishment

Suggested Scoring Rubric

4	• Very accurate data about costs of many items are gathered through detailed interviews with several people. • Comparison of costs of items is detailed, accurate, and clearly presented in a creative manner.
3	• Informative data about costs of several items are gathered through interviews with several people. • Comparison of costs of items is accurate and well organized.
2	• Adequate data about costs of some items are gathered through interviews with two or three people. • Comparison of costs of items is acceptable.
1	• Little data about costs of items are gathered through brief interviews. • Comparison of costs of items is limited.

Chapter Project

Students conduct interviews with senior citizens to gather data about the prices of items these citizens purchased when they were the student's age. Then students present a comparison of costs between then and now.

Resources
Chapter 7 Project Master

Introduce the Project

- Discuss which items would have been commonly available to senior citizens when they were in sixth grade.
- Talk about how to conduct an interview and how to find information about products senior citizens might have purchased as children.

Project Progress

Section A, page 378 Students individually conduct an interview with senior citizens to see how costs have changed over the years.

Section B, page 386 Students estimate the fraction or mixed number by which to multiply the old price to determine the new price.

Community Project

A community project for Chapter 7 is available in *Home and Community Connections.*

Cooperative Learning

You may want to use Teaching Tool Transparency 1: Cooperative Learning Checklist with **Explore** and other group activities in this chapter.

Problem Solving Focus

Identifying Missing Information

The Point
Students focus on determining whether any additional information is needed to solve a problem.

Resources
Teaching Tool Transparency 18: Problem-Solving Guidelines

Interactive CD-ROM Journal

About the Page

Using the Problem-Solving Process
It is critical that students be able to identify missing information when trying to solve a problem. Discuss the following suggestions.

- Determine what the problem is asking.
- Organize given information.
- Identify missing information needed to complete the problem-solving process.

Ask ...
- To find out how long it takes to get somewhere, as in Problem 1, what kind of information do you need? The total distance and the distance driven each day.
- In Problem 2, did Jennie eat more shrimp than David? This cannot be determined based on the information given.
- Can you solve any of the problems with the information given? Yes, Problem 4.

Answers for Problems
1. Distance to Arches National Park.
2. How much shrimp David and Mr. Halloran had, or how much shrimp Mrs. Halloran and Jennie had.
3. How much money she had.
4. No missing information.

Journal

Ask students to write a paragraph describing their favorite trip or experience. Check that they have included all necessary and important details.

Problem Solving
Understand
Plan
Solve
Look Back

Identifying Missing Information

When you plan a project, you are often told how the finished product should look. But you may not be told all the information you will need in order to complete that product. A critical problem-solving skill is being able to determine what information you need to complete a project or answer a question.

Problem Solving Focus

Identify what additional information would be needed to solve each problem. Some of the problems may not be missing any needed information.

1. Mr. and Mrs. Halloran and their children David and Jennie are planning to drive to Arches National Park. Mrs. Halloran suggests that they drive 400 miles each day. At this rate, how long will it take them to get there?

2. The Hallorans stopped at a restaurant and everyone ordered the all-you-can-eat shrimp. Mrs. Halloran had twice as much shrimp as David. Jennie had three more pieces than Mr. Halloran. Who ate the most shrimp?

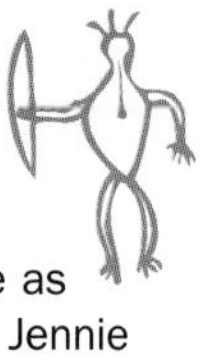

3. At the park, Jennie bought a souvenir map for $2.25, three postcards at $0.50 each, and a key ring for $1.00. How much money did she have left?

4. David had to write a 500-word report about the trip for his Language Arts class. He wrote half of the report at the park, and half of what was left on the way home. How many words did he have to write to finish the report?

364

Additional Problem

The sixth graders decided to present a play to raise money for a trip to a science museum in a nearby town. They charged $2 for adult tickets and $1.25 for student tickets. How much money did they make on the play?

1. What is the problem about? Determining the amount of money students raised by staging a play.
2. Is all the information given that you need to solve the problem? If not, what is missing? No; The number of each kind of ticket sold is missing.
3. If you had the missing information, how would you solve the problem? Multiply the number of student tickets sold by $1.25, the number of adult tickets sold by $2, and add the two amounts together.

Section 7A

Multiplying Fractions

Visit www.teacher.mathsurf.com for links to lesson plans from teachers and other professionals, NCTM information, and other sites.

LESSON PLANNING GUIDE

Student Edition | **Ancillaries***

LESSON		MATERIALS	VOCABULARY	DAILY	OTHER
	Chapter 7 Opener				Ch. 7 Project Master Ch. 7 Community Project Teaching Tool Trans. 1
	Problem Solving Focus				Teaching Tool Trans. 18 *Interactive CD-ROM Journal*
	Section 7A Opener				
7-1	**Estimation: Products and Quotients of Fractions**			7-1	
7-2	**Multiplying by a Whole Number**	colored pencils		7-2	Lesson Enhancement Trans. 33 Technology Master 31 *Interactive CD-ROM Lesson*
7-3	**Multiplying by a Fraction**	colored pencils		7-3	Teaching Tool Trans. 2, 3 Lesson Enhancement Trans. 34 Technology Master 32 Ch. 7 Project Master *Interactive CD-ROM Lesson*
	Connect				Interdisc. Team Teaching 7A
	Review				Practice 7A; Quiz 7A; *TestWorks*

* Daily Ancillaries include Practice, Reteaching, Problem Solving, Enrichment, and Daily Transparency. Teaching Tool Transparencies are in *Teacher's Toolkits*. Lesson Enhancement Transparencies are in *Overhead Transparency Package*.

SKILLS TRACE

LESSON	SKILL	FIRST INTRODUCED GR. 4	GR. 5	GR. 6	DEVELOP	PRACTICE/ APPLY	REVIEW
7-1	**Estimating products and quotients.**			✗ p. 366	pp. 366–367	pp. 368–369	pp. 380, 400, 471
7-2	**Multiplying whole numbers by fractions.**		✗		pp. 370–372	pp. 373–374	pp. 380, 400, 475
7-3	**Multiplying a fraction by a fraction.**		✗		pp. 375–376	pp. 377–378	pp. 380, 400, 480

CONNECTED MATHEMATICS

Investigation 5 in the unit *Bits and Pieces II (Using Rational Numbers),* from the **Connected Mathematics** series, can be used with Section 7A.

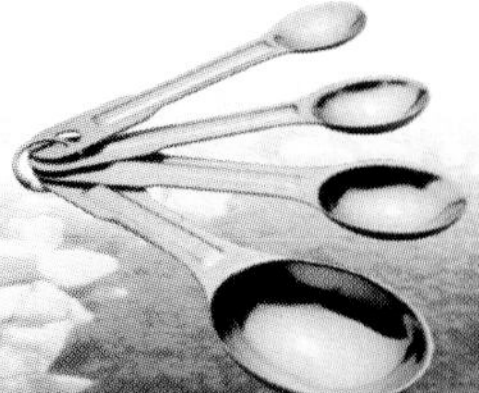

INTERDISCIPLINARY TEAM TEACHING

Math and Science/Technology

(Worksheet pages 33–34: Teacher pages T33–T34)

In this lesson, students multiply fractions to study human growth.

Name ______________________ ***Math and Science/Technology***

Big, Bigger...Wow!

Multiply fractions to study human growth.

Some of the most remarkable leaps in human growth take place before a baby is born. For example, during the second half of a baby's stay in its mother, it grows from about $1\frac{3}{5}$ ounces to about 7 pounds 11 ounces. That means that during this period of time, the developing baby increases in weight by an amazing factor of 77. If this happened to you now, in a little over four months you would weigh 77 times more than you do now!

Everyone's growth rate is different. Some young people grow very fast early and stop. Others do not grow tall until they are older. A girl who is very tall before her twelfth birthday will probably grow only a few inches after age twelve. Another girl might have a growth spurt after 12. Many factors influence the way a person grows, including nutrition, health, and genes—the "directions" for development you inherited from your parents.

To determine whether a person is growing within a normal range, doctors make a variety of measurements. For example, a doctor will regularly measure the circumference of an infant's head. In infancy, a baby's head grows at a relatively rapid rate. During a baby's first year, the circumference of a baby's head is greater than the circumference of its chest. But after a baby's first year, its chest becomes larger in proportion to the head because the growth of its head slows. So doctors monitor proportions like this to make sure a baby is developing as it should.

In addition to the head size, physicians measure a baby's height, and they keep measuring height at least until it stops increasing—around age 17 in girls and age 21 in boys. The speeding up or slowing down of this kind of growth can provide information about the health of a person.

You may have seen a chart on which a physician has plotted your height at various ages. If your growth rate had not been within a certain range, the physician would have searched for a reason.

1. On average, the circumference of an infant's head increases $\frac{1}{2}$ inch per month during the first four months after birth. From four months to one year of age, its head size increases a total of about two more inches. From age 1 to age 18, the increase is about four inches. What is the total increase in circumference from birth to age 18?

$(\frac{1}{2} \times 4) + 2 + 4 = 8$ inches

2. Physicians have noticed that healthy children tend to follow the same pattern of growth, even though they may not be the same height.

a. Child A and Child B are both normal. Child A is $\frac{7}{8}$ the height of Child B who is 2 feet $10\frac{1}{2}$ inches tall. How tall is Child A?

See below.

b. Assume that the same relationship of heights exists 15 years later when Child B is 5 feet 9 inches tall. How tall is Child A?

See below.

Name ______________________ ***Math and Science/Technology***

3. Babies gain an average of 2 pounds $3\frac{1}{5}$ ounces per month for the first three months after birth. If a baby starts out weighing $8\frac{1}{2}$ pounds, predict what it will weigh three months later? (Hint: 1 pound = 16 ounces)

See below.

4. a. Why is it important for physicians to regularly measure a child's growth?

See below.

b. Why is the ability to work with fractions an important tool for physicians?

See below.

5. Some physicians predict a person's adult height—plus or minus an inch—by doubling the person's height on his or her second birthday.

Do some research to locate the heights of some famous male and female basketball stars. Then complete the table below, which includes a prediction of the stars' heights at age 2.

Answers will vary.

6. Girls tend to have a growth spurt earlier than boys. That means that on average, girls tend to be taller than boys at certain ages and shorter at a certain other ages. And at still other ages, they are about the same height. Survey the heights of boys and girls at different ages from 10 to 17 and find the mean height for each group at each age. Graph your findings below. Based on the graph, at what ages are the mean heights of boys and girls about the same? How do you know?

See below.

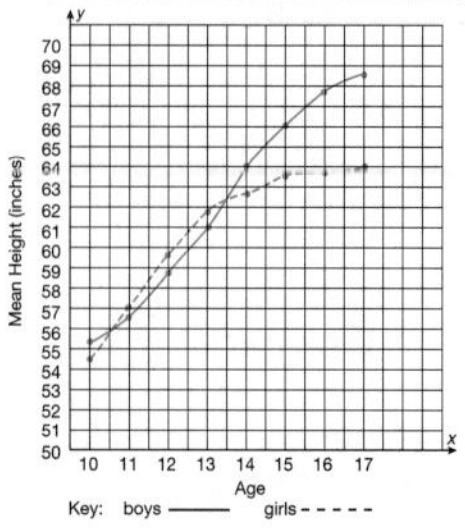

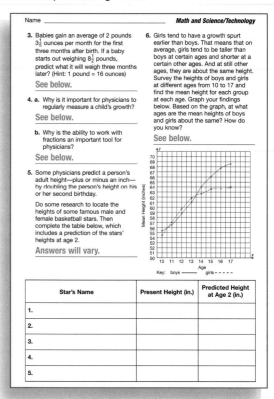

	Star's Name	Present Height (in.)	Predicted Height at Age 2 (in.)
1.			
2.			
3.			
4.			
5.			

Answers

2. a. $\frac{7}{8} \times 34\frac{1}{2}$ in. $= 30\frac{3}{16}$ in. or 2 ft $6\frac{3}{16}$ in.

   b. $\frac{7}{8} \times 69$ in. $= 60\frac{3}{8}$ in. or 5 ft $\frac{3}{8}$ in.

3. Change all values to ounces; 136 oz + (3 × 32 oz) + ($3 \times 3\frac{1}{5}$oz) = $241\frac{3}{5}$ oz = 15 pounds $1\frac{3}{5}$oz.

4. a. Possible answer: Frequent measurements help a doctor detect problems.

   b. Possible answer: When taking measurements, the results are often expressed in fractional parts.

6. According to statistics the answers should be about $10\frac{3}{4}$ and $13\frac{1}{2}$ years; These are the points on the graph where the lines for boys and girls intersect.

BIBLIOGRAPHY

FOR TEACHERS

Freidel, Frank Burt. *Franklin D. Roosevelt.* Boston, MA: Little Brown, 1990.

Geddes, Dorothy, et al. *Geometry in the Middle Grades: Addenda Series, Grades 5–8.* Reston, VA: NCTM, 1992.

Kenda, Margaret and Williams, Phyllis. *Math Wizardry for Kids.* Hauppauge, NY: Baron's, 1995.

McMillan, Bruce. *Eating Fractions.* New York, NY: Scholastic, 1991.

Spangler, David. *Math for Real Kids.* Glenview, IL: Good Year Books, 1997.

Weidensaul, Scott. *Hummingbirds.* New York, NY: Gallery Books, 1991.

FOR STUDENTS

Brown, Robert. *The World of Humingbirds.* Milwaukee, WI: Gareth Stevens, 1990.

Stienecker, David. *Fractions.* New York, NY: Benchmark Books, 1996.

SECTION **7A**

Multiplying Fractions

▶ Industry Link ▶ www.mathsurf.com/6/ch7/recipes

A TASTE FROM THE NORTH PACIFIC

The four recipes below are all authentic recipes. One of the four is different than the other three. Can you tell which recipe it is?

Chicken-Fried Muskrat	Sweet and Sour Porcupine	Wallpaper Paste	Eskimo Ice Cream (Akutaq)
Dressed muskrat Marinade: 1 quart water plus 1 tablespoon salt Salt, pepper, paprika, to taste Flour Bacon fat Sliced onions 1 cup sour cream	Legs of porcupine 2 sliced onions 1 cup cider vinegar $\frac{3}{4}$ cup brown sugar $\frac{1}{2}$ teaspoon nutmeg Fat	4 cups flour 1 cup sugar 1 gallon warm water 1 quart cold water	2 cups seal oil Bowl of loose snow $1\frac{1}{2}$ pounds of reindeer fat Wild berries

All the recipes are for food dishes, except for the third one. That's a recipe for the paste used when putting up wallpaper.

As you can see, recipes aren't used just for food. There are recipes for making candles, air fresheners, soap, paint, and cold cream. All recipes, whether they're food recipes or not, have one thing in common ... they all use mathematics.

1 What does something have to have in order for it to be considered a "recipe"?

2 Other than the examples above, what are some nonfood recipes?

3 Why does working with a recipe require an understanding of mathematics?

365

Where are we now?

In Chapter 6, students estimated sums and differences of fractions and mixed numbers. They learned to solve equations by adding and subtracting fractions and mixed numbers.

They learned how to

- use rounding to estimate sums and differences of mixed numbers.
- add and subtract fractions with like and unlike denominators.
- add and subtract mixed numbers.

Where are we going?

In Section 7A, students will

- estimate products and quotients of fractions.
- multiply fractions and mixed numbers by whole numbers.
- multiply fractions and mixed numbers by fractions.

Theme: Recipes

World Wide Web

If your class has access to the World Wide Web, you might want to use the information found at the Web site address given. The interdisciplinary link relates to topics discussed in this section.

About the Page

This page introduces the theme of the section, recipes, and discusses the characteristics of and uses for recipes.

Ask ...

- Have you ever followed a recipe to make a food or nonfood item? Answers may vary.
- Why do you think nonfood items such as paint have recipes? Possible answer: To guarantee uniformity of product.

Extension

The following activity does not require access to the World Wide Web.

Industry

Famous restaurant chefs may create recipes; supervise ordering, preparation, and presentation of the food; and write cookbooks. Have students identify other types of responsibilities within the food industry.

Answers for Questions

1. Possible answer: It has to have directions and a list of materials.
2. Possible answer: Dye, glue, potting soil, potpourri, shampoo.
3. Possible answer: You need to measure ingredients and you may need to alter recipes.

Connect

On page 379, students determine menu prices in a restaurant.

7-1

Lesson Organizer

Objective

- Estimate products and quotients of fraction problems.

NCTM Standards

- 1–4, 7

Review

Decide whether each fraction is greater than, less than, or equal to $\frac{1}{2}$.

1. $\frac{2}{3}$ Greater than
2. $\frac{3}{7}$ Less than
3. $\frac{4}{8}$ Equal to
4. $\frac{4}{9}$ Less than

Available on Daily Transparency 7-1

1 Introduce

Explore

The Point
Students explore estimating products of fractions by approximating quantities needed to modify a recipe and approximate prices.

Ongoing Assessment
Ask students about the reasonableness of their answers. For example, in Step 1, the amount of flour estimated for 90 ornaments should be less than that for 100 ornaments.

Answers for Explore

1. a. $6\frac{1}{2}$ cups flour, 2 cups salt, 3 cups water.
   b. 13 cups flour, 4 cups salt, 6 cups water.
   c. 9 cups flour, $2\frac{3}{4}$ cups salt, 4 cups water.
   d. 12 cups flour, $3\frac{1}{2}$ cups salt, 5 cups water.
   e. $1\frac{1}{2}$ cups flour, $\frac{1}{2}$ cup salt, $\frac{3}{4}$ cup water.
2. \$3; $\frac{3}{4}$ of 4 is 3.
3. \$11; $2\frac{2}{3}$ of \$4 is about \$11.
4. About 8; He's making about $\frac{1}{3}$ of the recipe.

7-1 Estimation: Products and Quotients of Fractions

You'll Learn ...

- to estimate products and quotients of fraction problems

... How It's Used

Farmers estimate fraction products when ordering feed for their animals.

► Lesson Link In the last chapter you learned to estimate sums and differences of fractions. Now you'll use these skills to estimate products and quotients of fractions. ◄

Explore Estimating Products of Fractions

Bringing Home the Dough

Ramon plans to use this recipe to make bread dough ornaments to sell at the school fair.

Ornaments

$3\frac{1}{4}$ cups flour
1 cup salt
$1\frac{1}{2}$ cups water
Makes 25 snowflake ornaments

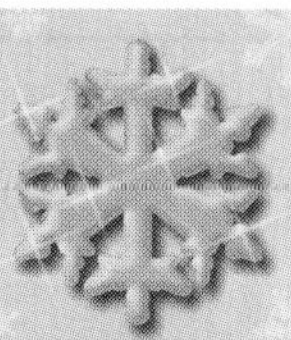

1. About how much flour, how much salt, and how much water will Ramon need to make each of the following numbers of snowflake ornaments?

   a. 50 **b.** 100 **c.** 70 **d.** 90 **e.** 12

2. Ramon will charge \$4 for a snowflake ornament. A star ornament is $\frac{3}{4}$ the size of a snowflake. If Ramon charges $\frac{3}{4}$ the price of a snowflake, about how much should he charge? Explain.
3. A bell ornament is $2\frac{2}{3}$ times the size of a snowflake. If Ramon charges $2\frac{2}{3}$ times the price of a snowflake, about how much should he charge?
4. If Ramon only had 1 cup of flour, and he adjusted the recipe accordingly, about how many snowflake ornaments could he make? Explain.

Learn Estimation: Products and Quotients of Fractions

You can use rounding to estimate products and quotients of fractions and mixed numbers.

- Round each factor to the nearest whole number.
- Multiply or divide the whole numbers.

MEETING INDIVIDUAL NEEDS

Resources

- 7-1 Practice
- 7-1 Reteaching
- 7-1 Problem Solving
- 7-1 Enrichment
- 7-1 Daily Transparency
  - Problem of the Day
  - Review
  - Quick Quiz

Learning Modalities

Social Have students work in groups and take turns explaining how estimates were found when multiplying and dividing fractions.

Verbal Have students describe techniques used to find estimates of products and quotients involving fractions.

Inclusion

Concrete activities may help some students make estimates. Have students use Fraction Bars or fraction circles to represent some of the fractions. Students can use these representations to help them estimate when multiplying or dividing the fraction by a number.

Examples

1 Estimate: $3\frac{1}{4} \times 5\frac{7}{8}$.

$\frac{1}{4} < \frac{1}{2}$, so $3\frac{1}{4}$ rounds down to 3.

$\frac{7}{8} > \frac{1}{2}$, so $5\frac{7}{8}$ rounds up to 6.

Estimate: $3 \times 6 = 18$.

2 Estimate: $8\frac{2}{3} \div 1\frac{1}{5}$.

$\frac{2}{3} > \frac{1}{2}$, so $8\frac{2}{3}$ rounds up to 9.

$\frac{1}{5} < \frac{1}{2}$, so $1\frac{1}{5}$ rounds down to 1.

Estimate: $9 \div 1 = 9$.

Remember

A fraction is less than $\frac{1}{2}$ if the numerator is less than half the denominator. [Page 343]

Try It

Estimate: **a.** $4\frac{3}{4} \times 3\frac{1}{6}$ 15 **b.** $1\frac{1}{3} \times 2\frac{1}{2}$ 3 **c.** $5\frac{2}{3} \div 1\frac{4}{5}$ 3 **d.** $1\frac{1}{3} \div \frac{3}{4}$ 1

When finding a product, if you round one number up, your result will be an *over*estimate.

When finding a quotient, if you round the dividend up, you will also get an overestimate. However, rounding the divisor up results in an *under*estimate. This is because the rounded number will divide the dividend into larger groups, so your estimate will have a smaller number of groups than the exact answer.

Example 3

A gardener wants to build a 36 ft fence using $3\frac{1}{2}$ ft long planks. About how many planks should the gardener buy to be sure there are enough?

Problem Solving TIP

You can also solve the problem by rewriting $3\frac{1}{2}$ as a decimal before you divide.

Estimate: $36 \div 3\frac{1}{2}$. To be sure there is enough wood, you should overestimate. Round the divisor *down*. This will give you a smaller number to divide by. As a result, the quotient will be greater: $36 \div 3 = 12$.

The gardener should buy 12 planks.

Check Your Understanding

1. When rounding fractions to the closest whole number, when do you round up?
2. Give a real-world circumstance with fractions where you should overestimate.

2 Teach

Learn

Alternate Examples

1. Estimate: $5\frac{3}{4} \times 4\frac{1}{3}$.

   $\frac{3}{4} > \frac{1}{2}$, so $5\frac{3}{4}$ rounds up to 6.

   $\frac{1}{3} < \frac{1}{2}$, so $4\frac{1}{3}$ rounds down to 4.

   Estimate: $6 \times 4 = 24$.

2. Estimate: $9\frac{1}{4} \div 2\frac{3}{4}$.

   $\frac{1}{4} < \frac{1}{2}$, so $9\frac{1}{4}$ rounds down to 9.

   $\frac{3}{4} > \frac{1}{2}$, so $2\frac{3}{4}$ rounds up to 3.

   Estimate: $9 \div 3 = 3$.

3. Jacob is making picture frames to sell. Each frame requires $2\frac{1}{2}$ ft of wood. He wants to make at least 10 frames. He has 30 ft of wood. Does he have enough wood?

   Estimate: $30 \div 2\frac{1}{2}$. To be sure that he has enough wood, he should overestimate the amount of wood he needs for each frame. Round the divisor up. The quotient will then be smaller: $30 \div 3 = 10$.

   Jacob will be able to make at least 10 frames.

3 Practice and Assess

Check

Answers for Check Your Understanding

1. When the numerator is greater than or equal to half of the denominator.
2. Possible answer: When buying $2\frac{3}{4}$ lb of fruit at $0.89 per pound, round both numbers up before multiplying to estimate how much money you will need.

MATH EVERY DAY

Problem of the Day

Put the given fractions in each circle so that each side of the triangle adds up to 1

Use these fractions:

$\frac{1}{3}, \frac{1}{4}, \frac{1}{6}, \frac{1}{12}, \frac{5}{12}, \frac{7}{12}$

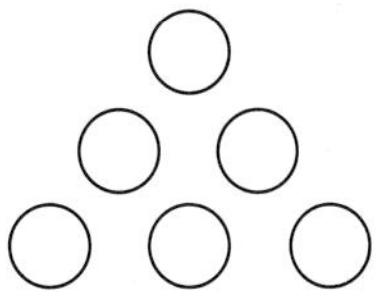

Possible answer:

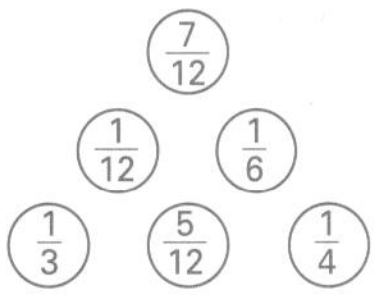

Available on Daily Transparency 7-1

An Extension is provided in the transparency package.

Fact of the Day

In 1790, the population of Massachusetts was 379,000. In 1990, Boston's population was 574,283.

Mental Math

Find each product mentally.

1. 2.2×10 22
2. 3.14×100 314
3. 4.589×1000 4589
4. 78.42×100 7842
5. 9.2×1000 9200

7-1 Exercises and Applications

Assignment Guide

- **Basic** 1–18, 31, 32, 34, 37–55 odds
- **Average** 1–3, 7–18, 31–35, 37, 39–55 odds
- **Enriched** 19–38, 40–56 evens

Exercise Notes

Exercises 1–30

Error Prevention If students are having difficulty estimating the answers, suggest that they use a number line to help them round the mixed numbers to whole numbers.

Exercise 31

Test Prep If students incorrectly choose D point out that although the fractions in III round down to 2×5, the actual product will be greater than 10.

Reteaching

Activity

- Draw a number line and label it from 0 to 5, placing a mark at each number and halfway between each number.
- Locate the following numbers on the number line and decide which whole number each is closest to.

  1. $3\frac{1}{3}$ 3
  2. $1\frac{4}{5}$ 2
  3. $4\frac{1}{6}$ 4
  4. $2\frac{3}{4}$ 3

- Then estimate the product of $3\frac{1}{3}$ times each of the numbers listed above. 9, 6, 12, 9

7-1 Exercises and Applications

PRACTICE 7-1

Practice and Apply

Getting Started **Round each mixed number to the nearest whole number.**

1. $4\frac{2}{3}$ 5 **2.** $3\frac{3}{7}$ 3 **3.** $6\frac{1}{8}$ 6 **4.** $5\frac{7}{10}$ 6 **5.** $8\frac{1}{2}$ 9 **6.** $8\frac{4}{8}$ 9

Estimate. Possible answers given for Exercises 7–30.

7. $3\frac{1}{5} \times 4\frac{7}{8}$ 15 **8.** $12\frac{1}{8} \div 6\frac{1}{3}$ 2 **9.** $9\frac{1}{2} \times 4\frac{7}{8}$ 50 **10.** $15\frac{1}{7} \div 2\frac{9}{10}$ 5

11. $2\frac{2}{3} \times 3\frac{6}{7}$ 12 **12.** $12\frac{9}{10} \div 6\frac{7}{8}$ 2 **13.** $8\frac{3}{5} \times 7\frac{3}{4}$ 72 **14.** $10\frac{2}{5} \div 5\frac{4}{13}$ 2

15. $6\frac{3}{8} \times 10\frac{2}{5}$ 60 **16.** $10\frac{4}{7} \div 5\frac{1}{2}$ 2 **17.** $6\frac{8}{10} \times 5\frac{3}{9}$ 35 **18.** $13\frac{4}{7} \div 3\frac{2}{7}$ 5

19. $4\frac{1}{4} \times 7\frac{3}{13}$ 28 **20.** $12\frac{2}{6} \div 4\frac{1}{3}$ 3 **21.** $2\frac{1}{2} \times 4\frac{1}{9}$ 12 **22.** $17\frac{5}{11} \div 3\frac{3}{10}$ 6

23. $5\frac{2}{11} \times 8\frac{1}{10}$ 40 **24.** $8\frac{5}{10} \div 3\frac{5}{6}$ 2 **25.** $10\frac{2}{7} \times 3\frac{4}{9}$ 30 **26.** $14\frac{6}{9} \div 6\frac{3}{8}$ 2

27. $9\frac{5}{9} \times 2\frac{2}{9}$ 20 **28.** $7\frac{5}{8} \div 2\frac{1}{4}$ 4 **29.** $6\frac{1}{3} \times 1\frac{3}{11}$ 6 **30.** $3\frac{2}{3} \div 1\frac{2}{4}$ 2

31. **Test Prep** Which products are less than 10? A

I. $1\frac{7}{8} \times 4\frac{5}{8}$ II. $6\frac{1}{2} \times 3\frac{1}{3}$ III. $2\frac{1}{3} \times 5\frac{1}{5}$

Ⓐ only I Ⓑ only II Ⓒ only III Ⓓ I and III

32. **Estimation** Mrs. McLaren wants to store some math books on a shelf. There are 21 books. Each book is $1\frac{5}{8}$ inches thick. Can she fit them all on a shelf that is $42\frac{1}{2}$ inches long? Yes

33. **History** Native Americans and the early European settlers used every part of the common swamp cattail as food. A recipe for cattail pancakes calls for $2\frac{2}{3}$ cups of cattail pollen. You have 6 cups of cattail pollen. Do you have enough to triple the recipe? No

PRACTICE

Name ____________

Practice 7-1

Estimation: Products and Quotients of Fractions

Estimate.

1. $6\frac{1}{3} \times 12\frac{1}{7}$ ≈ 72
2. $7\frac{9}{10} \div 3\frac{1}{3}$ $\approx 2\frac{2}{3}$
3. $4\frac{2}{3} \times 3\frac{3}{4}$ ≈ 20
4. $7\frac{2}{5} \div 2\frac{2}{3}$ $\approx 2\frac{1}{3}$
5. $3\frac{1}{3} \times 5\frac{1}{7}$ ≈ 15
6. $12\frac{3}{5} \div 7\frac{1}{5}$ $\approx 1\frac{6}{7}$
7. $7\frac{5}{8} \times 9\frac{3}{5}$ ≈ 80
8. $8\frac{2}{9} \div 3\frac{3}{5}$ ≈ 2
9. $7\frac{1}{4} \times 13\frac{4}{5}$ ≈ 98
10. $9\frac{1}{4} \div 3\frac{3}{4}$ $\approx 2\frac{1}{4}$
11. $2\frac{1}{2} \times 3\frac{4}{9}$ ≈ 9
12. $8\frac{7}{8} \div 3\frac{2}{9}$ ≈ 3
13. $4\frac{4}{5} \times 5\frac{1}{2}$ ≈ 30
14. $8\frac{2}{3} \div 4\frac{1}{3}$ $\approx 2\frac{1}{4}$
15. $7\frac{2}{5} \times 7\frac{1}{2}$ ≈ 56
16. $6\frac{1}{7} \div 2\frac{2}{5}$ ≈ 3
17. $9\frac{3}{4} \times 13\frac{5}{6}$ ≈ 140
18. $10\frac{1}{9} \div 5\frac{1}{6}$ ≈ 2
19. $11\frac{5}{7} \times 4\frac{2}{3}$ ≈ 60
20. $8\frac{3}{7} \div 4\frac{1}{6}$ ≈ 2
21. $7\frac{2}{3} \times 6\frac{1}{3}$ ≈ 48
22. $11\frac{2}{9} \div 6\frac{3}{7}$ ≈ 2
23. $3\frac{7}{10} \times 11\frac{1}{9}$ ≈ 44
24. $12\frac{4}{5} \div 6\frac{1}{9}$ $\approx 1\frac{6}{7}$
25. $8\frac{2}{3} \times 9\frac{8}{9}$ ≈ 90
26. $10\frac{3}{8} \div 5\frac{2}{5}$ ≈ 2
27. $4\frac{2}{5} \times 6\frac{1}{2}$ ≈ 28
28. $10\frac{4}{9} \div 5\frac{5}{6}$ $\approx 1\frac{2}{3}$
29. $11\frac{3}{4} \times 10\frac{5}{7}$ ≈ 132
30. $10\frac{1}{6} \div 6\frac{1}{3}$ $\approx 1\frac{2}{3}$
31. $3\frac{2}{3} \times 10\frac{2}{5}$ ≈ 40
32. $11\frac{1}{8} \div 6\frac{1}{4}$ $\approx 1\frac{5}{6}$
33. $12\frac{1}{3} \times 7\frac{1}{2}$ ≈ 96
34. $8\frac{3}{5} \div 4\frac{1}{10}$ $\approx 2\frac{1}{4}$
35. $3\frac{3}{4} \times 3\frac{7}{10}$ ≈ 16
36. $13\frac{3}{4} \div 7\frac{1}{2}$ $\approx 1\frac{3}{4}$
37. $9\frac{4}{7} \times 12\frac{5}{7}$ ≈ 130
38. $9\frac{2}{5} \div 4\frac{1}{3}$ $\approx 2\frac{1}{4}$
39. $8\frac{7}{9} \times 9\frac{4}{9}$ ≈ 81
40. A CD box measures $5\frac{5}{8}$ inches across. A music store manager wants to display 7 CDs side-by-side on a 42-inch shelf. Is there enough room for the display? Yes
41. Computer sales to dealers increased from about $\$2\frac{2}{5}$ billion in 1984 to about $\$8\frac{1}{2}$ billion in 1995. About how many times larger was the dollar amount of sales in 1995? About $4\frac{1}{2}$ times as large

RETEACHING

Name ____________

Alternative Lesson 7-1

Estimation: Products and Quotients of Fractions

You can use rounding to estimate products and quotients of fractions and mixed numbers.

- Round each factor to the nearest whole number.
- Multiply or divide the whole numbers.

Example 1

Estimate: $4\frac{3}{5} \times 2\frac{3}{8}$.

$4\frac{3}{5}$ × $2\frac{3}{8}$

$\frac{3}{5} > \frac{1}{2}$ Round up. $\frac{3}{8} < \frac{1}{2}$ Round down.

5 × 2 = 10 So, the estimate of $4\frac{3}{5} \times 2\frac{3}{8}$ is 10.

Try It

Estimate: $4\frac{2}{3} \times 5\frac{4}{9}$.

a. Round to the nearest whole number: $4\frac{2}{3} \to$ 5 $5\frac{4}{9} \to$ 5

b. Multiply. 5 × 5 = 25

Estimate.

c. $3\frac{7}{9} \times 5\frac{4}{15}$ 20 **d.** $8\frac{4}{9} \times 6\frac{5}{8}$ 56

Example 2

Estimate: $9\frac{7}{16} \div 2\frac{2}{3}$.

$9\frac{7}{16}$ ÷ $2\frac{2}{3}$

$\frac{7}{16} < \frac{1}{2}$ Round down. $\frac{2}{3} > \frac{1}{2}$ Round up.

9 ÷ 3 = 3 So, the estimate of $9\frac{7}{16} \div 2\frac{2}{3}$ is 3.

Try It

Estimate: $12\frac{3}{14} \div 3\frac{7}{8}$.

e. Round to the nearest whole number: $12\frac{3}{14} \to$ 12 $3\frac{7}{8} \to$ 4

f. Divide. 12 ÷ 4 = 3

Estimate.

g. $14\frac{7}{8} \div 5\frac{2}{5}$ 3 **h.** $75\frac{5}{24} \div 24\frac{17}{30}$ 3

34. A plumber needs 15 pieces of pipe, each $4\frac{1}{4}$ feet long. Will 58 feet of pipe be enough? No

35. Social Studies The population of Massachusetts in 1890 was $2\frac{1}{4}$ million. The population in 1990 was $6\frac{1}{6}$ million. About how many times larger was the population in 1990? 3

Boston, Massachusetts – 1890

Boston, Massachusetts – 1990

PROBLEM SOLVING 7-1

Problem Solving and Reasoning

36. Critical Thinking Use estimation to complete the table. Explain your reasoning.

Full Price	\$3.73	\$4.65	\$6.99	\$8.23
$\frac{1}{2}$ Price				
$\frac{3}{4}$ Price				

37. Critical Thinking Give five pairs of values for x and y so that $5\frac{x}{y}$ will round to 6 when rounded to the nearest whole number. What do all of your pairs of numbers have in common?

GPS

38. Journal In $6\frac{1}{4} \div 1\frac{1}{2}$, if you round only the first number up, you will get an overestimate. If you round only the second number up, you will get an underestimate. Explain why.

Mixed Review

Convert. *[Lesson 4-2]*

39. 8 m = ☐ cm 800 **40.** 126 L = ☐ mL 126,000 **41.** 976 mm = ☐ cm 97.6

42. 29 mL = ☐ L 0.029 **43.** 453 g = ☐ kg 0.453 **44.** 0.34 km = ☐ m 340

Tell whether the first number is divisible by the second. *[Lesson 5-1]*

45. 34, 9 No **46.** 55, 5 Yes **47.** 62, 4 No **48.** 88, 11 Yes **49.** 76, 2 Yes **50.** 54, 3 Yes

51. 1520, 10 Yes **52.** 63, 6 No **53.** 50, 7 No **54.** 32, 8 Yes **55.** 72, 6 Yes **56.** 5556, 5 No

PROBLEM SOLVING

Name ____________________

Guided Problem Solving 7-1

GPS **PROBLEM 37, STUDENT PAGE 369**

Give five pairs of values for x and y so that $5\frac{x}{y}$ will round to 6 when rounded to the nearest whole number. What do all of your pairs of numbers have in common?

— Understand —

1. Which whole number are you asked to round $5\frac{x}{y}$ to? 6

— Plan —

2. Will you round $5\frac{x}{y}$ up or down? Up.
3. If a fraction is less than $\frac{1}{2}$ will you round up or down to the nearest whole number? Round down.
4. Will the fractional part of $5\frac{x}{y}$ be less than or greater than or equal to $\frac{1}{2}$? Greater than or equal to.

— Solve —

5. Complete the table. Give five pairs of values for x and y so that $5\frac{x}{y}$ will round to 6.

x	2	3	4	5	6
y	3	4	5	6	7

6. What do all the pairs of numbers have in common?
Possible answer: Value of x is at least one half of value of y.

— Look Back —

7. Why did you decide whether to round $5\frac{x}{y}$ up or down before deciding on values for x and y? Possible answer: To determine whether the value of the fractions should be less than or greater than or equal to $\frac{1}{2}$.

SOLVE ANOTHER PROBLEM

Complete the table. Give five pairs of values for x and y so that $5\frac{x}{y}$ will round to 5 when rounded to the nearest whole number. What do all of your pairs of numbers have in common?

x	1	1	1	1	1
y	3	4	5	6	7

Possible answer: The value of x is less than one half the value of y.

ENRICHMENT

Name ____________________

Extend Your Thinking 7-1

Patterns in Numbers

For each of the sets of integers below, find the square of the middle number. Then multiply the first and last numbers, and add 1 to their product. The first one is completed for you.

	Square	Product + 1
1. 2, 3, 4	$3^2 = 9$	$(2 \times 4) + 1 = 8 + 1 = 9$
2. 3, 4, 5	$4^2 = 16$	$(3 \times 5) + 1 = 16$
3. 5, 6, 7	$6^2 = 36$	$(5 \times 7) + 1 = 36$
4. 11, 12, 13	$12^2 = 144$	$(11 \times 13) + 1 = 144$
5. 45, 46, 47	$46^2 = 2116$	$(45 \times 47) + 1 = 2116$
6. 99, 100, 101	$100^2 = 10{,}000$	$(99 \times 101) + 1 = 10{,}000$

Possible answers: Items 7–10

7. What pattern do you see in your calculations? The square of the middle number equals the product of the first and third number plus 1.

The integers in each set above are examples of consecutive integers. Consecutive integers are integers with a difference of 1.

8. Choose three other consecutive integers that each have at least four digits. Complete the same calculations as above. Does the pattern hold true?
2000, 2001, 2002; $2001^2 = 4{,}004{,}001$; $2000 \times 2002 + 1 = 4{,}004{,}001$; Yes, the pattern holds true.

9. Choose three integers that are not consecutive. Complete the same calculations as above. Does the pattern hold true? 2, 5, 10; $5^2 = 25$; $2 \times 10 + 1 = 21$. No, the pattern does not hold true.

10. Write a rule for the pattern. Given three *consecutive* integers, the square of the middle integer equals the product of the first and third integer plus 1.

Exercise Notes

■ Exercise 37

Extension Have students find five pairs of values for x and y so that $5\frac{x}{y}$ will round to 5 when rounded to the nearest whole number. Possible answers: (1, 3), (1, 4), (1, 5), (1, 6), (2, 5)

■ Exercises 45–56

Error Prevention If students have difficulty with these exercises, review the rules of divisibility and then have them check their answers with a calculator.

Exercise Answers

36. $\frac{1}{2}$ price: \$2, \$2.50, \$3.50, \$4; $\frac{3}{4}$ price: \$3, \$3.75, \$5.25, \$6; Round full price to nearest whole number, then multiply by $\frac{1}{2}$ and $\frac{3}{4}$.

37. (1,2), (2,4), (3,5), (4,5), (5,6); Each x is greater than or equal to half of its corresponding y.

38. When you round the dividend up, you are dividing a larger number of items into the same amount of groups, so each group will have more items. When you round the divisor up, you are dividing the same number of items into more groups, so each group will have fewer items.

Alternate Assessment

You may want to use the *Interactive CD-ROM Journal* with this assessment.

Journal Write a paragraph describing how to find estimates when multiplying or dividing mixed numbers.

▶ Quick Quiz

Estimate.

1. $2\frac{4}{5} \times 3\frac{1}{3}$ 9
2. $7\frac{1}{2} \times 2\frac{1}{12}$ 16
3. $12\frac{1}{4} \div 6\frac{3}{10}$ 2
4. $8\frac{3}{4} \div 2\frac{5}{6}$ 3

Available on Daily Transparency 7-1

INTERACTIVE LESSON

7-2 Lesson Organizer

Objective

- Multiply whole numbers by fractions.

Materials

- Explore: Colored pencils

NCTM Standards

- 1–4, 7, 10

Review

Write each mixed number as an improper fraction.

1. $3\frac{1}{2}$ $\frac{7}{2}$
2. $2\frac{3}{4}$ $\frac{11}{4}$
3. $5\frac{2}{3}$ $\frac{17}{3}$
4. $4\frac{1}{6}$ $\frac{25}{6}$

Available on Daily Transparency 7-2

1 Introduce

Explore

You may wish to use Lesson Enhancement Transparency 33 with **Explore**.

The Point
Students explore multiplying a whole number by a fraction by drawing a number of fraction sketches, shading the fractional part of each strip, and counting the shaded parts.

Ongoing Assessment
As students are drawing the models, make sure that they are drawing separate sketches with sections of approximately the same size. Students should realize that each strip represents 1.

For Groups That Finish Early
Multiply without drawing models.

1. $3 \times \frac{1}{4}$ $\frac{3}{4}$
2. $2 \times \frac{4}{5}$ $1\frac{3}{5}$
3. $4 \times \frac{2}{3}$ $2\frac{2}{3}$

Draw models to check your answers.

7-2 Multiplying by a Whole Number

You'll Learn ...

- to multiply whole numbers by fractions

... How It's Used

Zoologists multiply whole numbers and fractions when describing an animal's diet.

▶ Lesson Link In earlier lessons, you learned to multiply decimals by whole numbers. Now you'll multiply fractions by whole numbers. ◀

Explore Multiplying by a Whole Number

A Strip in Time

Materials: Colored pencils

Multiplying a Fraction by a Whole Number

- Draw a number of strips equal to the whole number.
- Divide the strips into equal sections. The number of sections should be equal to the fraction denominator.
- In each strip, color in the number of sections equal to the numerator.
- Describe the number modeled.

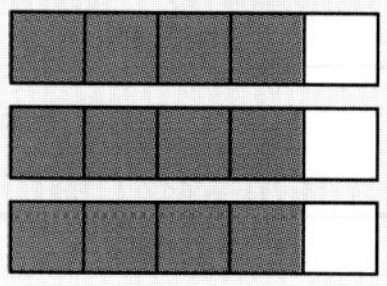

1. Model these problems.

a. $2 \times \frac{2}{5}$ **b.** $7 \times \frac{1}{2}$ **c.** $\frac{2}{3} \times 5$ **d.** $4 \times \frac{5}{9}$

e. $\frac{4}{5} \times 3$ **f.** $\frac{2}{7} \times 1$ **g.** $6 \times \frac{2}{2}$ **h.** $\frac{1}{8} \times 8$

2. Why does your answer have the same denominator as the fraction in the problem? Why does your answer have a different numerator?

3. Is your answer bigger than the whole number you started with or smaller than the whole number you started with? Why?

Learn Multiplying by a Whole Number

You can model the product 3×5 by showing 3 sets with 5 objects in each set. In the same way, you can model the product $3 \times \frac{5}{6}$ by showing 3 sets with $\frac{5}{6}$ in each set.

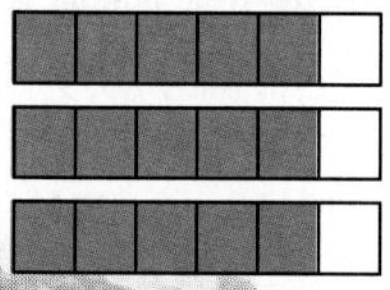

MEETING INDIVIDUAL NEEDS

Resources

- 7-2 Practice
- 7-2 Reteaching
- 7-2 Problem Solving
- 7-2 Enrichment
- 7-2 Daily Transparency
  - Problem of the Day
  - Review
  - Quick Quiz
- Lesson Enhancement Transparency 33
- Technology Master 31
- *Interactive CD-ROM Lesson*

Learning Modalities

Verbal Have students write several different word problems that could be solved by finding $3 \times \frac{3}{4}$.

Kinesthetic Have students fold sheets of paper and shade the same amount of each to illustrate multiplying a whole number by a fraction.

English Language Development

Have students work in pairs to discuss the parts of models used to multiply a fraction by a whole number. Have students name the parts and the shaded sections. They may conclude, for example, that 4 groups of 2 thirds is the same as 8 thirds, or 2 wholes and 2 thirds.

To multiply a fraction or mixed number by a whole number, write both factors as fractions. Then write the product of the numerators over the product of the denominators. Simplify if necessary.

Example 1

A recipe for hummingbird food calls for $1\frac{5}{8}$ cups of sugar. How much sugar should you use to triple the recipe?

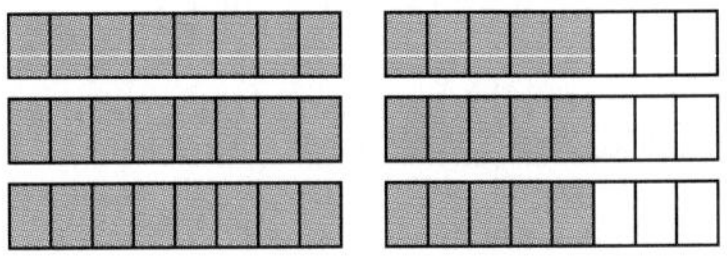

Multiply: $3 \times 1\frac{5}{8}$

$3 \times 1\frac{5}{8} = \frac{3}{1} \times \frac{13}{8}$ Write the factors as fractions.

$= \frac{3 \times 13}{1 \times 8}$ Multiply the numerators. Multiply the denominators.

$= \frac{39}{8}$ or $4\frac{7}{8}$ Simplify.

You should use $4\frac{7}{8}$ cups of sugar.

Some problems ask you to find the fractional part of a whole number. These problems can be solved using multiplication with fractions.

Example 2

About $\frac{2}{3}$ of the 360 students at Kensington Middle School belong to an after-school club or activity. How many students is this?

$360 \times \frac{2}{3} = \frac{360}{1} \times \frac{2}{3}$ Write the factors as fractions.

$= \frac{360 \times 2}{1 \times 3}$ Multiply the numerators. Multiply the denominators.

$= \frac{720}{3}$ or 240 Simplify.

240 students participate in a club or activity.

Try It

Simplify.

a. $4 \times \frac{2}{3}$ $2\frac{2}{3}$ **b.** $3 \times 1\frac{3}{4}$ $5\frac{1}{4}$ **c.** $\frac{1}{2}$ of 16 8 **d.** $\frac{5}{6}$ of 30 25

▶ Science Link

Because the hummingbird has a rapid metabolism, it must consume a tremendous amount of calories. If a hummingbird were the size of a man, it would need to consume 155,000 calories each day, the equivalent of 80 gallons of yogurt.

Problem Solving TIP

In math problems, the word *of* frequently suggests multiplication.

MATH EVERY DAY

▶ Problem of the Day

You know that every even number greater than two can be written as the sum of two prime numbers. Is the following statement true?

Any odd number can be written as the sum of three prime numbers.

Explain your answer. Yes. Even numbers can be written as the sum of two prime numbers, so odd numbers can be written as 3 plus the sum of two prime numbers.

Available on Daily Transparency 7-2

An Extension is provided in the transparency package.

Fact of the Day

The maximum recorded life span of the hippopotamus is 54 years, 4 months. For the African elephant it is 70 years.

Estimation

Estimate each product.

1. 8×36 320
2. 4×98 400
3. 99×115 10,000

Follow Up

Have students share the answers found in Step 1. Have students discuss the answers to Steps 2 and 3.

Answers for Explore

1. See page C1.
2. The sizes of the sections stay the same, but the number of sections changes.
3. Possible answer: When a whole number is multiplied by a fraction less than 1, the answer is smaller than the whole number. When a whole number is multiplied by a fraction greater than 1, the answer is larger than the whole number.

2 Teach

Learn

Alternate Examples

1. Jack wants to display 4 pictures, each one being $5\frac{3}{4}$ inches wide. How wide must the bulletin board be so that he can display the pictures side by side?

   Multiply: $4 \times 5\frac{3}{4}$

   $4 \times 5\frac{3}{4} = \frac{4}{1} \times \frac{23}{4}$

   $= \frac{4 \times 23}{1 \times 4}$

   $= \frac{92}{4}$ or 23

   The bulletin board must be 23 inches wide.

2. The sixth-grade class wants to sell 250 tickets to the school play. $\frac{4}{5}$ of the tickets have been sold. How many tickets have been sold?

   $250 \times \frac{4}{5} = \frac{250}{1} \times \frac{4}{5}$

   $= \frac{250 \times 4}{1 \times 5}$

   $= \frac{1000}{5}$ or 200

   200 tickets have been sold.

WHAT DO YOU THINK?

Students see two methods of multiplying a mixed number by a whole number. One method uses the Distributive Property and the other method uses improper fractions.

Answers for What Do You Think?

1. To use the Distributive Property, you break the number apart, multiply each piece, and then add the pieces back together.
2. Answers may vary.

3 Practice and Assess

Check

Answers for Check Your Understanding

1. Possible answer: No; The product is always smaller than the whole number and larger than or equal to the fraction.
2. Yes; In multiplication expressions, the factors can be written in any order and the product will always be the same.

WHAT DO YOU THINK?

Lauren and Skye are making wallpaper paste. They have $2\frac{3}{4}$ cups of sugar, and they want to adjust the recipe to use all of it. They need to determine how much flour to use in the adjusted recipe.

Wallpaper Paste

4 cups flour
1 cup sugar
1 gallon warm water
1 quart cold water

Lauren thinks ...

I'll multiply the 4 cups of flour by $2\frac{3}{4}$ using the Distributive Property.

First, I'll multiply 4 times the whole number in $2\frac{3}{4}$. $4 \times \mathbf{2} = 8$

Next, I'll multiply 4 times the fraction in $2\frac{3}{4}$. $4 \times \frac{\mathbf{3}}{\mathbf{4}} = +\ 3$

Now I'll add the results. 11

We need 11 cups of flour.

Skye thinks ...

I'll multiply by writing both factors as fractions.

$$4 \times 2\frac{3}{4} = \frac{4}{1} \times \frac{11}{4} = \frac{4 \times 11}{1 \times 4} = \frac{44}{4} = 11$$

We need 11 cups of flour.

What do you think?

1. Why did Lauren add 8 + 3 instead of multiplying 8 × 3?
2. Which method is easier to use mentally? Explain.

Check Your Understanding

1. Is the product of a whole number and a proper fraction always larger than either number? Explain.
2. Are the products $12 \times \frac{3}{5}$ and $\frac{3}{5} \times 12$ equal? Explain.

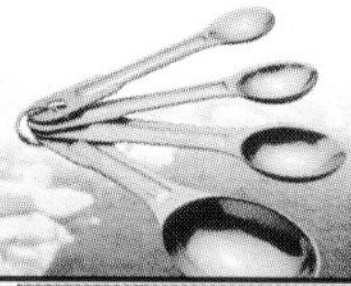

MEETING MIDDLE SCHOOL CLASSROOM NEEDS

Tips from Middle School Teachers

In learning about multiplication of fractions, I use sets of fraction models and recipes that list a number of fractions. First, I ask students to assemble all the necessary fraction models for the recipe. Then I have them multiply the recipe portions by 2 to show how twice the recipe could be made.

Team Teaching

Work with a home economics teacher to demonstrate and prepare a recipe that has to be doubled, tripled, or quadrupled to feed the entire class.

Science Connection

The smallest hummingbird, the bee hummingbird, lives in Cuba. It measures about $2\frac{1}{4}$ inches from the tip of its bill to the end of its tail. The smallest hummingbird in the United States is the calliope hummingbird, which measures about $2\frac{3}{4}$ inches.

7-2 Exercises and Applications

Practice and Apply

Getting Started Write the multiplication problem each model represents.

1.

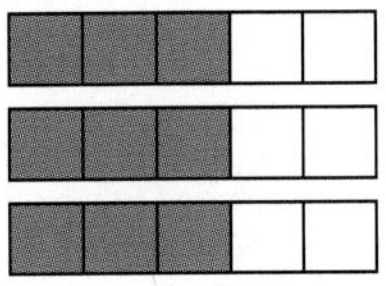

$3 \times \frac{3}{5}$

2.

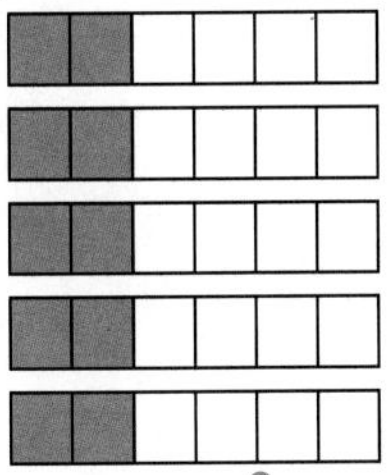

$5 \times \frac{2}{6}$

3.

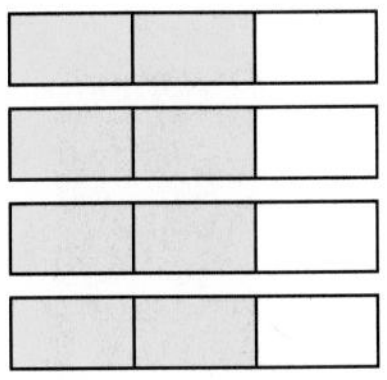

$4 \times \frac{2}{3}$

4.

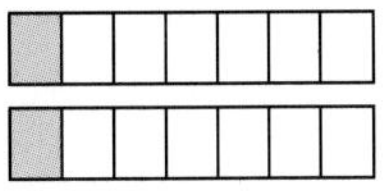

$2 \times \frac{1}{7}$

Simplify.

5. $\frac{1}{3} \times 2$ $\frac{2}{3}$

6. $\frac{1}{6} \times 8$ $1\frac{1}{3}$

7. $2 \times \frac{3}{10}$ $\frac{3}{5}$

8. $3\frac{3}{8} \times 5$ $16\frac{7}{8}$

9. $10 \times \frac{2}{3}$ $6\frac{2}{3}$

10. $\frac{2}{7} \times 7$ 2

11. $\frac{2}{3} \times 3$ 2

12. $4 \times \frac{5}{7}$ $2\frac{6}{7}$

13. $\frac{1}{4} \times 6$ $1\frac{1}{2}$

14. $3 \times \frac{3}{11}$ $\frac{9}{11}$

15. $\frac{3}{5} \times 11$ $6\frac{3}{5}$

16. $\frac{4}{8} \times 6$ 3

17. $5 \times \frac{4}{9}$ $2\frac{2}{9}$

18. $\frac{3}{7} \times 9$ $3\frac{6}{7}$

19. $9 \times \frac{6}{10}$ $5\frac{2}{5}$

20. $1 \times \frac{11}{12}$ $\frac{11}{12}$

21. $3 \times 1\frac{7}{12}$ $4\frac{3}{4}$

22. $4\frac{5}{9} \times 12$ $54\frac{2}{3}$

23. $7 \times 1\frac{5}{6}$ $12\frac{5}{6}$

24. $12 \times 2\frac{10}{11}$ $34\frac{10}{11}$

25. $2\frac{2}{5} \times 4$ $9\frac{3}{5}$

26. $6 \times \frac{3}{7}$ $2\frac{4}{7}$

27. $8 \times 3\frac{3}{8}$ 27

28. $5\frac{2}{7} \times 10$ $52\frac{6}{7}$

29. Health Complete the table for calories in orange juice.

Servings	$\frac{1}{4}$	$\frac{1}{2}$	$\frac{3}{4}$	1	$1\frac{1}{2}$	2
Ounces			8			
Calories			110			

30. **Test Prep** Andrew has read $\frac{3}{4}$ of his 304-page book. How many pages has he read? C

Ⓐ 76 Ⓑ 152 Ⓒ 228 Ⓓ None of these

PRACTICE

Name ______________________

Practice 7-2

Multiplying by a Whole Number

Simplify.

1. $5\frac{1}{2} \times 3$ $16\frac{1}{2}$
2. $3 \times 4\frac{5}{6}$ $14\frac{1}{2}$
3. $4 \times 5\frac{2}{3}$ $22\frac{2}{3}$
4. $10 \times 3\frac{5}{6}$ $38\frac{1}{3}$
5. $12\frac{4}{7} \times 4$ $50\frac{2}{7}$
6. $10 \times 2\frac{1}{3}$ $23\frac{1}{3}$
7. $6 \times 6\frac{1}{7}$ $36\frac{6}{7}$
8. $4\frac{1}{2} \times 2$ 9
9. $3\frac{4}{7} \times 8$ $28\frac{4}{7}$
10. $12 \times 3\frac{1}{4}$ 39
11. $5 \times 5\frac{1}{3}$ $26\frac{2}{3}$
12. $14 \times 3\frac{1}{2}$ 49
13. $3\frac{3}{4} \times 2$ $7\frac{1}{2}$
14. $4 \times 9\frac{5}{9}$ $38\frac{2}{9}$
15. $3 \times 6\frac{2}{3}$ 20
16. $8 \times 5\frac{3}{5}$ $44\frac{4}{5}$
17. $10 \times 4\frac{1}{2}$ 45
18. $4 \times 12\frac{2}{3}$ $50\frac{2}{3}$
19. $8\frac{1}{6} \times 4$ $32\frac{2}{3}$
20. $11 \times 4\frac{1}{3}$ $47\frac{2}{3}$
21. $10\frac{1}{2} \times 5$ $52\frac{1}{2}$
22. $14 \times 3\frac{1}{5}$ $44\frac{4}{5}$
23. $2\frac{1}{2} \times 5$ $12\frac{1}{2}$
24. $7 \times 7\frac{5}{9}$ $52\frac{8}{9}$
25. $10\frac{1}{2} \times 2$ 21
26. $7\frac{1}{5} \times 6$ $43\frac{1}{5}$
27. $13 \times 2\frac{1}{2}$ $32\frac{1}{2}$
28. $6\frac{5}{6} \times 4$ $27\frac{1}{3}$
29. $4\frac{1}{5} \times 4$ $16\frac{4}{5}$
30. $12\frac{5}{7} \times 4$ $50\frac{6}{7}$
31. $4 \times 10\frac{1}{2}$ 42
32. $11\frac{7}{10} \times 4$ $46\frac{4}{5}$
33. $2 \times 13\frac{1}{4}$ $26\frac{1}{2}$
34. $12 \times 2\frac{4}{7}$ $30\frac{6}{7}$
35. $4 \times 11\frac{2}{3}$ $46\frac{2}{3}$
36. $8\frac{1}{7} \times 4$ $32\frac{4}{7}$
37. $4 \times 12\frac{1}{2}$ 50
38. $10\frac{3}{4} \times 4$ 43
39. $3 \times 12\frac{1}{5}$ $36\frac{3}{5}$

40. **Health** Complete the table for calories in a certain brand of granola cereal.

Servings	$\frac{1}{2}$	$\frac{2}{3}$	$\frac{3}{4}$	1	$1\frac{1}{3}$	$2\frac{1}{2}$
Ounces	1	$1\frac{1}{3}$	$1\frac{1}{2}$	2	$2\frac{2}{3}$	5
Calories	120	160	180	240	320	600

41. **Science** The longest recorded jump by a kangaroo covered a distance of 45 feet. This is $3\frac{3}{4}$ times the longest jump from a standing position by a human. Find the length of the longest jump from a standing position by a human. 12 ft

RETEACHING

Name ______________________

Alternative Lesson 7-2

Multiplying by a Whole Number

To multiply a fraction or mixed number by a whole number, first write both numbers as fractions. Then write the product of the numerators over the product of the denominators. Simplify if necessary.

Example 1

Multiply: $6 \times \frac{3}{4}$.

Write the whole number as an improper fraction. $6 \times \frac{3}{4} = \frac{6}{1} \times \frac{3}{4}$

Multiply the numerators. Then multiply the denominators. $= \frac{6 \times 3}{1 \times 4}$

Multiply and simplify. $= \frac{18}{4} = 4\frac{2}{4} = 4\frac{1}{2}$

So, $6 \times \frac{3}{4} = 4\frac{1}{2}$.

Example 2

Multiply: $4 \times 1\frac{3}{5}$.

Write the mixed number as an improper fraction. $4 \times 1\frac{3}{5} = \frac{4}{1} \times \frac{8}{5}$

Multiply the numerators. Then multiply the denominators. $= \frac{4 \times 8}{1 \times 5}$

Simplify. $= \frac{32}{5} = 6\frac{2}{5}$

So, $4 \times 1\frac{3}{5} = 6\frac{2}{5}$.

Try It

Multiply: $\frac{2}{3} \times 5$.

a. Write the whole number as an improper fraction. $5 = \frac{5}{1}$

b. Multiply numerators and denominators. $\frac{2}{3} \times \frac{5}{1} = \frac{10}{3}$

c. Simplify. $\frac{10}{3} = 3\frac{1}{3}$

Multiply.

d. $\frac{3}{8} \times 9$ $3\frac{3}{8}$

e. $8 \times \frac{3}{5}$ $4\frac{4}{5}$

f. $1\frac{1}{2} \times 8$ 12

g. $\frac{5}{8} \times 9$ $5\frac{5}{8}$

h. $12 \times \frac{4}{5}$ $9\frac{3}{5}$

i. $1\frac{1}{2} \times 7$ $10\frac{1}{2}$

j. $2 \times \frac{5}{6}$ $1\frac{2}{3}$

k. $9 \times 3\frac{2}{3}$ 33

PRACTICE 7-2

Assignment Guide

- **Basic**
  1–16, 29–32, 36–39, 43–46
- **Average**
  1–27 odds, 29–39, 43–45
- **Enriched**
  3, 13–27 odds, 29–36, 38–48 evens

Exercise Notes

Exercises 5–28

Error Prevention If students are not getting the correct answers, check that they are writing each whole number as a fraction with a denominator of 1 before they multiply.

Exercise 30

Test Prep If students incorrectly choose A or B, tell them to recheck their multiplication.

Exercise Answers

29. Ounces: $2\frac{2}{3}$, $5\frac{1}{3}$, 8, $10\frac{2}{3}$, 16, $21\frac{1}{3}$; Calories: $36\frac{2}{3}$, $73\frac{1}{3}$, 110, $146\frac{2}{3}$, 220, $293\frac{1}{3}$.

Reteaching

Activity

Materials: Small paper squares

- Put 10 paper squares on your desk. Model $\frac{1}{2} \times 10$ by separating the squares into 2 equal groups. What is $\frac{1}{2} \times 10$? 5
- Model $\frac{1}{2} \times 5$ by separating 5 squares into 2 equal groups. You will need to cut one square in half. What is $\frac{1}{2} \times 5$? $2\frac{1}{2}$
- Model $\frac{2}{3} \times 6$ by separating 6 squares into 3 equal groups. Count the number of squares in 2 groups. What is $\frac{2}{3} \times 6$? 4
- Find the product by modeling each problem.
  1. $\frac{1}{3} \times 9$ 3
  2. $\frac{3}{4} \times 12$ 9
  3. $\frac{1}{2} \times 11$ $5\frac{1}{2}$
  4. $\frac{2}{5} \times 15$ 6

Exercise Notes

■ Exercise 36

Error Prevention Students may need to be reminded that there are 16 oz in a pound. Some students may find it useful to rewrite 1 lb 9 oz as $1\frac{9}{16}$ lb.

Exercise Answers

34. Possible answer: Less than; The product of a whole number and a proper fraction is always less than the whole number.

36. \$12.50; 1 lb 9 oz = $1\frac{9}{16}$ lb, $8 \times 1\frac{9}{16} = 12.5$.

Alternate Assessment

Performance Have students work in small groups to write three real-life problems which would be solved by multiplying a fraction by a whole number.

► Quick Quiz

Multiply.

1. $3 \times \frac{3}{4}$ $2\frac{1}{4}$
2. $\frac{2}{3} \times 7$ $4\frac{2}{3}$
3. $5 \times 2\frac{1}{5}$ 11

Available on Daily Transparency 7-2

PROBLEM SOLVING 7-2

31. History In colonial times, houses in New England were often painted with a glazed whitewash. One gallon of whitewash includes $\frac{3}{4}$ lb rice and $\frac{1}{2}$ lb sugar. How much of these ingredients are needed for 3 gallons of whitewash? $2\frac{1}{4}$ lb rice and $1\frac{1}{2}$ lb sugar

Science **Use the Life Span graph for Exercises 32 and 33.**

32. The maximum recorded life span for a baboon is $2\frac{1}{4}$ times the average. What is the maximum recorded life span? 45 years

33. The maximum recorded life span of a domestic cat is $2\frac{1}{3}$ times the average life span. What is the maximum recorded life span? 28 years

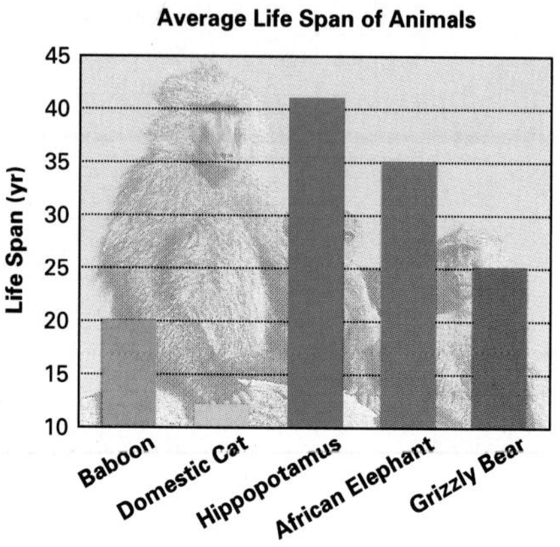

Problem Solving and Reasoning

34. Journal Explain how you can tell without multiplying if the product of $\frac{9}{10}$ and 15 is more than 15 or less than 15.

35. Critical Thinking Which does *not* have the same product as $6 \times 2\frac{1}{2}$? Explain. B; $\frac{2}{5}$ is not equivalent to $2\frac{1}{2}$

Ⓐ $6 \times \frac{5}{2}$ Ⓑ $\frac{6}{1} \times \frac{2}{5}$ Ⓒ $2\frac{1}{2} \times 6$ Ⓓ 6×2.5

36. Critical Thinking GPS Castile soap is named for the kingdom of Castile in Spain where the soap was first produced. To make about 36 bars, 1 pound 9 ounces of olive oil is needed. If a pound of olive oil costs \$8.00, how much does the olive oil for this recipe cost? Explain.

Mixed Review

Convert. *[Lesson 4-3]*

37. 1176 inches = ☐ feet 98 **38.** 38 feet = ☐ inches 456 **39.** 96 inches = ☐ feet 8

40. 102 feet = ☐ inches 1224 **41.** 204 inches = ☐ feet 17 **42.** 48 feet = ☐ inches 576

Find the prime factorization. *[Lesson 5-2]*

43. 63 $3^2 \times 7$ **44.** 1060 $2^2 \times 5 \times 53$ **45.** 17 17 **46.** 99 $3^2 \times 11$ **47.** 57 3×19 **48.** 34 2×17

PROBLEM SOLVING

Name ______

Guided Problem Solving 7-2

GPS PROBLEM 36, STUDENT PAGE 374

Castile soap is named for the kingdom of Castile in Spain where the soap was first produced. To make about 36 bars, 1 pound 9 ounces of olive oil is needed. If a pound of olive oil costs \$8.00, how much does the olive oil for this recipe cost? Explain.

— Understand —

1. Underline what you are asked to find.
2. What is the cost per pound of the olive oil? \$8.00
3. How much olive oil is used to make 36 bars of soap? 1 pound 9 ounces

— Plan —

4. There are 16 ounces in one pound. How many ounces of olive oil are used to make 36 bars of soap? 25 ounces
5. Write the quantity of olive oil as an improper fraction. $\frac{25}{16}$
6. Write an expression to show how to find the cost of the olive oil used in 36 bars of Castile soap. $\frac{25}{16} \times 8$

— Solve —

7. What is the cost to make 36 bars of soap? \$12.50
8. Explain how you found the answer. Possible answer: Found number of ounces used and cost per ounce; then multiplied these two amounts.

— Look Back —

9. How could you find your answer in a different way? Possible answer: Find cost of fractional part, $\frac{9}{16} \times 8 = 4.50$. Add to cost of a pound, \$8.

SOLVE ANOTHER PROBLEM

To make about 72 bars, 3 pounds 2 ounces of olive oil is needed. If a pound of olive oil costs \$9.00, how much does the olive oil for this recipe cost? Round your answer to the nearest cent. Explain.
\$28.13; 3 pounds 2 ounces = 50 ounces; $50 \times \frac{9}{16} = 28.125$.

ENRICHMENT

Name ______

Extend Your Thinking 7-2

Decision Making

An important thing to learn about fractions is that the size of the fraction is related to the size of the whole. For instance, $\frac{1}{2}$ of a large pizza is much larger than $\frac{1}{2}$ of a small pizza, even though each is a half. A half of a dime is much less than a half of a dollar!

1. Would you rather have $\frac{1}{2}$ of two pounds of pennies or $\frac{1}{3}$ of one pound of silver dollars? Explain.
   Possible answer: $\frac{1}{3}$ of one pound of silver dollars. Even though there are fewer pounds, the value is greater.
2. Would you rather have $\frac{1}{2}$ of one million dollars or $\frac{1}{3}$ of two million dollars? Explain.
   Possible answer: $\frac{1}{3}$ of two million dollars. $\frac{1}{3}$ of two million is about \$666,667; $\frac{1}{2}$ of one million is only \$500,000.
3. Which would be less, $\frac{7}{8}$ of a collection of 250,000 baseball cards, or $\frac{1}{2}$ of another collection of 500,000 baseball cards? How did you find the answer?
   Possible answer: $\frac{1}{2}$ of 500,000; $\frac{1}{2}$ of 500,000 is 250,000 which is more than any fraction of 250,000.
4. Which would be more, $\frac{1}{2}$ of 3 dozen chocolate chip cookies or $\frac{1}{6}$ of 12 dozen chocolate chip cookies? How do you know?
   Possible answer: $\frac{1}{6}$ of 12 dozen; $\frac{1}{6}$ of 12 is 2 which is greater than $\frac{1}{2}$ of 3, or $1\frac{1}{2}$.
5. Write a similar problem that has you compare the value of fractions. Trade problems with a classmate and solve.
   Check students' problems.

Multiplying by a Fraction

7-3

▶ Lesson Link In the last lesson, you learned to multiply fractions and mixed numbers by whole numbers. Now you'll multiply fractions and mixed numbers by fractions. ◀

You'll Learn ...

■ to multiply a fraction by another fraction

... How It's Used

Consumers multiply fractions by fractions when calculating the price of an item with multiple discounts.

Explore Multiplying by a Fraction

Inner Sections

Materials: Colored pencils

Multiplying a Fraction by a Fraction

- Draw a rectangle. Divide it vertically into equal sections. There should be as many sections as the denominator of the first number.
- Divide the rectangle horizontally into equal sections. There should be as many sections as the denominator of the second number.
- Color in a number of vertical strips equal to the numerator in the first number.
- Use a different color to shade a number of horizontal strips equal to the numerator in the second number.
- Describe the area where both colors overlap.

$\frac{2}{5} \times \frac{3}{4} = \frac{6}{20}$

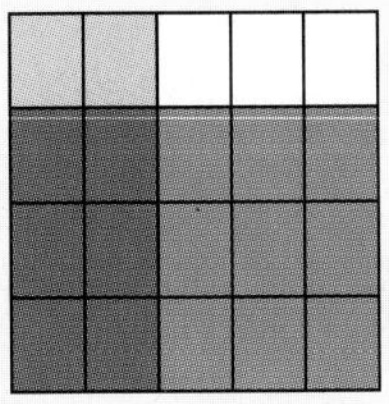

1. Model these problems.

a. $\frac{1}{2} \times \frac{1}{3}$ **b.** $\frac{1}{4} \times \frac{2}{5}$ **c.** $\frac{5}{6} \times \frac{2}{3}$

d. $\frac{2}{7} \times \frac{2}{7}$ **e.** $\frac{1}{5} \times \frac{3}{5}$ **f.** $\frac{1}{2} \times \frac{5}{8}$

2. Describe the pattern between the numerators in the problem and the numerator in the answer.

3. Describe the pattern between the denominators in the problem and the denominator in the answer.

4. Is your answer bigger or smaller than both of the fractions you started with? Why?

MEETING INDIVIDUAL NEEDS

Resources

7-3 Practice
7-3 Reteaching
7-3 Problem Solving
7-3 Enrichment
7-3 Daily Transparency
Problem of the Day
Review
Quick Quiz
Teaching Tool Transparencies 2, 3
Lesson Enhancement Transparency 34
Technology Master 32
Chapter 7 Project Master
Interactive CD-ROM Lesson

Learning Modalities

Verbal Have students write a paragraph describing the process used in **Explore** to find products using rectangular models.

Visual Have students draw rectangular grids and shade sections horizontally and vertically to show that the product of two fractions is the section shaded twice.

Inclusion

Some students may benefit from working with partners to draw models. For example, to model $\frac{1}{4} \times \frac{2}{3}$, one student might shade $\frac{2}{3}$ of a rectangle. The other student might shade $\frac{1}{4}$ of the $\frac{2}{3}$. Together, they can describe the region where the colors overlap.

INTERACTIVE LESSON

7-3 Lesson Organizer

Objective

■ Multiply a fraction by another fraction.

Materials

■ Explore: Colored pencils

NCTM Standards

■ 1–4, 7

▶ Review

Write each improper fraction as a mixed number.

1. $\frac{13}{4}$ $3\frac{1}{4}$
2. $\frac{29}{6}$ $4\frac{5}{6}$
3. $\frac{18}{5}$ $3\frac{3}{5}$
4. $\frac{43}{8}$ $5\frac{3}{8}$

Available on Daily Transparency 7-3

1 Introduce

Explore

You may wish to use Lesson Enhancement Transparency 34 with **Explore**.

The Point

Students explore multiplying fractions by drawing rectangular models. Students shade one part of the rectangle horizontally and another part vertically. Students find the product of the fractional parts by determining the part of the rectangle where both colors overlap.

Ongoing Assessment

As students are drawing the models, ask them to describe what each shaded section represents and what the area that is shaded with both colors represents.

For Groups That Finish Early

Multiply without drawing models.

1. $\frac{1}{4} \times \frac{1}{3}$ $\frac{1}{12}$
2. $\frac{2}{3} \times \frac{2}{5}$ $\frac{4}{15}$

Draw models to check your answers.

Answers for Explore on next page.

Answers for Explore

1. See page C1.
2. The numerator in the product is the product of the numerators in the problem.
3. The denominator in the product is the product of the denominators in the problem.
4. Smaller; The product of two proper fractions is always less than both of the fractions.

2 Teach

Learn

Alternate Examples

1. Juan needs to buy glass for a picture frame that is $\frac{2}{3}$ ft by $\frac{3}{4}$ ft. What is the area of the glass?

   $= \frac{2}{3} \times \frac{3}{4} = \frac{2 \times 3}{3 \times 4}$

   $= \frac{6}{12}$ or $\frac{1}{2}$

   The area of the glass is $\frac{1}{2}$ ft^2.

2. Sara has a board $3\frac{1}{2}$ feet long. She needs two boards for a project. If she cuts the board in half, how long will each half be?

   $3\frac{1}{2} \times \frac{1}{2} = \frac{7}{2} \times \frac{1}{2}$

   $= \frac{7 \times 1}{2 \times 2}$

   $= \frac{7}{4}$ or $1\frac{3}{4}$

   Each half will be $1\frac{3}{4}$ ft long.

3 Practice and Assess

Check

Answers for Check Your Understanding

1. Possible answer: $\frac{2}{5} \times \frac{4}{3}$; $\frac{2 \times 4}{3 \times 5} = \frac{8}{15}$.
2. Possible answer: You don't need a common denominator to multiply fractions.

Learn Multiplying by a Fraction

When adding fractions with unlike denominators, you must first rename the fractions so they have like denominators. You do not need to do this for multiplication. To multiply with fractions, write both factors as fractions. Then write the product of the numerators over the product of the denominators.

Example 1

A recipe for dying wool calls for $\frac{1}{4}$ pound of tea leaves for each pound of wool. Find the amount of leaves needed to dye $\frac{2}{3}$ pound of wool.

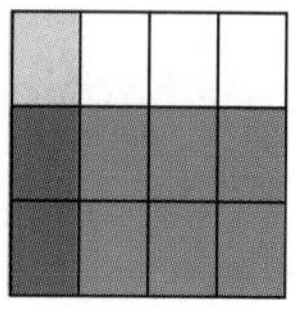

$\frac{1}{4} \times \frac{2}{3} = \frac{1 \times 2}{4 \times 3}$ Multiply the numerators. Multiply the denominators.

$= \frac{2}{12}$ or $\frac{1}{6}$ Simplify.

You need $\frac{1}{6}$ pound of tea leaves.

DID YOU KNOW?

Many different colors of dyes can be made from common plants. The bark of the American black oak tree can be used to make bright yellow. The flowers and stems from Queen Anne's lace can be used to make pale green.

Some problems may ask you to find the fractional part of a fraction. You can solve these problems using multiplication.

Example 2

Mr. Hamilton bought $2\frac{1}{2}$ gallons of milk. He used half of it to make ice cream. How much did he use?

$2\frac{1}{2} \times \frac{1}{2} = \frac{5}{2} \times \frac{1}{2}$ Write the mixed number as a fraction.

$= \frac{5 \times 1}{2 \times 2}$ Multiply the numerators. Multiply the denominators.

$= \frac{5}{4}$ or $1\frac{1}{4}$ Simplify.

He used $1\frac{1}{4}$ gallons of milk.

Try It

Multiply.

a. $\frac{4}{5} \times \frac{3}{7}$ $\frac{12}{35}$ **b.** $\frac{8}{9}$ of $1\frac{1}{2}$ $1\frac{1}{3}$ **c.** $1\frac{2}{3} \times 1\frac{3}{7}$ $2\frac{8}{21}$ **d.** $\frac{1}{9}$ of $\frac{2}{5}$ $\frac{2}{45}$

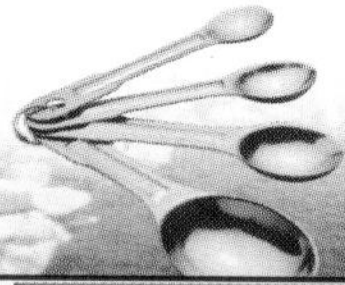

MATH EVERY DAY

Problem of the Day

Patsy stacked cans that were 9 cm tall. Pierre stacked cans that were 15 cm tall. Pietro stacked cans that were 12 cm tall. How tall will each stack be when the stacks are all the same height for the first time? 180 cm

Available on Daily Transparency 7-3

An Extension is provided in the transparency package.

Fact of the Day

Gilbert Stuart's famous portrait of George Washington is in the Museum of Fine Arts in Boston. Stuart made about 75 copies of the portrait.

Mental Math

Find each product mentally.

1. 7 × 13 91
2. 6 × 15 90
3. 11 × 16 176

Check Your Understanding

1. Give two fractions whose product is $\frac{8}{15}$. Explain your reasoning.
2. How is multiplying two fractions different from adding two fractions?

PRACTICE 7-3

7-3 Exercises and Applications

Practice and Apply

Getting Started Write the multiplication problem each model represents.

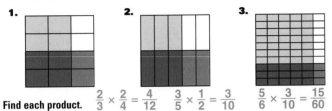

1. 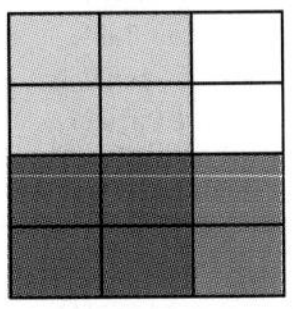 $\frac{2}{3} \times \frac{2}{4} = \frac{4}{12}$

2. 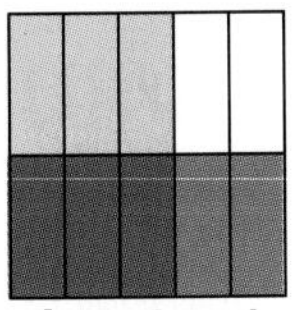 $\frac{3}{5} \times \frac{1}{2} = \frac{3}{10}$

3.  $\frac{5}{6} \times \frac{3}{10} = \frac{15}{60}$

4. 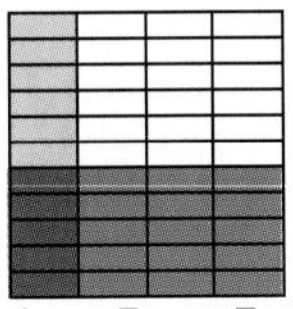 $\frac{1}{4} \times \frac{5}{11} = \frac{5}{44}$

Find each product.

5. $\frac{3}{7} \times \frac{2}{3}$ $\frac{2}{7}$
6. $\frac{5}{9} \times \frac{1}{2}$ $\frac{5}{18}$
7. $\frac{3}{4} \times \frac{7}{10}$ $\frac{21}{40}$
8. $\frac{1}{5} \times \frac{1}{5}$ $\frac{1}{25}$
9. $\frac{11}{15} \times 4\frac{6}{7}$ $3\frac{59}{105}$
10. $7\frac{1}{3} \times \frac{7}{9}$ $5\frac{19}{27}$
11. $\frac{13}{17} \times \frac{6}{11}$ $\frac{78}{187}$
12. $\frac{1}{9} \times \frac{7}{13}$ $\frac{7}{117}$
13. $\frac{4}{5} \times 10\frac{3}{8}$ $8\frac{3}{10}$
14. $6\frac{2}{5} \times \frac{9}{11}$ $5\frac{13}{55}$
15. $\frac{13}{20} \times \frac{1}{3}$ $\frac{13}{60}$
16. $\frac{2}{5} \times \frac{10}{11}$ $\frac{4}{11}$
17. $\frac{9}{13} \times 2\frac{9}{13}$ $1\frac{146}{169}$
18. $\frac{2}{5} \times \frac{7}{10}$ $\frac{7}{25}$
19. $\frac{4}{7} \times 2\frac{3}{8}$ $1\frac{5}{14}$
20. $5\frac{5}{7} \times 5\frac{8}{9}$ $33\frac{41}{63}$
21. $\frac{11}{21} \times \frac{1}{2}$ $\frac{11}{42}$
22. $9\frac{2}{9} \times 3\frac{4}{9}$ $31\frac{62}{81}$
23. $\frac{1}{8} \times \frac{3}{8}$ $\frac{3}{64}$
24. $\frac{4}{5} \times \frac{3}{8}$ $\frac{3}{10}$
25. $\frac{6}{11} \times \frac{6}{11}$ $\frac{36}{121}$
26. $8\frac{2}{5} \times \frac{3}{7}$ $3\frac{3}{5}$
27. $\frac{4}{7} \times 4\frac{9}{14}$ $2\frac{32}{49}$
28. $\frac{5}{8} \times \frac{8}{9}$ $\frac{5}{9}$

29. **Science** An alligator is $12\frac{1}{2}$ feet long. Its tail is half as long as its total length. How long is the alligator's tail? $6\frac{1}{4}$ ft

30. **Test Prep** Which of these expressions has the greatest product? A

Ⓐ $\frac{4}{5} \times 4$ Ⓑ $\frac{4}{5} \times 2\frac{1}{2}$ Ⓒ $\frac{4}{5} \times \frac{4}{5}$ Ⓓ $\frac{4}{5} \times 3$

PRACTICE

Name ____________

Practice 7-3

Multiplying by a Fraction

Find each product.

1. $5\frac{1}{2} \times \frac{1}{2}$ $2\frac{3}{4}$
2. $\frac{2}{3} \times \frac{9}{10}$ $\frac{3}{5}$
3. $\frac{1}{4} \times \frac{3}{5}$ $\frac{3}{20}$
4. $8\frac{1}{4} \times \frac{1}{2}$ $4\frac{1}{8}$
5. $\frac{5}{6} \times \frac{2}{3}$ $\frac{5}{9}$
6. $\frac{5}{8} \times \frac{1}{9}$ $\frac{5}{72}$
7. $\frac{1}{7} \times \frac{1}{2}$ $\frac{1}{14}$
8. $\frac{2}{3} \times \frac{4}{9}$ $\frac{8}{27}$
9. $\frac{5}{8} \times \frac{3}{8}$ $\frac{15}{64}$
10. $\frac{1}{2} \times \frac{4}{13}$ $\frac{2}{13}$
11. $\frac{1}{3} \times \frac{2}{7}$ $\frac{2}{21}$
12. $\frac{13}{15} \times \frac{1}{4}$ $\frac{13}{60}$
13. $\frac{2}{5} \times \frac{4}{5}$ $\frac{8}{25}$
14. $\frac{1}{11} \times \frac{2}{5}$ $\frac{2}{55}$
15. $\frac{7}{9} \times \frac{2}{11}$ $\frac{14}{99}$
16. $\frac{3}{4} \times \frac{1}{2}$ $\frac{3}{8}$
17. $\frac{1}{2} \times \frac{14}{15}$ $\frac{7}{15}$
18. $\frac{1}{5} \times \frac{1}{3}$ $\frac{1}{15}$
19. $\frac{11}{15} \times \frac{1}{10}$ $\frac{11}{150}$
20. $\frac{8}{9} \times \frac{2}{7}$ $\frac{16}{63}$
21. $\frac{7}{8} \times \frac{11}{14}$ $\frac{11}{16}$
22. $\frac{1}{2} \times \frac{5}{7}$ $\frac{5}{14}$
23. $\frac{3}{4} \times \frac{1}{3}$ $\frac{1}{4}$
24. $\frac{1}{2} \times \frac{7}{8}$ $\frac{7}{16}$
25. $\frac{2}{15} \times \frac{1}{2}$ $\frac{1}{15}$
26. $\frac{1}{3} \times \frac{4}{5}$ $\frac{4}{15}$
27. $\frac{10}{11} \times 5\frac{2}{3}$ $5\frac{5}{33}$
28. $\frac{10}{11} \times \frac{5}{6}$ $\frac{25}{33}$
29. $\frac{1}{5} \times \frac{1}{2}$ $\frac{1}{10}$
30. $\frac{3}{10} \times 2\frac{1}{2}$ $\frac{3}{4}$
31. $\frac{12}{13} \times \frac{3}{10}$ $\frac{18}{65}$
32. $\frac{2}{3} \times \frac{1}{3}$ $\frac{2}{9}$
33. $\frac{2}{3} \times \frac{7}{9}$ $\frac{14}{27}$
34. $\frac{5}{12} \times 3\frac{7}{12}$ $1\frac{71}{144}$
35. $\frac{1}{6} \times \frac{2}{7}$ $\frac{1}{21}$
36. $\frac{3}{5} \times \frac{7}{11}$ $\frac{21}{55}$
37. $\frac{1}{2} \times 7\frac{9}{13}$ $3\frac{11}{13}$
38. $\frac{2}{3} \times \frac{2}{5}$ $\frac{4}{15}$
39. $\frac{2}{7} \times \frac{1}{10}$ $\frac{1}{35}$

40. **Science** The total weight of all of the insects in the world is about $\frac{7}{20}$ of a billion tons. The total weight of all humans is about $\frac{1}{3}$ of this amount. Find the total weight of all humans. About $\frac{7}{60}$ billion tons

41. A recipe for minestrone soup calls for $3\frac{1}{2}$ cups of vegetable stock. How much stock would you use to make $\frac{2}{3}$ of the amount of soup in the original recipe? $2\frac{1}{3}$ cups

RETEACHING

Name ____________

Alternative Lesson 7-3

Multiplying by a Fraction

You can multiply two fractions by writing the product of the numerators over the product of the denominators.

Example

Multiply: $1\frac{1}{2} \times 3\frac{1}{2}$.

Write each mixed number as an improper fraction. $1\frac{1}{2} \times 3\frac{1}{2} =$ ↓ ↓

Multiply the numerators. Then multiply the denominators. $\frac{3}{2} \times \frac{7}{2} = \frac{3}{2} \times \frac{7}{2}$

Multiply and simplify. $= \frac{21}{4} = 5\frac{1}{4}$

So, $1\frac{1}{2} \times 3\frac{1}{2} = 5\frac{1}{4}$.

Try It

Multiply: $\frac{3}{5} \times \frac{7}{12}$.

a. Multiply numerators and denominators. $\frac{3}{5} \times \frac{7}{12} = \frac{21}{60}$

b. Simplify. $\frac{21}{60} = \frac{7}{20}$

Multiply: $\frac{7}{8} \times 1\frac{1}{4}$.

c. Write the mixed number as an improper fraction. $1\frac{1}{4} = \frac{5}{4}$

d. Multiply numerators and denominators. $\frac{7}{8} \times \frac{5}{4} = \frac{35}{32}$

e. Simplify. $\frac{35}{32} = 1\frac{3}{32}$

Multiply: $1\frac{3}{4} \times 2\frac{1}{2}$.

f. Write the whole numbers as improper fractions. $1\frac{3}{4} = \frac{7}{4}$ $2\frac{1}{2} = \frac{5}{2}$

g. Multiply numerators and denominators. $\frac{7}{4} \times \frac{5}{2} = \frac{35}{8}$

h. Simplify. $\frac{35}{8} = 4\frac{3}{8}$

Multiply.

i. $\frac{1}{4} \times \frac{9}{10}$ $\frac{9}{40}$
j. $\frac{5}{6} \times \frac{2}{3}$ $\frac{5}{9}$
k. $\frac{3}{5} \times 1\frac{3}{5}$ $\frac{24}{25}$
l. $2\frac{1}{2} \times \frac{7}{8}$ $2\frac{3}{16}$
m. $2\frac{3}{5} \times 1\frac{1}{3}$ $3\frac{7}{15}$
n. $\frac{9}{10} \times \frac{4}{5}$ $\frac{18}{25}$

o. Amal's bones make up about $\frac{1}{5}$ of his body weight. He weighs $158\frac{1}{2}$ pounds. How much do his bones weigh? $31\frac{7}{10}$ lb

7-3 Exercises and Applications

Assignment Guide

- **Basic**
  1–16, 29–31, 33, 36–52 evens
- **Average**
  1–16, 29–33, 36–38, 42–52 evens
- **Enriched**
  3, 17–30, 33–38, 43–53 odds

Exercise Notes

Exercise 8

Error Prevention Some students may write the denominator as 5. Remind them that when multiplying fractions you multiply both the numerators and the denominators.

Exercise 29

Science The body of an alligator is suited for living in water and on land. The side-to-side motion of its tail allows it to swim in water, and its short legs are used for walking on land.

Exercise 30

Test Prep Point out to students that they should look at all four expressions before they begin any computation. They may be able to answer the question without doing any computation.

Reteaching

Activity

- Fold a sheet of paper vertically into 4 equal sections. Then, fold it horizontally into 3 equal sections.
- Shade $\frac{1}{4}$ of the paper vertically. Shade $\frac{1}{3}$ of the paper horizontally. What part of the paper was shaded twice? $\frac{1}{12}$
- Fold two more sheets of paper as you folded the first. Shade them to solve the following.

  $\frac{3}{4} \times \frac{1}{3}$ $\frac{3}{12}$ or $\frac{1}{4}$

  $\frac{3}{4} \times \frac{2}{3}$ $\frac{6}{12}$ or $\frac{1}{2}$

Exercise Notes

■ Exercise 33

Problem-Solving Tip You may wish to use Teaching Tool Transparencies 2 and 3: Guided Problem Solving, pages 1–2.

■ Exercise 34

Extension Have students write generalizations about factors and their products when multiplying mixed numbers and fractions. Possible answers: a. The product of two fractions is less than one. b. and c. The product of a fraction and a mixed number is less than the mixed number. d. The product of two mixed numbers is greater than either mixed number.

Project Progress

You may want to have students use Chapter 7 Project Master.

Exercise Answers

33. $\frac{2}{3}$ cup milk, $\frac{2}{3}$ cup water; You must multiply $\frac{3}{4}$ by $\frac{4}{3}$ to get 1, so multiply the amount of each ingredient by $\frac{4}{3}$ to find the new recipe.

34. a. Less than; The first fraction is less than 1.
   b. Greater than; The first factor is greater than 1.
   c. Less than; The first fraction is less than 1.
   d. Greater than; The first factor is greater than 1.

35. $14\frac{1}{4}$ in. long and $11\frac{13}{16}$ in. wide;
   Area of painting: $673\frac{5}{16}$ in^2.
   Area of print: $168\frac{21}{64}$ in^2.

Alternate Assessment

Portfolio Have students select work that they have completed which shows how the multiplication of two fractions can be modeled. Have students write a description of how the model illustrates the product of the two fractions and add it to their portfolios.

► Quick Quiz

Multiply.

1. $\frac{3}{7} \times \frac{2}{7}$ $\frac{6}{49}$
2. $\frac{5}{6} \times \frac{2}{3}$ $\frac{10}{18}$ or $\frac{5}{9}$
3. $2\frac{1}{4} \times \frac{3}{5}$ $1\frac{7}{20}$
4. $\frac{3}{8} \times 4\frac{4}{5}$ $1\frac{4}{5}$

Available on Daily Transparency 7-3

PROBLEM SOLVING 7-3

$\frac{1}{8}$ cup sugar, $\frac{1}{8}$ cup flour and $\frac{7}{8}$ cup water

31. The recipe for a pint of paste includes $\frac{1}{4}$ cup sugar, $\frac{1}{4}$ cup flour, $1\frac{3}{4}$ cups water, and $\frac{1}{4}$ teaspoon cinnamon oil. How much sugar, flour, and water is needed to make a half pint of paste?

32. The distance between Tad's house and his school is $\frac{2}{3}$ of a mile. If he walks halfway to school, how far has he walked? $\frac{1}{3}$ of a mile

Problem Solving and Reasoning

33. Choose a Strategy To make $\frac{3}{4}$ cup of powdered-milk paint, you mix $\frac{1}{2}$ cup of powdered nonfat milk and $\frac{1}{2}$ cup of water. Adjust this recipe to make one whole cup of paint. Explain your method. GPS

34. Critical Thinking Without using multiplication, explain whether the product is greater than or less than the second factor.

a. $\frac{2}{3} \times \frac{5}{8}$ **b.** $\frac{9}{6} \times \frac{1}{2}$ **c.** $\frac{1}{4} \times \frac{12}{5}$ **d.** $5\frac{3}{4} \times 5\frac{3}{4}$

35. Critical Thinking A painting of George Washington by Gilbert Stuart is $28\frac{1}{2}$ inches long and $23\frac{5}{8}$ inches wide. The museum wants to make a print of the painting that will be half as long and half as wide. What will the dimensions of the print be? What is the area of each print?

Problem Solving STRATEGIES

- Look for a Pattern
- Make an Organized List
- Make a Table
- Guess and Check
- Work Backward
- Use Logical Reasoning
- Draw a Diagram
- Solve a Simpler Problem

Mixed Review

Convert. *[Lesson 4-3]*

36. 1 mile = ☐ feet 5280
37. 10,560 feet = ☐ inches 126,720
38. 6 miles = ☐ feet 31,680
39. 15,840 feet = ☐ inches 190,080
40. 10 miles = ☐ feet 52,800
41. 5280 feet = ☐ inches 63,360

Find the LCM of each pair. *[Lesson 5-3]*

42. 99, 3 99 **43.** 6, 3 6 **44.** 2, 45 90 **45.** 8, 4 8 **46.** 16, 24 48 **47.** 5, 7 35

48. 14, 4 28 **49.** 18, 8 72 **50.** 6, 10 30 **51.** 29, 1 29 **52.** 27, 6 54 **53.** 3, 9 9

Project Progress

Make a list of at least 15 things you buy today that you think senior citizens purchased when they were your age. Then, interview your senior citizen and record the amounts paid for each item. Make sure that you collect data about at least 10 items.

Problem Solving
Understand
Plan
Solve
Look Back

PROBLEM SOLVING

Name ______________________

Guided Problem Solving 7-3

GPS **PROBLEM 33, STUDENT PAGE 378**

To make $\frac{3}{4}$ cup of powdered-milk paint, you mix $\frac{1}{2}$ cup of powdered nonfat milk and $\frac{1}{2}$ cup of water. Adjust this recipe to make one whole cup of paint. Explain your method.

Possible answers: Items 7, 8

— Understand —

1. Circle the quantity of paint that is made from the recipe.
2. Underline the quantities of the paint ingredients.

— Plan —

3. How many fourths are in $\frac{3}{4}$? Three.
4. To rewrite the recipe for $\frac{1}{4}$ cup of paint, you could divide each quantity by the number in Item 3 or multiply by $\frac{1}{3}$.
5. Once the recipe has been written for $\frac{1}{4}$ cup of paint, you can rewrite it for 1 cup of paint by multiplying each quantity by 4.

— Solve —

6. Complete the table for $\frac{1}{4}$ cup of paint. Then use your answer to find the quantities for 1 cup of paint.

Paint (cups)	Milk (cups)	Water (cups)
$\frac{3}{4}$	$\frac{1}{2}$	$\frac{1}{2}$
$\frac{1}{4}$	$\frac{1}{6}$	$\frac{1}{6}$
1	$\frac{2}{3}$	$\frac{2}{3}$

7. Explain how you found the quantities.
Found quantities needed to make $\frac{1}{4}$ cup of paint, used those to find quantities needed for 1 cup of paint.

— Look Back —

8. Explain how you could use division to rewrite the recipe. Divide 1 by $\frac{3}{4}$. Then multiply the quotient by amounts of ingredients.

SOLVE ANOTHER PROBLEM

To make $\frac{3}{4}$ cup of powdered-milk paint, you mix $\frac{1}{2}$ cup of powdered nonfat milk and $\frac{1}{2}$ cup of water. Adjust this recipe to make $1\frac{1}{8}$ cup of paint. Explain your method. Possible answer:
$\frac{3}{4}$ cup each; Find $\frac{1}{8}$ cup: $\frac{1}{6} \times \frac{1}{2} = \frac{1}{12}$; $1\frac{1}{8} = \frac{9}{8}$; $9 \times \frac{1}{12} = \frac{3}{4}$

ENRICHMENT

Name ______________________

Extend Your Thinking 7-3

Critical Thinking

Robert and Marsha found the answer for $\frac{2}{3} \times \frac{5}{12}$ using these two different methods.

Robert's Method

$\frac{2}{3} \times \frac{5}{12} = \frac{2 \times 5}{3 \times 12} = \frac{10}{36} = \frac{10 \div 2}{26 \div 2} = \frac{5}{18}$

(Divide the numerator by 2.) (Divide the denominator by 2.)

Marsha's Method

$\frac{\not{2}^{1}}{3} \times \frac{5}{\not{12}_{6}} = \frac{1 \times 5}{3 \times 6} = \frac{5}{18}$

1. What did Robert do in order to write the answer in lowest terms?
Divided numerator and denominator of answer by 2.
2. What did Marsha do before she multiplied the numerators and denominators?
Divided a numerator and denominator by 2.
3. Why do you think both answers were correct?
Robert and Marsha both divided by $\frac{2}{2}$, which is equal to 1. When you divide by 1, the value does not change.

Use Marsha's shortcut to multiply. Show your work.

4. $\frac{1}{2} \times \frac{2}{3} =$ $\frac{1}{3}$
5. $\frac{3}{4} \times \frac{4}{5} =$ $\frac{3}{5}$
6. $\frac{2}{5} \times \frac{7}{12} =$ $\frac{7}{30}$
7. $\frac{5}{6} \times \frac{3}{4} =$ $\frac{5}{8}$
8. $\frac{7}{8} \times \frac{8}{15} =$ $\frac{7}{15}$
9. $\frac{11}{12} \times \frac{3}{4} =$ $\frac{11}{16}$
10. $\frac{3}{10} \times \frac{5}{8} =$ $\frac{3}{16}$
11. $\frac{5}{6} \times \frac{2}{3} =$ $\frac{5}{9}$
12. $\frac{2}{3} \times \frac{5}{8} =$ $\frac{5}{12}$

Try using the shortcut two times in each of the following exercises. Show your work.

13. $\frac{5}{6} \times \frac{3}{5} =$ $\frac{1}{2}$
14. $\frac{2}{3} \times \frac{3}{8} =$ $\frac{1}{4}$
15. $\frac{3}{4} \times \frac{4}{27} =$ $\frac{1}{9}$

Section 7A Connect

In this section, you've learned to multiply fractions and mixed numbers. You've also seen how this skill can be used to adjust the sizes of recipes. Now you'll use what you've learned to decide how much a restaurant owner should charge for items on the menu.

A Taste from the North Pacific

The appetizer menu for Li's Chinese Restaurant is shown here. Each "order" consists of several pieces of the same food.

Mr. Li has decided to change the number of pieces he serves in an order. The new numbers are shown here but the prices are missing.

1. Express the new number of pieces in an order as a fraction of the old number. Write each fraction in lowest terms. (For example, the new egg roll order is $\frac{3}{2}$ as large as the old order.)
2. Estimate the new prices Mr. Li should charge.
3. Find the exact new prices by multiplying the fractions you found in Question 1 by the old prices.
4. Explain a method for finding the new prices that doesn't involve fractions.

379

Answers for Connect

1. Egg rolls: $\frac{3}{2}$; Won Ton: $\frac{4}{5}$; Spareribs: $\frac{3}{2}$; Prawns: $\frac{4}{3}$; Pot Stickers: $\frac{2}{3}$.
2. Answers may vary.
3. Egg rolls \$4.50; Won Ton \$1.60; Spareribs \$9; Prawns \$6; Pot Stickers \$3.50.
4. Possible answer: Find the cost for one piece, then use multiplication to find the cost of the new order.

A Taste from the North Pacific

The Point

In *A Taste from the North Pacific* on page 365, students reviewed recipes. Now they will use the mathematics they learned to make adjustments in menu prices.

About the Page

- Discuss the menu with students so that they understand that each appetizer is made up of a number of separate pieces.
- Some students may find the new prices mentally by determining the per-unit cost and then multiplying. Ask them to use multiplication of fractions to check their solutions.
- Discuss with students that the fraction for the number of pieces in Question 1 will be equal to the fraction of the new prices. For example, $\frac{3}{2} = \frac{4.50}{3.00}$.

Ongoing Assessment

Check that students have expressed the fractions in Question 1 and the new menu prices correctly.

Extension

Have students solve the following problem.

Mr. Li has also decided to offer some combination appetizer plates. Determine what he should charge for each appetizer plate:

Appetizer Plate A
2 Egg rolls, 2 Won Ton, 2 Spareribs, 3 Prawns, and 3 Pot Stickers
\$10.80

Appetizer Plate B
2 Egg rolls, 3 Won Ton, 4 Spareribs, 5 Prawns, and 6 Pot Stickers
\$17.45

7A Review

Review Correlation

Item(s)	Lesson(s)
1–8	7-1
9–11	7-2
12–15	7-3

Test Prep

Test-Taking Tip

Tell students to avoid answering any questions in a hurry. Here, the phrase "lowest terms" is important to the answer.

Answers for Review

9. 3 oz wax; $19\frac{1}{2}$ Tbs oil; 9 Tbs water; $\frac{3}{4}$ tsp borax.
10. 6 oz wax; 39 Tbs oil; 18 Tbs water; $1\frac{1}{2}$ tsp borax.

Section 7A Review

REVIEW 7A

Estimate each product or quotient.

1. $8\frac{7}{8} \div 3\frac{1}{3}$ 3 **2.** $8\frac{9}{10} \times 2\frac{7}{8}$ 27 **3.** $9\frac{3}{5} \times 2\frac{7}{8}$ 30 **4.** $15\frac{1}{7} \div 2\frac{9}{10}$ 5

5. $1\frac{5}{6} \div 1\frac{1}{6}$ 2 **6.** $15\frac{2}{3} \div 4\frac{3}{7}$ 4 **7.** $10\frac{4}{5} \times 1\frac{3}{9}$ 11 **8.** $12\frac{1}{6} \times 3\frac{5}{8}$ 48

Measurement For Exercises 9 and 10, use the cold cream recipe.

9. For each ingredient, find the amount you would use to triple the cold cream recipe.

10. For each ingredient, find the amount you would use to make 6 times as much cold cream.

Homemade Cold Cream
1 ounce bowstring wax*
6½ tablespoons mineral oil
3 tablespoons water
¼ teaspoon borax
*Used for archery.
Found in sports specialty stores.

11. Boneless chicken breasts are selling for \$2.99 a pound. Can you buy $1\frac{3}{4}$ pounds for \$6? Yes

12. Kele bought $3\frac{1}{4}$ pound of trail mix. On his hike, he ate $\frac{2}{3}$ of it. How much trail mix did he eat? $2\frac{1}{6}$ lb

13. Communicate An urban planner designed a bridge that was $3\frac{1}{3}$ miles long. The construction manager reported that $\frac{1}{2}$ of the bridge was complete. How many miles of bridge had been completed? $1\frac{2}{3}$

Test Prep

If a test question asks you to give an answer in lowest terms, you can eliminate any answers that are not in lowest terms.

14. What is $\frac{3}{4} \times \frac{10}{12}$ in lowest terms? A

Ⓐ $\frac{5}{8}$ Ⓑ $\frac{15}{24}$ Ⓒ $\frac{30}{48}$ Ⓓ $1\frac{18}{30}$

15. What is $\frac{9}{10} \times \frac{2}{6}$ in lowest terms? D

Ⓐ $\frac{18}{60}$ Ⓑ $\frac{9}{30}$ Ⓒ $\frac{6}{20}$ Ⓓ Not here

Resources

Practice Masters
Section 7A Review
Assessment Sourcebook
Quiz 7A
TestWorks
Test and Practice Software

PRACTICE

Name ____________________

Practice

Section 7A Review

Estimate each product or quotient.

1. $4\frac{5}{6} \times 12\frac{2}{5}$ ≈ 60 **2.** $7\frac{3}{4} \div 2\frac{2}{3}$ $\approx 2\frac{2}{3}$ **3.** $3\frac{4}{9} \times 10\frac{2}{7}$ ≈ 30

4. $9\frac{1}{4} \div 4\frac{4}{7}$ $\approx 1\frac{4}{5}$ **5.** $11\frac{1}{2} \times 13\frac{2}{5}$ ≈ 156 **6.** $8\frac{4}{7} \div 3\frac{5}{9}$ $\approx 2\frac{1}{4}$

Simplify.

7. $4\frac{1}{9} \times 4$ $16\frac{4}{9}$ **8.** $8 \times 3\frac{1}{2}$ 28 **9.** $1\frac{1}{3} \times 2\frac{1}{2}$ $3\frac{1}{3}$

10. $4\frac{1}{10} \times 8$ $32\frac{4}{5}$ **11.** $\frac{1}{2} \times 4$ 2 **12.** $5 \times 2\frac{3}{8}$ $11\frac{7}{8}$

13. The table shows the ingredients in a recipe for papaya ice cream from *Kathy Cooks Naturally*. Complete the table to show how much of each ingredient you would use to make 4 times or 6 times the amount of the original recipe.

Ingredient	Ripe papaya	Orange juice	Lemon juice	Whipping cream	Honey
Original recipe	$1\frac{1}{2}$ cups	$\frac{1}{2}$ cup	$\frac{[illegible]}{16}$ cup	$1\frac{1}{2}$ cups	$\frac{1}{2}$ cup
4 times	6 cups	2 cups	$\frac{3}{4}$ cup	6 cups	2 cups
6 times	9 cups	3 cups	$1\frac{1}{8}$ cups	9 cups	3 cups

14. Fancy tomatoes are selling for \$1.95 per pound. Can you buy $2\frac{1}{4}$ pounds if you only have \$4.00? No

15. Mrs. Gonzales bought $3\frac{1}{8}$ pounds of candy for Halloween. She gave away $\frac{3}{5}$ of the candy. How much candy was left over? $1\frac{1}{4}$ lb

16. Fine Arts Rodney is making a macramé belt that is to be $1\frac{1}{4}$ meters long. If $\frac{1}{3}$ of the belt has been completed, how many meters of the belt have been completed? $\frac{5}{12}$ m

17. Some giant dump trucks use tires with a diameter of 12.5 feet. Find the area of a wheel with this tire. *[Lesson 4-8]* About 122.7 ft^2

18. Rick had $\frac{7}{8}$ of a cup of lemon juice. After making a pie, he had $\frac{1}{2}$ cup of lemon juice left. How much lemon juice did he use in the pie? *[Lesson 6-3]* $\frac{3}{8}$ cup

Section 7B

Dividing Fractions

Visit **www.teacher.mathsurf.com** for links to lesson plans from teachers and other professionals, NCTM information, and other sites.

LESSON PLANNING GUIDE

Student Edition / Ancillaries*

LESSON		MATERIALS	VOCABULARY	DAILY	OTHER
	Section 7B Opener				
7-4	**Dividing Whole Numbers by Fractions**		reciprocal	7-4	Lesson Enhancement Trans. 35 Technology Master 33 Ch. 7 Project Master
7-5	**Dividing Fractions by Fractions**	Fraction Bars®		7-5	Teaching Tool Trans. 14 Lesson Enhancement Trans. 36 Technology Master 34
	Technology	fraction calculator			Teaching Tool Trans. 24
7-6	**Solving Fraction Equations: Multiplication and Division**			7-6	Teaching Tool Trans. 2, 3 Technology Master 35
	Connect	masking tape			Interdisc. Team Teaching 7B
	Review				Practice 7B; Quiz 7B; *TestWorks*
	Extend Key Ideas				
	Chapter 7 Summary and Review				
	Chapter 7 Assessment				Ch. 7 Tests Forms A–F *TestWorks;* Ch.7 Letter Home
	Cumulative Review, Chapters 1–7				Cumulative Review Ch. 1–7

* Daily Ancillaries include Practice, Reteaching, Problem Solving, Enrichment, and Daily Transparency. Teaching Tool Transparencies are in *Teacher's Toolkits*. Lesson Enhancement Transparencies are in *Overhead Transparency Package*.

SKILLS TRACE

LESSON	SKILL	FIRST INTRODUCED GR. 4	GR. 5	GR. 6	DEVELOP	PRACTICE/ APPLY	REVIEW
7-4	**Dividing a whole number by a fraction.**		✗		pp. 382–384	pp. 385–386	pp. 398, 401, 484
7-5	**Dividing a fraction by a fraction or whole number.**		✗		pp. 387–388	pp. 389–390	pp. 398, 401, 491
7-6	**Solving fraction equations using multiplication and division.**			✗ p. 392	pp. 392–394	pp. 395–396	pp. 398, 401, 497

CONNECTED MATHEMATICS

Investigation 5 in the unit *Bits and Pieces II (Using Rational Numbers)*, from the **Connected Mathematics** series, can be used with Section 7B.

INTERDISCIPLINARY TEAM TEACHING

Math and Language Arts

(Worksheet pages 35–36: Teacher pages T35–T36)

In this lesson, students divide fractions to design and analyze newspaper page layouts.

Name ____________________ ***Math and Language Arts***

Newsy Fractions

Divide fractions to design and analyze newspaper page layouts.

The first successful American newspaper was printed in 1704 in Boston, Massachusetts. It was called the *Boston News-Letter*. It was very small—about the size of one sheet of notebook paper, with printing on both sides. The printing was divided into two columns. Today's newspapers are much larger, and they are divided into several columns.

The size of a newspaper and its staff is usually related to how many copies of the newspaper are sold. The average number of copies sold over a given period of time is called the newspaper's *circulation*. Some newspapers have a large circulation. *USA Today* has one of the largest circulations of any daily newspaper in the United States. More than 2 million copies are sold each day.

Large newspapers have several departments. The editorial department includes the people who prepare the stories for the newspapers. Reporters gather and write the news. Photographers take pictures to go with the news stories. Editors read the stories to make sure they are easy to follow and fit in the space allowed for them. Editors also choose the most important stories for the front page.

Another department of a large newspaper is the mechanical department. Its job is to print the newspaper. Most large newspapers have their own printing presses. Printing presses are machines that can print many copies of a newspaper in a very short time. For instance, there are presses that print more than 70,000 newspapers per hour.

A third department of the newspaper is the business department. One of this department's biggest jobs is to sell advertising space. Many newspapers make more money from selling advertising space than from selling newspapers. Space is sold by the part of a page. A half-page ad, for example, would cost more than a quarter-page ad.

In every phase of newspaper production, newspaper personnel must consider how everything, including stories, photographs, sketches, cartoons, and advertisements, fits on the newspaper's pages. For this reason, a system of measurement is used by all newspapers. The basic units of this system are *points* and *picas*.

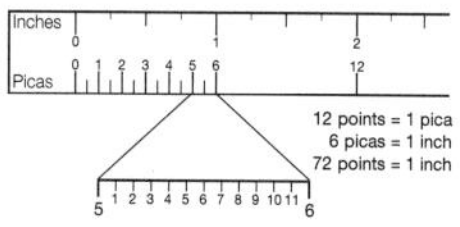

Newspapers are measured from left to right in columns. The width of the columns varies. For example, the columns of one newspaper may be 12 picas, or 2 inches, wide while the columns of another newspaper may be wider. Also, the number of columns across the page may vary.

Name ____________________ ***Math and Language Arts***

1. Compare and contrast several newspapers, including your community's local newspaper, to determine how the pages are divided into columns. Keep in mind that some newspapers let their stories run across two columns or two and one-half columns. Look at several pages of each newspaper to get an idea of how many columns are on a page. Then, carefully examine the front page of one newspaper. Describe at least three things that you think were done to make the stories fit together on the page.

See below.

2. A newspaper editor decides to print 4 pages that contain only advertisements. Each advertisement will be a quarter-page. How many advertisements will appear on the 4 pages?

16; $4 \div \frac{1}{4} = 4 \times \frac{4}{1} = 16$

3. An editor requests that 6 points of space separate a photograph from its caption. Express this as a fraction of an inch. Simplify.

$\frac{6}{72} = \frac{3}{36} = \frac{1}{12}$ inch

4. The columns of a local newspaper are 10 picas wide. There are 6 columns across the page, which is 12 in. wide. The space between columns is 1 pica. How many inches of space are left for the 2 margins? Hint: Draw a picture of the page. The answer is a mixed fraction.

See below.

5. a. If you type a paper on a school computer using 12 point type, what fraction of an inch is the type?

$\frac{12}{72} = \frac{1}{6}$

b. If you wanted a title to be $\frac{1}{2}$ inch tall, what size type (in points) would you use?

36 points

6. Why do you think newspaper people use points and picas instead of parts of an inch such as $\frac{1}{4}$ inch or $\frac{1}{16}$ inch?

See below.

7. Report events at your school by turning your classroom into a newspaper office and printing a newspaper. Class members should choose a role, such as reporter, photographer, editor, page designer, cartoonist, or columnist. (Columnists are people who give their opinion about a topic or provide special information—such as information about computer games, cooking, or music.) Have a staff meeting with your teacher to decide roles, what will be in the newspaper, and how the newspaper will be divided and produced.

In addition to deciding how to divide your newspaper, you must decide on the size of the type you will use for the title of your newspaper, its headlines, and the body copy. Remember, you want everything to fit together on each newspaper page. If your class has access to computers, you may be able to choose from a variety of type styles and sizes for your newspaper.

Upon completion, circulate the paper among the students, faculty, and staff in your school and community.

Answers

1. Student responses will vary. Possible responses: Continuing a story on another page, varying the headline type sizes, and adding images.

4. $1\frac{1}{6}$ inches; $(10 \times 6) + (1 \times 5) = 65$ picas; 72 picas (12 inches) – 65 picas = 7 picas; 7 picas = $1\frac{1}{6}$ inches

6. Possible answers: Differences in the size of type and spacing between lines are very small fractions, such as $\frac{1}{72}$ of an inch, and units such as points are more convenient to use for such measurements.

BIBLIOGRAPHY

FOR TEACHERS

Freidel, Frank Burt. *Franklin D. Roosevelt.* Boston, MA: Little Brown, 1990.

Geddes, Dorothy, et al. *Geometry in the Middle Grades: Addenda Series, Grades 5–8.* Reston, VA: NCTM, 1992.

Konda, Margaret and Williams, Phyllis. *Math Wizardry for Kids.* Hauppauge, NY: Baron's, 1995.

McMillan, Bruce. *Eating Fractions.* New York, NY: Scholastic, 1991.

Spangler, David. *Math for Real Kids.* Glenview, IL: Good Year Books, 1997.

Weidensaul, Scott. *Hummingbirds.* New York, NY: Gallery Books, 1991.

FOR STUDENTS

Fekete, Irene and Deyer, Jamine. *Mathematics.* New York, NY: Facts on File, 1990.

Sharp, Richard M. and Metzner, Seymour. *The Sneaky Square and 113 Other Math Activities for Kids.* Blue Ridge Summit, PA: TAB Books, 1990.

White, Laurence and Broekel, Ray. *Math-a-Magic: Number Tricks for Magicians.* Morton Grove, IL: A. Whitman, 1991.

SECTION **7B**

Dividing Fractions

▶ History Link ▶ Industry Link ▶ www.mathsurf.com/6/ch7/measures

364.4 Smoots and One Ear

In 1958, several students at the Massachusetts Institute of Technology (M.I.T.) measured the length of the Massachusetts Avenue Bridge. However, they didn't measure the length in feet, yards, or meters. Their unit of measurement was a fellow student named Oliver R. Smoot, Jr.

They laid Oliver down on the sidewalk and painted a mark to show his height. They repeated the process over 300 times until they had measured the entire bridge.

In 1989, the city rebuilt the bridge, but they preserved the Smoot. A plaque on the bridge now reads:

THIS PLAQUE PLACED IN HONOR OF

THE SMOOT

WHICH JOINED THE ANGSTROM, METER AND LIGHT YEAR AS STANDARDS OF LENGTH, WHEN IN OCTOBER 1958 THE SPAN OF THIS BRIDGE WAS MEASURED, USING THE BODY OF OLIVER REED SMOOT, M.I.T. '62 AND FOUND TO BE PRECISELY *364.4 SMOOTS AND ONE EAR*

COMMEMORATED AT OUR 25TH REUNION JUNE 6, 1987 M.I.T. CLASS OF 1962

There are many unusual and interesting measurements used in the world. Like the Smoot, they may not be well known. But they all involve mathematics.

1 **What other kinds of units could the students have used to measure the bridge?**

2 **When might it be better to use a made-up unit as opposed to a well-known unit?**

381

Where are we now?

In Section 7A, students learned to multiply fractions and mixed numbers.

They learned how to

- estimate products and quotients of fractions.
- multiply fractions and mixed numbers by whole numbers.
- multiply fractions and mixed numbers by fractions.

Where are we going?

In Section 7B, students will

- divide whole numbers by fractions.
- divide fractions by fractions.
- solve multiplication and division equations involving fractions.

Theme: Measurements

World Wide Web

If your class has access to the World Wide Web, you might want to use the information found at the Web site address given. The interdisciplinary links relate to topics discussed in this section.

About the Page

This page introduces the theme of the section, measurements, and discusses measuring a bridge, using the length of a person.

Ask ...

- Have you ever seen anyone measure a room using the length of his or her foot?
  Possible answer: Yes; When a person wants to get an estimate of the room's dimensions.

Extensions

The following activities do not require access to the World Wide Web.

History

The ancient Roman *pace* consisted of two steps and measured about 5 feet. Have students research other units of measure used by ancient civilizations and report their information to the class.

Industry

The publication of any book, magazine, or newspaper requires the use of different measurements. Have students research the various measurements used in the publishing industry and report their findings to the class.

Answers for Questions

1. Possible answers: Miles, feet, meters.
2. Possible answers: When you want to be noticed and get recognition.

Connect

On page 397, students use an unusual unit to measure a particular length.

7-4

Lesson Organizer

Objective

- Divide a whole number by a fraction.

Vocabulary

- Reciprocal

NCTM Standards

- 1–4, 7

Review

Multiply.

1. $\frac{1}{3} \times \frac{2}{5}$ $\frac{2}{15}$
2. $\frac{3}{4} \times \frac{1}{6}$ $\frac{3}{24}$ or $\frac{1}{8}$
3. $\frac{5}{8} \times \frac{1}{2}$ $\frac{5}{16}$
4. $\frac{3}{10} \times \frac{1}{4}$ $\frac{3}{40}$

Available on Daily Transparency 7-4

1 Introduce

Explore

You may wish to use Lesson Enhancement Transparency 35 with **Explore**.

The Point

Students explore dividing whole numbers by fractions by drawing a number of fraction sketches, circling groups of the divisor, and counting the number of groups.

Ongoing Assessment

As students are working, check to see that they are dividing each fraction sketch into the correct number of parts and that they are circling groups of the fraction divisor.

For Groups That Finish Early

Multiply each of the following:

1. $6 \times \frac{3}{2}$ 9
2. $5 \times \frac{6}{5}$ 6
3. $2 \times \frac{7}{2}$ 7

Are any of these like those in Step 1? Answers are the same as a, c, and e.

7-4 Dividing Whole Numbers by Fractions

You'll Learn ...

■ to divide a whole number by a fraction

... How It's Used

Structural engineers divide whole numbers by fractions when building tunnels.

Vocabulary

reciprocal

▶ Lesson Link In the last section, you learned to multiply whole numbers by fractions. Now you'll divide whole numbers by fractions. ◀

Explore Dividing Whole Numbers by Fractions

Circles and Strips Forever

Dividing a Whole Number by a Fraction

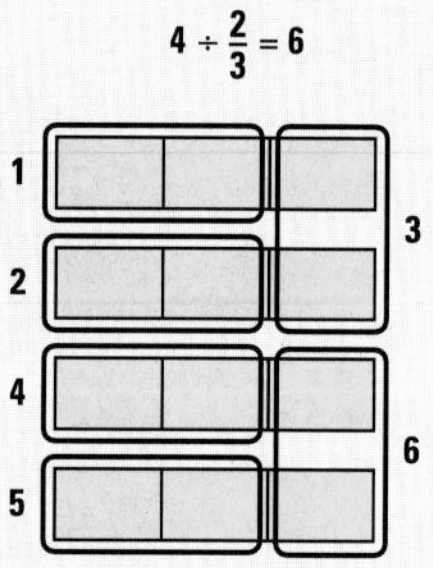

- Draw a number of strips equal to the whole number.
- Divide the strips into equal pieces. The number of pieces in each strip should be equal to the fraction denominator.
- Circle groups of equal pieces. The number of pieces in each circled group should equal the numerator.
- Describe the number of groups circled.

1. Model these problems.

a. $6 \div \frac{2}{3}$ **b.** $7 \div \frac{1}{2}$ **c.** $5 \div \frac{5}{6}$ **d.** $4 \div \frac{3}{6}$ **e.** $2 \div \frac{2}{7}$

2. When you divide a whole number by a fraction less than 1, is the quotient larger or smaller than the original whole number? Why?

3. Will $3 \div \frac{2}{5}$ have a whole-number answer? Explain.

Learn Dividing Whole Numbers by Fractions

You can think of division as taking a given amount and breaking it down into groups of a certain size. For example, 6 ÷ 2 can be modeled as 6 loaves of bread divided into groups of 2. The quotient, 3, is the number of groups you have.

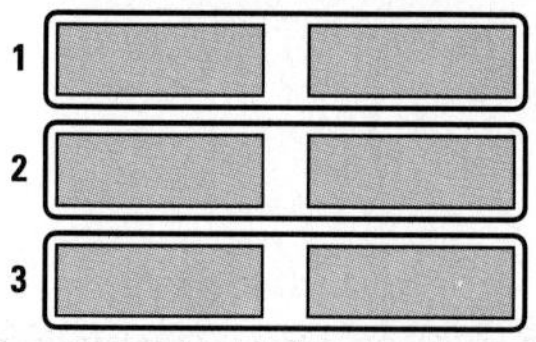

MEETING INDIVIDUAL NEEDS

Resources

- **7-4** Practice
- **7-4** Reteaching
- **7-4** Problem Solving
- **7-4** Enrichment
- **7-4** Daily Transparency
  - Problem of the Day
  - Review
  - Quick Quiz
- Lesson Enhancement Transparency 35
- Technology Master 33
- Chapter 7 Project Master

Learning Modalities

Musical Have students determine the number of quarter notes or half notes in 3 or 4 measures.

Kinesthetic Have students make fraction strips to model division of fraction problems.

English Language Development

The *Multilingual Handbook*, with its glossary of math terms, illustrations, and worked-out examples, can help you with students who have limited English language skills. The glossary is provided in multiple languages.

You can think of dividing by fractions in the same way. For example, $6 \div \frac{2}{3}$ is the same as 6 loaves of bread divided into groups of $\frac{2}{3}$. The number of groups you have, 9, is the quotient.

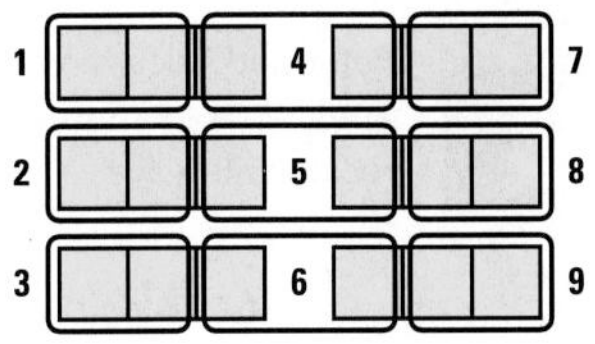

Notice that to find the answer, you first found the number of thirds by multiplying the number of loaves, 6, by the denominator, 3. Then, you divided the number of thirds by the numerator, 2.

$$6 \div \frac{2}{3} = 6 \times 3 \div 2 = 9$$

Remember

The numerator is the number on top of a fraction. The denominator is the number on the bottom. [Page 287]

Dividing by a fraction is the same as multiplying by its **reciprocal**. Reciprocals are numbers whose numerators and denominators have been switched. When two numbers are reciprocals, their product is 1.

Dividing	Multiplying by reciprocal
$6 \div \frac{2}{3} = 9$	$6 \times \frac{3}{2} = \frac{6}{1} \times \frac{3}{2}$
	$= \frac{18}{2}$
	$= 9$

Examples

1 Divide: $2 \div \frac{3}{4}$

$2 \div \frac{3}{4} = \frac{2}{1} \times \frac{4}{3}$ Multiply by the reciprocal of the fraction.

$= \frac{2 \times 4}{1 \times 3}$

$= \frac{8}{3}$ or $2\frac{2}{3}$

$2 \div \frac{3}{4} = 2\frac{2}{3}$

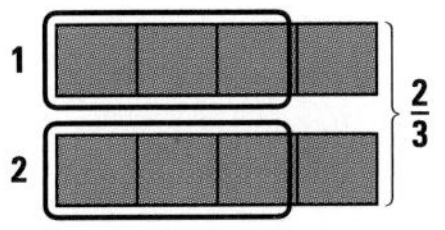

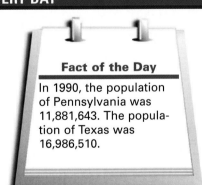

2 1 *nail* = $\frac{9}{4}$ in. of cloth. Find the length of 5 in. of cloth in nails.

$5 \div \frac{9}{4} = \frac{5}{1} \times \frac{4}{9}$ Multiply by the reciprocal.

$= \frac{20}{9}$ or $2\frac{2}{9}$ Simplify.

A 5-inch piece of cloth is $2\frac{2}{9}$ nails long.

Try It

Divide. **a.** $4 \div \frac{3}{5}$ $6\frac{2}{3}$ **b.** $1 \div \frac{4}{7}$ $1\frac{3}{4}$ **c.** $10 \div \frac{17}{4}$ $2\frac{6}{17}$ **d.** $3 \div \frac{3}{5}$ 5

DID YOU KNOW?

Three measurements used primarily for cloth include the *nail*, the *finger*, and the *span*. A *finger* is equal to $4\frac{1}{2}$ inches. A *span* is equal to 9 inches.

Answers for Explore

1. a. 9

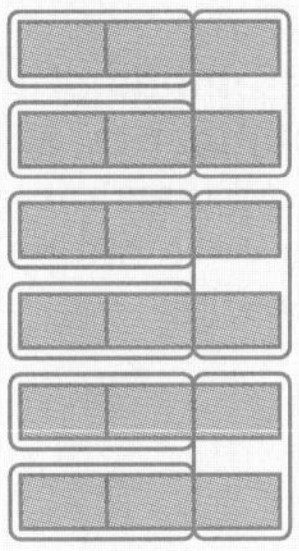

b. 14

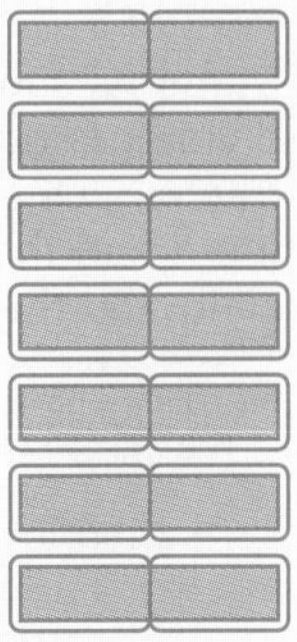

c. 6

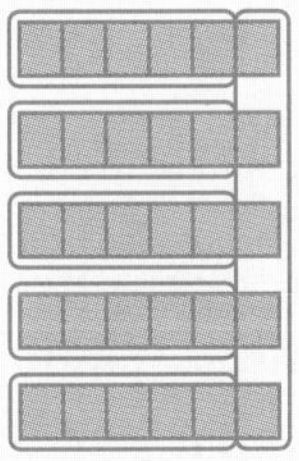

d. 8

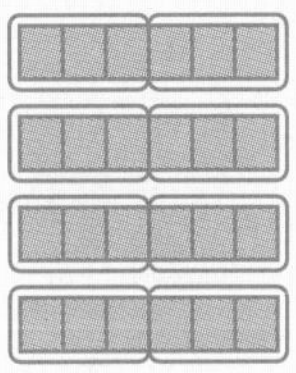

e. 7

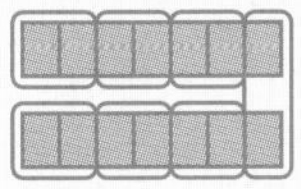

2. Larger; Possible answer: You are putting less than one object in each group, so the number of groups has to be larger than the number of objects.
3. No; Possible answer: The 15 sections cannot be grouped into equal groups with 2 pieces in each group.

2 Teach

Learn

Alternate Examples

1. Divide: $3 \div \frac{2}{5}$

   $3 \div \frac{2}{5} = \frac{3}{1} \times \frac{5}{2}$

   $= \frac{3 \times 5}{1 \times 2}$

   $= \frac{15}{2}$ or $7\frac{1}{2}$

2. A quarter is about $\frac{1}{16}$ in. thick. How many quarters would be in a stack 4 in. high?

   $4 \div \frac{1}{16} = \frac{4}{1} \times \frac{16}{1}$

   $= \frac{64}{1}$ or 64

   A 4-inch stack of quarters would contain about 64 quarters.

MATH EVERY DAY

Problem of the Day

Erica and six friends went on summer vacations, each to a different part of the United States. The friends promised to mail each of the others a postcard. How many postcards will be mailed? 42 postcards, since each of 7 people sends out 6 cards

Available on Daily Transparency 7-4

An Extension is provided in the transparency package.

Fact of the Day

In 1990, the population of Pennsylvania was 11,881,643. The population of Texas was 16,986,510.

Mental Math

Find each product mentally.

1. 24 × 4 96
2. 24 × 40 960
3. 24 × 4000 96,000

WHAT DO YOU THINK?

Students see two methods of dividing a whole number by a fraction. One method uses mental math and the other uses multiplication by the reciprocal.

Answers for What Do You Think?

1. Answers may vary.
2. Possible answer: Use mental math to decide what number multiplied by $\frac{3}{4}$ equals $\frac{36}{4}$.

3 Practice and Assess

Check

Answers for Check Your Understanding

1. Multiply 20 by $\frac{1}{5}$.
2. Larger; Possible answer: Dividing by a proper fraction is the same as multiplying by its reciprocal, which is an improper fraction. Multiplying by a number greater than 1 results in a larger product.

WHAT DO YOU THINK?

Peter and Erica have a recipe that makes 9 quarts of punch. They want to know how many $\frac{3}{4}$-quart (3-cup) servings the recipe will make.

Peter thinks ...

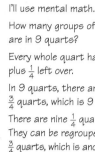

I'll use mental math.

How many groups of $\frac{3}{4}$ quart are in 9 quarts?

Every whole quart has one $\frac{3}{4}$ in it, plus $\frac{1}{4}$ left over.

In 9 quarts, there are nine $\frac{3}{4}$ quarts, which is 9 servings.

There are nine $\frac{1}{4}$ quarts left over. They can be regrouped as three $\frac{3}{4}$ quarts, which is another 3 servings.

That equals 9 + 3 or 12 groups of $\frac{3}{4}$ quart.

We will have 12 servings.

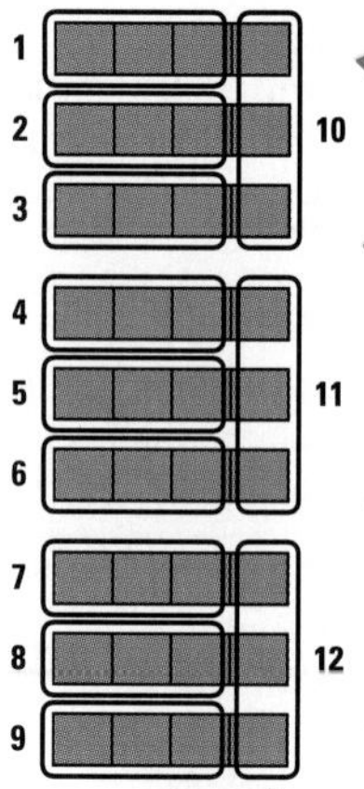

Erica thinks ...

I'll divide 9 by $\frac{3}{4}$. To do that, I'll multiply $\frac{9}{1}$ by the reciprocal of $\frac{3}{4}$.

$$9 \div \frac{3}{4} = \frac{9}{1} \times \frac{4}{3} = 12$$

We will have 12 servings.

What do *you* think?

1. Whose method is easier to use without paper and pencil? Explain.
2. How could you find the answer by writing 9 quarts as $\frac{36}{4}$ quarts?

Check Your Understanding

1. How could you use the "multiply by the reciprocal" rule to divide 20 by 5?
2. If you divide a whole number by a proper fraction, is the quotient larger or smaller than the whole number? Explain.

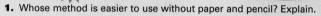

MEETING MIDDLE SCHOOL CLASSROOM NEEDS

Tips from Middle School Teachers

To help students understand the meaning of reciprocal, I have them complete a table like the one shown.

Number	Reciprocal	Number × Reciprocal
1	$\frac{1}{1}$	1
4	$\frac{1}{4}$	1
$\frac{4}{5}$	$\frac{5}{4}$	1
$5\frac{1}{8}$ or $\frac{41}{8}$	$\frac{8}{41}$	1

Cooperative Learning

Have students work in groups of three or four. On a sheet of paper, I have each student write a division problem with a whole number and a fraction. Then I ask each student to pass his or her problem along to the next student in a clockwise fashion. Then I have each student complete one step in the problem and pass it on to the next student who completes the next step, and so on until the problem is solved.

Health Connection

Have students examine the nutritional information given on food packages. Have students use fraction statements such as "$\frac{1}{3}$ less fat" or dietary exchanges, to create word problems.

7-4 Exercises and Applications

Practice and Apply

Getting Started State the reciprocal.

1. $\frac{5}{7}$ $\frac{7}{5}$ **2.** $\frac{1}{2}$ 2 **3.** $\frac{2}{9}$ $\frac{9}{2}$ **4.** $\frac{10}{14}$ $\frac{14}{10}$ **5.** $\frac{1}{4}$ 4 **6.** $\frac{4}{5}$ $\frac{5}{4}$

Simplify.

7. $6 \div \frac{2}{3}$ 9 **8.** $2 \div \frac{3}{5}$ $3\frac{1}{3}$ **9.** $3 \div \frac{6}{7}$ $3\frac{1}{2}$ **10.** $1 \div 1\frac{1}{2}$ $\frac{2}{3}$

11. $9 \div \frac{4}{5}$ $11\frac{1}{4}$ **12.** $7 \div \frac{6}{5}$ $5\frac{5}{6}$ **13.** $4 \div 3\frac{5}{8}$ $1\frac{3}{29}$ **14.** $5 \div \frac{1}{4}$ 20

15. $10 \div 7\frac{2}{3}$ $1\frac{7}{23}$ **16.** $8 \div 8\frac{7}{8}$ $\frac{64}{71}$ **17.** $3 \div \frac{10}{11}$ $3\frac{3}{10}$ **18.** $5 \div \frac{9}{2}$ $1\frac{1}{9}$

19. $16 \div \frac{2}{5}$ 40 **20.** $7 \div 6\frac{3}{4}$ $1\frac{1}{27}$ **21.** $8 \div 2\frac{1}{6}$ $3\frac{9}{13}$ **22.** $2 \div 4\frac{2}{7}$ $\frac{7}{15}$

23. $1 \div 3\frac{5}{9}$ $\frac{9}{32}$ **24.** $4 \div 1\frac{1}{2}$ $2\frac{2}{3}$ **25.** $9 \div \frac{6}{7}$ $10\frac{1}{2}$ **26.** $6 \div \frac{8}{12}$ 9

27. $11 \div \frac{13}{2}$ $1\frac{9}{13}$ **28.** $10 \div 9\frac{8}{9}$ $1\frac{1}{89}$ **29.** $3 \div 11\frac{1}{3}$ $\frac{9}{34}$ **30.** $7 \div 2\frac{3}{8}$ $2\frac{18}{19}$

31. **Test Prep** Which two expressions have the same quotient as $6 \div 1\frac{3}{4}$? B

I. $\frac{6}{1} \div \frac{7}{4}$ II. $\frac{6}{1} \times \frac{7}{4}$ III. $\frac{6}{1} \div \frac{4}{7}$ IV. $\frac{6}{1} \times \frac{4}{7}$

Ⓐ I and II Ⓑ I and IV

Ⓒ III and II Ⓓ III and IV

32. **Science** $\frac{4}{5}$ of a cubic foot of copper weighs 440 pounds. What is the weight of 1 cubic foot of copper? 550 lb

33. **Social Studies** GPS As a result of the 1990 census, Pennsylvania has 21 seats in the House of Representatives. This is $\frac{7}{10}$ as many seats as Texas has. How many seats does Texas have? 30

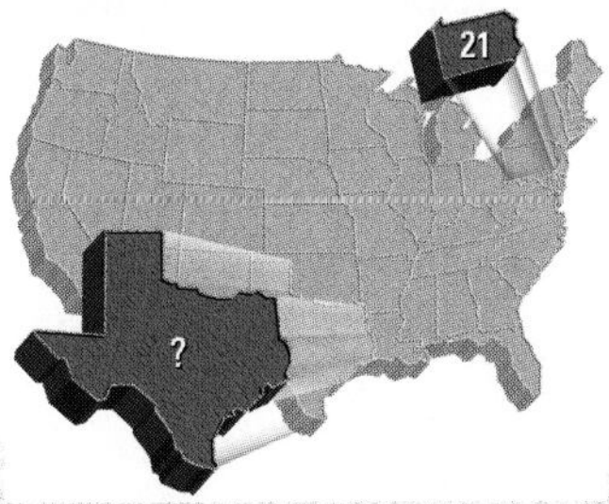

7-4 Exercises and Applications

Assignment Guide

- **Basic** 1–18, 31, 33, 35, 38–40, 44–46
- **Average** 1–31 odds, 32–34, 36, 41–46
- **Enriched** 10–30 evens, 31–37 odds, 41–49 odds

Exercise Notes

Exercises 7–30

Error Prevention Some students may multiply without finding the reciprocal of the divisor. Suggest that they write out each step of the division process.

Exercise 31

Test Prep If students incorrectly chose A, they failed to recognize that dividing by a fraction is the same as multiplying by its reciprocal.

Exercises 32–33

Problem-Solving Tip Students may find it helpful to write these problems as missing-factor problems. $\frac{4}{5} \times ? = 440$ and $21 = \frac{7}{10} \times ?$.

PRACTICE

Name ______________________

Practice 7-4

Dividing Whole Numbers by Fractions

Simplify.

1. $11 \div \frac{1}{7}$ 77 2. $6 \div \frac{1}{3}$ 18 3. $3 \div 1\frac{5}{8}$ $1\frac{11}{13}$
4. $7 \div \frac{2}{3}$ $10\frac{1}{2}$ 5. $4 \div \frac{3}{4}$ $5\frac{1}{3}$ 6. $11 \div \frac{3}{4}$ $14\frac{2}{3}$
7. $12 \div \frac{2}{5}$ 30 8. $11 \div \frac{4}{9}$ $24\frac{3}{4}$ 9. $12 \div 3\frac{1}{2}$ $3\frac{3}{7}$
10. $7 \div \frac{3}{10}$ $23\frac{1}{3}$ 11. $11 \div \frac{1}{2}$ 22 12. $3 \div \frac{2}{5}$ $7\frac{1}{2}$
13. $5 \div 2\frac{2}{9}$ $2\frac{1}{4}$ 14. $7 \div 2\frac{8}{9}$ $2\frac{11}{26}$ 15. $8 \div \frac{1}{3}$ 24
16. $8 \div 1\frac{1}{4}$ $6\frac{2}{5}$ 17. $8 \div 1\frac{5}{6}$ $4\frac{4}{11}$ 18. $10 \div 1\frac{7}{9}$ $5\frac{5}{8}$
19. $7 \div 1\frac{1}{5}$ $5\frac{5}{6}$ 20. $4 \div 4\frac{1}{3}$ $\frac{12}{13}$ 21. $3 \div 4\frac{1}{5}$ $\frac{5}{7}$
22. $10 \div 1\frac{1}{2}$ $6\frac{2}{3}$ 23. $6 \div \frac{1}{2}$ 12 24. $7 \div \frac{2}{9}$ $31\frac{1}{2}$
25. $3 \div 2\frac{3}{5}$ $1\frac{2}{13}$ 26. $11 \div 1\frac{3}{10}$ $8\frac{6}{13}$ 27. $10 \div 1\frac{5}{9}$ $6\frac{3}{7}$
28. $7 \div 2\frac{4}{7}$ $2\frac{13}{18}$ 29. $8 \div 1\frac{1}{3}$ 6 30. $8 \div 1\frac{1}{2}$ $5\frac{1}{3}$
31. $12 \div 1\frac{1}{3}$ 9 32. $8 \div \frac{3}{7}$ $18\frac{2}{3}$ 33. $5 \div 2\frac{2}{5}$ $2\frac{1}{12}$
34. $8 \div \frac{1}{7}$ 56 35. $8 \div 2\frac{1}{3}$ $3\frac{3}{7}$ 36. $5 \div \frac{2}{3}$ $7\frac{1}{2}$
37. $7 \div 2\frac{5}{9}$ $2\frac{17}{23}$ 38. $3 \div \frac{1}{3}$ 9 39. $11 \div 2\frac{2}{3}$ $4\frac{1}{8}$
40. $3 \div 2\frac{1}{3}$ $1\frac{2}{7}$ 41. $5 \div 1\frac{1}{5}$ $4\frac{1}{6}$ 42. $4 \div \frac{2}{5}$ 10

43. **Science** A baby walrus is 4 feet long. This is $\frac{2}{5}$ of the length of an adult male. What is the length of an adult male walrus? 10 ft

44. **Measurement** One yard (36 inches) is equal to $\frac{2}{11}$ of a rod. How many inches are in a rod? 198 in.

RETEACHING

Name ______________________

Alternative Lesson 7-4

Dividing Whole Numbers by Fractions

Dividing by a fraction is the same as multiplying by its **reciprocal.** Reciprocals are numbers whose numerators and denominators have been switched. When two numbers are reciprocals, their product is 1. For example, $\frac{2}{3}$ and $\frac{3}{2}$ are reciprocals because $\frac{2}{3} \times \frac{3}{2}$ is 1.

Study these whole numbers to learn how to divide by fractions.

$8 \div 4 = 2$ $7 \div 8 = \frac{7}{8}$

$8 \times \frac{1}{4} = 2$ $7 \times \frac{1}{8} = \frac{7}{8}$

4 and $\frac{1}{4}$ are reciprocals. 8 and $\frac{1}{8}$ are reciprocals.

Example

Divide: $4 \div \frac{3}{8}$.

Write 4 as an improper fraction.
Multiply by the reciprocal of $\frac{3}{8}$.
The reciprocal of $\frac{3}{8}$ is $\frac{8}{3}$.

$4 \div \frac{3}{8} = \frac{4}{1} \times \frac{8}{3}$

Simplify. $= \frac{32}{3} = 10\frac{2}{3}$

So, $4 \div \frac{3}{8} = 10\frac{2}{3}$.

Try It

a. Divide: $21 \div \frac{4}{3}$.

Multiply. $\frac{21}{1}$ (Improper fraction) $\times$ $\frac{3}{4}$ (Reciprocal) $= \frac{63}{4} = 15\frac{3}{4}$

b. Divide: $10 \div \frac{4}{3}$.

Multiply. $\frac{10}{1}$ (Improper fraction) $\times$ $\frac{3}{4}$ (Reciprocal) $= \frac{30}{4} = 7\frac{2}{4} = 7\frac{1}{2}$

Divide.

c. $3 \div \frac{3}{7}$ 7 **d.** $6 \div \frac{2}{5}$ 15
e. $8 \div \frac{6}{7}$ $9\frac{1}{3}$ **f.** $20 \div \frac{3}{5}$ $33\frac{1}{3}$
g. $4 \div \frac{5}{6}$ $4\frac{4}{5}$ **h.** $25 \div \frac{5}{8}$ 40
i. $12 \div \frac{2}{3}$ 18 **j.** $16 \div \frac{4}{9}$ 36

Reteaching

Activity

Materials: Fraction Bars

Have students use Fraction Bars to model each problem and find each quotient.

1. $4 \div \frac{1}{2}$ 8
2. $3 \div \frac{3}{4}$ 4
3. $6 \div \frac{3}{4}$ 8
4. $2 \div \frac{1}{3}$ 6
5. $8 \div \frac{1}{4}$ 32
6. $5 \div \frac{5}{6}$ 6

Project Progress

You may want to have students use Chapter 7 Project Master.

Exercise Answers

35. a. About $3\frac{1}{2}$; Change 2 lb to cups, then divide by $2\frac{1}{4}$ c.
    b. 2; Change 1 lb to cups, then divide by 1 cup.
    c. About 11; Change 4 lb to cups, then divide by $\frac{3}{4}$ c.

36. No; $4 \div \frac{2}{5} = 10$ and $\frac{2}{5} \div 4 = \frac{1}{10}$. Division is not commutative.

37. No; A quire should be smaller than a ream. It is 25 sheets.

44.
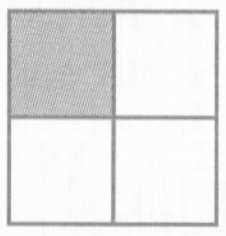

45
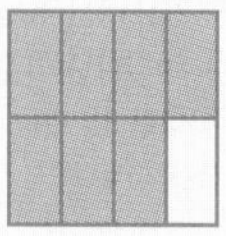

46.
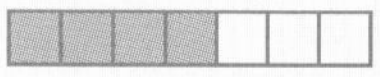

47.
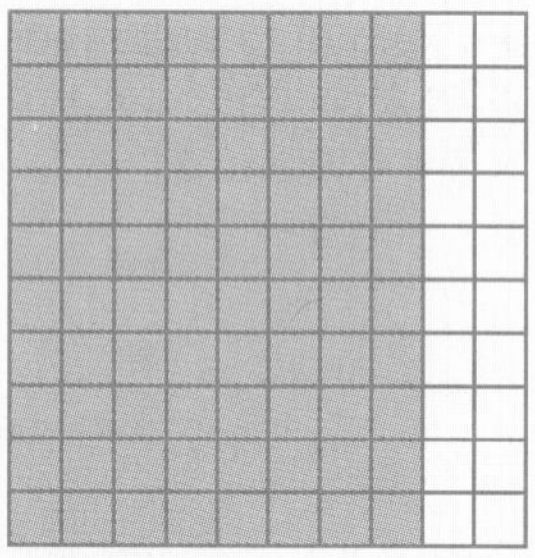

48.
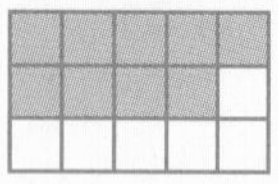

49.
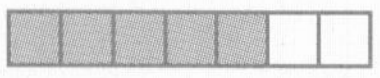

Alternate Assessment

You may want to use the *Interactive CD-ROM Journal* with this assessment.

Journal Have students write a paragraph describing how they divide a whole number by a fraction. Encourage them to include a drawing of a model which shows the solution of a division problem.

➤ Quick Quiz

Divide.

1. $4 \div \frac{3}{4}$ $5\frac{1}{3}$
2. $7 \div \frac{2}{3}$ $10\frac{1}{2}$
3. $5 \div 1\frac{1}{2}$ $3\frac{1}{3}$

Available on Daily Transparency 7-4

PROBLEM SOLVING 7-4

Problem Solving and Reasoning

34. Journal Explain how you can tell if two numbers are reciprocals of each other.
Their product is 1.

35. Critical Thinking This recipe makes 1 batch of cookies. About how many batches can you make if you change the recipe to include the following? Explain your answers.

a. A 2-pound bag of flour? (1 cup = $\frac{1}{4}$ pound)

b. A pound of margarine? (1 cup = $\frac{1}{2}$ pound)

c. A 4-pound bag of white sugar? (1 cup = $\frac{1}{2}$ pound)

36. Communicate Is $4 \div \frac{2}{5}$ the same as $\frac{2}{5} \div 4$? Explain your reasoning.

37. Critical Thinking A *ream* of paper is 500 sheets. A *quire* of paper is $\frac{1}{20}$ of a ream. Monique wanted to know how many sheets of paper were in a quire. She calculated $500 \div \frac{1}{20} = 10{,}000$, and decided a quire of paper was 10,000 sheets. Is her answer reasonable? Explain.

Mixed Review

Convert. *[Lesson 4-3]*

38. 144 ounces = ☐ pounds 9
39. 56 pounds = ☐ ounces 896
40. 80 ounces = ☐ pounds 5
41. 100 gallons = ☐ quarts 400
42. 64 quarts = ☐ gallons 16
43. 40 gallons = ☐ quarts 160

For each fraction, draw a model. *[Lesson 5-4]*

44. $\frac{1}{4}$ **45.** $\frac{7}{8}$ **46.** $\frac{4}{7}$ **47.** $\frac{80}{100}$ **48.** $\frac{9}{15}$ **49.** $\frac{5}{7}$

Project Progress

Choose 10 of the items from your list. Make a chart detailing how much each item cost when your senior citizen was your age, and how much it costs today. Estimate the fraction or mixed number you would need to multiply the old price by to get the current price.

Problem Solving
Understand
Plan
Solve
Look Back

PROBLEM SOLVING

Name ____________

Guided Problem Solving 7-4

GPS PROBLEM 33, STUDENT PAGE 385

As a result of the 1990 census, Pennsylvania has 21 seats in the House of Representatives. This is $\frac{7}{10}$ as many seats as Texas has. How many seats does Texas have?

— Understand —

1. Underline what you are asked to find.
2. How many seats did Pennsylvania have as a result of the 1990 census? 21 seats.
3. The number of Representatives from Pennsylvania is what fraction of the number of Representatives from Texas? $\frac{7}{10}$

— Plan —

4. Will Texas have fewer or more Representatives than Pennsylvania? More.
5. Which operation will you use to find the number of seats Texas has in the House of Representatives? Division.
6. Which would be a reasonable number of seats for Texas to have in the House of Representatives? c
   a. 15 seats b. 21 seats c. 30 seats

— Solve —

7. Write an equation showing the number of seats Texas has in the House of Representatives. $21 \div \frac{7}{10}$
8. How many seats does Texas have? 30 seats.

— Look Back —

9. How could you use decimals to find your answer? Possible answer: Convert $\frac{7}{10}$ to 0.7. Then divide 21 by 0.7.

SOLVE ANOTHER PROBLEM

As a result of the 1990 census, Colorado has 6 seats in the House of Representatives. This is $\frac{3}{10}$ as many seats as Illinois has. How many seats does Illinois have? 20 seats.

ENRICHMENT

Name ____________

Extend Your Thinking 7-4

Visual Thinking

Four figures in each row are identical. Circle the letter of the figure that is different.

1.
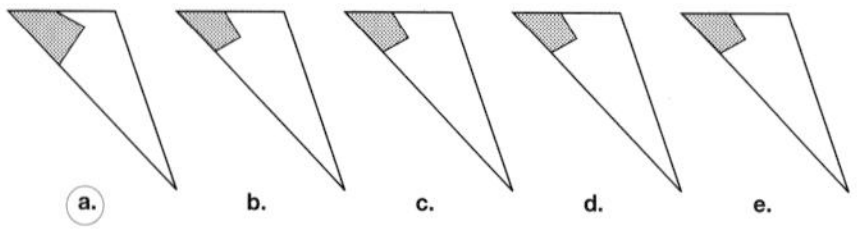
a. b. c. d. e.

2.

a. b. c. d. e.

3.
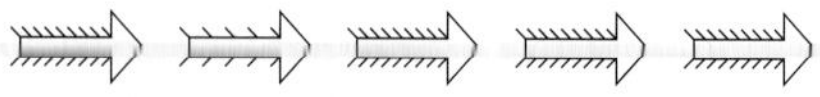
a. b. c. d. e.

4.
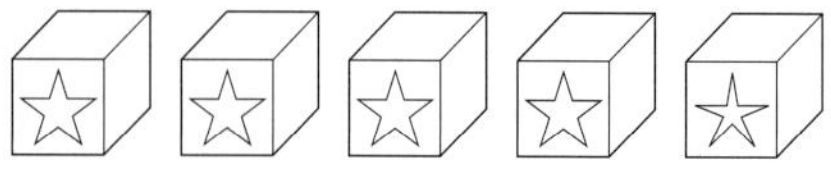
a. b. c. d. e.

5.

a. b. c. d. e.

Dividing Fractions by Fractions

7-5

▶ Lesson Link In the last lesson, you learned to divide whole numbers by fractions. Now you'll divide fractions by fractions. ◀

You'll Learn ...

■ to divide a fraction by a fraction or a whole number

... How It's Used

Choreographers divide fractions by fractions when fitting a dance routine to a particular tempo of music.

Explore Dividing Fractions by Fractions

Materials: Fraction Bars®

Wish Upon a Bar

Dividing a Fraction by a Fraction

$\frac{2}{3} \div \frac{1}{12} = 8$

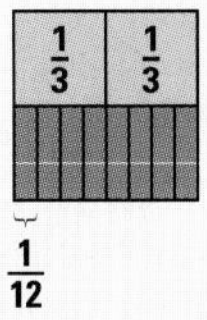

- Using a Fraction Bar®, draw and label the first fraction.
- Under that, use a Fraction Bar® to draw as many diagrams of the second fraction as will fit.
- Describe the number of diagrams below the first fraction.

1. Model each problem.

a. $\frac{3}{6} \div \frac{1}{12}$ **b.** $\frac{1}{2} \div \frac{1}{4}$ **c.** $\frac{2}{3} \div \frac{1}{6}$ **d.** $\frac{2}{4} \div \frac{2}{12}$

2. When you divide a fraction by a fraction less than 1, why is the answer bigger than the fraction you started with?

3. How is dividing a fraction by a fraction similar to dividing a whole number by a fraction?

4. Can you use Fraction Bars® to divide $\frac{1}{2} \div \frac{1}{5}$? Explain.

Learn Dividing Fractions by Fractions

When you divide a whole number by a fraction, you get the same result as if you had multiplied the whole number by the fraction's reciprocal. This is also true when you divide a fraction by a fraction.

Dividing	Multiplying by Reciprocal
$\frac{6}{7} \div \frac{3}{7} = 2$	$\frac{6}{7} \times \frac{7}{3} = \frac{42}{21}$ or 2

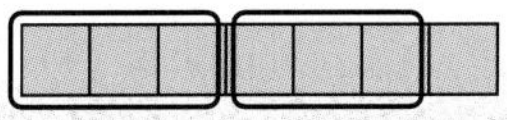

MEETING INDIVIDUAL NEEDS

Resources

7-5 Practice
7-5 Reteaching
7-5 Problem Solving
7-5 Enrichment
7-5 Daily Transparency
- Problem of the Day
- Review
- Quick Quiz

Teaching Tool Transparency 14
Lesson Enhancement Transparency 36
Technology Master 34

Learning Modalities

Kinesthetic Have students cut paper strips and fold and shade them to model division of fractions.

Verbal Have students indicate true or false by showing thumbs up or thumbs down for the following statements about dividing fractions.

1. To divide by a fraction, first find the common denominator. False
2. To divide by a whole number, you can multiply by its reciprocal. True
3. To divide by a mixed number, first change it to an improper fraction. True

Challenge

Have students simplify the following exercises.

1. $\frac{3}{4} \times \frac{5}{9} \div \frac{5}{8}$ $\frac{2}{3}$
2. $\frac{1}{9} \div \frac{2}{3} \div 1\frac{1}{2}$ $\frac{1}{9}$
3. $2\frac{1}{3} \div 1\frac{3}{4} \times 4\frac{1}{5}$ $\frac{28}{5}$ or $5\frac{3}{5}$

7-5 Lesson Organizer

Objective
- Divide a fraction by a fraction or a whole number.

Materials
- Explore: Fraction Bars

NCTM Standards
- 1–4, 7, 13

▶ Review

Write the reciprocal.

1. $\frac{3}{4}$ $\frac{4}{3}$
2. 6 $\frac{1}{6}$
3. $1\frac{1}{3}$ $\frac{3}{4}$
4. $3\frac{1}{4}$ $\frac{4}{13}$

Available on Daily Transparency 7-5

▶ Lesson Link

Have students discuss situations in which a whole number would be divided by a fraction and decide whether or not similar situations could require dividing a fraction by a fraction.

1 Introduce

Explore

You may wish to use Lesson Enhancement Transparency 36 or Teaching Tool Transparency 14: Fraction Bars with **Explore.**

The Point
Students explore division of fractions by using Fraction Bars to determine the number of fractional parts given by the divisor, and in another fractional region, given by the dividend.

Ongoing Assessment
As students are working, ask them to describe how their diagrams represent the given division problems.

Answers for Explore on next page.

Answers for Explore

1. a. 6 b. 2

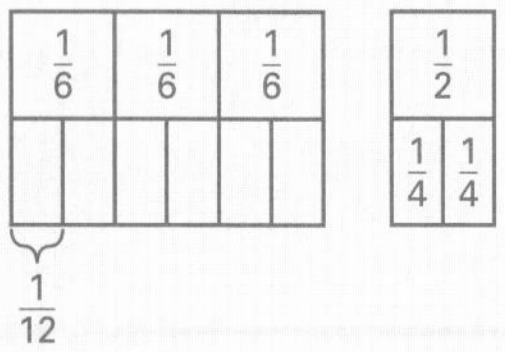

c. 4 d. 3

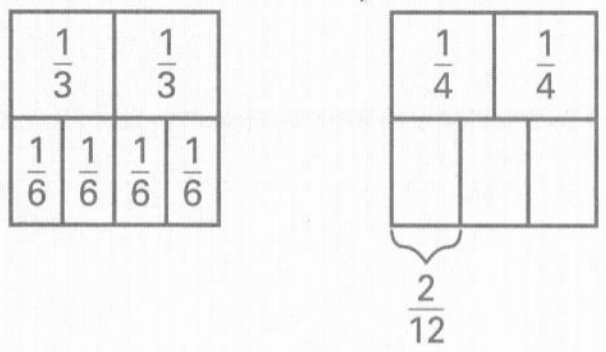

2. Possible answer: Dividing by a fraction less than 1 is the same as multiplying by its reciprocal, which is greater than 1.
3. Possible answer: You multiply the first factor by the reciprocal of the second.
4. No; The answer is not a whole number.

2 Teach

Learn

Alternate Examples

1. Stan has made $3\frac{1}{2}$ gallons of punch for a party. How many one-cup servings of punch are there? (1 cup = $\frac{1}{16}$ gallon)

$$3\frac{1}{2} \div \frac{1}{16} = \frac{7}{2} \div \frac{1}{16}$$
$$= \frac{7}{2} \times \frac{16}{1}$$
$$= 56$$

There are 56 one-cup servings.

2. What is $\frac{5}{8} \div 4$?

$$\frac{5}{8} \div 4 = \frac{5}{8} \div \frac{4}{1}$$
$$= \frac{5}{8} \times \frac{1}{4}$$
$$= \frac{5}{32}$$

3 Practice and Assess

Check

Answers for Check Your Understanding

1. No; You can't change the order of fractions in division problems without changing the result.
2. 1

▶ History Link

The term *furlong* originated in the Middle Ages. The furlong was originally a "furrow long," the length of a plowed strip of land on a standard-size field.

Example 1

Horse races are measured in *furlongs* (1 furlong = $\frac{1}{8}$ mi). The Kentucky Derby is $1\frac{1}{4}$ mi long. How long is the Kentucky Derby in furlongs?

$1\frac{1}{4} \div \frac{1}{8} = \frac{5}{4} \div \frac{1}{8}$ Write the numbers as fractions.

$= \frac{5}{4} \times \frac{8}{1}$ Multiply by the reciprocal.

$= 10$

The Kentucky Derby is 10 furlongs long.

When dividing a fraction by a whole number, you can write the whole number as a fraction with 1 as its denominator. You can then multiply the fraction by the reciprocal of the whole number.

Remember

You can write a fraction in lowest terms when the numerator and the denominator share a common factor.
[Page 292]

Example 2

What is $\frac{3}{5} \div 6$?

$\frac{3}{5} \div 6 = \frac{3}{5} \div \frac{6}{1}$ Write the whole number as a fraction with a denominator of 1.

$= \frac{3}{5} \times \frac{1}{6}$ Multiply by the reciprocal of $\frac{6}{1}$.

$= \frac{3}{30}$ or $\frac{1}{10}$ Simplify.

Try It

Divide. **a.** $\frac{4}{5} \div \frac{5}{8}$ $1\frac{7}{25}$ **b.** $\frac{3}{7} \div \frac{2}{7}$ $1\frac{1}{2}$ **c.** $\frac{1}{5} \div 2$ $\frac{1}{10}$ **d.** $\frac{2}{5} \div 10$ $\frac{1}{25}$

Check Your Understanding

1. $\frac{1}{2} \times \frac{1}{4} = \frac{1}{4} \times \frac{1}{2}$. Does $\frac{1}{2} \div \frac{1}{4} = \frac{1}{4} \div \frac{1}{2}$? Explain.
2. If you find the reciprocal of a whole number, what will the numerator of that reciprocal be equal to?

MATH EVERY DAY

▶ Problem of the Day

How many squares can you find in the drawing below?

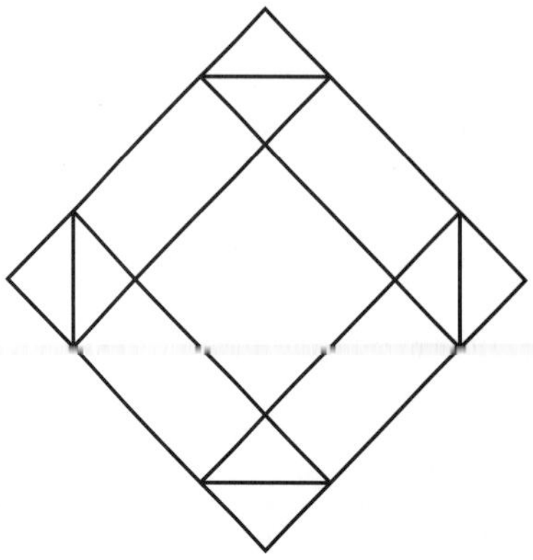

10 squares

Available on Daily Transparency 7-5

An Extension is provided in the transparency package.

Fact of the Day

In 1973, Secretariat ran the fastest Kentucky Derby in 1 minute 59.2 seconds. The slowest was 2 minutes and 10.4 seconds in 1929.

Estimation

Estimate.

1. 1123 + 510 1600
2. 20,336 + 698 21,000
3. 2982 − 983 2000

7-5 Exercises and Applications

Practice and Apply

Getting Started Write the division problem that each model represents.

1.

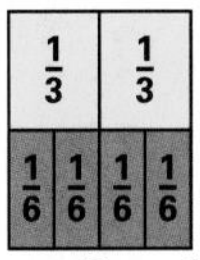

$\frac{2}{3} \div \frac{1}{6} = 4$

2.

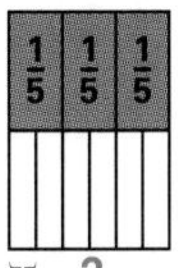

$\frac{1}{10}$

$\frac{3}{5} \div \frac{1}{10} = 6$

3.

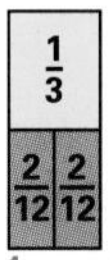

$\frac{1}{3} \div \frac{2}{12} = 2$

4.

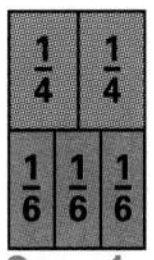

$\frac{2}{4} \div \frac{1}{6} = 3$

Simplify.

5. $\frac{6}{15} \div \frac{3}{3}$ $\frac{2}{5}$ **6.** $\frac{1}{3} \div 6\frac{1}{4}$ $\frac{4}{75}$ **7.** $\frac{7}{8} \div \frac{1}{8}$ 7 **8.** $\frac{6}{7} \div \frac{2}{7}$ 3

9. $\frac{15}{16} \div \frac{3}{4}$ $1\frac{1}{4}$ **10.** $\frac{1}{4} \div \frac{1}{2}$ $\frac{1}{2}$ **11.** $\frac{5}{7} \div 6\frac{3}{4}$ $\frac{20}{189}$ **12.** $\frac{1}{2} \div \frac{2}{3}$ $\frac{3}{4}$

13. $\frac{2}{3} \div 9\frac{4}{3}$ $\frac{2}{31}$ **14.** $1\frac{1}{2} \div \frac{1}{2}$ 3 **15.** $2\frac{1}{2} \div 8$ $\frac{5}{16}$ **16.** $2\frac{7}{8} \div 1\frac{1}{2}$ $1\frac{11}{12}$

17. $2\frac{1}{2} \div \frac{1}{4}$ 10 **18.** $4\frac{1}{3} \div 3$ $1\frac{4}{9}$ **19.** $2\frac{2}{3} \div \frac{1}{3}$ 8 **20.** $\frac{1}{2} \div 3\frac{3}{4}$ $\frac{2}{15}$

21. $\frac{4}{5} \div 5$ $\frac{4}{25}$ **22.** $\frac{9}{14} \div \frac{3}{7}$ $1\frac{1}{2}$ **23.** $3\frac{4}{5} \div 8\frac{1}{5}$ $\frac{19}{41}$ **24.** $\frac{11}{13} \div \frac{13}{11}$ $\frac{121}{169}$

25. **Measurement** Caroline received a letter from England telling her about the birth of a new baby. The baby weighed $\frac{1}{2}$ of a stone. One pound equals $\frac{1}{14}$ of a stone. How many pounds did the baby weigh? 7

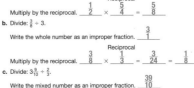

26. One peck equals $\frac{1}{4}$ of a bushel. If Peter Piper had picked a half bushel of pickled peppers, how many pecks of pickled peppers would Peter Piper have picked? 2

27. **Test Prep** Choose the expression with the smallest quotient. B

Ⓐ $6\frac{1}{2} \div \frac{1}{2}$ Ⓑ $6\frac{1}{2} \div 3\frac{1}{2}$ Ⓒ $6\frac{1}{2} \div \frac{1}{4}$ Ⓓ $6\frac{1}{2} \div 2$

28. **Test Prep** Choose the expression with the largest quotient. C

Ⓐ $5\frac{1}{2} \div \frac{1}{4}$ Ⓑ $3\frac{1}{3} \div \frac{1}{4}$ Ⓒ $7 \div \frac{1}{4}$ Ⓓ $\frac{1}{10} \div \frac{1}{4}$

PRACTICE

Name ____________________

Practice 7-5

Dividing Fractions by Fractions

Simplify.

1. $1\frac{4}{5} \div \frac{1}{3}$ $5\frac{2}{5}$ 2. $1\frac{2}{3} \div \frac{1}{8}$ $13\frac{1}{3}$ 3. $3\frac{4}{7} \div 3\frac{1}{2}$ $1\frac{1}{49}$
4. $3\frac{4}{5} \div 1\frac{5}{7}$ $2\frac{13}{60}$ 5. $\frac{2}{5} \div 4\frac{3}{5}$ $\frac{2}{23}$ 6. $4\frac{1}{8} \div \frac{3}{7}$ $9\frac{5}{8}$
7. $\frac{1}{2} \div \frac{2}{5}$ $1\frac{1}{4}$ 8. $2\frac{4}{5} \div 4\frac{3}{4}$ $\frac{56}{95}$ 9. $\frac{5}{6} \div 1\frac{3}{4}$ $\frac{10}{21}$
10. $1\frac{5}{7} \div 1\frac{2}{3}$ $1\frac{1}{35}$ 11. $\frac{8}{9} \div \frac{1}{2}$ $1\frac{7}{9}$ 12. $\frac{1}{4} \div \frac{2}{5}$ $\frac{5}{8}$
13. $\frac{1}{3} \div 2\frac{1}{6}$ $\frac{2}{13}$ 14. $1\frac{4}{9} \div \frac{6}{7}$ $1\frac{37}{54}$ 15. $1\frac{3}{4} \div \frac{4}{5}$ $2\frac{3}{16}$
16. $\frac{1}{3} \div \frac{2}{5}$ $\frac{5}{6}$ 17. $1\frac{1}{3} \div 1\frac{3}{4}$ $\frac{16}{21}$ 18. $\frac{1}{3} \div \frac{2}{7}$ $1\frac{1}{6}$
19. $\frac{1}{2} \div 3\frac{1}{4}$ $\frac{2}{13}$ 20. $2\frac{1}{4} \div 3\frac{4}{9}$ $\frac{81}{124}$ 21. $4\frac{2}{7} \div 1\frac{1}{6}$ $3\frac{33}{49}$
22. $\frac{4}{5} \div 3\frac{2}{5}$ $\frac{4}{17}$ 23. $1\frac{1}{5} \div \frac{1}{3}$ $3\frac{3}{5}$ 24. $\frac{4}{5} \div \frac{1}{6}$ $4\frac{4}{5}$
25. $\frac{8}{9} \div 2\frac{5}{7}$ $\frac{56}{171}$ 26. $1\frac{1}{4} \div 2\frac{2}{3}$ $\frac{15}{32}$ 27. $\frac{1}{4} \div 1\frac{5}{9}$ $\frac{9}{56}$
28. $\frac{1}{4} \div \frac{1}{4}$ 1 29. $1\frac{7}{8} \div 1\frac{1}{4}$ $1\frac{1}{2}$ 30. $1\frac{3}{4} \div \frac{1}{5}$ $8\frac{3}{4}$
31. $4\frac{2}{7} \div 1\frac{1}{2}$ $2\frac{6}{7}$ 32. $5\frac{1}{7} \div 2\frac{1}{2}$ $2\frac{2}{35}$ 33. $1\frac{1}{9} \div \frac{1}{5}$ $5\frac{5}{9}$
34. $1\frac{1}{2} \div 1\frac{2}{3}$ $\frac{9}{10}$ 35. $\frac{7}{8} \div \frac{2}{7}$ $3\frac{1}{16}$ 36. $1\frac{5}{8} \div \frac{5}{9}$ $2\frac{37}{40}$
37. $\frac{1}{4} \div \frac{4}{5}$ $\frac{5}{16}$ 38. $1\frac{1}{2} \div 3\frac{1}{2}$ $\frac{3}{7}$ 39. $1\frac{3}{5} \div \frac{1}{3}$ $4\frac{4}{5}$
40. $\frac{1}{2} \div 3\frac{5}{7}$ $\frac{7}{52}$ 41. $1\frac{1}{3} \div 1\frac{2}{3}$ $\frac{4}{5}$ 42. $1\frac{1}{2} \div 2\frac{3}{4}$ $\frac{6}{11}$

43. **Measurement** A cake recipe calls for $\frac{5}{8}$ of a cup of butter. One tablespoon equals $\frac{1}{16}$ of a cup. How many tablespoons of butter are used to make the cake? 10 tablespoons

44. **Geography** One square mile equals $\frac{1}{36}$ of a township. The area of Austin, Texas, is $6\frac{4}{9}$ townships. Find the area in square miles. 232 mi^2

RETEACHING

Name ____________________

Alternative Lesson 7-5

Dividing Fractions by Fractions

Dividing by a fraction is the same as multiplying by its reciprocal.
For example, $\frac{3}{5} \div \frac{2}{3}$ is the same as $\frac{3}{5} \times \frac{2}{3}$.

Example

Divide: $2\frac{4}{5} \div \frac{3}{4}$.

Write $2\frac{4}{5}$ as an improper fraction.
Multiply by the reciprocal of $\frac{3}{4}$.

$2\frac{4}{5} \div \frac{3}{4} = \frac{14}{5} \times \frac{4}{3}$

Simplify. $= \frac{56}{15} = 3\frac{11}{15}$

So, $2\frac{4}{5} \div \frac{3}{4} = 3\frac{11}{15}$.

Try It

a. Divide: $\frac{1}{2} \div \frac{4}{5}$.

Multiply by the reciprocal. $\frac{1}{2} \times \frac{5}{4}$ (Reciprocal) $= \frac{5}{8}$

b. Divide: $\frac{3}{8} \div 3$.

Write the whole number as an improper fraction. $\frac{3}{1}$

Multiply by the reciprocal. $\frac{3}{8} \times \frac{1}{3}$ (Reciprocal) $= \frac{3}{24} = \frac{1}{8}$

c. Divide: $3\frac{9}{10} \div \frac{2}{3}$.

Write the mixed number as an improper fraction. $\frac{39}{10}$

Write the reciprocal of the divisor. $\frac{3}{2}$

Multiply. $\frac{39}{10}$ (Improper fraction) $\times \frac{3}{2}$ (Reciprocal) $= 5\frac{17}{20}$

Divide. Remember to simplify if necessary.

d. $\frac{7}{8} \div \frac{2}{3}$ $1\frac{5}{16}$ **e.** $\frac{2}{5} \div \frac{3}{4}$ $\frac{8}{15}$
f. $\frac{4}{7} \div 2$ $\frac{2}{7}$ **g.** $3\frac{1}{3} \div \frac{4}{5}$ $4\frac{1}{6}$
h. $2\frac{3}{8} \div \frac{1}{10}$ $23\frac{3}{4}$ **i.** $15 \div 2\frac{1}{2}$ 6
j. $4\frac{1}{5} \div \frac{7}{8}$ $4\frac{4}{5}$ **k.** $1\frac{3}{4} \div 1\frac{2}{5}$ $1\frac{1}{4}$

Assignment Guide

- **Basic**
  1–16, 25, 27–30, 34–40 evens
- **Average**
  1–23 odds, 26–31, 34–40 evens
- **Enriched**
  5–27 odds, 28–33, 35–41 odds

Exercise Notes

Exercises 5–24

Error Prevention If students have difficulty with these exercises, encourage them to rewrite the original exercise on their papers and then show all steps in working it out.

Exercises 25–26

Error Prevention Have students state division questions to help them understand the division problems. For example, for $\frac{1}{2} \div \frac{1}{14}$, students should ask, "How many fourteens are there in one-half?"

Reteaching

Activity

Materials: Rulers

- Draw a line segment that is $\frac{3}{4}$-inch long.
- Mark $\frac{1}{8}$-inch units along the segment, and count the number of eighths.
- Into how many eighths can $\frac{3}{4}$-inch be divided? 6
- What is $\frac{3}{4} \div \frac{1}{8}$? 6
- Draw line segments to model the following problems. Find each quotient.

1. $\frac{3}{4} \div \frac{1}{8}$ 6
2. $\frac{5}{8} \div \frac{1}{8}$ 5
3. $\frac{1}{2} \div \frac{1}{8}$ 4

Exercise Notes

■ Exercises 38–41

Extension Ask students to identify the fraction that represents the unshaded part to the shaded part of each figure. $\frac{1}{1}, \frac{4}{6}, \frac{2}{1}, \frac{6}{2}$.

Exercise Answers

30. Possible answer: Two $\frac{1}{2}$ cup measures equal 1 cup, then estimate half of the $\frac{1}{2}$-cup measure for each $\frac{1}{4}$ cup.

31. 3; The fraction has to equal its reciprocal, so the numerator has to equal the denominator.

32. Estimate: 2; Exact: $2\frac{2}{45}$; Estimate is low.

33. Possible answer: $2\frac{1}{2}$ is larger than $\frac{1}{2}$; Dividing by a larger number results in a smaller quotient.

Alternate Assessment

Self Assessment Ask students to identify what they find most difficult about dividing fractions by fractions or whole numbers, and what about dividing fractions they feel most confident about.

▶ Quick Quiz

Divide.

1. $\frac{3}{4} \div \frac{1}{2}$ $1\frac{1}{2}$
2. $1\frac{1}{2} \div \frac{2}{3}$ $2\frac{1}{4}$
3. $2\frac{1}{3} \div 1\frac{1}{3}$ $1\frac{3}{4}$

Available on Daily Transparency 7-5

PROBLEM SOLVING 7-5

29. Industry The size of letters in printed material such as newspapers or books is measured in points. One point equals $\frac{1}{72}$ of an inch.

a. What is the point size of type that is $\frac{1}{8}$ of an inch high? 9

b. What is the point size of type that is $1\frac{1}{2}$ inches high? 108

12 pt The Brown Fox Jumped over the
14 pt The Brown Fox Jumped ove
18 pt The Brown Fox Jump
24 pt The Brown Fox
28 pt The Brown Fo

Problem Solving and Reasoning

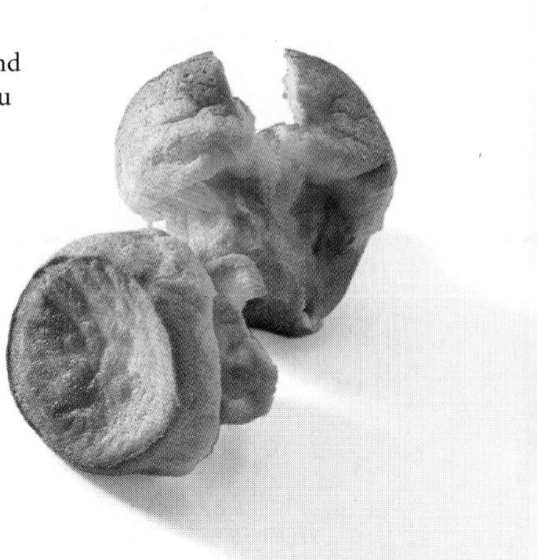

30. Critical Thinking A popover recipe calls for $1\frac{1}{4}$ cups of flour and $1\frac{1}{4}$ cups of milk. If you only had a $\frac{1}{2}$-cup measure, how could you use it to complete the recipe?

31. Critical Thinking If $5 \div \frac{x}{3} = 5 \times \frac{x}{3}$, what is the value of x? Explain your reasoning.

32. Communicate Use rounding to estimate the quotient of $3\frac{5}{6}$ and $1\frac{7}{8}$. Compare your estimate to the exact quotient.

33. Journal Explain why $5\frac{1}{2} \div \frac{1}{2}$ has a larger quotient than $5\frac{1}{2} \div 2\frac{1}{2}$.

Mixed Review

Find the missing measurements for each circle, where r = radius, d = diameter, and C = circumference. *[Lesson 4-7]*

34. $r = \square$, $d = 1.4$ km, $C = \square$ $r = 0.7$ km; $C = 4.396$ km

35. $r = \square$, $d = \square$, $C = 50.24$ cm $r = 8$ cm; $d = 16$ cm

36. $r = 4.2$ m, $d = \square$, $C = \square$ $d = 8.4$ m; $C = 26.376$ m

37. $r = \square$, $d = \square$, $C = 25.12$ mm $r = 4$ mm; $d = 8$ mm

What fraction does each shaded part represent? *[Lesson 5-4]*

38.

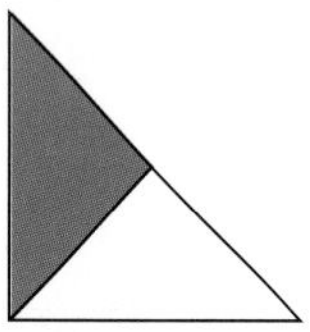

$\frac{1}{2}$

39.

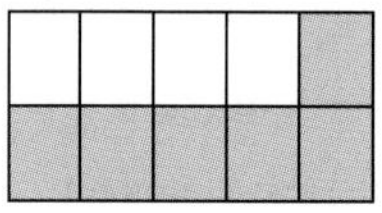

$\frac{6}{10}$

40.

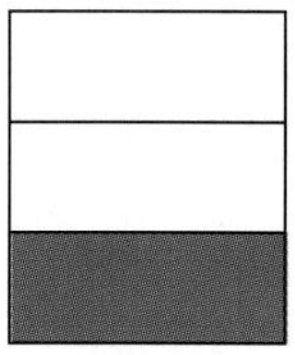

$\frac{1}{3}$

41.

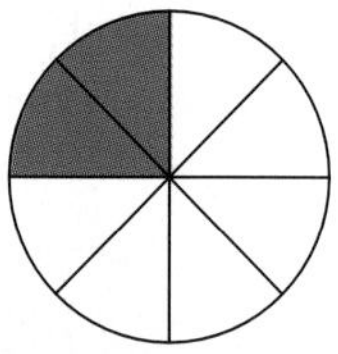

$\frac{2}{8}$

PROBLEM SOLVING

Name ______________________

Guided Problem Solving 7-5

GPS PROBLEM 29, STUDENT PAGE 390

The size of letters in printed material such as newspapers or books is measured in points. One point equals $\frac{1}{72}$ of an inch.

a. What is the point size of type that is $\frac{1}{8}$ of an inch high?

b. What is the point size of type that is $1\frac{1}{2}$ inches high?

— Understand —

1. What part of an inch is equal to one point? $\frac{1}{72}$ of an inch.

2. What are you asked to find? The point sizes of types that measure $\frac{1}{8}$ in. and $1\frac{1}{2}$ in.

— Plan —

3. Will each type size be more than or less than 72 points?

a. $\frac{1}{8}$ inch type Less than.

b. $1\frac{1}{2}$ inches More than.

4. Write $1\frac{1}{2}$ as an improper fraction. $\frac{3}{2}$

5. Write an expression to show how to use division to find each point size.

a. $\frac{1}{8}$ inch type $\frac{1}{8} \div \frac{1}{72}$

b. $1\frac{1}{2}$ inches $1\frac{1}{2} \div \frac{1}{72}$

— Solve —

6. Simplify your expressions to find the number of points in each.

a. $\frac{1}{8}$ inch type 9 points. b. $1\frac{1}{2}$ inches 108 points.

— Look Back —

7. How can you use multiplication to check your answer? Possible answer: Multiply 72 times the type size in inches.

SOLVE ANOTHER PROBLEM

What is the point size of type that is $\frac{1}{6}$ of an inch? 12 points.

ENRICHMENT

Name ______________________

Extend Your Thinking 7-5

Critical Thinking

Complete each triangle by filling in the missing fractions.

1. The "magic" sum of the fractions on each side of this triangle is the same. Fill in the missing fractions. Then find the "magic" sum.

Sum 1

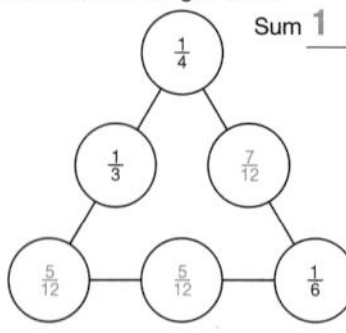

2. Multiply each fraction in the first triangle by $\frac{2}{5}$. Write each product in the corresponding circle below. Then find the "magic" sum.

Sum $\frac{2}{5}$

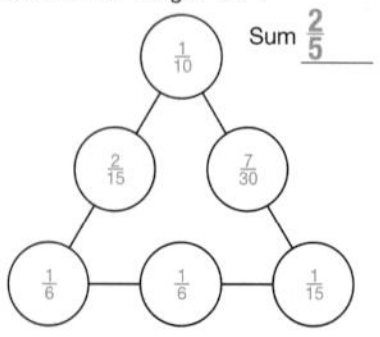

3. Divide each fraction in the first triangle by $\frac{1}{2}$. Write each product in the corresponding circle below. Then find the "magic" sum.

Sum 2

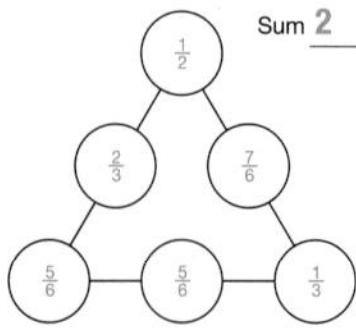

4. Multiply or divide each fraction in the first triangle by any fraction you choose. Write each answer in the corresponding circle below. Then find the "magic" sum.

Check students' answers.

Sum ______

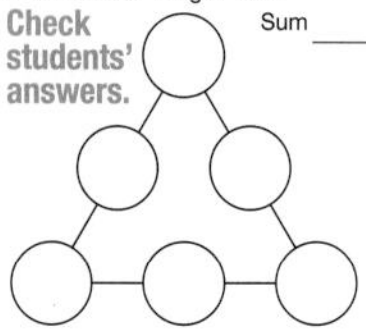

5. Suppose Jane tells you that she has multiplied each fraction in the first triangle by $\frac{7}{8}$. Sara says she has divided each fraction by $\frac{5}{6}$. How can you tell both your friends each "magic" sum without doing any calculations?

Jane's "magic" sum is $\frac{7}{8}$, the multiplier × 1. Sara's "magic" sum is $\frac{6}{5}$, the reciprocal of the divisor × 1.

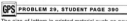

TECHNOLOGY

Using a Fraction Calculator • Finding Fraction Products and Quotients

Problem: What is the quotient of $\frac{4}{70} \div \frac{14}{51}$?

Fractions may involve large numbers that are not easy to work with. A fraction calculator can help you multiply or divide such fractions.

1 Type in the numerator of the first fraction, and then press the [/] button.

2 Type in the denominator of the first fraction, and then press the [÷] button.

3 Type in the numerator of the second fraction, and then press the [/] button.

4 Type in the denominator of the second fraction, and then press the [=] button.

5 The calculator may indicate that the fraction is not in lowest terms. Press the [simp] button and then the [=] button to see the fraction in lowest terms.

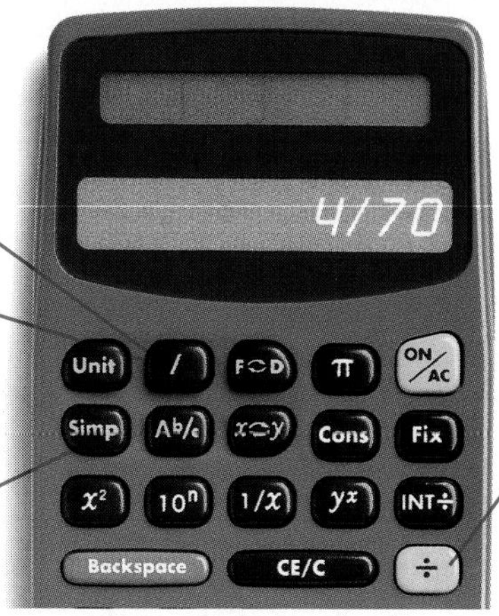

Solution: The answer is $\frac{204}{980}$ or, in lowest terms, $\frac{51}{245}$.

TRY IT

a. What is $\frac{7}{25} \times \frac{18}{31}$? $\frac{126}{775}$

b. What is $\frac{10}{19} \div \frac{6}{37}$? $\frac{185}{57}$

ON YOUR OWN

- When multiplying fractions, is using a fraction calculator always the fastest way to find the product? Explain.
- The product of the fractions $\frac{25}{91} \times \frac{25}{91}$ has a denominator bigger than 1000. What does the calculator do when the answer has a four-digit denominator?
- How could you use a nonfraction calculator to divide fractions?

Technology

Using a Fraction Calculator • Finding Fraction Products and Quotients

The Point

Students use a fraction calculator to multiply and divide fractions.

Materials

Fraction calculator

Resources

Teaching Tool Transparency 24: Fraction Calculator

About the Page

- Some calculators have a [/] key that performs operations with fractions.
- When using some of the newer fraction calculators, knowing the order of operations is important. Each fraction must be inside parentheses; otherwise, the calculator will divide the numbers in order from left to right. The calculator will give the answer as a decimal, but is able to convert it to a fraction.

Ask ...

- If you use a calculator to find $\frac{4}{70} \times \frac{14}{51}$, how is the process similar to the example shown? You use the same key sequence, but use the [×] key instead of the [÷] key.
- How does your calculator enable you to work with fractions? Answers may vary.

On Your Own

These questions point out some of the limitations of the fraction calculator. You might seek students' opinions about the usefulness of a fraction calculator.

Answers for On Your Own

- No; Sometimes mental math is quicker.
- The calculator changes it to a decimal.
- Possible answer: Rewrite the fractions as decimals.

7-6 Lesson Organizer

Objective

- Solve multiplication and division equations containing fractions.

NCTM Standards

- 1–5, 7, 9

▶ Review

Solve.

1. $y + 3 = 21$ $y = 18$
2. $y + 12 = 29$ $y = 17$
3. $5y = 55$ $y = 11$

Available on Daily Transparency 7-6

▶ Lesson Link

Discuss types of equations that have been previously solved. Ask students questions, such as "Two-thirds of what amount is 40?" Discuss equations that could be written to answer such questions.

1 Introduce

Explore

The Point
Students explore solving fraction equations by determining whether the variable is greater or less than a number and then determining its value.

Ongoing Assessment
As students are working, ask them to describe their thinking for Steps 1 and 2. If students are having difficulty, suggest that they substitute different numbers for the variables to help them get a feel for the approximate value of the variable.

For Groups That Finish Early
For each equation, find the value of x.

1. $\frac{1}{3}x = 5$ $x = 15$
2. $x \div \frac{1}{2} = 8$ $x = 4$

7-6 Solving Fraction Equations: Multiplication and Division

You'll Learn ...

- to solve multiplication and division equations containing fractions

... How It's Used

Magazine editors use fraction equations when converting a measurement from one unit to another.

▶ Lesson Link In earlier lessons, you solved multiplication and division equations that involved whole numbers and decimals. Now you'll use similar methods to solve multiplication and division equations involving fractions. ◀

Explore Solving Fraction Equations

Truth or Dare

Each equation is followed by only one correct statement. Use your number sense to choose the correct statement, and explain how you know it's true.

1. Equation: $5w = 3$

a. The value of w is a fraction greater than 1.

b. The value of w is a fraction less than 1.

2. Equation: $\frac{1}{2}x = 10$

a. The value of x is greater than 10.

b. The value of x is less than 10.

3. Equation: $y \div \frac{2}{3} = 6$

a. y multiplied by $\frac{2}{3}$ equals 6.

b. y multiplied by $\frac{3}{2}$ equals 6.

4. Equation: $\frac{3}{4} \div z = \frac{3}{4}$

a. The value of z can be written as a fraction.

b. The value of z cannot be written as a fraction.

5. Four of the values below will make one of the above equations true. Which value will not make *any* of the above equations true?

a. 20 **b.** $\frac{3}{5}$ **c.** 1 **d.** $\frac{4}{3}$ **e.** 4

Learn Solving Fraction Equations

Recall that you used mental math to solve addition and subtraction equations involving fractions. You can use the same method to solve multiplication and division equations involving fractions.

MEETING INDIVIDUAL NEEDS

Resources

7-6 Practice
7-6 Reteaching
7-6 Problem Solving
7-6 Enrichment
7-6 Daily Transparency
  Problem of the Day
  Review
  Quick Quiz
Teaching Tool Transparencies 2, 3
Technology Master 35

Learning Modalities

Verbal Have students write in words the questions that are asked by the equations in **Explore**.

Social Have students work in small groups to discuss the solutions of equations.

Challenge

Have students find five numbers that would solve the following inequalities.

1. $1\frac{1}{2}x < 20$ Possible answers: $\frac{1}{2}$, 1, 3, 6, 8
2. $x \div \frac{2}{3} > 10$ Possible answers: 10, 14, 16, 20, 21

When solving multiplication equations, it may help to first find the numerator of the missing value, and then the denominator.

Example 1

Solve: $\frac{2}{3}x = \frac{8}{15}$

$\frac{2}{3}x = \frac{8}{15}$ Read as "What number times $\frac{2}{3}$ equals $\frac{8}{15}$?"

$\frac{2}{3} \times \frac{\mathbf{4}}{?} = \frac{8}{15}$ Using mental math, find the numerator.

$\frac{2}{3} \times \frac{\mathbf{4}}{\mathbf{5}} = \frac{8}{15}$ Using mental math, find the denominator.

$\frac{8}{15} = \frac{8}{15}$ ✓ Check to see that the equation is true.

x is equal to $\frac{4}{5}$.

If the equation includes whole numbers or mixed numbers, you may need to rewrite these numbers as fractions.

Remember

To find the product of two fractions, multiply the numerators of both fractions. Then multiply the denominators of both fractions.

[Page 375]

Example 2

Surveyors often measure distances in *chains*. A parking lot 33 yards long measured $1\frac{1}{2}$ chains. How many yards are there in a chain?

Let x = the number of yards in a chain

$1\frac{1}{2}x = 33$ Read as "What number times $1\frac{1}{2}$ equals 33?"

$\frac{3}{2}x = 33$ Write the mixed number as an improper fraction.

$\frac{3}{2}x = \frac{66}{2}$ Write the whole number as a fraction with the same denominator.

$\frac{3}{2} \times \frac{\mathbf{22}}{\mathbf{1}} = \frac{66}{2}$ Use mental math.

1 chain equals 22 yards.

Try It

Solve for x.

a. $\frac{1}{2}x = 3$ 6 **b.** $\frac{3}{4}x = \frac{15}{16}$ $\frac{5}{4}$ **c.** $1\frac{1}{4}x = 15$ 12

DID YOU KNOW?

A *chain* can be subdivided into 100 equal units. Each of those units is called a *link*.

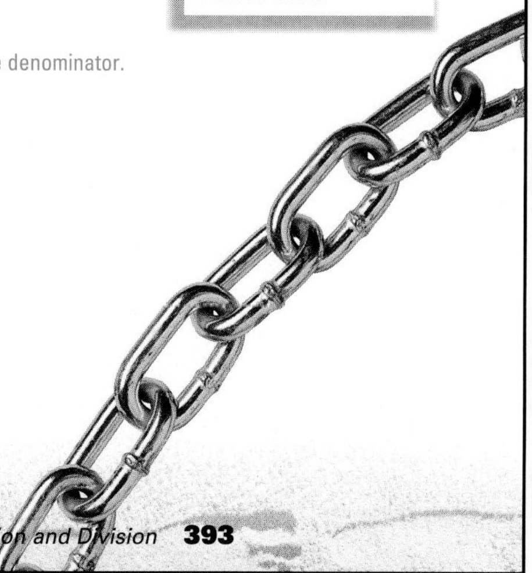

MATH EVERY DAY

Problem of the Day

The flag of the United Arab Emirates looks like this:

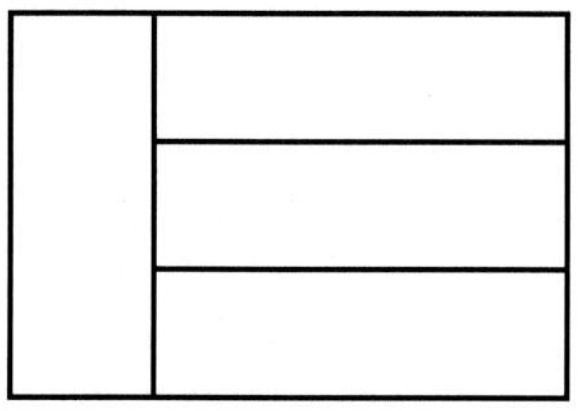

The colors used are black, green, red, and white. In how many different ways can the flag be colored?

24 ways

Available on Daily Transparency 7-6

An Extension is provided in the transparency package.

Fact of the Day

Apothecaries' weight has 12 ounces per pound, 8 drams per ounce, 3 scruples per dram, and 20 grains per scruple.

Estimation

Estimate each product.

1. $7\frac{3}{4} \times 8\frac{1}{4}$ 64
2. $5 \times 2\frac{2}{3}$ 15
3. $3\frac{5}{6} \times 4\frac{1}{3}$ 16

Follow Up

Have students discuss how they determined whether the variable was greater than or less than 1 in Step 1 and greater than or less than 10 in Step 2. Have students share their answers to Steps 3, 4, and 5.

Answers for Explore

1. b; The product is smaller than the whole number 5, so w must be a fraction less than 1.
2. a; The first factor is less than 1, so x must be greater than 10.
3. b; A division problem can be turned into a multiplication problem using the reciprocal.
4. a; $z = 1$, which can always be written as a fraction.
5. d; a is the solution to equation 2; b is the solution to equation 1; c is the solution to equation 4; e is the solution to equation 3.

2 Teach

Learn

Alternate Examples

1. Solve: $\frac{3}{4}x = \frac{9}{20}$

   $\frac{3}{4}x = \frac{9}{20}$

   $\frac{3}{4} \times \frac{\mathbf{3}}{?} = \frac{9}{20}$

   $\frac{3}{4} \times \frac{3}{5} = \frac{9}{20}$

   $\frac{9}{20} = \frac{9}{20}$

   x is equal to $\frac{3}{5}$.

2. The height of a horse is usually measured in hands. A horse 62 inches high is $15\frac{1}{2}$ hands high. How many inches are there in a hand?

   Let x = the number of inches in a hand.

   $15\frac{1}{2}x = 62$

   $\frac{31}{2}x = 62$

   $\frac{31}{2}x = \frac{124}{2}$

   $\frac{31}{2} \times \frac{4}{1} = \frac{124}{2}$

   1 hand equals 4 inches.

Alternate Examples

3. Solve: $y \div \frac{3}{5} = \frac{5}{9}$

   $y \times \frac{5}{3} = \frac{5}{9}$

   $\mathbf{\frac{1}{3}} \times \frac{5}{3} = \frac{5}{9}$

   $\frac{5}{9} = \frac{5}{9}$

   y is equal to $\frac{1}{3}$.

4. Solve: $\frac{2}{7} \div z = \frac{8}{21}$

   $\frac{2}{7} \times z = \frac{8}{21}$

   $\frac{2}{7} \times \mathbf{\frac{4}{3}} = \frac{8}{21}$

   $z = \frac{3}{4}$

3 Practice and Assess

Check

Answers for Check Your Understanding

1. Possible answer: You might be able to use mental math to solve the problem.
2. Possible answer: No; Like denominators are only necessary when adding or subtracting fractions.
3. Possible answer: First find a reasonable estimate using mental math.

When solving division equations, it may help to rewrite the equation as a multiplication equation by using the reciprocal of the divisor.

Study TIP

You can check your work by dividing the product by one of the factors. Your result should be the dividend.

Example 3

Solve: $y \div \frac{2}{3} = \frac{9}{10}$

$y \times \frac{3}{2} = \frac{9}{10}$ — Rewrite as a multiplication equation.

$\mathbf{\frac{3}{5}} \times \frac{3}{2} = \frac{9}{10}$ — Use mental math.

$\frac{9}{10} = \frac{9}{10}$ ✓ — Check to see that the equation is true.

y is equal to $\frac{3}{5}$.

If the variable in the original equation is the divisor, you can still rewrite the equation as a multiplication equation. Don't forget that your final answer will be the reciprocal of the answer to the multiplication equation.

Example 4

Solve: $\frac{4}{5} \div z = \frac{12}{25}$

$\frac{4}{5} \times z = \frac{12}{25}$ — Rewrite as a multiplication equation.

$\frac{4}{5} \times \mathbf{\frac{3}{5}} = \frac{12}{25}$ — Use mental math to solve the multiplication equation.

$z = \frac{5}{3}$ — Use the reciprocal for the answer to the original equation.

Try It

Solve. **a.** $\frac{7}{3} \div x = 1\frac{1}{6}$ **2** **b.** $\frac{4}{3} \div x = \frac{8}{21}$ $\mathbf{\frac{7}{2}}$ **c.** $x \div 2\frac{2}{3} = \frac{9}{16}$ $\mathbf{1\frac{1}{2}}$

Check Your Understanding

1. Why is it sometimes a good idea to rewrite a division equation as a multiplication equation?
2. If the fractions in a multiplication equation have unlike denominators, do you need to change them to fractions with like denominators? Explain.
3. What ideas are used in solving equations regardless of whether they contain whole numbers, decimals, or fractions?

MEETING MIDDLE SCHOOL CLASSROOM NEEDS

Tips from Middle School Teacher

I find that students understand the concept of solving equations with fractions better if I first present a real-life example. For instance, Davis earns time-and-a-half wages working overtime. If he makes $18 per hour working overtime, what is his regular hourly wage? $1\frac{1}{2}w = 18$, so $w = 12$.

Team Teaching

Work with a science teacher to reinforce the use of formulas involving fractions. Students might discuss techniques for solving such equations in science class.

Cultural Connection

Have students find examples of units of measure which were used by different cultures at other times in history. Have them write equations that relate two different units.

7-6 Exercises and Applications

Practice and Apply

Getting Started For each equation, state if the given value will make the equation true.

1. $\frac{3}{5}x = \frac{9}{10}$; $x = \frac{3}{2}$ Yes **2.** $\frac{1}{3}x = \frac{1}{15}$; $x = \frac{1}{4}$ No **3.** $z \div \frac{4}{5} = \frac{10}{16}$; $z = \frac{4}{2}$ No

Solve.

4. $\frac{1}{2}g = 6$ 12 **5.** $3\frac{1}{6}k = \frac{4}{7}$ $\frac{24}{133}$ **6.** $\frac{8}{9} \div r = \frac{16}{18}$ 1 **7.** $p \div \frac{5}{4} = 12$ 15

8. $e \div \frac{6}{7} = \frac{1}{3}$ $\frac{2}{7}$ **9.** $\frac{4}{5}w = \frac{3}{5}$ $\frac{3}{4}$ **10.** $\frac{5}{6}t = 16$ $19\frac{1}{5}$ **11.** $a \div 2\frac{2}{3} = \frac{3}{4}$ 2

12. $q \div \frac{10}{3} = \frac{3}{4}$ $2\frac{1}{2}$ **13.** $s \div 10\frac{7}{9} = 11\frac{3}{5}$ $125\frac{1}{45}$ **14.** $\frac{5}{9}d = \frac{2}{7}$ $\frac{18}{35}$ **15.** $\frac{5}{7}f = 1\frac{4}{5}$ $2\frac{13}{25}$

16. $7g = \frac{5}{8}$ $\frac{5}{56}$ **17.** $j \div 16 = 4\frac{1}{4}$ 68 **18.** $\frac{3}{8}z = 2\frac{5}{9}$ $6\frac{22}{27}$ **19.** $\frac{9}{2} \div c = 3\frac{3}{8}$ $1\frac{1}{3}$

20. $\frac{5}{4} \div v = \frac{10}{16}$ 2 **21.** $\frac{2}{3} \div b = \frac{16}{30}$ $1\frac{1}{4}$ **22.** $6\frac{4}{5}m = \frac{2}{3}$ $\frac{5}{51}$ **23.** $i \div 8 = \frac{6}{7}$ $6\frac{6}{7}$

24. **Test Prep** Mina made 12 cups of Jell-O. She divided it into equal servings, and each serving was $\frac{3}{4}$ of a cup. Which equation can you use to find out how many servings she has? C

Ⓐ $\frac{3}{4} \div s = 12$ Ⓑ $12s = \frac{3}{4}$

Ⓒ $12 \div s = \frac{3}{4}$

25. **History** Length was once measured in palms and spans. One inch equaled $\frac{1}{3}$ of a palm and $\frac{1}{9}$ of a span.

GPS

a. Which equation could you use to find the number of palms in 12 inches? A

Ⓐ $p \div \frac{1}{3} = 12$ Ⓑ $\frac{1}{3}p = 12$

b. How many palms are in 12 inches? 4

c. Write and solve an equation to find the number of spans in 18 inches. $s \div \frac{1}{9} = 18$; $s = 2$

26. **Operation Sense** Shaun said, "I'm thinking of a fraction. If I divide it by $\frac{1}{2}$, I get $\frac{7}{12}$." What fraction was Shaun thinking of? $\frac{7}{24}$

27. **Operation Sense** Caroline says, "I'm thinking of a fraction. If I multiply it by $\frac{2}{3}$, I get $\frac{4}{9}$. What fraction am I thinking of?" $\frac{2}{3}$

PRACTICE

Name ____________________

Practice 7-6

Solving Fraction Equations: Multiplication and Division

Solve.

1. $n \div 4\frac{1}{3} = \frac{1}{2}$ $n = 2\frac{1}{6}$ **2.** $2\frac{6}{7}f = \frac{1}{3}$ $f = \frac{7}{60}$ **3.** $f \div 2\frac{5}{7} = \frac{1}{2}$ $f = 1\frac{5}{14}$ **4.** $n \div 3\frac{3}{5} = 2\frac{1}{3}$ $n = 8\frac{2}{5}$

5. $n \div 1\frac{3}{5} = 1$ $n = 1\frac{3}{5}$ **6.** $\frac{1}{2}u = 5\frac{3}{5}$ $u = 11\frac{1}{5}$ **7.** $q \div 2\frac{1}{3} = \frac{3}{8}$ $q = \frac{7}{8}$ **8.** $c \div 2\frac{4}{5} = \frac{1}{2}$ $c = 1\frac{2}{5}$

9. $b \div \frac{2}{3} = 2\frac{6}{7}$ $b = 1\frac{19}{21}$ **10.** $\frac{1}{4}n = 2$ $n = 8$ **11.** $t \div 1\frac{1}{7} = 3$ $t = 3\frac{3}{7}$ **12.** $h \div 2\frac{2}{5} = \frac{3}{5}$ $h = 1\frac{11}{25}$

13. $2f = \frac{1}{4}$ $f = \frac{1}{8}$ **14.** $2z = 3\frac{2}{3}$ $z = 1\frac{5}{6}$ **15.** $2\frac{1}{4}v = \frac{1}{4}$ $v = \frac{1}{9}$ **16.** $h \div 3\frac{1}{8} = 2$ $h = 6\frac{1}{4}$

17. $v \div \frac{1}{3} = \frac{2}{5}$ $v = \frac{2}{15}$ **18.** $3\frac{7}{10}q = 1$ $q = \frac{10}{37}$ **19.** $h \div \frac{7}{10} = \frac{1}{2}$ $h = \frac{7}{20}$ **20.** $1c = 1\frac{1}{3}$ $c = 1\frac{1}{3}$

21. $w \div 1\frac{1}{2} = 3\frac{1}{4}$ $w = 4\frac{7}{8}$ **22.** $d \div 2\frac{1}{8} = 2\frac{1}{3}$ $d = 4\frac{23}{24}$ **23.** $v \div \frac{2}{3} = 1\frac{1}{2}$ $v = 1$ **24.** $z \div \frac{1}{3} = 1$ $z = \frac{1}{3}$

25. $t \div 2 = 2$ $t = 4$ **26.** $b \div 1 = 1\frac{2}{5}$ $b = 1\frac{2}{5}$ **27.** $\frac{5}{9}z = \frac{1}{3}$ $z = \frac{3}{5}$ **28.** $1\frac{7}{10}m = 4$ $m = 2\frac{6}{17}$

29. The largest U.S. standard postage stamp ever issued has a width of $1\frac{1}{11}$ inches, which was $\frac{3}{4}$ of the height of the stamp. Write and solve an equation to find the height of the stamp.

Possible answer: $\frac{3}{4}x = 1\frac{1}{11}$; $1\frac{5}{11}$ in.

30. Candace said, "I'm thinking of a fraction. If I divide it by $2\frac{1}{2}$, I get $\frac{3}{11}$." What fraction was Candace thinking of? $\frac{15}{22}$

RETEACHING

Name ____________________

Alternative Lesson 7-6

Solving Fraction Equations: Multiplication and Division

When solving multiplication equations, it may help to first find the numerator of the missing value and then the denominator. If the equation includes whole numbers or mixed numbers, you may need to rewrite these numbers as fractions.

Example 1

Solve: $\frac{2}{5}x = \frac{4}{25}$.

Think: What number times $\frac{2}{5}$ equals $\frac{4}{25}$? Then use mental math to find the numerator. ($2 \times 2 = 4$) $\frac{2}{5} \times \frac{?}{?} = \frac{4}{25}$

Use mental math to find the denominator. $\frac{2}{5} \times \frac{2}{?} = \frac{4}{25}$ ($5 \times 5 = 25$)

Check to see that the equation is true. $\frac{2}{5} \times \frac{2}{5} = \frac{4}{25}$ ✓

So, $x = \frac{2}{5}$.

Try It Solve for x.

a. $\frac{2}{3}x = \frac{8}{15}$ $x = \frac{4}{5}$ **b.** $\frac{3}{4}x = \frac{9}{20}$ $x = \frac{3}{5}$

c. $\frac{1}{3}x = 4$ $x = 12$ **d.** $\frac{3}{8}x = \frac{18}{16}$ $x = \frac{6}{2} = 3$

Example 2

Solve: $x \div \frac{3}{4} = \frac{8}{9}$.

Rewrite as a multiplication equation. ($2 \times 4 = 8$)

Use mental math to find the numerator. $\frac{?}{?} \times \frac{4}{3} = \frac{8}{9}$

Use mental math to find the denominator. ($3 \times 3 = 9$)

Check to see that the equation is true. $\frac{2}{3} \div \frac{3}{4} = \frac{8}{9}$ ✓

So, $x = \frac{2}{3}$.

Try It Solve for x.

e. $x \div \frac{2}{3} = \frac{6}{10}$ $x = \frac{2}{5}$ **f.** $x \div \frac{5}{9} = \frac{9}{25}$ $x = \frac{1}{5}$

g. $x \div \frac{3}{8} = \frac{16}{27}$ $x = \frac{2}{9}$ **h.** $x \div \frac{4}{5} = \frac{35}{48}$ $x = \frac{7}{12}$

i. $x \div \frac{7}{9} = \frac{27}{35}$ $x = \frac{3}{5}$ **j.** $x \div \frac{3}{10} = \frac{20}{27}$ $x = \frac{2}{9}$

7-6 Exercises and Applications

Assignment Guide

- **Basic**
  1–15, 24, 25, 28–30, 34–44 evens
- **Average**
  1–23 odds, 24–27, 32–33, 36–44 evens
- **Enriched**
  2–24 evens, 25, 28–33, 35–43 odds

Exercise Notes

Exercise 25

History Many units of measure relate to parts of the body. The ancient Egyptian cubit was the length of a man's arm from his elbow to the end of his middle finger. A cubit had 7 palms. A palm was divided into 4 digits, or fingers. Of course, everybody's cubit was slightly different.

Exercises 26–27

Problem-Solving Tip Students should first write an equation for each exercise. Then the equation can be solved by using the method taught in the lesson.

Reteaching

Activity

Materials: Graph paper, colored pencils

- Draw a rectangle. Divide it vertically into 4 equal sections. Divide it horizontally into 3 equal sections.
- Shade $\frac{3}{4}$ vertically. What should you shade horizontally so that $\frac{3}{12}$ of the rectangle is shaded twice? $\frac{1}{3}$
- If $\frac{3}{4}x = \frac{3}{12}$, what is x? $\frac{1}{3}$
- Draw another rectangle the same size. Shade the rectangle to find x if $\frac{1}{4}x = \frac{2}{12}$. $x = \frac{2}{3}$

Exercise Notes

■ Exercise 31

Problem-Solving Tip You may wish to use Teaching Tool Transparencies 2 and 3: Guided Problem Solving, pages 1–2.

■ Exercise 33

Extension Have interested students research the Avoirdupois and Troy systems of weight measurement. These students can present their findings to the rest of the class.

Exercise Answers

28. $\frac{301}{989} = \frac{7}{23}$; There are 989 mangos and 301 of them went to Jack's.
29. Jack's Fruit Stand; 301 is about 300. 989 is about 1000. $\frac{300}{1000}$ is equal to $\frac{3}{10}$.
30. $\frac{550}{989}$
31. Possible answer: Subtract $\frac{3}{4}$ from both sides, then divide each side by $\frac{2}{3}$.
32. Possible answer: If $\frac{7}{8}$ of a number is equal to 43, then the number must be greater than 43.
33. a. 256; b. 7000; c. 240; d. 5760; e. x = Avoirdupois; y = Troy; Explanations may vary.

Alternate Assessment

Interview Ask students to tell you how, in general, they would solve a multiplication or division equation.

Quick Quiz

Solve.

1. $\frac{2}{3}x = \frac{8}{9}$ $x = \frac{4}{3}$
2. $y \div \frac{2}{5} = \frac{5}{6}$ $y = \frac{1}{3}$
3. $\frac{5}{3}z = \frac{1}{2}$ $z = \frac{3}{10}$

Available on Daily Transparency 7-6

PROBLEM SOLVING 7-6

Problem Solving and Reasoning

Critical Thinking Use the circle graph for Exercises 28–30.

28. What fraction of the total mangos went to Jack's Fruit Stand? Explain your reasoning.

29. Which place received about $\frac{3}{10}$ of the total mangos? Explain how you can use estimation skills to determine this.

30. What fraction of the total mangos went to either Glendale Grocery or the Rosewood School?

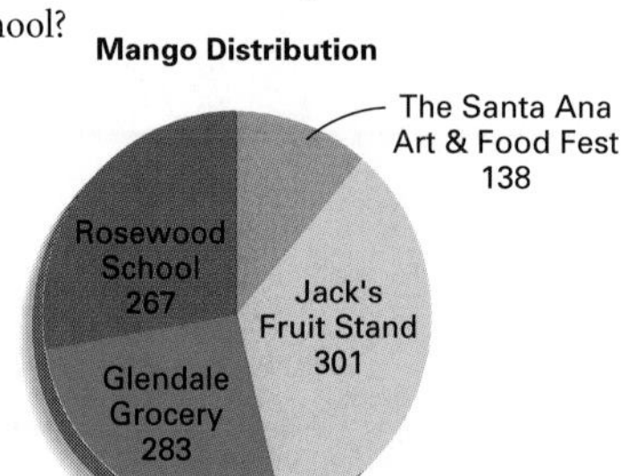

31. Choose a Strategy Explain the steps you would take to solve $\frac{2}{3}x + \frac{3}{4} = 3\frac{1}{2}$.

32. Communicate Explain why the solution of $\frac{7}{8}x = 43$ is more than 43.

Problem Solving STRATEGIES

- Look for a Pattern
- Make an Organized List
- Make a Table
- Guess and Check
- Work Backward
- Use Logical Reasoning
- Draw a Diagram
- Solve a Simpler Problem

33. Critical Thinking The Avoirdupois [a-VWA-du-PWA] system of weight measurement is the part of the customary system used to measure most things in everyday life, such as food, cars, or people. The Troy system is used to measure the weight of precious metals and jewels, such as gold, silver, or diamonds.

Avoirdupois Weight	Troy Weight
$27\frac{11}{32}$ grains = 1 drachma	24 grains = 1 pennyweight
16 drachmas = 1 ounce	20 pennyweights = 1 ounce
16 ounces = 1 pound	12 ounces = 1 pound

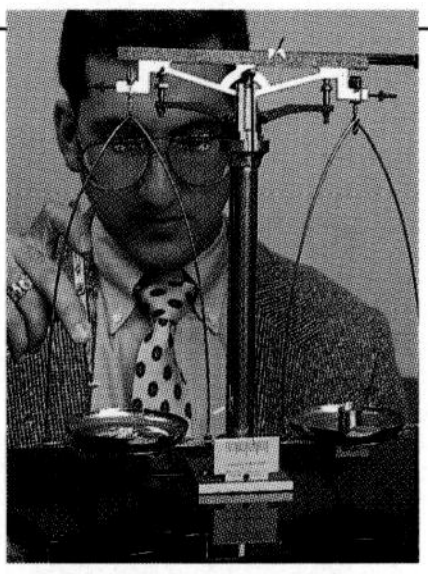

a. How many drachmas are in an Avoirdupois pound?

b. How many grains are in an Avoirdupois pound?

c. How many pennyweights are in a Troy pound?

d. How many grains are in a Troy pound?

e. The equation $x\frac{5760}{7000} = y$ can be used to convert from one type of pound to the other. Which variable represents an Avoirdupois pound? Which variable represents the Troy pound? Explain your reasoning.

Mixed Review

Name two equivalent fractions. *[Lesson 5-4]* Possible answers for Ex. 34–39.

34. $\frac{6}{8}$ $\frac{3}{4}, \frac{12}{16}$ **35.** $\frac{3}{8}$ $\frac{9}{24}, \frac{6}{16}$ **36.** $\frac{2}{5}$ $\frac{4}{10}, \frac{6}{15}$ **37.** $\frac{10}{20}$ $\frac{1}{2}, \frac{2}{4}$ **38.** $\frac{6}{24}$ $\frac{1}{4}, \frac{2}{8}$ **39.** $\frac{11}{14}$ $\frac{22}{28}, \frac{33}{42}$

Find the GCF of each pair. *[Lesson 5-5]*

40. 4, 8 4 **41.** 3, 27 3 **42.** 18, 96 6 **43.** 7, 15 1 **44.** 33, 66 33

396 *Chapter 7 • Multiplying and Dividing Fractions*

PROBLEM SOLVING

Name ____________

Guided Problem Solving 7-6

GPS PROBLEM 25, STUDENT PAGE 395

Length was once measured in palms and spans. One inch equaled $\frac{1}{3}$ of a palm and $\frac{1}{9}$ of a span.

a. Which equation could you use to find the number of palms in 12 inches?

A $p \div \frac{1}{3} = 12$ **B** $\frac{1}{3}p = 12$

b. How many palms are in 12 inches?

c. Write and solve an equation to find the number of spans in 18 inches.

— Understand —

1. How many palms equal one inch? $\frac{1}{3}$ palm. How many spans? $\frac{1}{9}$ span.

— Plan —

2. In division, you break down a given amount into equal parts. In multiplication, you find how many items in all. Which operation will you use to find how many
   a. palms are in 12 inches? Division.
   b. spans are in 18 inches? Division.
3. How are the equations used to find the number of palms in 12 inches and the number of spans in 18 inches similar? Possible answer: Both use the same operation and have fractional amounts.

— Solve —

4. Which equation would you use to find the number of palms? A
5. How many palms are in 12 inches? 4 palms.
6. Write an equation to find the number of spans in 18 inches. $s \div \frac{1}{9} = 18$
7. How many spans are in 18 inches? 2 spans.

— Look Back —

8. How can you check your answer? Possible answer: Substitute the answer into the equation. Then solve.

SOLVE ANOTHER PROBLEM

Write and solve an equation to find the number of inches in 16 palms.
Possible answer: $16 \div \frac{1}{3} = p$; $p = 48$ inches.

ENRICHMENT

Name ____________

Extend Your Thinking 7-6

Patterns in Numbers

Possible answers: Items 1–10

You have found rules for number sequences. For example, you know that the rule for the sequence 3, 9, 27, 81 is *Multiply by 3.*

You can also find rules for sequences that contain fractions. Some rules also contain fractions. Write the next three terms in each sequence below. Then write the rule.

1. 81, 27, 9, 3, 1, $\frac{1}{3}$, $\frac{1}{9}$ … Rule: Divide by 3.
2. 250, 50, 10, 2, $\frac{2}{5}$, $\frac{2}{25}$, $\frac{2}{125}$ … Rule: Divide by 5.
3. 1, 8, 64, 512, 4096, 32,768, 262,144 … Rule: Multiply by 8.
4. 1000, 100, 10, 1, $\frac{1}{10}$, $\frac{1}{100}$, $\frac{1}{1000}$ … Rule: Divide by 10.
5. $\frac{1}{8}$, $\frac{1}{2}$, 2, 8, 32, 128, 512 … Rule: Multiply by 4.
6. $\frac{3}{2}$, 1, $\frac{2}{3}$, $\frac{4}{9}$, $\frac{8}{27}$, $\frac{16}{81}$, $\frac{32}{243}$ … Rule: Multiply by $\frac{2}{3}$.
7. How could you rewrite the rule *Divide by 2* using a fraction in the rule? Think: $4 \div 2 = 2$, $4 \times x = 2$ Multiply by $\frac{1}{2}$.
8. Rewrite each rule for Questions 1–6 above.
   a. 81, 27, 9, … Multiply by $\frac{1}{3}$.
   b. 250, 50, 10, … Multiply by $\frac{1}{5}$.
   c. 1, 8, 64, … Divide by $\frac{1}{8}$.
   d. 1000, 100, 10, … Multiply by $\frac{1}{10}$.
   e. $\frac{1}{8}$, $\frac{1}{2}$, 2, … Divide by $\frac{1}{4}$.
   f. $\frac{3}{2}$, 1, $\frac{2}{3}$, … Divide by $\frac{3}{2}$.
9. Draw the next figure in the pattern. Then write two rules for the pattern.

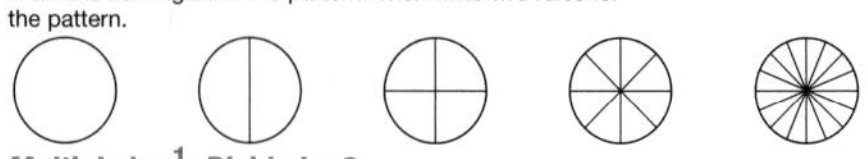

Multiply by $\frac{1}{2}$; Divide by 2.

10. Draw the next figure in the pattern. Then write two rules for the pattern.

Multiply by 2; Divide by $\frac{1}{2}$.

Section 7B Connect

At the beginning of this section, you read that the Massachusetts Avenue Bridge was once measured using Oliver R. Smoot, Jr. as the unit of measurement. In the following exploration, you will model that activity using one of your fellow students as the unit of measurement.

364.4 Smoots and One Ear

Materials: Masking tape

Choose a length to measure. For example, you could choose the length of the cafeteria or the length of a corridor. Choose one student in your group to be "Smoot."

Oliver Reed Smoot, M.I.T. 1962

1. Estimate the number of Smoot heights in the length that you choose to measure.
2. Use Student X to make the measurement. Use masking tape to mark off each Smoot height measurement. When you have finished measuring, post a sign that tells the measurement. Compare your measurement with your estimate.
3. Now measure the same length using a standard unit of measurement. Use fractional units if necessary. Measure your Smoot using the same standard unit of measurement.
4. Use your measurements from Step 3 and what you have learned in this section to calculate the number of Smoot heights in the length.
5. Compare your actual Smoot measurement from Step 2 with your calculation from Step 4. Which do you think is more accurate? Why? Which measurement was easier to find?

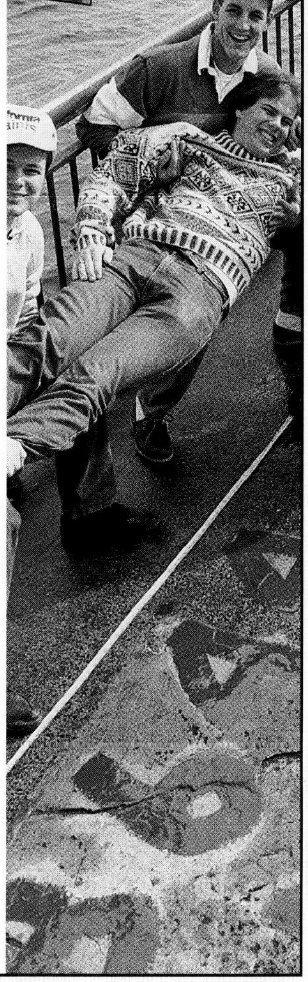

364.4 Smoots and One Ear

The Point

In *364.4 Smoots and One Ear* on page 381, students read about an unusual unit of measure. Now students will do an activity which uses a fellow student as a unit of measure.

Materials

Masking tape

About the Page

- Ask for a volunteer to serve as the unit of measure.
- Have students record their estimates before they begin to measure.
- Students might enjoy doing this activity in small groups. Each group could use a different student as the unit of measure. Then they could compare their results.
- After students have measured in "student lengths," they may use either metric or customary units to measure both the students and the length they measured.

Ongoing Assessment

Check that students have measured with their student unit and the standard unit accurately.

Extension

Have students use the span of their outstretched hands to measure the distance across their desks. Ask them how they handled fractional distances when they used the "hand span" unit.

Answers may vary.

Answers for Connect

1–5. Answers may vary.

7B Review

Review Correlation

Item(s)	Lesson(s)
1, 2	7-4
3	7-2
4, 5	7-5
6–8	7-3
9	7-4
10	7-3
11	7-2
12	7-5
13, 14	7-4
15–25	7-6
26	7-5
27	7-3

Test Prep

Test-Taking Tip

Tell students to reread the question before selecting an answer. Here, students may divide, ignoring the fact that the answer must be a mixed number.

Answers for Review

23. You can divide 11 by $\frac{1}{4}$ or multiply 11 by 4. Let x = height, $11 \div \frac{1}{4} = x$ or $\frac{1}{4}x = 11$, $x = 44$ in.

24. $5 \times 2\frac{1}{2} = x$; $x = 12.5$ cm.

25. $x = 12 \times \frac{1}{4}$; $x = 3$ gal.

Section 7B Review

REVIEW 7B

Simplify.

1. $4 \div \frac{1}{2}$ 8
2. $\frac{2}{3} \div 12$ $\frac{1}{18}$
3. $2\frac{1}{2} \times 3$ $7\frac{1}{2}$
4. $\frac{9}{4} \div \frac{1}{4}$ 9
5. $\frac{6}{7} \div \frac{1}{3}$ $2\frac{4}{7}$
6. $\frac{5}{4} \times \frac{6}{7}$ $1\frac{1}{14}$
7. $2\frac{8}{11} \times 1\frac{3}{4}$ $4\frac{17}{22}$
8. $\frac{9}{10} \times \frac{4}{5}$ $\frac{18}{25}$
9. $10 \div \frac{1}{5}$ 50
10. $\frac{2}{5} \times \frac{2}{3}$ $\frac{4}{15}$
11. $3\frac{1}{4} \times 4$ 13
12. $\frac{6}{10} \div \frac{1}{2}$ $1\frac{1}{5}$
13. **Health** Ellen needs to take 2 teaspoons of medicine. She has only a $\frac{1}{2}$-teaspoon measure. How many $\frac{1}{2}$ teaspoons should she take? Explain whether Ellen should use an estimate or an exact answer.
    4; Exact; Taking too much or too little could be harmful.
14. **Measurement** The rod was once used to measure distance. There are $5\frac{1}{2}$ yards in 1 rod. How many rods are in 11 yards? 2

Solve.

15. $\frac{1}{2}v = 16$ $v = 32$
16. $\frac{3}{5} \div k = 2\frac{1}{2}$ $k = \frac{6}{25}$
17. $x \div 6 = \frac{1}{3}$ $x = 2$
18. $\frac{1}{3}w = 2\frac{2}{3}$ $w = 8$
19. $2p = \frac{4}{5}$ $p = \frac{2}{5}$
20. $\frac{9}{5} \div e = 5$ $e = \frac{9}{25}$
21. $\frac{1}{2}u = \frac{4}{5}$ $u = 1\frac{3}{5}$
22. $c \div 4\frac{1}{3} = \frac{1}{3}$ $c = 1\frac{4}{9}$
23. A Shetland pony is 11 hands high. One inch = $\frac{1}{4}$ hand. Explain how you could use either multiplication or division to find this pony's height in inches.
24. Write and solve an equation to find the number of centimeters in 5 inches. ($1 \text{ inch} \approx 2\frac{1}{2}$ centimeters)
25. Write and solve an equation to find the number of gallons in 12 quarts. (1 quart = $\frac{1}{4}$ gallon)

Test Prep

If a test question asks you to give an answer as a mixed number, you can eliminate any answers that are not mixed numbers.

26. What is $\frac{4}{5} \div \frac{1}{3}$ as a mixed number? D
    Ⓐ $\frac{4}{15}$ Ⓑ $\frac{12}{5}$ Ⓒ $1\frac{2}{5}$ Ⓓ $2\frac{2}{5}$
27. What is $\frac{2}{3} \times \frac{5}{2}$ as a mixed number? A
    Ⓐ $1\frac{2}{3}$ Ⓑ $1\frac{1}{6}$

Resources

Practice Masters
Section 7B Review

Assessment Sourcebook
Quiz 7B

TestWorks
Test and Practice Software

PRACTICE

Name ______________________

Practice

Section 7B Review

Simplify.

1. $1\frac{7}{8} \div 1\frac{5}{7}$ $1\frac{3}{32}$
2. $7 \div 3\frac{3}{5}$ $1\frac{17}{18}$
3. $1\frac{5}{6} \times 5\frac{2}{3}$ $10\frac{7}{18}$
4. $3 \div 2\frac{1}{2}$ $1\frac{1}{5}$
5. $3\frac{1}{3} \times 7\frac{1}{2}$ 25
6. $3\frac{3}{5} \div \frac{1}{3}$ $10\frac{4}{5}$
7. $2\frac{1}{2} \div 7\frac{2}{3}$ $\frac{15}{46}$
8. $2\frac{3}{5} \times 8$ $20\frac{4}{5}$
9. **Measurement** One teaspoon is $\frac{1}{3}$ of a tablespoon. A bread recipe calls for 2 tablespoons of yeast. How many teaspoons is this? 6 teaspoons
10. **Measurement** There are $1\frac{3}{25}$ American tons in one British ton (long ton). How many British tons are in 7 American tons? $6\frac{1}{4}$ British tons

Solve.

11. $1\frac{2}{7}g = \frac{1}{2}$ $g = \frac{7}{18}$
12. $x \div \frac{1}{2} = 1\frac{1}{3}$ $x = \frac{2}{3}$
13. $\frac{7}{8}f = \frac{3}{5}$ $f = \frac{24}{35}$
14. $s \div 3 = \frac{3}{4}$ $s = 2\frac{1}{4}$
15. Write and solve an equation to find the number of furlongs in 12 rods. (1 rod = $\frac{1}{40}$ furlong)
    Possible answer: $x \times 40 = 12$; $\frac{3}{10}$ furlong
16. Write and solve an equation to find the number of pounds in 8 kilograms. (1 kilogram ≈ $2\frac{1}{5}$ pounds)
    Possible answer: $x \div 2\frac{1}{5} = 8$; $17\frac{3}{5}$ lb
17. The road distance from Toledo, Ohio, to Detroit, Michigan, is 4720 chains. One mile = 80 chains. Explain how you could use either multiplication or division to find the number of miles from Toledo to Detroit.
    Possible answer: $4720 \times \frac{1}{80} = 4720 \div 80 = 59$ miles
18. **Science** The largest birds' egg ever measured was laid by an ostrich in 1988 and had a mass of 2.32 kilograms. A typical albatross egg has about one fourth of this mass. Find the mass of an albatross egg. *[Lesson 3-12]* About 0.58 kg
19. **Fine Arts** Rodin's bronze sculpture of Jules Dalov is $20\frac{3}{4}$ inches tall. His marble *Hand of God* is $15\frac{7}{8}$ inches taller. Find the height of the *Hand of God*. $36\frac{5}{8}$ in.

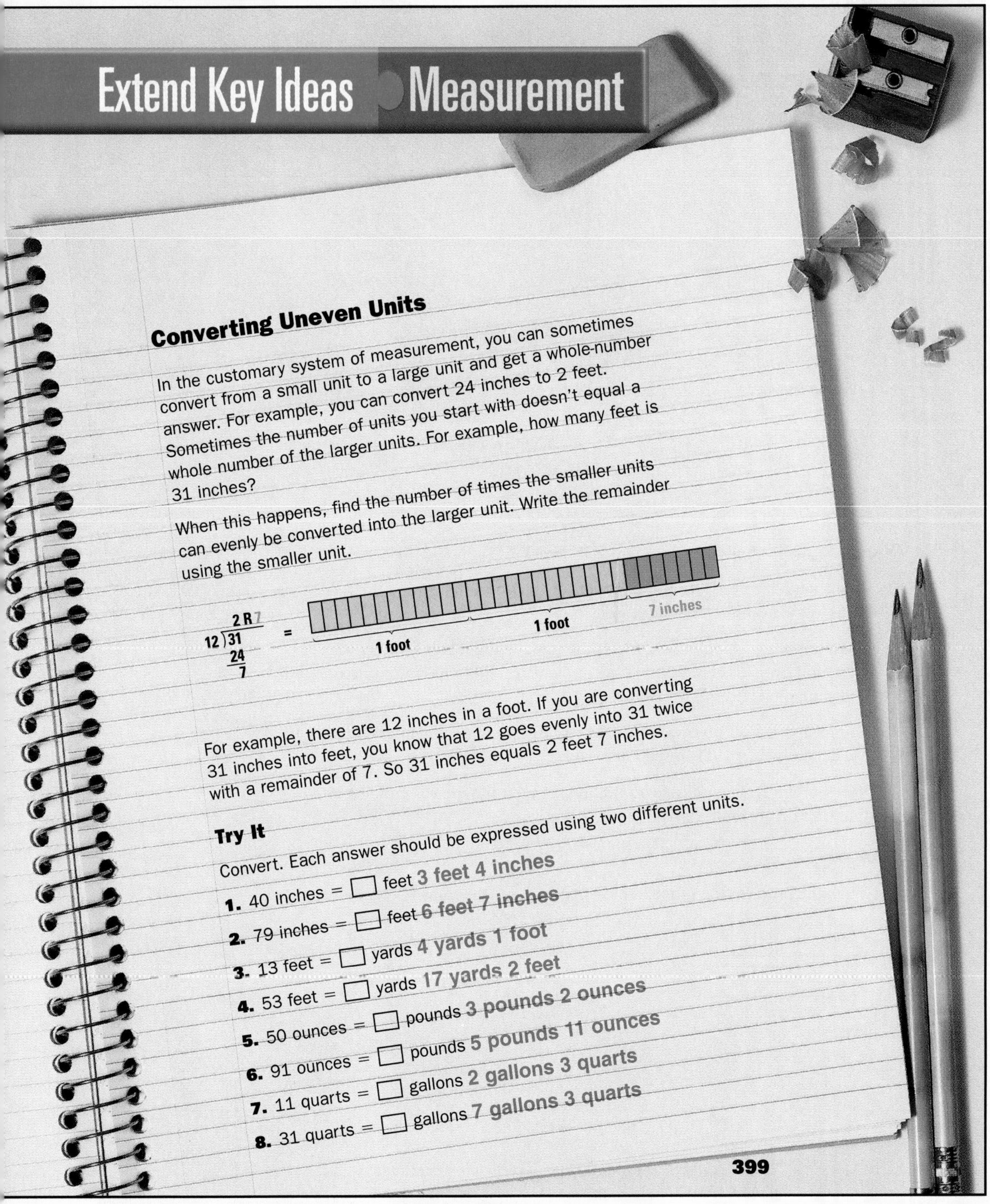

Extend Key Ideas ● Measurement

Converting Uneven Units

In the customary system of measurement, you can sometimes convert from a small unit to a large unit and get a whole-number answer. For example, you can convert 24 inches to 2 feet. Sometimes the number of units you start with doesn't equal a whole number of the larger units. For example, how many feet is 31 inches?

When this happens, find the number of times the smaller units can evenly be converted into the larger unit. Write the remainder using the smaller unit.

$$12\overline{)31} = 2\text{ R }7,\quad 31 - 24 = 7$$

For example, there are 12 inches in a foot. If you are converting 31 inches into feet, you know that 12 goes evenly into 31 twice with a remainder of 7. So 31 inches equals 2 feet 7 inches.

Try It

Convert. Each answer should be expressed using two different units.

1. 40 inches = ☐ feet 3 feet 4 inches
2. 79 inches = ☐ feet 6 feet 7 inches
3. 13 feet = ☐ yards 4 yards 1 foot
4. 53 feet = ☐ yards 17 yards 2 feet
5. 50 ounces = ☐ pounds 3 pounds 2 ounces
6. 91 ounces = ☐ pounds 5 pounds 11 ounces
7. 11 quarts = ☐ gallons 2 gallons 3 quarts
8. 31 quarts = ☐ gallons 7 gallons 3 quarts

399

Extend Key Ideas

Converting Uneven Units

The Point

Students convert smaller units to larger units, with a remainder.

About the Page

Discuss with students why this lesson is done with customary units and not with metric units. Point out the converting within the metric system is done by moving the decimal point. Explain that there is usually no need to express a metric measurement using two different units.

Ask ...

- How do you convert from a smaller unit to a larger unit? Divide the number of smaller units by the number of smaller units in 1 larger unit.
- When converting a whole number of inches to feet, what is the greatest number of inches that can be the remainder? 11
- When converting a whole number of feet to yards, what is the greatest number of feet that can be the remainder? 2
- When converting a whole number of ounces to pounds, what is the greatest number of ounces that can be the remainder? 15
- When converting a whole number of quarts to gallons, what is the greatest number of quarts that can be the remainder? 3

Extension

Create some other conversion problems, using conversions that are different than the ones already used. Trade problems with classmates, and try to solve their conversion problems.

Chapter 7 Summary and Review

Review Correlation

Item(s)	Lesson(s)
1	7-2
2, 3	7-1
4–7	7-3
8	7-2
9	7-3
10	7-2
11,12	7-3
13	7-2
14–16	7-4
17–20	7-5
21–24	7-4
25–28	7-5
29–33	7-6

For additional review, see page 668.

Chapter 7 Summary and Review

Graphic Organizer

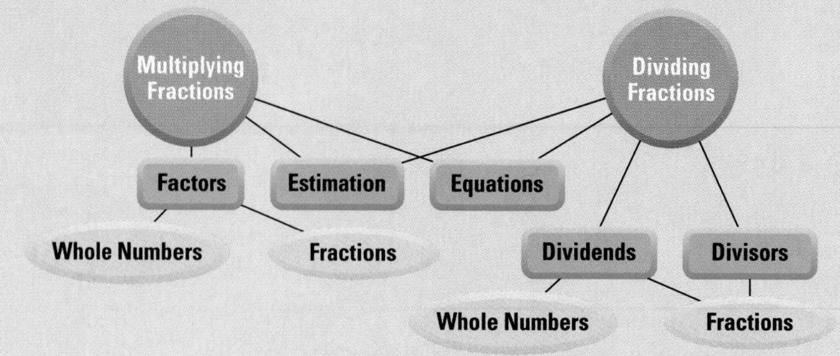

Section 7A Multiplying Fractions

Summary

- To estimate the products and quotients of fractions, first round the fractions to the nearest whole numbers.
- To multiply a fraction by a whole number, write the whole number as a fraction over 1. Then multiply the numerators, then the denominators, and simplify if necessary.
- To multiply a fraction by a fraction, first multiply the numerators, then the denominators, and simplify if necessary.
- When multiplying with mixed numbers, convert the mixed numbers into fractions before multiplying.

Review

1. Write the problem the model represents.

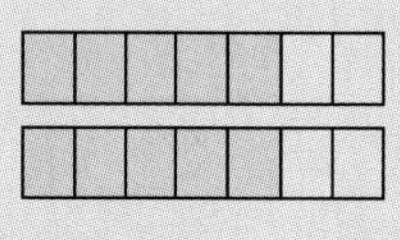

$2 \times \frac{5}{7} = \frac{10}{7}$

Estimate.

2. $7 \times 2\frac{3}{8} \approx 14$

3. $9\frac{3}{4} \div 2\frac{3}{7} \approx 5$

Simplify.

4. $\frac{3}{4} \times \frac{1}{8}$ $\frac{3}{32}$ 5. $\frac{1}{9} \times \frac{1}{9}$ $\frac{1}{81}$ 6. $\frac{2}{5} \times \frac{2}{3}$ $\frac{4}{15}$ 7. $\frac{3}{7} \times \frac{4}{7}$ $\frac{12}{49}$

8. $6\frac{1}{4} \times 4$ 25 9. $1\frac{5}{7} \times 1\frac{1}{6}$ 2 10. $5 \times 2\frac{1}{4}$ $11\frac{1}{4}$ 11. $3\frac{1}{6} \times 3\frac{1}{3}$ $10\frac{5}{9}$

Resources

Practice Masters
Cumulative Review Chapters 1–7

PRACTICE

Name ______________________ **Practice**

Cumulative Review Chapters 1–7

Write the phrase as an expression. *[Lesson 2-11]*

1. y divided by 7 $\frac{y}{7}$
2. m times 5 $m \times 5$
3. 15 less than u $u - 15$
4. one-third of k $\frac{1}{3} \times k$
5. d increased by 12 $d + 12$
6. c doubled $2c$
7. half of g $\frac{g}{2}$
8. p cubed p^3

Multiply. *[Lesson 3-9]*

9. 0.01×6.45 0.0645 10. 895×0.001 0.895 11. 2.83×9.7 27.451
12. 0.38×0.08 0.0304 13. 12.7×0.85 10.795 14. 2.3×18 41.4
15. 0.43×0.7 0.301 16. 8.41×0.03 0.2523 17. 34.8×1.2 41.76

Convert. *[Lesson 4-2]*

18. 85 g = 0.085 kg 19. 42 kg = 42,000 g 20. 3.82 mL = 0.00382 L
21. 73 cm = 0.73 m 22. 6.2 L = 6,200 mL 23. 9.4 m = 9,400 mm
24. 183 m = 0.183 km 25. 31 mm = 0.031 m 26. 2.9 km = 290,000 cm

Simplify. *[Lessons 7-2 to 7-5]*

27. $\frac{1}{3} \div 4\frac{1}{2}$ $\frac{2}{27}$ 28. $3 \div 1\frac{3}{4}$ $1\frac{5}{7}$ 29. $2 \div 10\frac{1}{2}$ $\frac{4}{21}$ 30. $4\frac{1}{2} \div 15$ $\frac{3}{10}$
31. $2 \div 3\frac{3}{4}$ $\frac{8}{15}$ 32. $2\frac{2}{5} \times 6$ $14\frac{2}{5}$ 33. $4\frac{3}{4} \div 1\frac{1}{5}$ $3\frac{23}{24}$ 34. $6\frac{1}{2} \times 7\frac{1}{2}$ $48\frac{3}{4}$

Solve. *[Lesson 7-6]*

35. $\frac{1}{9}q = \frac{1}{6}$ $q = 1\frac{1}{2}$
36. $k \div \frac{1}{6} = \frac{7}{9}$ $k = \frac{7}{54}$
37. $g \div 1\frac{3}{4} = 4$ $g = 7$
38. $p \div 2\frac{1}{2} = 2\frac{1}{4}$ $p = 5\frac{5}{8}$
39. $p \div \frac{1}{4} = \frac{7}{9}$ $p = \frac{7}{36}$
40. $\frac{1}{4}n = 2\frac{2}{3}$ $n = 10\frac{2}{3}$
41. $v \div \frac{1}{5} = 3$ $v = \frac{3}{5}$
42. $f \div \frac{5}{9} = 2\frac{1}{2}$ $f = 1\frac{7}{18}$

Section 7A Dividing Fractions *continued*

12. A recipe calls for two and one-half cups of milk. If you are making half a recipe, how much milk would you use? $1\frac{1}{4}$ cups

13. Is the product of a whole number and an improper fraction always larger than either number? Explain.

Section 7B Dividing Fractions

Summary

- A number times its reciprocal equals 1. To find the **reciprocal** of a fraction, switch the numerator and the denominator.
- To divide a whole number by a fraction, multiply by the reciprocal of the fraction.
- To divide a fraction by a fraction, multiply by the reciprocal of the divisor fraction.
- To divide a fraction by a whole number, write the whole number as a fraction over 1. Then multiply by the reciprocal of this fraction.
- When solving fraction equations with multiplication and division, find the numerator of the variable first, and then the denominator. If necessary, rewrite division equations as multiplication equations.

Review

14. Write the problem the model represents.

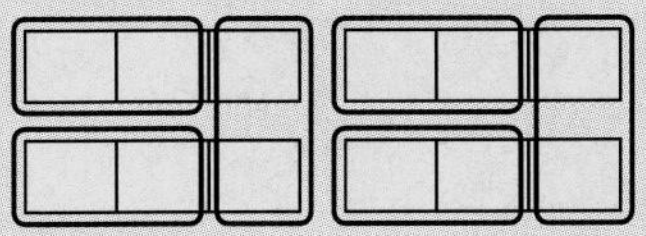

$4 \div \frac{2}{3} = 6$

State the reciprocal.

15. $\frac{5}{8}$ $\frac{8}{5}$

16. 3 $\frac{1}{3}$

Simplify.

17. $\frac{3}{4} \div \frac{1}{6}$ $4\frac{1}{2}$

18. $\frac{5}{9} \div \frac{2}{3}$ $\frac{5}{6}$

19. $\frac{6}{7} \div \frac{10}{3}$ $\frac{9}{35}$

20. $\frac{4}{7} \div \frac{5}{2}$ $\frac{8}{35}$

21. $\frac{3}{7} \div 4$ $\frac{3}{28}$

22. $\frac{4}{9} \div 7$ $\frac{4}{63}$

23. $\frac{2}{10} \div 8$ $\frac{1}{40}$

24. $\frac{7}{11} \div 2$ $\frac{7}{22}$

For each equation, state if the given value will make the equation true.

25. $\frac{2}{3}t = \frac{4}{9}$; $t = \frac{2}{3}$ Yes

26. $y \div \frac{1}{3} = \frac{6}{10}$; $y = \frac{2}{10}$ Yes

27. $\frac{3}{4}j = \frac{9}{16}$; $j = \frac{4}{3}$ No

28. $\frac{1}{5} \div p = \frac{2}{5}$; $p = 2$ No

Solve.

29. $\frac{3}{5}x = \frac{27}{30}$ $x = \frac{3}{2}$

30. $\frac{5}{6}m = \frac{30}{48}$ $m = \frac{3}{4}$

31. $w \div \frac{2}{3} = \frac{21}{60}$ $w = \frac{7}{30}$

32. $q \div \frac{6}{5} = \frac{35}{18}$ $q = \frac{7}{3}$

33. Ursula has a string that is $2\frac{1}{2}$ feet long. If she cuts the string into equal pieces and each piece is $\frac{1}{4}$ foot long, how many pieces does she have? 10 pieces

Answers for Review

13. Not necessarily. If the whole number has a value of one, the product of the improper fraction and the whole number will be the same as the value of the improper fraction. If the whole number has a value greater than one, the product will be greater than either number.

Chapter 7 Assessment

Assessment Correlation

Item(s)	Lesson(s)
1	7-2
2	7-3
3	7-4
4–7	7-1
8–11	7-4
12, 13	7-2
14, 15	7-3
16, 17	7-2
18, 19	7-3
20, 21	7-4
22	7-5
23–25	7-4
26	7-5
27	7-4
28–35	7-6

Answer for Performance Task

Students should show an 11 × 11 grid with the following entries:

Row 1: Empty, $\frac{1}{2}$, $\frac{1}{3}$, $\frac{2}{3}$, $\frac{1}{4}$, $\frac{2}{4}$, $\frac{3}{4}$, $\frac{1}{5}$, $\frac{2}{5}$, $\frac{3}{5}$, $\frac{4}{5}$

Row 2: $\frac{1}{2}$, $\frac{1}{4}$, $\frac{1}{6}$, $\frac{2}{6}$ or $\frac{1}{3}$, $\frac{1}{8}$, $\frac{2}{8}$ or $\frac{1}{4}$, $\frac{3}{8}$, $\frac{1}{10}$, $\frac{2}{10}$ or $\frac{1}{5}$, $\frac{3}{10}$, $\frac{4}{10}$ or $\frac{2}{5}$

Row 3: $\frac{1}{3}$, $\frac{1}{6}$, $\frac{1}{9}$, $\frac{2}{9}$, $\frac{1}{12}$, $\frac{2}{12}$ or $\frac{1}{6}$, $\frac{3}{12}$ or $\frac{1}{4}$, $\frac{1}{15}$, $\frac{2}{15}$, $\frac{3}{15}$ or $\frac{1}{5}$, $\frac{4}{15}$

Row 4: $\frac{2}{3}$, $\frac{2}{6}$ or $\frac{1}{3}$, $\frac{2}{9}$, $\frac{4}{9}$, $\frac{2}{12}$ or $\frac{1}{6}$, $\frac{4}{12}$ or $\frac{1}{3}$, $\frac{6}{12}$ or $\frac{1}{2}$, $\frac{2}{15}$, $\frac{4}{15}$, $\frac{6}{15}$ or $\frac{2}{5}$, $\frac{8}{15}$

Row 5: $\frac{1}{4}$, $\frac{1}{8}$, $\frac{1}{12}$, $\frac{2}{12}$ or $\frac{1}{6}$, $\frac{1}{16}$, $\frac{2}{16}$ or $\frac{1}{8}$, $\frac{3}{16}$, $\frac{1}{20}$, $\frac{2}{20}$ or $\frac{1}{10}$, $\frac{3}{20}$, $\frac{4}{20}$ or $\frac{1}{5}$

Row 6: $\frac{2}{4}$, $\frac{2}{8}$ or $\frac{1}{4}$, $\frac{2}{12}$ or $\frac{1}{6}$, $\frac{4}{12}$ or $\frac{1}{3}$, $\frac{2}{16}$ or $\frac{1}{8}$, $\frac{4}{16}$ or $\frac{1}{4}$, $\frac{6}{16}$ or $\frac{3}{8}$, $\frac{2}{20}$ or $\frac{1}{10}$, $\frac{4}{20}$ or $\frac{1}{5}$, $\frac{6}{20}$ or $\frac{3}{10}$, $\frac{8}{20}$ or $\frac{2}{5}$

Row 7: $\frac{3}{4}$, $\frac{3}{8}$, $\frac{3}{12}$ or $\frac{1}{4}$, $\frac{6}{12}$ or $\frac{1}{2}$, $\frac{3}{16}$, $\frac{6}{16}$ or $\frac{3}{8}$, $\frac{9}{16}$, $\frac{3}{20}$, $\frac{6}{20}$ or $\frac{3}{10}$, $\frac{9}{20}$, $\frac{12}{20}$ or $\frac{3}{5}$

Row 8: $\frac{1}{5}$, $\frac{1}{10}$, $\frac{1}{15}$, $\frac{2}{15}$, $\frac{1}{20}$, $\frac{2}{20}$ or $\frac{1}{10}$, $\frac{3}{20}$, $\frac{1}{25}$, $\frac{2}{25}$, $\frac{3}{25}$, $\frac{4}{25}$

Row 9: $\frac{2}{5}$, $\frac{2}{10}$ or $\frac{1}{5}$, $\frac{2}{15}$, $\frac{4}{15}$, $\frac{2}{20}$ or $\frac{1}{10}$, $\frac{4}{20}$ or $\frac{1}{5}$, $\frac{6}{20}$ or $\frac{3}{10}$, $\frac{2}{25}$, $\frac{4}{25}$, $\frac{6}{25}$, $\frac{8}{25}$

Row 10: $\frac{3}{5}$, $\frac{3}{10}$, $\frac{3}{15}$ or $\frac{1}{5}$, $\frac{6}{15}$ or $\frac{2}{5}$, $\frac{3}{20}$, $\frac{6}{20}$ or $\frac{3}{10}$, $\frac{9}{20}$, $\frac{3}{25}$, $\frac{6}{25}$, $\frac{9}{25}$, $\frac{12}{25}$

Row 11: $\frac{4}{5}$, $\frac{4}{10}$ or $\frac{2}{5}$, $\frac{4}{15}$, $\frac{8}{15}$, $\frac{4}{20}$ or $\frac{1}{5}$, $\frac{8}{20}$ or $\frac{2}{5}$, $\frac{12}{20}$ or $\frac{3}{5}$, $\frac{4}{25}$, $\frac{8}{25}$, $\frac{12}{25}$, $\frac{16}{25}$

Chapter 7 Assessment

Write the problem that each model represents.

1. 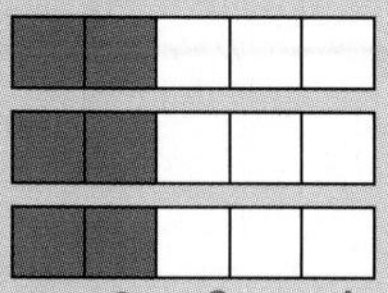

$3 \times \frac{2}{5} = \frac{6}{5}$ or $1\frac{1}{5}$

2. 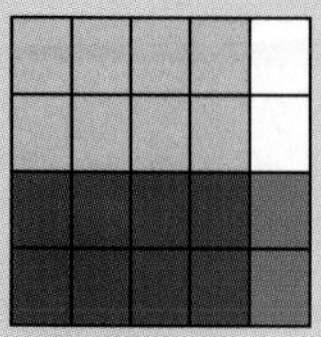

$\frac{4}{5} \times \frac{2}{4} = \frac{8}{20}$ or $\frac{2}{5}$

3. 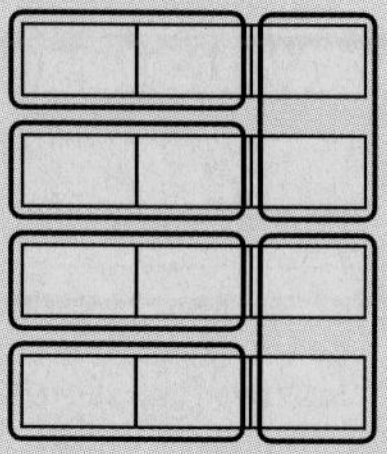

$4 \div \frac{2}{3} = 6$

Estimate.

4. $5\frac{2}{5} \times 2\frac{6}{8} \approx 15$ **5.** $7\frac{3}{9} \times 10\frac{1}{4} \approx 70$ **6.** $11\frac{1}{3} \div 1\frac{5}{6} \approx 5\frac{1}{2}$ **7.** $8\frac{4}{5} \div 3\frac{8}{11} \approx 2\frac{1}{4}$

State the reciprocal.

8. $\frac{5}{9}$ $\frac{9}{5}$ **9.** $\frac{6}{11}$ $\frac{11}{6}$ **10.** 4 $\frac{1}{4}$ **11.** $4\frac{1}{3}$ $\frac{3}{13}$

Simplify.

12. $3 \times \frac{4}{9}$ $1\frac{1}{3}$ **13.** $6 \times 3\frac{3}{7}$ $20\frac{4}{7}$ **14.** $\frac{1}{4} \times \frac{7}{8}$ $\frac{7}{32}$ **15.** $8\frac{4}{5} \times \frac{4}{7}$ $5\frac{1}{35}$

16. $6 \times \frac{2}{5}$ $2\frac{2}{5}$ **17.** $7 \times \frac{3}{10}$ $2\frac{1}{10}$ **18.** $\frac{7}{10} \times \frac{1}{5}$ $\frac{7}{50}$ **19.** $9\frac{1}{2} \times \frac{7}{11}$ $6\frac{1}{22}$

20. $9 \div \frac{2}{5}$ $22\frac{1}{2}$ **21.** $8 \div 1\frac{1}{9}$ $7\frac{1}{5}$ **22.** $\frac{1}{7} \div \frac{2}{8}$ $\frac{4}{7}$ **23.** $4\frac{2}{3} \div 7$ $\frac{2}{3}$

24. $10 \div \frac{2}{9}$ 45 **25.** $8 \div 6\frac{1}{5}$ $1\frac{9}{31}$ **26.** $\frac{3}{8} \div \frac{5}{9}$ $\frac{27}{40}$ **27.** $1\frac{1}{3} \div 4$ $\frac{1}{3}$

For each equation, state if the given value will make the equation true.

28. $\frac{1}{3}g = 10; g = 2$ No **29.** $\frac{4}{7}w = \frac{12}{49}; w = \frac{3}{7}$ Yes **30.** $p \div \frac{1}{4} = 2; p = \frac{1}{8}$ No **31.** $\frac{2}{9} \div r = \frac{2}{9}; r = \frac{2}{9}$ No

Solve.

32. $\frac{2}{5}g = 8$ $g = 20$ **33.** $\frac{3}{11}w = \frac{15}{88}$ $w = \frac{5}{8}$ **34.** $p \div \frac{3}{2} = \frac{2}{15}$ $p = \frac{3}{15}$ **35.** $\frac{5}{7} \div r = \frac{20}{21}$ $r = \frac{3}{4}$

Performance Task

The multiplication table pictured shows the products when multiplying with $\frac{1}{2}$, $\frac{1}{3}$, and $\frac{1}{4}$. Draw a multiplication table that shows the products when multiplying with $\frac{1}{2}$, $\frac{1}{3}$, $\frac{2}{3}$, $\frac{1}{4}$, $\frac{2}{4}$, $\frac{3}{4}$, $\frac{1}{5}$, $\frac{2}{5}$, $\frac{3}{5}$, and $\frac{4}{5}$. If the product can be rewritten in lowest terms, show the original fraction *and* the fraction in lowest terms. Describe any patterns you see.

	$\frac{1}{2}$	$\frac{1}{3}$	$\frac{1}{4}$
$\frac{1}{2}$	$\frac{1}{4}$	$\frac{1}{6}$	$\frac{1}{8}$
$\frac{1}{3}$	$\frac{1}{6}$	$\frac{1}{9}$	$\frac{1}{12}$
$\frac{1}{4}$	$\frac{1}{8}$	$\frac{1}{12}$	$\frac{1}{16}$

Resources

Assessment Sourcebook

Chapter 7 Tests
- Forms A and B (free response)
- Form C (multiple choice)
- Form D (performance assessment)
- Form E (mixed response)
- Form F (cumulative chapter test)

TestWorks
Test and Practice Software

Home and Community Connections
- Letter Home for Chapter 7 in English and Spanish

Cumulative Review Test Prep

Cumulative Review Chapters 1–7 — Test Prep

Performance Assessment

Choose one problem.

The 2-3-4-5 Scramble

You can form 24 mixed numbers using three of the digits 2, 3, 4, and 5 without repeating any digits. $2\frac{3}{5}$ and $4\frac{3}{2}$ are two possibilities. $2\frac{2}{3}$ is not a possibility because it repeats the digit 2.

Find the 24 possible mixed numbers and their decimal equivalents.

Recipes of Data

Collect copies of at least 8 cake recipes. Each recipe should call for a specific amount of flour and milk or water. Compile two lists, one for the amount of flour called for, and one for the amount of milk or water called for. (For example, if a recipe calls for $4\frac{1}{2}$ cups of flour, you would write $4\frac{1}{2}$ on your flour list.) For each list of amounts: What fraction of the list are fractions? What is the mode amount? Is the mode amount a fraction?

Horsing Around

The table lists the range of height, in hands, of several breeds of draft horses.

Horse	Height (in hands)	Colors
Belgian	15.3 to 17.0	chestnut, roan
Percheron	16.0 to 17.0	gray, black
Clydesdale	16.0 to 16.2	bay, brown
Shire	17.0 to 17.1	black, bay brown, roan
German Coach	15.2 to 16.3	black
Suffolk	15.2 to 16.2	chestnut

One inch equals $\frac{1}{4}$ of a hand. Rewrite the chart to show the range of heights in inches.

High Bars

Measure the heights of seven people, including yourself. Draw a bar graph of the data. Find the mean height. Which person is closest to having the mean height? Find the median height. Are there more people shorter than the median height, or taller than the median height? Why?

About Performance Assessment

The Performance Assessment options ...

- provide teachers with an alternate means of assessing students.
- address different learning modalities.
- allow students to choose one problem.

Teachers may encourage students to choose the most challenging problem.

Learning Modalities
The 2-3-4-5 Scramble **Intrapersonal** Students write twenty-four mixed numbers, using the digits 1 through 4.
Recipes of Data **Kinesthetic** Students collect recipes and find fractional amounts of ingredients.
Horsing Around **Logical** Students change a chart by using a stated ratio.
High Bars **Social** Students compare heights of people they know.

Answers for Assessment

• The 2-3-4-5 Scramble

Mixed numbers, decimals:

$2\frac{3}{4}$, 2.75; $2\frac{4}{3}$, $3.\overline{3}$; $2\frac{4}{5}$, 2.8; $2\frac{5}{4}$, 3.25; $2\frac{3}{5}$, 2.6; $2\frac{5}{3}$, $3.\overline{6}$; $3\frac{2}{4}$, 3.5; $3\frac{4}{2}$, 5.0; $3\frac{2}{5}$, 3.4; $3\frac{5}{2}$ 5.5; $3\frac{4}{5}$, 3.8; $3\frac{5}{4}$, 4.25; $4\frac{2}{3}$, $4.\overline{6}$; $4\frac{3}{2}$, 5.5; $4\frac{2}{5}$, 4.4; $4\frac{5}{2}$, 6.5; $4\frac{3}{5}$, $4.\overline{6}$; $4\frac{5}{3}$, $5.\overline{6}$; $5\frac{2}{3}$, $5.\overline{6}$; $5\frac{3}{2}$, 6.5; $5\frac{2}{4}$, 5.5; $5\frac{4}{2}$, 7; $5\frac{3}{4}$, 5.75; $5\frac{4}{3}$, $6.\overline{3}$

• Horsing Around

Heights in inches: Belgian, 61.2 to 68; Percheron, 64 to 68; Clydesdale, 64 to 64.8; Shire, 68 to 68.4; German Coach, 60.8 to 65.2; Suffolk, 60.8 to 64.8.

Suggested Scoring Rubric

See key on page 363.

Recipes of Data

Score	Criteria
4	•Compiled appropriate lists for at least 8 cake recipes. •Correctly calculated fractional amounts; identified all modes.
3	•Compiled appropriate lists for 8 cake recipes. •Some errors in calculating fractional amounts; identified most modes.
2	•Attempted to compile appropriate lists for at least 6 cake recipes. •Attempted to calculate fractional amounts; identified some modes.
1	•Incorrectly compiled all lists for cake recipes. •Was not able to identify related statistical data.

High Bars

Score	Criteria
4	•Accurately drew and labeled bar graph with required data. •Correctly calculated mean and median heights; correctly answered questions.
3	•Drew and labeled bar graph with required data. •Calculated mean and median heights; answered questions.
2	•Drew an adequate bar graph with data for 5 people. •Calculated mean and median with some degree of error; did not answer questions completely.
1	•Attempted to draw a bar graph with minimum amount of data. •Did not know how to find the mean or median heights; did not answer questions.

Chapter 8

The Geometry of Polygons

▶ OVERVIEW

Section 8A

Lines and Angles: Students learn to describe different kinds of lines and angles. They learn to measure the size of angles using a protractor.

8-1 Classifying Lines

8-2 Classifying Angles

8-3 Measuring Angles

Section 8B

Polygons: Students learn to classify triangles by the measures of their angles and by the lengths of their sides. They also classify polygons and quadrilaterals.

8-4 Exploring Angles in a Triangle

8-5 Exploring Sides of a Triangle

8-6 Polygons

8-7 Quadrilaterals

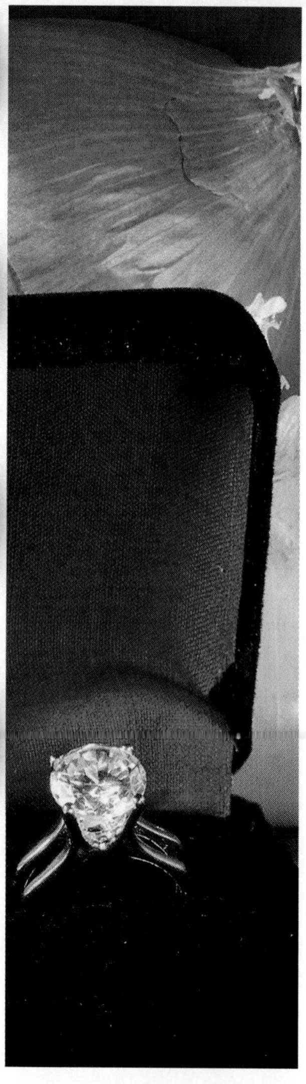

Section 8C

Transformations: Students investigate polygons whose shapes consist of repeated patterns. They examine figures that are flipped over a line, rotated around a point, and slid to a new position.

8-8 Flips and Line Symmetry

8-9 Turns and Rotational Symmetry

8-10 Slides and Tessellations

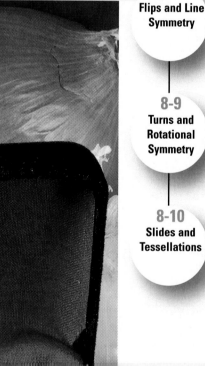

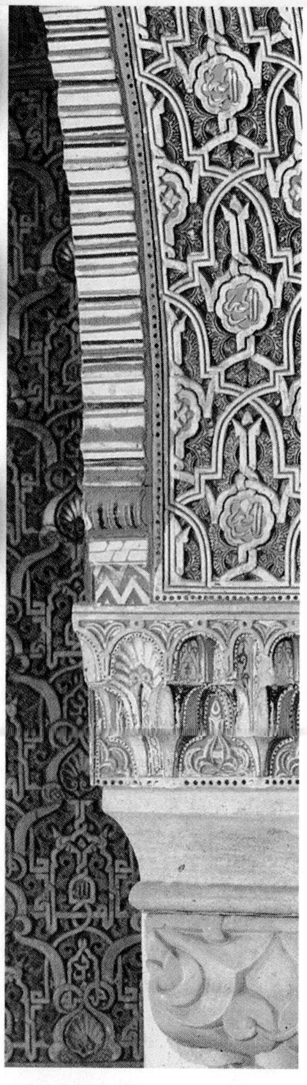

Meeting NCTM Standards

Curriculum Standards

STANDARD			pages
1	**Problem Solving**	Skills and Strategies	406, 415, 427, 456
		Applications	410–411, 414–415, 419–420, 421, 426–427, 430–431, 434–435, 438–439, 441, 446–447, 451–452, 455–456, 457
		Exploration	405, 408, 412, 416, 420, 424, 428, 431, 432, 436, 444, 448, 453, 456
2	**Communication**	Oral	407, 413, 423, 427, 429, 437, 445, 450, 454
		Written	411, 420, 431, 435, 439, 452, 456
		Cooperative Learning	*408, 412, 416, 424, 428, 432, 436, 444, 448, 453*
3	**Reasoning**	Critical Thinking	411, 415, 420, 427, 431, 435, 439, 447, 452, 456
4	**Connections**	Mathematical	See Standards 7, 12, 13 below.
		Interdisciplinary	Social Studies 404; Arts & Literature 404; Entertainment 405; Science 405, *423*, 427, 435, *450*; Fine Arts *407*, 410, 415, 419, *443*, 446, 451, 452; Language 413, 437; History *418*, 430, 438, 443, 445; Geography *407*, 449; Sports 418; Industry *423*
		Technology	440
		Cultural	404
7	**Computation and Estimation**		419, 425, 451
12	**Geometry**		408–459
13	**Measurement**		414, 416–420, 426, 439

Italic type indicates Teacher Edition reference.

Teaching Standards

Focus on Mathematical Tasks

Teachers are responsible for the quality of mathematical tasks in which students engage. Teachers should sometimes

- create their own tasks for students.
- choose from commercially prepared materials.

Assessment Standards

Focus on Openness

Ongoing The Openness Standard seeks to ensure that students have a clear understanding of what is expected of them and how they will be asked to demonstrate their understanding. In Chapter 8, the teacher checks that students have

- correctly illustrated a term.
- correctly identified terms.
- designed a reasonable tessellation.

TECHNOLOGY

For the Teacher

- **Teacher Resource Planner CD-ROM**
  Use the teacher planning CD-ROM to view resources available for Chapter 8. You can prepare custom lesson plans or use the default lesson plans provided.
- **World Wide Web**
  Visit **www.teacher.mathsurf.com** for links to lesson plans from teachers and other professionals, NCTM information, and other sites.
- **TestWorks**
  TestWorks provides ready-made tests and can create custom tests and practice worksheets.

For the Parent

- **World Wide Web**
  Parents can use the Web site at **www.parent.mathsurf.com.**

For the Student

- **Interactive CD-ROM**
  Lesson 8-9 has an *Interactive CD-ROM Lesson*. The *Interactive CD-ROM Journal* and *Interactive CD-ROM Geometry Tool* are also used in Chapter 8.
- **Wide World of Mathematics**
  Lesson 8-5 Middle School: Youthbuild
- **World Wide Web**
  Use with Chapter and Section Openers;
  Students can go online to the Scott Foresman-Addison Wesley Web site at **www.mathsurf.com/6/ch8** to collect information about chapter themes.
- **Jasper Woodbury Videodisc**
  Lesson 8-3: The Great Circle Race
  Lesson 8-4: The Right Angle

STANDARDIZED - TEST CORRELATION

SECTION 8A

LESSON	OBJECTIVE	ITBS Form M	CTBS 4th Ed.	CAT 5th Ed.	SAT 9th Ed.	MAT 7th Ed.	Your Form
8-1	• Describe different kinds of lines.		✗	✗		✗	
8-2	• Name and describe angles.		✗		✗		
8-3	• Measure angles.			✗			

SECTION 8B

LESSON	OBJECTIVE	ITBS Form M	CTBS 4th Ed.	CAT 5th Ed.	SAT 9th Ed.	MAT 7th Ed.	Your Form
8-4	• Classify triangles according to their angles.	✗	✗				
8-5	• Classify triangles according to their sides.	✗	✗				
8-6	• Classify polygons.	✗	✗	✗	✗		
8-7	• Classify quadrilaterals.	✗	✗	✗	✗		

SECTION 8C

LESSON	OBJECTIVE	ITBS Form M	CTBS 4th Ed.	CAT 5th Ed.	SAT 9th Ed.	MAT 7th Ed.	Your Form
8-8	• Identify reflections of figures. • Identify line symmetry.		✗	✗ ✗	✗ ✗	✗ ✗	
8-9	• Identify rotations of figures. • Identify rotational symmetry.				✗		
8-10	• Identify translations of figures and tessellations.			✗	✗	✗	

Key: ITBS - Iowa Test of Basic Skills; CTBS - Comprehensive Test of Basic Skills; CAT - California Achievement Test; SAT - Stanford Achievement Test; MAT - Metropolitan Achievement Test

ASSESSMENT PROGRAM

Traditional Assessment

QUICK QUIZZES	SECTION REVIEW	CHAPTER REVIEW	CHAPTER ASSESSMENT FREE RESPONSE	CHAPTER ASSESSMENT MULTIPLE CHOICE	CUMULATIVE REVIEW
TE: pp. 411, 415, 420, 427, 431, 435, 439, 447, 452, 456	SE: pp. 422, 442, 458 *Quiz 8A, 8B, 8C	SE: pp. 460–461	SE: p. 462 *Ch. 8 Tests Forms A, B, E	*Ch. 8 Tests Forms C, E	SE: p. 463 *Ch. 8 Test Form F

Alternate Assessment

INTERVIEW	JOURNAL	ONGOING	PERFORMANCE	PORTFOLIO	PROJECT	SELF
TE: p. 427	SE: pp. 415, 420, 427, 435, 439, 447 TE: pp. 406, 411, 431, 435	TE: pp. 408, 412, 416, 424, 428, 432, 436, 444, 449, 453	SE: p. 462 TE: pp. 420, 447 *Ch. 8 Tests Forms D, E	TE: pp. 415, 456	SE: pp. 420, 431, 456 TE: p. 405	TE: pp. 439, 452

*Tests and quizzes are in *Assessment Sourcebook*. Test Form E is a mixed response test.
Forms for Alternate Assessment are also available in *Assessment Sourcebook*.

TestWorks: Test and Practice Software

MIDDLE SCHOOL PACING CHART

REGULAR PACING

Day	5 classes per week
1	Chapter 8 Opener; Problem Solving Focus
2	Section **8A** Opener; Lesson **8-1**
3	Lesson **8-2**
4	Lesson **8-3**
5	**8A** Connect; **8A** Review
6	Section **8B** Opener; Lesson **8-4**
7	Lesson **8-5**
8	Lesson **8-6**
9	Lesson **8-7**; Technology
10	**8B** Connect; **8B** Review
11	Section **8C** Opener; Lesson **8-8**
12	Lesson **8-9**
13	Lesson **8-10**
14	**8C** Connect; **8C** Review; Extend Key Ideas
15	Chapter 8 Summary and Review
16	Chapter 8 Assessment Cumulative Review, Chapters 1–8

BLOCK SCHEDULING OPTIONS

Block Scheduling for
Complete Course

Chapter 8 may be presented in

- ten 90-minute blocks
- thirteen 75-minute blocks

Each block consists of a combination of

- Chapter and Section Openers
- Explores
- Lesson Development
- Problem Solving Focus
- Technology
- Extend Key Ideas
- Connect
- Review
- Assessment

For details, see *Block Scheduling Handbook.*

Block Scheduling for
Interdisciplinary Course

Each block integrates math with another subject area.

In Chapter 8, interdisciplinary topics include

- Origami
- Crystals
- Islamic Art

Themes for Interdisciplinary Team Teaching 8A, 8B, and 8C are

- Bees
- Pyramids
- Symmetry and Animals

For details, see *Block Scheduling Handbook.*

Block Scheduling for
Lab-Based Course

In each block, 30–40 minutes is devoted to lab activities including

- Explores in the Student Edition
- Connect pages in the Student Edition
- Technology options in the Student Edition
- Reteaching Activities in the Teacher Edition

For details, see *Block Scheduling Handbook.*

Block Scheduling for
Course with *Connected Mathematics*

In each block, investigations from **Connected Mathematics** replace or enhance the lessons in Chapter 8.

Connected Mathematics topics for Chapter 8 can be found in

- *Shapes and Designs*
- *Ruins of Montarek*

For details, see *Block Scheduling Handbook.*

INTERDISCIPLINARY BULLETIN BOARD

Set Up

Prepare a bulletin board with a sample of a maze.

Procedure

- Ask interested students to design a maze on paper. They should use intersecting, perpendicular, and parallel lines. They also should use different kinds of angles—acute, right, and obtuse.
- Volunteers should display their mazes anonymously so the class can decide which mazes to reproduce on the bulletin board.
- Small groups of students could be responsible for completing specific sections of the maze, such as the northeast corner, and so on.

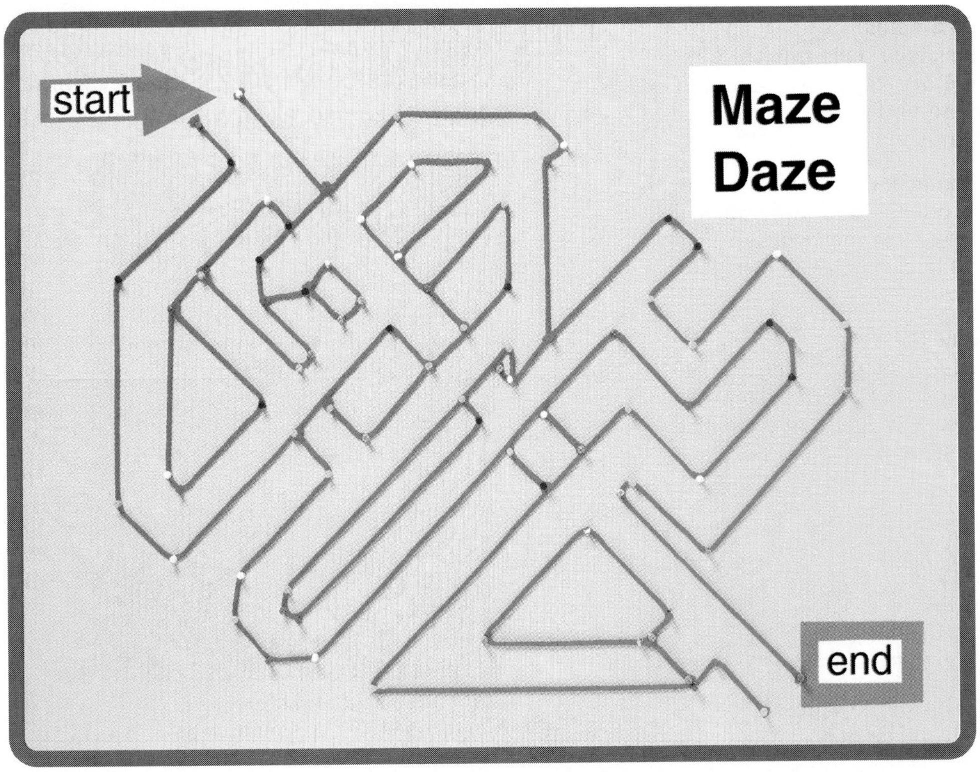

Chapter 8

The information on these pages shows how geometry is used in real-life situations.

World Wide Web

If your class has access to the World Wide Web, you might want to use the information found at the Web site addresses given.

Extensions

The following activities do not require access to the World Wide Web.

People of the World

Suggest that students work in groups to investigate the astrolabe and other methods of navigation, such as the sextant and loran, and share their findings with the class. Students may also wish to investigate what effect the Global Positioning satellite (G. P. S.) has had on navigation.

Arts & Literature
M. C. Escher (1898–1972) was a Dutch artist who explored the relationship of shapes. He experimented with the repetition of interlocking figures. Ask students to research the work of M. C. Escher and share examples of his work with the class.

Social Studies
Discuss why buildings are often square or rectangular. Ask students to find pictures of other buildings with unusual shapes.

Entertainment
Ask students to identify other distances on the mat which might be useful to gymnasts in planning their routines.

Science
Ask students to investigate the shape of the cells in a beehive. Discuss why that particular shape is constructed.

8 The Geometry of Polygons

Cultural Link
www.mathsurf.com/6/ch8/people

Social Studies Link
www.mathsurf.com/6/ch8/social

People of the World

The astrolabe was a device used by early Islamic astronomers to help them determine the time of day. In order to use it properly, an astronomer had to have a good knowledge of the stars and an understanding of how to measure angles.

Social Studies

The Pentagon is the headquarters for the United States Department of Defense. The building itself is shaped like a regular pentagon, with each side measuring 921 feet long. It contains over $17\frac{1}{2}$ miles of corridors and 7700 windows.

Arts & Literature

A tessellation is a design created by repeating a shape that fits together with no space in between. M. C. Escher (1898–1972) was an artist who is perhaps best remembered for his tessellations.

Escher, Maurits Cornelius. "Circle Limit IV," 1960. Woodcut.

404

TEACHER TALK

Meet Allison McNaughton

Barnstable Middle School
Marstons Mills, Massachusetts

I have students work with a partner to complete a project that demonstrates their understanding of quadrilaterals and triangles. They may write a song or rap, a poem in the shape of a polygon, or a creative story about Polly Gon and her family. I give them a list of requirements for each project, and try to include a variety of learning modalities in the choice of projects.

Students' projects must demonstrate an understanding of the differences and similarities between quadrilaterals or triangles. I give them a rubric ahead of time which includes demonstrating their understanding of polygons, and their creativity.

Science Link
www.mathsurf.com/6/ch8/science

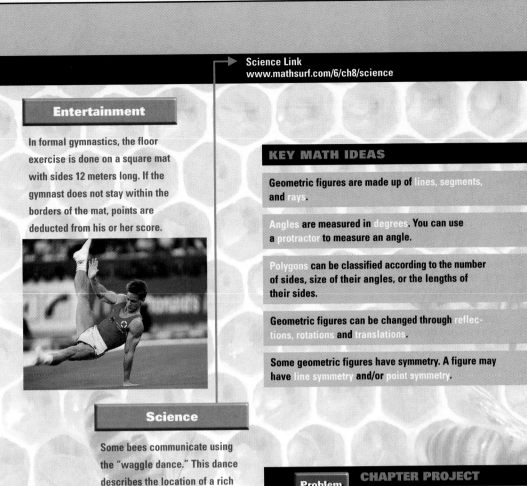

Entertainment

In formal gymnastics, the floor exercise is done on a square mat with sides 12 meters long. If the gymnast does not stay within the borders of the mat, points are deducted from his or her score.

KEY MATH IDEAS

Geometric figures are made up of lines, segments, and rays.

Angles are measured in degrees. You can use a protractor to measure an angle.

Polygons can be classified according to the number of sides, size of their angles, or the lengths of their sides.

Geometric figures can be changed through reflections, rotations and translations.

Some geometric figures have symmetry. A figure may have line symmetry and/or point symmetry.

Science

Some bees communicate using the "waggle dance." This dance describes the location of a rich source of pollen. The angle formed by the bee's motion and the sun indicates the direction of the pollen.

CHAPTER PROJECT

Problem Solving
Understand
Plan
Solve
Look Back

In this project, you will create a logo for yourself, your class, your team, or any group you belong to. Start by thinking about who you want to design a logo for, and what you would want the logo to look like.

405

Chapter Project

Students use their understanding of geometric concepts to create a logo for themselves or for their class, a sports team, or any other group to which they may belong.

Resources
Chapter 8 Project Master

Introduce the Project

- Talk about what a logo is and why teams or companies might use logos.
- Discuss the aspects of a logo that make it distinctive and easily remembered, such as design and color.

Project Progress

Section A, page 420 Students include a variety of shapes, including some shapes with straight sides only, in a rough sketch of their logo.

Section B, page 431 Students add necessary polygons to the revision of the draft of their logo.

Section C, page 456 Students incorporate at least one shape with either line or rotational symmetry into the final draft of their logo.

Community Project

A community project for Chapter 8 is available in *Home and Community Connections.*

Cooperative Learning

You may want to use Teaching Tool Transparency 1: Cooperative Learning Checklist with **Explore** and other group activities in this chapter.

PROJECT ASSESSMENT

You may choose to use this project as a performance assessment for the chapter.

Performance Assessment Key

Level 4 Full Accomplishment

Level 3 Substantial Accomplishment

Level 2 Partial Accomplishment

Level 1 Little Accomplishment

Suggested Scoring Rubric

4
- Logo is original and creative.
- Logo incorporates all required shapes and at least one shape with line or rotational symmetry.

3
- Logo is creative.
- Logo incorporates most required shapes and one shape with line or rotational symmetry.

2
- Logo displays some creativity.
- Logo incorporates some required shapes and attempts one shape with line or rotational symmetry.

1
- Logo displays little creativity.
- Logo incorporates few required shapes, and no shapes with line or rotational symmetry.

Problem Solving Focus

Interpreting Math Phrases

The Point
Students focus on identifying and interpreting key phrases that are needed to develop a plan for solving the problem.

Resources
Teaching Tool Transparency 18: Problem-Solving Guidelines

Interactive CD-ROM Journal

About the Page

Using the Problem-Solving Process
In order to develop a plan for solving a problem, students may need to interpret phrases that indirectly tell them what operation to use. Discuss the following suggestions for interpreting these phrases:

- Read the problem more than once.
- Determine what the problem is asking.
- Determine the meaning of any comparison phrases.

Ask ...

- In Problem 1, what is another way to indicate that Hanna practices 10 minutes more than Lynn? Lynn practices 10 minutes less than Hanna.
- In Problem 3, which person has more sheets of music? How do you know? Rebecca; She has twice as many as Dawn.
- Describe two ways to solve Problem 7. You can multiply 12 by $\frac{1}{2}$ or divide 12 by 2.

Answers for Problems

1. $30 - 10 = 20$
2. $7 - 2 = 5$
3. $34 \times 2 = 68$
4. $10 \div 2 = 5$
5. $5 + 6 = 11$
6. $8 \div 2 = 4$
7. $12 \div 2 = 6$

Problem Solving
Understand
Plan
Solve
Look Back

Interpreting Math Phrases

Many problem-solving situations use phrases like *more than, fewer than, twice as much,* or *half as much.* When developing a plan to solve the problem correctly, you need to know how to interpret these phrases.

Problem Solving Focus

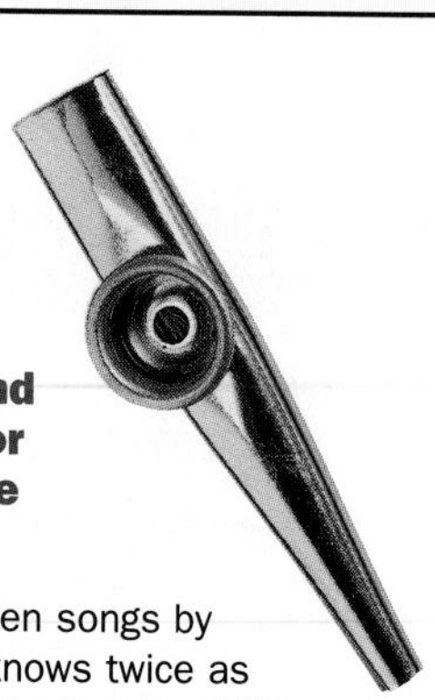

For each problem, write down the answer and the equation for how you got the answer. For example, if you added 5 to 7 to get 12, write "5 + 7 = 12."

1. Hanna practices the flute for thirty minutes a day. Hanna practices for ten minutes more than Lynn. For how many minutes does Lynn practice?
2. Andrea has seven drums. James has two fewer drums than Andrea. How many drums does James have?
3. Dawn has thirty-four sheets of music. Rebecca has twice as many sheets of music as Dawn. How many sheets of music does Rebecca have?
4. Tito knows ten songs by heart. Tito knows twice as many songs by heart as Will. How many songs does Will know by heart?
5. Miranda has performed in five more concerts than Crystal. Crystal has performed in six concerts. In how many concerts has Miranda performed?
6. Donte has twice as many spare guitar strings as Loren. Donte has eight spare strings. How many spare strings does Loren have?
7. Marco's kazoo cost half as much as Julie's harmonica. Julie's harmonica cost twelve dollars. How much did Marco's kazoo cost?

406

Additional Problem

Lee collected baseball cards. He had 48 cards in all. Rosy had five more cards than Lee, and Chas has half as many as Lee. How many cards did each person have?

1. What does the problem ask you to find? The number of cards each person has.
2. Suppose Chas has 96 cards. Write a descriptive phrase that describes Chas's cards. Possible answer: Chas has twice as many cards as Lee.
3. Solve the problem. Rosy had 53 cards and Chas had 24.

Journal

Have students write a problem that uses a phrase introduced in this lesson.

Section 8A

Lines and Angles

Visit www.teacher.mathsurf.com for links to lesson plans from teachers and other professionals, NCTM information, and other sites.

LESSON PLANNING GUIDE

Student Edition / **Ancillaries***

LESSON		MATERIALS	VOCABULARY	DAILY	OTHER
	Chapter 8 Opener				Ch. 8 Project Master Ch. 8 Community Project Teaching Tool Trans. 1
	Problem Solving Focus				Teaching Tool Trans. 18 *Interactive CD-ROM Journal*
	Section 8A Opener				
8-1	**Classifying Lines**		line, segment, endpoint, ray, intersect, perpendicular, parallel	8-1	Technology Master 36
8-2	**Classifying Angles**	index cards	angle, side, vertex, acute angle, right angle, obtuse angle, straight angle	8-2	Teaching Tool Trans. 2, 3
8-3	**Measuring Angles**	scissors	degree, complementary angles, supplementary angles, protractor	8-3	Teaching Tool Trans. 6, 17 Lesson Enhancement Trans. 37 Technology Master 37 Ch. 8 Project Master
	Connect	squares of paper, ruler			Interdisc. Team Teaching 8A
	Review				Practice 8A; Quiz 8A; *TestWorks*

* Daily Ancillaries include Practice, Reteaching, Problem Solving, Enrichment, and Daily Transparency. Teaching Tool Transparencies are in *Teacher's Toolkits*. Lesson Enhancement Transparencies are in *Overhead Transparency Package*.

SKILLS TRACE

LESSON	SKILL	FIRST INTRODUCED GR. 4	GR. 5	GR. 6	DEVELOP	PRACTICE/ APPLY	REVIEW
8-1	**Classifying lines and parts of lines.**	✗			pp. 408–409	pp. 410–411	pp. 422, 460, 471
8-2	**Naming and classifying angles.**			✗ p. 412	pp. 412–413	pp. 414–415	pp. 422, 460, 475
8-3	**Measuring angles.**		✗		pp. 416–418	pp. 419–420	pp. 422, 460, 480

CONNECTED MATHEMATICS

Investigation 3 in the unit *Shapes and Designs (3-D Geometry)*, from the **Connected Mathematics** series, can be used with Section 8A.

INTERDISCIPLINARY TEAM TEACHING

Math and Science/Technology

(Worksheet pages 37–38: Teacher pages T37–T38)

In this lesson, students use angles to understand how bees find nectar.

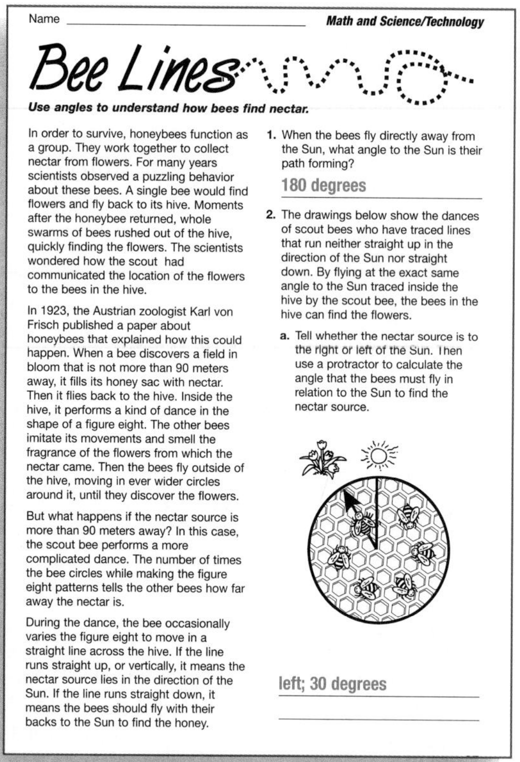

Name ______________ *Math and Science/Technology*

Bee Lines

Use angles to understand how bees find nectar.

In order to survive, honeybees function as a group. They work together to collect nectar from flowers. For many years scientists observed a puzzling behavior about these bees. A single bee would find flowers and fly back to its hive. Moments after the honeybee returned, whole swarms of bees rushed out of the hive, quickly finding the flowers. The scientists wondered how the scout had communicated the location of the flowers to the bees in the hive.

In 1923, the Austrian zoologist Karl von Frisch published a paper about honeybees that explained how this could happen. When a bee discovers a field in bloom that is not more than 90 meters away, it fills its honey sac with nectar. Then it flies back to the hive. Inside the hive, it performs a kind of dance in the shape of a figure eight. The other bees imitate its movements and smell the fragrance of the flowers from which the nectar came. Then the bees fly outside of the hive, moving in ever wider circles around it, until they discover the flowers.

But what happens if the nectar source is more than 90 meters away? In this case, the scout bee performs a more complicated dance. The number of times the bee circles while making the figure eight patterns tells the other bees how far away the nectar is.

During the dance, the bee occasionally varies the figure eight to move in a straight line across the hive. If the line runs straight up, or vertically, it means the nectar source lies in the direction of the Sun. If the line runs straight down, it means the bees should fly with their backs to the Sun to find the honey.

1. When the bees fly directly away from the Sun, what angle to the Sun is their path forming?
   180 degrees
2. The drawings below show the dances of scout bees who have traced lines that run neither straight up in the direction of the Sun nor straight down. By flying at the exact same angle to the Sun traced inside the hive by the scout bee, the bees in the hive can find the flowers.
   a. Tell whether the nectar source is to the right or left of the Sun. Then use a protractor to calculate the angle that the bees must fly in relation to the Sun to find the nectar source.
   left; 30 degrees

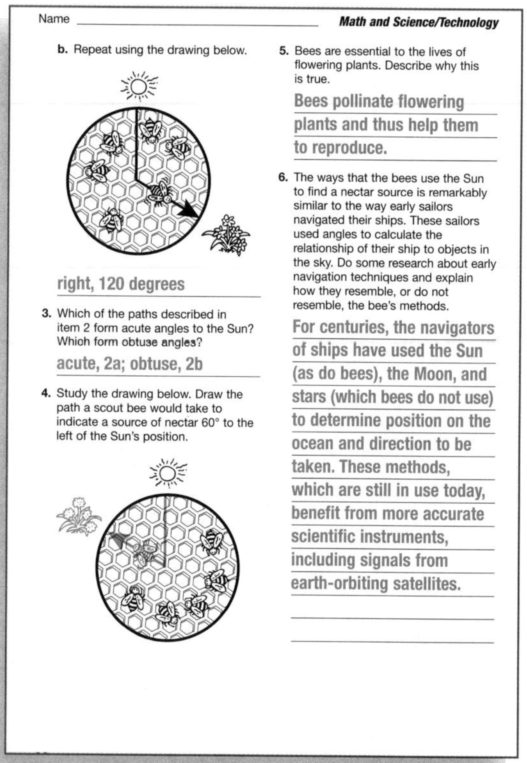

Name ______________ *Math and Science/Technology*

b. Repeat using the drawing below.
   right, 120 degrees
3. Which of the paths described in item 2 form acute angles to the Sun? Which form obtuse angles?
   acute, 2a; obtuse, 2b
4. Study the drawing below. Draw the path a scout bee would take to indicate a source of nectar 60° to the left of the Sun's position.
5. Bees are essential to the lives of flowering plants. Describe why this is true.
   Bees pollinate flowering plants and thus help them to reproduce.
6. The ways that the bees use the Sun to find a nectar source is remarkably similar to the way early sailors navigated their ships. These sailors used angles to calculate the relationship of their ship to objects in the sky. Do some research about early navigation techniques and explain how they resemble, or do not resemble, the bee's methods.
   For centuries, the navigators of ships have used the Sun (as do bees), the Moon, and stars (which bees do not use) to determine position on the ocean and direction to be taken. These methods, which are still in use today, benefit from more accurate scientific instruments, including signals from earth-orbiting satellites.

BIBLIOGRAPHY

FOR TEACHERS

Fowler, Allan. *Busy, Buzzy Bees.* Chicago, IL: Children's Press, 1995.

Hirsch, Christian R., ed. *Geometry from Multiple Perspectives.* Palo Alto, CA: Dale Seymour Publications, 1996.

Kallevig, Christine Petrell. *Folding Stories.* Newburgh, IN: Storytime Ink International, 1991.

Leff, Lawrence S. *Barron's Geometry the Easy Way.* New York, NY: Barron's Educational Series, 1990.

Pluckrose, Henry Arthur. *Shape.* London, England: Watts, 1986.

Symes, R. F. *Crystal & Gem.* New York, NY: Knopf, 1991.

FOR STUDENTS

Cook, Harry. *Samurai, the Story of the Warrior Tradition.* New York, NY: Sterling Publications, 1993.

Jackson, Paul. *The Ultimate Papercraft and Origami Book.* New York, NY: Smithmark, 1992.

Lang, Robert J. *Origami Zoo.* New York, NY: St. Martin's Press, 1990.

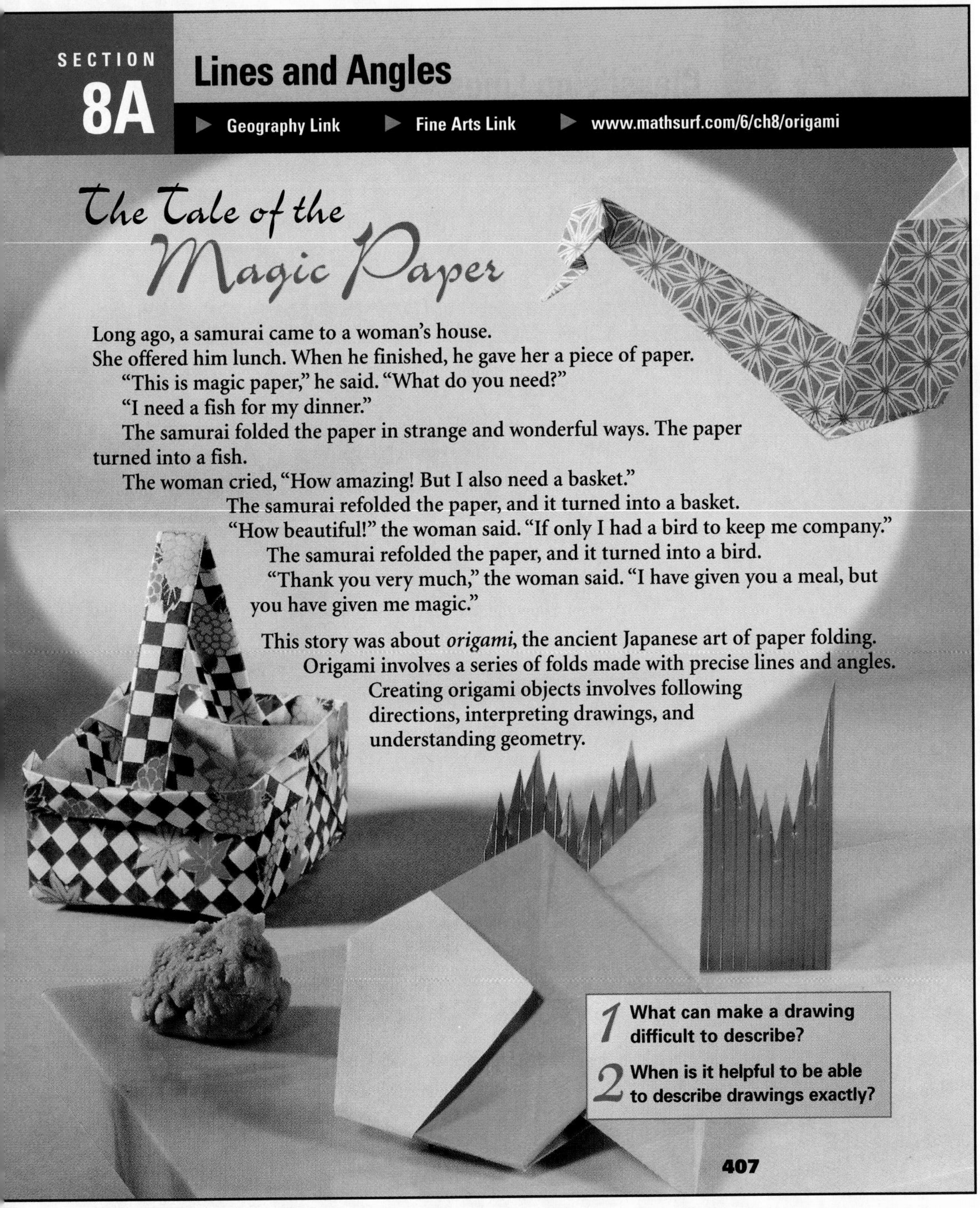

SECTION **8A**

Lines and Angles

▶ Geography Link ▶ Fine Arts Link ▶ www.mathsurf.com/6/ch8/origami

The Tale of the Magic Paper

Long ago, a samurai came to a woman's house. She offered him lunch. When he finished, he gave her a piece of paper.

"This is magic paper," he said. "What do you need?"

"I need a fish for my dinner."

The samurai folded the paper in strange and wonderful ways. The paper turned into a fish.

The woman cried, "How amazing! But I also need a basket."

The samurai refolded the paper, and it turned into a basket.

"How beautiful!" the woman said. "If only I had a bird to keep me company."

The samurai refolded the paper, and it turned into a bird.

"Thank you very much," the woman said. "I have given you a meal, but you have given me magic."

This story was about *origami*, the ancient Japanese art of paper folding. Origami involves a series of folds made with precise lines and angles. Creating origami objects involves following directions, interpreting drawings, and understanding geometry.

1. What can make a drawing difficult to describe?
2. When is it helpful to be able to describe drawings exactly?

407

Where are we now?

In Grade 5, students explored angles and polygons. They studied the characteristics of triangles and quadrilaterals.

They learned how to

- measure angles.
- recognize similar and congruent polygons.
- recognize line symmetry.

Where are we going?

In Grade 6, Section 8A, students will

- classify and describe lines.
- name and describe angles.
- measure angles.

Theme: Origami

World Wide Web

If your class has access to the World Wide Web, you might want to use the information found at the Web site address given. The interdisciplinary links relate to topics discussed in this section.

About the Page

This page introduces the theme of the section, origami, and discusses this ancient Japanese art of paper folding.

Ask ...

- Have you ever made something using paper folding?
- What information would you need to make the origami bird?

Extensions

The following activities do not require access to the World Wide Web.

Geography

Origami originated in China, but flourished in Japan. Paper folding and cutting activities, such as making snowflakes and paper dolls are popular in the United States. Have students research paper folding activities in other countries.

Fine Arts

The art of paper folding is fun and challenging. Ask students to find instructions for an origami shape and create an example of an origami figure.

Answers for Questions

1. Possible answer: If it has a lot of lines, colors, or shapes in it.
2. Possible answer: When you have to be very precise about something, as in describing plans for how to build a house.

Connect

On page 421, students create paper patterns describing geometric terms.

8-1 Lesson Organizer

Objective

- Describe different kinds of lines.

Vocabulary

- Line, segment, endpoint, ray, intersect, perpendicular, parallel

NCTM Standards

- 1–4, 12

Review

1. Name as many kinds of lines in daily life as you can. Possible answers: Power lines, telephone lines, clothes lines.
2. Would any of the lines you named extend forever? Explain. No. Any line in real life would eventually end, no matter how long it might be.

Available on Daily Transparency 8-1

1 Introduce

Explore

The Point
Students look at groups of four pictures showing various kinds of lines and decide which of the four lines is different from the other three.

Ongoing Assessment
Some students might give different answers from those listed. For example, in Step 2 some might say that the first picture is different because the lines are farthest apart. Allow such answers if they are reasonable.

For Groups That Finish Early
For each question, suppose each picture is turned on its side. Does that affect your original answers? Explain.

8-1 Classifying Lines

You'll Learn ...

- to describe different kinds of lines

... How It's Used

Hotel receptionists use line vocabulary when giving directions to hotel guests.

Vocabulary

line
segment
endpoint
ray
intersect
perpendicular
parallel

▶ **Lesson Link** You've used number lines to order decimals, and you've used line plots to display data. Now you'll look more closely at lines to see what they are and how they are classified. ◀

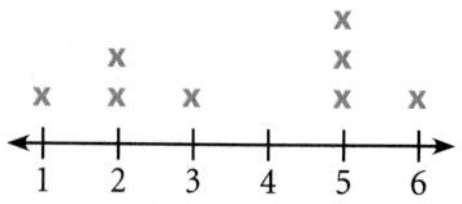

Explore Lines

What's My Line?

In each group, one picture is different from the others. Decide which picture is different and explain how it is different.

1.

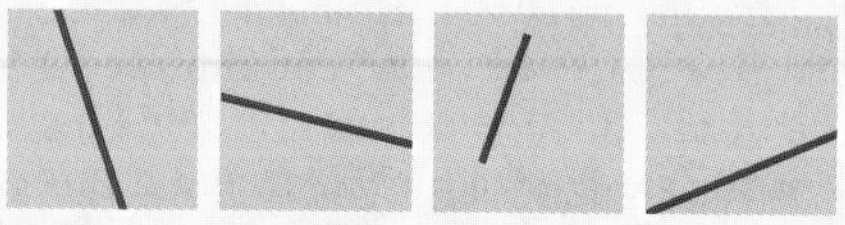

2.

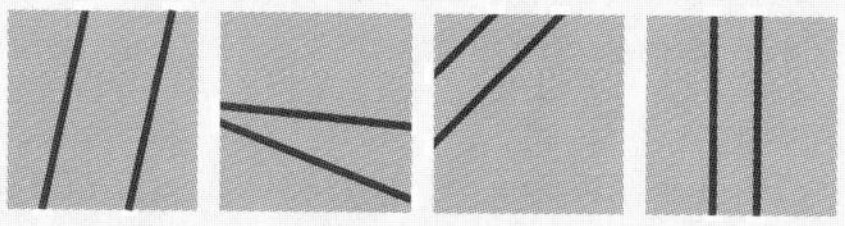

3.

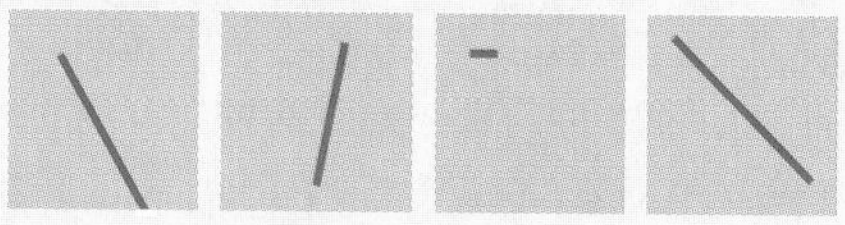

4.

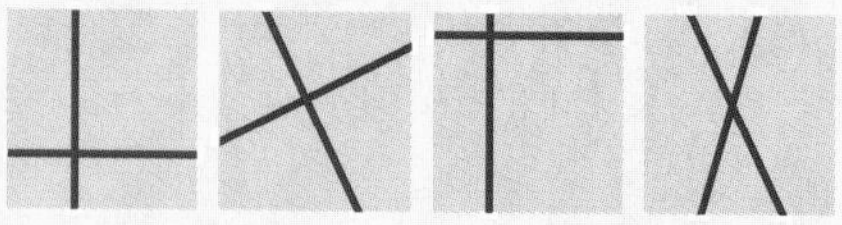

Learn Classifying Lines

Geometry is the branch of mathematics that studies shapes and figures. In order to describe shapes exactly, mathematicians use words with precise meanings. One class of words describes the different kinds of lines used to make figures.

MEETING INDIVIDUAL NEEDS

Resources

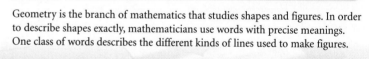

- 8-1 Practice
- 8-1 Reteaching
- 8-1 Problem Solving
- 8-1 Enrichment
- 8-1 Daily Transparency
  - Problem of the Day
  - Review
  - Quick Quiz

Technology Master 36

Learning Modalities

Visual Have students use magazines and newspapers to find pictures that illustrate parallel and perpendicular lines.

Social Allow students to work in pairs. Each student should draw pictures of various lines, line segments, and rays, with labels included on the drawings. Then they should name the figures drawn by the other person.

English Language Development

Point out that in daily life the word *line* is often used to describe a *line segment*. But in mathematics, words are used more precisely to avoid confusion. Stress that a line goes on forever, but a segment does not.

A **line** extends forever in both directions. To show that a figure is a line, draw an arrow at each end.

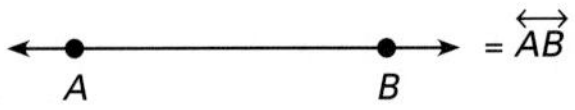

A line **segment** has two **endpoints**. The segment does not extend beyond these endpoints. To show that a figure is a segment, draw the endpoints.

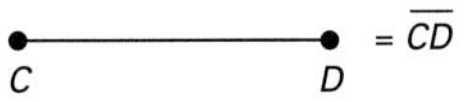

A **ray** has one endpoint, and extends forever in the other direction. To show that a figure is a ray, use an endpoint on one end and an arrow through a point on the other.

If lines cross through the same point, they **intersect**. If they intersect at right angles, they are **perpendicular**. If they do not intersect no matter how far they extend, they are **parallel**.

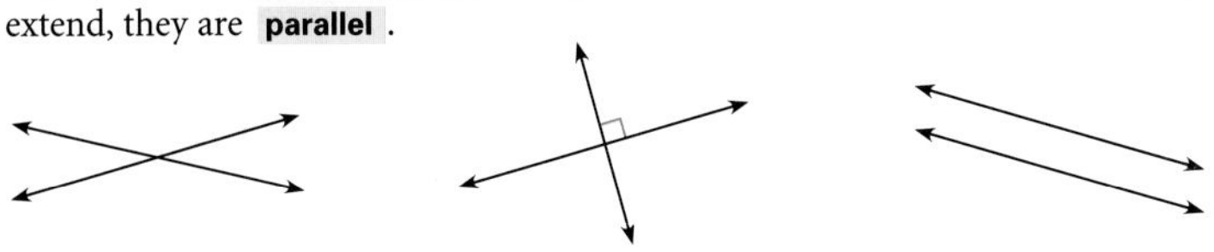

The lines intersect. The lines are perpendicular. The lines are parallel.

Rays and segments can also intersect, or be perpendicular or parallel.

Example 1

The origami angelfish has been labeled with several points. Describe the relationships between $\overline{AE}$ and $\overline{BE}$, $\overline{BE}$ and $\overline{CE}$, and $\overline{AD}$ and $\overline{BC}$.

$\overline{AE}$ and $\overline{BE}$ are intersecting line segments. $\overline{BE}$ and $\overline{CE}$ are perpendicular line segments. $\overline{AD}$ and $\overline{BC}$ are parallel line segments.

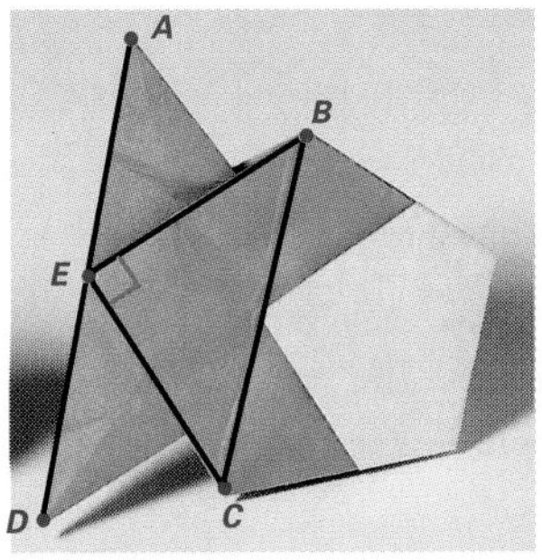

DID YOU KNOW?

John Smith developed the Origami Instructional Language, which converts lengthy written origami instructions into a compact list of numbers and symbols.

Check Your Understanding

1. Which is longer, a segment or a line? How much longer?

2. If two segments do not intersect, does that mean they are parallel? Explain.

MATH EVERY DAY

Problem of the Day

Kimberly bought some grapes. She and her friends ate of them on the way home. Her family ate $\frac{1}{2}$ of what was left as they watched television. Her brother put $\frac{1}{2}$ of what was left in a sack for lunch tomorrow. There was still $\frac{3}{4}$ pound of grapes left. How many pounds of grapes did Kimberly buy? 6 pounds

Available on Daily Transparency 8-1

An Extension is provided in the transparency package.

Fact of the Day

Trains run on two-railed parallel tracks. The tracks of the world's main routes extend about 750,000 miles.

Mental Math

Find each product mentally.

1. 8×70 560
2. 9×20 180
3. 4×90 360
4. 7×70 490

Answers for Explore

1. Third; The line does not extend to the edges of the picture.
2. Second; The lines are not parallel.
3. First; The line is not completely contained within the border of the picture.
4. Fourth; The lines do not intersect at right angles.

2 Teach

Learn

Point out that a line can be named by using any two points on the line, but a segment must be named by using the endpoints.

Alternate Examples

The diagram of a flag has been labeled with several points. Describe the relationships between $\overline{RS}$ and $\overline{ST}$, $\overline{RE}$ and $\overline{ST}$, and $\overline{RT}$ and $\overline{ES}$.

$\overline{RS}$ and $\overline{ST}$ are perpendicular line segments.

$\overline{RS}$ and $\overline{ET}$ are parallel line segments.

$\overline{RT}$ and $\overline{ES}$ are intersecting line segments.

3 Practice and Assess

Check

Answers for Check Your Understanding

1. A line goes on forever and a segment ends, so a line is longer; You can't measure the length of a line, so you can't measure how much longer it is.
2. No; Since a segment doesn't extend beyond its endpoints, it is possible for two segments to have no point of intersection yet not be parallel.

8-1 Exercises and Applications

Assignment Guide

- **Basic** 1–22, 24, 29, 32–50 evens
- **Average** 6–28, 31–51 odds
- **Enriched** 9–30, 32–52 evens

Exercise Notes

Exercise 17

Error Prevention Watch for students who think the lines are not intersecting because the point of intersection is not shown. Point out that the lines extend forever, so they do intersect.

Exercises 20–21

Fine Arts Origami figures range from simple figures that young children can make to quite complicated figures that even many adults would have difficulty making.

Exercise Answers

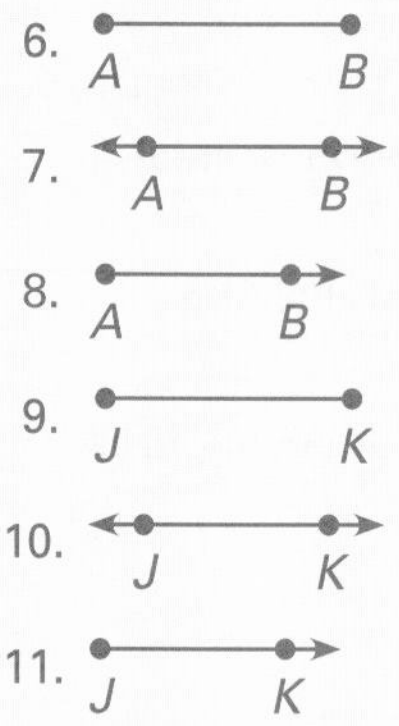

20. Possible answer: $\overline{AB}$ and $\overline{CH}$, $\overline{EG}$ and $\overline{FH}$, $\overline{BG}$ and $\overline{CD}$.

21. Possible answer: $\overline{BG}$ and $\overline{EG}$

Reteaching

Activity

Materials: Index cards

- Work in small groups. Use index cards as a device for drawing parallel lines, as well as perpendicular lines.
- Once you have drawn these lines, label them with enough points so that you can describe them in several ways.

8-1 Exercises and Applications

Practice and Apply

Getting Started State whether each figure is a line, a ray, or a segment.

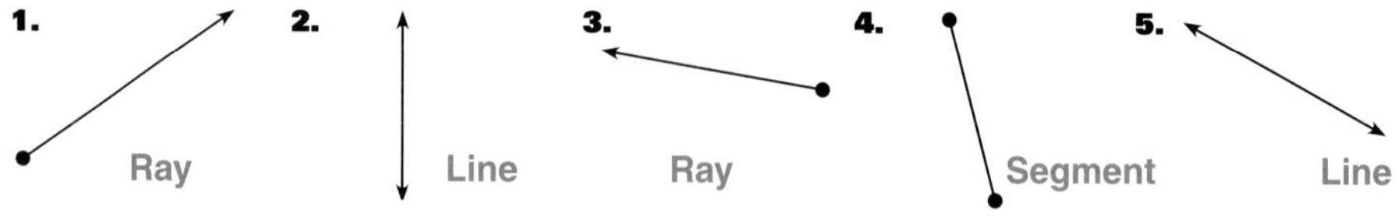

1. Ray 2. Line 3. Ray 4. Segment 5. Line

Draw an example of each.

6. $\overline{AB}$ 7. $\overleftrightarrow{AB}$ 8. $\overrightarrow{AB}$ 9. $\overline{JK}$ 10. $\overleftrightarrow{JK}$ 11. $\overrightarrow{JK}$

Describe the relationship between the lines, rays, or segments.

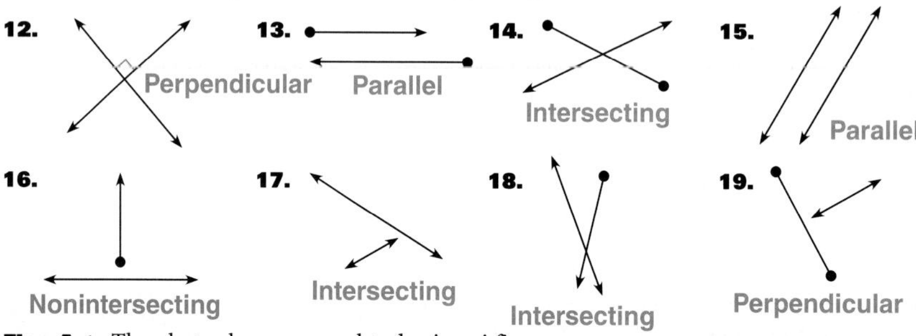

12. Perpendicular 13. Parallel 14. Intersecting 15. Parallel

16. Nonintersecting 17. Intersecting 18. Intersecting 19. Perpendicular

PRACTICE 8-1

Fine Arts The photo shows a completed origami figure.

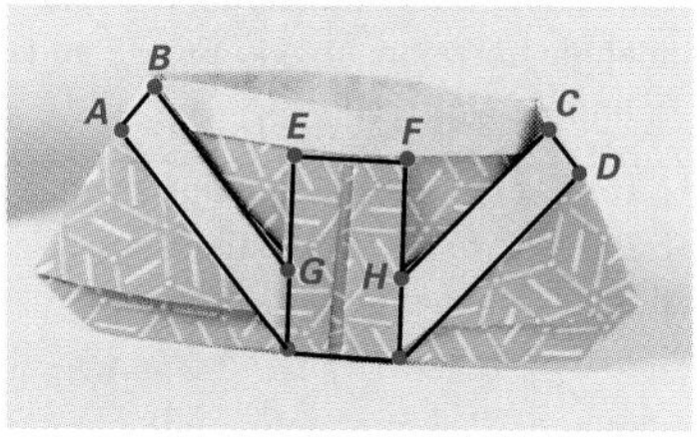

20. Name three pairs of parallel segments.

21. Name two segments that intersect but are not perpendicular.

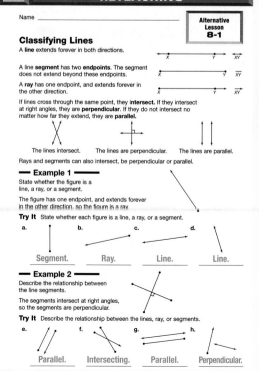

22. **Test Prep** Choose the lines that are parallel. D

GPS

Ⓐ A and D

Ⓑ C and E

Ⓒ A and C

Ⓓ E and D

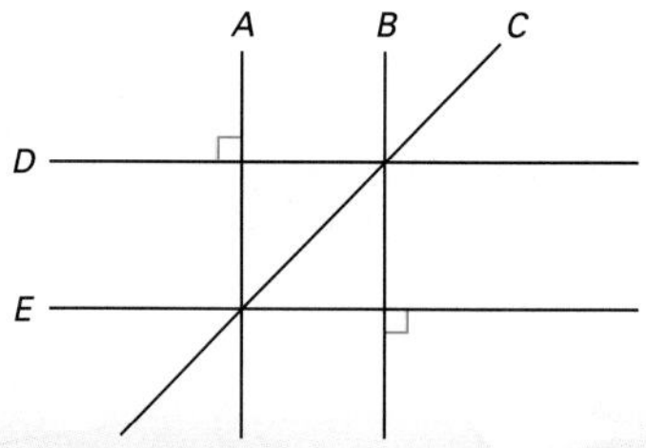

PRACTICE

Name ______________________

Practice 8-1

Classifying Lines

Draw an example of each. Possible answers:

1. $\overline{GH}$ 2. $\overrightarrow{GH}$ 3. $\overleftrightarrow{GH}$

4. $\overrightarrow{PQ}$ 5. $\overleftrightarrow{PQ}$ 6. $\overline{PQ}$

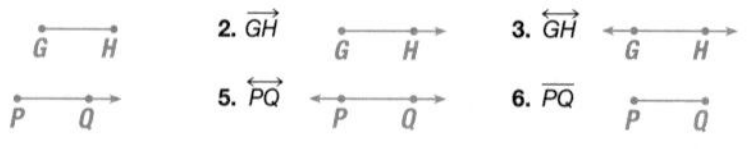

Describe the relationship between the lines, rays, or segments.

7. Parallel segments

8. Perpendicular line and ray

9. Intersecting rays

10. Perpendicular segments

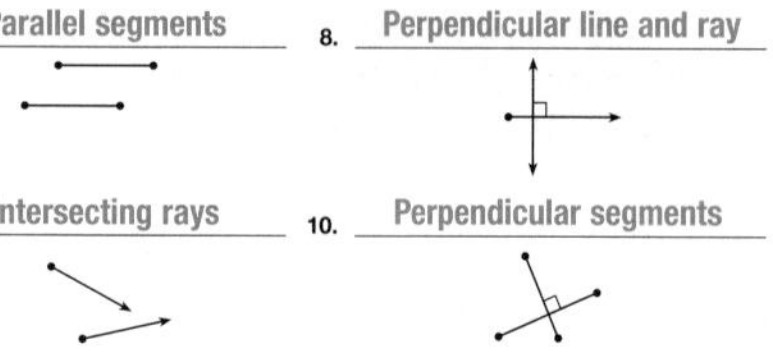

Tell whether each statement is always, sometimes, or never true.

11. Perpendicular lines intersect. Always true

12. Rays that are not parallel intersect. Sometimes true

13. The blue lines on a sheet of standard notebook paper are perpendicular. Never true

14. The diagram shows a simplified drawing of a truck.

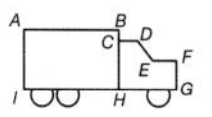

a. Name two pairs of parallel line segments.
Possible answers: $\overline{AB}$ and $\overline{IG}$, $\overline{BH}$ and $\overline{AI}$

b. Name two pairs of perpendicular line segments.
Possible answers: $\overline{AB}$ and $\overline{AI}$, $\overline{BH}$ and $\overline{CD}$

c. Name two line segments that intersect but are not perpendicular.
Possible answers: $\overline{CD}$ and $\overline{DE}$

RETEACHING

Name ______________________

Alternative Lesson 8-1

Classifying Lines

A **line** extends forever in both directions.

A line **segment** has two **endpoints**. The segment does not extend beyond these endpoints.

A **ray** has one endpoint, and extends forever in the other direction.

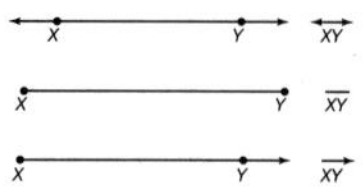

If lines cross through the same point, they **intersect.** If they intersect at right angles, they are **perpendicular**. If they do not intersect no matter how far they extend, they are **parallel.**

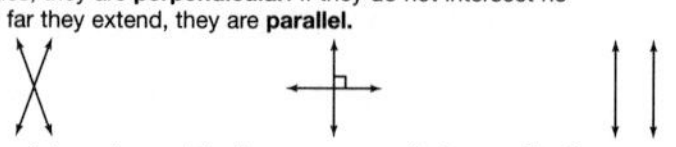

The lines intersect. The lines are perpendicular. The lines are parallel.

Rays and segments can also intersect, be perpendicular or parallel.

Example 1

State whether the figure is a line, a ray, or a segment.

The figure has one endpoint, and extends forever in the other direction, so the figure is a ray.

Try It State whether each figure is a line, a ray, or a segment.

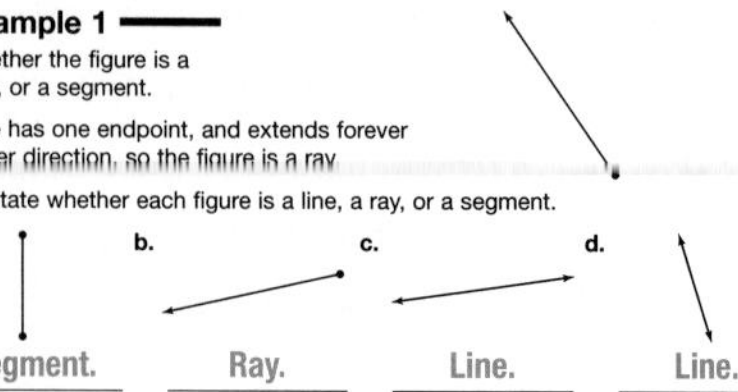

a. Segment. b. Ray. c. Line. d. Line.

Example 2

Describe the relationship between the line segments.

The segments intersect at right angles, so the segments are perpendicular.

Try It Describe the relationship between the lines, ray, or segments.

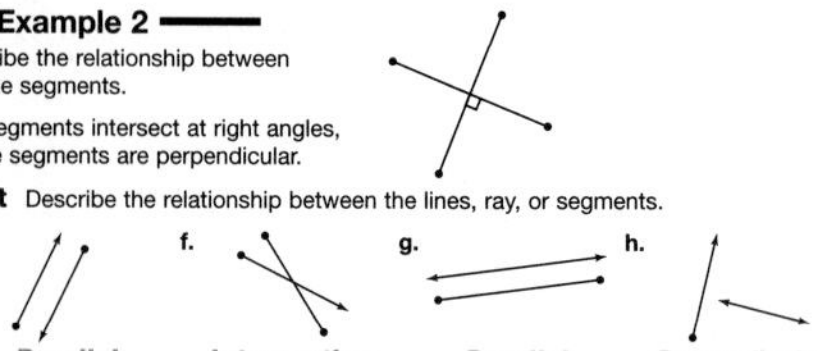

e. Parallel. f. Intersecting. g. Parallel. h. Perpendicular.

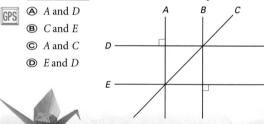

23. Miranda and Hien are walking along parallel streets in a neighborhood. If the girls are 150 feet apart when they start walking, how long will they have to walk until their paths cross? Their paths will never cross.

Logic Tell whether each statement is always, sometimes, or never true.

24. The rails on a set of train tracks are parallel. Always

25. Two intersecting streets are perpendicular. Sometimes

26. The paths of two airplanes flying above Texas will intersect. Sometimes

27. A line is longer than a segment. Always

Problem Solving and Reasoning

28. Critical Thinking Jarred studied 50 pairs of lines. He labeled each pair with the terms *parallel, perpendicular,* and *intersecting*. The bar graph shows the number of times he used each label. The numbers in the graph do not add up to 50. Other than being a mistake, explain how this is possible.

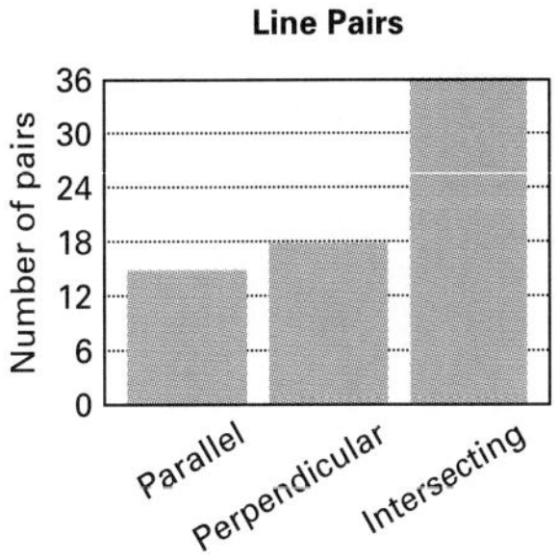

29. Communicate List three real-world situations that involve parallel lines. Do the situations also involve perpendicular lines? Explain.

30. Communicate Is the distance between two parallel lines always the same? Explain. Use a picture or diagram in your explanation.

PROBLEM SOLVING 8-1

Mixed Review

Write as a mixed number. *[Lesson 5-6]*

31. $\frac{5}{3}$ $1\frac{2}{3}$ **32.** $\frac{3}{2}$ $1\frac{1}{2}$ **33.** $\frac{7}{3}$ $2\frac{1}{3}$ **34.** $\frac{9}{4}$ $2\frac{1}{4}$ **35.** $\frac{7}{2}$ $3\frac{1}{2}$ **36.** $\frac{14}{6}$ $2\frac{1}{3}$

37. $\frac{9}{5}$ $1\frac{4}{5}$ **38.** $\frac{18}{4}$ $4\frac{1}{2}$ **39.** $\frac{6}{4}$ $1\frac{1}{2}$ **40.** $\frac{10}{7}$ $1\frac{3}{7}$ **41.** $\frac{12}{5}$ $2\frac{2}{5}$ **42.** $\frac{8}{3}$ $2\frac{2}{3}$

Simplify. Write your answer as a mixed number. *[Lesson 6-1]*

43. $\frac{2}{7}+\frac{5}{7}$ 1 **44.** $\frac{4}{5}-\frac{1}{5}$ $\frac{3}{5}$ **45.** $\frac{7}{10}+\frac{9}{10}$ $1\frac{3}{5}$ **46.** $\frac{55}{100}+\frac{46}{100}$ $1\frac{1}{100}$ **47.** $\frac{8}{4}-\frac{3}{4}$ $1\frac{1}{4}$

48. $\frac{4}{3}-\frac{3}{3}$ $\frac{1}{3}$ **49.** $\frac{12}{15}+\frac{13}{15}$ $1\frac{2}{3}$ **50.** $\frac{7}{8}-\frac{4}{8}$ $\frac{3}{8}$ **51.** $\frac{9}{12}+\frac{3}{12}$ 1 **52.** $\frac{3}{5}-\frac{1}{5}$ $\frac{2}{5}$

PROBLEM SOLVING

Name ______________________

Guided Problem Solving 8-1

GPS PROBLEM 22, STUDENT PAGE 410

Choose the lines that are parallel.

(A) *A* and *D* (B) *C* and *E*

(C) *A* and *C* (D) *E* and *D*

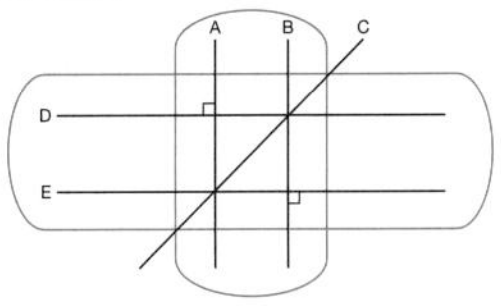

Understand

1. What are you asked to do? Decide which lines are parallel.
2. Do parallel lines intersect? No.

Plan

3. Circle all pairs of parallel lines in the diagram.
4. How many pairs of parallel lines did you circle? 2 pairs.

Solve

5. Write the letters of all the pairs of parallel lines. D and E; A and B
6. Compare your answer to Item 5 with the given answer choices.
   a. Choice (A) says lines A and D are parallel. Is that correct? No.
   b. Choice (B) says lines C and E are parallel. Is that correct? No.
   c. Choice (C) says lines A and C are parallel. Is that correct? No.
   d. Choice (D) says lines E and D are parallel. Is that correct? Yes.
7. Which choice—A, B, C, or D—is the correct answer? Choice D.

Look Back

8. Why are lines A and B not the correct answer? While they are a pair of parallel lines, they are not one of the choices.

SOLVE ANOTHER PROBLEM

Which lines in the diagram above are perpendicular?
Lines A and D, A and E, B and D, B and E.

ENRICHMENT

Name ______________________

Extend Your Thinking 8-1

Patterns in Geometry

You can use a corner or a ruler to draw perpendicular lines.

1. Draw a line perpendicular to radius 1 at point *A*. Label its intersection with radius 2, *B*.
2. Draw a line perpendicular to radius 2 at point *B*. Label its intersection with radius 3, *C*.
3. Draw a line perpendicular to radius 3 at point *C*. Label its intersection with radius 4, *D*.
4. Describe the pattern in the drawing. Possible answer: Connect each point to an adjacent radius by drawing a perpendicular line.
5. Continue this pattern until you reach the outer edge circle.

Possible answer: Item 4

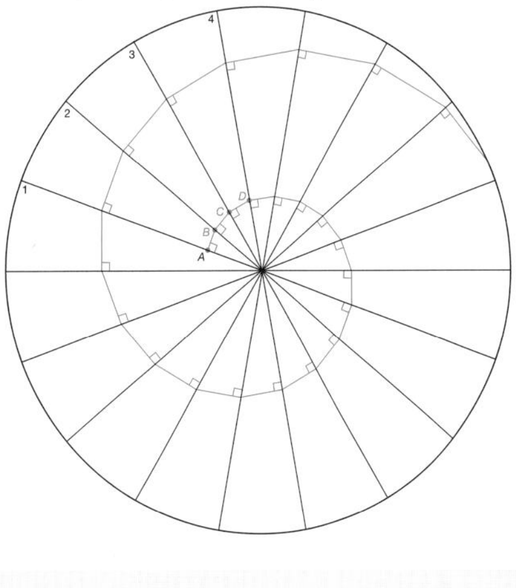

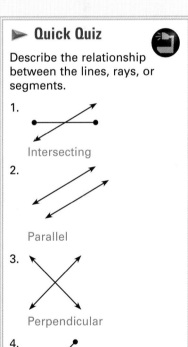

Exercise Answers

28. Perpendicular lines are also intersecting, so they have been counted twice in the graph.

29. Possible answer: Edges of a book are both parallel and perpendicular. Lines on a street are sometimes parallel and sometimes perpendicular. Grid lines on a map are both parallel and perpendicular. Situations with parallel lines do not always contain perpendicular lines.

30. Yes; If it were not, the lines would eventually cross.

Alternate Assessment

You may want to use the *Interactive CD-ROM Journal* with this assessment.

Journal Have students draw diagrams in their journals to illustrate a line, a line segment, and a ray, as well as parallel, perpendicular, and intersecting lines. Then have them write a brief description for each of the figures.

Quick Quiz

Describe the relationship between the lines, rays, or segments.

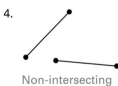

1. 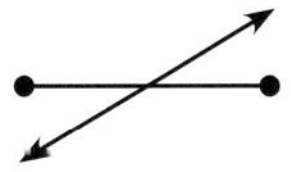
Intersecting

2. 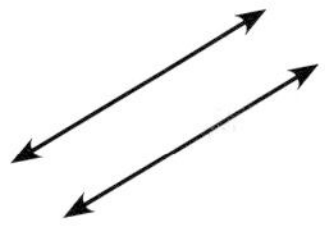
Parallel

3. 
Perpendicular

4. 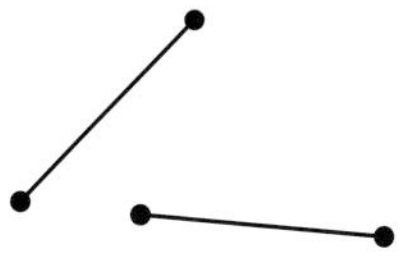
Non-intersecting

Available on Daily Transparency 8-1

8-2 Lesson Organizer

Objective

- Name and describe angles.

Vocabulary

- Angle, side, vertex, acute angle, right angle, obtuse angle, straight angle

Materials

- Explore: Index cards

NCTM Standards

- 1–4, 7, 12, 13

Review

Draw an example of each.

1. $\overleftrightarrow{XY}$
2. $\overleftrightarrow{PQ}$
3. $\overrightarrow{RT}$

Check students' drawings.

Available on Daily Transparency 8-2

1 Introduce

Explore

The Point
Students use an index card to determine if angles are less than, greater than, or equal to a right angle.

Ongoing Assessment
Watch for students who do not know how to place the corner of the index card in the right location to determine the answers.

For Groups That Finish Early
Name at least two pairs of angles in the figure that have a shared side. Possible answers: ∠1 and ∠3, ∠4 and ∠6, ∠7 and ∠8, ∠9 and ∠10

8-2 Classifying Angles

You'll Learn ...

- to name and describe angles

... How It's Used

Campers must understand angle descriptions when assembling tents.

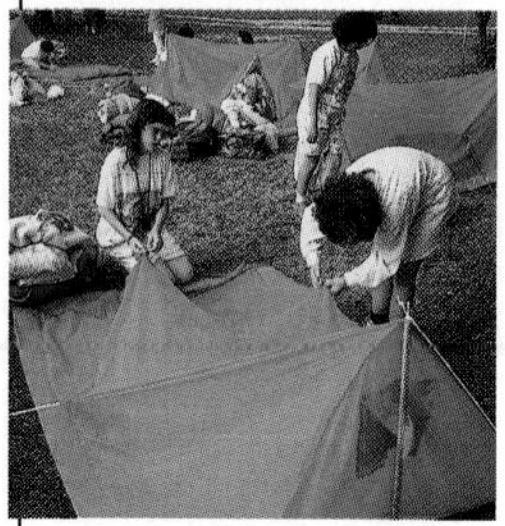

Vocabulary

angle
side
vertex
acute angle
right angle
obtuse angle
straight angle

▶ Lesson Link In the last lesson, you learned that lines, rays, and segments are basic elements in geometry. Now you'll learn about a simple figure made up of these parts—the angle. ◀

Explore Angles

Materials: Index cards

Sailing at an Angle

The sailboat is the symbol of Origami USA, the largest U.S. organization for origami enthusiasts.

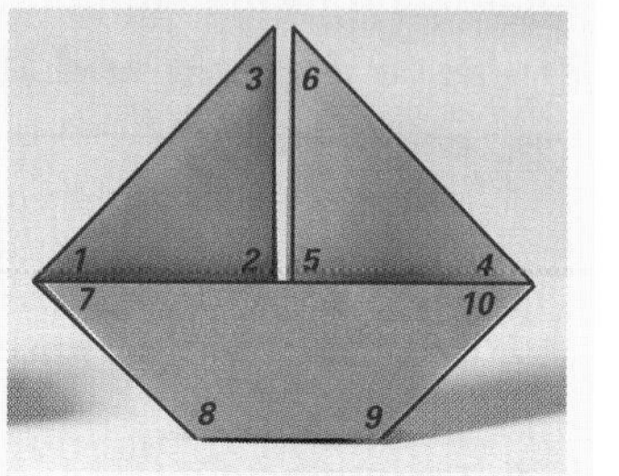

1. The edges of an index card meet to form a right angle. Use an index card to determine if each corner is less than a right angle, about equal to a right angle, or greater than a right angle.
2. Several pairs of angles in the drawing can be put together to form a single angle about equal to a right angle. Find two pairs of angles like this. Explain how you can tell that they form a right angle.
3. Without an index card, how can you decide whether an angle is about equal to, greater than, or smaller than a right angle?

Learn Classifying Angles

An **angle** is formed by two rays with the same endpoint. The rays are the **sides** of the angle. The common endpoint is the **vertex**.

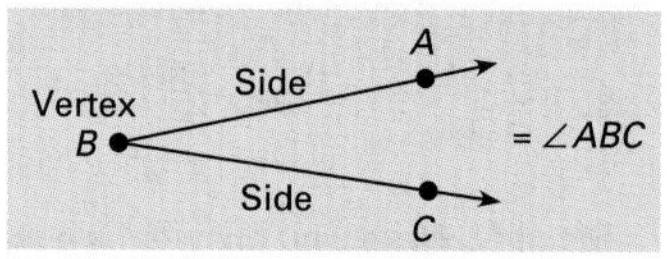

You can name an angle using a point on each side and the vertex. The angle shown can be called ∠*ABC*, read angle *ABC*, or ∠*CBA*. The vertex must appear as the middle letter.

When it is not confusing, you can name an angle using the vertex alone. The angle shown can also be called ∠*B*.

MEETING INDIVIDUAL NEEDS

Resources

8-2 Practice
8-2 Reteaching
8-2 Problem Solving
8-2 Enrichment
8-2 Daily Transparency
- Problem of the Day
- Review
- Quick Quiz

Teaching Tool Transparencies 2, 3

Learning Modalities

Visual Have students use magazines and newspapers to find pictures that illustrate acute, obtuse, right, and straight angles.

Verbal Have students work in groups and write fill-in-the-blank sentences using the vocabulary introduced in this lesson. Allow each student to read his or her sentence aloud, and have the other members fill in the missing words.

Inclusion

For students who are visually impaired, use cut-out models of the different kinds of angles. Allow students to examine the models closely. Be sure to include several different types of acute and obtuse angles to help them realize that the sizes of the angles vary.

Have students add new vocabulary with examples to their reference book.

Angles can be classified by their size.

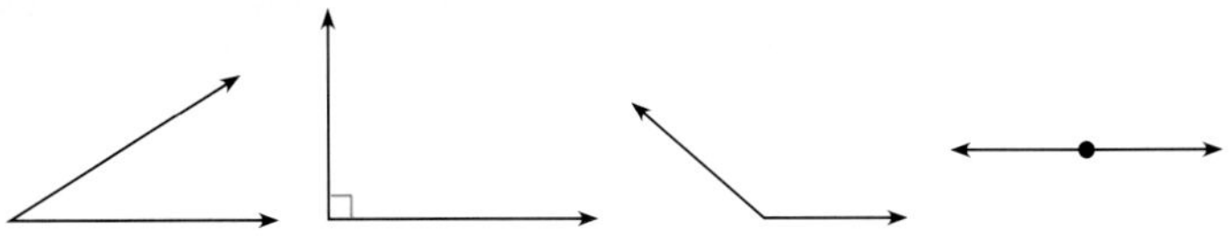

An **acute angle** is smaller than a right angle.

A **right angle** is like the corner of an index card.

An **obtuse angle** is greater than a right angle but smaller than a straight angle.

A **straight angle** is a line.

> **▶ Language Link**
>
> Some words have a nonmathematical meaning that is similar to their mathematical meaning. The word *acute* can also mean "having a sharp point." The word *obtuse* can also mean "blunt, not sharp."

Example 1

Classify each angle as acute, right, obtuse, or straight.

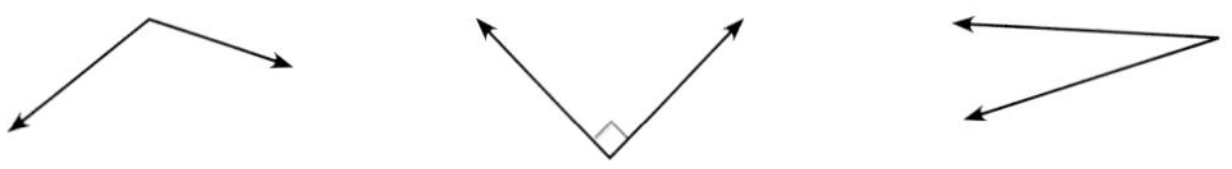

The angle is obtuse. The angle is a right angle. The angle is acute

Try It

Classify each angle as acute, right, obtuse, or straight.

a.

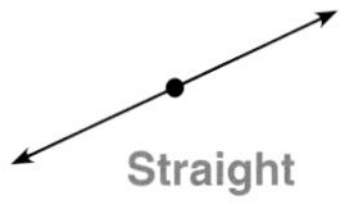

Straight

b.

Right

c.

Obtuse

d.

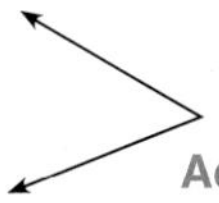

Acute

Check Your Understanding

1. Find an example of each type of angle in your classroom.

2. Why do mathematicians sometimes use three letters to name an angle instead of just using the vertex?

Answers for Explore

1. Angles 1, 3, 4, 6, 7, and 10 are less than a right angle; Angles 2 and 5 are right angles; Angles 8 and 9 are greater than a right angle.
2. Possible answer: Any combination of angles 1, 3, 6, and 4; They each take up about half of the corner of the index card, so together they would form a right angle.
3. Possible answer: Estimate by looking; A right angle is formed by perpendicular lines.

2 Teach

Learn

Point out that when an angle is named, any point on each side of an angle can be used in naming the angle, but only one point can be named as the vertex.

Alternate Examples

1. Classify each angle as acute, right, obtuse, or straight.

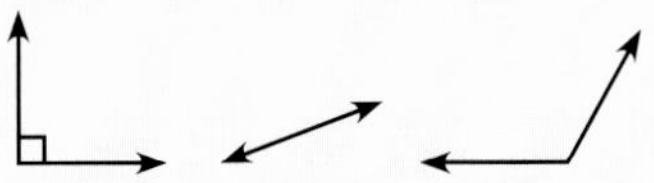

The first angle is right, the second is straight, and the third is obtuse.

3 Practice and Assess

Check

For Question 2, it might be helpful to show a diagram illustrating a case where one letter is enough and another where three letters are needed.

Answers for Check Your Understanding

1. Possible answers: Right angle: Corner of the room; Acute angle: Tip of a pencil; Obtuse angle: Edges of pages of an open book; Straight angle: Lines on the floor.
2. The vertex might be a vertex to several angles. Three letters are used to clarify which angle is being named.

MATH EVERY DAY

▶ Problem of the Day

Each of the books has 100 pages. A bookworm eats from page 1 of Volume I through page 100 of Volume III. How many pages and how many covers did he eat through?

4 covers plus 102 pages. [Page 1 is on the right-hand side of Volume I and page 100 is on the left-hand side of volume III.]

Available on Daily Transparency 8-2

An Extension is provided in the transparency package.

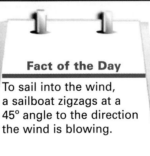

Fact of the Day

To sail into the wind, a sailboat zigzags at a 45° angle to the direction the wind is blowing.

Estimation

Estimate each sum.

1. 8.9 + 9.9 19
2. 1.14 + 6.89 8
3. 0.81 + 0.73 1.5
4. 0.58 + 0.97 1.6

8-2 Exercises and Applications

Assignment Guide

- Basic
  1–25, 28–29, 34–50 evens
- Average
  3–29, 31–51 odds
- Enriched
  5–32, 34–54 evens

Exercise Notes

Exercises 17–19

Error Prevention If students have difficulty with these statements, suggest that they draw a diagram to help them answer each question.

Exercise 28

Test Prep If students selected D, they probably thought that a right angle would always have one side horizontal and the other vertical. Remind them that the angles can be in any position.

Reteaching

Activity

Materials: Watch or clock with movable hands

- Work with a partner.
- List at least two times for which the hands form an acute angle, a right angle, an obtuse angle, and a straight angle. Answers may vary.
- Be sure to use times other than those listed in Exercises 20–25.

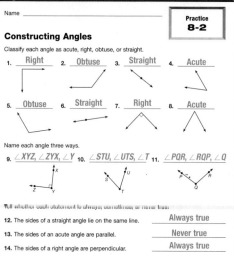

8-2 Exercises and Applications

Practice and Apply

Getting Started State the vertex of each angle.

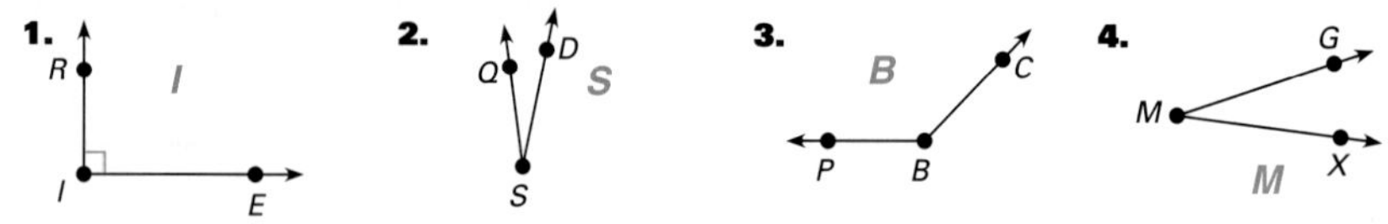

Classify each angle as acute, right, obtuse, or straight.

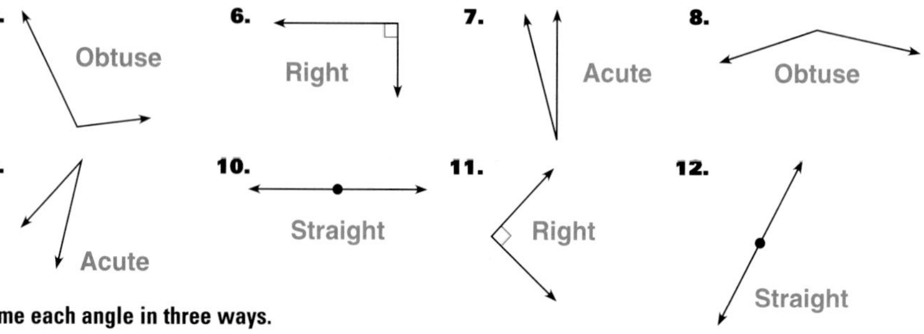

Name each angle in three ways.

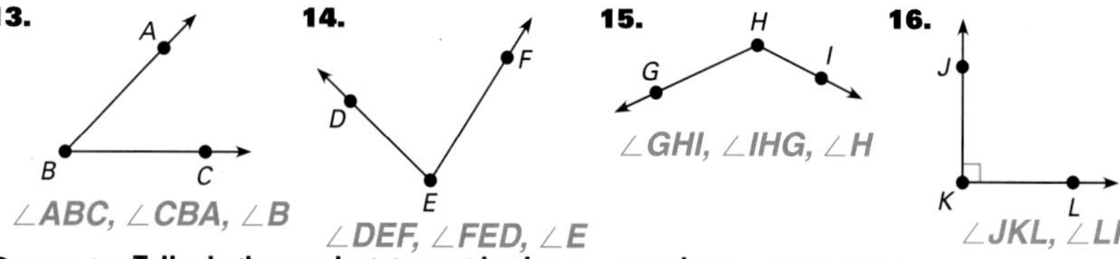

Geometry Tell whether each statement is always, sometimes, or never true.

GPS **17.** Two acute angles of the same size form a right angle. Sometimes

18. A right angle and an acute angle form an obtuse angle. Always

19. An angle consists of two endpoints, a vertex, and a ray. Never

Measurement Classify the angle made by the hands of a clock at each time.

20. 3:00 Right **21.** 7:15 Obtuse **22.** 2:45 Obtuse **23.** 6:00 Straight **24.** 1:00 Acute **25.** 10:00 Acute

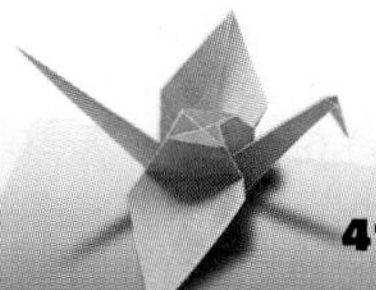

PRACTICE

Name ______ **Practice 8-2**

Constructing Angles

Classify each angle as acute, right, obtuse, or straight.

1. Right 2. Obtuse 3. Straight 4. Acute

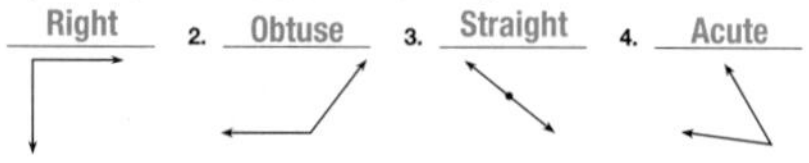

5. Obtuse 6. Straight 7. Right 8. Acute

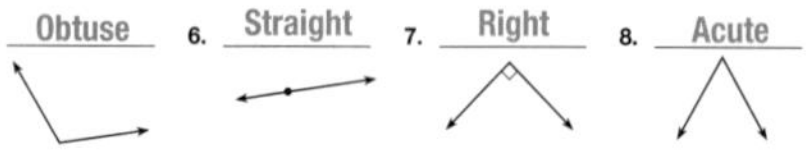

Name each angle three ways.

9. ∠XYZ, ∠ZYX, ∠Y 10. ∠STU, ∠UTS, ∠T 11. ∠PQR, ∠RQP, ∠Q

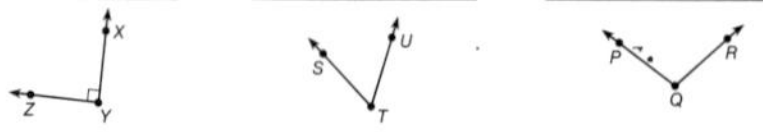

Tell whether each statement is always, sometimes, or never true.

12. The sides of a straight angle lie on the same line. Always true
13. The sides of an acute angle are parallel. Never true
14. The sides of a right angle are perpendicular. Always true

Measurement Classify the angle made by the hands of a clock at each time.

15. 2:00 Acute 16. 5:00 Obtuse 17. 7:45 Acute
18. 9:00 Right 19. 10:15 Obtuse 20. 4:40 Obtuse

21. Use the figure at the right. Name two angles of each type. Possible answers:

Acute: ∠CAD, ∠EAF Right: ∠BAD, ∠DAE
Obtuse: ∠CAE, ∠DAF Straight: ∠BAE, ∠CAF

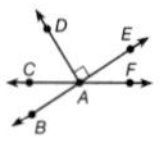

RETEACHING

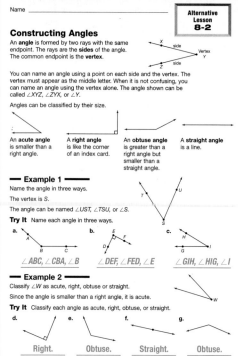

Name ______ **Alternative Lesson 8-2**

Constructing Angles

An **angle** is formed by two rays with the same endpoint. The rays are the **sides** of the angle. The common endpoint is the **vertex**.

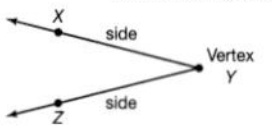

You can name an angle using a point on each side and the vertex. The vertex must appear as the middle letter. When it is not confusing, you can name an angle using the vertex alone. The angle shown can be called ∠XYZ, ∠ZYX, or ∠Y.

Angles can be classified by their size.

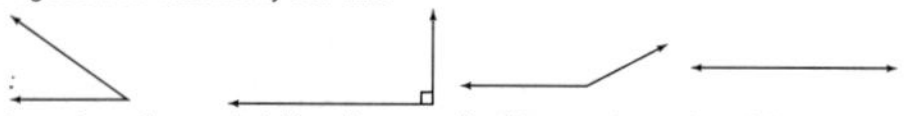

An **acute angle** is smaller than a right angle. A **right angle** is like the corner of an index card. An **obtuse angle** is greater than a right angle but smaller than a straight angle. A **straight angle** is a line.

Example 1

Name the angle in three ways.

The vertex is *S*.

The angle can be named ∠UST, ∠TSU, or ∠S.

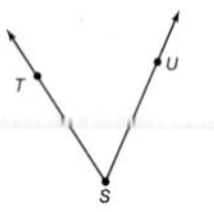

Try It Name each angle in three ways.

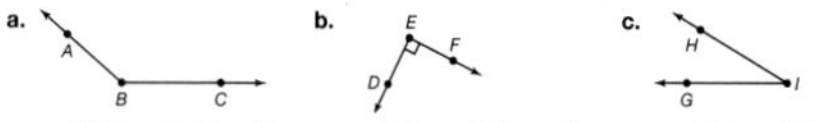

a. ∠ABC, ∠CBA, ∠B b. ∠DEF, ∠FED, ∠E c. ∠GIH, ∠HIG, ∠I

Example 2

Classify ∠W as acute, right, obtuse, or straight.

Since the angle is smaller than a right angle, it is acute.

Try It Classify each angle as acute, right, obtuse, or straight.

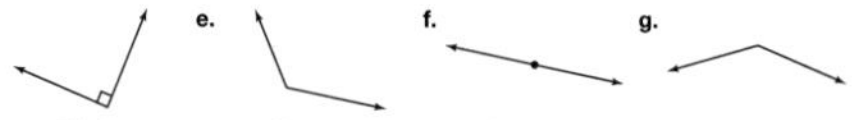

d. Right. e. Obtuse. f. Straight. g. Obtuse.

Fine Arts Use the unfolded pattern of the inside reverse fold for Exercises 26 and 27.

26. Name five angles and classify each as acute, right, or obtuse.

27. Name and classify two angles which make up a straight angle.

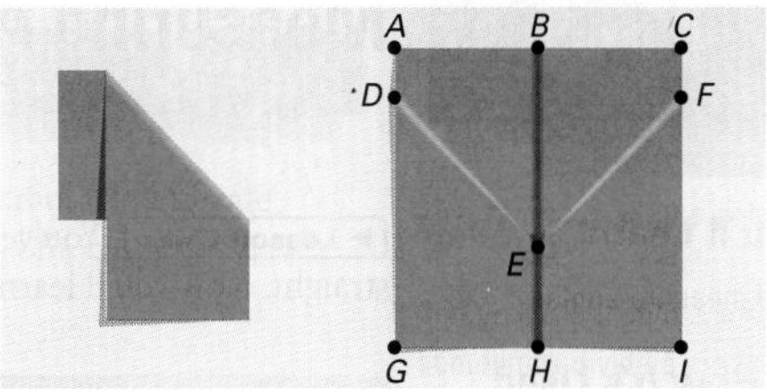

28. **Test Prep** Choose the acute angle. **A**

Ⓐ Ⓑ Ⓒ Ⓓ

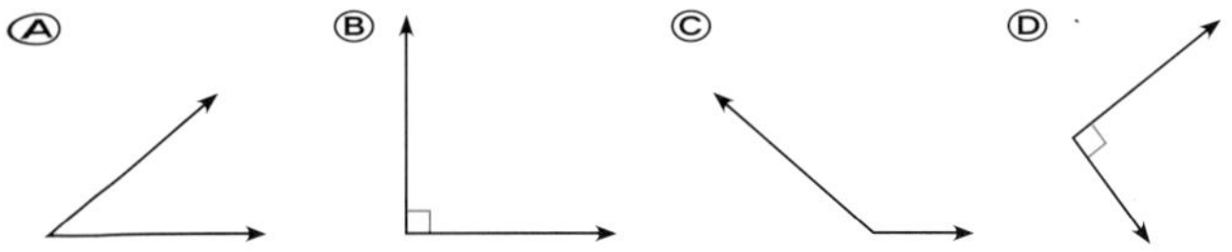

Problem Solving and Reasoning

29. **Choose a Strategy** What is the smallest number of sides needed to draw a polygon with exactly 5 right angles? Explain.

30. **Journal** What kind of angles are made between two perpendicular lines? Two parallel lines? Explain.

31. **Communicate** Two angles placed together make a straight line. If one is an obtuse angle, what is the other? Explain.

32. **Critical Thinking** Draw two rays that don't make an angle. Explain your drawing.

Problem Solving STRATEGIES
- Look for a Pattern
- Make an Organized List
- Make a Table
- Guess and Check
- Work Backward
- Use Logical Reasoning
- Draw a Diagram
- Solve a Simpler Problem

PROBLEM SOLVING 8-2

Mixed Review

Write each mixed number as an improper fraction. *[Lesson 5-6]*

33. $6\frac{3}{5}$ $\frac{33}{5}$ **34.** $12\frac{2}{3}$ $\frac{38}{3}$ **35.** $3\frac{1}{2}$ $\frac{7}{2}$ **36.** $2\frac{4}{5}$ $\frac{14}{5}$ **37.** $10\frac{9}{11}$ $\frac{119}{11}$ **38.** $4\frac{1}{4}$ $\frac{17}{4}$

39. $9\frac{3}{4}$ $\frac{39}{4}$ **40.** $5\frac{2}{5}$ $\frac{27}{5}$ **41.** $2\frac{1}{6}$ $\frac{13}{6}$ **42.** $6\frac{2}{3}$ $\frac{20}{3}$ **43.** $3\frac{6}{7}$ $\frac{27}{7}$ **44.** $7\frac{3}{5}$ $\frac{38}{5}$

Simplify. *[Lesson 6-2]*

45. $\frac{7}{9}+\frac{3}{4}$ $1\frac{19}{36}$ **46.** $\frac{6}{12}-\frac{2}{6}$ $\frac{1}{6}$ **47.** $\frac{2}{3}+\frac{6}{9}$ $1\frac{1}{3}$ **48.** $\frac{3}{4}-\frac{5}{8}$ $\frac{1}{8}$ **49.** $\frac{1}{2}-\frac{1}{8}$ $\frac{3}{8}$

50. $\frac{12}{18}+\frac{5}{9}$ $1\frac{2}{9}$ **51.** $\frac{9}{10}-\frac{2}{5}$ $\frac{1}{2}$ **52.** $\frac{2}{3}+\frac{3}{8}$ $1\frac{1}{24}$ **53.** $\frac{6}{11}+\frac{6}{22}$ $\frac{9}{11}$ **54.** $\frac{4}{5}-\frac{3}{4}$ $\frac{1}{20}$

Exercise Notes

■ Exercise 29

Problem-Solving Tip You may wish to use Teaching Tool Transparencies 2 and 3: Guided Problem Solving, pages 1–2.

Exercise Answers

26. Possible answer: ∠BCF, ∠BAD right; ∠FEB, acute; ∠FEH, ∠ADE obtuse.

27. Possible answer: ∠BED, acute and ∠DEH, obtuse.

29. 6;

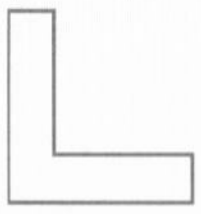

30. Perpendicular angles make right angles by definition; Parallel lines don't cross, so they don't make angles.

31. Acute; An obtuse angle is between 90° and 180°, so to get a straight angle of 180°, you have to add an angle between 0° and 90°, which is an acute angle.

32.

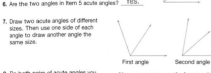

The rays do not share a common point because they start at different places and point away from each other.

Alternate Assessment

Portfolio Have students draw a diagram to illustrate each of the vocabulary words in this lesson. Have them add these drawings to their portfolio.

PROBLEM SOLVING

Name ____________________ **Guided Problem Solving 8-2**

GPS PROBLEM 17, STUDENT PAGE 414

Tell whether this statement is always, sometimes, or never true.

Two acute angles of the same size form a right angle.

— Understand — Possible answers: Items 7, 8, and 10

1. What part of an index card forms a right angle? The corner.
2. Is an acute angle smaller or greater than a right angle? Smaller.
3. How many acute angles are you asked to find? Two.
4. Are the acute angles the same or different sizes? Same size.

— Plan —

5. Draw a right angle. Then draw a line to divide the right triangle into two angles of the same size.

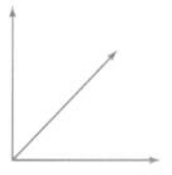

6. Are the two angles in Item 5 acute angles? Yes.
7. Draw two acute angles of different sizes. Then use one side of each angle to draw another angle the same size.

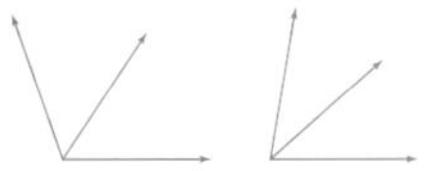

8. Do both pairs of acute angles you drew in Item 7 form right angles? Explain. No, one new angle is greater than a right angle and the other is smaller.

— Solve —

9. Use your answers to Items 6 and 8 to tell whether the statement is always, sometimes, or never true. Sometimes.

— Look Back —

10. What other strategy could you use to find the answer? Use Logical Reasoning.

SOLVE ANOTHER PROBLEM

Is the statement always, sometimes, or never true: "Three acute angles of the same size form a straight angle." Sometimes.

ENRICHMENT

Name ____________________ **Extend Your Thinking 8-2**

Visual Thinking

For each row, circle the letter of the fraction that is shown by the shading in the figure on the left.

1. 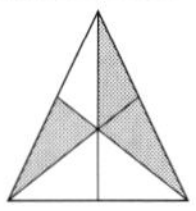 a. $\frac{2}{3}$ (b.) $\frac{1}{2}$ c. $\frac{6}{7}$ d. $\frac{1}{4}$

2. 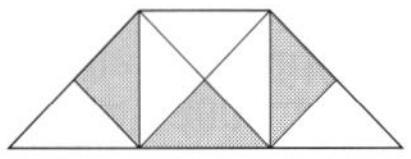 a. $\frac{1}{5}$ b. $\frac{2}{4}$ c. $\frac{1}{2}$ (d.) $\frac{3}{8}$

3. 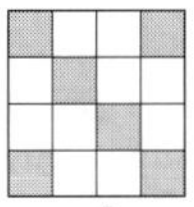 (a.) $\frac{3}{8}$ b. $\frac{3}{12}$ c. $\frac{3}{4}$ d. $\frac{7}{12}$

4. 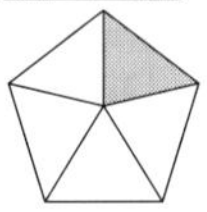 a. $\frac{3}{5}$ b. $\frac{2}{3}$ (c.) $\frac{1}{5}$ d. $\frac{1}{3}$

5. 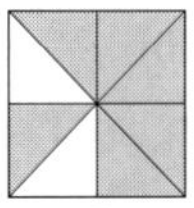 a. $\frac{1}{4}$ (b.) $\frac{3}{4}$ c. $\frac{1}{3}$ d. $\frac{3}{8}$

6. 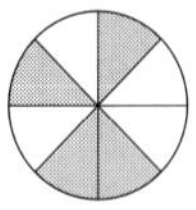 (a.) $\frac{1}{2}$ b. $\frac{5}{8}$ c. $\frac{1}{4}$ d. $\frac{4}{9}$

▶ Quick Quiz

Classify each angle as acute, right, obtuse, or straight.

1. 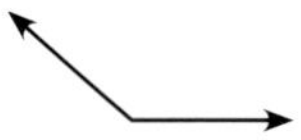

Obtuse

2. 

Straight

3. 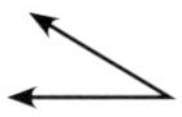

Acute

4. 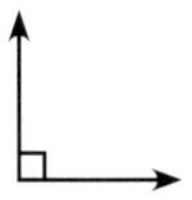

Right

Available on Daily Transparency 8-2

WHAT DO YOU THINK?

Students see two methods of measuring an angle. One method involves placing the protractor so that its bottom edge falls along one side of the angle. The other method involves placing the bottom edge of the protractor parallel to the edge of the photo. Students can decide which of the two correct methods is easier for them.

Answers for What Do You Think?

1. She knew it was an acute angle, so the measurement had to be between 0° and 90°.
2. An angle measure is the difference between whatever angle measures the two sides of an angle pass through on a protractor. If Zack had lined up the protractor on one of the sides, he would have found the difference between 15° and 0°. As long as Zack places the vertex of the angle at the middle of the protractor, he can use any measurements the lines pass through.

3 Practice and Assess

Check

Answers for Check Your Understanding

1. An acute angle is between 0° and 90°. A right angle is exactly 90°. An obtuse angle is between 90° and 180°.
2. Angles

WHAT DO YOU THINK?

The smaller the angle between a ski jumper's body and the skis, the farther the skier will travel. Sonia and Zack help coach the ski team. They photographed the team's best jumper. Now they want to measure the angle between her body and the skis.

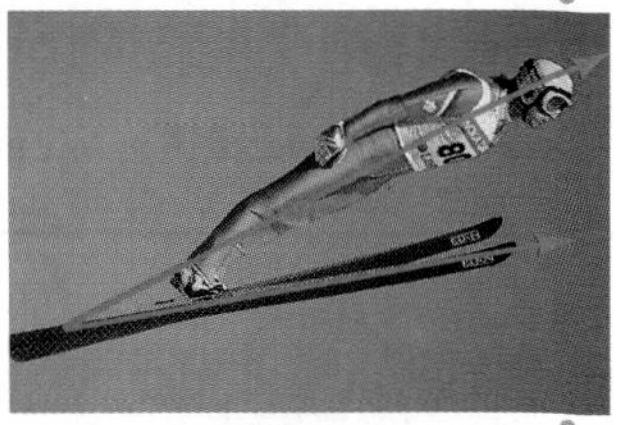

Sonia thinks ...

I'll place the bottom edge of the protractor on the ray on the ski. The other ray crosses the protractor at 15°, so the angle measures 15°.

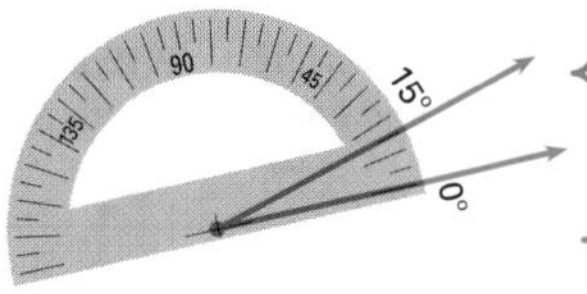

Zack thinks ...

I'll place the center of the protractor on the vertex of the angle. The two rays cross at 20° and 35°. 35° − 20° = 15°. The angle measures 15°.

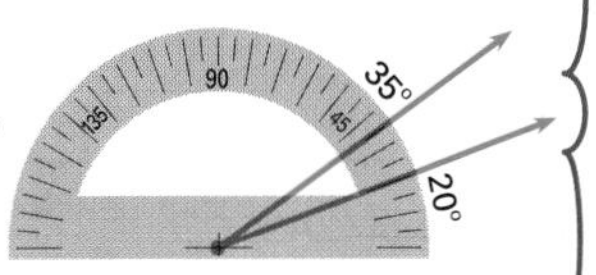

What do you think?

1. The protractor is labeled with pairs of measurements. How did Sonia know that the 20° measure was the correct measure to use?
2. Explain Zack's reasoning. Could he place the protractor in other ways and still find the measure of the angle?

MEETING MIDDLE SCHOOL CLASSROOM NEEDS

Tips from Middle School Teachers

I like to use an overhead projector for teaching students how to measure with a protractor. Students can actually see the procedure being performed step by step. I involve students as much as possible in all the steps.

Team Teaching

Work with a drafting teacher or art teacher and discuss how measurement of angles is important for drawing many diagrams of real-world objects.

Sports Connection

Skiing first began as a way to travel more than 5000 years ago. Skiers first served in battle in 1200 A.D. People began enjoying skiing as a sport in the early 1800s. Men and women's downhill, slalom, and giant slalom skiing are now major sports during the winter Olympics.

Fine Arts Use the unfolded pattern of the inside reverse fold for Exercises 26 and 27.

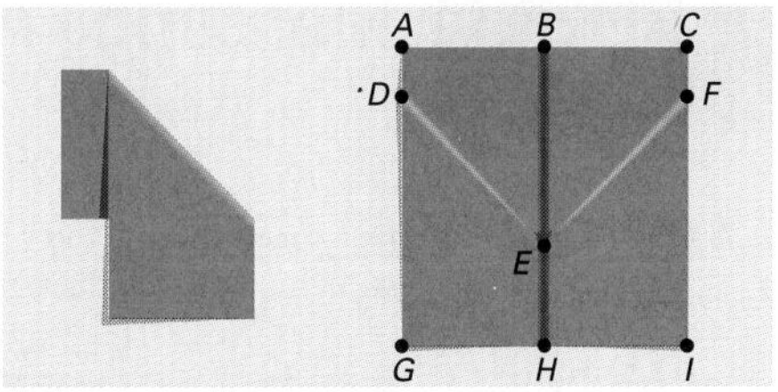

26. Name five angles and classify each as acute, right, or obtuse.

27. Name and classify two angles which make up a straight angle.

28. **Test Prep** Choose the acute angle. A

Ⓐ Ⓑ Ⓒ Ⓓ

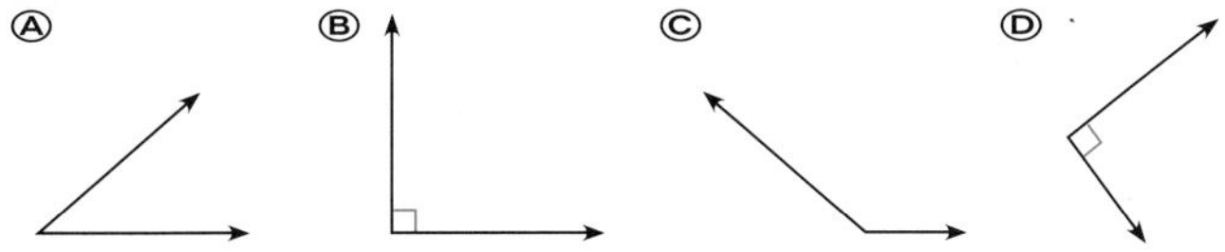

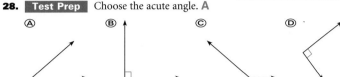

Problem Solving and Reasoning

29. Choose a Strategy What is the smallest number of sides needed to draw a polygon with exactly 5 right angles? Explain.

30. Journal What kind of angles are made between two perpendicular lines? Two parallel lines? Explain.

31. Communicate Two angles placed together make a straight line. If one is an obtuse angle, what is the other? Explain.

32. Critical Thinking Draw two rays that don't make an angle. Explain your drawing.

Problem Solving STRATEGIES

- Look for a Pattern
- Make an Organized List
- Make a Table
- Guess and Check
- Work Backward
- Use Logical Reasoning
- Draw a Diagram
- Solve a Simpler Problem

Mixed Review

Write each mixed number as an improper fraction. *[Lesson 5-6]*

33. $6\frac{3}{5}$ $\frac{33}{5}$ **34.** $12\frac{2}{3}$ $\frac{38}{3}$ **35.** $3\frac{1}{2}$ $\frac{7}{2}$ **36.** $2\frac{4}{5}$ $\frac{14}{5}$ **37.** $10\frac{9}{11}$ $\frac{119}{11}$ **38.** $4\frac{1}{4}$ $\frac{17}{4}$

39. $9\frac{3}{4}$ $\frac{39}{4}$ **40.** $5\frac{2}{5}$ $\frac{27}{5}$ **41.** $2\frac{1}{6}$ $\frac{13}{6}$ **42.** $6\frac{2}{3}$ $\frac{20}{3}$ **43.** $3\frac{6}{7}$ $\frac{27}{7}$ **44.** $7\frac{3}{5}$ $\frac{38}{5}$

Simplify. *[Lesson 6-2]*

45. $\frac{7}{9} + \frac{3}{4}$ $1\frac{19}{36}$ **46.** $\frac{6}{12} - \frac{2}{6}$ $\frac{1}{6}$ **47.** $\frac{2}{3} + \frac{6}{9}$ $1\frac{1}{3}$ **48.** $\frac{3}{4} - \frac{5}{8}$ $\frac{1}{8}$ **49.** $\frac{1}{2} - \frac{1}{8}$ $\frac{3}{8}$

50. $\frac{12}{18} + \frac{5}{9}$ $1\frac{2}{9}$ **51.** $\frac{9}{10} - \frac{2}{5}$ $\frac{1}{2}$ **52.** $\frac{2}{3} + \frac{3}{8}$ $1\frac{1}{24}$ **53.** $\frac{6}{11} + \frac{6}{22}$ $\frac{9}{11}$ **54.** $\frac{4}{5} - \frac{3}{4}$ $\frac{1}{20}$

PROBLEM SOLVING 8-2

PROBLEM SOLVING

Name ____________________

Guided Problem Solving 8-2

GPS PROBLEM 17, STUDENT PAGE 414

Tell whether this statement is always, sometimes, or never true.

Two acute angles of the same size form a right angle.

— Understand — Possible answers: Items 7, 8, and 10

1. What part of an index card forms a right angle? The corner.
2. Is an acute angle smaller or greater than a right angle? Smaller.
3. How many acute angles are you asked to find? Two.
4. Are the acute angles the same or different sizes? Same size.

— Plan —

5. Draw a right angle. Then draw a line to divide the right triangle into two angles of the same size.

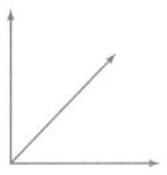

6. Are the two angles in Item 5 acute angles? Yes.
7. Draw two acute angles of different sizes. Then use one side of each angle to draw another angle the same size.

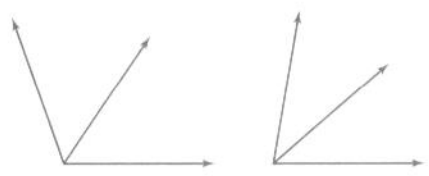

8. Do both pairs of acute angles you drew in Item 7 form right angles? Explain. No, one new angle is greater than a right angle and the other is smaller.

— Solve —

9. Use your answers to Items 6 and 8 to tell whether the statement is always, sometimes, or never true. Sometimes.

— Look Back —

10. What other strategy could you use to find the answer? Use Logical Reasoning.

SOLVE ANOTHER PROBLEM

Is the statement always, sometimes, or never true: "Three acute angles of the same size form a straight angle." Sometimes.

ENRICHMENT

Name ____________________

Extend Your Thinking 8-2

Visual Thinking

For each row, circle the letter of the fraction that is shown by the shading in the figure on the left.

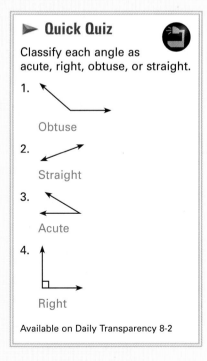

1. 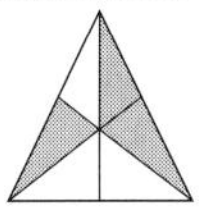 a. $\frac{2}{3}$ (b.) $\frac{1}{2}$ c. $\frac{6}{7}$ d. $\frac{1}{4}$
2. 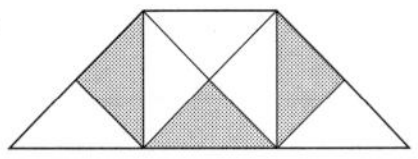 a. $\frac{1}{5}$ b. $\frac{2}{4}$ c. $\frac{1}{2}$ (d.) $\frac{3}{8}$
3. 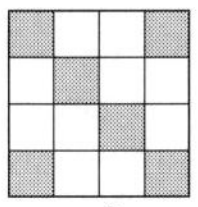 (a.) $\frac{3}{8}$ b. $\frac{3}{12}$ c. $\frac{3}{4}$ d. $\frac{7}{12}$
4. 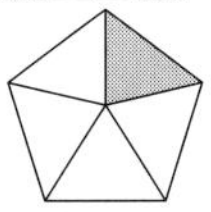 a. $\frac{3}{5}$ b. $\frac{2}{3}$ (c.) $\frac{1}{5}$ d. $\frac{1}{3}$
5. 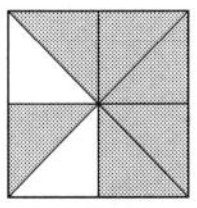 a. $\frac{1}{4}$ (b.) $\frac{3}{4}$ c. $\frac{1}{3}$ d. $\frac{3}{8}$
6. 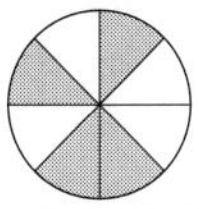 (a.) $\frac{1}{2}$ b. $\frac{5}{8}$ c. $\frac{1}{4}$ d. $\frac{4}{9}$

Exercise Notes

■ Exercise 29

Problem-Solving Tip You may wish to use Teaching Tool Transparencies 2 and 3: Guided Problem Solving, pages 1–2.

Exercise Answers

26. Possible answer: ∠*BCF*, ∠*BAD* right; ∠*FEB*, acute; ∠*FEH*, ∠*ADE* obtuse.

27. Possible answer: ∠*BED*, acute and ∠*DEH*, obtuse.

29. 6;

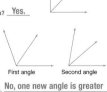

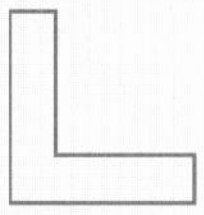

30. Perpendicular angles make right angles by definition; Parallel lines don't cross, so they don't make angles.

31. Acute; An obtuse angle is between 90° and 180°, so to get a straight angle of 180°, you have to add an angle between 0° and 90°, which is an acute angle.

32.

The rays do not share a common point because they start at different places and point away from each other.

Alternate Assessment

Portfolio Have students draw a diagram to illustrate each of the vocabulary words in this lesson. Have them add these drawings to their portfolio.

▶ Quick Quiz

Classify each angle as acute, right, obtuse, or straight.

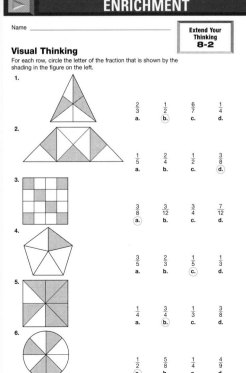

1. 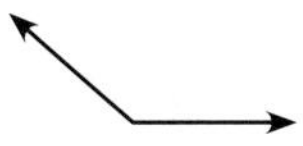 Obtuse
2.  Straight
3. 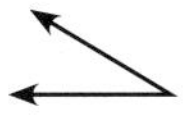 Acute
4. 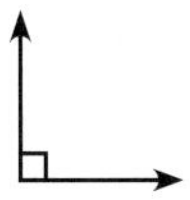 Right

Available on Daily Transparency 8-2

8-3 Lesson Organizer

Objective

- Measure angles.

Vocabulary

- Degree, complementary angles, supplementary angles, protractor

Materials

- Explore: Scissors

NCTM Standards

- 1–4, 7, 12, 13

Review

Classify each angle as acute, right, obtuse, or straight.

1. 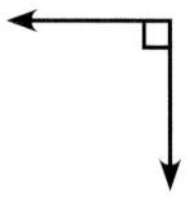

Right

2. 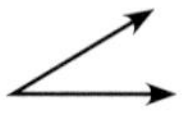

Acute

3. 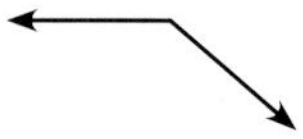

Obtuse

4. 

Straight

Available on Daily Transparency 8-3

1 Introduce

Explore

You may wish to use Lesson Enhancement Transparency 37 with **Explore**.

The Point
Students use a model of an angle to measure angles and then classify the angles as acute, right, or obtuse.

Ongoing Assessment
Watch for students who have trouble measuring angles **d** and **f** because they involve a fraction of the given "slice."

8-3 Measuring Angles

You'll Learn ...

- to measure angles

... How It's Used

Surveyors measure angles when determining the height of an object that is too large to measure with a meter stick.

Vocabulary

degree

complementary angles

supplementary angles

protractor

▶ Lesson Link You've learned to classify angles as acute, right, obtuse, or straight. Now you'll learn to measure the sizes of angles using a protractor. ◀

Explore Measuring Angles

I'd Like a Glass of Milk and a Right Angle

Materials: Scissors

1. Trace and cut out a copy of the "slice." Then determine the number of "slices" that fit into each angle.

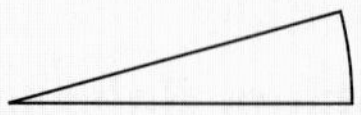

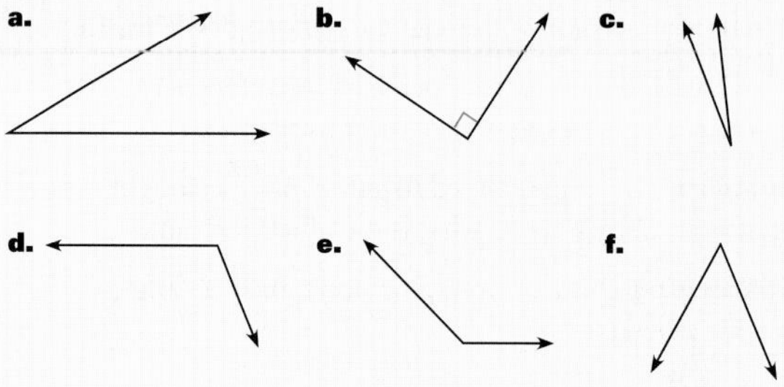

2. Rank the angles in order from fewest slices to most slices.
3. Classify each angle as acute, right, or obtuse.
4. What is the greatest number of pie slices an acute angle can have? What is the greatest number a right angle can have? What is the greatest number an obtuse angle can have?
5. If the sides of an angle are longer, then you can fit more slices into the angle. Do you agree or disagree? Explain.
6. In Step 1, if everyone in the classroom used a different-sized slice, would everyone get different answers? Explain.

MEETING INDIVIDUAL NEEDS

Resources

- **8-3** Practice
- **8-3** Reteaching
- **8-3** Problem Solving
- **8-3** Enrichment
- **8-3** Daily Transparency
  - Problem of the Day
  - Review
  - Quick Quiz
- Teaching Tool Transparencies 6, 17
- Lesson Enhancement Transparency 37
- Technology Master 37
- Chapter 8 Project Master

Learning Modalities

Verbal Have students describe how measuring with a protractor is different from measuring with a ruler.

Kinesthetic Have students make a model of an angle by connecting two strips of cardboard with a brass fastener. Then have them position the sides of the angle in different positions to illustrate various sizes of angles.

English Language Development

Some students will confuse angle degrees with temperature degrees. Point out that the two are unrelated and the context will make it clear which is being discussed.

Learn Measuring Angles

Angles are measured in units called **degrees**. Use the symbol ° to indicate degrees. A complete circle measures 360°. A 1° angle is $\frac{1}{360}$ of a circle.

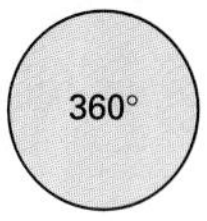

An acute angle measures more than 0° and less than 90°.

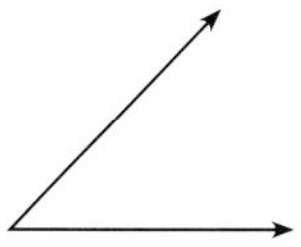

A right angle measures exactly 90°.

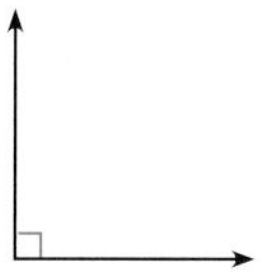

An obtuse angle measures more than 90° and less than 180°.

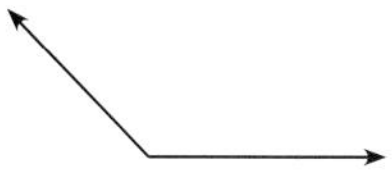

Two angles are **complementary angles** if the sum of their measures equals 90°. Two angles are **supplementary angles** if the sum of their measures equals 180°.

A **protractor** is a tool that measures angles.

Example 1

What is the measure of ∠*ABC*?

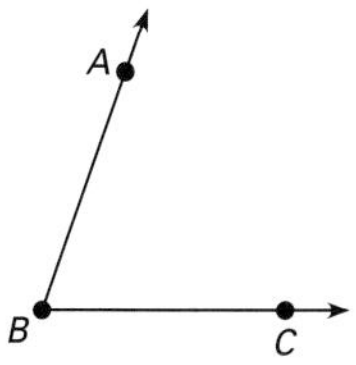

Place the protractor so that the middle of its bottom edge is over the vertex, and one side of the bottom edge is over one side of the angle. Read the pair of numbers where the other side of the angle passes underneath the protractor. If the angle is an acute angle, use the smaller number in the pair. If the angle is obtuse, use the larger number.

∠*ABC* is 70°.

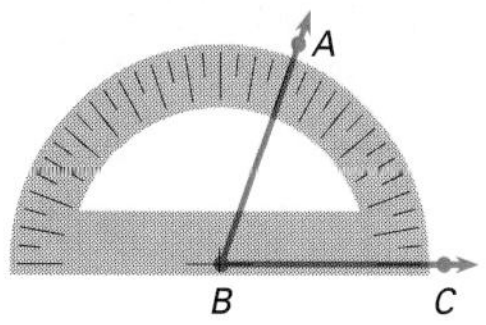

Place hole over vertex.

Place protractor line over side of angle.

DID YOU KNOW?

The *degree* is not the only measure of an angle's opening. Mathematicians sometimes divide a circle into *radians.* A radian measures a little more than 57°. There are a little more than 6 radians in a complete circle.

For Groups That Finish Early

Use a different sized slice than the one shown in Step 1. Measure angles **a–f.** Answers may vary.

Answers for Explore

1. a. 2; b. 6; c. 1; d. $7\frac{1}{2}$; e. 9; f. $3\frac{1}{2}$.
2. c, a, f, b, d, e.
3. a. Acute; b. Right; c. Acute; d. Obtuse; e. Obtuse; f. Acute.
4. Acute: 5; Right: 6; Obtuse: 11.
5. Disagree; The size of an angle does not change if the sides get longer or shorter.
6. Yes; If the size of the slice was larger, fewer slices would fit into an angle. If a slice was really small, then the number of slices that would fit into each angle would be large.

2 Teach

Learn

You may wish to use Teaching Tool Transparencies 6: Cuisenaire Angle Ruler and 17: Protractor with this lesson.

Alternate Examples

1. What is the measure of ∠*DEF*?

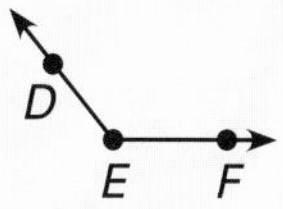

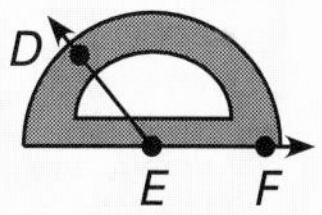

Place the protractor so that the middle of the protractor bottom is over the vertex, and one side of the protractor is over one side of the angle.

Read the pair of numbers where the other side of the angle passes underneath the protractor. If the angle is an acute angle, use the smaller number in the pair. If the angle is obtuse, use the larger number.

∠*DEF* measures 130°.

MATH EVERY DAY

Problem of the Day

I am thinking of a three-digit number. The number is divisible by 5 and 9. One of the digits is 8. The number is greater than 250 and less than 750. What number am I thinking of? Possible answer: 585

Available on Daily Transparency 8-3

An Extension is provided in the transparency package.

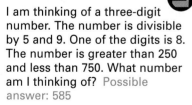

Fact of the Day

Sundials were first developed about 4000 years ago. However, clocks had no dials or hands until the mid-1300s.

Mental Math

Find each sum mentally.

1. 9 + 1 + 7 + 3 + 8 + 2 30
2. 17 + 3 + 16 + 4 40
3. 47 + 13 + 24 + 26 110
4. 87 + 13 + 75 + 25 + 150 + 50 400

WHAT DO YOU THINK?

Students see two methods of measuring an angle. One method involves placing the protractor so that its bottom edge falls along one side of the angle. The other method involves placing the bottom edge of the protractor parallel to the edge of the photo. Students can decide which of the two correct methods is easier for them.

Answers for What Do You Think?

1. She knew it was an acute angle, so the measurement had to be between 0° and 90°.
2. An angle measure is the difference between whatever angle measures the two sides of an angle pass through on a protractor. If Zack had lined up the protractor on one of the sides, he would have found the difference between 15° and 0°. As long as Zack places the vertex of the angle at the middle of the protractor, he can use any measurements the lines pass through.

3 Practice and Assess

Check

Answers for Check Your Understanding

1. An acute angle is between 0° and 90°. A right angle is exactly 90°. An obtuse angle is between 90° and 180°.
2. Angles

WHAT DO YOU THINK?

The smaller the angle between a ski jumper's body and the skis, the farther the skier will travel. Sonia and Zack help coach the ski team. They photographed the team's best jumper. Now they want to measure the angle between her body and the skis.

Sonia thinks ...

I'll place the bottom edge of the protractor on the ray on the ski. The other ray crosses the protractor at 15°, so the angle measures 15°.

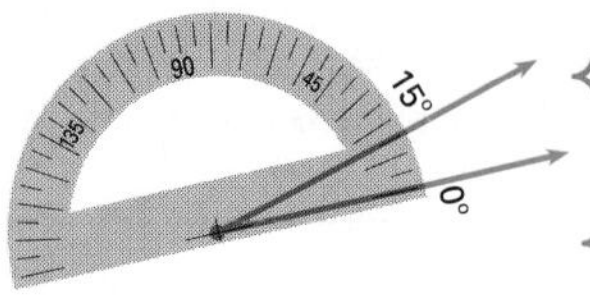

Zack thinks ...

I'll place the center of the protractor on the vertex of the angle. The two rays cross at 20° and 35°. 35° − 20° = 15°. The angle measures 15°.

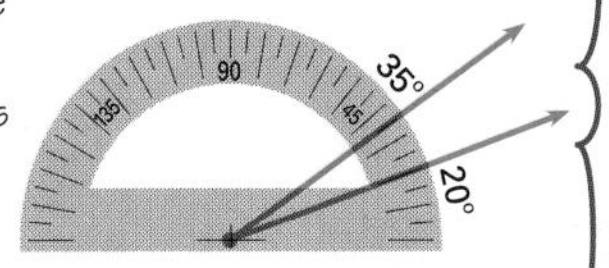

What do you think?

1. The protractor is labeled with pairs of measurements. How did Sonia know that the 20° measure was the correct measure to use?
2. Explain Zack's reasoning. Could he place the protractor in other ways and still find the measure of the angle?

MEETING MIDDLE SCHOOL CLASSROOM NEEDS

Tips from Middle School Teachers

I like to use an overhead projector for teaching students how to measure with a protractor. Students can actually see the procedure being performed step by step. I involve students as much as possible in all the steps.

Team Teaching

Work with a drafting teacher or art teacher and discuss how measurement of angles is important for drawing many diagrams of real-world objects.

Sports Connection

Skiing first began as a way to travel more than 5000 years ago. Skiers first served in battle in 1200 A.D. People began enjoying skiing as a sport in the early 1800s. Men and women's downhill, slalom, and giant slalom skiing are now major sports during the winter Olympics.

Check Your Understanding

1. If someone tells you the measure of an angle, how can you tell if the angle is an acute angle, a right angle, or an obtuse angle?

2. What is a degree a measurement of?

8-3 Exercises and Applications

Practice and Apply

Getting Started State whether the measure of each angle is less than 90° or greater than 90°.

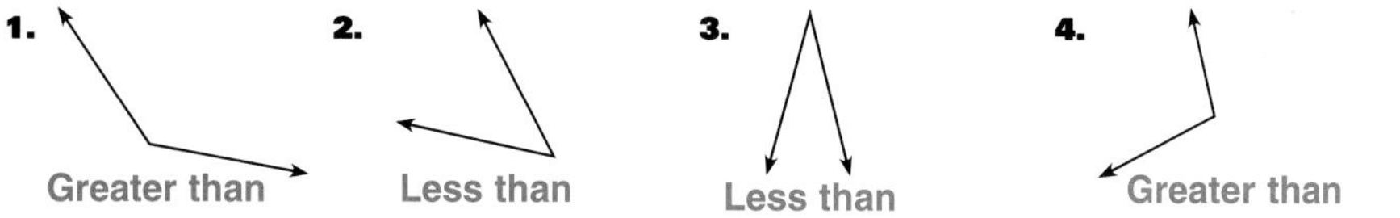

1. Greater than **2.** Less than **3.** Less than **4.** Greater than

Estimation Estimate the measure of each angle. Then measure each with a protractor.

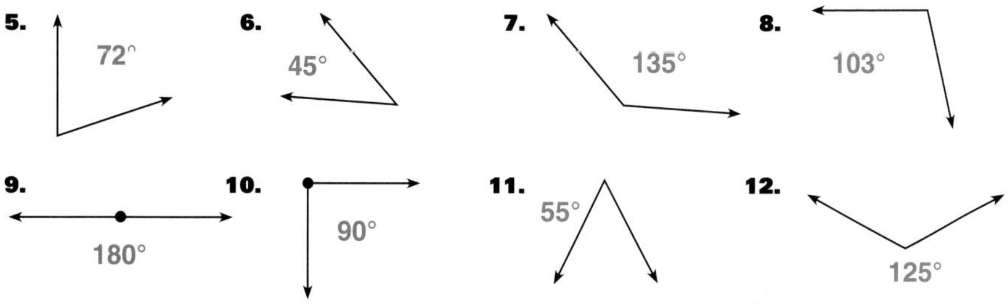

5. 72° **6.** 45° **7.** 135° **8.** 103° **9.** 180° **10.** 90° **11.** 55° **12.** 125°

13. Fine Arts Name two supplementary angles and two complementary angles in the origami photo.

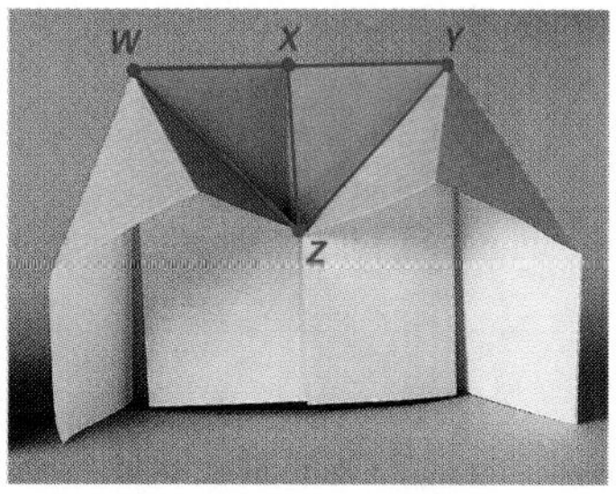

Draw the angle for each measure. Then classify each as acute, obtuse, or right.

14. 50° **15.** 140° **16.** 70° **17.** 110°

State the angle measure that is complementary to the given angle.

18. 23° 67° **19.** 79° 11° **20.** 62° 28° **21.** 3° 87°

State the angle measure that is supplementary to the given angle.

22. 127° 53° **23.** 52° 128° **24.** 60° 120° **25.** 90° 90°

PRACTICE

Name ____________________

Practice 8-3

Measuring Angles

Estimate the measure of each angle. Then measure each with a protractor.

1. 120° 2. 85° 3. 38° 4. 145°

Draw an angle of each measure. Then classify each as acute, obtuse, or right.

5. 60° Acute 6. 105° Obtuse 7. 90° Right 8. 15° Acute

State the angle measure that is complementary to the given angle.

9. 18° 72° 10. 88° 2° 11. 32° 58° 12. 60° 30°
13. 41° 49° 14. 26° 64° 15. 7° 83° 16. 78° 12°

State the angle measure that is supplementary to the given angle.

17. 85° 95° 18. 100° 80° 19. 23° 157° 20. 163° 17°
21. 135° 45° 22. 36° 144° 23. 120° 60° 24. 71° 109°

Read each statement and tell if it is always, sometimes, or never true.

25. An obtuse angle and an acute angle are complementary. Never true

26. A pair of supplementary angles includes an obtuse angle and an acute angle. Sometimes true

27. Name a pair of complementary angles and a pair of supplementary angles in the figure. Possible answers:

Complementary: ∠*DAE* and ∠*BAE*

Supplementary: ∠*BEC* and ∠*CED*

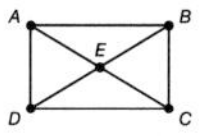

RETEACHING

Name ____________________

Alternative Lesson 8-3

Measuring Angles

Angles are measured in units called **degrees.** Use the symbol ° to indicate degrees. A complete circle measures 360°.

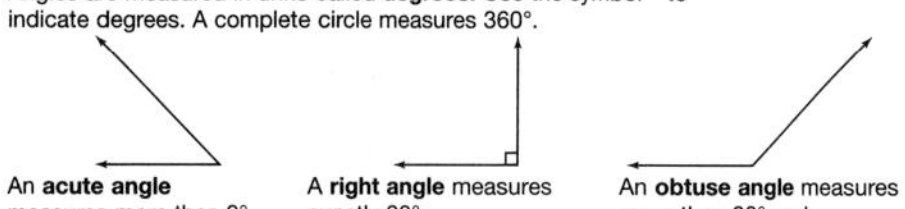

An **acute angle** measures more than 0° and less than 90.

A **right angle** measures exactly 90°.

An **obtuse angle** measures more than 90° and less than 180°.

A **protractor** is a tool that measures angles.

Example

What is the measure of ∠*FGH*?

Step 1: Place your protractor so that the middle mark (hole) on its bottom side is exactly on the vertex of the angle.

Step 2: Place the protractor line, with the zero mark on the scale, over one side of the angle.

Step 3: Read the number where the other side of the angle meets the degree scale on the protractor. Since the angle is an acute angle, use the smaller number in the pair.

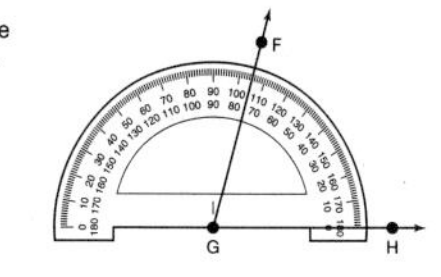

The measure of ∠*FGH* is 75°.

Try It Find the measure of each angle.

a. 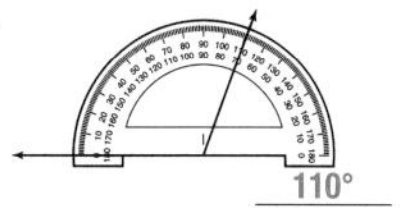 110°

b. 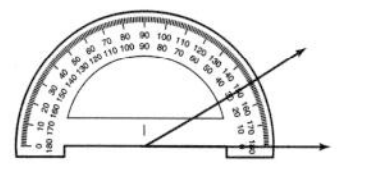 30°

c. 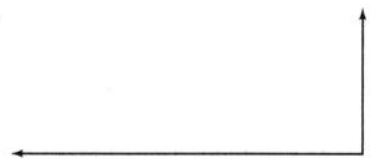 90°

d.  145°

8-3 Exercises and Applications

Assignment Guide

- **Basic** 1–51 odds
- **Average** 3–31 odds, 34–52 evens
- **Enriched** 13–29 odds, 30–32, 33–51 odds

Exercise Notes

Exercises 18–25

Extension Point out that equations can be used to find either the complement or supplement of a known angle. To find the complement, use x + known measure = 90. To find the supplement, use x + known measure = 180.

Exercise Answers

13. Supplementary: ∠*WXZ* and ∠*ZXY*; Complementary: ∠*WZX* and ∠*XZY*

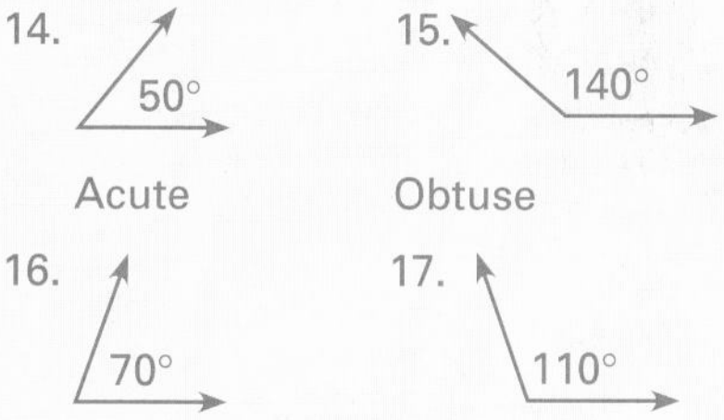

14. 50° Acute 15. 140° Obtuse 16. 70° Acute 17. 110° Acute

PRACTICE 8-3

Reteaching

Activity

Materials: Protractor or angle ruler, straightedge.

- Work in groups of three or four.
- Play the following game in which a round consists of each person performing the following steps.
- Use a straightedge to draw an angle. Estimate the measure of the angle.
- Measure the angle with a protractor or angle ruler.
- Determine the difference between the estimated measure and the actual measure.
- The person whose estimated measure is closest to the actual measure is the winner for that round.

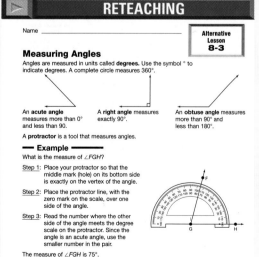

Project Progress

You may want to have students use Chapter 8 Project Master

Exercise Answers

30. 24 hours; 9 hours. The minute hand travels 360° in 12 hours.
31. Possible answer: 91°; A 1° angle will be so narrow that it would be difficult to distinguish from a straight line.
32. There is no limit to the number of angles you can draw. Angle measures can be in decimals or fractions.

Alternate Assessment

Performance Have students work with a partner. Have each student draw five different angles on a sheet of paper. Then have students switch papers with their partners and use a protractor to measure the partner's angles.

Quick Quiz

Draw an angle of each measure and classify each as acute, obtuse, or right. Drawings will vary.

1. 28° Acute
2. 110° Obtuse

State the angle measure that is complementary to the given angle.

3. 42° 48°
4. 80° 10°

State the angle measure that is supplementary to the given angle.

5. 54° 126°
6. 120° 60°

Available on Daily Transparency 8-3

Read each statement and tell if it is always, sometimes, or never true.

26. Degrees are used to measure the sides of angles. Never

27. Two angles whose measures are 45° and 45° are complementary. Always

28. Two obtuse angles are supplementary. Never

29. **Test Prep** Estimate the measurement of the obtuse angle. B

GPS

Ⓐ 45° Ⓑ 135°

Ⓒ 90° Ⓓ 270°

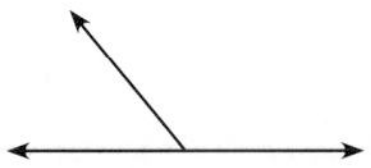

Problem Solving and Reasoning

30. Journal A clock face is divided into 360°. About how long does it take the hour hand to travel 720°? 270°? Explain.

31. **Critical Thinking** Is it easier to draw a 1° angle or a 91° angle? Explain.

32. **Communicate** How many angles can you draw that measure between 72° and 73°? Explain.

PROBLEM SOLVING 8-3

Mixed Review

Write each fraction as a decimal. *[Lesson 5-7]*

33. $\frac{1}{2}$ 0.5 **34.** $\frac{2}{3}$ $0.\overline{6}$ **35.** $\frac{1}{4}$ 0.25 **36.** $\frac{3}{4}$ 0.75 **37.** $\frac{1}{3}$ $0.\overline{3}$ **38.** $\frac{5}{6}$ $0.8\overline{3}$

39. $\frac{4}{9}$ $0.\overline{4}$ **40.** $\frac{3}{5}$ 0.6 **41.** $\frac{12}{22}$ $0.\overline{54}$ **42.** $\frac{7}{8}$ 0.875 **43.** $\frac{673}{673}$ 1.0 **44.** $\frac{5}{8}$ 0.625

Solve. *[Lesson 6-3]*

45. $\frac{5}{6} + w = \frac{7}{8}$ $\frac{1}{24}$ **46.** $t + \frac{4}{9} = \frac{3}{4}$ $\frac{11}{36}$ **47.** $p - \frac{5}{6} = \frac{6}{11}$ $1\frac{25}{66}$ **48.** $n - \frac{3}{4} = \frac{1}{2}$ $1\frac{1}{4}$

49. $a + \frac{3}{8} = \frac{4}{9}$ $\frac{5}{72}$ **50.** $\frac{60}{10} - j = 5$ 1 **51.** $b - \frac{4}{5} = \frac{1}{10}$ $\frac{9}{10}$ **52.** $4 - m = \frac{3}{5}$ $3\frac{2}{5}$

Project Progress

Draw a rough sketch of your logo. Include as many shapes as possible in your logo. Make sure some of the shapes have only straight sides.

Problem Solving
Understand
Plan
Solve
Look Back

PROBLEM SOLVING

Name ______________________

Guided Problem Solving 8-3

GPS **PROBLEM 29, STUDENT PAGE 420**

Estimate the measurement of the obtuse angle.

(A) 45° (B) 135°
(C) 90° (D) 270°

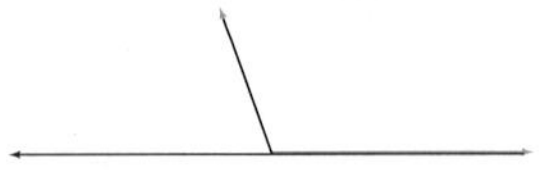

— Understand —

1. What is the definition of an obtuse angle? An angle with a measure between 90° and 180°.
2. Which of these kinds of angles are shown in the diagram? C
   a. acute and right b. right and obtuse c. acute and obtuse

— Plan —

3. Darken the rays that make up the obtuse angle in the diagram.
4. Classify the type of angle given in each choice as acute, obtuse, right, or none of these.
   a. Choice A (45°) Acute. b. Choice B (135°) Obtuse.
   c. Choice C (90°) Right. d. Choice D (270°) None.

— Solve —

5. Which choice is an obtuse angle? Choice B.

— Look Back —

6. Why does classifying the angle help estimate the measure? Possible answer: The classification narrows the range of measurement.

SOLVE ANOTHER PROBLEM

Which of the answer choices is a reasonable estimate for the measurement of the acute angle in the drawing above? Choice A.

(A) 45° (B) 135°
(C) 90° (D) 270°

ENRICHMENT

Name ______________________

Extend Your Thinking 8-3

Critical Thinking

Use this figure to answer the questions below. Answer each question in as many ways as possible.

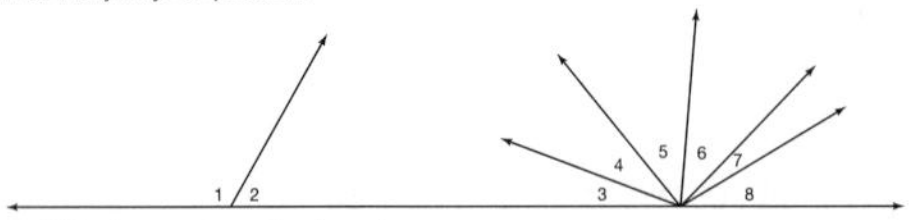

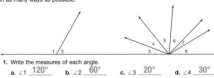

1. Write the measures of each angle.
   a. ∠1 120° b. ∠2 60° c. ∠3 20° d. ∠4 30°
   e. ∠5 45° f. ∠6 40° g. ∠7 15° h. ∠8 30°
2. Which two angles have the same measure? ∠4 and ∠8.
3. Which of the eight angles are acute angles? ∠2 – ∠8.
4. Which of the eight angles are obtuse angles? ∠1.
5. Which two angles can be joined to form a right angle? ∠2 and ∠4; ∠2 and ∠8.
6. Which three angles can be joined to form a right angle? ∠3, ∠4, and ∠6; ∠5, ∠7, and ∠8; ∠3, ∠6, and ∠8.
7. Which three angles can be joined to form a straight angle? ∠1, ∠3, and ∠6; ∠1, ∠4, and ∠8; ∠1, ∠5, and ∠7.
8. Choose an angle. Use a protractor to draw two angles with the same measure as the chosen angle. Then use from four to six other angle measures from the diagram above to make a circle. Label each angle measure. Remember that a circle measures 360°.
   Possible answer:

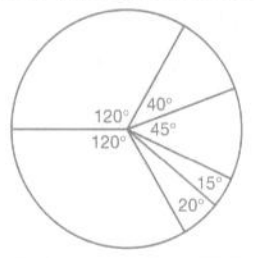

Section 8A Connect

In this section, you've seen how traditional origami folds produce patterns of lines and angles. Now you'll start your own "tradition" by creating folds to illustrate what you've learned about lines and angles.

The Tale of the Magic Paper

Materials: Squares of paper, Ruler

The instructions for the octopus appear in Kunihiko Kasahara's book, *Creative Origami.* If you unfold the paper used to create the octopus, you can see many interesting line and angle patterns.

Create patterns in paper squares to model at least 12 of the terms you have learned in this lesson. Fold and then open squares to make the patterns. Darken creases with a pencil or pen. Label each figure with the term it models.

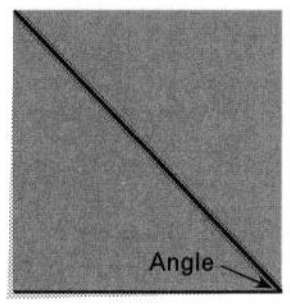

Here's a list of some of the terms you've studied in this section:

acute angle	angle	complementary angles
degree	endpoint	intersect
line	obtuse angle	parallel
perpendicular	protractor	ray
right angle	segment	side
straight angle	supplementary angles	vertex

You may use a different square to model each term. You may sometimes find it easier to create patterns that model several terms at once. Let the geometry of the square help you create useful patterns.

8A Connect

The Tale of the Magic Paper

The Point

In *The Tale of the Magic Paper* on page 407, students learned about origami, the ancient Japanese art of paper folding. Now students will create patterns in paper squares to model what they learned about lines and angles in this section.

Materials

Squares of paper, ruler

About the Page

- Discuss the various ways the squares might be folded, for example, in half on the diagonal or straight across, in quarters forming right angles, into fans, and so on.
- Review the list of terms and their definitions before students begin to illustrate them.
- Show students how you want them to label the figures.

Ongoing Assessment

Check that students have created patterns that correctly illustrate the terms.

Extension

During the winter season students often make paper snowflakes. Ask students to design a snowflake from a square of white paper. After they have folded their paper, have them cut four geometric shapes into the folds. When they have finished their snowflake, ask students to write a set of directions so that someone else could make a copy of the snowflake they created.

Answers for Connect

Answers may vary.

8A Review

Review Correlation

Item(s)	Lesson(s)
1–4	8-1
5–8	8-2
9–12	8-3
13	8-2

Test Prep

Test-Taking Tip

Tell students to take a few brief rest breaks. To help them answer Exercise 13, students can shut their eyes and picture the required answer, then look for the answer that matches their image.

REVIEW 8A

Section 8A Review

Describe the relationship between the lines, rays, or segments.

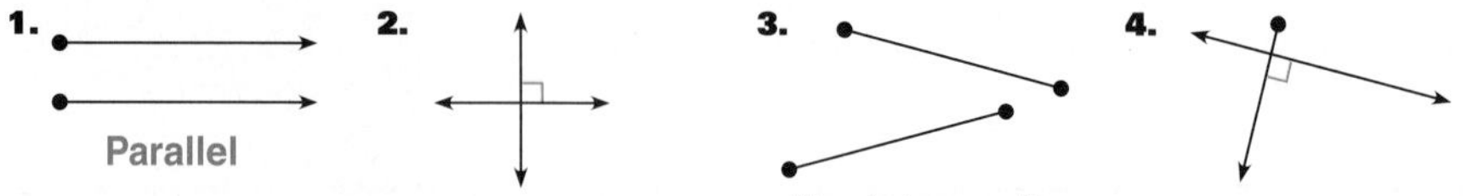

1. Parallel **2.** Perpendicular **3.** Nonintersecting **4.** Perpendicular

Classify each angle as acute, right, obtuse, or straight.

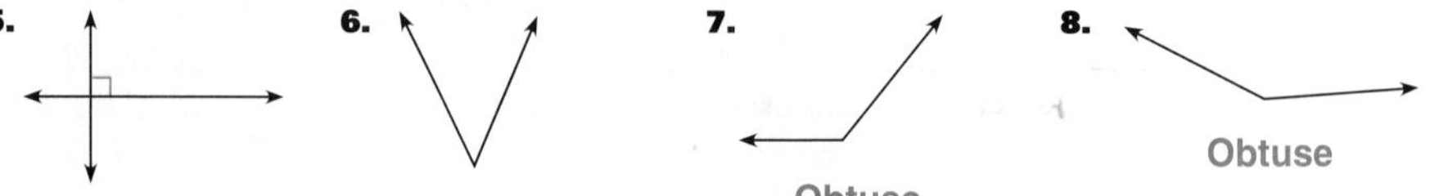

5. All right **6.** Acute **7.** Obtuse **8.** Obtuse

Measure each angle and find its complement and supplement.

9. 37°; C = 53°; S = 143°

10. 41°; C = 49°; S = 139°

11. 75°; C = 15°; S = 105°

12. 25°; C = 65°; S = 155°

Test Prep

When estimating the measurement of an angle, remember that a right angle is 90° and half of a right angle is 45°.

13. Rosemary is building a birdhouse. She wants the roof of the birdhouse to be at an angle more than 90° but less than 135°. Choose the angle that she could use for the roof. A

Ⓐ Ⓑ Ⓒ Ⓓ

Resources

Practice Masters
Section 8A Review

Assessment Sourcebook
Quiz 8A

TestWorks
Test and Practice Software

PRACTICE

Name ____________

Practice

Section 8A Review

Describe the relationship between the lines, rays, or segments.

1. Parallel line and segment
2. Perpendicular segments
3. Intersecting rays
4. Intersecting line and ray

Classify each angle as acute, right, obtuse, or straight.

5. Obtuse 6. Acute 7. Right 8. Acute

Measure each angle and find its complement and supplement.

9. measure: 51° complement: 39° supplement: 129°

10. measure: 82° complement: 8° supplement: 98°

11. measure: 10° complement: 80° supplement: 170°

12. Science The gar is an armored fish that has survived since the age of dinosaurs. It is 150 centimeters long. How many meters is this? *[Lesson 4-2]* 1.5 m

13. During the 1896 Olympic Games, Thomas Burke completed the 400-meter dash in $54\frac{1}{5}$ seconds. In 1992, Quincy Watts beat this time by $10\frac{7}{10}$ seconds. What was Watts' time? *[Lesson 6-6]* $43\frac{1}{2}$ sec

Section 8B

Polygons

Visit www.teacher.mathsurf.com for links to lesson plans from teachers and other professionals, NCTM information, and other sites.

LESSON PLANNING GUIDE

Student Edition | **Ancillaries***

LESSON		MATERIALS	VOCABULARY	DAILY	OTHER
	Section 8B Opener				
8-4	**Exploring Angles in a Triangle**	ruler, scissors, protractor	triangle, acute triangle, right triangle, obtuse triangle	8-4	Teaching Tool Trans. 6 Technology Master 38
8-5	**Exploring Sides of a Triangle**	Cuisenaire rods®	equilateral triangle, isosceles triangle, scalene triangle	8-5	Technology Master 39 Ch. 8 Project Master *WW Math*–Middle School
8-6	**Polygons**		polygon, quadrilateral, pentagon, hexagon, octagon, regular polygon	8-6	Teaching Tool Trans. 20 Lesson Enhancement Transparencies 38, 39 Technology Master 40
8-7	**Quadrilaterals**		trapezoid, parallelogram, rhombus, rectangle, square	8-7	Lesson Enhancement Transparencies 40, 41 Technology Master 41
	Technology	dynamic geometry software			*Interactive CD-ROM Geometry Tool*
	Connect	ruler			Teaching Tool Trans. 16 Lesson Enhancement Trans. 42 Interdisc. Team Teaching 8B
	Review				Practice 8B; Quiz 8B; *TestWorks*

* Daily Ancillaries include Practice, Reteaching, Problem Solving, Enrichment, and Daily Transparency. Teaching Tool Transparencies are in *Teacher's Toolkits*. Lesson Enhancement Transparencies are in *Overhead Transparency Package*.

SKILLS TRACE

LESSON	SKILL	FIRST INTRODUCED GR. 4	GR. 5	GR. 6	DEVELOP	PRACTICE/ APPLY	REVIEW
8-4	**Classifying triangles according to angles.**			✗ p. 424	pp. 424–425	pp. 426–427	pp. 442, 461, 484
8-5	**Classifying triangles according to sides.**			✗ p. 428	pp. 428–429	pp. 430–431	pp. 442, 461, 491
8-6	**Classifying polygons.**			✗ p. 432	pp. 432–433	pp. 434–435	pp. 442, 461, 497
8-7	**Classifying quadrilaterals.**			✗ p. 436	pp. 436–437	pp. 438–439	pp. 442, 461, 502

CONNECTED MATHEMATICS

Investigation 2 in the unit *Shapes and Designs (3-D Geometry)*, from the **Connected Mathematics** series, can be used with Section 8B.

INTERDISCIPLINARY TEAM TEACHING

Math and Social Studies

(Worksheet pages 39–40: Teacher pages T39–T40)

In this lesson, students identify polygons to distinguish the parts of pyramids.

Name ______________________ *Math and Social Studies*

Secrets of the Pyramids

Identify polygons to distinguish the parts of pyramids.

A pyramid is a solid figure made up of a base and planes whose edges meet at a single point above the base called the *vertex.* There is something mysterious and appealing about the pyramid. Throughout history, ancient civilizations have used this geometrical shape to build great monuments.

Egyptian pyramids were constructed from about 2700 B.C. to about 1700 B.C. They were used as gigantic tombs for royalty. Inside the pyramids a maze of stairs and passageways led to several rooms containing the royal person's body as well as many valuable treasures. The largest Egyptian pyramid, called the Great Pyramid at Giza, was built around 2600 B.C. It was considered one of the Seven Wonders of the World. It was originally 147 meters tall. It is made of five polygons and is comprised of four sides and a base. Each side of its base measures 230 meters. The Great Pyramid is made of huge limestone blocks and covers 13 acres of land.

People once assumed that the Egyptians influenced the building of pyramids in the Americas, which came later. However, a close look at the New World pyramids shows that they aren't copies of the Egyptian model. In fact they aren't really pyramids.

Take the Pyramid of the Sun at Teotihuacán, in Mexico, as an example. It has four sides that do not meet at the top at a single point. Thus, it has no vertex. The Pyramid of the Sun looks like a pyramid with the top chopped off. This is called a *truncated pyramid.* Unlike the Egyptian pyramids, the New World versions were never used to bury royalty. Their truncated tops formed bases for religious temples.

The sides of Egyption pyramids, such as the Great Pyramid at Giza, Egypt, come to a single point at the top.

Name ______________________ *Math and Social Studies*

The sides of New World pyramids, such as the Pyramid of the Sun at Teotihuacán, Mexico, have truncated, or flat, tops.

1. What kind of quadrilateral is the base of the Great Pyramid?
   a square
2. Look at the sides of the pyramid. What kind of polygons do they form?
   triangles
3. The sides of the Great Pyramid are identical in shape. Are they regular or irregular polygons?
   regular
4. What kinds of polygon form the sides of the Pyramid of the Sun?
   trapezoid
5. Suppose you extended the lines of the Pyramid of the Sun until they met at a vertex. What kinds of polygons would the sides change into?
   triangles
6. How were people able to move huge blocks of stone to build ancient pyramids? Do some research on the subject and write a short report on what you find.
   Students should become aware that such marvels as the Great Pyramid at Giza were built without the use of cranes, pulleys, or lifting tackle. However, modern scholars suggest that simple machines, such as inclined planes, rollers, and sleds were used to move the stone blocks.

BIBLIOGRAPHY

FOR TEACHERS

Fowler, Allan. *Busy, Buzzy Bees.* Chicago, IL: Children's Press, 1995.

Hirsch, Christian R., ed. *Geometry from Multiple Perspectives.* Palo Alto, CA: Dale Seymour Publications, 1996.

Kallevig, Christine Petrell. *Folding Stories.* Newburgh, IN: Storytime Ink International, 1991.

Leff, Lawrence S. *Barron's Geometry the Easy Way.* New York, NY: Barron's Educational Series, 1990.

Pluckrose, Henry Arthur. *Shape.* London, England: Watts, 1986.

Symes, R. F. *Crystal & Gem.* New York, NY: Knopf, 1991.

FOR STUDENTS

Kappraff, Jay. *Connections: The Geometric Bridge.* New York, NY: McGraw-Hill Publications, 1990.

Stangl, Jean. *Crystals and Crystal Gardens You Can Grow.* New York, NY: F. Watts, 1990.

SECTION **8B**

Polygons

▶ Science Link ▶ Industry Link ▶ www.mathsurf.com/6/ch8/crystals

The Geometry of Gems

Not long ago, a diamond was found in the African nation of Guinea. The diamond was the size of a small onion. The owner sold it for $10 million. At that rate, 1 pound of diamonds is worth about $90 million! (One pound of onions is worth about 59¢.)

An uncut diamond is an example of a crystal. Most of the world's rocks and minerals occur as crystals. Some display fascinating geometric shapes and patterns.

A few crystals, such as diamonds, emeralds, and rubies, are prized for their rarity and beauty. Skilled gem cutters grind the crystals into attractive three-dimensional shapes.

Then they cut flat geometric shapes called facets into the surface. Their work produces jewels that are mathematical as well as artistic—and worth much more than a bag of onions!

In this section, you'll learn about the geometry of crystals and facets.

1 **Why are diamonds worth more than onions?**

2 **What does it mean to say, "At that rate, 1 pound of diamonds is worth about $90 million"?**

Where are we now?

In Section 8A, students learned about line segments and angles.

They learned how to

- classify and describe lines.
- name and describe angles.
- measure angles.

Where are we going?

In Section 8B, students will

- classify triangles according to their angles.
- classify triangles according to their sides.
- classify polygons.
- identify and classify quadrilaterals.

Theme: Crystals

World Wide Web

If your class has access to the World Wide Web, you might want to use the information found at the Web site address given. The interdisciplinary links relate to topics discussed in this section.

About the Page

This page introduces the theme of the section, crystals, and discusses diamonds and other minerals that are crystals.

Ask ...

- Have you ever seen crystals? If so, where?
- What are facets? Flat, polished surfaces cut on a gemstone.

Extensions

The following activities do not require access to the World Wide Web.

Science

Crystals are classified by the geometry of the surfaces that give them their shape. Have students research and identify six basic types. Isometric, orthorhombic, tetragonal, hexagonal, triclinic, monoclinic.

Industry

A diamond is the hardest naturally occurring substance. Have students investigate diamond mines and how the value of diamonds is determined.

Answers for Questions

1. Possible answer: Diamonds are more rare and more beautiful than onions.
2. Answers may vary.

Connect

On page 441, students use geometric terms to describe a diamond design.

8-4 Lesson Organizer

Objective

- Classify triangles according to their angles.

Vocabulary

- Triangle, acute triangle, right triangle, obtuse triangle

Materials

- Explore: Ruler, scissors, protractor

NCTM Standards

- 1–4, 7, 13

Review

Name the possible measures for each type of angle.

1. Acute Between 0° and 90°
2. Right 90°
3. Obtuse Between 90° and 180°

Solve each equation.

4. $t + 20 + 30 = 180$ $t = 130$
5. $y + 42 + 110 = 180$ $y = 28$

Available on Daily Transparency 8-4

1 Introduce

Explore

The Point
Students use paper models of triangles and cut out angles to discover that the sum of the angles is 180°.

Ongoing Assessment
Watch for students who have trouble placing the three angles together correctly. Emphasize that the vertices of all three angles should touch.

For Groups That Finish Early
If you increase the size of the triangles by doubling the lengths of the sides, how will the angle sum be affected? The sum is still 180°.

8-4 Exploring Angles in a Triangle

You'll Learn ...

■ to classify triangles according to their angles

... How It's Used

Diamond cutters classify triangles when describing the cut of a particular stone.

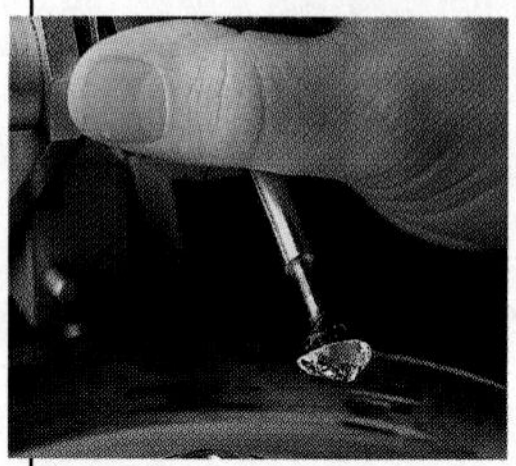

Vocabulary

triangle
acute triangle
right triangle
obtuse triangle

▶ Lesson Link You've learned about line segments and angles. Now you'll investigate the triangle, a figure with three line segments and three angles. ◀

Explore Angles in a Triangle

Straight to the Sum

Materials: Ruler, Scissors, Protractor

1. Draw and cut out a large triangle. Label the angles as 1, 2, and 3.
2. Tear the triangle into three pieces as shown. Each piece should have one and only one labeled angle.
3. Put the three pieces together so that the angles are touching. Estimate the sum of the three angles of your triangle.

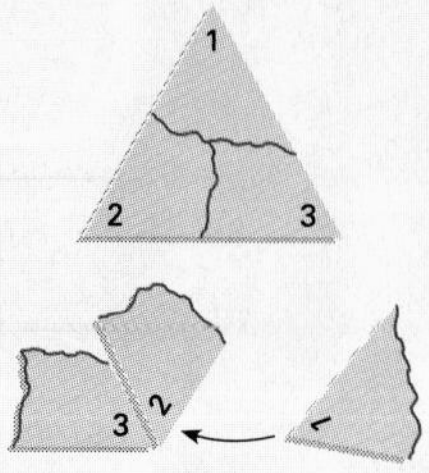

4. Using a protractor, find the measure of each angle. Calculate the sum of the angles. How does the sum compare to your estimate?
5. Repeat Steps 1–4 with two more triangles. Compare the sums of the angles for your three triangles. Describe any patterns you see in the sums.

Learn Angles in a Triangle

A **triangle** is a closed figure made from three line segments. Like angles, triangles can be classified using the terms *acute, right,* and *obtuse.*

An **acute triangle** has three acute angles.

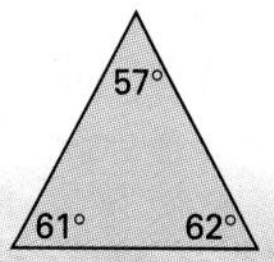

A **right triangle** has exactly one right angle.

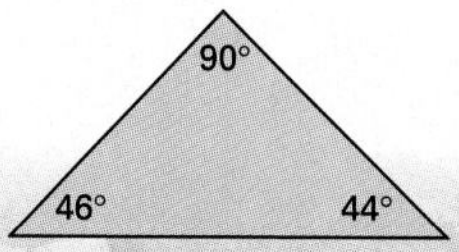

An **obtuse triangle** has exactly one obtuse angle.

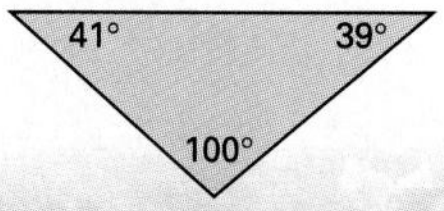

MEETING INDIVIDUAL NEEDS

Resources

8-4 Practice
8-4 Reteaching
8-4 Problem Solving
8-4 Enrichment
8-4 Daily Transparency
Problem of the Day
Review
Quick Quiz
Teaching Tool Transparency 6
Technology Master 38

Learning Modalities

Logical Have students explain how they can find the measure of the third angle of a triangle if they only know two of the measures. Ask them to give examples to support their reasoning.

Visual Have students create a classroom display of all of the triangles they drew and cut apart in **Explore**. The display will reinforce the concept that the sum of the angles of any triangle is 180°.

Challenge

Have students repeat the steps in **Explore**, but have them start with a quadrilateral instead of a triangle. Then ask them to make a generalization. For a quadrilateral, the sum of the angles is always 360°.

Example 1

Classify each triangle as acute, right, or obtuse.

a.

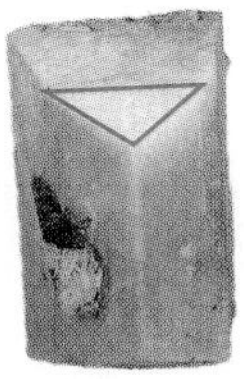

The face has one obtuse angle, so the triangle is obtuse.

b.

The face has three acute angles, so the triangle is acute.

c.

The face has a right angle, so the triangle is a right triangle.

The sum of the angles of any triangle is always equal to 180°.

Example 2

Find the measure of the missing angle in each triangle.

a.

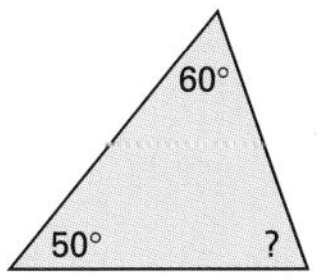

$50° + 60° + ? = 180°$

$110° + ? = 180°$

$110° + \mathbf{70°} = 180°$

The angle measures 70°.

b.

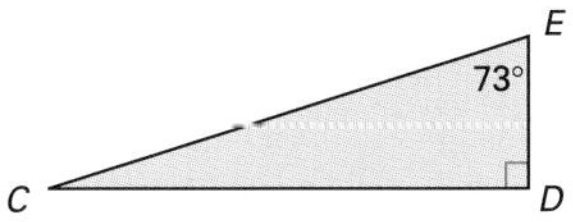

$\angle D$ is a right angle, so it measures 90°.

$90° + 73° + ? = 180°$

$163° + ? = 180°$

$163° + \mathbf{17°} = 180°$

$m\angle C = 17°$

Try It

Find the measure of the missing angle in each triangle. Then classify the triangle.

a.

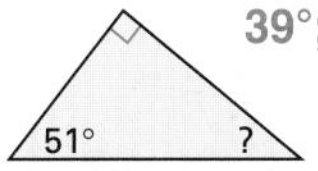

39°; right

b.

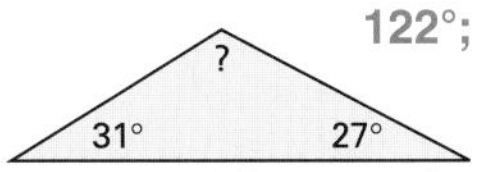

122°; obtuse

MENTAL MATH

It is easy to add 50 and 60 because they both end in the same number of zeros. $5 + 6 = 11$, so $50 + 60 = 110$.

MATH EVERY DAY

Problem of the Day

Look for a pattern. What number should replace the *X*?

4 (pattern: top left ÷ top right − 1)

Available on Daily Transparency 8-4

An Extension is provided in the transparency package.

Fact of the Day

Angles of a crystal can change when the crystal is heated. Quartz crystals melt only when heated above 1600°C.

Estimation

Estimate each quotient.

1. 543 ÷ 9 60
2. 348 ÷ 7 50
3. 239 ÷ 8 30
4. 531 ÷ 6 90
5. 165 ÷ 82 2

Answers for Explore

1–5. Answers may vary. The sum of the three angles is always 180°.

2 Teach

Learn

Alternate Examples

1. Classify each triangle as acute, right, or obtuse.

a.

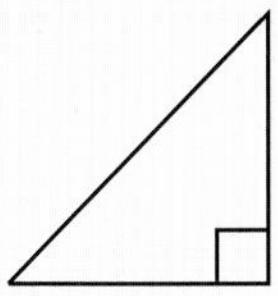

Right

b.

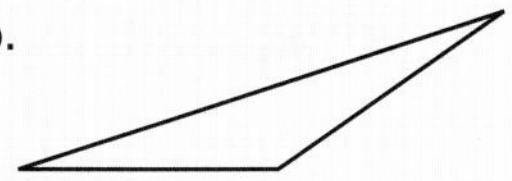

Obtuse

c.

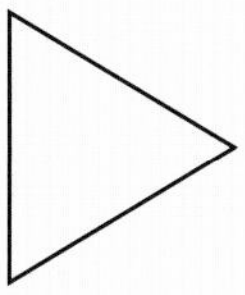

Acute

2. Find the measure of the missing angle in each triangle.

a.

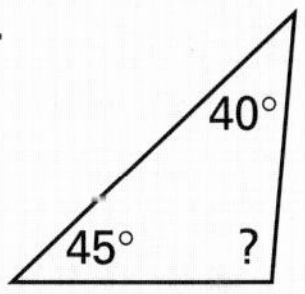

$45° + 40° + ? = 180°$

$85° + ? = 180°$

$85° + \mathbf{95°} = 180°$

The angle measures 95°.

b.

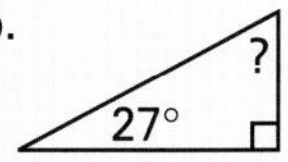

$90° + 27° + ? = 180°$

$117° + ? = 180°$

$117° + \mathbf{63°} = 180°$

The angle measures 63°.

8-4 Exercises and Applications

Assignment Guide

- **Basic**
  2–38 evens, 41, 42–60 evens
- **Average**
  7–18, 19–35 odds, 38–41, 43–61 odds
- **Enriched**
  11–18, 19–37 odds, 38–41, 45–61 odds

3 Practice and Assess

Check

Answers for Check Your Understanding

1. No; The sum of the angles must be 180°.
2. The sum of the three angles would not be 180°. The sum of two obtuse angles is always more than 180°.

Exercise Notes

Exercises 19–26

Extension Have students identify each triangle as acute, obtuse, or right before they measure the angles. You may want to trace these angles on a transparency and have students use Teaching Tool Transparency 6: Cuisenaire Angle Ruler, to measure the angles.

Reteaching

Activity

- Work with a partner and follow these steps.
- Draw a large triangle on a sheet of paper. Label the angles 1, 2, and 3.
- Draw a different triangle on another sheet of paper. Label the angles 4, 5, and 6.
- Tear the angle off each triangle and put all six pieces together. Shuffle the pieces. Pick three and put them together. Will they form a straight angle? Explain. Sometimes; Only if they come from the same triangle.

Check Your Understanding

1. Can any three angles form a triangle? Explain.
2. Why can't a triangle have more than one obtuse angle?

8-4 Exercises and Applications

PRACTICE 8-4

Practice and Apply

Getting Started Given the two angles of a triangle, find the third.

1. 100°, 40° 40°
2. 60°, 60° 60°
3. 80°, 20° 80°
4. 50°, 50° 80°
5. 30°, 50° 100°
6. 80°, 90° 10°

For Exercises 7–18, classify each triangle as acute, right, or obtuse.

7. 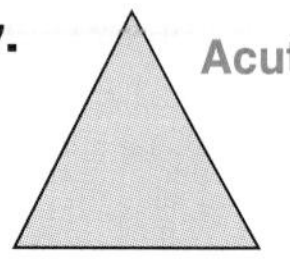 Acute

8. 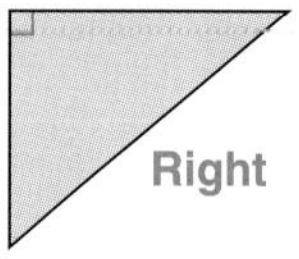 Right

9. 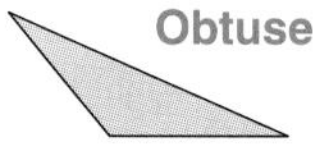 Obtuse

10. 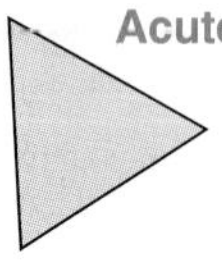 Acute

11. 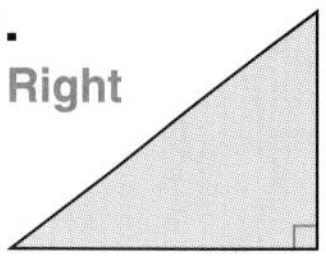 Right

12. 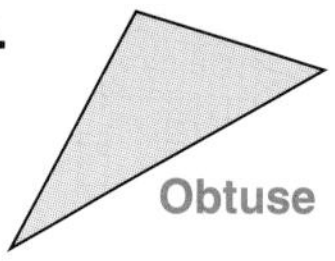 Obtuse

13.  Obtuse

14. 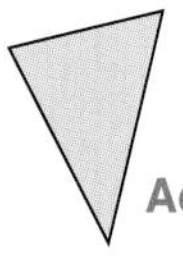 Acute

15. $\angle T = 67°$, $\angle H = 34°$, $\angle W = 79°$ Acute
16. $\angle S = 124°$, $\angle D = 50°$, $\angle P = 6°$ Obtuse
17. $\angle V = 30°$, $\angle R = 60°$, $\angle F = 90°$ Right
18. $\angle E = 60°$, $\angle J = 60°$, $\angle B = 60°$ Acute

Use a protractor to determine the measure of all angles in each triangle.

19. 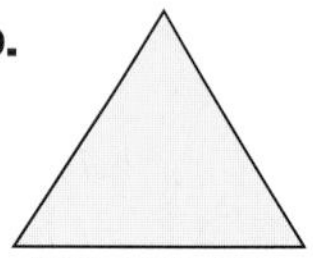 66°, 56°, 58°

20. 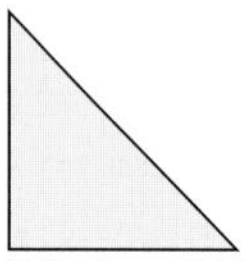 45°, 45°, 90°

21. 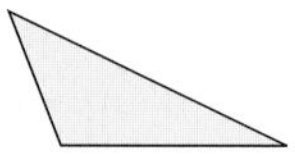 43°, 112°, 25°

22. 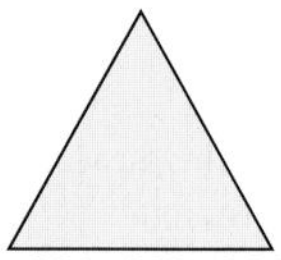 60°, 60°, 60°

23. 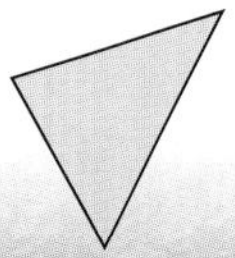 77°, 45°, 58°

24. 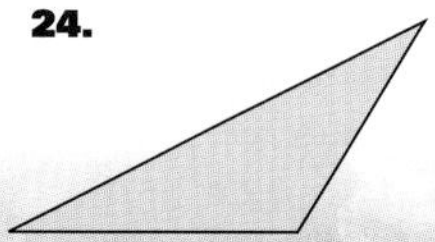 26°, 32°, 122°

25. 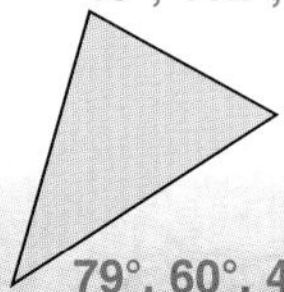 79°, 60°, 41°

26. 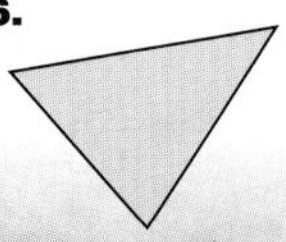 57°, 47°, 76°

PRACTICE

Name ______________________

Practice 8-4

Exploring Angles in a Triangle

For Exercises 1–8, classify each triangle as acute, right, or obtuse.

1. Obtuse 2. Acute 3. Right 4. Acute

5. $m\angle T = 47°$, $m\angle U = 87°$, $m\angle V = 46°$ Acute
6. $m\angle D = 73°$, $m\angle E = 90°$, $m\angle F = 17°$ Right
7. $m\angle G = 51°$, $m\angle P = 68°$, $m\angle Z = 61°$ Acute
8. $m\angle A = 67°$, $m\angle R = 13°$, $m\angle F = 100°$ Obtuse

Use a protractor to determine the measures of all angles in each triangle.

9. 40°, 52°, 88° 10. 35°, 80°, 65° 11. 22°, 57°, 101° 12. 36°, 54°, 90°

Find the measure of the missing angle in each triangle.

13. $m\angle G = 94°$, $m\angle H = 47°$, $m\angle I =$ 39°
14. $m\angle K = 81°$, $m\angle L = 53°$, $m\angle M =$ 46°
15. $m\angle P = 38°$, $m\angle Q = 45°$, $m\angle R =$ 97°
16. $m\angle B = 30°$, $m\angle S = 60°$, $m\angle U =$ 90°

For Exercises 17–20, decide whether the angle measurements can form a triangle. If a triangle can be formed, draw and classify it.

17. 35°, 65°, 90° Cannot form a triangle
18. 70°, 55°, 55° Acute triangle
19. 30°, 40°, 110° Obtuse triangle
20. 45°, 55°, 65° Cannot form a triangle

RETEACHING

Name ______________________

Alternative Lesson 8-4

Exploring Angles In a Triangle

A **triangle** is a closed figure made from three line segments. The sum of the angles in any triangle always equals 180°.

Triangles can be classified by the size of their angles.

An **acute triangle** has three acute angles. (70°, 55°, 55°)
A **right triangle** has exactly one right angle. (60°, 90°, 30°)
An **obtuse triangle** has exactly one obtuse angle. (40°, 40°, 100°)

Example 1

Classify this triangle as acute, right or obtuse.

All three angles of the triangle are less than 90°, so the triangle is acute.

Try It Classify each triangle as acute, right, or obtuse.

a. Obtuse. b. Acute. c. Obtuse. d. Right.

Example 2

Find the measure of the missing angle in the triangle.

The sum of the angles of a triangle is equal to 180°.

Write an equation using the given measures. 35 + 60 + ? = 180

Add the given measures. 95 + ? = 180

Use mental math to find the missing measure. 95 + 85 = 180

So, the angle measures 85°.

Try It Find the measure of the missing angle in each triangle.

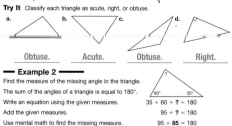

e. 40° f. 80° g. 90° h. 75°

Find the measure of the missing angle in each triangle.

27. $\angle A = 56°, \angle B = 93°, \angle C = \square$ 31° **28.** $\angle X = 115°, \angle Y = 34°, \angle Z = \square$ 31°

29. $\angle L = 170°, \angle M = 5°, \angle N = \square$ 5° **30.** $\angle R = 48°, \angle S = 63°, \angle T = \square$ 69°

31. $\angle I = 78°, \angle J = 12°, \angle K = \square$ 90° **32.** $\angle D = 25°, \angle G = 80°, \angle P = \square$ 75°

Geometry For Exercises 33–36, decide whether the angle measurements can form a triangle. If a triangle can be formed, draw and classify it.

33. 35°, 65°, 80° **34.** 45°, 45°, 90° **35.** 95°, 45°, 40° **36.** 55°, 50°, 50°

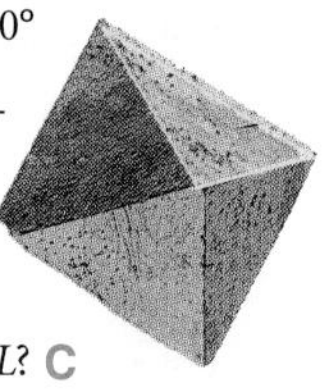

37. Science Magnetite is one of only two common minerals that are magnetic. Magnetite was used in early versions of modern-day compasses. What are the angle measures for the magnetite crystal shown? 30°, 43°, 107°

38. Test Prep A triangle has angles *J*, *K*, and *L*. $\angle J$ is 58°, and $\angle K$ is larger than $\angle J$. Which of the following is not a possible measure for $\angle L$? C

Ⓐ 58° Ⓑ 32° Ⓒ 70° Ⓓ 51.5°

Problem Solving and Reasoning

39. Journal If you know the angle measurements of two triangles, can you determine which triangle has the larger area? Explain.

40. Critical Thinking Is the shadow of a right triangle always a right triangle? Explain.

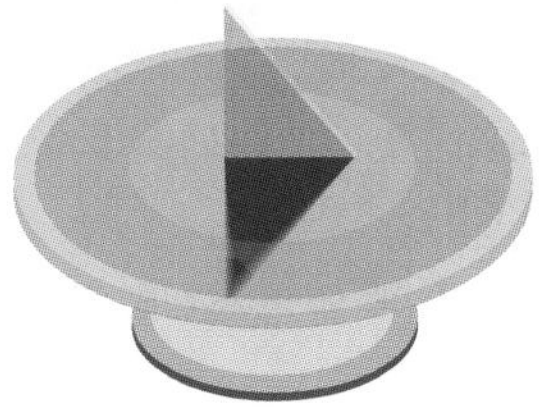

41. Choose a Strategy GPS A triangle has angles *A*, *B*, and *C*. The complement of $\angle A$ is 58°, and the supplement of $\angle B$ is 60°. What is the measure of $\angle C$? Explain your strategy.

Problem Solving STRATEGIES

- Look for a Pattern
- Make an Organized List
- Make a Table
- Guess and Check
- Work Backward
- Use Logical Reasoning
- Draw a Diagram
- Solve a Simpler Problem

Mixed Review

Write each decimal as a fraction in lowest terms. *[Lesson 5-7]*

42. 0.75 $\frac{3}{4}$ **43.** 0.78 $\frac{39}{50}$ **44.** 0.596 $\frac{149}{250}$ **45.** 0.9 $\frac{9}{10}$ **46.** 0.38 $\frac{19}{50}$ **47.** 0.72 $\frac{18}{25}$

48. 0.55 $\frac{11}{20}$ **49.** 0.138 $\frac{69}{500}$ **50.** 0.7 $\frac{7}{10}$ **51.** 0.375 $\frac{3}{8}$ **52.** 0.2 $\frac{1}{5}$ **53.** 0.999 $\frac{999}{1000}$

Estimate. *[Lesson 6-4]*

54. $5\frac{1}{2} - 4\frac{6}{8}$ 1 **55.** $2\frac{6}{7} + 2\frac{1}{9}$ 5 **56.** $4\frac{8}{9} - 2\frac{1}{3}$ 3 **57.** $9\frac{5}{6} + 5\frac{3}{4}$ 16

58. $6\frac{2}{7} + 9\frac{3}{7} + 4\frac{10}{11}$ 20 **59.** $8\frac{9}{14} - 3\frac{5}{6}$ 5 **60.** $7\frac{5}{7} + 7\frac{5}{7} + 6\frac{3}{5}$ 23 **61.** $9\frac{4}{8} - 4\frac{3}{6}$ 5

PROBLEM SOLVING 8-4

Exercise Answers

33.

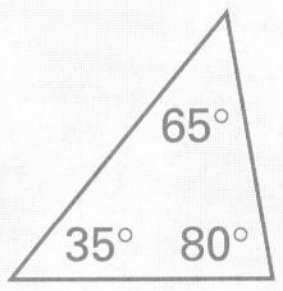

Acute

34.

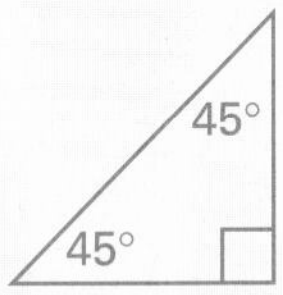

Right

35.

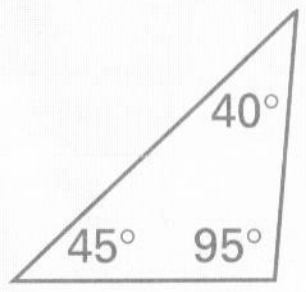

Obtuse

36. A triangle cannot be formed.

39. No; The area of a triangle depends on the lengths of the sides.

40. No; The shadow will be distorted depending on where the sun is.

41. 28°; $\angle A$ measures 90° − 58° which is 32°. $\angle B$ measures 180° − 60° which is 120°. $\angle C$ measures 180° − 32° − 120° which is 28°.

Alternate Assessment

Interview Ask students to explain how to classify a triangle as acute, right, or obtuse given the three angle measures of a triangle.

Quick Quiz

Classify each triangle as acute, right, or obtuse.

1. $\angle R = 70°, \angle S = 20°, \angle T = 90°$ Right
2. $\angle L = 41°, \angle M = 100°, \angle K = 39°$ Obtuse

Find the measure of the missing angle in each triangle.

3. $\angle A = 43°, \angle B = 22°, \angle C = ?$ 115°
4. $\angle P = 55°, \angle Q = 65°, \angle R = ?$ 60°

Available on Daily Transparency 8-4

PROBLEM SOLVING

Name ______________________

Guided Problem Solving 8-4

GPS **PROBLEM 41, STUDENT PAGE 427**

A triangle has angles *A, B,* and *C*. The complement of $\angle A$ is 58° and the supplement of $\angle B$ is 60°. What is the measure of $\angle C$? Explain your strategy.

Understand

1. Which angle's measurement are you to find? $\angle C$
2. Underline the information you need.

Plan

3. What is sum of the measures of two complementary angles? 90°
4. The complement of $\angle A$ is 58°. What is the measure of $\angle A$? 32°
5. What is sum of the measures of two supplementary angles? 180°
6. The supplement of $\angle B$ is 60°. What is the measure of $\angle B$? 120°
7. What is sum of the measures of the three angles in a triangle? 180°

Solve

8. Add the measurements of $\angle A$ and $\angle B$: 32° + 120° = 152°
9. Find the measure of $\angle C$: 180° − 152° = 28°
10. What is the measure of $\angle C$? 28°
11. What strategy did you use to find the measure of $\angle C$?
Possible answer: Use Logical Reasoning.

Look Back

12. What other strategies could you use to find the measure of $\angle C$?
Possible answers: Draw a Diagram. Solve a Simpler Problem.

SOLVE ANOTHER PROBLEM

A triangle has angles *D, E,* and *F.* The complement of $\angle D$ is 42° and the supplement of $\angle E$ is 54°. What is the measure of $\angle F$? 6°

ENRICHMENT

Name ______________________

Extend Your Thinking 8-4

Decision Making

Mandy wants to buy a necklace for a friend. She will buy a chain and gold letters to spell out a message. Consonants are on square "beads", and vowels (a, e, i, o, and u) are on triangular "beads." Each consonant costs $7. Each vowel costs $8. Gold beads to place between words are $5 each. She can buy a 16-inch chain for $10 or a 20-inch chain for $15.

1. Mandy wants the necklace to spell "MY BEST FRIEND." Draw the necklace with the appropriately shaped "beads."

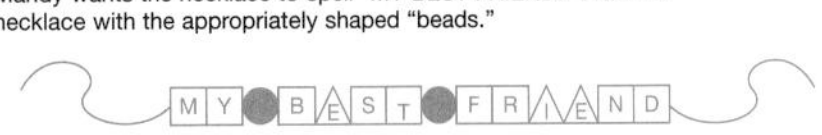

2. What will it cost to buy the beads for the necklace? $97
3. Mandy needs to buy a chain for the letters. What will the total cost be for the letters and the 16-inch chain? $107
4. Mandy decided that the necklace was too expensive. Write a phrase she could use with a 20-inch chain that would cost less than $70. Possible answers 4–6: "LOVE"
5. What is the cost of the necklace in Question 4? $45
6. Draw the necklace with the phrase you selected in Question 4.

7. Another store has the "beads" in plastic rather than gold. The price for each plastic bead is $\frac{1}{4}$ the cost of the gold beads. What is the cost of a 20-inch necklace with the phrase "My Best Friend?" $39.25
8. What is the advantage in buying the gold "beads." Possible answer: Gold "beads" are sturdier and better looking.
9. What is the advantage in buying the plastic "beads." Possible answer: Plastic "beads" have a more reasonable cost.
10. Suppose you buy a "bead" necklace for a friend. Choose a phrase and draw the necklace. Write the length of the chain and whether or not you are using plastic or gold "beads." Then find the cost.
Check students' work.

8-5 Lesson Organizer

Objective

- Classify triangles according to their sides.

Vocabulary

- Equilateral triangle, isosceles triangle, scalene triangle

Materials

- Explore: Cuisenaire rods

NCTM Standards

- 1–4, 12

▶ Review

Answer the following questions. Draw pictures if necessary.

1. Can a right triangle have two sides of equal length? Yes Three sides of equal length? No
2. Can an acute triangle have two sides of equal length? Yes Three sides of equal length? Yes
3. Can an obtuse triangle have two sides of equal length? Yes Three sides of equal length? No

Available on Daily Transparency 8-5

1 Introduce

Explore

The Point
Students use sets of three Cuisenaire rods to discover that the length of two rods together has to be longer than the third to form a triangle.

Ongoing Assessment
Watch for students who have difficulty determining if the rods can actually form a triangle.

For Groups That Finish Early
If three identical rods are used, will they always form a triangle? Yes

8-5 Exploring Sides of a Triangle

You'll Learn ...
- to classify triangles according to their sides

... How It's Used
Sculptors classify triangles when designing a sculpture.

Vocabulary
equilateral triangle
isosceles triangle
scalene triangle

▶ **Lesson Link** You have investigated classifying triangles by their angles. Now you'll see how to classify triangles by the lengths of their sides. ◀

Explore Sides of a Triangle

Pick Up Sticks

Materials: Cuisenaire rods

1. For each given set of rods, determine if the rods can be placed together to form a triangle. In order to count as a triangle, every rod must be touching corner to corner.

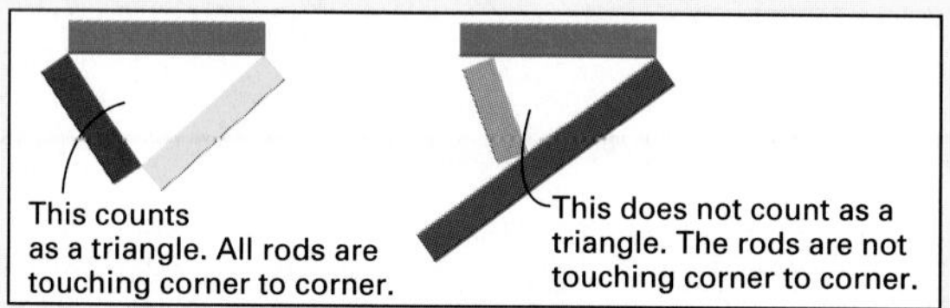

This counts as a triangle. All rods are touching corner to corner.
This does not count as a triangle. The rods are not touching corner to corner.

   a. Orange, blue, dark green
   b. Light green, yellow, dark green
   c. Red, white, black
   d. Yellow, brown, light green
   e. Dark green, yellow, red
   f. Purple, dark green, white
   g. Orange, blue, white
   h. Black, dark green, red

2. Find five new sets of three rods that can form a triangle. Find five new sets of three rods that cannot form a triangle.
3. Without actually putting them together, how can you tell whether or not three rods will form a triangle?

Learn Sides of a Triangle

An **equilateral triangle** has three sides of the same length.

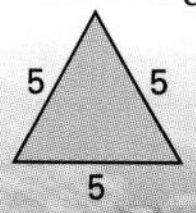

An **isosceles triangle** has two sides of the same length.

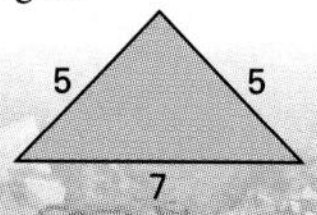

A **scalene triangle** has no sides of equal length.

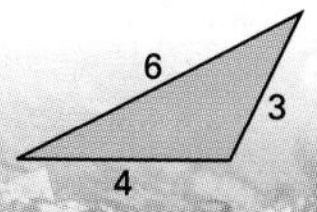

MEETING INDIVIDUAL NEEDS

Resources

- 8-5 Practice
- 8-5 Reteaching
- 8-5 Problem Solving
- 8-5 Enrichment
- 8-5 Daily Transparency
  - Problem of the Day
  - Review
  - Quick Quiz
- Technology Master 39
- Chapter 0 Project Master
- *Wide World of Mathematics* Middle School: Youthbuild

Learning Modalities

Kinesthetic Wood strips or twigs of various lengths are useful if Cuisenaire rods are not available.

Social Give students the chance to work together if they are having trouble understanding why some side lengths will not form a triangle.

English Language Development

The vocabulary words in this lesson may be difficult for many students. It might be helpful to write *equilateral*, *isosceles*, and *scalene* on index cards and break the words apart into syllables with phonic markings. The index cards should contain a drawing of each triangle.

Example 1

The diamond is cut in the "American brilliant" style. Classify the triangles as shown that form facets *a*, *b*, and *c*.

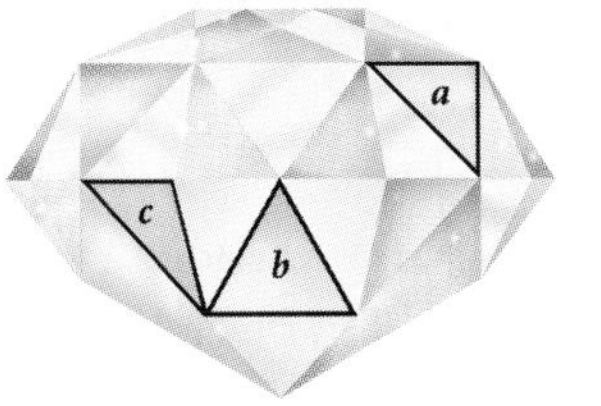

Triangle *a* has 2 equal sides, so it is isosceles. Triangle *b* has 3 equal sides, so it is equilateral. Triangle *c* has no equal sides, so it is scalene.

In order for three lengths to form a triangle, the sum of the two shortest lengths must be greater than the longest length.

In the first cabin, the combined heights of the walls was *greater than* the length of the floor.

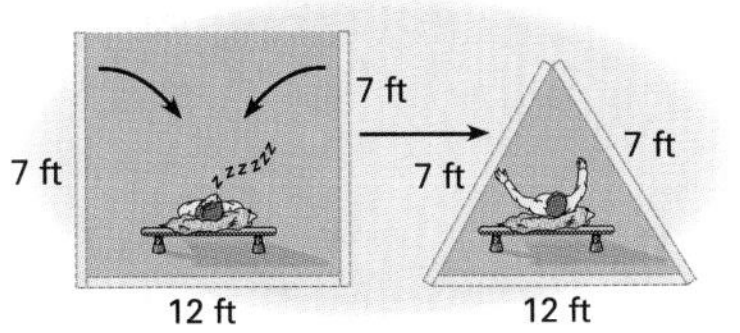

In the second cabin, the combined heights of the walls was *less than* the length of the floor.

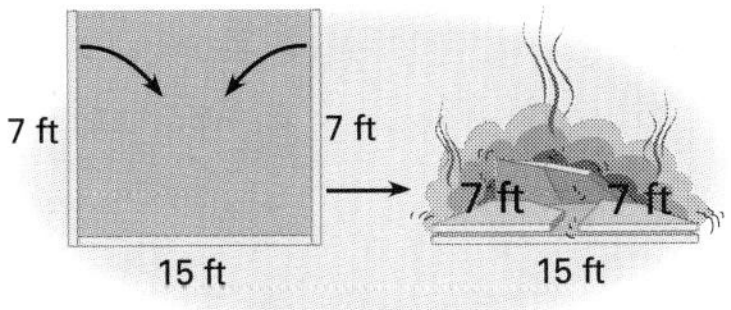

Examples

State whether the given lengths can form a triangle.

2 5 in., 9 in., 13 in.

$5 + 9 > 13$
A triangle can be formed.

3 10 cm, 14 cm, 25 cm

$10 + 14 < 25$
A triangle cannot be formed.

Try It

State whether the given lengths can form a triangle.

a. 2 ft, 5 ft, 6 ft Yes **b.** 11 in., 3 in., 8 in. No **c.** 3 m, 6 m, 2 m No

Check Your Understanding

1. Can a right triangle also be isosceles? Explain.

2. Do all equilateral triangles have the same shape? The same size? Explain.

DID YOU KNOW?

The four measures of the quality of a diamond are known to some jewelers as the "four C's": color, cut, clarity, and carat (weight).

MATH EVERY DAY

Problem of the Day

How many triangles are in the figure below?

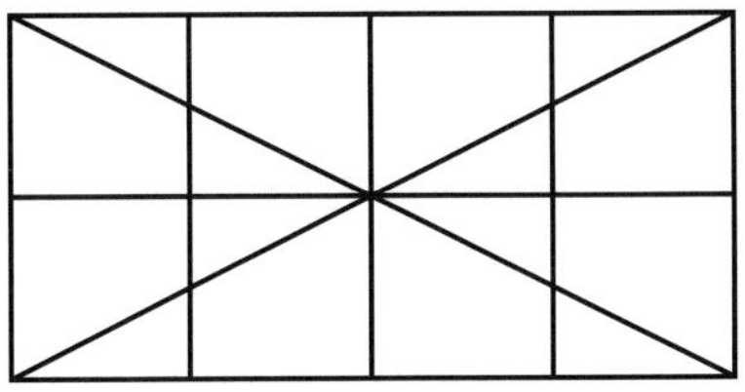

30 triangles

Available on Daily Transparency 8-5

An Extension is provided in the transparency package.

Fact of the Day

Diamonds are weighed in carats. One carat is 200 milligrams. The famous Blue Hope diamond weighs 44.5 carats.

Mental Math

Find each sum mentally.

1. $80 + 90$ 170
2. $70 + 40$ 110
3. $50 + 70$ 120
4. $90 + 90$ 180
5. $30 + 90$ 120

Answers for Explore

1. a. Yes; b. Yes; c. No; d. No; e. Yes; f. No; g. No; h. Yes
2. Possible answers: Orange, dark green, black; Orange, dark green, yellow; Orange, dark green, brown. Possible answers: Orange, dark green, purple; Orange, dark green, white; orange, dark green, red; Orange, dark green, light green.
3. The two shorter rods together have to be longer than the third.

2 Teach

Learn

Alternate Examples

1. Classify the triangles.

a. Scalene

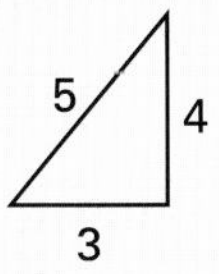

b. Isosceles

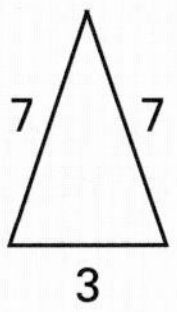

c. Equilateral

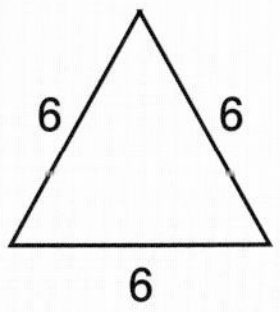

State whether the given lengths can form a triangle.

2. 10 in., 7 in., 18 in.

$10 + 7 < 18$
A triangle cannot be formed.

3. 9 cm, 12 cm, 15 cm

$9 + 12 > 15.$
A triangle can be formed.

3 Practice and Assess

Check

Answers for Check Your Understanding

1. Yes; The sides making the right angle need to be the same length.
2. Yes; The angles are always 60°; No; The lengths of the sides of one triangle can be different from the lengths of the sides of another.

8-5 Exercises and Applications

Assignment Guide

- **Basic** 1–4, 6–28 evens, 29–33, 38–42, 43–49 odds
- **Average** 3–4, 8–28 evens, 29–49 odds
- **Enriched** 3–4, 10–28 evens, 29–37, 38–50 evens

Exercise Notes

Exercise 18

Error Prevention Watch for students who think that the lengths can form a triangle because the sum of the first two lengths is greater than the third. Stress that the sum of the two shortest lengths must be greater than the third.

Exercise 28

Test Prep Stress the importance of reading the question carefully. Choices A and C classify the triangle by the measure of its angles. Only choices B and D classify the triangle by the lengths of its sides. Therefore, there are only two possible answers to choose from.

Reteaching

Activity

Materials: Cardboard or paper, centimeter ruler

- Work with a partner.
- Make cardboard or paper strips of the following lengths: 3 cm, 4 cm, 5 cm, 6 cm, 7 cm, 8 cm, 9 cm, 10 cm, 11 cm, and 12 cm.
- Label each strip with the correct length. Then put all the strips in a bag.
- Pick three strips at random. Record the lengths of each strip. Form a triangle if possible. If not, write no after the lengths.
- Replace the strips and repeat the process.
- Make a list of all sets of three strips that do form a triangle.
- Explain to your partner how you can always tell whether three lengths will form a triangle.

8-5 Exercises and Applications

Practice and Apply

Getting Started **Given the lengths of two sides of a triangle, state the greatest whole-number measurement that is possible for the third.**

1. 1 m, 4 m **4 m** **2.** 2 in., 6 in. **7 in.** **3.** 10 ft, 11 ft **20 ft** **4.** 4 cm, 6 cm **9 cm** **5.** 5 yd, 5 yd **9 yd**

For Exercises 6–17, classify each triangle as scalene, equilateral, or isosceles.

6.

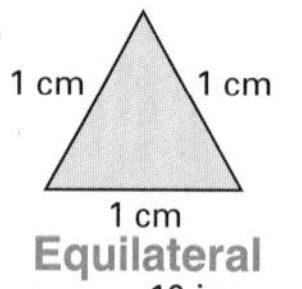

Equilateral

7.

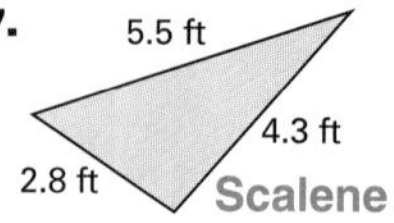

Scalene

8.

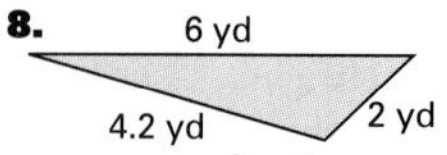

Scalene

9.

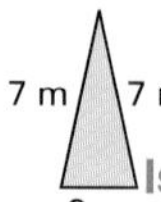

Isosceles

10.

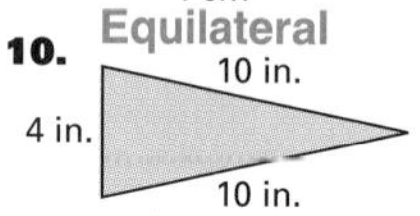

Isosceles

11.

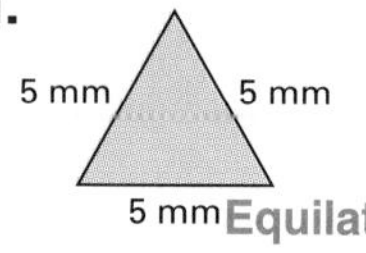

Equilateral

12.

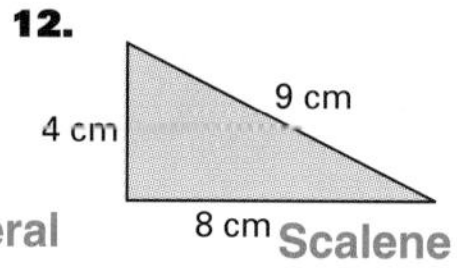

Scalene

13.

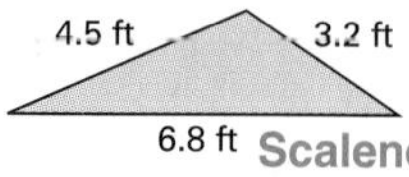

Scalene

14. Sides: 40 cm, 55 cm, 45 cm **Scalene**

15. Sides: 1.67 in., 1.53 in., 0.28 in. **Scalene**

16. Sides: 3 yd, 9 yd, 9 yd **Isosceles**

17. Sides: 6 in., 6 in., 6 in. **Equilateral**

State whether the given lengths can form a triangle. If they can, draw the triangle and classify it.

18. 5 cm, 3 cm, 2 cm **No** **19.** 3 in., 6 in., 8 in. **Yes** **20.** 7 m, 7 m, 10 m **Yes**

21. 2.1 ft, 4.6 ft, 3.1 ft **Yes** **22.** 15 cm, 7 cm, 7 cm **No** **23.** 3 in., 6 in., 9 in. **No**

24. 10 mm, 10 mm, 10 mm **Yes** **25.** 9.6 yd, 9.4 yd, 9.3 yd **Yes** **26.** 2 yd, 14 yd, 7 yd **No**

27. History In ancient times it was thought that rock crystal was ice that had frozen so hard it would never melt. We know now that it is formed by other molecules, like silicon dioxide. Classify the triangular face of the smokey quartz rock crystal shown by the lengths of its sides. **Scalene**

28. **Test Prep** Classify the triangle by the lengths of its sides. **B**

Ⓐ acute
Ⓑ isosceles
Ⓒ obtuse
Ⓓ scalene

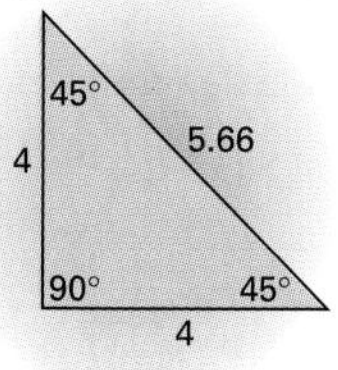

PRACTICE

Name ____________________ **Practice 8-5**

Exploring Sides of a Triangle

For Exercises 1–8, classify each triangle as scalene, equilateral, or isosceles.

1. Scalene 2. Equilateral 3. Scalene 4. Isosceles

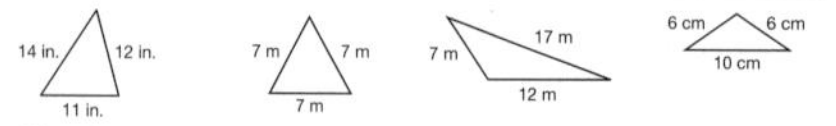

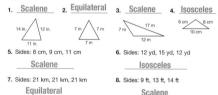

5. Sides: 8 cm, 9 cm, 11 cm **Scalene**
6. Sides: 12 yd, 15 yd, 12 yd **Isosceles**
7. Sides: 21 km, 21 km, 21 km **Equilateral**
8. Sides: 9 ft, 13 ft, 14 ft **Scalene**

State whether the given lengths can form a triangle. If they can, draw the triangle and classify it. **Drawings are possible answers.**

9. 9 in., 3 in., 10 in. **Scalene triangle**
10. 20 cm, 15 cm, 5 cm **Cannot form a triangle**

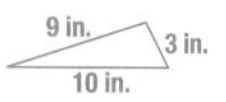

11. 8 ft, 8 ft, 8 ft **Equilateral triangle**
12. 8 m, 8 m, 12 m **Isosceles triangle**

13. Carolyn made a triangular painting and measured its sides. The numbers she wrote down were 35 cm, 55 cm, and 95 cm. She said, "That can't be right. I must have made a mistake." How did she know?
Possible answer: 35 + 55 is not greater than 95.

RETEACHING

Name ____________________ **Alternative Lesson 8-5**

Exploring Sides of a Triangle

Triangles can be classified by the lengths of their sides.

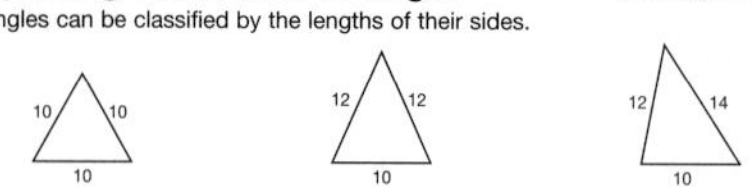

An **equilateral triangle** has three sides of the same length. An **isosceles triangle** has two sides of the same length. A **scalene triangle** has no sides of equal length.

In order for three lengths to form a triangle, the sum of the two shortest lengths must be greater than the longest length.

— Example 1 —

Classify the triangle as scalene, equilateral, or isosceles.

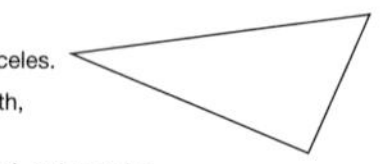

None of the sides of the triangle are the same length, so the figure is a scalene triangle.

Try It Classify each triangle as scalene, equilateral, or isosceles.

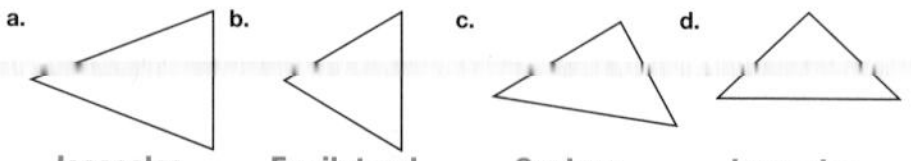

a. **Isosceles.** b. **Equilateral.** c. **Scalene.** d. **Isosceles.**

— Example 2 —

State whether these lengths can form a triangle: 19 cm, 14 cm, 28 cm.

Add the lengths of the two shortest sides. 19 + 14 = 33

Compare the sum to the lengths of the longest side. 33 > 28

Since the sum of the lengths of the two shorter sides is greater than the length of the longest side, a triangle can be formed.

Try It State whether the given lengths can form a triangle. Write *yes* or *no*.

e. 3 in., 3 in., 3 in. Write the sum of the lengths of the two shorter sides. **6 in.**
Compare sum to longer line's length. Can a triangle be formed? **Yes.**

f. 23 cm, 27 cm, 78 cm **No.** g. 1.5 yd, 4.2 yd, 2.7 yd **No.**

h. 13 ft, 18 ft, 13 ft **Yes.** i. 113 mm, 143 mm, 192 mm **Yes.**

29. Geometry Jeremy has two poles for the end of his tent. They are each 4 feet long. Can he form the triangular end of his tent if he puts two ends together and places the other ends 9 feet apart? No

GPS

Problem Solving and Reasoning

Critical Thinking Classify each triangle as acute, right, or obtuse, and also as equilateral, isosceles, or scalene.

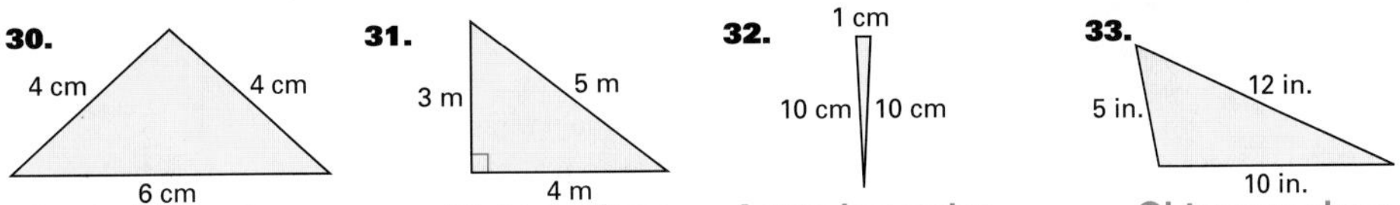

30. Acute isosceles
31. Right scalene
32. Acute isosceles
33. Obtuse scalene

Critical Thinking Explain whether it is possible to draw each triangle. If it is possible, draw the triangle.

34. An obtuse right triangle **35.** A scalene acute triangle **36.** An isosceles right triangle

37. Communicate If you fold an equilateral triangle in half, what kind of triangles are the smaller two triangles? Explain.

Mixed Review

Compare using, >, <, or =. *[Lesson 5-8]*

38. $\frac{3}{4}$ [>] $\frac{1}{3}$ **39.** $\frac{7}{8}$ [>] $\frac{6}{7}$ **40.** $\frac{5}{9}$ [<] $\frac{7}{10}$ **41.** $\frac{2}{4}$ [=] $\frac{9}{18}$ **42.** $\frac{20}{10}$ [<] $\frac{15}{3}$

Simplify. *[Lesson 6-5]*

43. $4\frac{3}{5} + 6\frac{2}{3}$ $11\frac{4}{15}$ **44.** $3\frac{1}{4} + 4\frac{3}{7}$ $7\frac{19}{28}$ **45.** $10 + 13\frac{4}{8}$ $23\frac{1}{2}$ **46.** $62\frac{3}{4} + 3\frac{5}{9}$ $66\frac{11}{36}$

47. $6\frac{1}{5} + 5\frac{2}{7}$ $11\frac{17}{35}$ **48.** $8\frac{4}{7} + 9\frac{10}{14}$ $18\frac{2}{7}$ **49.** $5\frac{6}{7} + 1\frac{4}{5}$ $7\frac{23}{35}$ **50.** $7\frac{2}{7} + 4\frac{6}{9}$ $11\frac{20}{21}$

Project Progress

When you have finished your rough sketch, draw a revised version. Add any polygons as needed, and describe these polygons.

Problem Solving
Understand
Plan
Solve
Look Back

PROBLEM SOLVING

Name ______________________

Guided Problem Solving 8-5

GPS PROBLEM 29, STUDENT PAGE 431

Jeremy has two poles for the end of his tent. They are each 4 feet long. Can he form the triangular end of his tent if he puts two ends together and places the other ends 9 feet apart?

— Understand —

1. What figure will be formed by the two poles and the ground? Triangle.
2. What are the lengths of each of the two poles? 4 feet.
3. How far apart will Jeremy place the ends of the poles? 9 feet.

— Plan —

4. Is the sum of the two shorter sides of a triangle greater or less than the length of the longer side? Greater than.
5. What is the length of the longest side of the figure formed? 9 feet.
6. Write an equation to find the sum of the two shorter tent poles? 4 + 4 = 8

— Solve —

7. Is the sum in Item 6 greater than or less than the length of the longest side? Less than.
8. Can Jeremy place the poles 9 feet apart? No.

— Look Back —

9. What other strategy could you use to find the answer? Possible answer: Draw a diagram.

SOLVE ANOTHER PROBLEM

Diana has two poles for the end of her tent. They are each 8 feet long. Can she form the triangular end of her tent if she puts two ends together and places the other ends 10 feet apart? Explain.

Yes, the sum of the shorter sides is 16. Since 16 is greater than 10, the poles could form a triangle.

ENRICHMENT

Name ______________________

Extend Your Thinking 8-5

Visual Thinking

Circle the letters of the two shapes that are identical.

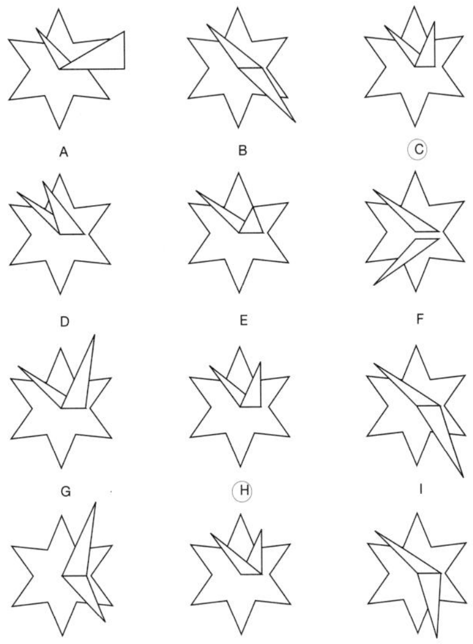

Project Progress

You may want to have students use Chapter 8 Project Master.

Exercise Answers

19. 6 in., 3 in., 8 in. Scalene

20. 7 m, 7 m, 10 m Isosceles

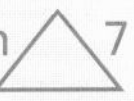

21. 3.1 ft, 2.1 ft, 4.6 ft Scalene

24. 10 mm, 10 mm, 10 mm Equilateral

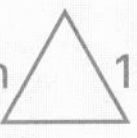

25. 9.4 yd, 9.3 yd, 9.6 yd Scalene

34. No; A right triangle must also have two acute angles.

35. Yes

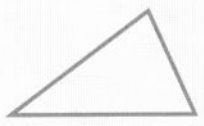

36. Yes

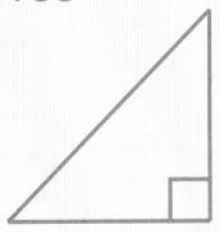

37. Right scalene triangles

Alternate Assessment

You may want to use *Interactive CD-ROM Journal* with this assessment.

Journal Write a paragraph comparing classifying triangles according to angles and according to lengths of the sides.

Quick Quiz

Classify each triangle as scalene, equilateral, or isosceles.

1. Sides: 17 cm, 21 cm, 17 cm Isosceles
2. Sides: 24 in., 19 in., 12 in. Scalene

State whether the given lengths can form a triangle.

3. 8 cm, 10 cm, 12 cm Yes
4. 24 ft, 10 ft, 10 ft No

Available on Daily Transparency 8-5

8-6 Lesson Organizer

Objective

- Classify polygons.

Vocabulary

- Polygon, quadrilateral, pentagon, hexagon, octagon, regular polygon

NCTM Standards

- 1–7, 12

► Review

Which figures are rectangles? If a figure is not a rectangle, explain why.

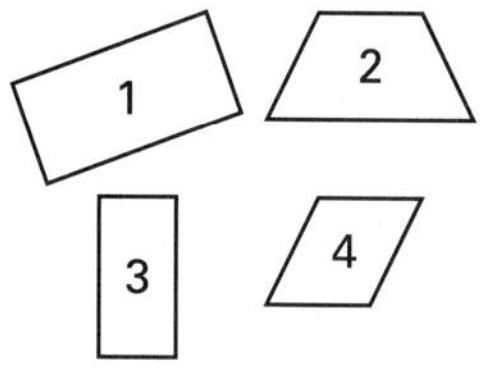

1 and 3 are rectangles; 2 and 4 are not rectangles because the angles are not all right angles.

Available on Daily Transparency 8-6

1 Introduce

Explore

You may wish to use Lesson Enhancement Transparency 38 with **Explore**.

The Point
Students sort a group of 12 shapes into four groups of three so that the shapes in each group have something in common.

Ongoing Assessment
Watch for students who consider characteristics that would cause a group to have more or less than three figures. For example, they might put triangles in one group, but there are four triangles pictured.

For Groups That Finish Early
Which figures have all angles equal? 1, 8, 10

8-6 Polygons

You'll Learn ...

- to classify polygons

... How It's Used

Motorists classify shapes when reading traffic signs.

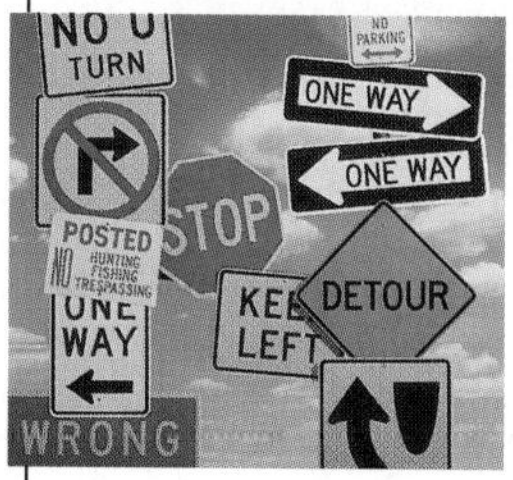

Vocabulary

polygon
quadrilateral
pentagon
hexagon
octagon
regular polygon

► Lesson Link In the last lesson, you studied triangles—figures with three sides and three angles. Now you'll look at figures with more than three sides and three angles. ◄

Explore Geometric Figures

Shape Shifters

1. Put the twelve figures at the right into four groups of three. The figures within a group must have something in common. Every figure must belong to one and only one group.
2. For each group, write one or two sentences explaining what the figures have in common.
3. Add a fifth group of three figures. These three figures must also have a common feature, but it cannot be the same as any of the features used for the first four groups.
4. In general, what features of a figure are important when comparing it to other figures?

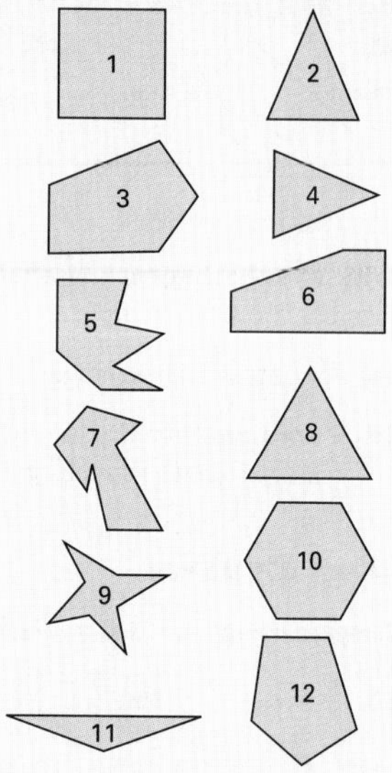

Learn Polygons

A **polygon** is a closed figure made of line segments. The word *polygon* comes from Greek and means "many angled."

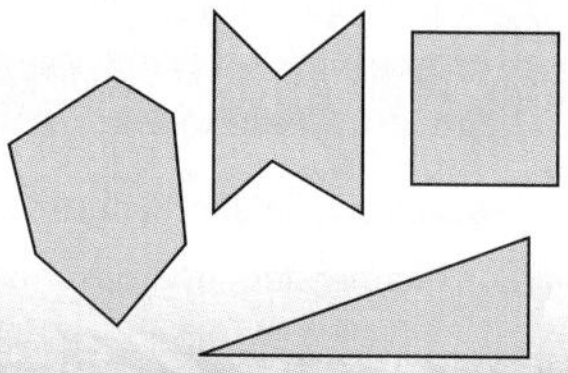

MEETING INDIVIDUAL NEEDS

Resources

8-6 Practice
8-6 Reteaching
8-6 Problem Solving
8-6 Enrichment
8-6 Daily Transparency
Problem of the Day
Review
Quick Quiz
Teaching Tool Transparency 20
Lesson Enhancement Transparencies 38, 39
Technology Master 40

Learning Modalities

Verbal Have students describe the polygons shown in **Explore**. Encourage students to be as specific as possible with their descriptions.

Visual Give students the opportunity to identify various examples of polygons found in books, magazines, or newspapers.

English Language Development

Students are presented with an unusual amount of vocabulary in this lesson. Have students prepare index cards with drawings and names of each type of polygon discussed in this lesson. Their drawings should include regular and irregular figures. Stress that the word *regular* is used to mean *the same* when describing polygons. A regular polygon has all sides the same length and all angles the same measure.

Polygons are classified by the number of sides they have. You've already studied the *triangle*, which has 3 sides. These are also polygons:

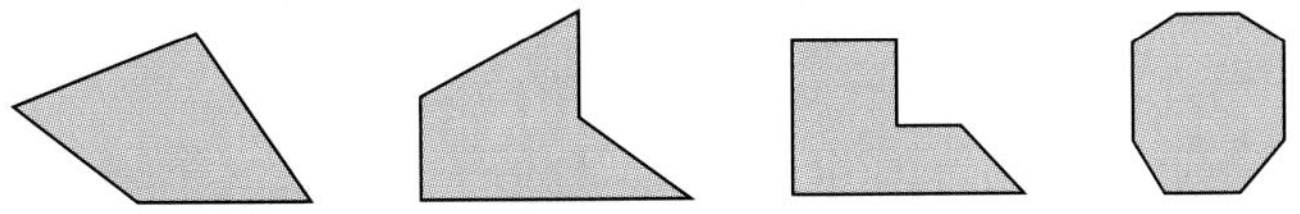

quadrilateral	**pentagon**	**hexagon**	**octagon**
4 sides	5 sides	6 sides	8 sides

In a **regular polygon**, all the sides and all the angles have the same measures.

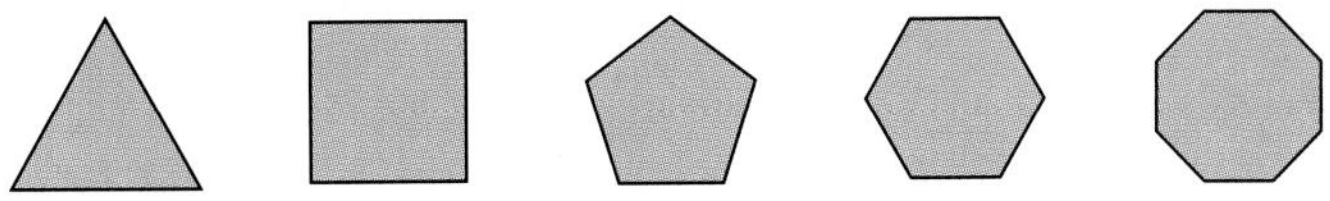

DID YOU KNOW?

The terms *heptagon* (7-sided figure), *nonagon* (9-sided figure), *decagon* (10-sided figure), and *dodecagon* (12-sided figure) are less common geometry terms.

Examples

Name each polygon and tell if it is regular or irregular.

1

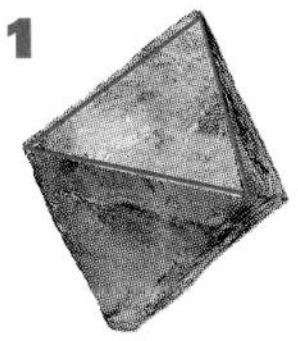

The figure is a triangle. Its sides and angles are equal, so it is regular.

2

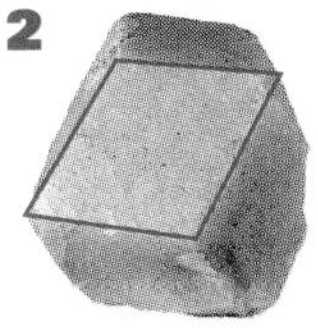

The figure is a quadrilateral. Neither its sides nor its angles are equal, so it is irregular.

3

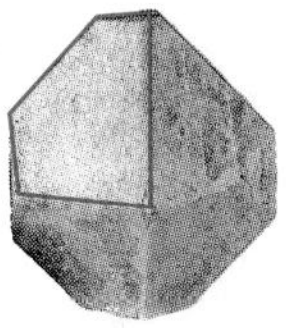

The figure is a pentagon. Neither its sides nor its angles are equal, so it is irregular.

Try It

Name each polygon and tell if it is regular or irregular.

a.

Regular quadrilateral

b.

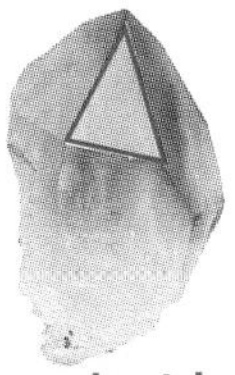

Irregular triangle

c.

Irregular pentagon

MATH EVERY DAY

Problem of the Day

Martha wants to go to a movie. Andy wants to go skating. Priscilla wants to play basketball. Mario wants to go to a museum. The four friends decide they have time to do two of the four activities. They write each activity on a card and put all the cards in a box. If two cards are drawn out of the box, what are the chances that they will go to a movie and play basketball? 1 out of 6

Available on Daily Transparency 8-6

An Extension is provided in the transparency package.

Fact of the Day

The black-and-white devilfish, a kind of manta ray, measures more than 6.5 meters from the tip of one wing to the tip of the other.

Estimation

Estimate each sum.

1. 188 + 308 500
2. 721 + 102 800
3. 4567 + 3076 8000
4. 1211 + 7891 + 4321 13,000
5. 6789 + 1211 + 5905 14,000

Answers for Explore

1–2. 5, 7, 9: eight sides; 2, 4, 11: isosceles triangles; 3, 6, 12: five sides; 1, 8, 10: angles within a shape are the same size and sides within a shape are same length.

3. Possible answer: Draw three right triangles.

4. Number of sides, angle size, and side length.

2 Teach

Learn

You may wish to use Teaching Tool Transparency 20: Tangrams and Lesson Enhancement Transparency 39 with this lesson.

Alternate Examples

Name each polygon and tell if it is regular or irregular.

1. 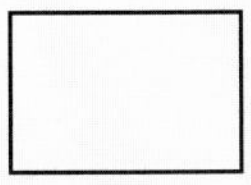

The figure is a quadrilateral. Its angles are equal but its sides are not, so it is irregular.

2. 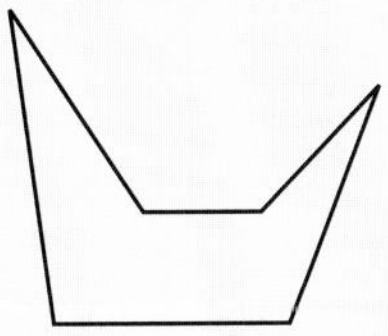

The figure is a hexagon. Neither its sides nor its angles are equal, so it is irregular.

3. 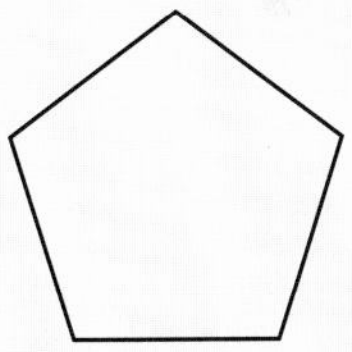

The figure is a pentagon. Its sides and angles are equal, so it is regular.

8-6 Exercises and Applications

Assignment Guide

- Basic
  1–25, 19–28, 30–48 evens
- Average
  1–12, 16–48 evens
- Enriched
  9–31, 33–49 odds

3 Practice and Assess

Check

Answers for Check Your Understanding

1. Yes; The angles and the sides have the same measures.
2. Possible answers: Books, ceiling tiles, floor tiles, windows, stop signs, panes, desks.

Exercise Answers

13. acute angles

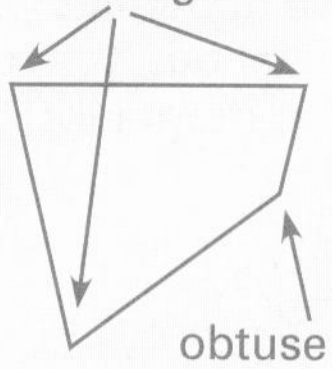

obtuse angle

14.

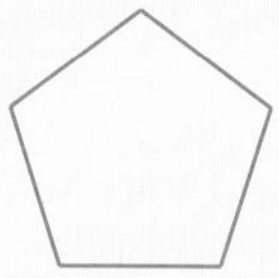

obtuse angles

15.

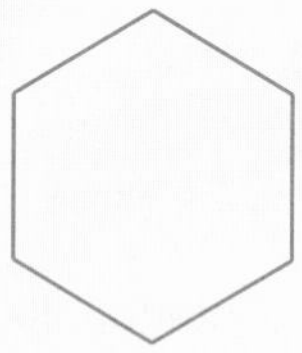

obtuse angles

Reteaching

Activity

Materials: Photos from magazines or newspapers

- Work in groups of three. Use photos from magazines or newspapers and find examples of at least four different polygons that you studied in this lesson.
- Cut out the photos and label them with their correct names.

Check Your Understanding

1. Is an equilateral triangle a regular polygon? Explain.
2. Name something that is the shape of a quadrilateral; a pentagon; a hexagon; an octagon.

8-6 Exercises and Applications

PRACTICE 8-6

Practice and Apply

Getting Started State why each figure is not a polygon.

1. 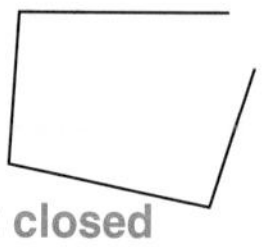
Not closed

2. 
No line segments

3. 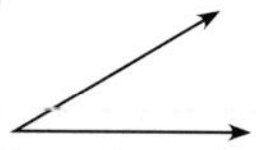
Not closed

4. 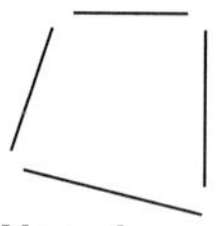
Not closed

Name each polygon and tell if it is regular or irregular.

5. 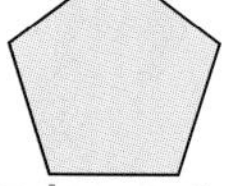
Regular pentagon

6. 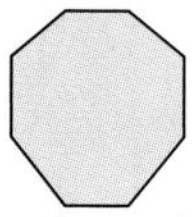
Irregular octagon

7. 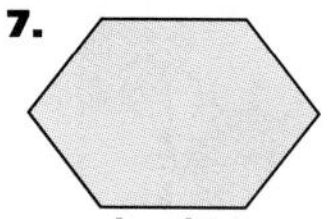
Irregular hexagon

8. 
Regular quadrilateral

9. 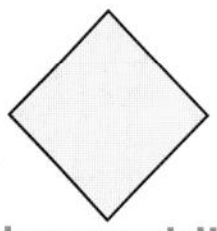
Regular quadrilateral

10. 
Irregular quadrilateral

11. 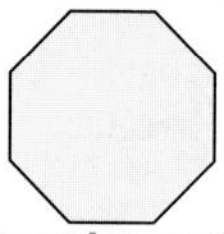
Regular octagon

12. 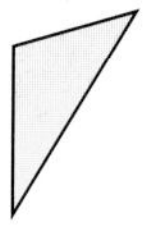
Irregular triangle

Draw an example of each figure and classify each of the angles in your drawing.

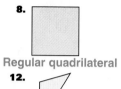

13. Irregular quadrilateral
14. Regular pentagon
15. Regular hexagon
16. Irregular octagon
17. Regular triangle
18. Irregular pentagon

Industry What kind of polygon is each traffic sign?

19. 

Octagon

20. 

Triangle

21. 
Pentagon

22. 

Quadrilateral

PRACTICE

Name ______________________

Practice 8-6

Polygons

Name each polygon and tell if it is regular or irregular.

1. Hexagon, regular

2. Pentagon, irregular

3. Octagon, irregular

4. Quadrilateral, irregular
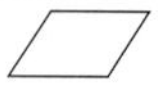

Draw an example of each figure and classify each of the angles in your drawing.
Possible answers:

5. Irregular hexagon

2 acute angles,
4 obtuse angles

6. Regular quadilateral

4 right angles

7. Irregular triangle

1 right angle,
2 acute angles

8. Regular octagon
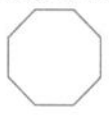
8 obtuse angles

What kind of polygon is each mask?

9. Pentagon 10. Octagon 11. Quadrilateral 12. Triangle

13. **Social Science** The offices of the U.S. Department of Defense are located in an Arlington, Virginia, building called the Pentagon. How many sides do you think the shape of this building has? 5

RETEACHING

Name ______________________

Alternative Lesson 8-6

Polygons

A **polygon** is a closed figure made of line segments. Polygons are classified by the number of sides they have. A triangle is a polygon with 3 sides. In a **regular polygon**, all the sides and all the angles have the same measures.

Irregular Polygon / Regular Polygon

A **quadrilateral** has 4 sides.
A **pentagon** has 5 sides.
A **hexagon** has 6 sides.
An **octagon** has 8 sides.

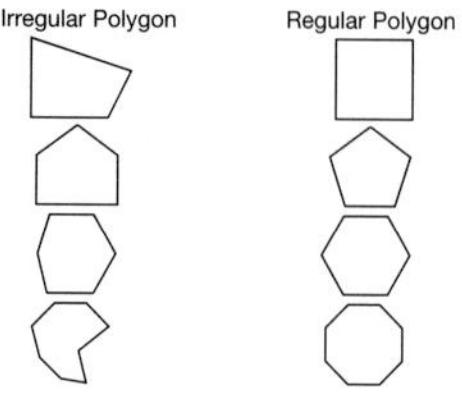

Example

Name the polygon and tell if it is regular or irregular.

The polygon has five sides, so it is a pentagon.
Its sides and angles are equal, so it is regular.
The polygon is a regular pentagon.

Try It Name each polygon and tell if it is regular or irregular.

a. 
Regular octagon.

b. 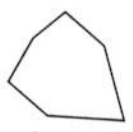
Irregular hexagon.

c. 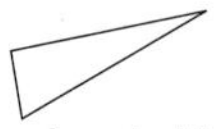
Irregular triangle.

d. 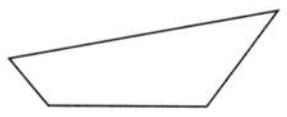
Irregular quadrilateral.

e. 
Regular hexagon.

f. 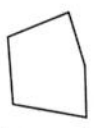
Irregular pentagon.

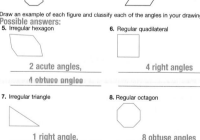

23. **Science** Rays and skates are relatives of sharks. Their fins are greatly enlarged and flap like wings when they swim. What polygon can the shape of the ray shown be most closely classified as? Triangle

Geometry State the shape of the crystal face.

24.  Triangle

25.  Quadrilateral

26. 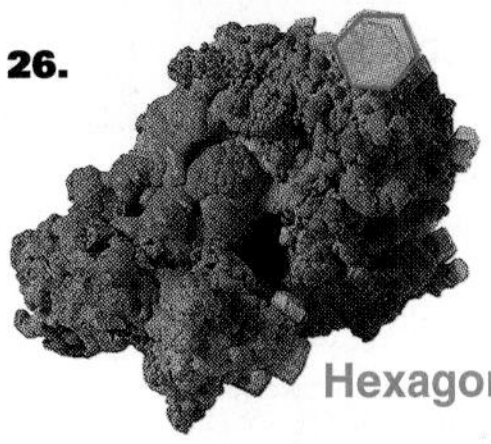 Hexagon

27. The floor of a ballroom in a large hotel is shaped like an octagon. How many walls does the room have? 8

28. **Test Prep** Classify the polygon. D

Ⓐ Regular quadrilateral Ⓑ Irregular pentagon

Ⓒ Regular hexagon Ⓓ Irregular octagon

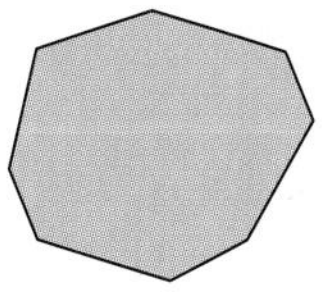

Problem Solving and Reasoning

29. **Critical Thinking** Find the perimeter of a regular octagon with one side measuring 5 inches. Explain how you could find the area of the figure.

30. **Critical Thinking** The lengths of the sides of a quadrilateral are 3.5 ft, $\frac{7}{2}$ ft, $3\frac{1}{2}$ ft, and $2\frac{3}{2}$ ft. Is the quadrilateral regular or irregular? Explain. GPS

31. Journal Classify acute, right, obtuse, equilateral, isosceles, and scalene triangles as regular or irregular polygons. Explain your reasoning.

PROBLEM SOLVING 8-6

Mixed Review

Order from smallest to largest. *[Lesson 5-8]*

32. $\frac{3}{5}, \frac{3}{6}, \frac{3}{7}$ $\frac{3}{7}, \frac{3}{6}, \frac{3}{5}$

33. $\frac{8}{9}, \frac{4}{5}, \frac{7}{8}$ $\frac{4}{5}, \frac{7}{8}, \frac{8}{9}$

34. $\frac{13}{2}, \frac{12}{3}, \frac{14}{15}$ $\frac{14}{15}, \frac{12}{3}, \frac{13}{2}$

35. $\frac{6}{9}, \frac{9}{6}, \frac{6}{6}$ $\frac{6}{9}, \frac{6}{6}, \frac{9}{6}$

36. $\frac{24}{3}, \frac{24}{8}, \frac{24}{6}$ $\frac{24}{8}, \frac{24}{6}, \frac{24}{3}$

37. $\frac{1}{2}, \frac{1}{3}, \frac{1}{4}$ $\frac{1}{4}, \frac{1}{3}, \frac{1}{2}$

38. $\frac{4}{6}, \frac{6}{8}, \frac{8}{10}$ $\frac{4}{6}, \frac{6}{8}, \frac{8}{10}$

39. $\frac{6}{7}, \frac{7}{6}, \frac{9}{8}$ $\frac{6}{7}, \frac{9}{8}, \frac{7}{6}$

Simplify. *[Lesson 6-6]*

40. $3\frac{3}{4} - 1\frac{2}{3}$ $2\frac{1}{12}$

41. $5\frac{4}{7} - 3\frac{4}{5}$ $1\frac{27}{35}$

42. $6\frac{1}{3} - 3\frac{2}{6}$ 3

43. $4\frac{3}{8} - 4\frac{1}{4}$ $\frac{1}{8}$

44. $8\frac{5}{6} - 7\frac{1}{3}$ $1\frac{1}{2}$

45. $12\frac{5}{8} - 9\frac{3}{7}$ $3\frac{11}{56}$

46. $9\frac{2}{5} - 4\frac{6}{7}$ $4\frac{19}{35}$

47. $7\frac{1}{3} - \frac{8}{9}$ $6\frac{4}{9}$

48. $3\frac{3}{4} - 1\frac{3}{8}$ $2\frac{3}{8}$

49. $6\frac{4}{7} - 2\frac{1}{4}$ $4\frac{9}{28}$

PROBLEM SOLVING

Name ______________________

Guided Problem Solving 8-6

GPS **PROBLEM 30, STUDENT PAGE 435**

The lengths of the sides of a quadrilateral are 3.5 ft, $\frac{7}{2}$ ft, $3\frac{1}{2}$ ft, and $2\frac{3}{2}$ ft. Is the quadrilateral regular or irregular? Explain.

— Understand — Possible answer: Item 8

1. Underline the lengths of the sides of the quadrilateral.
2. Circle what the problem asks you to find.
3. How do you know if a polygon is regular? All sides and all angles have the same measures.

— Plan —

4. Write each measure as an improper fraction.

a. 3.5 $\frac{7}{2}$ b. $\frac{7}{2}$ $\frac{7}{2}$ c. $3\frac{1}{2}$ $\frac{7}{2}$ d. $2\frac{3}{2}$ $\frac{7}{2}$

5. Draw a quadrilateral using the given sides and making sure all 4 angles have the same measure. If possible, draw the quadrilateral using the given sides and making sure that all 4 angles do *not* have the same measure.

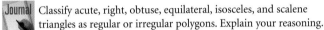

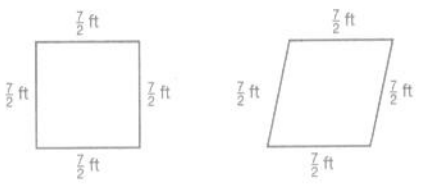

— Solve —

6. Is the quadrilateral regular or irregular? Explain. Possible answer: If all four angles have the same measure, the figure is regular (square). If not, it is irregular (rhombus).

— Look Back —

7. What ways could you have written the measures other than as improper fractions? As decimals or mixed numbers.

SOLVE ANOTHER PROBLEM

If a pentagon has sides of 2.25 in., $1\frac{5}{4}$ in., $\frac{7}{4}$ in., $2\frac{1}{4}$ in., and 1.75 in., is it regular or irregular? Explain.

Irregular, the sides do not have the same measures.

ENRICHMENT

Name ______________________

Extend Your Thinking 8-6

Critical Thinking

You can use a protractor to make a circle.

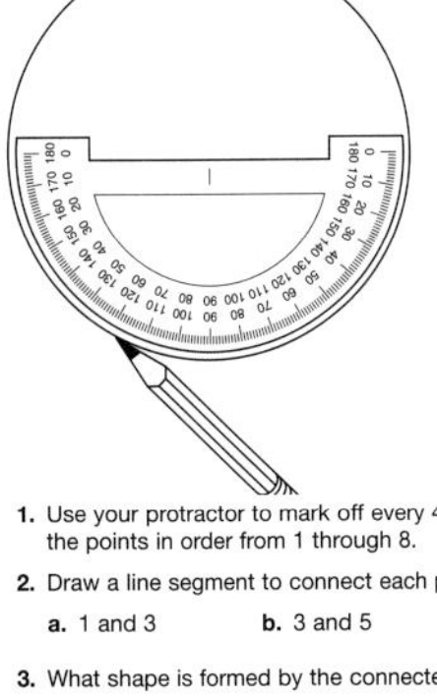

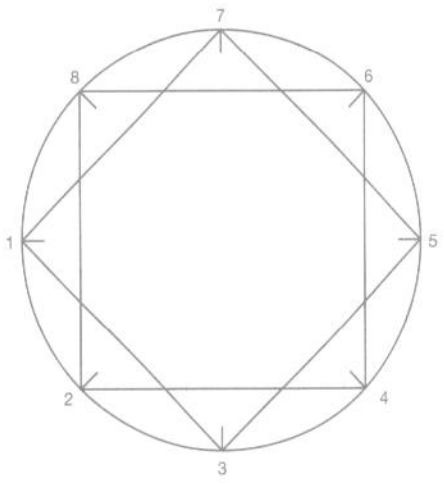

1. Use your protractor to mark off every 45° on the circle. Number the points in order from 1 through 8.
2. Draw a line segment to connect each pair of points.
   a. 1 and 3 b. 3 and 5 c. 5 and 7 d. 7 and 1
3. What shape is formed by the connected points? Square.
4. Draw a line segment to connect each pair of points.
   a. 2 and 4 b. 4 and 6 c. 6 and 8 d. 8 and 2
5. What shape is formed by the connected points? Square.
6. How many right triangles did you make? 8 right triangles.
7. What other polygons did you make? If you don't know the name of the polygon, describe it using the number of sides. Possible answers: pentagon, hexagon, heptagon, octagon, nonagon, decagon, 11-16 sided polygons.
8. Which of the polygons are regular polygons? Quadrilateral, octagon.

Exercise Answers

16. 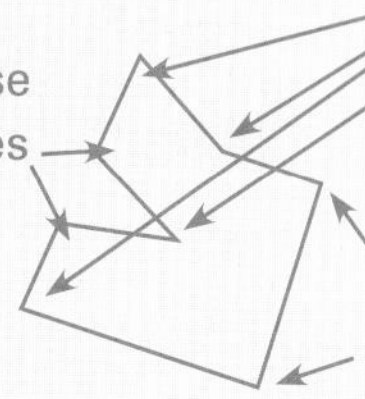

17. 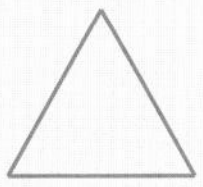
acute angles

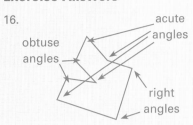

18. 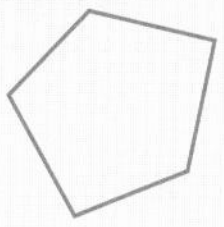
obtuse angles

29. 40 in.; Divide the octagon into triangles to find the area.

30. You can't tell; The sides are the same length, but you don't know the angle measures.

31. Equilateral triangles are always regular. Acute triangles can be regular or irregular. Right, obtuse, isosceles, and scalene are irregular.

Alternate Assessment

You may want to use the *Interactive CD-ROM Journal* with this assessment.

Journal Have students list examples of polygons from everyday life. They should draw each polygon and describe it as regular or irregular.

▶ Quick Quiz

Draw an example of each figure.

1. Irregular hexagon

Possible answer:

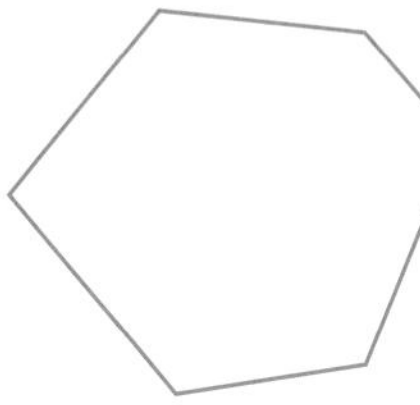

2. Regular octagon

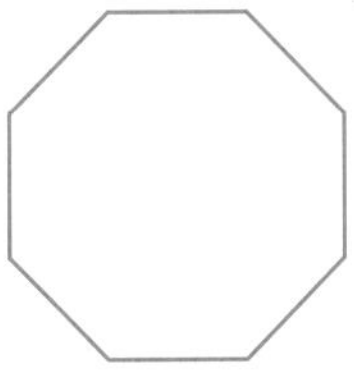

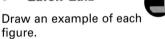

Available on Daily Transparency 8-6

8-7 Lesson Organizer

Objective

- Classify quadrilaterals.

Vocabulary

- Trapezoid, parallelogram, rhombus, rectangle, square

NCTM Standards

- 1–4, 12, 13

▶ Review

Refer to the following figures.

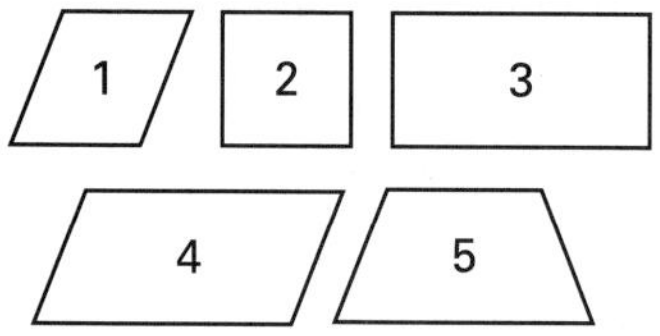

1. For which figures are opposite sides parallel? 1, 2, 3, 4
2. For which figures are opposite sides equal in length? 1, 2, 3, 4
3. For which figures are all angles right angles? 2, 3

Available on Daily Transparency 8-7

1 Introduce

Explore

You may wish to use Lesson Enhancement Transparency 40 with **Explore**.

The Point
Students look at diagrams of various types of quadrilaterals and write definitions of the quadrilaterals based on the diagrams.

Ongoing Assessment
Watch for students who fail to include all characteristics or who include too many characteristics when they write definitions.

For Groups That Finish Early
Complete the following statement using the words: alpha, beta, gamma, delta.

Every ______, ______, and ______ is also an ______. beta, gamma, delta, alpha

8-7 Quadrilaterals

You'll Learn ...

- to classify quadrilaterals

... How It's Used

Software engineers use quadrilaterals when drawing diagrams to illustrate how a program functions.

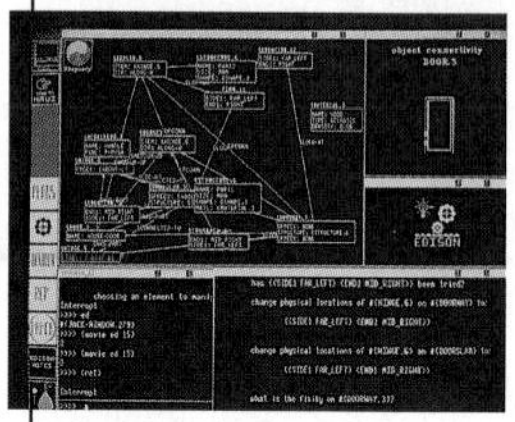

Vocabulary

trapezoid
parallelogram
rhombus
rectangle
square

▶ Lesson Link In the last lesson, you learned to identify quadrilaterals. Now you'll see how quadrilaterals are classified. ◀

Explore Quadrilaterals

In Your Own Words ...

Each group shows three examples of a particular type of quadrilateral, and one nonexample. For each type of quadrilateral, write a definition in your own words.

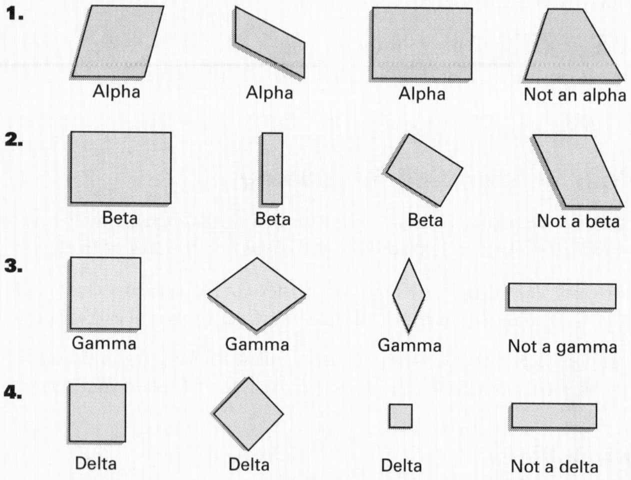

Learn Quadrilaterals

Any **polygon** with four sides is a quadrilateral. There are five special types of quadrilaterals: **trapezoid**, **parallelogram**, **rhombus**, **rectangle**, and **square**. Each has a different set of features, and some figures can be classified in more than one way.

MEETING INDIVIDUAL NEEDS

Resources

8-7 Practice
8-7 Reteaching
8-7 Problem Solving
8-7 Enrichment
8-7 Daily Transparency
  Problem of the Day
  Review
  Quick Quiz
Lesson Enhancement Transparencies 40, 41
Technology Master 41

Learning Modalities

Logical Hold up diagrams of various types of quadrilaterals. Have students name each quadrilateral in as many ways as possible.

Visual Have students draw Venn diagrams showing the relationship of the quadrilaterals discussed in this lesson.

Challenge

Have students use toothpicks (or pencils) to make the following figure. Then have them move only two toothpicks to form four squares of the same size.

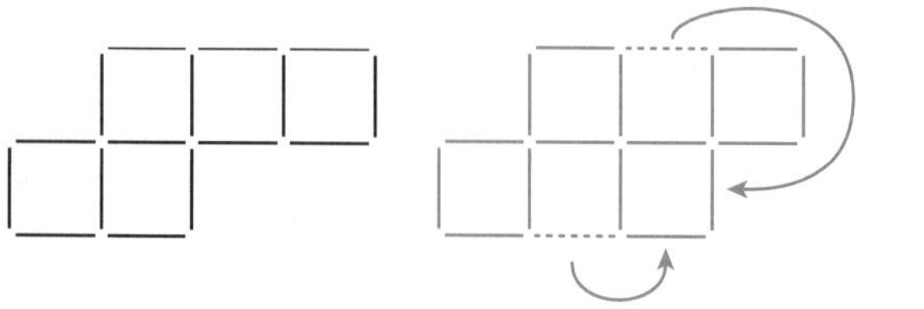

Definitions of Quadrilaterals

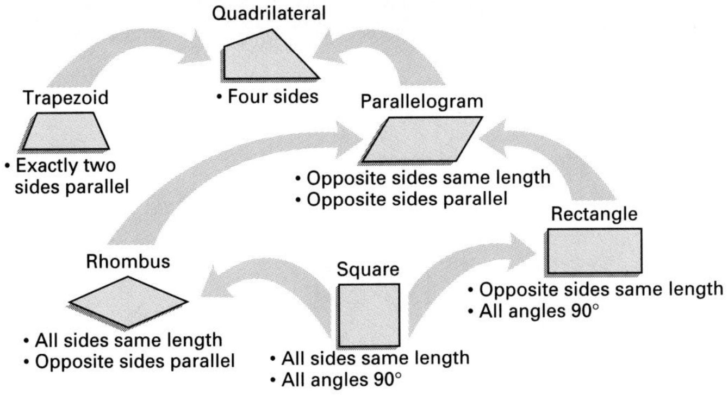

Examples

1 True or false: A square is a rectangle.

A square has opposite sides of the same length, and all angles are 90°. A square is a rectangle. The statement is true.

2 Classify the figure in as many ways as possible.

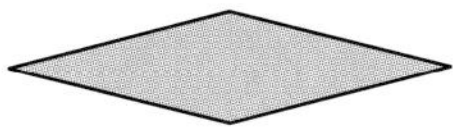

The figure is a *quadrilateral,* a *parallelogram,* and a *rhombus.*

Try It

Answer *true* or *false.*

a. A rhombus is a trapezoid. False **b.** A rectangle is a parallelogram. True

c. Classify the figure in as many ways as possible.

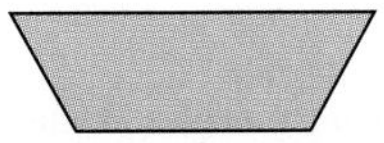

Trapezoid, quadrilateral

▶ Language Link

The prefix *quad-* means "four." For example, a quadruped is an animal with four legs. A sound system that is quadraphonic uses four separate sound tracks.

Problem Solving TIP

The chart above can help you find all the classifications for a figure. For example, "rhombus" points to "parallelogram," which points to "quadrilateral." So, any rhombus is also a parallelogram and also a quadrilateral.

Check Your Understanding

1. A geometry book said that a square is a "rectangular rhombus." Do you agree? Explain your reasoning.

2. How are trapezoids and parallelograms alike? How are they different?

3. Quadrilaterals can be classified based on whether or not their opposite sides are parallel. Can triangles also be classified in this way? Explain.

MATH EVERY DAY

▶ Problem of the Day

Here is the schedule for a television mini-series.

Monday	7 P.M. to 10 P.M.
Tuesday	7:30 P.M. to 10 P.M.
Thursday	7:30 P.M. to 11 P.M.
Friday	8 P.M. to 10:30 P.M.

How many video tapes will you need to tape the entire series if you use 6-hour tapes?
2 video tapes

Available on Daily Transparency 8-7

An Extension is provided in the transparency package.

Fact of the Day

The Crystal Palace in London took up almost 19 acres. More than 6,000,000 visitors saw displays by 15,000 exhibitors.

Mental Math

Find each product mentally.

1. 60 × 40 2400
2. 8 × 700 5600
3. 200 × 900 180,000
4. 70 × 900 63,000

Answers for Explore

1. The opposite sides are parallel.
2. All angles are right angles.
3. Sides are all the same length.
4. Sides are all the same length and all angles are right angles.

2 Teach

Learn

You may wish to use Lesson Enhancement Transparency 41 with this lesson.

Alternate Examples

1. True or false: A rhombus is a parallelogram.

   A rhombus has opposite sides that are the same length and parallel. A rhombus is a parallelogram. The statement is true.

2. Classify the figure in as many ways as possible.

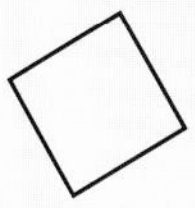

   The figure is a quadrilateral, a parallelogram, a rhombus, a rectangle, and a square.

3 Practice and Assess

Check

Answers for Check Your Understanding

1. Yes; A square has all the characteristics of both a rectangle and a rhombus.
2. Alike; They both have four sides and a pair of parallel lines; Different: Parallelograms have to have two pairs of parallel sides and the opposite sides have to be the same length.
3. No; Triangles do not have sides that are parallel.

8-7 Exercises and Applications

Assignment Guide

- **Basic**
  1–21, 23, 27–49 odds
- **Average**
  5–27, 29–49 odds
- **Enriched**
  5–23 odds, 24–29,
  30–48 evens

Exercise Notes

Exercise 22

History The Crystal Palace was the first building with a cast-iron frame and also the first building for which units were pre-fabricated and then assembled on site.

Exercise Answers

8. Irregular quadrilateral, polygon.
9. Rhombus, parallelogram, irregular quadrilateral, polygon.
10. Trapezoid, irregular quadrilateral, polygon.
11. Parallelogram, irregular quadrilateral, polygon.
12. Rectangle, parallelogram, irregular quadrilateral, polygon.
13. Irregular quadrilateral, polygon.
14. Square, rhombus, rectangle, parallelogram, regular quadrilateral, polygon.
15. Rhombus, parallelogram, irregular quadrilateral, polygon.

Reteaching

Activity

Materials: Graph paper

- Work in groups of three or four. Use several sheets of graph paper. Each person should cut out a quadrilateral from one of the sheets of paper.
- The other persons in the group should then classify the quadrilateral in as many ways as possible.

PRACTICE 8-7

8-7 Exercises and Applications

Practice and Apply

Getting Started For each figure, state how many pairs of opposites sides are parallel.

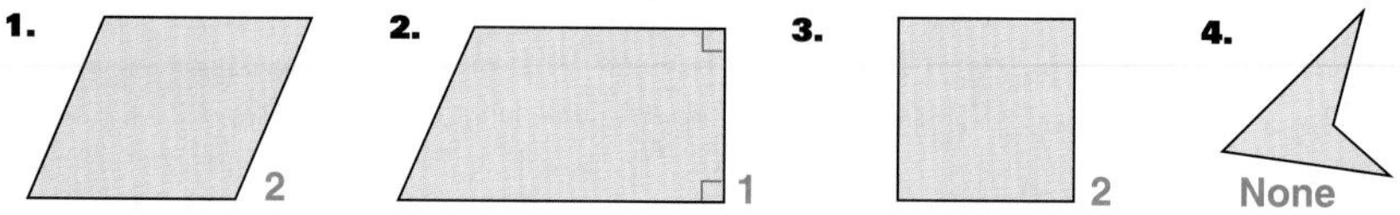

Answer true or false.

5. Every four-sided figure can be classified as more than one type of quadrilateral. False
6. A square is also a parallelogram. True
7. A trapezoid is never a rectangle. True

Classify each figure in as many ways as possible.

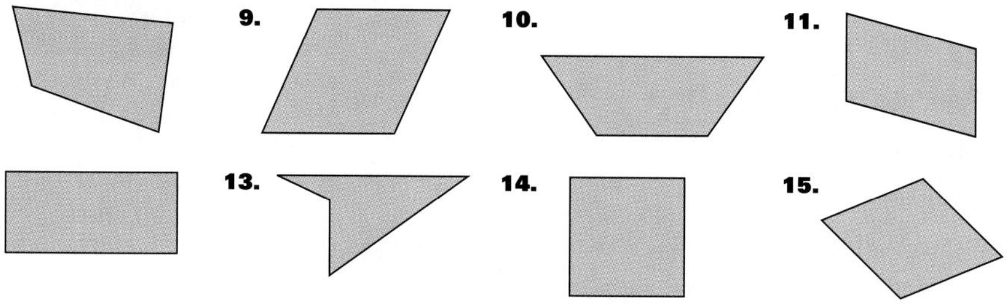

Draw an example of each figure. Classify each of the angles in your drawing.

16. Trapezoid
17. Parallelogram
18. Rhombus
19. Rectangle
20. Square
21. Quadrilateral

22. **History** In 1851, the Crystal Palace was built in London as an exhibition hall. The roof and outer walls were built of almost 300,000 panes of glass. Are any windows parallelograms?
Yes. The rectangular windows are also parallelograms

PRACTICE

Name ______________________

Practice 8-7

Quadrilaterals

Answer true or false.

1. Some rectangles are also rhombuses. True
2. All quadrilaterals are either trapezoids or parallelograms. False
3. A square is a kind of trapezoid. False

Classify each figure in as many ways as possible.

4. Quadrilateral, trapezoid
5. Quadrilateral, rhombus, parallelogram

Draw an example of each figure. Classify each of the angles in your drawing.

6. A rhombus that is not a square
7. A rectangle that is not a square
8. A parallelogram that is not a rectangle or a rhombus

6. 2 acute angles, 2 obtuse angles
7. 4 right angles
8. 2 acute angles, 2 obtuse angles

Measurement Given the information, can you determine the lengths of each figure's sides? If so, give the lengths.

9. A rhombus with a perimeter of 44 inches. Yes, four 11-inch sides
10. A trapezoid with three 5-meter sides No
11. Classify each shape in the jack-o-lantern in as many ways as possible.

Eyes Quadrilateral, parallelogram, rhombus
Nose Quadrilateral, trapezoid
Mouth Quadrilateral, parallelogram, rectangle

RETEACHING

Name ______________________

Alternative Lesson 8-7

Quadrilaterals

Any **polygon** with four sides is a quadrilateral. The five special types of quadrilaterals are shown below.

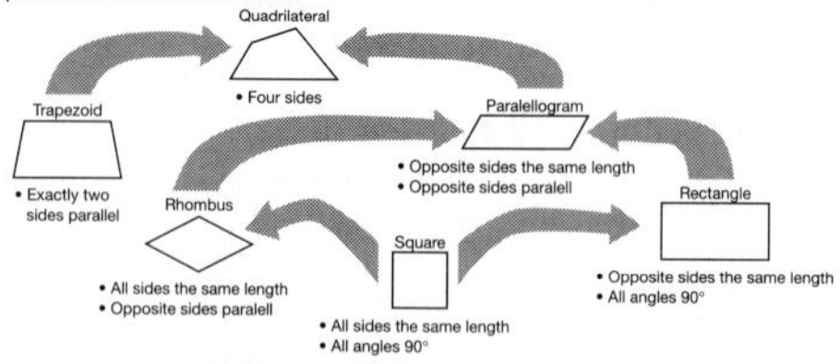

Some figures can be classified in more than one way.

Example

Classify the figure in as many ways as possible.

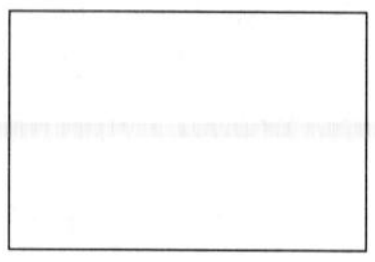

The figure has 4 sides, so it is a quadrilateral.

The figure has opposite sides that are parallel and the same length, so it is also a parallelogram.

All angles measure 90°, and opposite sides are the same length, so it is a rectangle.

The figure is a quadrilateral, a parallelogram, and a rectangle.

Try It Classify this figure in as many ways as possible.

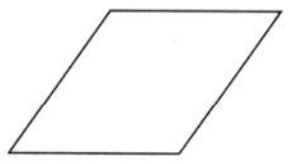

a. How many sides? 4 sides.
b. How many pairs of opposite sides are parallel? Two pairs.
c. Are opposite sides the same length? Yes.
d. Are all sides? Yes.
e. Do all angles measure 90°? No.
f. The polygon is a quadrilateral, parallelogram, rhombus.

Classify this figure in as many ways as possible.

g. Quadrilateral, trapezoid.

23. **Test Prep** What kind of quadrilaterals are the states of Nevada and Arkansas shaped like? **A**

Ⓐ Trapezoids

Ⓑ Squares

Ⓒ Rectangles

Ⓓ Rhombuses

Measurement Given the information, can you determine the lengths of each figure's sides? If so, give the lengths.

24. A parallelogram with a perimeter of 64 inches. No

25. A rhombus with a perimeter of 8 feet. Yes; All 2 ft

26. A trapezoid with a perimeter of 52 inches and a side of 12 inches. No

Problem Solving and Reasoning

27. Journal Every square is also a rectangle, but every rectangle is not necessarily a square. Explain.

28. **Critical Thinking** The sides of an octagon are the same length, and all opposite sides are parallel. Can the octagon be classified as a rhombus? Explain your reasoning.

29. **Communicate** Explain why the shape of the kite shown cannot be classified as a trapezoid, a parallelogram, a rhombus, a rectangle, or a square.

GPS

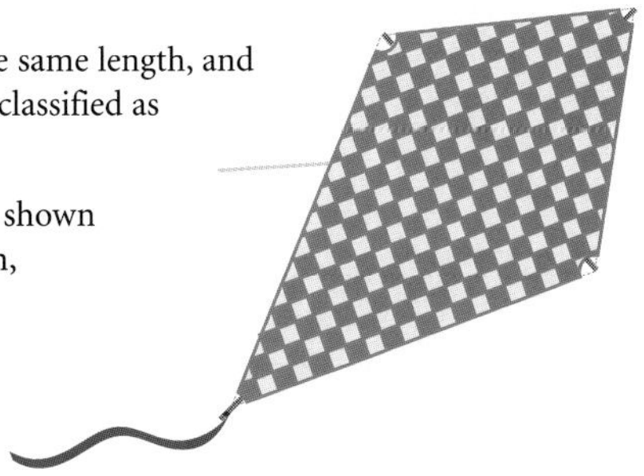

PROBLEM SOLVING 8-7

Mixed Review

Compare using >, <, or =. *[Lesson 5-8]*

30. $\frac{1}{2}$ [<] 0.54 **31.** $\frac{3}{4}$ [>] 0.65 **32.** $\frac{2}{9}$ [<] 0.4 **33.** $\frac{5}{6}$ [>] 0.83 **34.** $\frac{2}{3}$ [<] 0.67 **35.** $\frac{4}{5}$ [=] 0.8

36. $\frac{5}{8}$ [<] 0.652 **37.** $\frac{1}{7}$ [<] 0.2 **38.** $\frac{2}{5}$ [=] 0.4 **39.** $\frac{11}{22}$ [=] 0.5 **40.** $\frac{6}{9}$ [<] 0.75 **41.** $\frac{2}{6}$ [>] 0.25

Multiply. *[Lesson 3-8]*

42. 5 × 6.27 31.35 **43.** 12 × 2.45 29.4 **44.** 3 × 0.151 0.453 **45.** 56.7 × 4 226.8

46. 34.56 × 100 3456 **47.** 6.89 × 7 48.23 **48.** $34 × 1.4 $47.60 **49.** 0.04 × 10 0.4

Exercise Answers

16.

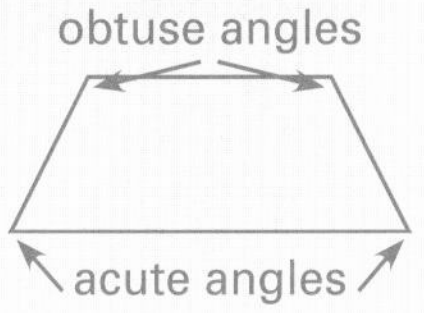

17.

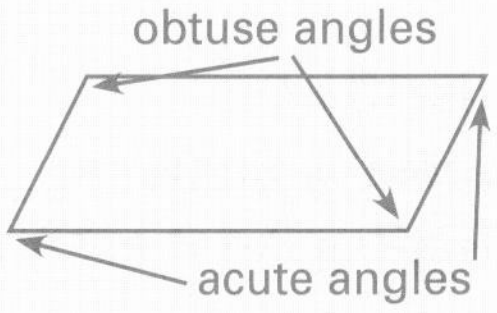

18.

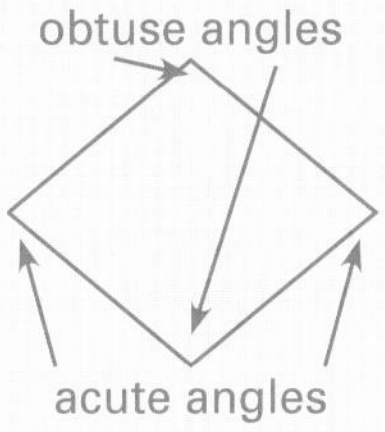

19.

20.

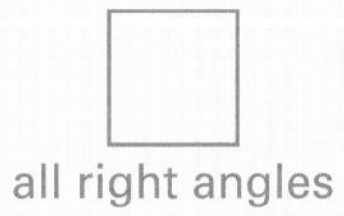

21.

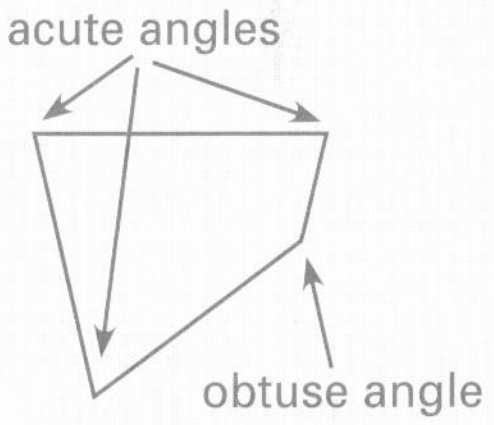

27. Squares have all sides of the same length and angles all of 90°, but rectangles don't have all sides of the same length.

28. No; A rhombus is a quadrilateral.

29. It doesn't have any sides that are parallel.

PROBLEM SOLVING

Name ______________________

Guided Problem Solving 8-7

GPS **PROBLEM 29, STUDENT PAGE 439**

Explain why the shape of the kite shown cannot be classified as a trapezoid, a parallelogram, a rhombus, a rectangle, or a square.

— Understand —

1. Underline the five quadrilaterals that are *not* classifications of the kite.

— Plan —

2. Which of the five quadrilaterals can be classified as a parallelogram? Parallelogram, rhombus, rectangle, square.
3. What do you know about the sides of a parallelogram? Opposite sides have the same length and are parallel.
4. What do you know about the sides of the fifth figure? Two sides parallel.
5. Does the kite have any parallel sides? No.
6. Does the kite shape have any pairs of opposite sides that are the same length? No.

— Solve —

7. Why can a kite not be classified as any of the given quadrilaterals? Possible answer: Its opposite sides do not have equal lengths and are not parallel.

— Look Back —

8. Does your answer to Item 7 rule out each figure named in the problem? Yes.

SOLVE ANOTHER PROBLEM

Classify the quadrilaterals that make up the patterns of the kite in as many ways as possible. Square, rhombus, rectangle, parallelogram, quadrilateral.

ENRICHMENT

Name ______________________

Extend Your Thinking 8-7

Decision Making

David is scheduling the order that the acts in the school variety show will appear on stage. He has made this list of the acts, the performers, and the approximate length of time it takes for each performance.

Performer	Act	Time	Performer	Act	Time
Kelsey and Adam	Dance routine	5 min	Glee Club	Song medley	6 min
Franco and Lonnie	Comedy routine	5 min	Nancy	Song	3 min
Aron	Magic tricks	8 min	Yori	Guitar solo	6 min
Zuri	Dance	5 min	Sara and Edna	Song	4 min
George and Kyle	Comedy	4 min	Clay	Piano solo	5 min

1. How long will the acts perform in all? 51 minutes.
2. How long will the show run if David allows 1 minute between each act for performers to enter and exit the stage? 60 minutes.
3. Should David plan for an intermission? Why or why not? Possible answer: No, the show is not long enough to require one.
4. Should David schedule similar acts to perform one after the other? For example, all singers perform, then all dancers, and so on. Why or why not? Possible answer: No, it would probably hold audiences' interest longer if the acts were varied.
5. Write a schedule of the performances. If necessary, place a star showing the first act to go on stage after the intermission. Remember to schedule the minute between acts. Possible answer:

Time	Performer	Act	Time	Performer	Act
8:00	F & L	Comedy	8:29	Zuri	Dance
8:06	Nancy	Song	8:35	Aron	Magic
8:10	Yori	Guitar	8:44	S & E	Song
8:17	K & A	Dance	8:49	G & K	Comedy
8:23	Clay	Piano	8:54	Glee	Song

Alternate Assessment

Self Assessment Have students make a list of any exercises in this lesson for which they had a wrong answer. Then have them explain why each answer was incorrect.

Quick Quiz

True or false.

1. A rectangle is a parallelogram. True
2. A trapezoid is a parallelogram. False
3. A square is a quadrilateral. True

Available on Daily Transparency 8-7

Technology

Using Dynamic Geometry Software • Finding Relationships in Triangles

The Point
Students use dynamic geometry software to discover that the longest side in a triangle is always opposite the largest angle.

Materials
Dynamic geometry software

Resources
Interactive CD-ROM Geometry Tool

About the Page

- Be sure that students are familiar with the software and how to use the necessary features for this lesson.
- The discovery here should make intuitive sense to students.

Ask ...

- Is it possible for one side of the triangle to be changed without at least one of the other two sides also being changed? No
- What happens if two angles happen to have the same measure? The opposite sides will have the same length.

Answers for Try It

a. The shortest side is opposite the smallest angle.

b. The angle measures are the same.

On Your Own
In the third question, it should be pointed out that while the larger angle can be determined from the longer side, there is no way to determine the actual measures of the angles.

Answers for On Your Own

- Yes; Then you have an easy way of knowing which angle is which.
- Possible answer: If you want to know the angle measurements and side lengths, it is easier on the computer because the program does it for you. Otherwise, it's easier to create examples on paper.
- Possible answer: Compare them to each other or to a right angle.

TECHNOLOGY

Using Dynamic Geometry Software • Finding Relationships in Triangles

Problem: How can you determine the relationship between the longest side of a triangle and the largest angle?

You can use geometry software to explore triangle relationships. Using the software, you can quickly create and analyze many different examples of triangles.

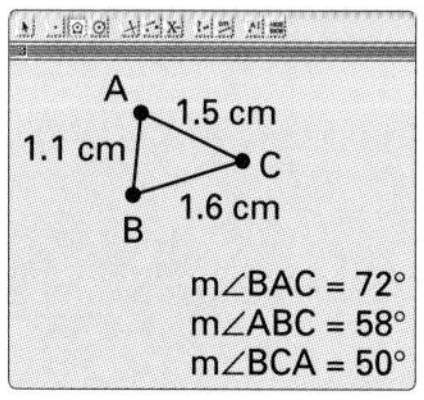

1. **Using your geometry software, draw a triangle. Label the vertices of the triangle *A*, *B*, and *C*. Use the measuring tool to measure the side lengths and the angles.**
2. **Record which side is the longest and which angle is the largest.**
3. **Drag one of the points to a new location, and record which side is now the longest, and which angle is now the largest.**
4. **Repeat Step 3 until you have looked at five or six triangles. Describe any patterns in your data.**

Solution: The longest side is always opposite the largest angle.

TRY IT

a. Find the relationship between the shortest side and the smallest angle.

b. Find the relationship between the angles opposite the equal sides of an isosceles triangle.

ON YOUR OWN

- Did it help your investigation to label the vertices of the triangle as *A*, *B*, and *C*? Explain.
- When investigating triangles, is it easier to create examples on paper or with geometry software? Why?
- Without using geometry software, how could you verify which of two angles is the larger?

Section 8B Connect

In this section, you've learned to classify polygons. Now you'll use what you've learned to describe the design of a beautiful and unusual diamond.

The Geometry of Gems

Materials: Ruler

The diagram shows an unusual diamond pattern called the "cross-rose." Each polygon is a face that has been ground into the crystal by the diamond cutter.

1. Copy the pattern onto a sheet of paper. Label the points as in the figure.

2. Find examples of as many of the following figures as you can in the cross-rose design. Use letters to identify each figure.

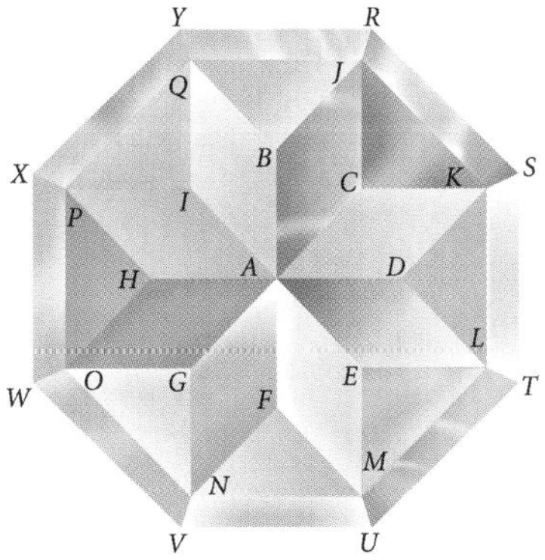

acute triangle	right triangle	obtuse triangle
equilateral triangle	isosceles triangle	scalene triangle
polygon	quadrilateral	pentagon
hexagon	octagon	regular polygon
parallelogram	rectangle	rhombus
square	trapezoid	

3. Some of the figures above cannot be found unless you add a line segment to the pattern. What figures could you find if you added a line segment? Where would you add the segment?

441

Answers for Connect

1. Check students' drawings.
2. First Column

Acute triangle	*AGF*
Equilateral triangle	not possible
Polygon	*RSTUVWXY*
Hexagon	*AHPIQB*
Parallelogram	*AEMF*
Square	not possible

Second Column

Right triangle	*JCK*
Isosceles triangle	*JCK*
Quadrilateral	*YQJR*
Octagon	*RSTUVWXY*
Rectangle	not possible
Trapezoid	*UVNM*

Third Column

Obtuse triangle	not possible
Scalene triangle	not possible
Pentagon	*AGNME*
Regular polygon	*RSTUVWXY*
Rhombus	*BJCA*

3. Possible answers:

Equilateral triangle	Cannot be done with only one new segment
Square	Cannot be done with only one new segment
Rectangle	*HONF* (if you connect *H* and *P*)
Obtuse triangle	*QBA* (if you connect *Q* and *A*)
Scalene triangle	*ADE* (if you connect *D* and *E*)

The Geometry of Gems

The Point

In *The Geometry of Gems* on page 423, students learned about how crystals are changed into jewels. Now, students will apply what they learned about polygons to describe the design of a diamond.

Materials

Ruler

Resources

Teaching Tool Transparency 16: Rulers

Lesson Enhancement Transparency 42

About the Page

- Students should trace or copy the diagram carefully.
- Review the terms listed to be sure students understand exactly what shapes they are trying to identify in the design.
- Ask students which shapes in the pattern could be named by more than one term.
- Suggest that students name each shape in the pattern by its most specific name, for example, *square* instead of *rectangle* or *polygon.*

Ongoing Assessment

Check that students have identified the terms correctly on the diamond pattern.

Extension

Ask students to design a pattern they think would enhance the beauty of a diamond. Have them determine the shape of the diamond and the number of facets it will have. Ask them to draw the pattern carefully. Display the work that the students create.

8B Review

Review Correlation

Item(s)	Lesson(s)
1–4	8-2
5–10	8-3
11–14	8-4, 8-5
15–17	8-6
18–21	8-7
22	8-4

Test Prep

Test-Taking Tip

Tell students to glance through the entire test before answering any question. In this question, they are told that every triangle has at least two acute angles. They need to choose between C and D.

Answers for Review

15.

16.

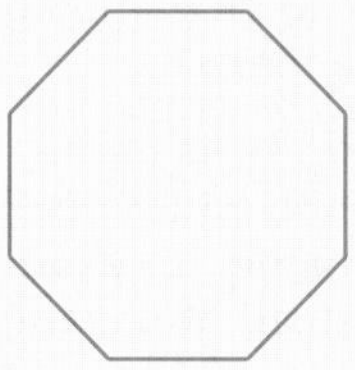

17.

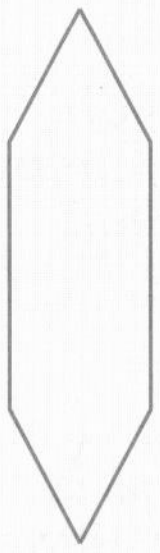

18. Square, rectangle, parallelogram, rhombus, regular quadrilateral, polygon.
19. Rhombus, parallelogram, irregular quadrilateral, polygon.
20. Irregular quadrilateral, polygon.
21. Trapezoid, irregular quadrilateral, polygon.

Section 8B Review

REVIEW 8B

Use the letters to name each angle in three ways.

1. **2.** **3.** **4.**

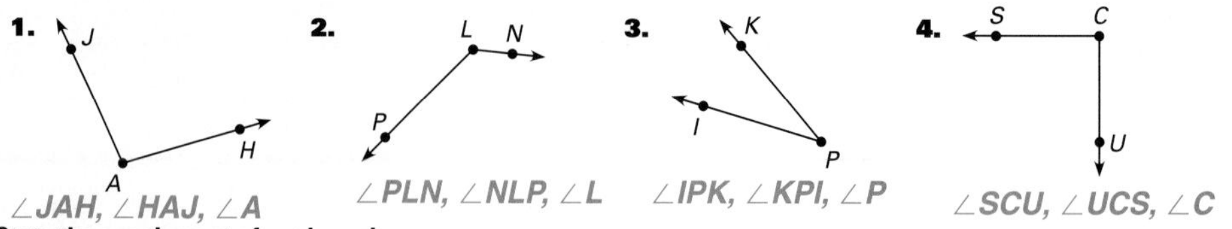

1. ∠JAH, ∠HAJ, ∠A 2. ∠PLN, ∠NLP, ∠L 3. ∠IPK, ∠KPI, ∠P 4. ∠SCU, ∠UCS, ∠C

State the supplement of each angle.

5. 156° 24° **6.** 119° 61° **7.** 45° 135° **8.** 26° 154° **9.** 52° 128° **10.** 179° 1°

Classify each triangle by its sides. Find the measure of each missing angle.

11. **12.** **13.** **14.**

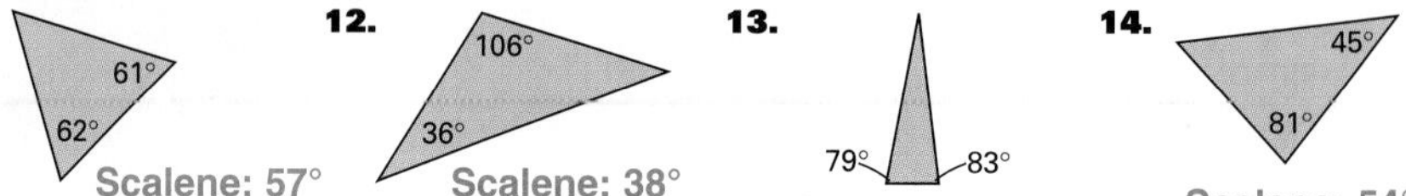

11. Scalene; 57° 12. Scalene; 38° 13. Scalene; 18° 14. Scalene; 54°

Draw an example of each figure.

15. Regular quadrilateral **16.** Regular octagon **17.** Irregular hexagon

Classify each figure in as many ways as possible.

18. **19.** **20.** **21.**

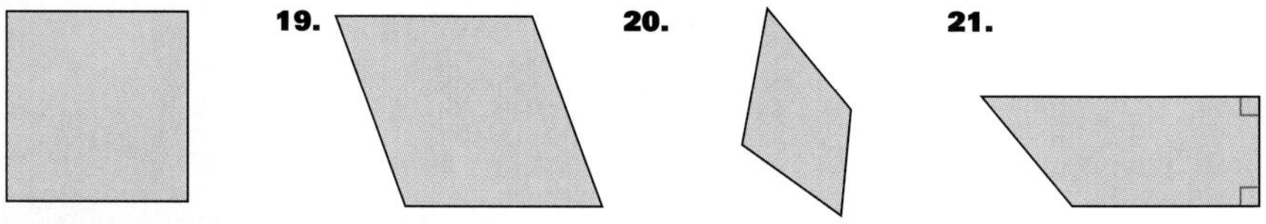

Test Prep

Every triangle has at least two acute angles. It's the measure of the third angle that determines what type of triangle it is.

22. How many acute angles does the triangle have? C

Ⓐ 0
Ⓑ 1
Ⓒ 2
Ⓓ 3

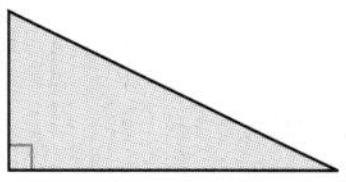

Resources

Practice Masters
Section 8B Review
Assessment Sourcebook
Quiz 8B
TestWorks
Test and Practice Software

PRACTICE

Name ______________________ **Practice**

Section 8B Review

Use the letters to name each angle in three ways.

1. ∠ABC, ∠CBA, ∠B 2. ∠PQR, ∠RQP, ∠Q 3. ∠WYX, ∠XYW, ∠Y

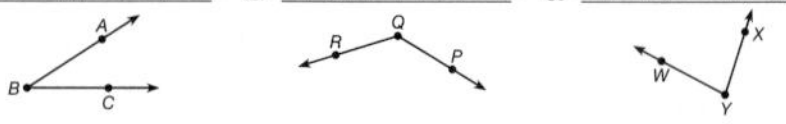

Classify each triangle by its sides. Find the measure of each missing angle.

4. Isosceles; 67° 5. Scalene; 108° 6. Equilateral; 60°

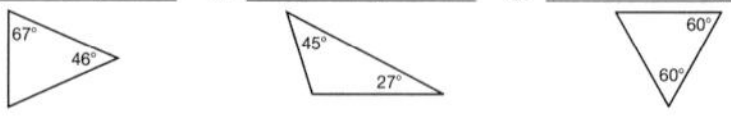

Draw an example of each figure. Possible answers:

7. Irregular octagon 8. Regular triangle 9. Irregular pentagon

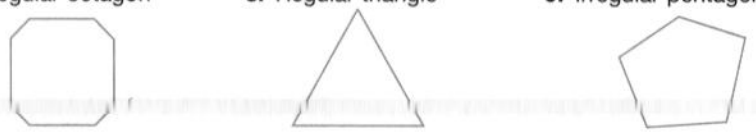

Classify each figure in as many ways as possible.

10.

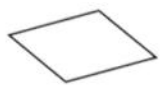

Quadrilateral, parallelogram

11.

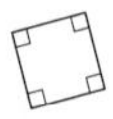

Quadrilateral, parallelogram, rectangle, rhombus, square

12. **Geography** The figure at the right shows the approximate shape of Manitoba, Canada. Find the approximate area of Manitoba. *[Lesson 4-9]x*

About 251,500 mi^2

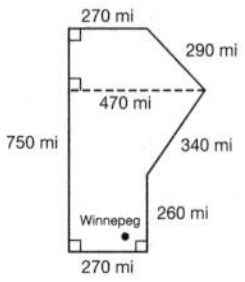

13. **Science** A typical female swallowtail butterfly weighs about $\frac{11}{20}$ gram. Find the weight of 12 female swallowtails. *[Lesson 7-2]*

About $6\frac{3}{5}$ g

Section 8C

Transformations

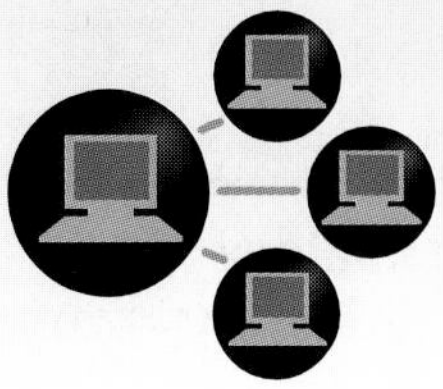

Visit **www.teacher.mathsurf.com** for links to lesson plans from teachers and other professionals, NCTM information, and other sites.

LESSON PLANNING GUIDE

Student Edition | **Ancillaries***

LESSON		MATERIALS	VOCABULARY	DAILY	OTHER
	Section 8C Opener				
8-8	**Flips and Line Symmetry**	unlined paper, scissors	congruent, line symmetry, reflection	8-8	Technology Master 42
8-9	**Turns and Rotational Symmetry**	tracing paper	rotation, clockwise, counterclockwise, rotational symmetry	8-9	Lesson Enhancement Trans. 43 Technology Master 43 *Interactive CD-ROM Lesson*
8-10	**Slides and Tessellations**	tracing paper, unlined paper	translation, tessellation	8-10	Teaching Tool Trans. 2, 3 Ch. 8 Project Master
	Connect	unlined paper, colored pencils or markers, ruler			Interdisc. Team Teaching 8C
	Review				Practice 8C; Quiz 8C; *TestWorks*
	Extend Key Ideas	compass, straightedge			
	Chapter 8 Summary and Review				
	Chapter 8 Assessment				Ch. 8 Tests Forms A–F *TestWorks*; Ch. 8 Letter Home
	Cumulative Review, Chapters 1–8				Cumulative Review Ch. 1–8

* Daily Ancillaries include Practice, Reteaching, Problem Solving, Enrichment, and Daily Transparency. Teaching Tool Transparencies are in *Teacher's Toolkits*. Lesson Enhancement Transparencies are in *Overhead Transparency Package*.

SKILLS TRACE

LESSON	SKILL	FIRST INTRODUCED GR. 4	GR. 5	GR. 6	DEVELOP	PRACTICE/ APPLY	REVIEW
8-8	**Identifying reflections and line symmetry.**		✗		pp. 444–445	pp. 446–447	pp. 458, 461, 517
8-9	**Identifying rotations and rotational symmetry.**			✗ p. 448	pp. 448–450	pp. 451–452	pp. 458, 461, 522
8-10	**Identifying translations and tessellations.**			✗ p. 453	pp. 453–454	pp. 455–456	pp. 458, 461, 526

CONNECTED MATHEMATICS

Investigations 1, 4, and 5 in the unit *Shapes and Designs (3-D Geometry)*, and the unit *Ruins of Montarek (Spatial Visualization)* from the **Connected Mathematics** series, can be used with Section 8C.

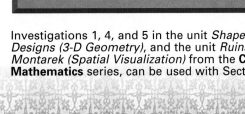

INTERDISCIPLINARY TEAM TEACHING

Math and Science/Technology

(Worksheet pages 41–42: Teacher pages T41–T42)

In this lesson, students use symmetry to compare and contrast animals.

Name ______________________ *Math and Science/Technology*

Classification Clues

Use symmetry to compare and contrast animals.

When biologists try to classify the arrangement of an animal's body parts, they first determine whether or not a body has symmetry. Some animals, such as humans, have line symmetry. Your body has a regular distribution of body parts on opposite sides of a linear axis.

Imagine a line drawn down the center of your forehead, down the bridge of your nose, and straight down the rest of your body. The parts on either side of that line would be nearly identical in shape. Such identical shapes, which you can imagine fitting over one another, are said to be *congruent*. Animals whose body parts show such line symmetry around a single axis are said to have *bilateral symmetry.*

Other animals have an arrangement of similar body parts around a central axis, like the spokes of a wheel. This arrangement is called *radial symmetry.* The starfish is an example. Each of its arms is similar in size and shape, and all radiate around a central axis.

Perfectly ball-shaped organisms, like some kinds of protozoa, have what is called *spherical symmetry*. Spherical symmetry is found in ball shaped objects organized about a central point, which is usually the organism's nucleus.

Finally, there are animals—like the sponge—whose body parts show no symmetry. There is no way to locate a dividing line, axis, or point of symmetry on their bodies.

1. Think of an animal other than a human being that has bilateral symmetry. Then draw it on a separate sheet of paper.
   possible drawings: mammals and most familiar insects
2. Does the starfish have any congruent parts? If so, what are they?
   Yes. Its arms are congruent. It cannot be folded over, but it still has congrent parts.

Name ______________________ *Math and Science/Technology*

3. Determining an animal's symmetry is one way to compare animals. Tell whether these 6 animals have symmetry, and if so, which kind.

   See below.
4. By the slow process of evolution, nature produces new species of animals. Using your knowledge of symmetry, draw in the space below a new species of animal with bilateral symmetry. Describe something about the place where it lives, how it moves, and how it gets food.
   See below.
5. Cut out photos of animals from magazines. Arrange them on a poster in groups to represent different examples of symmetry. Find out how the animals are classified (mammals, insects, birds, echinoderms, and the like). Describe any patterns you find. For example, ask yourself whether all or most animals in a group share the same kind of symmetry. Based on what you discover, state whether—and why—symmetry can or cannot be used to classify mammals.
   Possible answers: Animals in a particular group tend to share characteristics, including symmetry, so symmetry can be used to help classify animals.

Answers

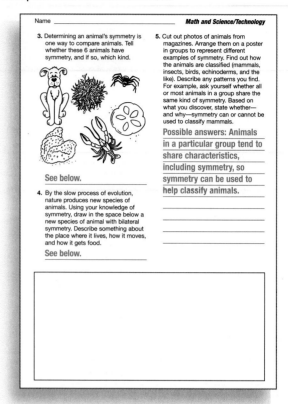

3. Dog, bilateral; crayfish, bilateral; sea urchin, radial; sand dollar, radial; sponge, no symmetry; spider, bilateral.
4. Answers will vary. Whatever students draw should be divisible into two identical halves by drawing a line down the center.

BIBLIOGRAPHY

FOR TEACHERS

Fowler, Allan. *Busy, Buzzy Bees*. Chicago, IL: Children's Press, 1995.

Hirsch, Christian R., ed. *Geometry from Multiple Perspectives*. Palo Alto, CA: Dale Seymour Publications, 1996.

Kallevig, Christine Petrell. *Folding Stories*. Newburgh, IN: Storytime Ink International, 1991.

Leff, Lawrence S. *Barron's Geometry the Easy Way*. New York, NY: Barron's Educational Series, 1990.

Pluckrose, Henry Arthur. *Shape*. London, England: Watts, 1986.

Symes, R. F. *Crystal & Gem*. New York, NY: Knopf, 1991.

FOR STUDENTS

Critchlow, Keith. *Islamic Patterns*. New York, NY: Schocken Books, 1976.

Feldman, Judy. *Shapes in Nature*. Chicago, IL: Children's Press, 1991.

Frishman, Martin, ed. *The Mosque, History and Architectural Development*. New York, NY: Thames and Hudson, 1994.

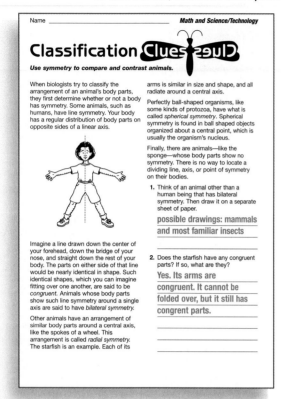

SECTION **8C**

Transformations

▶ Fine Arts Link ▶ History Link ▶ www.mathsurf.com/6/ch8/Islam_art

Artistic Solutions

The early Islamic artisans of the 600s faced a challenge in designing their pottery, rugs, and paintings. Their religion did not allow art to include images of humans, animals, or man-made objects. If they couldn't do these things, how could they create art?

The artisans developed several solutions. Some made images of plant life. Others used Arabic calligraphy as art. But the most well-known form of Islamic art is probably the use of geometric patterns. Series of repeating and interlocking shapes decorate all types of Islamic artwork, and demonstrate that Islamic artists are also expert mathematicians.

1. Other than Islamic art, what kinds of art styles are there?
2. How can geometric patterns be used to decorate things?

443

Where are we now?

In Section 8B, students learned to identify and classify polygons.

They learned how to

- classify triangles according to their angles.
- classify triangles according to their sides.
- classify polygons.
- identify and classify quadrilaterals.

Where are we going?

In Section 8C, students will

- identify reflections of figures.
- identify line symmetry.
- identify rotations of figures.
- identify rotational symmetry.
- identify translations and tessellations.

Theme: Islamic Art

World Wide Web

If your class has access to the World Wide Web, you might want to use the information found at the Web site address given. The interdisciplinary links relate to topics discussed in this section.

About the Page

This page introduces the theme of the section, Islamic art, and discusses the prohibitions faced by early Islamic artisans.

Ask …

- Why were human and animal images forbidden on Islamic art? People might regard statues or paintings as something divine.
- What images and shapes did the Islamic artisans use? Flowers, leaves, geometric patterns.

Extension

The following activities do not require access to the World Wide Web.

Fine Arts
Two famous examples of Islamic art are the Taj Mahal in India and the Alhambra in Spain. Have students research Islamic art and architecture.

History
Islamic art is the product of many cultures. In Spain, Islamic art is often referred to as Moorish art. Ask students to identify some of the cultures that contributed to its development.

Answers for Questions

1. Answers may vary.
2. Possible answer: Shapes put together can form patterns and cover surfaces.

Connect

On page 457, students use polygons to create a tessellation.

8-8 Lesson Organizer

Objectives

- Identify reflections of figures.
- Identify line symmetry.

Vocabulary

- Congruent, line symmetry, reflection

Materials

- Explore: Unlined paper, scissors

NCTM Standards

- 1–4, 7, 12

▶ Review

What would you see if each of the following letters was reflected in a mirror?

1. A A
2. D ᗡ
3. L ⅃
4. Name another letter that looks the same when it is reflected in a mirror. Possible answers: H, I, M, O, T, U, V, W, X, Y

Available on Daily Transparency 8-8

1 Introduce

Explore

The Point
Students cut polygons from paper that has been folded one, two, or three times and investigate the figures that are formed.

Ongoing Assessment
Watch for students who have trouble following the directions in **Explore**. Remind them not to cut through the fold line(s).

8-8 Flips and Line Symmetry

You'll Learn ...

- to identify reflections of figures
- to identify line symmetry

... How It's Used

Photographers use symmetry when composing portraits and landscape photographs.

Vocabulary

congruent
line symmetry
reflection

▶ Lesson Link In the last section, you learned to classify polygons. Now you'll investigate geometric figures involving repeated patterns. ◀

Explore Symmetry

Let's See What Unfolds ...

Materials: Unlined paper, Scissors

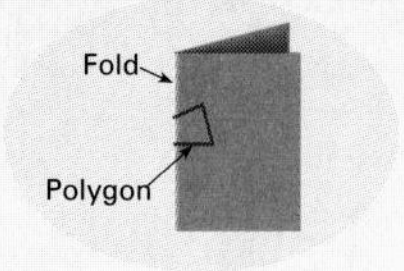

1. Fold a sheet of paper in half. Draw a polygon with one side *along the fold.* Cut out the figure. Do not cut through the fold. Sketch the shape you think it will have. Open the cutout and compare it with the one you predicted.

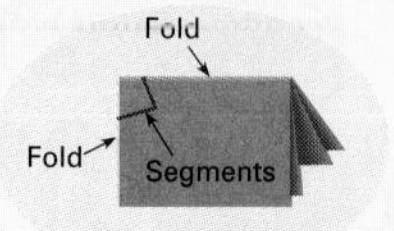

2. Fold a sheet from left to right, then top to bottom. With the paper as shown, draw 2 or 3 line segments from the top fold to the left fold. Repeat Step 1.

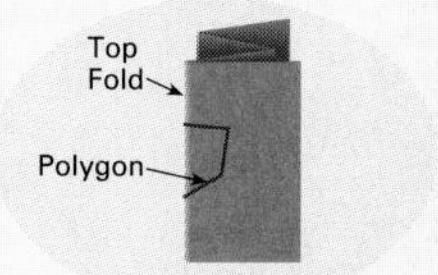

3. Fold a sheet "accordion style" with three folds. Draw a polygon with one side along the top fold. Repeat Step 1, cutting through all four layers.
4. Compare your paper shapes. Describe anything you can find that all three shapes have in common.

Learn Flips and Line Symmetry

Two figures are **congruent** if they have the same size and shape.

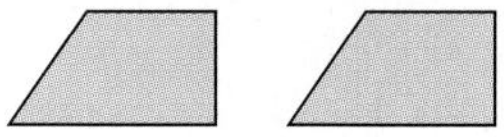

A figure that can be folded into congruent halves has **line symmetry**.

A **reflection** is the mirror image of a figure that has been "flipped" over a line.

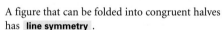

MEETING INDIVIDUAL NEEDS

Resources

8-8 Practice
8-8 Reteaching
8-8 Problem Solving
8-8 Enrichment
8-8 Daily Transparency
Problem of the Day
Review
Quick Quiz
Technology Master 42

Learning Modalities

Kinesthetic Have students use several sheets of paper to cut out various types of polygons. Then have them fold the polygons along all possible lines of symmetry.

Visual Have students find several photos from magazines or newspapers that show two or more congruent objects. Then have them paste the photos onto a poster and display the posters.

Inclusion

Some students may recognize congruent figures when they are side by side, but not when they have been turned or flipped. Use cardboard cutouts of congruent figures and show them in different positions to illustrate that the figures are congruent no matter how they are positioned. Use a flat-edged mirror to demonstrate reflection of a figure.

Examples

This Islamic design is an illuminated page of Nasta'liq script by Mir'Ali Haravi from the early 16th century Safavid dynasty in Iran. Tell whether each design has line symmetry. If it does, copy the figure and draw its line(s) of symmetry.

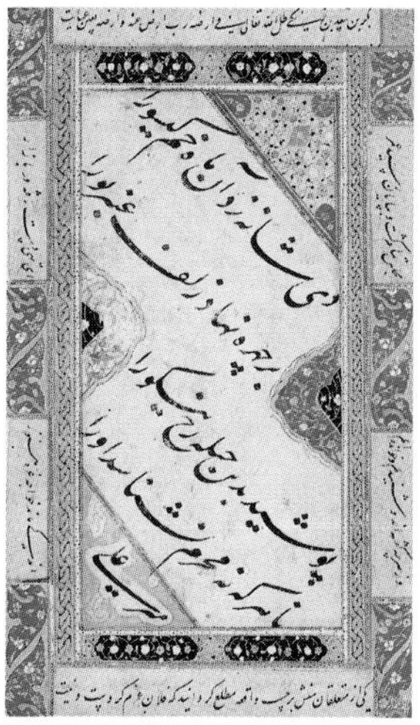

Ink and color on paper. Gift of the Todd G. Williams Memorial Fund and the Society for Asian Art. The Asian Art Museum of San Francisco. B87-D6.

1

Yes. The figure has two lines of symmetry.

2 No. The figure does not have line symmetry.

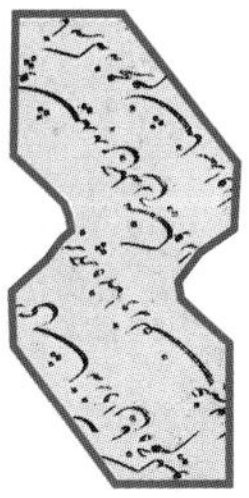

3 Draw the reflection of the figure over the line.

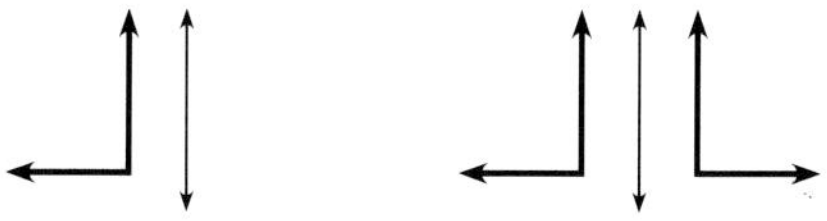

Try It

Tell whether each figure has line symmetry. If so, draw its line(s) of symmetry.

a. 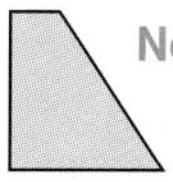 No

b. 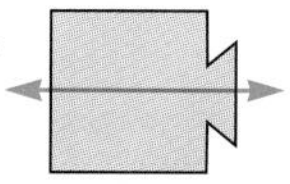 Yes

c. 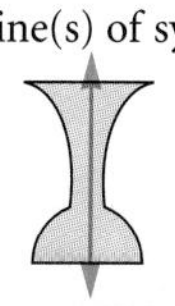 Yes

> **History Link**
>
> Early Islamic artists believed that the universe had a natural order to it. They chose to make their designs symmetrical as a representation of this natural order.

Check Your Understanding

1. What does it mean to say that a reflection is a "mirror image"?

2. *B* is the reflection of *A*. Are *A* and *B* congruent? Explain.

For Groups That Finish Early

In Steps 1–2, if the polygon that you start with is a square with one side along the fold, what will the shape be when the cutout is unfolded? A rectangle that is not a square.

Answers for Explore

1–3. Check students' cutouts.

4. The three paper shapes can each be cut in half and the halves will have the same shape.

2 Teach

Learn

Alternate Examples

Tell whether each figure has line symmetry. If it does, copy the figure and draw its line(s) of symmetry.

1. 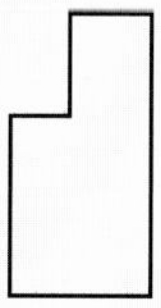

The figure does not have a line of symmetry.

2. 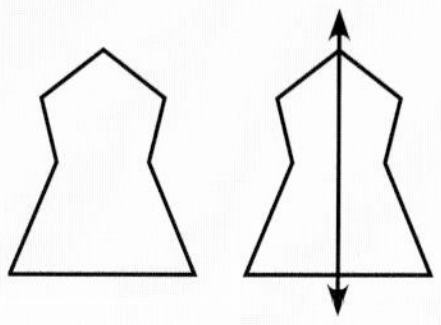

The figure has one line of symmetry.

3. Draw the reflection of the figure over the line.

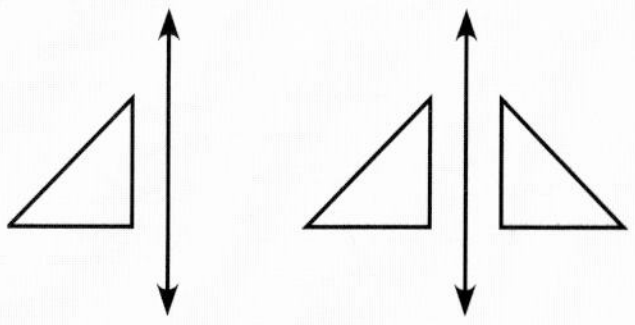

MATH EVERY DAY

Problem of the Day

In 1836, Norwegian Mensen Ernest walked from Constantinople, (now Istanbul) to Calcutta, India, and back in just 59 days. That is a distance of 5589 miles. What was his average speed in miles per hour? Round your answer to the nearest hundredth. 3.95 mi/hr (His actual speed was faster because he did stop to sleep and eat. The feat is more amazing considering that for much of the trip there were no roads!)

Available on Daily Transparency 8-8

An Extension is provided in the transparency package.

Fact of the Day

The use of glass mirrors was first recorded more than 2000 years ago, but they were not widely used until the thirteenth century.

Estimation

Estimate each sum.

1. 27 + 27 + 27 90
2. 41 + 41 + 41 + 41 160
3. 78 + 48 + 98 230
4. 81 + 49 + 62 + 31 220

3 Practice and Assess

Check

Answers for Check Your Understanding

1. When you hold a mirror up to an object, the image you see is its reflection.

2. Yes; An image and its reflection are always congruent.

8-8 Exercises and Applications

Assignment Guide

- **Basic**
  1–18, 20–36 evens
- **Average**
  3–20, 26–36 evens
- **Enriched**
  3–21, 23–37 odds

Exercise Notes

Exercises 9–12

Extension Have students determine if there are any other lines of symmetry for the given figures. For Exercise 10, there is one line of symmetry. For Exercise 12, there are four other lines of symmetry.

Exercise Answers

1.
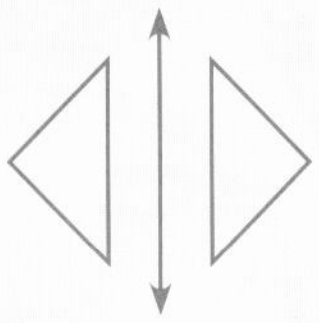

2.
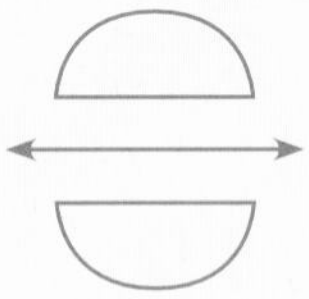

3.
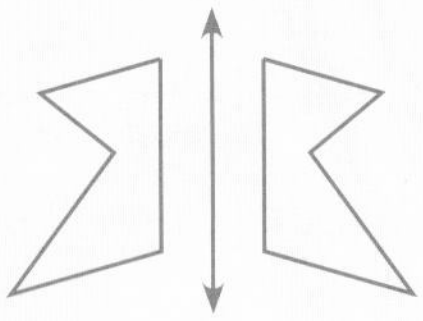

4.
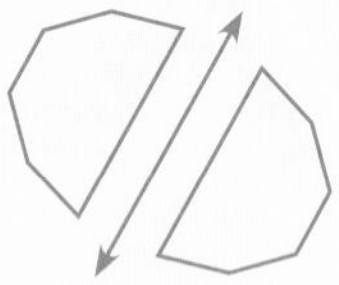

14. No
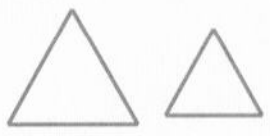

Reteaching

Activity

Materials: Index cards

- Work in groups of three or four. Use index cards. On each index card print a letter of the alphabet.
- Include all 26 possible letters. Take turns picking a card at random and telling how many lines of symmetry the letter has.

8-8 Exercises and Applications

PRACTICE 8-8

Practice and Apply

Getting Started Trace each figure and draw its reflection over the line.

1. 2. 3. 4.
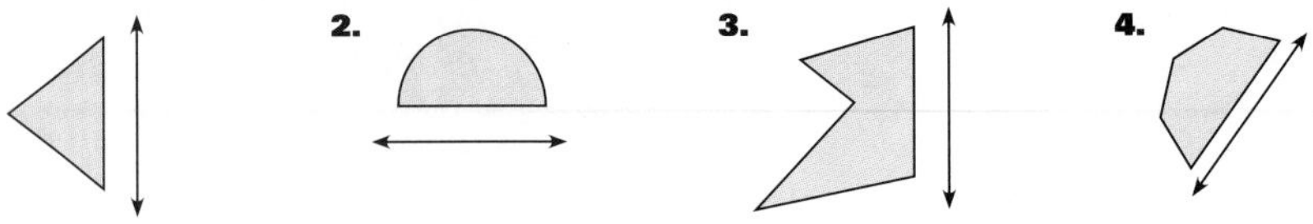

Tell if each photo has line symmetry. If it does, tell how many lines of symmetry it has.

5. 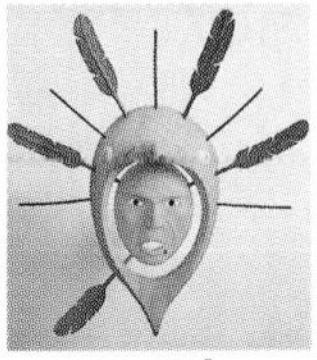
Not symmetric

6. 
Symmetric; 2

7. 
Not symmetric

8. 
Not symmetric

Tell if each line is a line of symmetry.

9. 10. 11. 12.

9. Yes 10. No 11. Yes 12. Yes

Tell if each pair of figures is congruent. If *not,* draw a figure that is congruent to each.

13. 14.
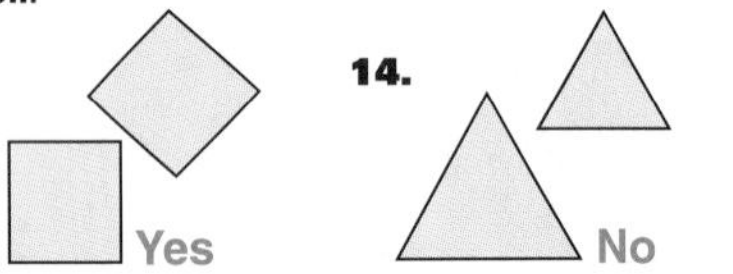

13. Yes 14. No

15. **Fine Arts** This window is from the Dome of the Rock mosque in Jerusalem, Israel. Describe the lines of symmetry in the window's design.

PRACTICE

Name ______________________

Practice 8-8

Flips and Line Symmetry

Tell if the picture has line symmetry. If it does, tell how many lines of symmetry it has.

1. No 2. Yes; 6 3. Yes; 1 4. Yes; 2
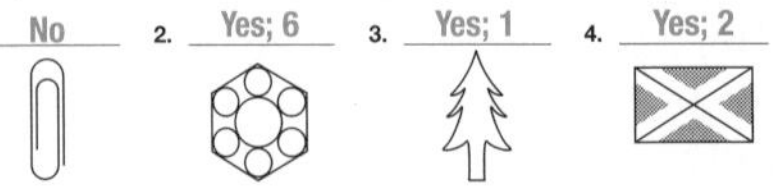

Tell if each line is a line of symmetry.

5. Yes 6. No 7. No 8. Yes
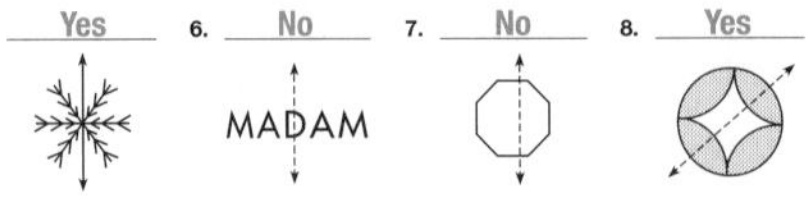

Tell if each pair of figures are congruent. If *not,* draw a figure congruent to each.

9. Congruent 10. Not congruent 11. Congruent
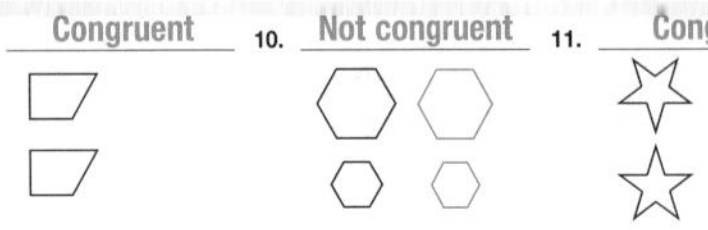

Use the design for Exercises 12 and 13.

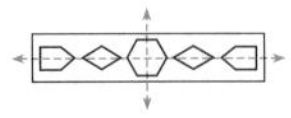

12. Name the congruent figures in the design.
Pentagons, rhombuses

13. Tell whether the design has line symmetry. If it does, draw the line(s) of symmetry.
Yes

14. Hexagonal tiles can be used to cover floors because they fit together nicely. Draw all lines of symmetry in the figure.

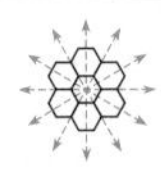

RETEACHING

Name ______________________

Alternative Lesson 8-8

Flips and Line Symmetry

Two figures are **congruent** if they have the same size and shape. A figure that can be folded into congruent halves has **line symmetry**. A **reflection** is the mirror image of a figure that has been "flipped" over a line.

Example 1

Draw the reflection of the figure over the line.

Draw the mirror image of the figure.

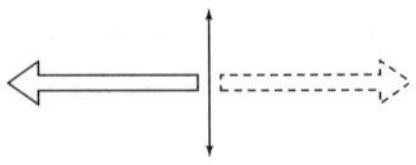

Try It Draw the reflection of each figure over the line.

a. b. c.
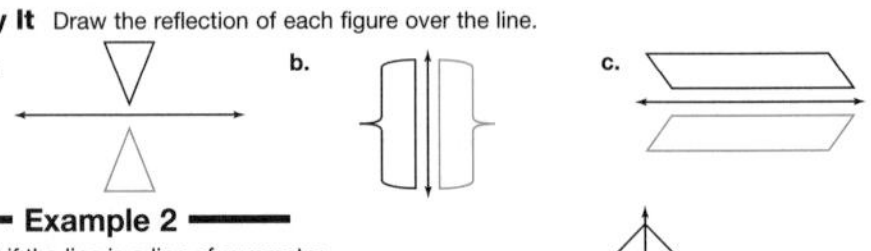

Example 2

Tell if the line is a line of symmetry.

If the figure was folded at the line, the two parts would match exactly. So, the line is a line of symmetry.

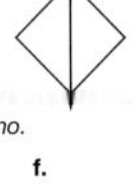

Try It Tell if each line is a line of symmetry. Write *yes* or *no.*

d. e. f.
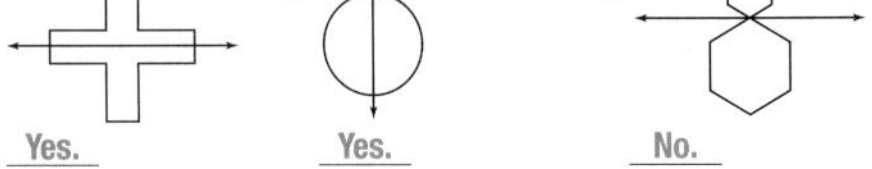

d. Yes. e. Yes. f. No.

Example 3

Tell if the pair of figures is congruent.

The figures are the same shape, but are different sizes. So, the figures are not congruent.

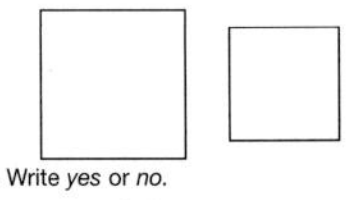

Try It Tell whether each pair of figures is congruent. Write *yes* or *no.*

g. h. i.
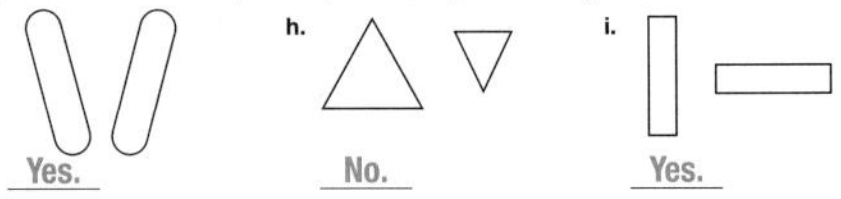

g. Yes. h. No. i. Yes.

Geometry **The front wall of the Islamic palace of Mshatta was built around 743. Use the design on the wall for Exercises 16 and 17.**

16. Sketch a pair of congruent figures in the design.

17. Determine the number of lines of symmetry that the design has. 2

18. **Test Prep** Look at the shape to the right. Choose the shape that is a reflection of this shape. A

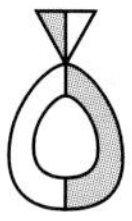

Problem Solving and Reasoning

19. **Critical Thinking** Draw a regular octagon, a regular hexagon, and a regular pentagon. Which polygon has the most lines of symmetry? Explain.

20. GPS **Critical Thinking** A triangle has one angle of 40°. The other angles are congruent to each other. What are the measurements of the other two angles? Explain.

21. Journal List five objects in your classroom or home that have line symmetry. Explain why and describe the line(s) of symmetry.

Mixed Review

Order from smallest to largest. *[Lesson 5-8]*

22. $\frac{5}{6}, 0.5, \frac{1}{3}$ $\frac{1}{3}, 0.5, \frac{5}{6}$

23. $\frac{7}{9}, \frac{2}{3}, 0.75$ $\frac{2}{3}, 0.75, \frac{7}{9}$

24. $\frac{14}{7}, \frac{7}{7}, 2.12$ $\frac{7}{7}, \frac{14}{7}, 2.12$

25. $1.1, \frac{7}{6}, 1.167$ $1.1, \frac{7}{6}, 1.167$

26. $2.2, 2.22, \frac{2}{22}$ $\frac{2}{22}, 2.2, 2.22$

27. $\frac{1}{3}, \frac{3}{1}, 1.3$ $\frac{1}{3}, 1.3, \frac{3}{1}$

28. $\frac{1}{10}, 1.10, 10.1$ $\frac{1}{10}, 1.10, 10.1$

29. $2.5, \frac{2}{5}, 0.25$ $0.25, \frac{2}{5}, 2.5$

Multiply. *[Lesson 3-9]*

30. 4.6 × 8.2 37.72

31. 9.54 × 3.2 30.528

32. 0.06 × 3.29 0.1974

33. 0.92 × 4.76 4.3792

34. 3.1 × 3.1 9.61

35. 1.9 × 9.1 17.29

36. 0.4 × 0.44 0.176

37. 6.6 × 0.6 3.96

PROBLEM SOLVING 8-8

Exercise Answers

15. Answers may vary.

16. Possible answer:

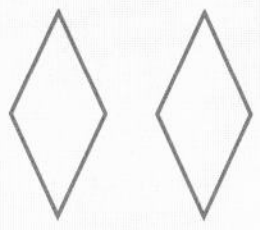

19.

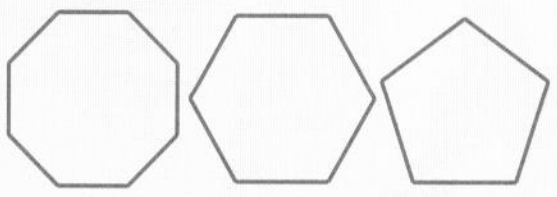

Octagon; There is a line of symmetry through every corner and every side of a regular polygon, and an octagon has more corners and sides than a hexagon and a pentagon.

20. 70°; The angle measure multiplied by two and then added to 40° must equal 180°.

21. Answers may vary.

Alternate Assessment

Performance Have students fold a sheet of paper in half and then draw a line down the fold. Then have students print their name horizontally on one half of the page and draw the reflection of their name over the line.

Quick Quiz

Tell if the dotted line is a line of symmetry.

1.

Yes

2.

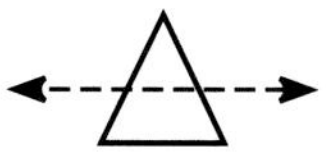

No

3.

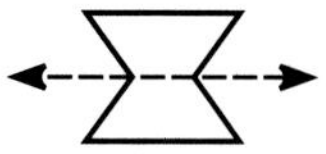

Yes

Available on Daily Transparency 8-8

PROBLEM SOLVING

Name ______________________

Guided Problem Solving 8-8

GPS **PROBLEM 20, STUDENT PAGE 447**

A triangle has one angle of 40°. The other angles are congruent to each other. What are the measurements of the other two angles? Explain.

— Understand —

1. What is the measurement of the given angle? 40°
2. What does *congruent* mean? The same size and shape.
3. Would congruent angles have the same or different measures? Same.

— Plan —

4. What is the sum of the measures of the three angles of a triangle? 180°
5. Which is a reasonable measure for one of the congruent angles? C
   a. about 360° b. about 180° c. less than 90°

— Solve —

6. Subtract to find the measure of the two congruent angles. 140°
7. Write an equation to find the measures of the congruent angles.
   140 ÷ 2 = 70
8. What are the measures of the congruent angles? 70°, 70°

— Look Back —

9. How could drawing a picture of the triangle help you decide if your answer is reasonable? Possible answer: You would be able to see if calculated measures are reasonable.

SOLVE ANOTHER PROBLEM

A parallelogram has two pairs of congruent angles. One angle measures 45°. What are the measurements of the other angles? Explain.

45°, 135°, 135°; 2 · 45 = 90; 360 − 90 = 270; 270 ÷ 2 = 135

ENRICHMENT

Name ______________________

Extend Your Thinking 8-8

Patterns in Geometry

You can flip small squares to make a larger square pattern.

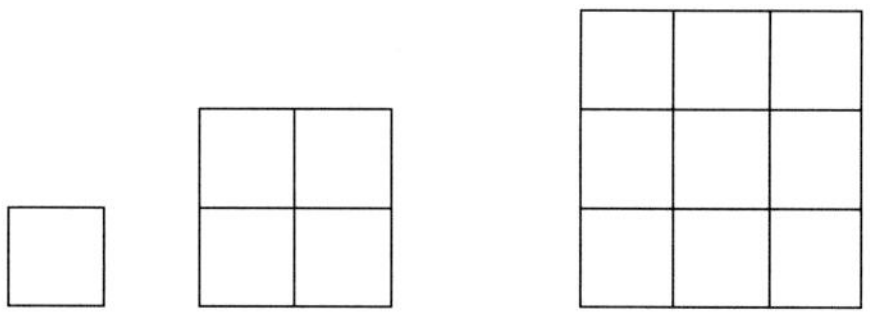

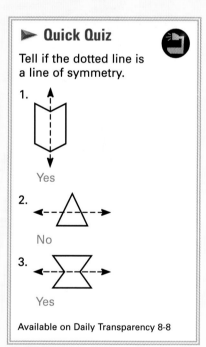

1. How many small squares are in the first figure? One square.
2. How many small squares are in the second figure? Four squares.
3. How many times was the small square flipped to make the second figure? Three times.
4. How many small squares are in the third figure? Nine squares.
5. How many times was the small square flipped to make the third figure? Eight times.
6. What pattern do you see in the number of small squares in each figure? It is the square of the figure's position in the pattern.
7. What pattern do you see in the number of flips made to make each figure? It is one less than the number of small squares in the figure.
8. How many small squares will make up the fourth figure in the pattern? How many flips? 16 squares; 15 flips.
9. A larger square was made with 49 small squares. What place is the figure in the pattern? Seventh place.
10. A larger square was made with 80 flips. How many small squares are in the figure? 81 small squares.
11. A larger square was made with 143 flips. What place is the figure in the pattern? Twelfth place.

INTERACTIVE LESSON

8-9 Lesson Organizer

Objectives

- Identify rotations of figures.
- Identify rotational symmetry.

Vocabulary

- Rotation, clockwise, counterclockwise, rotational symmetry

Materials

- Explore: Tracing paper

NCTM Standards

- 1–4, 7, 12

Review

Refer to the following diagram of a rectangle with a small square on top.

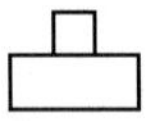

1. Draw the figure after it has been turned one-quarter turn to the right.

2. Draw the original figure after it has been turned one-half turn to the right.

3. Draw the original figure after it has been turned three-quarter turn to the right.

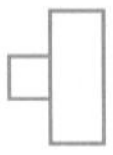

Available on Daily Transparency 8-9

1 Introduce

Explore

The Point
Students match pairs of identical figures, one of which has been rotated.

8-9 Turns and Rotational Symmetry

You'll Learn ...

- to identify rotations of figures
- to identify rotational symmetry

... How It's Used

Quilt makers use rotational symmetry when designing the pattern for a quilt.

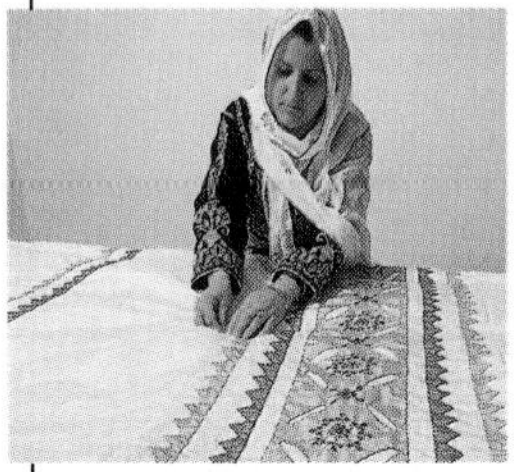

Vocabulary

rotation
clockwise
counterclockwise
rotational symmetry

▶ Lesson Link In the last lesson, you saw what happens when a figure is flipped over a line. Now you'll look at what happens when a figure is turned like a wheel. ◀

Explore Turns

It's Your Turn

Materials: Tracing paper

The 15 shapes below include 7 pairs of identical shapes. One of the shapes in each pair has been turned to face a different direction. One shape below has no match, no matter how you turn it.

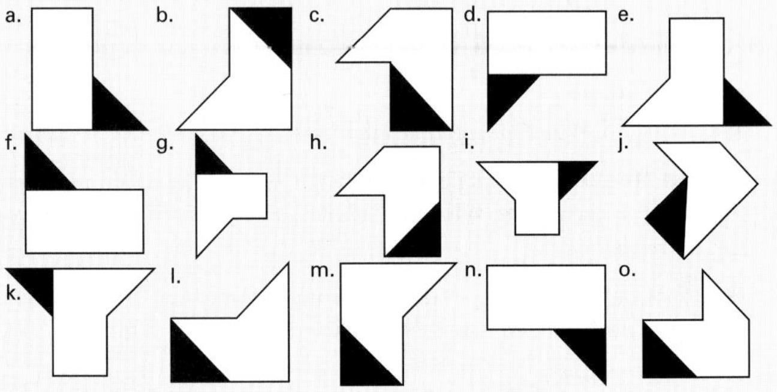

1. For each shape, find its match. Which shape has no match?
2. Draw a match for the leftover shape. Make sure it is turned to face a different direction. How can you prove the two shapes are a match?

Learn Turns and Rotational Symmetry

A **rotation** is the image of a figure that has been turned, as if it were on a wheel. When the top of a figure turns to the right, it is turned **clockwise**. When the top turns to the left, it is turned **counterclockwise**.

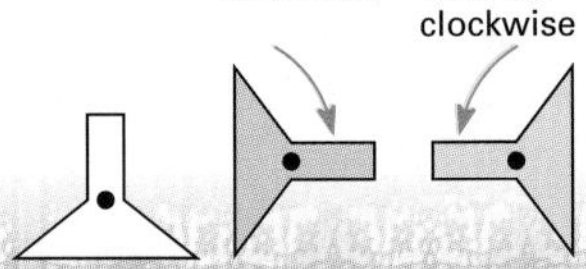

MEETING INDIVIDUAL NEEDS

Resources

8-9 Practice
8-9 Reteaching
8-9 Problem Solving
8-9 Enrichment
8-9 Daily Transparency
Problem of the Day
Review
Quick Quiz
Lesson Enhancement Transparency 43
Technology Master 43
Interactive CD-ROM Lesson

Learning Modalities

Visual Have students cut out pictures from newspapers or magazines that show rotational symmetry. Each picture should then be labeled with the least rotation that would land the figure on top of itself.

Kinesthetic Some students will find it helpful to trace, shade, and cut out the shapes in **Explore**. Then they can actually lift the shapes up and rotate them to find the pairs of identical shapes.

Challenge

Show students the following sign. Ask them to discover what is unusual about it.

NOW NO SWIMS ON MON

It has 180° rotational symmetry. If the sign is turned upside down, it still reads the same.

If a figure can be rotated less than a full circle, and the rotation exactly matches the original image, then the figure has **rotational symmetry**.

This figure has 180° rotational symmetry. If you turn it 180°, it will "land on itself," exactly matching the original image.

The figure at the right has 90°, 180°, and 270° rotational symmetry.

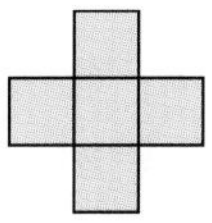

This figure does not have rotational symmetry.

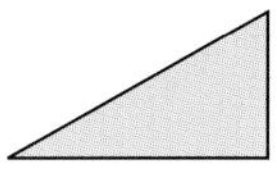

Examples

The following images have been taken from Islamic designs. Give the least number of degrees and the direction that each figure has been rotated.

1

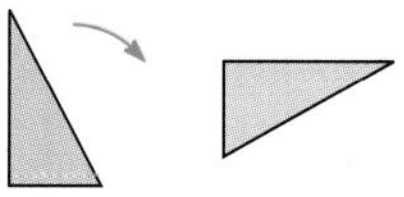

The figure has been rotated 90° clockwise.

2

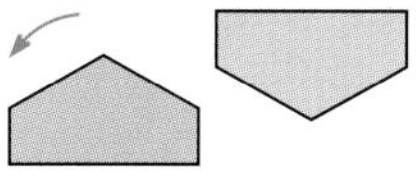

The figure has been rotated 180° counterclockwise.

3 If the figure is rotated 360°, how many times will it land on itself?

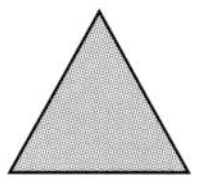

The figure will land on itself three times.

Try It

Give the number of degrees and the direction that each figure has been rotated.

a.

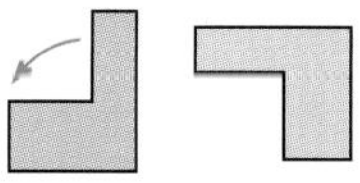

90° counterclockwise

b.

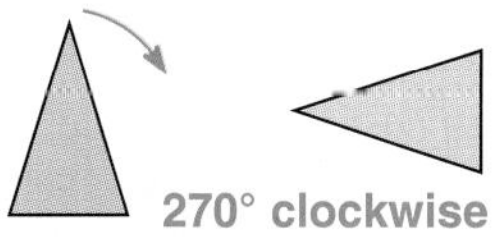

270° clockwise

c. If the figure is rotated 360°, how many times will it land on itself? 2

► Geography Link

The Islamic world stretches from Morocco on the northwest coast of Africa to Pakistan just west of India, and includes Bangladesh and Indonesia beyond India.

Ongoing Assessment

Some students will name pairs of figures that are mirror images. Remind them not to flip the paper when they trace figures.

For Groups That Finish Early

Name two figures that are mirror images. Possible answer: d and n

Answers for Explore

1. a, d; b, m; c, j; e, k; f, n; g, i; h, o; l has no match.
2. 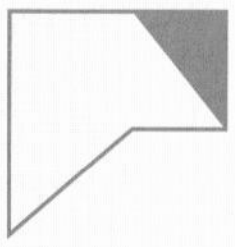

   Rotate one of the pieces so that it lands on the other.

2 Teach

Learn

Alternate Examples

Give the least number of degrees and the direction that each figure has been rotated.

1. 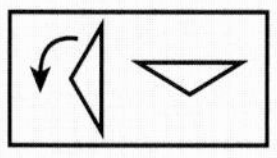

   The figure has been rotated 90° counterclockwise.
2. 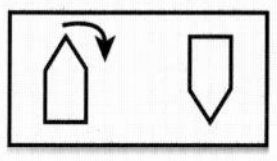

   The figure has been rotated 180° clockwise.
3. If the figure is rotated 360°, how many times will it land on itself?

   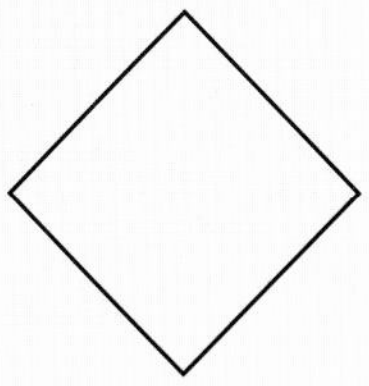

   The figure will land on itself four times.

MATH EVERY DAY

► Problem of the Day

Move one toothpick to make a true number sentence.

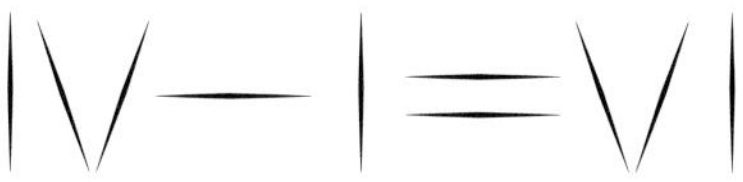

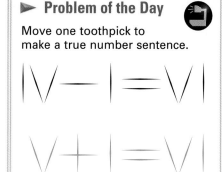

Available on Daily Transparency 8-9

An Extension is provided in the transparency package.

Fact of the Day

Tiles with geometric designs decorate buildings in Islamic countries. Some were turned and rotated to make larger patterns.

Estimation

Estimate each product.

1. 1.8×7 14
2. 4.2×6 24
3. 7.9×7.9 64
4. 9.8×12.3 120
5. 3.08×8.98 27

WHAT DO YOU THINK?

Students see two methods of solving a problem. One method involves tracing a figure and then rotating it. The other method involves reflecting the figure over a vertical line and then over a horizontal line. Students can decide which of the two correct methods is easier for them.

Answers for What Do You Think?

1. A vertical reflection and a horizontal reflection always result in the same outcome as a 180° rotation; Yes, you can always use it.
2. Peter only has to sketch the figure once. Tyreka sketches it twice.

3 Practice and Assess

Check

Be sure students realize that when a figure is rotated, it is rotated around the center, just as a wheel rotates about the center. Otherwise, no figure would ever land on itself unless it went through a complete rotation.

Answers for Check Your Understanding

1. 360°
2. Yes; Rotating a figure never changes its shape.

WHAT DO YOU THINK?

Peter and Tyreka are making a scrapbook of designs that display symmetry. They need a figure that has rotational symmetry for 180°. They want to know if they can use this mosque design.

Peter thinks ...

I'll trace the design on tracing paper. Then I'll rotate the paper 180°.

The rotated figure matches the design on the mosque. Therefore, the design shows 180° rotational symmetry.

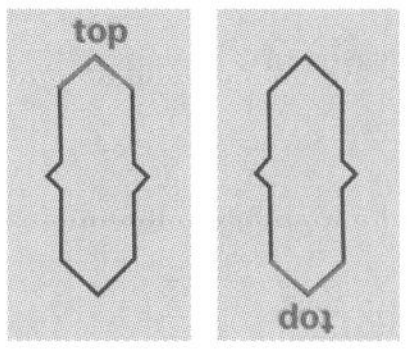

Tyreka thinks ...

I'll reflect the figure over a line vertically.

Then I'll reflect the resulting figure over a line horizontally.

The result matches the original figure. Therefore, the design shows 180° rotational symmetry

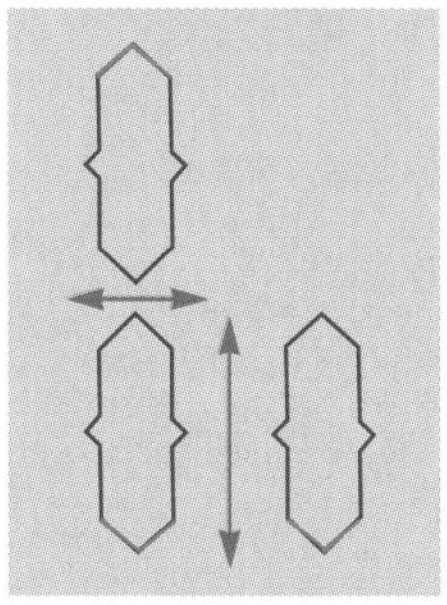

What do you think?

1. How does Tyreka's method work? Can you always use it to show that a design has 180° rotational symmetry?
2. What advantages does Peter's method have over Tyreka's method? Tyreka's method over Peter's?

MEETING MIDDLE SCHOOL CLASSROOM NEEDS

Tips from Middle School Teachers

I like to have students make up their own designs that show rotational symmetry. This allows students with artistic talent to illustrate their talent, and it also allows them to succeed in a mathematical setting.

Team Teaching

Work with an art teacher to show various examples of paintings or designs that illustrate rotational symmetry.

Science Connection

Some living things have radial symmetry; their parts are arranged around a central point, like the spokes of a wheel. Others have bilateral symmetry. They can be divided into right and left halves that are mirror images of each other.

Check Your Understanding

1. A figure has no rotational symmetry. How many degrees must you rotate it before it lands on itself?

2. If a figure is rotated, is it congruent to the original shape? Explain.

8-9 Exercises and Applications

Practice and Apply

Getting Started **Draw a 90° counterclockwise rotation of each figure.**

1. 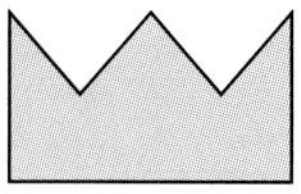 **2.** 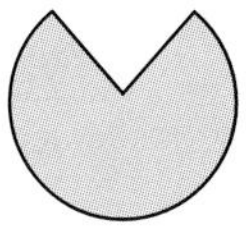 **3.** 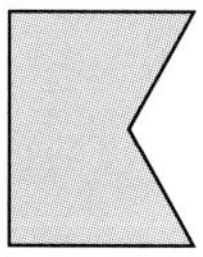 **4.** 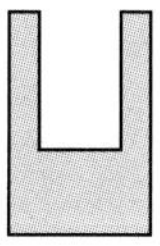

What is the least rotation that will land the figure on top of itself?

5.  360°

6.  90°

7. 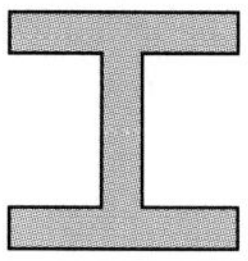 180°

8. 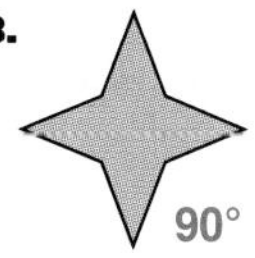 90°

Draw a 45° clockwise rotation of the figure.

9.  **10.** 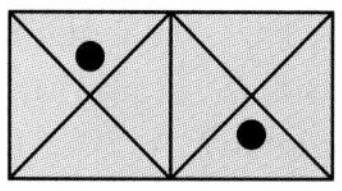 **11.** 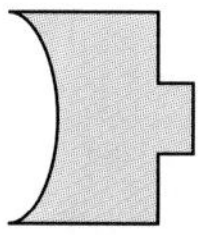 **12.** 

13. Fine Arts What is the least rotation that will land the design on top of itself? 45°

IL-KHANID STAR-SHAPED TILE, 1293. Earthenware with lustre decoration. The Avery Brundage Collection. The Asian Art Museum of San Francisco. B60 P2148.

PRACTICE 8-9

8-9 Exercises and Applications

Assignment Guide

- **Basic** 1–17, 19–21, 25–35 odds
- **Average** 4–22, 25–39 odds
- **Enriched** 4–23, 24–38 evens

Exercise Answers

1. 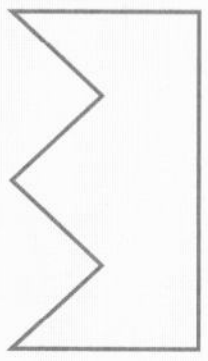

2. 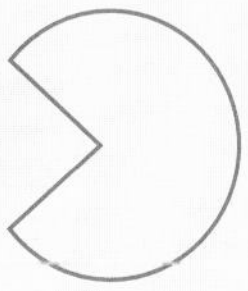

3. 

4. 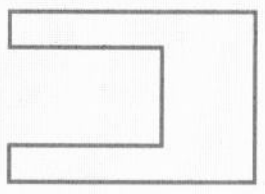

9–12 See page C2.

PRACTICE

Name ______________________

Practice 8-9

Turns and Rotational Symmetry

What is the least rotation that will land the figure on top of itself?

1. 180° 2. 90° 3. 360° 4. 60°

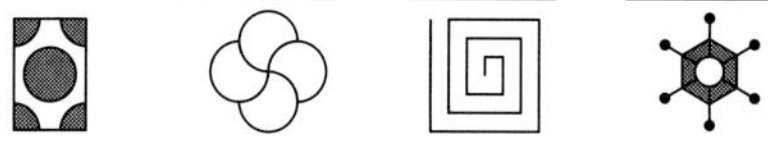

Draw a 45° clockwise rotation of the figure.

5. 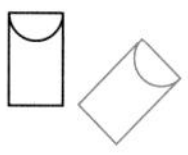 6. 

7. 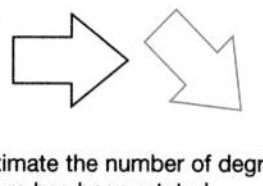 8. 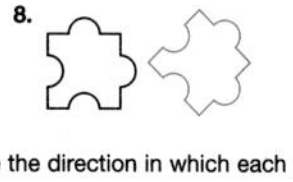

Estimate the number of degrees and state the direction in which each figure has been rotated.

9. 180° clockwise 
10. 90° clockwise 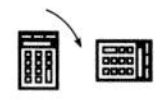
11. 135° counterclockwise 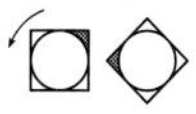
12. 90° counterclockwise 

13. **Fine Arts** A mirror illustrated in Jan van Eyck's *The Betrothal of the Arnolfini* has the shape shown at the right. If the mirror is rotated 360°, how many times will it land on itself? 10

RETEACHING

Name ______________________

Alternative Lesson 8-9

Turns and Rotational Symmetry

A **rotation** is the image of a figure that has been turned, as if it were on a wheel. When the top of a figure turns to the right, it is turned **clockwise.** When the top turns to the left, it is turned **counter-clockwise.** You can use degrees to describe the rotation. If a figure can be rotated less than a full circle, and the rotation exactly matches the original image, then the figure has **rotational symmetry.**

— Example 1 —

Draw a 45° clockwise rotation for the figure.

The rotation is to the right. There are 360° in a circle. Draw a 45° angle to see the rotation of the figure. Then use the angle to draw the rotation.

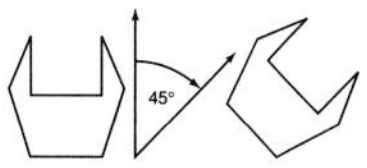

Try It Draw a 90° clockwise rotation for each figure.

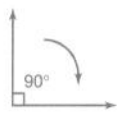

a. Draw a 90° angle to see the rotation of each figure.

b. 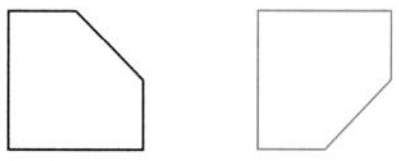 c. 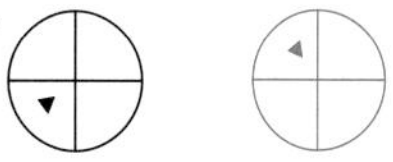

— Example 2 —

What is the least rotation that will land the figure on top of itself?

If the figure is rotated 360°, it will land on itself 2 times. The least rotation is half of 360°, or 180°.

Try It What it the least rotation that will land the figure on top of itself?

d. 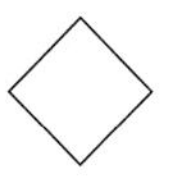 90°

e.  180°

f.  360°

Reteaching

Activity

Materials: Index cards

- Work with a partner. Each person should print each distinct letter of his or her name on a separate index card.
- All the letters should be put into a pile and shuffled.
- Each person should pick one letter at a time and determine if that letter has rotational symmetry and then tell the least rotation that will land the letter on top of itself.

Exercise Answers

21. Yes; Every figure can be rotated 360° and that rotation will always land a figure on top of itself.
22. No; The figure and its rotation are congruent, so the area, perimeter, and shape are the same.
23. Answers may vary; A figure with only one line of symmetry will not have rotational symmetry.

Alternate Assessment

Self Assessment Ask students to describe what they find most difficult to understand about the concept of rotational symmetry.

Quick Quiz

What is the least rotation that will land each figure on top of itself?

1. 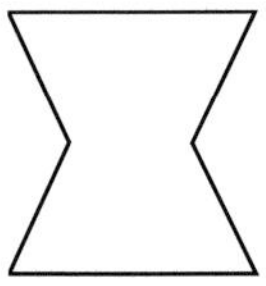

180°

2. 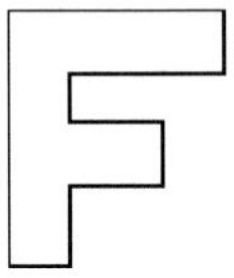

360°

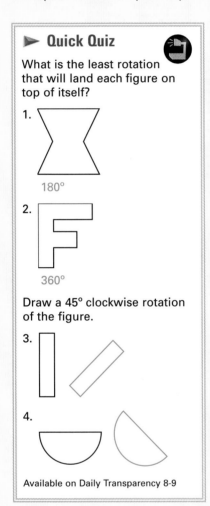

Draw a 45° clockwise rotation of the figure.

3. 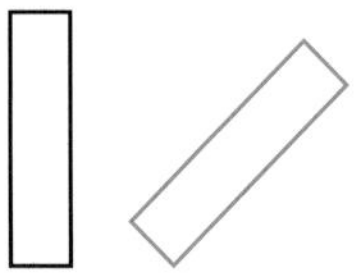

4. 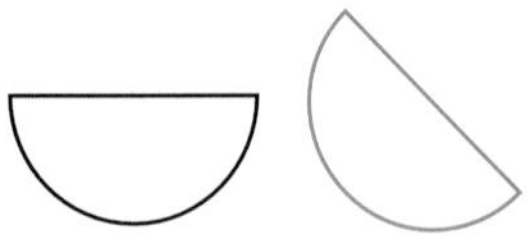

Available on Daily Transparency 8-9

Estimation Estimate the number of degrees that each figure has been rotated.

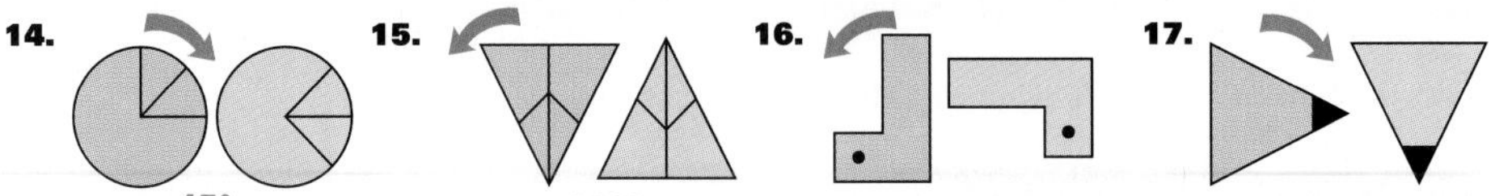

14. 45°
15. 180°
16. 90°
17. 90°

18. **Fine Arts** If one of the flowers in the pattern is rotated 360°, how many times will it land on itself? 5

19. **Fine Arts** What is the least number of degrees of rotation that will land a flower on top of itself? 72°

GPS

20. **Test Prep** Choose the example of a rotation. B

Ⓐ Ⓑ Ⓒ

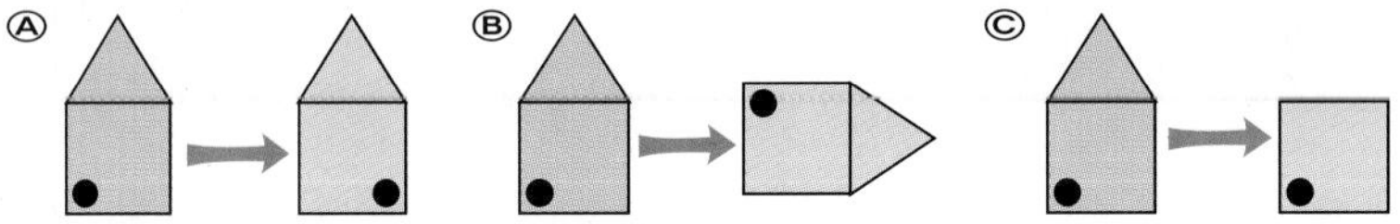

PROBLEM SOLVING 8-9

Problem Solving and Reasoning

21. **Communicate** Can every figure be rotated so that it will land on top of itself? Explain.

22. **Communicate** Does the area, perimeter, or shape of a figure change when it is rotated? Explain.

23. **Critical Thinking** Fold a piece of paper in half and then in half again. Cut out a figure that has rotational symmetry. Do the same with another piece of paper. Cut out a figure that has line symmetry but not rotational symmetry. Describe the differences between the symmetries of your figures.

Mixed Review

Divide. Round the quotient to the nearest hundredth. *[Lesson 3-10]*

24. 36.39 ÷ 5 7.28
25. 14.2 ÷ 4 3.55
26. 1.89 ÷ 10 0.19
27. 2.86 ÷ 22 0.13
28. 25.5 ÷ 5 5.1
29. 0.65 ÷ 11 0.06
30. 0.79 ÷ 8 0.1
31. 7.111 ÷ 3 2.37

Divide. Round to the nearest hundredth. *[Lesson 3-11]*

32. 13.26 ÷ 0.6 22.1
33. 98.28 ÷ 5.4 18.2
34. 16.324 ÷ 1.54 10.6
35. 57.2 ÷ 21.3 2.69
36. 37.97 ÷ 0.78 48.68
37. 100.82 ÷ 7.1 14.2
38. 0.75 ÷ 0.25 3
39. 39.2 ÷ 5.6 7

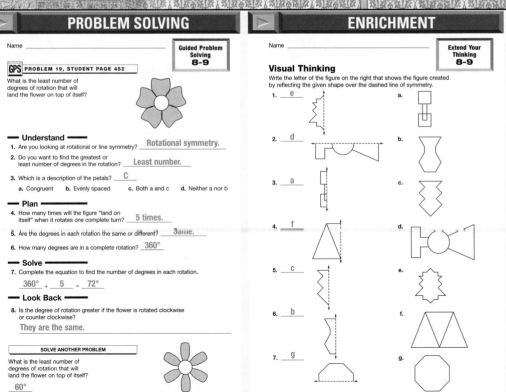

PROBLEM SOLVING

Name ______________________

Guided Problem Solving 8-9

GPS **PROBLEM 19, STUDENT PAGE 452**

What is the least number of degrees of rotation that will land the flower on top of itself?

Understand

1. Are you looking at rotational or line symmetry? Rotational symmetry.
2. Do you want to find the greatest or least number of degrees in the rotation? Least number.
3. Which is a description of the petals? C
   a. Congruent **b.** Evenly spaced **c.** Both a and c **d.** Neither a nor b

Plan

4. How many times will the figure "land on itself" when it rotates one complete turn? 5 times.
5. Are the degrees in each rotation the same or different? Same.
6. How many degrees are in a complete rotation? 360°

Solve

7. Complete the equation to find the number of degrees in each rotation.
   360° ÷ 5 = 72°

Look Back

8. Is the degree of rotation greater if the flower is rotated clockwise or counter clockwise?
   They are the same.

SOLVE ANOTHER PROBLEM

What is the least number of degrees of rotation that will land the flower on top of itself?

60°

ENRICHMENT

Name ______________________

Extend Your Thinking 8-9

Visual Thinking

Write the letter of the figure on the right that shows the figure created by reflecting the given shape over the dashed line of symmetry.

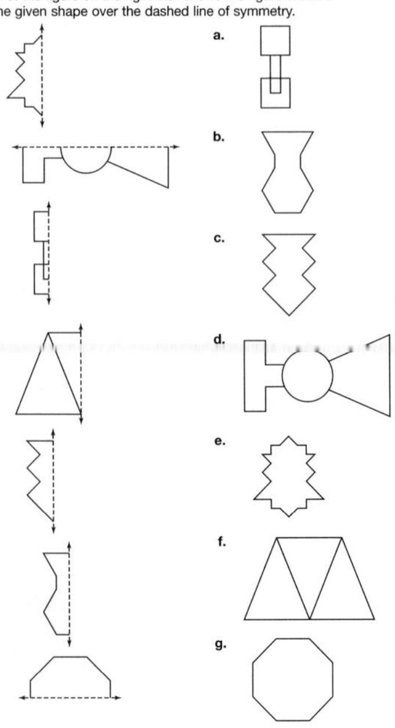

1. e
2. d
3. a
4. f
5. c
6. b
7. g

Slides and Tessellations

8-10

▶ Lesson Link You know what happens to a figure when you flip it or turn it. Now you'll see what happens when you slide a figure to a new position. ◀

You'll Learn ...

■ to identify translations of figures and tessellations

... How It's Used

Graphic designers use translations and tessellations when designing logos and graphic artwork.

Vocabulary

translation

tessellation

Explore Slides and Tessellations

I've Got You Covered!

Materials: Tracing paper, Unlined paper

These shapes represent different tiles for sale. Which of the shapes could be used to cover the floor without having any space in between tiles?

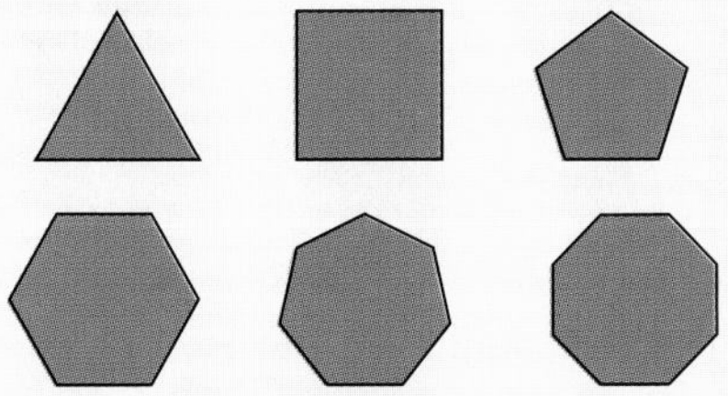

1. Copy each shape onto tracing paper several times. Copy the shapes as closely together as possible without overlaps. Then state whether each shape can or cannot be put together with copies of itself, leaving no spaces in between.
2. Draw a shape that does not appear above but that could be used to entirely cover a floor without any spaces in between.
3. Look at all of the shapes that can fit together without spaces in between. What patterns do you see that could help you determine if a shape would work without using tracing paper?

Learn Slides and Tessellations

When a figure is slid to a new position without flipping or turning, the new image is called a slide, or a **translation** .

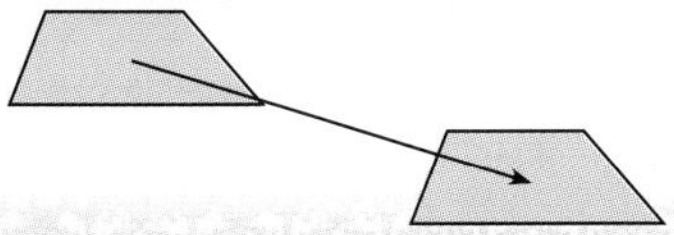

MEETING INDIVIDUAL NEEDS

Resources

8-10 Practice
8-10 Reteaching
8-10 Problem Solving
8-10 Enrichment
8-10 Daily Transparency
- Problem of the Day
- Review
- Quick Quiz

Teaching Tool Transparencies 2, 3
Chapter 8 Project Master

Learning Modalities

Kinesthetic Have students work with pattern blocks. Have them decide which of the shapes tessellate. You may wish to extend the activity by having students find pairs of shapes that will tessellate.

Visual Show students several different wallpaper patterns. Then have them discuss any tessellations that are involved and how the patterns might have been created.

English Language Development

Point out that a translation is often called a slide. You might also need to point out that the word *translation* as used in mathematics has nothing to do with translation from one language to another.

8-10 Lesson Organizer

Objective

- Identify translations of figures and tessellations.

Vocabulary

- Translation, tessellation

Materials

- Explore: Tracing paper, unlined paper

NCTM Standards

- 1–4, 12

▶ Review

How many sides does each of the following polygons have?

1. Pentagon 5
2. Hexagon 6
3. Octagon 8
4. Quadrilateral 4

Available on Daily Transparency 8-10

1 Introduce

Explore

The Point
Students use cutout figures of various polygons and determine if these figures can be used to completely cover a plane surface.

Ongoing Assessment
Watch for students who think that the figures can overlap.

For Groups That Finish Early
Which type of polygon is used most often for tiling floors?
Square

Answers for Explore on next page.

Answers for Explore

1. Yes: triangle, square, hexagon; No: pentagon, heptagon, octagon.
2. Possible answer:

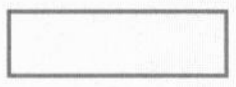

3. Using only the angles of that polygon, if you can make a circle or fill 360° without overlapping the angles, the polygon tessellates.

2 Teach

Learn

Alternate Examples

Does the figure tessellate? Make a drawing to show your answer.

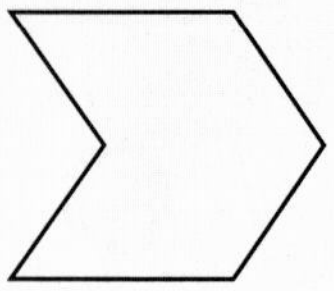

Yes, the figure tessellates.

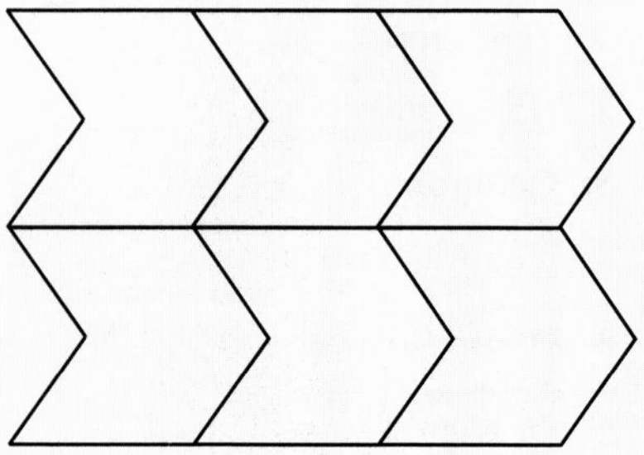

3 Practice and Assess

Check

Some students may need to review line symmetry and rotational symmetry from the two preceding lessons.

Answers for Check Your Understanding

1. Not necessarily. For example, a right scalene triangle tessellates and has neither line nor rotational symmetry.
2. No; Possible answer:

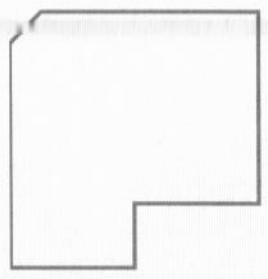

DID YOU KNOW?

There are only 17 basic tessellation patterns. Every tessellation can be broken down into one of these 17 patterns.

In Islamic art, the design of a mosaic wall sometimes consists of a single figure translated to every possible position on the wall. As a result, the wall is completely covered by the figure.

A pattern of congruent shapes like the one above, with no gaps or overlaps, is called a **tessellation**.

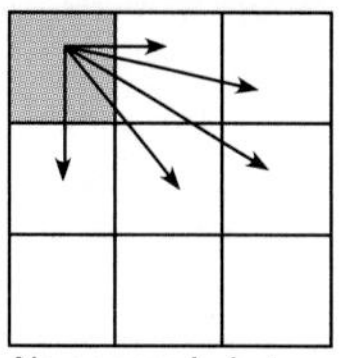

A square tessellates.

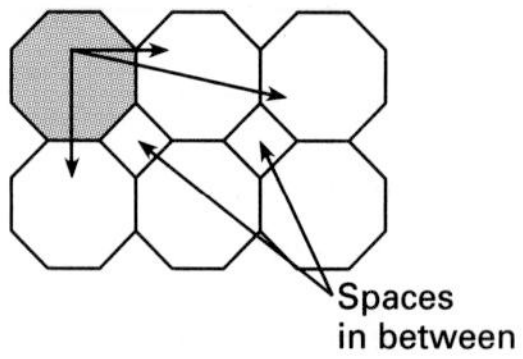

A regular octagon does not tessellate.

Example

Does the figure tessellate? Make a drawing to show your answer.

Yes, the figure tessellates.

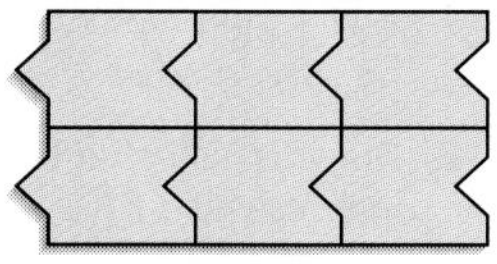

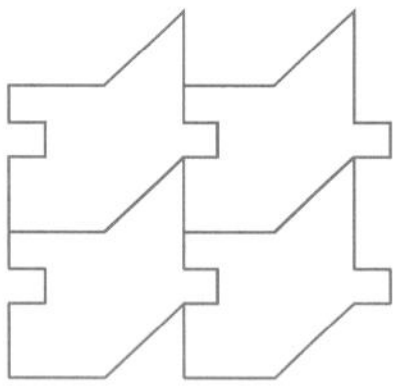

Try It

Does the figure tessellate? Make a drawing to show your answer. Yes

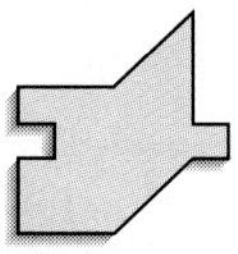

Check Your Understanding

1. Does a figure that tessellates have line symmetry? Rotational symmetry? Explain.
2. Can you tessellate any shape? Make a drawing to show your answer.

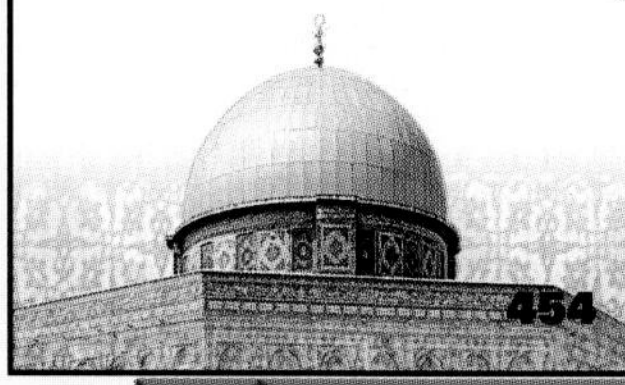

MATH EVERY DAY

Problem of the Day

Put five circles on the grid so that no two circles are in the same row, column, or diagonal.

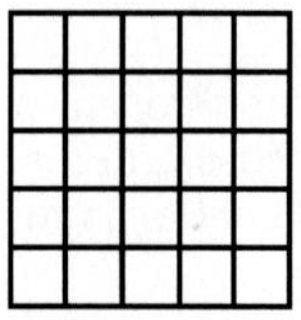

Possible answer:

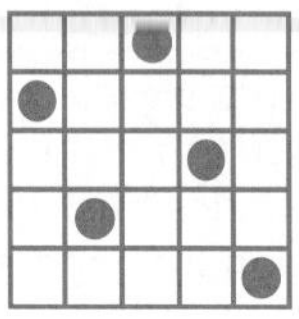

Available on Daily Transparency 8-10

An Extension is provided in the transparency package.

Fact of the Day

Building of the Dome of the Rock in Jerusalem began more than 1350 years ago.

Mental Math

Find each quotient mentally.

1. 80 ÷ 40 2
2. 360 ÷ 60 6
3. 4200 ÷ 60 70
4. 5600 ÷ 800 7

8-10 Exercises and Applications

Practice and Apply

Getting Started State whether one figure is a translation of the other.

1. 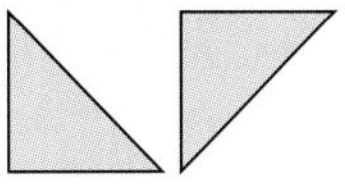 No

2. 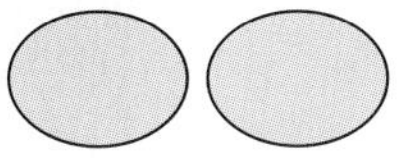 Yes

3. 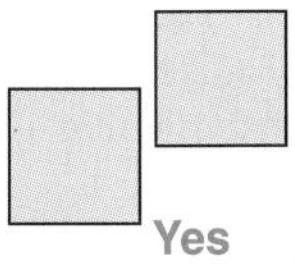 Yes

4. 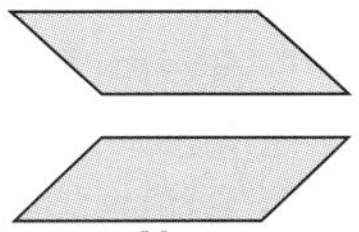 No

These designs can be found on the Dome of the Rock in Jerusalem, the oldest Islamic monument standing. Name the polygons that are tessellated in the designs.

5. 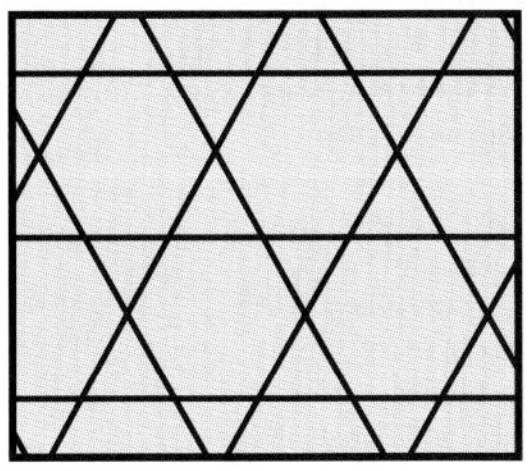

6. 

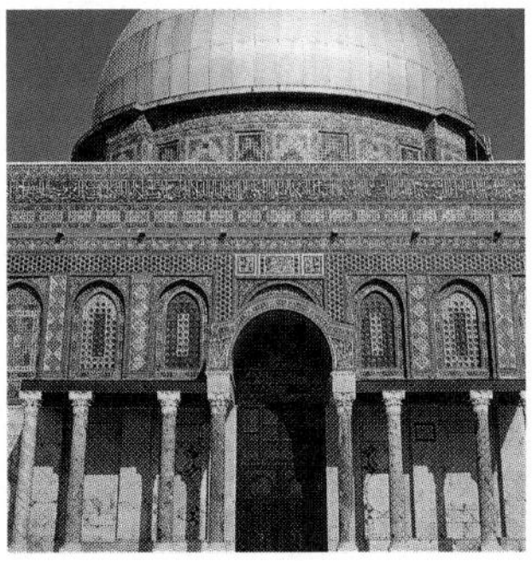

State if the figure tessellates. Make a drawing to show your answer.

7. Yes 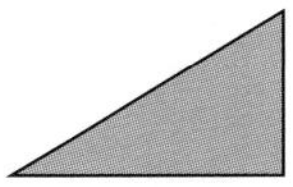

8. No 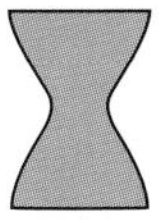

9. Yes 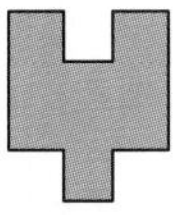

10. No 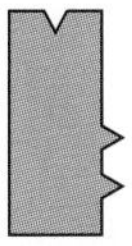

11. No 

12. Yes 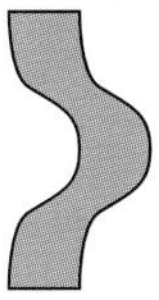

13. No 

14. No 

15. **Science** An individual cell of honeycomb starts off as a circle, but because the cells are so close together, the circles flatten out. The result is a tessellation. What polygon is tessellated in a honeycomb? Hexagon

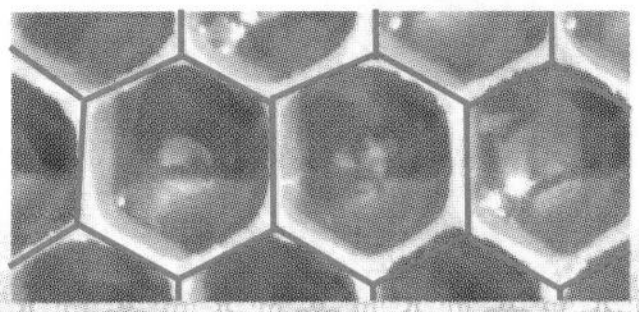

PRACTICE 8-10

PRACTICE

Name ______________________

Practice 8-10

Tessellations

Name the polygon that is tessellated in each design.

1. Equilateral triangle 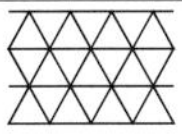

2. Parallelogram 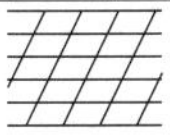

3. Pentagon 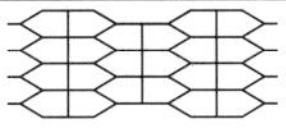

4. Trapezoid 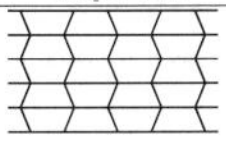

State if each figure tessellates. Make a drawing to show your answer.

5. Tessellates 

6. Does not tessellate 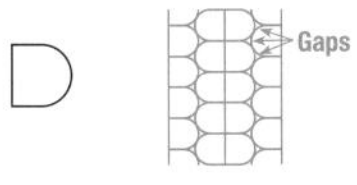

7. Tessellates 

8. Tessellates 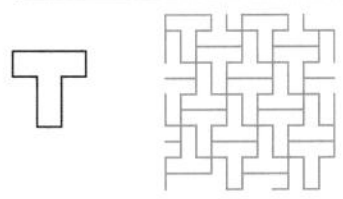

9. Is each shaded polygon a translation of one of the white polygons?
No; Possible answer: The shaded polygons are rotations of the white polygons.

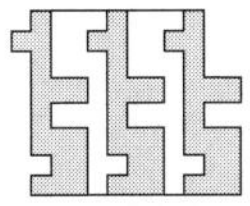

RETEACHING

Name ______________________

Alternative Lesson 8-10

Translations and Tessellations

When a figure is slid to a new position without flipping or turning, the new image is called a **translation.**

A pattern of congruent shapes with no gaps or overlaps, is called a **tessellation.**

Example 1

State whether the one figure is a translation of the other.

The figure is in a new position. The new position is not a flip or turn. So, the figure is a translation.

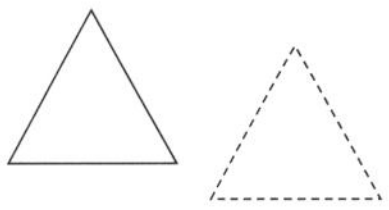

Try It State whether one figure is a translation of the other. Write *yes* or *no.*

a. Is the new position a flip? No.
Is the new position a rotation? Yes.
Is the new position a translation? No.

b. 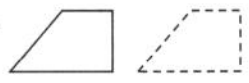 Yes.

c.  Yes.

d. 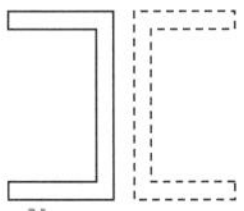 No.

Example 2

State if the figure tessellates.

The figure cannot be moved to make a pattern of congruent shapes with no gaps or overlaps, so it cannot tessellate.

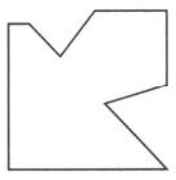

Try It Make a drawing to show whether or not each figure tessellates. Both figures tesselate. Check student's work.

e. 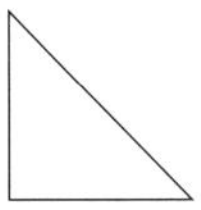

f. 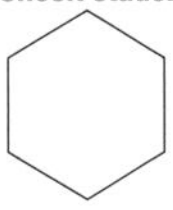

8-10 Exercises and Applications

Assignment Guide

- Basic
  1–6, 7–15 odds, 16, 19–29 odds
- Average
  1–17, 19–29 odds
- Enriched
  5–20, 22–28 evens

Exercise Notes

Exercise 3

Error Prevention Some students may think that the second square is not a translation of the first because the slide is not completely horizontal or vertical. Point out that a slide can involve a move in both a horizontal and a vertical direction.

Exercise Answers

5. Hexagons, triangles
6. Squares
7. Yes

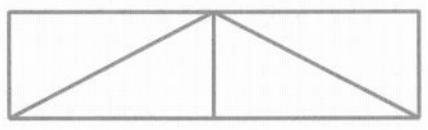

9. Yes

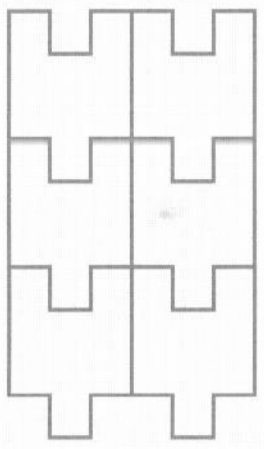

12. Yes

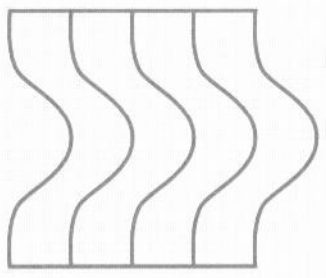

Reteaching

Activity

Materials: Cardboard

- Work in pairs. Start with a square piece of cardboard.
- Cut out a piece from one side of the square. The piece can be any shape.
- Slide the piece to the opposite side of the square so that the straight side of the piece is in exactly the same position as it was on the opposite side.
- Use the new figure to make a drawing of a tessellation.

Exercise Notes

■ Exercise 20

Problem-Solving Tip You may wish to use Teaching Tool Transparencies 2 and 3: Guided Problem Solving, pages 1–2.

Project Progress

You may want to have students use Chapter 8 Project Master.

Exercise Answers

17. Yes; The parallel lines can always be put next to each other with no gaps.
18. Answers may vary.
19. Check students' drawings. The answer to Exercise 12 is an example of a figure that tesselates that is not a polygon.

Alternate Assessment

Portfolio Have students draw the tile designs from floors they have seen in places such as schools, stores, restaurants, libraries, and museums. For each drawing, ask them to explain what shape(s) was tessellated.

▶ Quick Quiz

State if the figure tessellates. Make a drawing to show your answer.

1. 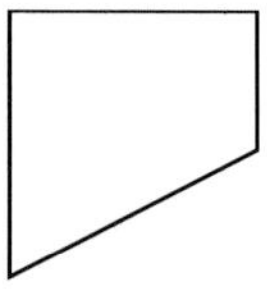

Yes

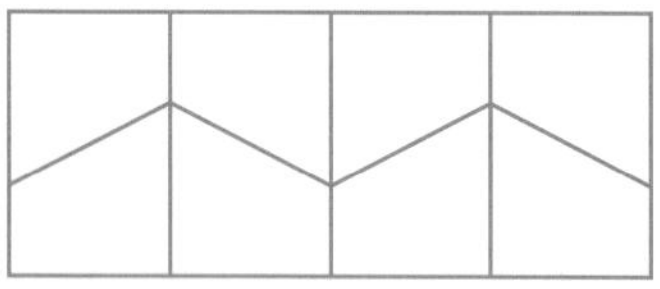

2. 

No

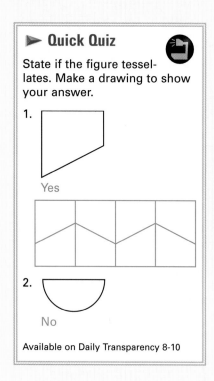

Available on Daily Transparency 8-10

---

16. **Test Prep** Which shape cannot be used to make a tessellation? B

Ⓐ Rectangle Ⓑ Circle Ⓒ Regular hexagon Ⓓ Not here

Problem Solving and Reasoning

17. Communicate Steve stated that all squares, rectangles, and parallelograms tessellate. Do you agree with Steve? Explain your reasoning.

18. Critical Thinking What is the base pattern of the tessellation running across the bottom of the stone carving?

19. Critical Thinking Draw a tessellation that does not use a polygon as the figure tessellated. Explain your tessellation.

GPS

20. Choose a Strategy Is the design on the door a tessellation? If so, draw the shape that is tessellated.
No

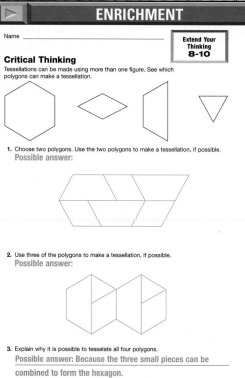

Problem Solving STRATEGIES

- Look for a Pattern
- Make an Organized List
- Make a Table
- Guess and Check
- Work Backward
- Use Logical Reasoning
- Draw a Diagram
- Solve a Simpler Problem

PROBLEM SOLVING 8-10

Mixed Review

Find the perimeter of each figure. *[Lesson 4-1]*

21. 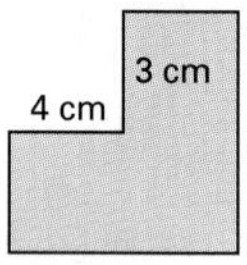

28 cm

22. 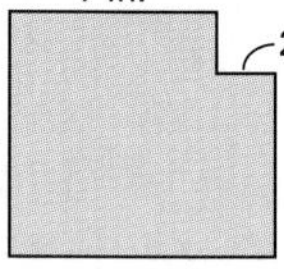

34 in.

23. 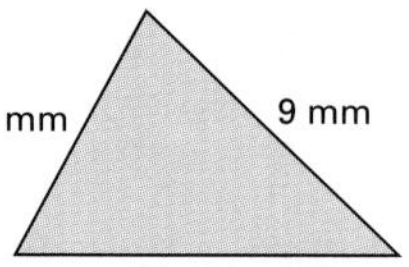

26 mm

Convert. *[Lesson 4-2]*

24. 6 kg = ☐ g 6000 **25.** 3.1 m = ☐ mm 3100 **26.** 650 mL = ☐ L 0.65

27. 5.6 cm = ☐ mm 56 **28.** 7.34 L = ☐ mL 7340 **29.** 106 mm = ☐ m 0.106

Project Progress

Prepare the final rough draft of your logo. Make sure that your logo has one shape with either line or rotational symmetry. Start working on your final draft.

Problem Solving
Understand
Plan
Solve
Look Back

456 *Chapter 8 • The Geometry of Polygons*

PROBLEM SOLVING

Name ______

Guided Problem Solving 8-10

GPS **PROBLEM 19, STUDENT PAGE 456**

Draw a tessellation that does not use a polygon as the figure tessellated. Explain your tessellation.

— Understand —

1. What are you asked to draw? A tessellation.
2. What shape figure are you *not* to use in your drawing? A polygon.

— Plan —

3. Can you use all straight line segments in your drawing? Explain. No, if all line segments are straight, then the figure is a polygon.
4. Which of the figures below will tessellate? a and b.

a. b. c. d.

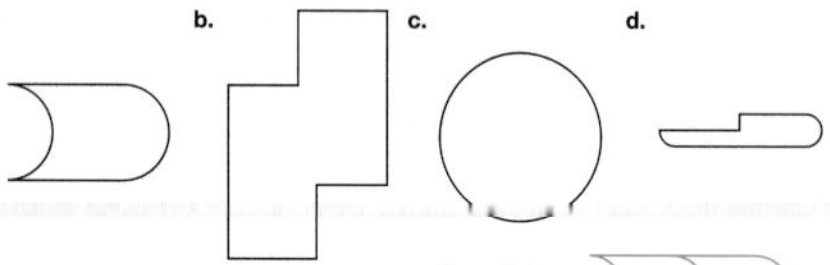

— Solve —

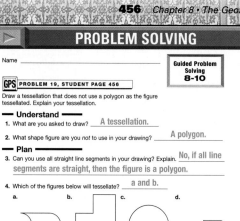

5. Choose one of the figures in Item 4 that meets the criteria of Item 3. Then make the drawing. Check students' work.

Possible answer:

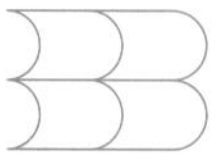

6. Explain. The tessellated figure has curved lines, therefore it is not a polygon.

— Look Back —

7. Draw a different figure to answer the question. Check students' work.

SOLVE ANOTHER PROBLEM

Draw a tessellation that does not use a quadrilateral as the figure tessellated. Explain your tessellation.
Possible answer: Tessellated figure is a hexagon.

ENRICHMENT

Name ______

Extend Your Thinking 8-10

Critical Thinking

Tessellations can be made using more than one figure. See which polygons can make a tessellation.

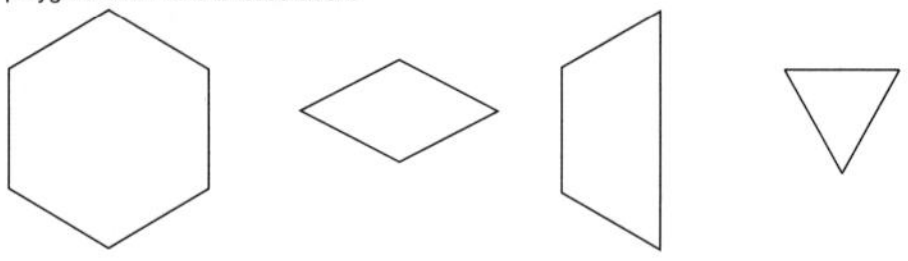

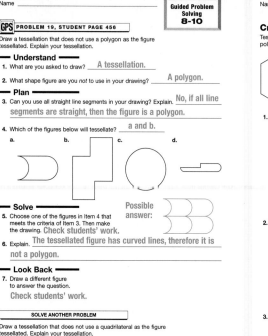

1. Choose two polygons. Use the two polygons to make a tessellation, if possible.
Possible answer:

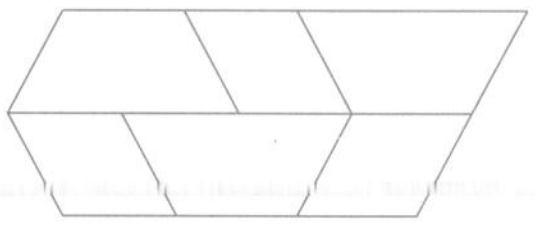

2. Use three of the polygons to make a tessellation, if possible.
Possible answer:

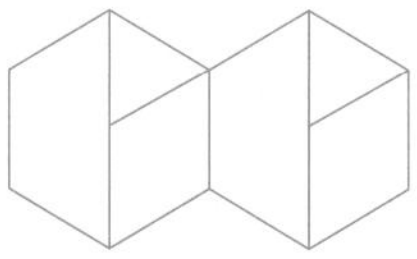

3. Explain why it is possible to tesselate all four polygons.
Possible answer: Because the three small pieces can be combined to form the hexagon.

Section 8C Connect

In this section, you've seen how polygons can be flipped, turned, and slid. You've also seen how geometric figures can be repeated to create designs known as tessellations. Now you'll use what you've learned to make a tessellation.

Artistic Solutions

Materials: Unlined paper, Colored pencils or markers, Ruler

1. Study the tiled floor in the Islamic painting. Notice that a square was used to create the tessellation.

2. Study this example to see how a square can be changed to produce a new tessellation pattern.

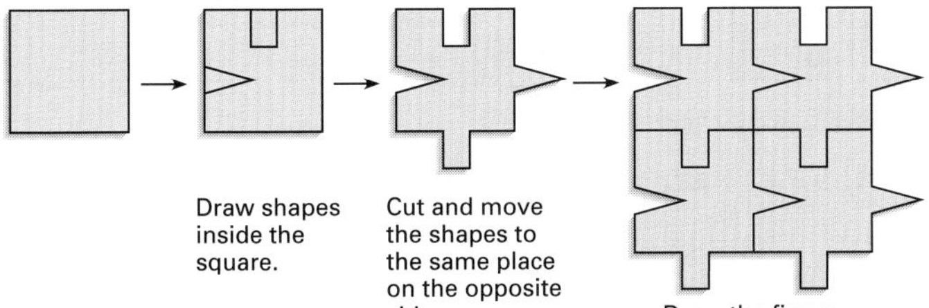

Draw shapes inside the square.

Cut and move the shapes to the same place on the opposite side.

Draw the figure repeatedly.

3. Create a design like the tiled floor above using a square tessellation of your own design.

Artistic Solutions

The Point

In *Artistic Solutions* on page 443, students learned that geometric patterns were used in much of Islamic art. Now they will make a tessellation.

Materials

Unlined paper, colored pencils or markers, ruler

About the Page

- Students should make a pattern out of a square piece of paper.
- Remind students that when they cut a piece out of their square, they should move that shape to the same place on the opposite side of the square. They can do this more than once to create their pattern.
- Discuss with students that their pattern pieces should fit together so that there aren't any spaces between the shapes as they are repeated throughout the tessellation.
- Suggest that students color their tessellation to create an interesting pattern.

Ongoing Assessment

Check that students have designed a reasonable tessellation.

Extension

Ask students to create a tessellation by cutting one or more pieces out of a square. Explain that the pieces should be placed on the opposite sides, but not directly across from the place from which it was removed. Create an area to display the most interesting tessellations.

Answers for Connect

1–2. No answer required.

3. Possible answer:

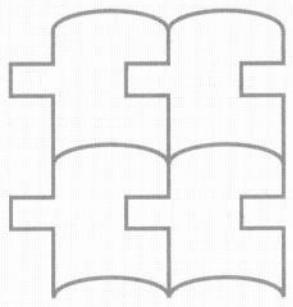

Review Correlation

Item(s)	Lesson(s)
1–6	8-1
7–10	8-4
11–14	8-8, 8-9
15–18	8-10
19–24	8-3
25	8-9

Test Prep

Test-Taking Tip

Tell students that when they select the answer "None of the above," they should double check to be sure that none of the first answers is correct. In this problem, one figure *is* a rotation of the other, so D is not correct.

Answers for Review

1. 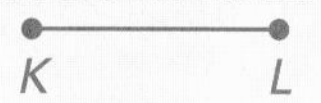
K L
2. 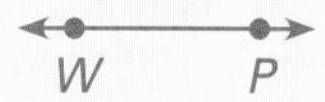
W P
3. 
S D
4. 
M N
5. 
F S
6. 
L O
7. Obtuse; 110°, 40°, 30°.
8. Acute; 60°, 70°, 50°.
9. Acute; 65°, 65°, 50°.
10. Right; 90°, 80°, 10°.
11. Regular octagon; Yes; 16.
12. Irregular pentagon; No.
13. Irregular triangle; No.
14. Irregular quadrilateral; No.
15. Yes

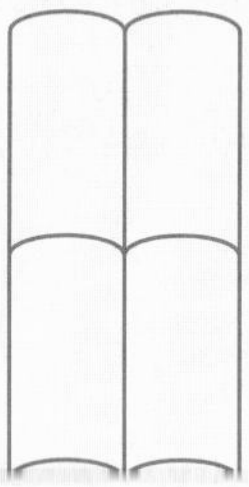

16. No

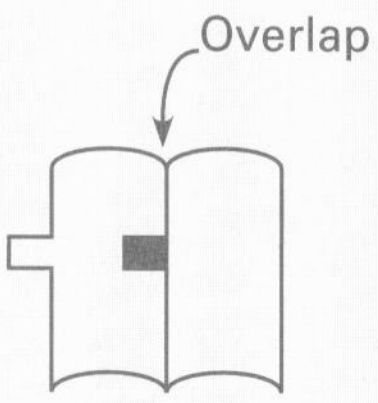

17–18. See page C2.

Section 8C Review

REVIEW 8C

Draw an example of each.

1. $\overline{KL}$ **2.** $\overleftrightarrow{WP}$ **3.** $\overrightarrow{SD}$ **4.** $\overline{MN}$ **5.** $\overleftrightarrow{FS}$ **6.** $\overrightarrow{LO}$

Classify each triangle by its angles. Estimate the measure of each angle.

7. 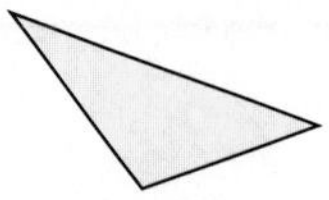
8. 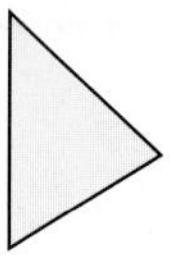
9. 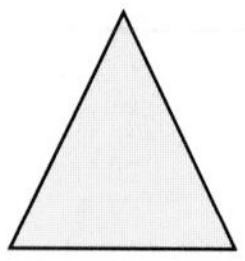
10. 

Name each polygon and tell if it has line symmetry. If it does, tell how many lines of symmetry it has.

11. 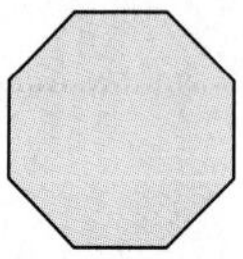
12. 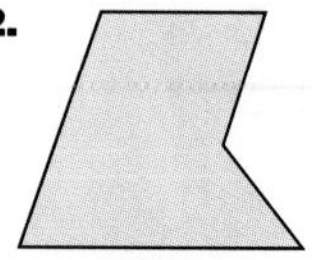
13. 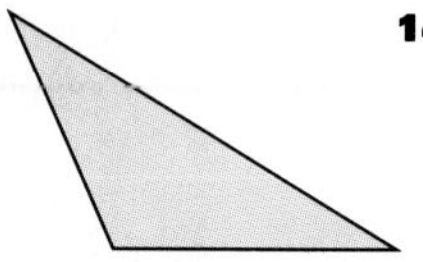
14. 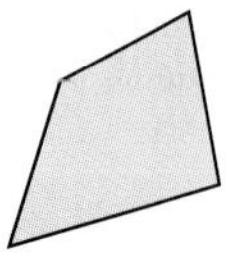

State if each figure will tessellate. Make a drawing to show your answer.

15. 
16. 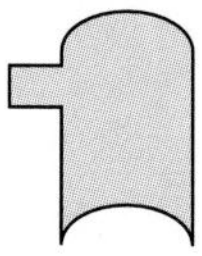
17. 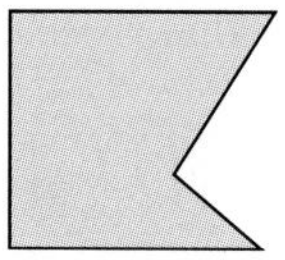
18. 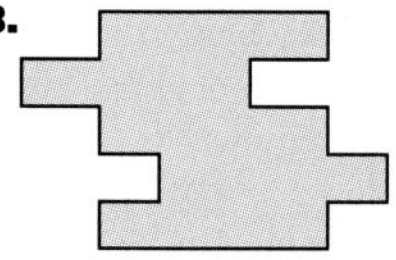

State the angle that is supplementary to each given angle.

19. 76° 104° **20.** 152° 28° **21.** 99° 81° **22.** 48° 132° **23.** 90° 90° **24.** 179° 1°

Test Prep

Rotating a figure 180° clockwise is the same as rotating the figure 180° counterclockwise.

25. How has the figure been rotated? C

Ⓐ 180° clockwise Ⓑ 180° counterclockwise
Ⓒ Either of the above Ⓓ None of the above

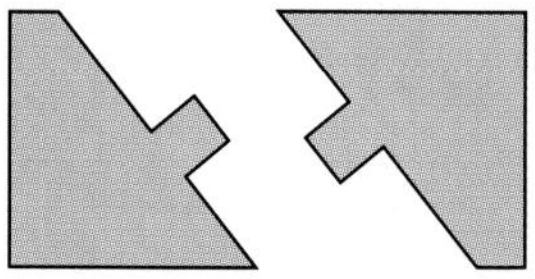

Resources

Practice Masters
Section 8C Review
Assessment Sourcebook
Quiz 8C
TestWorks
Test and Practice Software

PRACTICE

Name ______________________ Practice

Section 8C Review

Name each polygon and tell if it has line symmetry. If it does, tell how many lines of symmetry it has.

1. Quadrilateral; yes; 1 2. Pentagon; yes; 1

3. Octagon; yes; 2 4. Square; yes; 4

5. Hexagon; no 6. Parallelogram; no

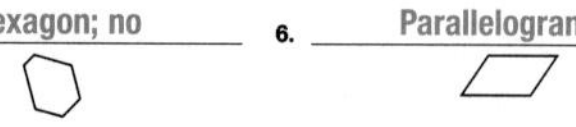

State if each figure will tessellate. Make a drawing to show your answer.

7. Tessellates 8. Tessellates

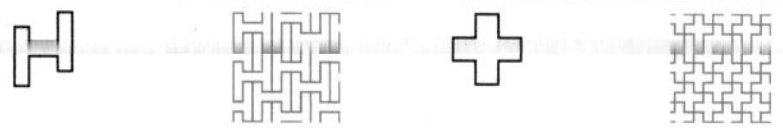

9. Tessellates 10. Does not tessellate

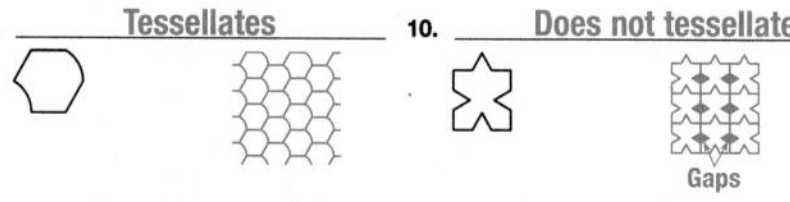

11. **Science** A running cheetah completed one stride (23 feet) in 0.28 seconds. Using the formula distance = rate × time, write and solve an equation to find this cheetah's speed in feet per second. *[Lesson 3-12]*

Possible answer: $23 = 0.28r$; about 82.1 ft/sec

12. A $7\frac{3}{4}$-pound tomato was grown in Oklahoma in 1986. Write and solve an equation to find the number of $\frac{3}{8}$-pound servings that could be made from this tomato. *[Lesson 7-6]*

Possible answer: $\frac{3}{8}x = 7\frac{3}{4}$; $20\frac{2}{3}$ servings

Extend Key Ideas

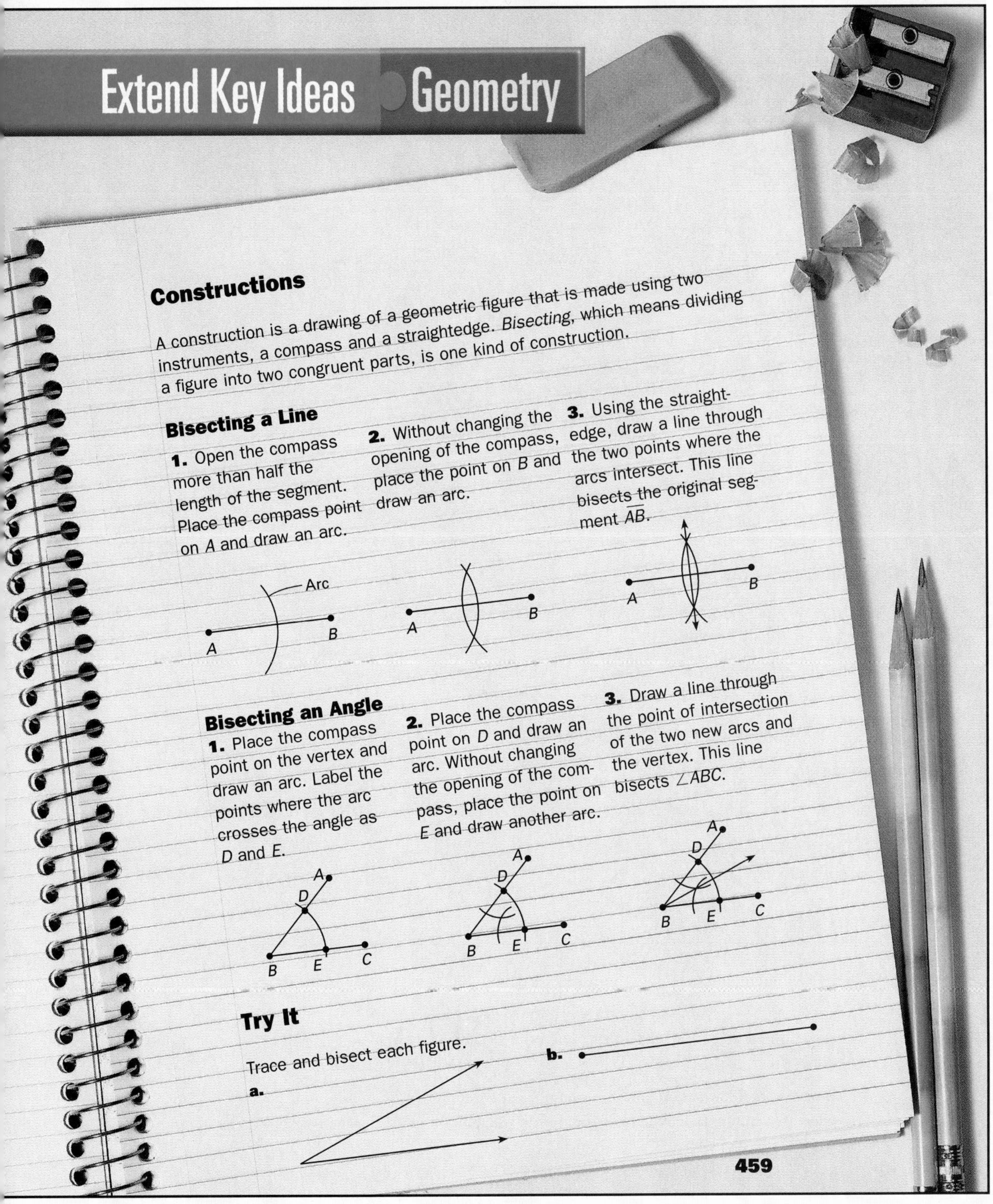

Extend Key Ideas Geometry

Constructions

A construction is a drawing of a geometric figure that is made using two instruments, a compass and a straightedge. *Bisecting*, which means dividing a figure into two congruent parts, is one kind of construction.

Bisecting a Line

1. Open the compass more than half the length of the segment. Place the compass point on *A* and draw an arc.

2. Without changing the opening of the compass, place the point on *B* and draw an arc.

3. Using the straightedge, draw a line through the two points where the arcs intersect. This line bisects the original segment $\overline{AB}$.

Bisecting an Angle

1. Place the compass point on the vertex and draw an arc. Label the points where the arc crosses the angle as *D* and *E*.

2. Place the compass point on *D* and draw an arc. Without changing the opening of the compass, place the point on *E* and draw another arc.

3. Draw a line through the point of intersection of the two new arcs and the vertex. This line bisects ∠*ABC*.

Try It

Trace and bisect each figure.

a.

b.

459

Constructions

The Point
Students use a compass and straightedge to construct a segment bisector and an angle bisector.

Materials
Compass, straightedge

About the Page

- You might also want to point out that the segment bisector is perpendicular to the original segment. This is one way to construct a right angle.
- The compass is difficult to manipulate if the distance from point to pencil is small. Encourage students to use segments and angles large enough to be able to use the compass easily.
- If students have difficulty drawing the intersecting arcs as shown in Step 2 of bisecting an angle, suggest that they draw the arcs outside the arc that passes through points *D* and *E*.

Ask …
To construct the segment bisector, why does the compass have to be open more than half the length of the segment? If it was not, the arcs drawn from each endpoint would not intersect, and so the points determining the bisector would not be created.

Extension

Draw any line segment. Divide the segment into four equal parts. Explain your work. Bisect the line segment, then bisect each half of the line segment.

Answers for Try It

a.

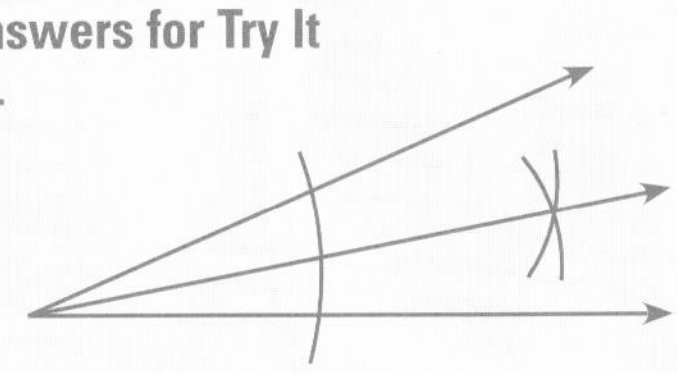

b.

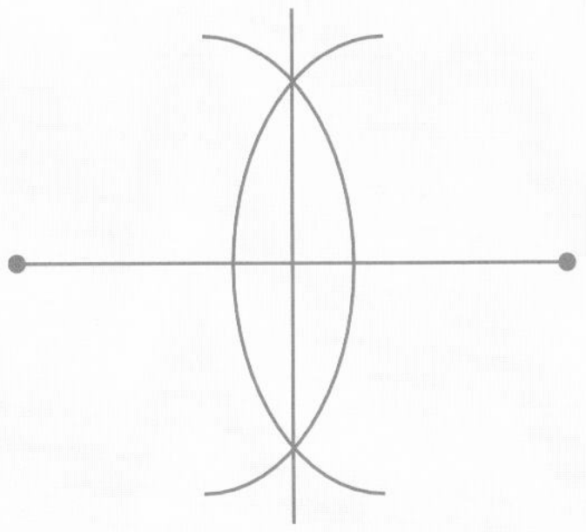

Chapter 8 Summary and Review

Review Correlation

Item(s)	Lesson(s)
1	8-1
2	8-2
3	8-1
4	8-4
5	8-7
6–8	8-8, 8-9, 8-10
9–11	8-8
12	8-9

For additional review, see page 669.

Answers for Review

1. 

2. 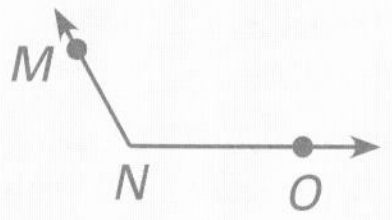

3. a. 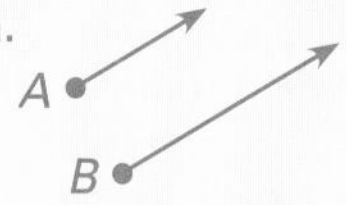

b. 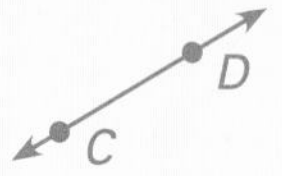

Chapter 8 Summary and Review

Graphic Organizer

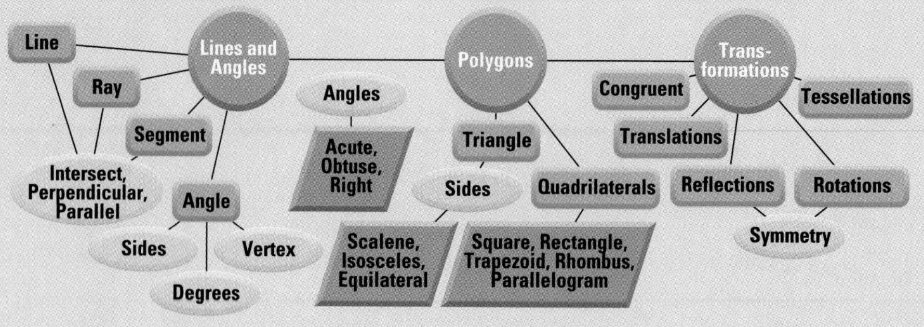

Section 8A Lines and Angles

Summary

- **Segments** and **rays** are parts of **lines**. They can **intersect**. They can be **perpendicular** or **parallel**.
- An **angle** is formed from two rays that meet at the **vertex**. Angles are classified by size as **acute, right, obtuse,** or **straight**.
- You can use a **protractor** to measure the **degrees** in an angle.

Review

1. Draw and label a line with points *A* and *B*.

2. Draw and label an obtuse angle through points *M*, *N*, and *O*, with *N* as the vertex.

3. Draw and label:

a. Two rays that are parallel. **b.** $\overleftrightarrow{CD}$

Section 8B Polygons

Summary

- **Triangles** can be classified by the measures of their angles as **acute, obtuse,** or **right,** or by the lengths of their sides as **scalene, isosceles,** or **equilateral.**
- **Polygons** are **regular** if their sides and angles are equal. If not, they are **irregular. Quadrilaterals** have four sides. Some side pairs may be parallel.

Resources

Practice Masters
Cumulative Review
Chapters 1–8

PRACTICE

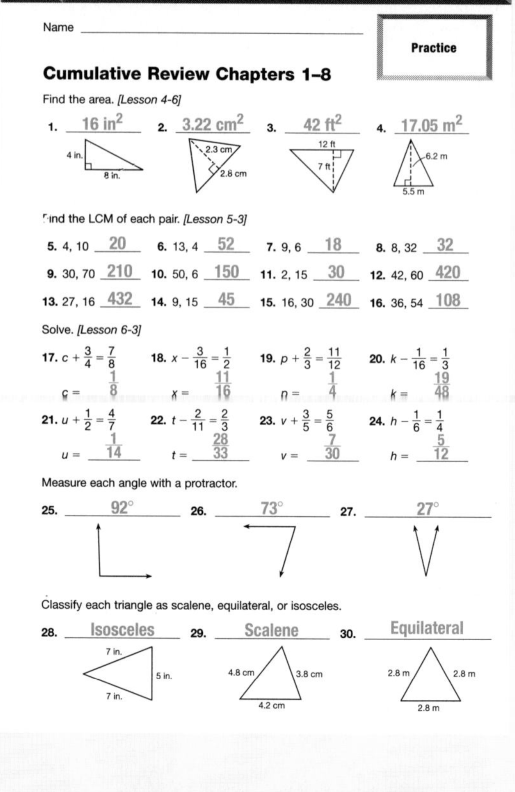
Name ____________ Practice

Cumulative Review Chapters 1–8

Find the area. *[Lesson 4-6]*

1. 16 in² 2. 3.22 cm² 3. 42 ft² 4. 17.05 m²

Find the LCM of each pair. *[Lesson 5-3]*

5. 4, 10 20 6. 13, 4 52 7. 9, 6 18 8. 8, 32 32
9. 30, 70 210 10. 50, 6 150 11. 2, 15 30 12. 42, 60 420
13. 27, 16 432 14. 9, 15 45 15. 16, 30 240 16. 36, 54 108

Solve. *[Lesson 6-3]*

17. $c + \frac{3}{4} = \frac{7}{8}$ $c = \frac{1}{8}$
18. $x - \frac{3}{16} = \frac{1}{2}$ $x = \frac{11}{16}$
19. $p + \frac{2}{3} = \frac{11}{12}$ $p = \frac{1}{4}$
20. $k - \frac{1}{16} = \frac{1}{3}$ $k = \frac{19}{48}$
21. $u + \frac{1}{2} = \frac{4}{7}$ $u = \frac{1}{14}$
22. $t - \frac{2}{11} = \frac{2}{3}$ $t = \frac{28}{33}$
23. $v + \frac{3}{5} = \frac{5}{6}$ $v = \frac{7}{30}$
24. $h - \frac{1}{6} = \frac{1}{4}$ $h = \frac{5}{12}$

Measure each angle with a protractor.

25. 92° 26. 73° 27. 27°

Classify each triangle as scalene, equilateral, or isosceles.

28. Isosceles 29. Scalene 30. Equilateral

Section 8B Polygons *continued*

Review

4. Classify the triangle whose angles measure 82°, 14°, and 84°. Acute Triangle

5. Explain why all rectangles are parallelograms, but not all parallelograms are rectangles.

Section 8C Transformations

Summary

- **Congruent** figures have the same size and shape.
- If you flip a figure over a line, its **reflection** is the mirror image of the figure. The original figure and its reflection have **line symmetry**.
- If you turn a figure as if it were on a wheel, the image of the figure is a **rotation**. If the image lands on itself before one full turn, it has **rotational symmetry**. Turns can be **clockwise** or **counterclockwise**.
- If you slide a figure, its image is called a **translation**.
- A pattern of congruent shapes, with no gaps or overlaps, is a **tessellation**.

Review

Tell whether each transformation is a reflection, translation, or rotation.

6. 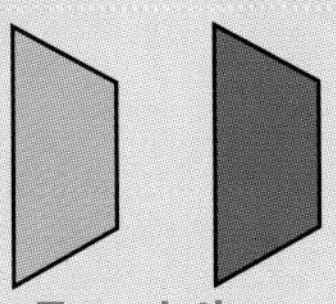
Translation

7. 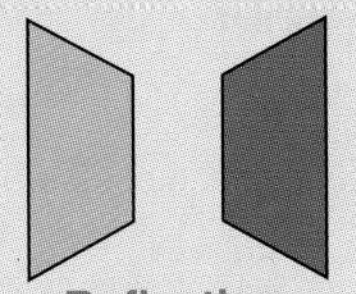
Reflection

8. 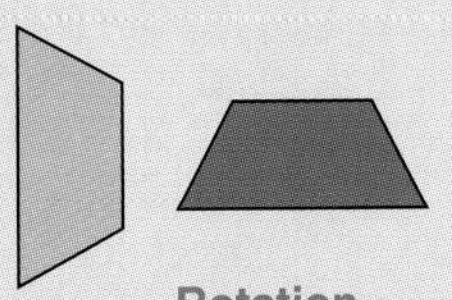
Rotation

9. Are the figures in Exercises 6–8 congruent? Explain.

10. Trace the figure and draw its reflection over the line.

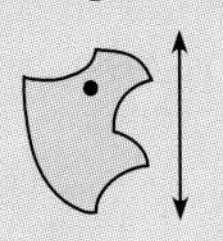

11. Tell whether the figure has line symmetry. If it does, draw its line(s) of symmetry.

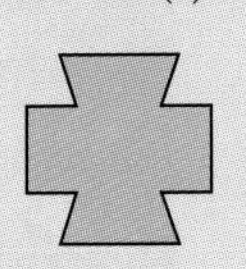

12. Give the number of degrees and the direction in which the figure has been rotated.

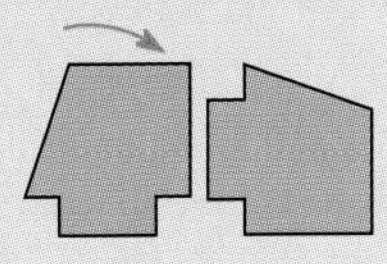
90° clockwise

Answers for Review

5. All rectangles are parallelograms because their opposite sides have the same lengths and are parallel. But some parallelograms do not have all 90° angles, which rectangles must have.

9. Yes; They are the same size and shape.

10. 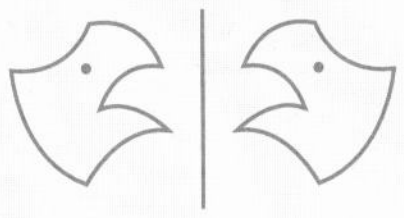

11. Yes; The figure has two lines of symmetry.

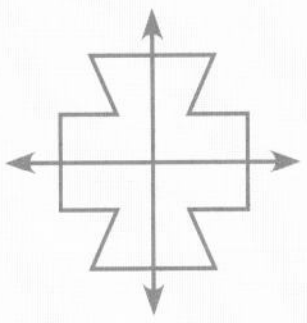

Chapter 8 Assessment

Assessment Correlation

Item(s)	Lesson(s)
1, 2	8-1
3	8-4
4	8-2
5	8-3
6	8-4
7	8-5
8	8-3
9	8-5
10–12	8-6
13	8-4
14	8-7
15–17	8-8, 8-9

Answers for Assessment

4. No; Yes; No. A line and a ray both have an end that continues forever.

7. Yes. Student's figure should be a scalene triangle with one of the shorter sides twice as long as the shortest side.

14. Polygon, quadrilateral, parallelogram, rectangle.

Answer for Performance Task

Possible answer: Section A; There are pairs of segments that are parallel, perpendicular, and intersecting. There are acute and right angles in triangles and right angles in rectangles. There are straight angles.
Section B; There are acute, right, and scalene triangles. There are polygons, quadrilaterals, rectangles, trapezoids, and parallelograms.
Section C; There is line and rotational symmetry. There are flips and turns.

Chapter 8 Assessment

For each group, describe the figures and their relationship.

1. 
Parallel lines

2. 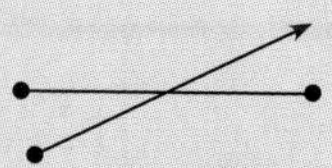
A segment and ray that intersect.

3. Classify the triangle whose angles measure 82°, 90°, and 8°. Right triangle

4. Can you measure the length of a line? A segment? A ray? Explain.

5. a. Name the vertex of the angle. *S*

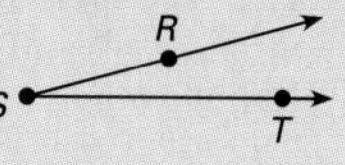

b. Name the angle in three ways. $\angle S$, $\angle RST$, $\angle TSR$

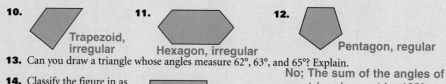

6. The sum of two angles of a triangle is 85°. What is the measure of the third angle? 95°

7. Can the lengths of 4 m, 8 m, and 10 m form a triangle? If so, draw the triangle and classify it.

8. Angles *A* and *B* are complements. If the measure of $\angle A$ is 37°, what is the measure of $\angle B$? 53°

9. Classify the triangle whose sides each measure 6 feet. Equilateral

Name each polygon and tell if it is regular or irregular.

10. 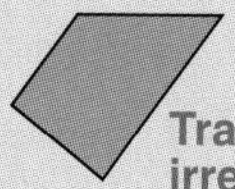
Trapezoid, irregular

11. 
Hexagon, irregular

12. 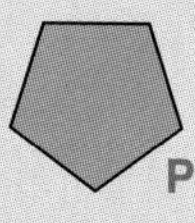
Pentagon, regular

13. Can you draw a triangle whose angles measure 62°, 63°, and 65°? Explain.
No; The sum of the angles of any triangle must be 180°.

14. Classify the figure in as many ways as possible. 

Identify each transformation. Tell if it has line or rotational symmetry.

15. 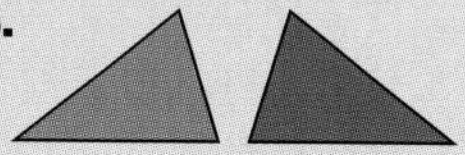
Reflection; Line symmetry

16. 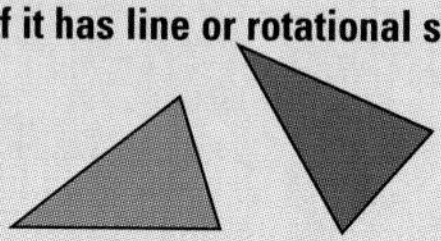
Rotation; Rotational symmetry

17. 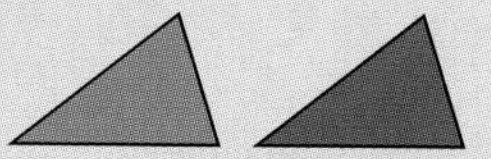
Translation

Performance Task

Make a list of 12 geometric concepts that are found in the design of the United Kingdom's flag. Four concepts must relate to lines and angles, four to polygons, and four to transformations and line or rotational symmetry.

Resources
Assessment Sourcebook
Chapter 8 Tests
Forms A and B (free response)
Form C (multiple choice)
Form D (performance assessment)
Form E (mixed response)
Form F (cumulative chapter test)
TestWorks *Test and Practice Software*
Home and Community Connections
Letter Home for Chapter 8 in English and Spanish

Cumulative Review Chapters 1–8

Test Prep

Multiple Choice

Choose the best answer.

1. Which graph uses wedge-shaped pieces to represent the data? *[Lesson 1-1]* B

Ⓐ Bar Ⓑ Circle Ⓒ Line Ⓓ Pictograph

2. One business plan calls for a change in employees of 2^5. A second plan calls for a change that is twice as large as 2^5. What is the change in employees for the second plan? *[Lesson 2-4]* A

Ⓐ 2^6 Ⓑ 2^7 Ⓒ 2^{10} Ⓓ 4^5

3. What is the decimal form for seven and twenty-nine thousandths. *[Lesson 3-1]* B

Ⓐ 7029.0 Ⓑ 7.029 Ⓒ 7.0029 Ⓓ 0.7029

4. Find the product of 0.001×32. *[Lesson 3-8]* C

Ⓐ 32000 Ⓑ 320 Ⓒ 0.032 Ⓓ 0.0032

5. What is the solution to the equation $0.01m = 25.2$? *[Lesson 3-12]* A

Ⓐ 2520 Ⓑ 252 Ⓒ 2.52 Ⓓ 0.252

6. Find the perimeter of the figure. *[Lesson 4-1]* A

Ⓐ 96 m Ⓑ 87 m Ⓒ 64 m Ⓓ 55 m

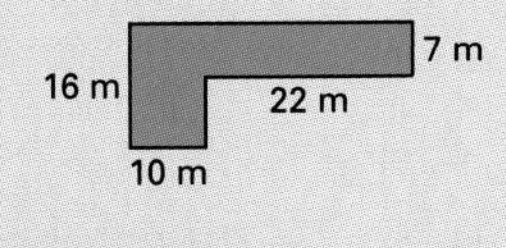

7. What is the area of a rectangle 4 ft long and 6 ft wide? *[Lesson 4-5]* D

Ⓐ 20 ft Ⓑ 24 ft Ⓒ 20 ft^2 Ⓓ 24 ft^2

8. Write $\frac{29}{9}$ as a mixed number. *[Lesson 5-6]* C

Ⓐ $20\frac{1}{9}$ Ⓑ $4\frac{2}{9}$ Ⓒ $3\frac{2}{9}$ Ⓓ $3\frac{1}{9}$

9. Simplify $\frac{3}{7} - \frac{1}{4}$. *[Lesson 6-2]* A

Ⓐ $\frac{5}{28}$ Ⓑ $\frac{2}{11}$ Ⓒ $\frac{2}{3}$ Ⓓ $\frac{19}{28}$

10. Simplify $3\frac{2}{3} + 1\frac{3}{4}$. *[Lesson 6-5]* B

Ⓐ $4\frac{5}{7}$ Ⓑ $5\frac{5}{12}$ Ⓒ $5\frac{7}{12}$ Ⓓ None of these

11. Simplify $32 \times 1\frac{1}{2}$. *[Lesson 7-2]* C

Ⓐ 16 Ⓑ 32.5 Ⓒ 48 Ⓓ None of these

12. Simplify $\frac{3}{5} \div 5$. *[Lesson 7-5]* B

Ⓐ $\frac{3}{55}$ Ⓑ $\frac{3}{25}$ Ⓒ $\frac{3}{10}$ Ⓓ 3

13. Solve for x, if $x \div \frac{3}{4} = \frac{8}{9}$. *[Lesson 7-6]* C

Ⓐ $\frac{3}{2}$ Ⓑ $\frac{27}{32}$ Ⓒ $\frac{2}{3}$ Ⓓ None of these

14. An angle that measures less than 90° is called a(n) ____ angle. *[Lesson 8-3]* D

Ⓐ Straight Ⓑ Right Ⓒ Obtuse Ⓓ Acute

15. What is the name of a triangle that has exactly two equal sides? *[Lesson 8-5]* A

Ⓐ Isosceles Ⓑ Obtuse Ⓒ Right Ⓓ Scalene

Cumulative Review Test Prep

About Multiple-Choice Tests

The Cumulative Review found at the end of Chapters 2, 4, 6, 8, 10, and 12 can be used to prepare students for standardized tests.

Students sometimes do not perform as well on standardized tests as they do on other tests. There may be several reasons for this related to the format and content of the test.

- **Format**
Students may have limited experience with multiple-choice tests. For some questions, such tests are harder because having options may confuse the students.

- **Content**
A standardized test may cover a broader range of content than normally covered on a test, and the relative emphasis given to various strands may be different than given in class. Also, some questions may assess general aptitude or thinking skills and not include specific pieces of mathematical content.

It is important not to let the differences between standardized tests and other tests shake your students' confidence.

Chapter 9

Integers and the Coordinate Plane

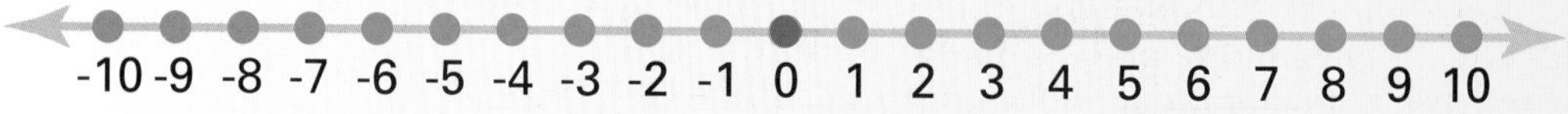

▶ OVERVIEW

Section 9A

Integers: Students learn the definition of integers. They learn the rules for addition, subtraction, multiplication, and division of integers. Then students use integers to solve problems.

9-1 Understanding Integers

9-2 Adding Integers

9-3 Subtracting Integers

9-4 Multiplying and Dividing Integers

Section 9B

Graphing on the Coordinate Plane: Students learn to locate points on the coordinate plane. Then they graph translations, reflections, and equations.

9-5 The Coordinate Plane

9-6 Graphing Slides and Flips

9-7 Graphing Equations

Meeting NCTM Standards

Curriculum Standards

STANDARDS

			pages
1	**Problem Solving**	Skills and Strategies	466, 480, 497, 499
		Applications	470–471, 474–475, 479–480, 483–484, 485, 490–491, 496–497, 501–502, 503
		Exploration	468, 472, 476, 481, 488, 493, 498
2	**Communication**	Oral	467, 469, 473, 478, 483, 487, 490, 495, 500
		Written	471, 475, 484, 491, 497, 502
		Cooperative Learning	*468, 472, 476, 481, 488, 493, 498*
3	**Reasoning**	Critical Thinking	471, 475, 480, 484, 491, 497, 502
4	**Connections**	Mathematical	See Standards 5–9, 12, 13 below.
		Interdisciplinary	Science 465, *467*, 469, *470*, 473, 477, *478*, 480, *500*; Entertainment 464; Consumer 501; Social Studies 464, *495*; Arts & Literature 464; Career 471, 491; Geography *467*, *479*, *487*; History *487*, 489, 494
		Technology	473, 481, 492
		Cultural	465
5	**Number and Number Relationships**		464–505
6	**Number Systems and Number Theory**		464–486
7	**Computation and Estimation**		472–484, *494*
8	**Patterns and Functions**		481, 483, 498–502
9	**Algebra**		498–502
12	**Geometry**		491, 493–497, 504
13	**Measurement**		474, 505

Italic type indicates Teacher Edition reference.

Teaching Standards

Focus on Classroom Environment

A successful learning environment will help students believe in themselves as successful mathematical thinkers. Teachers should

- encourage students to take intellectual risks by raising and formulating questions.
- allow students to work collaboratively as well as independently.

Assessment Standards

Focus on Equity

Portfolios The Equity Standard underscores the need to use a variety of assessment modes for every skill in order to allow all students to demonstrate their level of understanding. A portfolio of work chosen to illustrate that understanding may give both student and teacher valuable information about the student's preferred learning modality. In Chapter 9, students are asked to write problems that illustrate the use of integers.

TECHNOLOGY

For the Teacher

- **Teacher Resource Planner CD-ROM**
  Use the teacher planning CD-ROM to view resources available for Chapter 9. You can prepare custom lesson plans or use the default lesson plans provided.

- **World Wide Web**
  Visit **www.teacher.mathsurf.com** for links to lesson plans from teachers and other professionals, NCTM information, and other sites.

- **TestWorks**
  TestWorks provides ready-made tests and can create custom tests and practice worksheets.

For the Parent

- **World Wide Web**
  Parents can use the Web site at **www.parent.mathsurf.com.**

For the Student

- **Interactive CD-ROM**
  Lesson 9-2 has an *Interactive CD-ROM Lesson*. The *Interactive CD-ROM Journal* and *Interactive CD-ROM Spreadsheet/Grapher Tool* are also used in Chapter 9.

- **Wide World of Mathematics**
  Lesson 9-2 Middle School: Integer Football
  Lesson 9-5 Middle School: Balancing the Budget

- **World Wide Web**
  Use with Chapter and Section Openers; Students can go online to the Scott Foresman-Addison Wesley Web site at **www.mathsurf.com/6/ch9** to collect information about chapter themes.

STANDARDIZED - TEST CORRELATION

SECTION 9A

LESSON	OBJECTIVE	ITBS Form M	CTBS 4th Ed.	CAT 5th Ed.	SAT 9th Ed.	MAT 7th Ed.	Your Form
9-1	• Identify an integer.		✘	✘		✘	
	• Order integers.			✘		✘	
9-2	• Identify the opposite of an integer.		✘	✘		✘	
	• Add integers.		✘	✘			
9-3	• Subtract integers.		✘	✘			
9-4	• Multiply and divide integers.		✘	✘			

SECTION 9B

LESSON	OBJECTIVE	ITBS Form M	CTBS 4th Ed.	CAT 5th Ed.	SAT 9th Ed.	MAT 7th Ed.	Your Form
9-5	• Plot points on a coordinate plane.		✘		✘	✘	
	• Read the coordinates of points on a coordinate plane.		✘		✘	✘	
9-6	• Graph translations and reflections on the coordinate plane.		✘		✘		
9-7	• Draw the graph of an equation.						

Key: ITBS - Iowa Test of Basic Skills; CTBS - Comprehensive Test of Basic Skills; CAT - California Achievement Test; SAT - Stanford Achievement Test; MAT - Metropolitan Achievement Test

ASSESSMENT PROGRAM

Traditional Assessment

QUICK QUIZZES	SECTION REVIEW	CHAPTER REVIEW	CHAPTER ASSESSMENT FREE RESPONSE	CHAPTER ASSESSMENT MULTIPLE CHOICE	CUMULATIVE REVIEW
TE: pp. 471, 475, 480, 484, 491, 497, 502	SE: pp. 486, 504 *Quiz 9A, 9B	SE: pp. 506–507	SE: p. 508 *Ch. 9 Tests Forms A, B, E	*Ch. 9 Tests Forms C, E	SE: p. 509 *Ch. 9 Test Form F; Quarterly Test Ch. 1–9

Alternate Assessment

INTERVIEW	JOURNAL	ONGOING	PERFORMANCE	PORTFOLIO	PROJECT	SELF
TE: p. 484	SE: pp. 471, 475, 484, 491, 502 TE: pp. 466, 471, 502	TE: pp. 469, 472, 476, 481, 488, 493, 498	SE: p. 508, 509 TE: p. 491 *Ch. 9 Tests Forms D, E	TE: p. 475	SE: pp. 465, 484, 502 TE: p. 465	TE: p. 480

*Tests and quizzes are in *Assessment Sourcebook.* Test Form E is a mixed response test. Forms for Alternate Assessment are also available in *Assessment Sourcebook.*

TestWorks: Test and Practice Software

MIDDLE SCHOOL PACING CHART

REGULAR PACING

Day	5 classes per week
1	Chapter 9 Opener; Problem Solving Focus
2	Section **9A** Opener; Lesson **9-1**
3	Lesson **9-2**
4	Lesson **9-3**
5	Lesson **9-4**
6	**9A** Connect; **9A** Review
7	Section **9B** Opener; Lesson **9-5**
8	Technology; Lesson **9-6**
9	Lesson **9-7**
10	**9B** Connect; **9B** Review; Extend Key Ideas
11	Chapter 9 Summary and Review
12	Chapter 9 Assessment Cumulative Review, Chapters 1–9

BLOCK SCHEDULING OPTIONS

Block Scheduling for Complete Course

Chapter 9 may be presented in

- seven 90-minute blocks
- nine 75-minute blocks

Each block consists of a combination of

- Chapter and Section Openers
- Explores
- Lesson Development
- Problem Solving Focus
- Technology
- Extend Key Ideas
- Connect
- Review
- Assessment

For details, see *Block Scheduling Handbook.*

Block Scheduling for Interdisciplinary Course

Each block integrates math with another subject area.

In Chapter 9, interdisciplinary topics include

- Earth Science
- Treasure Maps

Themes for Interdisciplinary Team Teaching 9A and 9B are

- Banking
- Web Page Programming

For details, see *Block Scheduling Handbook.*

Block Scheduling for Lab-Based Course

In each block, 30–40 minutes is devoted to lab activities including

- Explores in the Student Edition
- Connect pages in the Student Edition
- Technology options in the Student Edition
- Reteaching Activities in the Teacher Edition

For details, see *Block Scheduling Handbook.*

Block Scheduling for Course with *Connected Mathematics*

In each block, investigations from **Connected Mathematics** replace or enhance the lessons in Chapter 9.

Connected Mathematics topics for Chapter 9 can be found in

- *Shapes and Designs*
- *Data About Us*

For details, see *Block Scheduling Handbook.*

INTERDISCIPLINARY BULLETIN BOARD

Set Up

Divide a bulletin board vertically into two sections. Label the left section *Atmosphere* and the right *Ocean.*

Procedure

- Explain that the atmosphere and ocean are divided into layers. Have small groups of students research layers of the atmosphere—troposphere, stratosphere, mesosphere, and thermosphere. Have other groups research ocean layers—mixed layer, thermocline, and deep ocean.
- Groups should graph information concerning the height and composition of the atmospheric layers on the left section of the board.
- Groups should graph information concerning the depth and composition of the oceanic layers on the right section of the board.

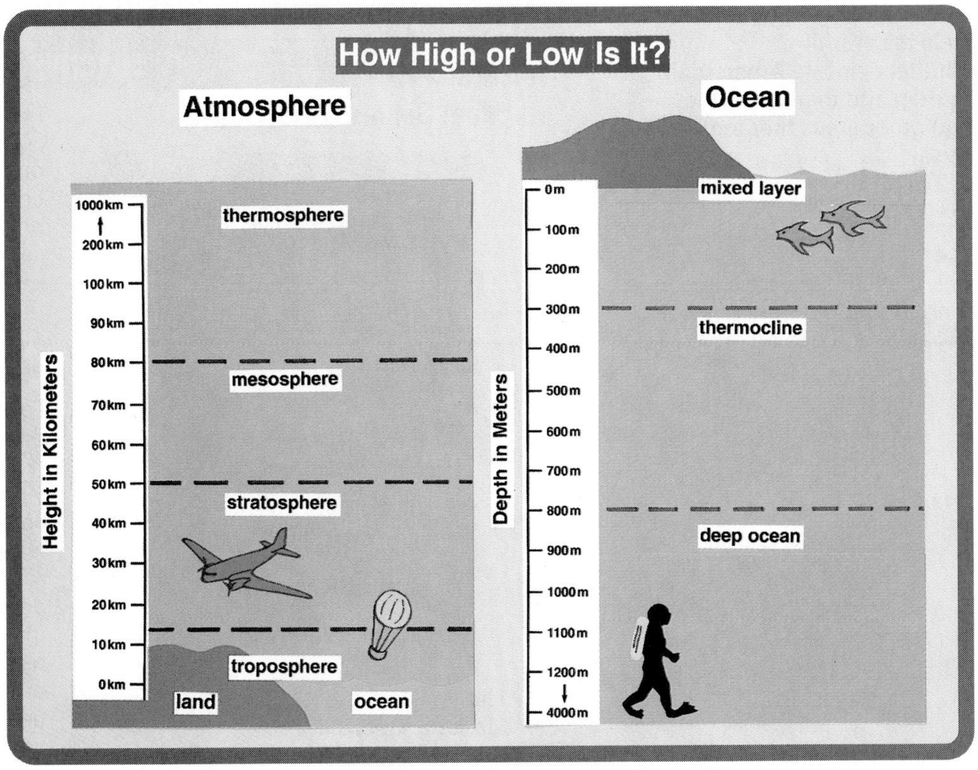

Chapter 9

The information on these pages shows how integers and coordinate grids are used in real-life situations.

World Wide Web

If your class has access to the World Wide Web, you might want to use the information found at the Web site addresses given.

Extensions

The following activities do not require access to the World Wide Web.

Arts & Literature
Suggest that students further explore the concept of "negative space." Ask them to bring in some photographs in which negative space has been used.

Entertainment
Have students find examples of golf scores in the newspaper and discuss how they are presented and what they mean.

Social Studies
Have students locate a particular place on a map and find the lines of latitude and longitude. Have them locate the 0° latitude and the 0° longitude points. Then suggest they choose a number of degrees of latitude and longitude and find what is located there.

People of the World
Have students locate Amsterdam on the map and then see if they can find other areas that are below sea level. Possible answer: Death Valley, California, is 282 ft below sea level.

Science
Suggest that students research lightning to find out how positive and negative charges are involved.

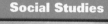

9 Integers and the Coordinate Plane

Entertainment Link
www.mathsurf.com/6/ch9/ent

Social Studies

The location of any place in the world can be described using the lines of longitude and latitude. Washington, DC, is located at 38° North, 77° West. The point at 0° latitude, 0° longitude is in the Gulf of Guinea, off the coast of Africa.

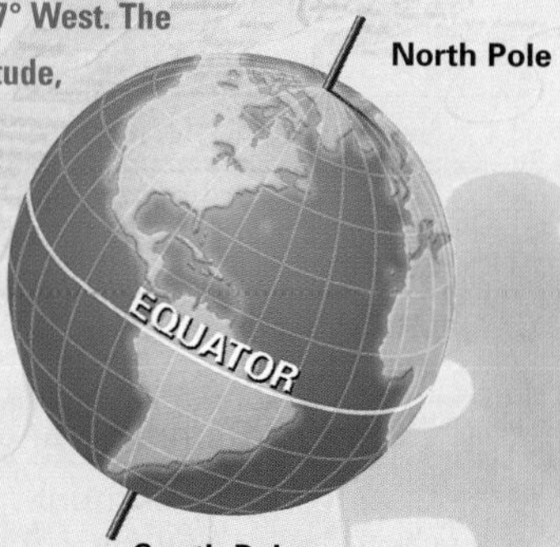

Arts & Literature

Some photographs use the spaces in between objects to create interesting shapes. Photographers say that these kinds of shapes create "negative space."

Entertainment

Golf scores are often compared using *par*, the number of strokes it should take for a player to get the ball in a particular hole. A score of 3 under par means the player needed three strokes less than the expected number to sink the ball in the hole.

464

TEACHER TALK

Meet Dennis McElhaney

The Walker School
Marietta, Georgia

I think that one of the most important concepts involved in graphing equations on the coordinate plane is recognizing and finding patterns. To begin this process, I show students a T-chart with several ordered pairs and then ask them to tell me any patterns or relationships that they see between the *x*- and *y*-coordinates. I ask them to be as specific as possible in giving their answer.

For example, if I show students the ordered pairs $(-2, 0)$ $(-1, 1)$ $(0, 2)$ $(1, 3)$ $(2, 4)$, I would like them to see that each *y*-coordinate is two greater than its corresponding *x*-coordinate. This would lead to the equation $y = x + 2$. After giving a few examples, I ask students to make their own T-chart. I ask for volunteers to write their ordered pairs on the board, and have the rest of the students find the relationship between *x* and *y* and to give the equation that describes it.

Cultural Link
www.mathsurf.com/6/ch9/people

People of the World

In the Netherlands, the city of Amsterdam, near the North Sea, has an elevation of −22 feet. Since it is below sea level, canals and dikes line the city to prevent flooding.

KEY MATH IDEAS

An integer can be a whole positive number, the opposite of a whole positive number, or 0.

Integers can be added and subtracted.

When multiplying and dividing integers, the sign of the product or the quotient depends on the sign of the factors or divisor and dividend.

The coordinate plane can be used to locate any point on a flat surface.

Algebra equations can be represented on the coordinate plane.

Science

Sometimes when you walk across a carpeted floor, you collect electrons and develop a negative charge. If you touch something with a positive charge, the electrons move to the positively charged object. This causes a small electric shock.

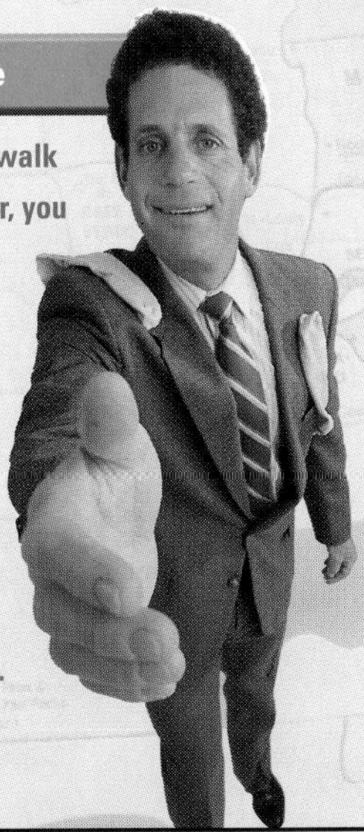

CHAPTER PROJECT

Problem Solving

Understand
Plan
Solve
Look Back

In this project, you will create a drawing of a real country on a coordinate plane, and collect facts about the country that involve positive and negative numbers. Begin by thinking about a country that you find interesting and that has an interesting shape.

465

PERFORMANCE ASSESMENT

You may choose to use this project as a performance assessment for the chapter.

Performance Assessment Key

Level 4 Full Accomplishment

Level 3 Substantial Accomplishment

Level 2 Partial Accomplishment

Level 1 Little Accomplishment

Suggested Scoring Rubric

4
- Drawing of country is created on an accurately drawn and labeled coordinate plane.
- Many interesting facts involving positive and negative integers are collected.

3
- Drawing of country is created on a coordinate plane.
- Several facts involving positive and negative integers are collected.

2
- Drawing of a country is attempted on a coordinate plane.
- Some facts involving positive and negative integers are collected.

1
- Drawing of a country is attempted, but does not include a coordinate plane.
- Very few facts involving positive and negative integers are collected.

Chapter Project

Students choose a country of interest, create a drawing of the country on a coordinate plane, and find interesting facts about the country that involve positive and negative numbers.

Resources
Teaching Tool Transparency 21: Map of the World

Chapter 9 Project Master

Introduce the Project

- You may want to use Teaching Tool Transparency 21 to introduce the project.
- Discuss information about a country that might involve positive and negative numbers, such as average temperatures, population growth and decline, imports and exports, and so on.
- Discuss how students might select a country and represent it on a coordinate plane.
- Talk about where students might find information about their countries of choice, such as encyclopedias, magazines, books, and the Internet.

Project Progress
Section A, page 484 Students use integers to express the facts they have collected about the country they have chosen to study.

Section B, page 502 Students draw a coordinate plane on an outline of their country and identify the coordinates of the points that trace out the country's shape.

Community Project

A community project for Chapter 9 is available in *Home and Community Connections.*

Cooperative Learning

You may want to use Teaching Tool Transparency 1: Cooperative Learning Checklist with **Explore** and other group activities in this chapter.

Problem Solving Focus

Solving Problems

The Point
Students focus on different methods of solving a problem and on choosing the methods that work for them.

Resources
Teaching Tool Transparency 18: Problem-Solving Guidelines

Interactive CD-ROM Journal

About the Page

Using the Problem-Solving Process
After students have read the problem and determined what is being asked, they must decide how to solve it. Sometimes there is more than one way to solve a problem, and students must be able to choose the way that makes the most sense to them. Discuss these steps for solving a problem:

- Determine what the problem is asking.
- Decide if making a list, drawing a picture, using number sense, or some other method is most appropriate.
- Apply the chosen method to solve the problem.

Ask ...

- Why does making a list seem like a good method? Possible answer: It helps you to consider all the possibilities.
- Why does using number sense seem like a good method? Possible answer: You can think about the problem logically.
- Why does drawing a picture seem like a good method? Possible answer: It helps you visualize what is happening.

Answers for Problems
12

Journal

Ask students to describe how they chose a method to use in solving the question about twins.

Problem Solving
Understand
Plan
Solve
Look Back

Solving Problems

You can solve most problems in more than one way. When solving a problem, you may find that one plan works more easily than another. An important part of good problem solving is choosing the easiest strategy to work with.

Problem Solving Focus

The following problem has already been solved using three different methods.

Five employees of the Carlson Company met at a meeting. These five employees had never met each other before, so each person shook everyone else's hand. How many handshakes were there?

Make a list	**Number sense**	**Draw a picture**
(Each pair represents one handshake.) 1-2 1-3 1-4 1-5 2-3 2-4 2-5 3-4 3-5 4-5	There are five people. Each person shook four other hands. $5 \times 4 = 20$ But this counts each handshake twice (once when 1 greets 2, and once when 2 greets 1). Therefore, you need to cut the number in half. $20 \div 2 = 10$	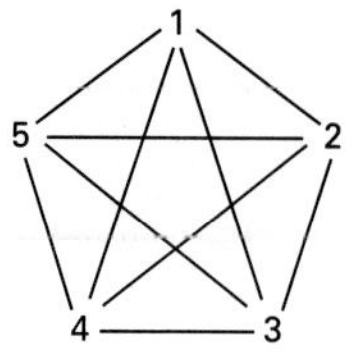 Each line equals one handshake. There are ten lines.
There were 10 handshakes.	There were 10 handshakes.	There were 10 handshakes.

Solve the following problem. You may use one of the above methods, or a method of your own.

Three sets of twins met at the park. At first, each person knew only his or her twin. But by the end of the day, every person had met everyone else. How many introductions were there?

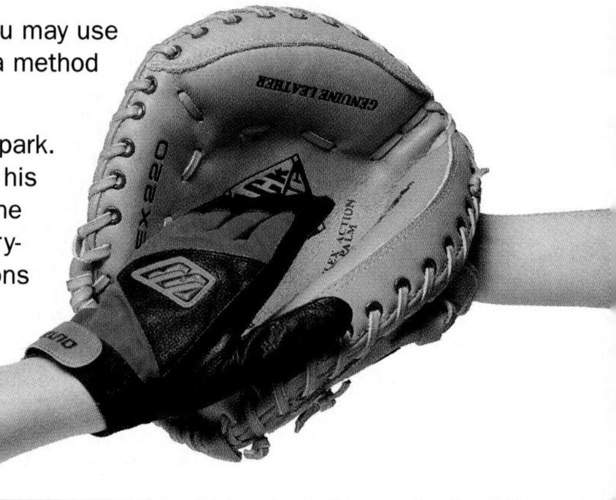

466

Additional Problem

Aaron invited six friends to a party. Each person decided to play a game of darts with each other person at the party. How many games of darts did Aaron and his guests play?

1. What does the problem ask you to find? The number of dart games played.
2. How could you solve the problem by making a list? Possible answer: Number the people and list all the possible pairs.
3. How could you solve the problem by using number sense? Possible answer: Multiply 7×6 and divide by 2 to give 21 games.
4. How could you solve the problem by drawing a picture? Possible answer: Draw 7 points and draw lines between them to represent the games.
5. Which method do you prefer? Why? Answers may vary.

Section 9A

Integers

Visit www.teacher.mathsurf.com for links to lesson plans from teachers and other professionals, NCTM information, and other sites.

LESSON PLANNING GUIDE

Student Edition | **Ancillaries***

LESSON		MATERIALS	VOCABULARY	DAILY	OTHER
	Chapter 9 Opener				Ch. 9 Project Master Ch. 9 Community Project Teaching Tool Trans. 1, 21
	Problem Solving Focus				Teaching Tool Trans. 18 *Interactive CD-ROM Journal*
	Section 9A Opener				
9-1	**Understanding Integers**		positive numbers, negative numbers, integers	9-1	Teaching Tool Trans. 5 Technology Master 44
9-2	**Adding Integers**	2-color counters	opposite	9-2	Teaching Tool Trans. 5, 15 Technology Master 45 *Interactive CD-ROM Lesson* *WW Math*–Middle School
9-3	**Subtracting Integers**	2-color counters		9-3	Teaching Tool Trans. 2, 3, 5, 15 Technology Master 46
9-4	**Multiplying and Dividing Integers**	spreadsheet software		9-4	Teaching Tool Trans. 5 Lesson Enhancement Trans. 44 Technology Master 47 Ch. 9 Project Master *Interactive CD-ROM Spreadsheet/Grapher Tool*
	Connect				Interdisc. Team Teaching 9A
	Review				Practice 9A; Quiz 9A; *TestWorks*

* Daily Ancillaries include Practice, Reteaching, Problem Solving, Enrichment, and Daily Transparency. Teaching Tool Transparencies are in *Teacher's Toolkits*. Lesson Enhancement Transparencies are in *Overhead Transparency Package*.

SKILLS TRACE

LESSON	SKILL	FIRST INTRODUCED GR. 4	GR. 5	GR. 6	DEVELOP	PRACTICE/ APPLY	REVIEW
9-1	**Identifying and ordering integers.**			✘ p. 468	pp. 468–469	pp. 470–471	pp. 486, 506, 533
9-2	**Adding integers.**			✘ p. 472	pp. 472–473	pp. 474–475	pp. 486, 506, 537
9-3	**Subtracting integers.**			✘ p. 476	pp. 476–478	pp. 479–480	pp. 486, 506, 542
9-4	**Multiplying and dividing integers.**			✘ p. 481	pp. 481–482	pp. 483–484	pp. 486, 506, 546

CONNECTED MATHEMATICS

Investigation 6 in the unit *Shapes and Designs (3-D Geometry)*, from the **Connected Mathematics** series, can be used with Section 9A.

9-1 Lesson Organizer

Objectives

- Learn what an integer is.
- Order integers.

Vocabulary

- Positive numbers, negative numbers, integers

NCTM Standards

- 1–6

Review

Order each set of numbers from least to greatest.

1. 0.5, 1, $2\frac{1}{2}$, 0   0, 0.5, 1, $2\frac{1}{2}$
2. 1.5, 0.1, 0.01, 0.15   0.01, 0.1, 0.15, 1.5
3. $1\frac{1}{2}$, 1.75, $\frac{3}{4}$, 1.3 $\frac{3}{4}$, 1.3, $1\frac{1}{2}$, 1.75

Available on Daily Transparency 9-1

Ans
2.

▶ Lesson Link

Have students discuss games they have played which involve gains and losses and have them discuss how the game is scored.

1 Introduce

Explore

You may wish to use Teaching Tool Transparency 5: Number Lines with this lesson.

The Point
Students explore five different situations in which individuals have money and also owe money. Students must then rank the individuals from the one having the most money to the one who owes the most after all monies owed have been paid.

9-1 Understanding Integers

You'll Learn ...

- what an integer is
- to order integers

... How It's Used

Hot-air balloon operators work with integers when determining how much ballast, or weight, is needed to maintain a certain altitude.

Vocabulary

positive numbers
negative numbers
integers

▶ Lesson Link You've learned to locate whole numbers on a number line. Now you'll investigate a set of numbers that are related to the whole numbers and graph them on a number line. ◀

Explore Integers

Connect the Debts

I owe John eleven dollars. I have fifteen dollars in my wallet.
Zack
I have eight dollars in my bank. My brother owes me four dollars.
Sonia
I owe my sister three dollars. I owe Molly nine dollars.
Tyreka
I have three dollars in my purse. I owe Tina eight dollars.
Peggy
I owe Raquel six dollars. I have six dollars in my bank.
Ricardo

1. Determine how much money each person will have or how much they will owe when all of the monies owed have been paid.
2. Rank the five friends from who has the most money to who owes the most money.
3. Copy this number line and indicate where each person is.

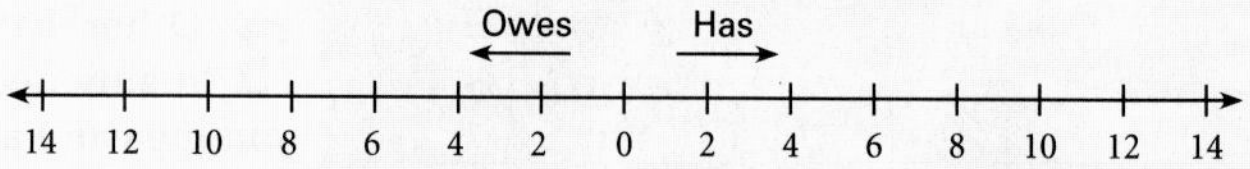
Owes
Has
14 12 10 8 6 4 2 0 2 4 6 8 10 12 14

4. Without using words, how could you indicate if an answer of "6" meant "has 6 dollars" or "owes 6 dollars?"

MEETING INDIVIDUAL NEEDS

Resources

- 9-1 Practice
- 9-1 Reteaching
- 9-1 Problem Solving
- 9-1 Enrichment
- 9-1 Daily Transparency
  - Problem of the Day
  - Review
  - Quick Quiz
- Teaching Tool Transparency 5
- Technology Master 44

Learning Modalities

Verbal Have students name several different situations where negative integers, as well as positive integers, are useful.

Kinesthetic Have students examine a thermometer that measures in both Fahrenheit and Celsius degrees and then have them point out where negative integers occur on each thermometer.

English Language Development

Have students make a list of phrases used in context that denote positive or negative integers. For example, degrees *above* zero, feet *below* sea level, pay *increase of* $2 an hour.

Section 9A

Integers

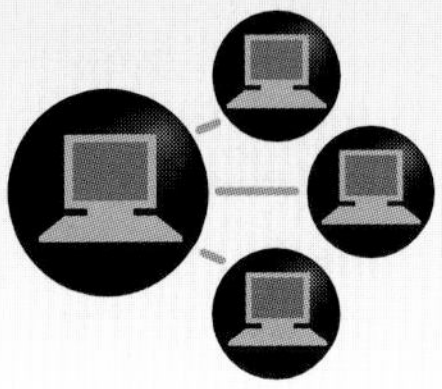

Visit **www.teacher.mathsurf.com** for links to lesson plans from teachers and other professionals, NCTM information, and other sites.

LESSON PLANNING GUIDE

Student Edition: LESSON		MATERIALS	VOCABULARY	Ancillaries*: DAILY	OTHER
	Chapter 9 Opener				Ch. 9 Project Master Ch. 9 Community Project Teaching Tool Trans. 1, 21
	Problem Solving Focus				Teaching Tool Trans. 18 *Interactive CD-ROM Journal*
	Section 9A Opener				
9-1	**Understanding Integers**		positive numbers, negative numbers, integers	9-1	Teaching Tool Trans. 5 Technology Master 44
9-2	**Adding Integers**	2-color counters	opposite	9-2	Teaching Tool Trans. 5, 15 Technology Master 45 *Interactive CD-ROM Lesson* *WW Math*–Middle School
9-3	**Subtracting Integers**	2-color counters		9-3	Teaching Tool Trans. 2, 3, 5, 15 Technology Master 46
9-4	**Multiplying and Dividing Integers**	spreadsheet software		9-4	Teaching Tool Trans. 5 Lesson Enhancement Trans. 44 Technology Master 47 Ch. 9 Project Master *Interactive CD-ROM Spreadsheet/Grapher Tool*
	Connect				Interdisc. Team Teaching 9A
	Review				Practice 9A; Quiz 9A; *TestWorks*

* Daily Ancillaries include Practice, Reteaching, Problem Solving, Enrichment, and Daily Transparency. Teaching Tool Transparencies are in *Teacher's Toolkits*. Lesson Enhancement Transparencies are in *Overhead Transparency Package*.

SKILLS TRACE

LESSON	SKILL	FIRST INTRODUCED GR. 4	GR. 5	GR. 6	DEVELOP	PRACTICE/ APPLY	REVIEW
9-1	**Identifying and ordering integers.**			✘ p. 468	pp. 468–469	pp. 470–471	pp. 486, 506, 533
9-2	**Adding integers.**			✘ p. 472	pp. 472–473	pp. 474–475	pp. 486, 506, 537
9-3	**Subtracting integers.**			✘ p. 476	pp. 476–478	pp. 479–480	pp. 486, 506, 542
9-4	**Multiplying and dividing integers.**			✘ p. 481	pp. 481–482	pp. 483–484	pp. 486, 506, 546

CONNECTED MATHEMATICS

Investigation 6 in the unit *Shapes and Designs (3-D Geometry)*, from the **Connected Mathematics** series, can be used with Section 9A.

INTERDISCIPLINARY TEAM TEACHING

Math and Social Studies

(Worksheet pages 43–44: Teacher pages T43–T44)

In this lesson, students use integers and positive and negative numbers in banking.

Name ______________________ *Math and Social Studies*

TAKE IT TO THE BANK

Use integers and positive and negative numbers in banking.

Banking has a long history. In ancient Rome, people went to money changers to borrow money, to deposit money, and to get bills of credit. Bills of credit were similar to today's checks. The money changers were so important to Roman commerce that an entire Roman street, called the Street of Janus, was set aside for money changing. During the Renaissance (between 1400 and 1600), money changers did business from benches in the street. The Italian word for bench is *banca*, from which comes the English word, *bank*.

In England during the early 1600s, goldsmiths were the bankers. Goldsmiths were people who made and repaired articles of gold. The goldsmiths kept money and other valuables in safe care for their customers. Over time, the goldsmiths noticed that the value of the deposits left in their care remained at a steady level. There were about as many deposits as there were withdrawals. (A *withdrawal* is the process by which money is taken out of a bank account.)

Apparently, people wanted only enough money to meet their everyday needs. They left the rest with the goldsmiths. The goldsmiths realized that they could use the money left in their safe keeping to make additional profits. They could lend the money to people and charge a fee—interest—as the cost for borrowing the money. The goldsmiths also allowed their customers to transfer any part of the money in their account to another person's account. This seems to be the beginning of modern check writing.

Modern banks provide many services. The most common ones are savings accounts, loans, and checking accounts. A checking account is an account in which a person deposits money and then writes checks against that money. For example, a person who deposits $300 into a checking account may write up to $300 worth of checks. If that person writes checks for more than $300, the checks are said to be "bad," because there is not enough money in his or her account to cover the check.

Name ______________________ *Math and Social Studies*

Item	Cost	Cost Rounded	Balance in Checking Account	Balance in Checking Account Rounded	+ or –	Do you have enough money?
sneakers	$99.95	$100	$86.79	$90	–$10	no
video game	$43.50	$40	$217.14	$200	+$160	yes
dinner at a restaurant	$17.23	$20	$3.89	$4	–$16	no
CD	$11.99	$10	$41.08	$40	+$30	yes
baseball cap	$22.50	$20	$25.62	$30	+$10	yes
bicycle	$269.79	$300	$177.45	$200	–$100	no

1. Complete the table by rounding to decide whether you have enough money in your checking account to pay for an item. If you have enough, select the positive sign and write the rounded amount of money you will have left after writing the check. If you do not have enough money, select the negative sign and write the rounded amount of money you will owe the account. An example has been provided to help you get started. Round each number so there is only one non-zero digit.

2. When is an amount of money an integer and when is it not an integer? Include an example of each in your explanation.

   See below.

3. When people make deposits, they add money to their checking account. When people write checks, they subtract money from their checking account. How can checkbook activities be expressed on a number line?

   See below.

4. Why do you think banking has existed for at least 2,000 years?

   Students' responses will vary. People have always needed a safe place to store their money and valuables. Also, people have always needed to borrow money.

5. **a.** Research ways that banks have helped to shape history.

   Students should discover such things as financing wars and helping businesses get started.

   b. Visit or call your local bank to find out their rules about checking accounts. Find out such things as how old a person must be to open a checking account and the penalties for writing bad checks. Also, find out about overdraft protection and how it can help a person to avoid writing bad checks.

Answers

2. Money is sometimes expressed as whole dollar amounts, such as $5. These are integers because they are whole numbers. Money can also be expressed as decimals, such as $5.34. Decimals are not integers.

3. A deposit into a checking account is a positive number. It is added to the checking account. On a number line, you would move to the right. The amount of a check written to someone or some place is a negative number. It is subtracted from the checking account. You would move to the left on the number line.

BIBLIOGRAPHY

FOR TEACHERS

Burton, Maurice and Robert, ed. *The Marshall Cavendish International Wildlife Encyclopedia.* New York, NY: Marshall Cavendish, 1990.

Few, Roger. *Animal Encyclopedia for Children.* New York, NY: Macmillan Publications, 1991.

McLeish, John, Ph.D. *Number.* New York, NY: Fawcett Columbine, 1992.

FOR STUDENTS

Fine, John Christopher. *Free Spirits in the Sky.* New York, NY: Atheneum, 1994.

Kane, Joseph Nathan. *Famous First Facts.* New York, NY: H. W. Wilson Company, 1991.

Nicholls, Richard. *Beginning Hydroponics: Soilless Gardening: A Beginner's Guide to Growing Vegetables,* Philadelphia, PA: Running Press, 1990.

SECTION 9A

Integers

▶ Science Link ▶ Geography Link ▶ www.mathsurf.com/6/ch9/earth

The Third Sphere From the Sun

How could you measure the height of a mountain?

PLAN A: Go to the top of the mountain, drill a hole to the bottom, and drop a long tape measure down the hole.

PLAN B: Build a gigantic ruler and have several hundred friends place it straight up into the air next to the mountain.

PLAN C: Find a mountain whose height you know and ask it to go stand back to back against the first mountain.

Nobody uses any of these methods, but many people do ask the question about how to measure and learn more about the earth. People who study the earth are collectively known as earth scientists. They include zoologists, who study animals; botanists, who study plants; geologists, who study rocks; meteorologists, who study weather; oceanographers, who study oceans; and many other types of scientists.

These scientists have to be able to describe how far a point is above or below sea level. They have to record temperatures above and below the freezing point of water. They have to keep track of how an animal population has grown or shrunk. All of these descriptions require a special set of numbers known as integers.

1 Other than the measurements mentioned above, what else could you measure about the earth?

2 Why is it useful for humans to have a better understanding of the earth?

Where are we now?

In Grade 5, students developed their number sense. They learned to estimate and operate with whole numbers.

They learned how to

- locate whole numbers on a number line.
- add and subtract whole numbers.
- multiply and divide whole numbers.

Where are we going?

In Grade 6, Section 9A, students will

- learn the meaning of integers.
- order integers.
- add and subtract integers.
- multiply and divide integers.

Theme: Earth Science

World Wide Web

If your class has access to the World Wide Web, you might want to use the information found at the Web site address given. These interdisciplinary links relate to topics discussed in this section.

About the Page

This page introduces the theme of the section, earth science, and discusses the scientists who study plants, animals, rocks, weather, and oceans.

Ask ...

- Why aren't Plans A, B, and C practical methods for measuring mountains?

Extensions

The following activities do not require access to the World Wide Web.

Science

Geology is the science of the changing Earth. Some of the things geologists study are the Earth's interior (geophysics) and its chemical composition (geochemistry). Have students research an area of geology.

Geography

The highest mountains in the world are the Himalaya Mountains in Asia. Have students research the locations of some of the other highest mountains. Possible answers: Mt. McKinley in Alaska is the highest mountain in the United States.

Answers for Questions

1. Possible answers: The weight of the Earth, the age of the Earth.
2. Possible answers: To plan for space exploration missions, to identify serious changes in the weather or environment.

Connect

On page 485, students use positive and negative numbers to record information about changes in elevation.

9-1 Lesson Organizer

Objectives

- Learn what an integer is.
- Order integers.

Vocabulary

- Positive numbers, negative numbers, integers

NCTM Standards

- 1–6

Review

Order each set of numbers from least to greatest.

1. 0.5, 1, $2\frac{1}{2}$, 0   0, 0.5, 1, $2\frac{1}{2}$
2. 1.5, 0.1, 0.01, 0.15   0.01, 0.1, 0.15, 1.5
3. $1\frac{1}{2}$, 1.75, $\frac{3}{4}$, 1.3 $\frac{3}{4}$, 1.3, $1\frac{1}{2}$, 1.75

Available on Daily Transparency 9-1

Lesson Link

Have students discuss games they have played which involve gains and losses and have them discuss how the game is scored.

1 Introduce

Explore

You may wish to use Teaching Tool Transparency 5: Number Lines with this lesson.

The Point
Students explore five different situations in which individuals have money and also owe money. Students must then rank the individuals from the one having the most money to the one who owes the most after all monies owed have been paid.

9-1 Understanding Integers

You'll Learn ...

- what an integer is
- to order integers

... How It's Used

Hot-air balloon operators work with integers when determining how much ballast, or weight, is needed to maintain a certain altitude.

Vocabulary

positive numbers
negative numbers
integers

Lesson Link You've learned to locate whole numbers on a number line. Now you'll investigate a set of numbers that are related to the whole numbers and graph them on a number line. ◄

Explore Integers

Connect the Debts

I owe John eleven dollars. I have fifteen dollars in my wallet.

Zack

I have eight dollars in my bank. My brother owes me four dollars.

Sonia

I owe my sister three dollars. I owe Molly nine dollars.

Tyreka

I have three dollars in my purse. I owe Tina eight dollars.

Peggy

I owe Raquel six dollars. I have six dollars in my bank.

Ricardo

1. Determine how much money each person will have or how much they will owe when all of the monies owed have been paid.
2. Rank the five friends from who has the most money to who owes the most money.
3. Copy this number line and indicate where each person is.

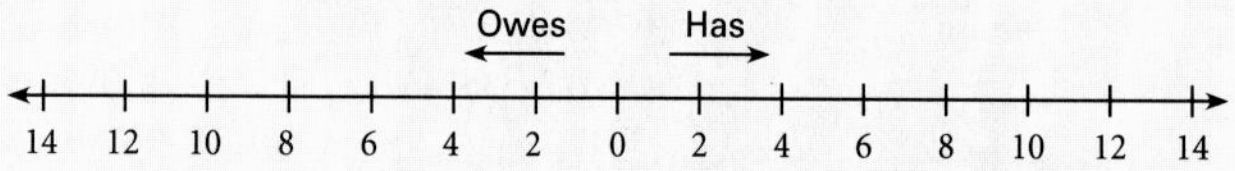

4. Without using words, how could you indicate if an answer of "6" meant "has 6 dollars" or "owes 6 dollars?"

MEETING INDIVIDUAL NEEDS

Resources

9-1 Practice
9-1 Reteaching
9-1 Problem Solving
9-1 Enrichment
9-1 Daily Transparency
  Problem of the Day
  Review
  Quick Quiz
Teaching Tool Transparency 5
Technology Master 44

Learning Modalities

Verbal Have students name several different situations where negative integers, as well as positive integers, are useful.

Kinesthetic Have students examine a thermometer that measures in both Fahrenheit and Celsius degrees and then have them point out where negative integers occur on each thermometer.

English Language Development

Have students make a list of phrases used in context that denote positive or negative integers. For example, degrees *above* zero, feet *below* sea level, pay *increase of* $2 an hour.

Learn Understanding Integers

Most of the numbers you have seen so far have been greater than or equal to 0. Numbers greater than 0 are known as **positive numbers**. There is another set of numbers that are all *less than 0.* They are known as **negative numbers**.

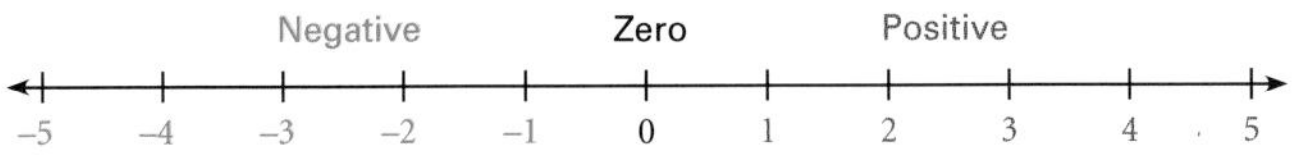

Negative numbers are used to keep track of values below a certain mark. They are used to describe debts, depths below sea level, and temperatures in degrees Celsius below freezing.

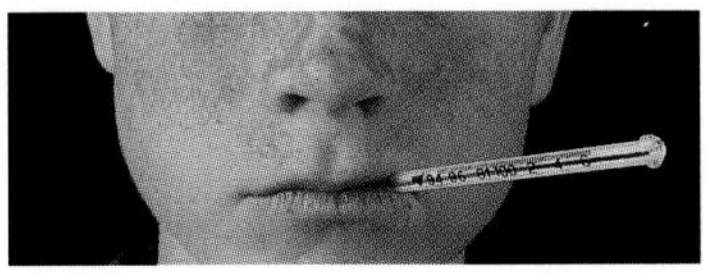

Negative numbers are always shown with a minus (−) sign. Positive numbers may or may not have a plus (+) sign. Whole numbers (1, 2, 3...), their negative counterparts (−1, −2, −3...), and 0 are known as **integers**. On a number line, the further to the right a number is, the greater it is. The further to the left it is, the less it is.

▶ Science Link

Most of the world uses degrees Celsius to measure temperature. In Celsius, water freezes at 0° and boils at 100°. People in the United States often use the Fahrenheit system, where water freezes at 32° and boils at 212°.

Example 1

Order the integers from least to greatest: 1, −2, 4, −5, 0.

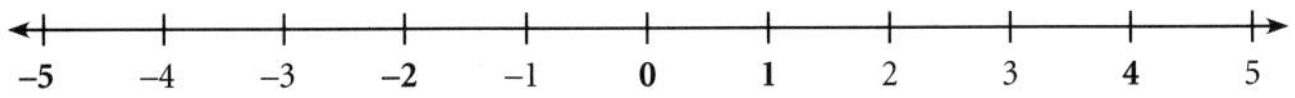

Locate the numbers on the number line. The least number, which is the one furthest to the left, is −5. It is followed by −2, 0, 1, and 4.

−5, −2, 0, 1, 4

Try It

Tell which Celsius temperature is greater. **a.** 4° or −4° 4° **b.** −7° or −6° −6°

Order the integers from least to greatest. **c.** 1, −3, −10, 7, 10, 0
−10, −3, 0, 1, 7, 10

DID YOU KNOW?

Zero is the only integer that is neither positive nor negative.

Check Your Understanding

1. What kinds of numbers are integers?

2. Is a negative number always less than a positive number? Explain.

MATH EVERY DAY

▶ Problem of the Day

The Kuba people of the Congo (Zaire) region of Africa use slides and flips when making the patterns on cloth. Identify the pattern used on the cloth below and continue the pattern.

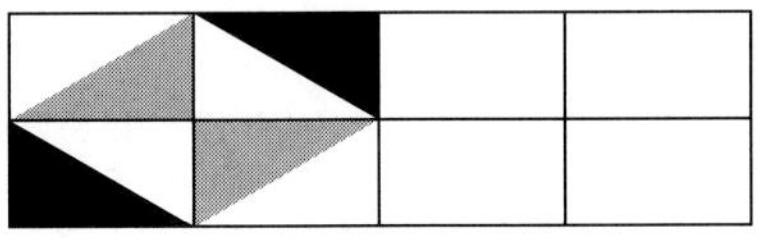

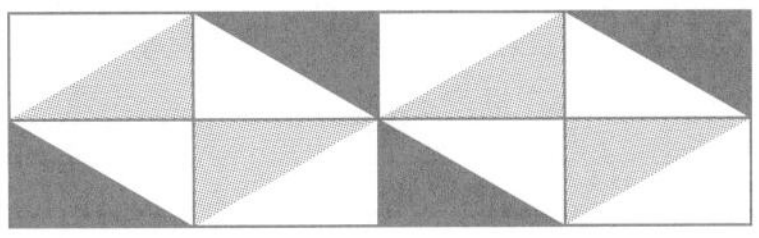

Available on Daily Transparency 9-1

An Extension is provided in the transparency package.

Fact of the Day

In 1994, American consumers had $925,000,000,000 debt outstanding in installment credit.

Mental Math

Find each sum mentally.

1. 20 + 90 110
2. 80 + 80 160
3. 700 + 900 1600
4. 900 + 600 1500

Ongoing Assessment

Be sure students understand that they are to determine how much each student has or owes after all debts are paid, not how much each has at the beginning.

For Groups That Finish Early

How much more money would Tyreka need in order to have as much money as Sonia? $24

Answers for Explore

1. Sonia will have $12; Tyreka will owe $12; Zack will have $4; Peggy will owe $5; Ricardo will have $0.
2. Sonia; Zack; Ricardo; Peggy; Tryeka.
3. See page C2.
4. Possible answer: Use a plus or minus sign: + 6 or −6.

2 Teach

Learn

Alternate Examples

Order the integers from least to greatest: 5, −3, 2, 0, −4.

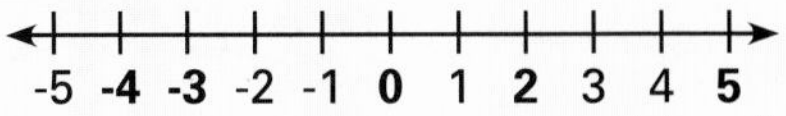

Locate the numbers on the number line. The least number, which is the one farthest to the left, is −4. It is followed by −3, 0, 2, and 5.

3 Practice and Assess

Check

Be sure students understand that integers include only whole numbers and their opposites and that there are other negative numbers that are not integers.

Answers for Check Your Understanding

1. Integers are whole numbers and their opposites.
2. Yes; A negative number is always less than 0 and a positive number is always greater than 0, so a negative number must be less than a positive number.

9-1 Exercises and Applications

Assignment Guide

- **Basic**
  1–12, 14–42 evens, 46–62 evens
- **Average**
  1–11 odds, 14–62 evens
- **Enriched**
  1–29 odds, 31–46, 47–61 odds

Exercise Notes

Exercise 31

Science Ethanol is also known as grain alcohol or ethyl alcohol. It has immense industrial importance as a solvent, in antifreeze, and as an antiseptic.

Exercise Answers

7–12.

Reteaching

Activity

Materials: Index cards

- Work in groups of three. Use index cards.
- On each index card write one of the integers from −10 through 10 so that you have 21 cards, each with a different integer written on it.
- Shuffle the cards and pick three at random.
- From a given starting point, take turns marking off the number of paces that is indicated by the integer on the card.
- If the number is positive, walk to the *right*; if the number is negative, walk to the *left*.
- Hold the cards up to see the 3 numbers ordered from least to greatest, such as −5, 0, 2.

9-1 Exercises and Applications

Practice and Apply

Getting Started Tell if each number is an integer. If it is not, explain why.

1. −78 Yes **2.** $\frac{1}{2}$ **3.** 56 Yes **4.** −54.7 **5.** 0 Yes **6.** +33 Yes

2. No; Fractions aren't integers.
4. No; Decimals aren't integers.

Draw a number line. Locate each integer on the number line.

7. −5 **8.** 2 **9.** 0 **10.** −4 **11.** 3 **12.** −2

Compare using > or <.

13. −8 [>] −10 **14.** −6 [<] 5 **15.** −1 [<] 1 **16.** 12 [>] −42 **17.** −66 [>] −68

18. −45 [>] −49 **19.** −16 [>] −26 **20.** −24 [<] −18 **21.** 5 [>] −5 **22.** −55 [<] −32

Order from greatest to least.

23. 3, −4, −5, 2 — 3, 2, −4, −5
24. −45, 67, −67, 45 — 67, 45, −45, −67
25. −78, 13, −16, −56 — 13, −16, −56, −78
26. −2, −42, −24, −4 — −2, −4, −24, −42

27. 16, −10, 12, 0 — 16, 12, 0, −10
28. −45, −32, −59, −14 — −14, −32, −45, −59
29. 16, 17, −18, 19 — 19, 17, 16, −18
30. −99, −100, −89, −47 — −47, −89, −99, −100

Write each number as an integer.

31. Ethanol freezes at 114°C below zero. −114

32. Bryan has a debt of $49. −49

33. Lori is 62 inches tall. 62

34. The picture is 37 in. wide. 37

35. Todd lost 7 pounds. −7

36. Chelsea hopped 5 ft backwards.

37. Kay completed five dives to the following depths below sea level: −107, −52, −213, −211, −76. Order these integers from smallest to largest. −213, −211, −107, −76, −52

38. Byron is making up a board game. He wants to write the following on the board spaces: Go back two spaces; Move ahead four spaces; Move ahead three spaces; Go back five spaces; Move ahead one space. If he writes these instructions using integers, will he have more negative numbers or more positive numbers? Positive

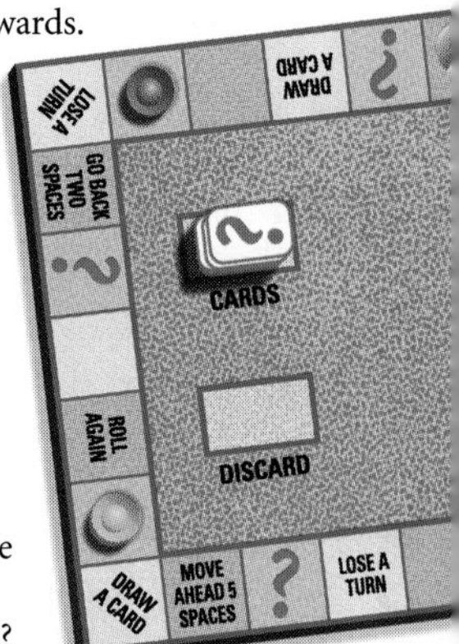

39. At the Spring Carnival Go-Fish booth, the 6th-grade class had expenses of $12. They took in $22. Write the money amounts as integers. −12, 22

40. Lori is saving money to buy a new bicycle. She deposited $30 into a bank account. Later, she withdrew $25 to buy a new helmet. Write these amounts as integers. 30; −25

PRACTICE

Name ______________________

Practice 9-1

Understanding Integers

Locate each integer on the number line.

1. 1
2. −3
3. −1
4. 4

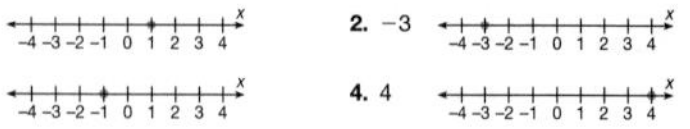

Compare using > or <.

5. 7 (>) −7 **6.** −5 (>) −6 **7.** 0 (>) −3 **8.** 16 (>) −17

9. −12 (<) 9 **10.** 4 (>) 0 **11.** −11 (<) −7 **12.** 14 (>) −12

13. −6 (<) 8 **14.** 12 (>) −11 **15.** −8 (<) 0 **16.** 5 (>) −1

Order from greatest to least.

17. 17, −15, −20, 19 — 19, 17, −15, −20

18. −74, −83, −62, −77 — −62, −74, −77, −83

19. 5, 0, −8, 3, −6 — 5, 3, 0, −6, −8

20. −66, 78, 42, −58 — 78, 42, −58, −66

Write each number as an integer.

21. Jason has $318 in his bank account. 318

22. The temperature is 9°F below zero. −9

23. Rover weighs 36 pounds. 36

24. Sylvia owes $520. −520

25. The Aslam family made $253 at their garage sale, but they had to pay $18 for advertising and signs. Write the money amounts as integers. 253; −18

26. Science High and low tide levels are reported using positive and negative numbers. The tides for June 6, 1997, in Broad Creek, South Carolina, were −12, 232, −17, and 272 centimeters. Write these numbers in order from the lowest tide to the highest. −17, −12, 232, 272

RETEACHING

Name ______________________

Alternative Lesson 9-1

Understanding Integers

Numbers greater than 0 are known as **positive numbers.** The set of numbers that are all *less than 0* are **negative numbers.** Negative numbers are always shown with a minus (–) sign. Whole numbers and their negative counterparts are known as **integers.** Zero is the only integer that is neither positive nor negative.

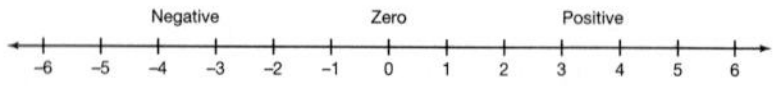

Example 1

Tell if $\frac{3}{4}$ is an integer.

Since fractions and decimals are not integers, $\frac{3}{4}$ is *not* an integer.

Try It Tell if each number is an integer. If it is not, explain why.

a. 2.4 No, it is a decimal. **b.** $3\frac{1}{3}$ No, it is a fraction.

c. 1 Yes. **d.** 12 Yes.

Example 2

Order from least to greatest: –2, 0, 5, –3, 1

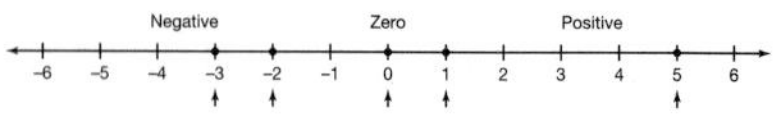

Locate the numbers on the number line. Numbers on a number line increase from left to right. The least number is furthest to the left, so the least number is –3. Then list the numbers as they appear from left to right on the number line: –2, 0, 1, and 5.

The numbers in order from least to greatest are –3, –2, 0, 1, 5.

Try It Order from least to greatest. Draw a number line if you need help.

e. 8, 0, –3, –1 —3, –1, 0, 8 **f.** –3, 5, –1, 1, –2 —3, –2, –1, 1, 5

g. 6, –2, 0, 7, –4 —4, –2, 0, 6, 7 **h.** 12, –15, –9, 7 —15, –9, 7, 12

41. **Career** Before a space shuttle takes off, astronauts count the time remaining in negative numbers. Order these takeoff times from earliest to latest: −4 minutes, −15 minutes, −3 minutes, −20 minutes, −5 minutes, −1 minute, −2 minutes.

42. **Test Prep** Choose the set of integers that is ordered from least to greatest. C

Ⓐ 5, −6, 7, 8 Ⓑ −3, −1, 4, 0

Ⓒ −5, −3, 0, 7 Ⓓ 9, 3, −6, −7

Problem Solving and Reasoning

43. **Communicate** Is $\frac{1}{2}$ an integer? Is $-\frac{1}{2}$? Explain your reasoning.

44. **Critical Thinking** Like integers, decimals can be either positive or negative. Order each set of decimals from least to greatest.

a. 1.6, −2.7, −5.6 **b.** −7.3, −2.5, −5.8 **c.** −0.25, 0.5, −0.75 **d.** −0.3, −0.5, −0.4

45. Journal What is the largest positive integer? The largest negative integer? Explain your reasoning.

46. **Critical Thinking** Order −5, −26, 8, 19, and −20 from least to greatest. Then order these same numbers from closest to zero to furthest from zero. Explain the similarities and differences between your two lists.

Mixed Review

Estimate. *[Lesson 7-1]*

47. $6\frac{2}{3} \times 2\frac{1}{3}$ 14 **48.** $11\frac{3}{4} \div 3\frac{5}{8}$ 3 **49.** $2\frac{6}{7} \times \frac{1}{2}$ 3 **50.** $15\frac{3}{7} \div 3\frac{1}{3}$ 5

51. $4\frac{1}{4} \times 10\frac{4}{5}$ 44 **52.** $9\frac{8}{9} \div 1\frac{7}{8}$ 5 **53.** $20\frac{2}{5} \times 8\frac{5}{6}$ 180 **54.** $5\frac{7}{8} \div 2\frac{8}{9}$ 2

Describe the relationship between the lines, rays, or segments. *[Lesson 8-1]*

55.

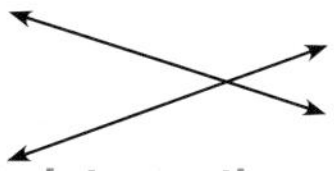

Intersecting

56.

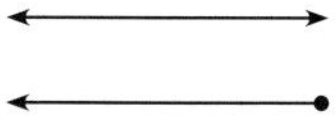

Parallel

57.

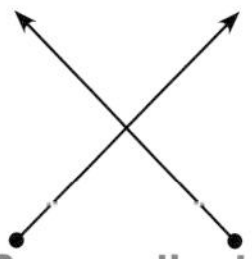

Perpendicular

58.

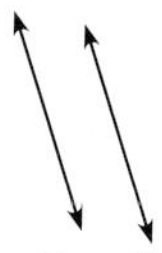

Parallel

59.

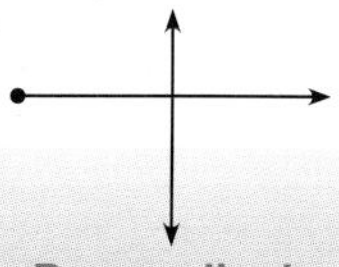

Perpendicular

60.

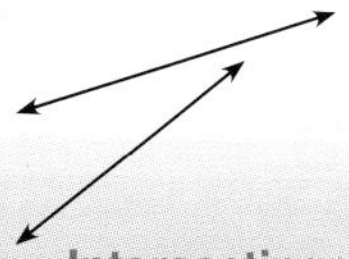

Intersecting

61.

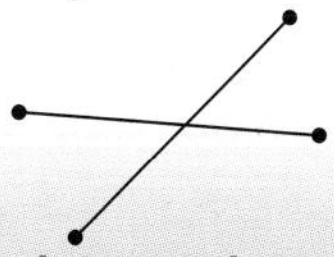

Intersecting

62.

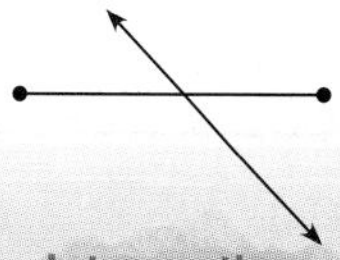

Intersecting

PROBLEM SOLVING 9-1

PROBLEM SOLVING

Name ______________________

Guided Problem Solving 9-1

GPS **PROBLEM 46, PAGE 471**

Order −5, −26, 8, 19, and −20 from least to greatest. Then order these same numbers from closest to zero to furthest from zero. Explain the similarities and differences between your two lists.

Understand

1. Underline the integers you are asked to order.

Plan

2. Show each integer on the number line. Add any necessary labels.

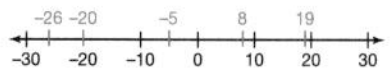

Solve

3. Order the numbers from least to greatest. −26, −20, −5, 8, 19

4. The integer +6 is 6 "steps" from zero. So is the integer −6. How many "steps" is each of the following integers from zero?

a. −5 5 steps. **b.** −26 26 steps. **c.** 8 8 steps.

d. 19 19 steps. **e.** −20 20 steps.

5. Use your answers to Item 4 to write the integers in order from closest to zero to furthest from zero. −5, 8, 19, −20, −26

6. How are your lists alike? Different? Similar: The same integers are used; Different: Distance from zero is not related to integer sign.

Look Back

7. How could you write the numbers in order from least to greatest without using a number line? Order by sign, then by proximity to zero. Negative numbers furthest to closest, positive numbers closest to furthest.

SOLVE ANOTHER PROBLEM

Order 12, −3, 5, −14, 19 from least to greatest. Then order these same numbers from closest to zero to furthest from zero.

Order: −14, −3, 5, 12, 19; Distance: −3, 5, 12, −14, 19.

ENRICHMENT

Name ______________________

Extend Your Thinking 9-1

Critical Thinking

You have learned that all integers, except zero, are either positive or negative numbers. Fractions and decimals can also be positive and negative numbers. A number line is a useful tool for ordering numbers.

The number line below shows some positive and negative fractions.

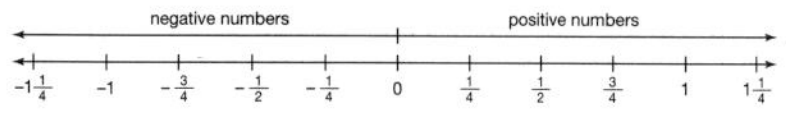

As with integers, the further to the right a fraction is located on a number line, the greater it is. The further to the left it is, the less it is.

Order from greatest to least. Use the number line above. Locate and add fractions to the number line if necessary.

1. $\frac{1}{2}, -\frac{1}{2}, -\frac{1}{4}$ $\frac{1}{2}, -\frac{1}{4}, -\frac{1}{2}$

2. $\frac{2}{3}, -\frac{3}{4}, \frac{3}{8}$ $\frac{2}{3}, \frac{3}{8}, -\frac{3}{4}$

3. $-\frac{1}{8}, -\frac{5}{8}, \frac{3}{8}, \frac{3}{4}$ $\frac{3}{4}, \frac{3}{8}, -\frac{1}{8}, -\frac{5}{8}$

4. $-\frac{1}{3}, \frac{2}{3}, \frac{1}{6}, -\frac{5}{6}$ $\frac{2}{3}, \frac{1}{6}, -\frac{1}{3}, -\frac{5}{6}$

The number line below shows some positive and negative decimals.

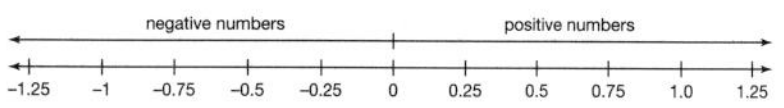

As with integers, the further to the right a decimal is located on a number line, the greater it is. The further to the left it is, the less it is.

Order from greatest to least. Use the number line above. Locate and add decimals to the number line if necessary.

5. −0.3, 0.25, −0.45 0.25, −0.3, −0.45

6. 0.75, −0.25, 0.5 0.75, 0.5, −0.25

7. 0.44, −0.89, −0.6 0.44, −0.6, −0.89

8. 0.1, −0.15, −0.51, 0.05 0.1, 0.05, −0.15, −0.51

Exercise Notes

■ Exercise 42

Test Prep If students selected A, they ordered the numbers without regard as to whether they are positive or negative.

Exercise Answers

41. −20, −15, −5, −4, −3, −2, −1 minutes

43. No; No; Each is a fraction between two consecutive integers.

45. There is no largest positive integer; The largest negative integer is −1 because the next largest integer is 0 which is neither positive nor negative.

46. −26, −20, −5, 8, 19; −5, 8, 19, −20, −26; The lists are in different orders. The second list orders the numbers from least to greatest as if they were all positive, since the distance from zero is always a positive number.

Alternate Assessment

You may want to use the *Interactive CD-ROM Journal* with this assessment.

Journal Have students name some situations in daily life for which integers would be useful.

Quick Quiz

Compare using > or <.

1. −7 ☐ 5 <
2. −2 ☐ −8 >
3. 1 ☐ −4 >
4. −10 ☐ 0 <

Order from greatest to least.

5. 11, −3, 7, −15
   11, 7, −3, −15
6. −49, 48, −50, 50
   50, 48, −49, −50

Available on Daily Transparency 9-1

INTERACTIVE LESSON

9-2 Lesson Organizer

Objectives

- Learn what an opposite is.
- Add integers.

Vocabulary

- Opposite

Materials

- Explore: 2-Color Counters

NCTM Standards

- 1–7, 13

Review

Give the opposite for each situation.

1. 7-yard gain 7-yard loss
2. 5-degree rise 5-degree drop
3. 3-pound loss 3-pound gain
4. $50 withdrawal $50 deposit

Available on Daily Transparency 9-2

1 Introduce

Explore

You may wish to use Teaching Tool Transparencies 5: Number Lines and 15: 2-Color Counters with this lesson.

The Point
Students use 2-color counters to model sums of integers.

Ongoing Assessment
Watch for students who have difficulty pairing opposite integers. Point out that in some cases, there are no opposite pairs.

For Groups That Finish Early
Name at least three pairs of integers having a sum of 0. Possible answers: 1 + (−1), 2 + (−2), 3 + (−3).

9-2 Adding Integers

You'll Learn ...

- what an opposite is
- to add integers

... How It's Used

Football referees add integers when determining how many yards a team must move the football in order to make it to first down.

Vocabulary

opposite

Lesson Link In the last lesson, you learned that integers include positive and negative numbers. Now you'll add integers together.

The **opposite** of an integer is the integer on the opposite side of zero but at the same distance from zero. 8 and −8 are the same distance from zero, so they are opposites.

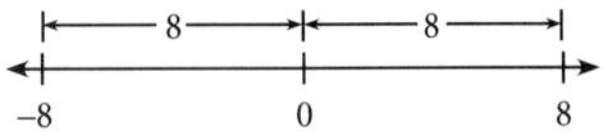

The sum of an integer and its opposite will always equal 0.

Explore Adding Integers

Two Nothings Are Nothing!

Materials: 2-color counters

Adding Integers

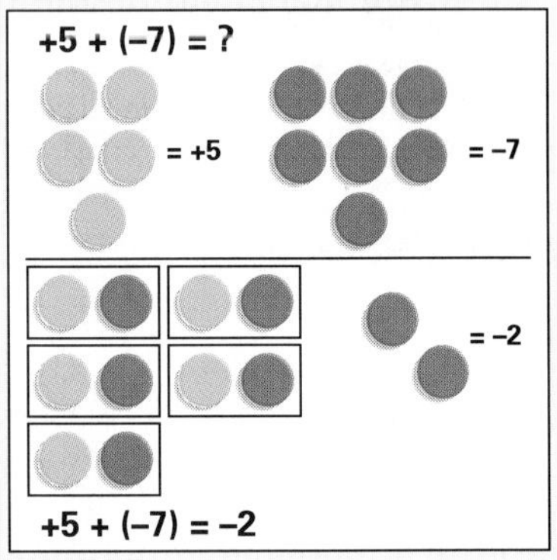

- Count out enough counters to represent the first number. If the number is positive, put the yellow sides up. If it is negative, put the red sides up.
- Repeat the first step for the second number.
- Make as many opposite pairs of one yellow and one red counter as possible. Since each pair equals 0 when added together, remove each pair.
- Describe the number and color of the counters left over.

1. Model each problem, and state the answer.

a. 10 + (−7) **b.** −6 + 5 **c.** −3 + (−8) **d.** 6 + 2
e. 4 + (−12) **f.** −5 + 0 **g.** −4 + 4 **h.** −7 + 7

2. Is the sum positive or negative when you add two positive integers? Two negative integers? Explain.

3. How can you predict the sign of the sum when you add a positive integer to a negative integer?

MEETING INDIVIDUAL NEEDS

Resources

9-2 Practice
9-2 Reteaching
9-2 Problem Solving
9-2 Enrichment
9-2 Daily Transparency
Problem of the Day
Review
Quick Quiz
Teaching Tool Transparencies 5, 15
Technology Master 45
Interactive CD-ROM Lesson
Wide World of Mathematics Middle School: Integer Football

Learning Modalities

Verbal Have students write a paragraph describing how they know whether a sum of two integers is positive, negative, or zero.

Visual Have students make number-line drawings to illustrate the sums in several exercises, such as Exercises 20–24 on page 474.

Social Have students assume that the entire class has a joint savings account in which they can make deposits and withdrawals. Have them start with $50 in the account and then determine the final balance after several transactions in preparation for a class party.

English Language Development

Help students distinguish between the various meanings of the minus sign. Always refer to a negative number as "negative," rather than "minus." Use "minus" for subtraction. Ask students to share terms used in their native language for minus sign and negative number.

Learn Adding Integers

You can add integers using a number line. Find the first number on the line. Move *right* to add a positive number. Move *left* to add a negative number.

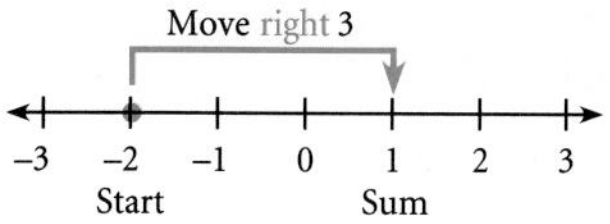

Examples

1 Add: $-3 + 5$

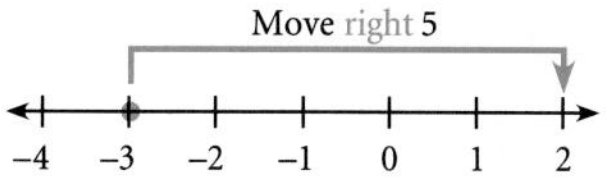

$-3 + 5 = 2$

2 Add: $2 + (-4)$

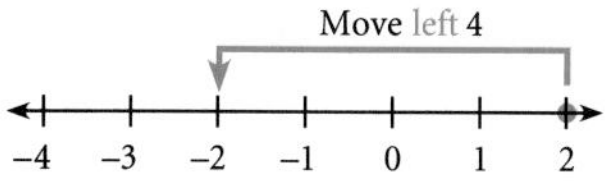

$2 + (-4) = -2$

3 A geologist removed a rock sample from 12 feet below sea level. She then climbed 31 feet up and removed another rock sample. From what height was the second rock sample removed?

$-12 + 31$ Write an expression.

19 Add.

The rock sample was removed from 19 feet above sea level.

Try It

Add.

a. $6 + 4$ 10 **b.** $-3 + (-5)$ −8 **c.** $-7 + 8$ 1 **d.** $2 + (-2)$ 0

e. $10 + (-3)$ 7 **f.** $-6 + 12$ 6 **g.** $5 + (-2)$ 3 **h.** $5 + (-8)$ −3

HINT

To enter a negative number into a calculator, enter the number and then press the +/- key.

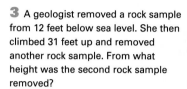

Science Link

The skin that surrounds the surface of the Earth is called the *crust.* The crust varies in thickness, from 5 miles to 25 miles, and the deepest parts of the crust are hot enough to melt rocks.

Check Your Understanding

1. If you add a positive integer to a negative integer, will the sum be positive or negative? Explain.

2. What is the sum of an integer and its opposite? Explain.

MATH EVERY DAY

Problem of the Day

Use the even integers from −2 to −18 to make a magic square where the sum of each column, row, and diagonal is −30.

-12	-14	
-2		-18
		-8

Possible answer:

-12	-14	-4
-2	-10	-18
-16	-6	-8

Available on Daily Transparency 9-2

An Extension is provided in the transparency package.

Fact of the Day

In 1948, August Piccard designed a deep-sea diving ship called a *bathyscaph.* Today such vessels can dive more than 6 miles to explore ocean depths.

Estimation

Estimate each sum.

1. 28 + 91 120
2. 81 + 89 170
3. 789 + 902 1700
4. 921 + 616 1500

Answers for Explore

1. a. 3; b. −1; c. −11; d. 8; e. −8; f. −5; g. 0; h. 0
2. Positive; Negative; There are no opposite pairs.
3. Possible answer: If the positive number is farther from 0 than the negative number, the sum will be positive. If the positive number is closer to 0, the sum will be negative. If they are the same distance from 0, the sum will be 0.

2 Teach

Learn

Alternate Examples

1. Add: $-5 + 3$

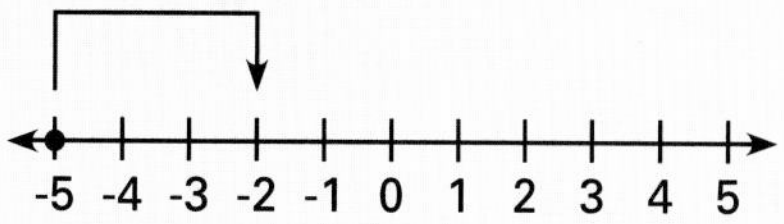

$-5 + 3 = -2$

2. Add: $4 + (-1)$

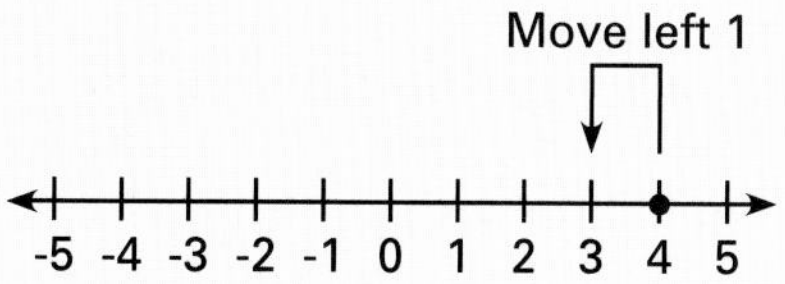

$4 + (-1) = 3$

3. A diver descended 58 feet below sea level to observe a ship wreck and then ascended 20 feet to make some photos. At what depth were the photos made?

$-58 + 20 = -38$

The photos were made at 38 feet below sea level.

3 Practice and Assess

Check

Answers for Check Your Understanding

1. If the positive number is farther from 0 than the negative number, the sum will be positive. If the positive number is closer to 0, it will be negative. If they are the same distance from 0, the sum will be 0.
2. 0; They are the same distance from 0 but on opposite sides, so the sum is 0.

9-2 Exercises and Applications

Assignment Guide

- Basic
  1–3, 5–69 odds
- Average
  5–55 odds, 56–58, 59–69 odds
- Enriched
  10–50 evens, 51–58, 60–70 evens

Exercise Notes

Exercise 8

Error Prevention Some students may use −0 as the opposite of 0. Remind students that 0 is its own opposite.

Exercises 10–19

Extension Have students make up real-life situations in which they would have to find the given integer sums.

Exercises 20–49

Error Prevention Some students will simply add the given numbers without regard to the signs. Remind them that they can use a number line to help them.

Reteaching

Activity

Materials: Index cards

- Work in groups of three.
- On index cards write the integers from −10 through 10, one integer per card. Shuffle the cards.
- Write an addition sign on an index card.
- One person draws 2 cards and forms an addition problem, such as $10 + (-6)$.
- Another person uses the addition problem and tells a story about yardage gained or lost on a football field.
- For example, the quarterback gained 10 yards and then he was pushed back 6 yards for a net gain of 4 yards.
- Take turns drawing pairs of cards and telling an appropriate football story.
- Record the results so that all types of addition problems are recorded, such as $10 + 6$, $10 + (-6)$, $-10 + 6$, $-10 + (-6)$.

9-2 Exercises and Applications

Practice and Apply

Getting Started State each equation that is modeled.

1.

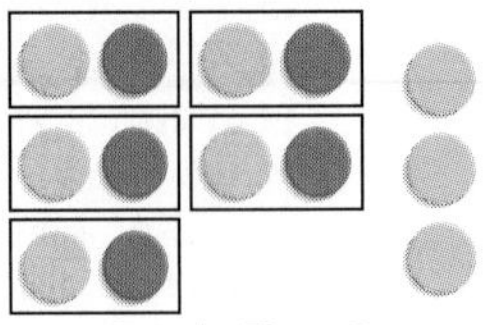

$8 + (-5) = 3$

2.

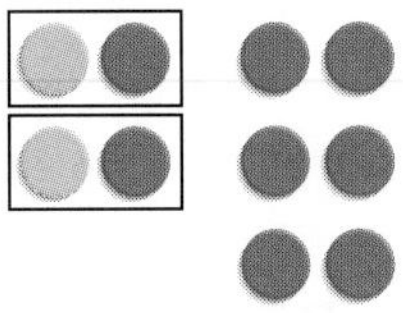

$2 + (-8) = -6$

3.

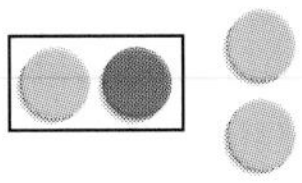

$3 + (-1) = 2$

State each number's opposite.

4. 6 −6 **5.** 12 −12 **6.** −35 35 **7.** −40 40 **8.** 0 0 **9.** −1589 1589

State if the sum is positive, negative, or zero.

10. $10 + 4$ Positive **11.** $-7 + (-3)$ Negative **12.** $-8 + 2$ Negative **13.** $-3 + 7$ Positive **14.** $5 + (-3)$ Positive

15. $21 + (-21)$ Zero **16.** $63 + (-32)$ Positive **17.** $-47 + 35$ Negative **18.** $-15 + 15$ Zero **19.** $-6 + (-22)$ Negative

Add.

20. $2 + (-6)$ −4 **21.** $-8 + (-4)$ −12 **22.** $-2 + 19$ 17 **23.** $2 + (-4)$ −2 **24.** $4 + (-4)$ 0

25. $7 + (-1)$ 6 **26.** $-7 + (-1)$ −8 **27.** $-7 + (-5)$ −12 **28.** $7 + (-5)$ 2 **29.** $-14 + (-3)$ −17

30. $-10 + (-2)$ −12 **31.** $-6 + 7$ 1 **32.** $-9 + 4$ −5 **33.** $-10 + 12$ 2 **34.** $5 + (-7)$ −2

35. $-13 + 7$ −6 **36.** $6 + (-3)$ 3 **37.** $16 + (-3)$ 13 **38.** $-17 + (-5)$ −22 **39.** $-20 + 6$ −14

40. $-8 + 9$ 1 **41.** $11 + (-2)$ 9 **42.** $18 + (-12)$ 6 **43.** $-4 + 3$ −1 **44.** $-5 + 2$ −3

45. $-16 + (-15)$ −31 **46.** $-13 + 16$ 3 **47.** $-5 + (-9)$ −14 **48.** $-6 + (-6)$ −12 **49.** $8 + (-8)$ 0

50. Leona runs a lemonade stand. One week she spent \$7 on ingredients and sold \$12 worth of lemonade. What was Leona's profit? \$5

51. Number Sense Which depth is lower, −157 feet or the opposite of 211 feet? Opposite of 211

52. Measurement Which number is farther from zero, −5 or the opposite of +3? −5

PRACTICE 9-2

PRACTICE

Name ______________ **Practice 9-2**

Adding Integers

State each number's opposite.

1. −2 2 2. 7 −7 3. 14 −14 4. −52 52
5. −16 16 6. 11 −11 7. −23 23 8. 36 −36

State if the sum is positive, negative, or zero.

9. −5 + 5 Zero 10. 9 + (−12) Negative 11. −38 + 5 Negative 12. −3 + 17 Positive
13. 21 + (−9) Positive 14. −2 + 1 Negative 15. 6 + (−6) Zero 16. −64 + 38 Negative
17. 7 + (−3) Positive 18. 17 + (−3) Positive 19. −47 + 47 Zero 20. 43 + (−35) Positive

Add.

21. −7 + 12 5 22. 35 + (−1) 34 23. −10 + (−12) −22
24. −6 + (−5) −11 25. 0 + (−6) −6 26. 50 + (−2) 48
27. 1 + (−7) −6 28. −15 + 15 0 29. 2 + (−9) −7
30. −31 + 3 −28 31. 4 + (−12) −8 32. −23 + 8 −15
33. 10 + (−15) −5 34. 42 + 16 58 35. −1 + (−4) −5
36. −9 + (−14) −23 37. 12 + (−12) 0 38. 25 + 6 31
39. 5 + (−65) −60 40. −20 + 0 −20 41. 3 + (−8) −5
42. −4 + 27 23 43. −8 + 4 −4 44. 8 + 2 10

45. Which height is higher, −83 feet or the opposite of −88 feet? The opposite of −88 feet

46. U.S. business inventories decreased 10 billion dollars in 1991, then increased 7 billion dollars the next year. What was the overall change in business inventories for the two years? −3 billion dollars

RETEACHING

Name ______________ **Alternative Lesson 9-2**

Adding Integers

The **opposite** of an integer is the integer on the opposite side of zero but at the same distance from zero. For example, 2 and −2 are opposites because each is the same distance from zero. The sum of an integer and its opposite is always zero.

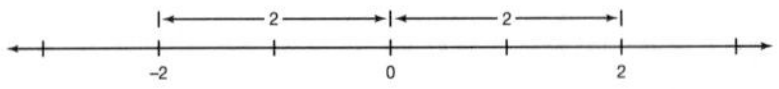

You can use different color counters or a number line to help you add.

Example 1

State the opposite of 28.

The opposite of 28 is the same distance from zero as 28. Opposite numbers have different signs.

The opposite of 28 is −28.

Try It State each number's opposite.

a. 11 b. −32 c. −7 d. 9

Example 2

Add: 6 + (−3).

Count out or draw six same color counters to represent +6.

Count out or draw three counters of a different color to represent −3.

Make as many opposite pairs as possible. Match one of each color counter or cross out one of each color counter in your diagram. You can make three pairs.

Count the remaining counters. There are 3 positive counters left, so 6 + (−3) = 3

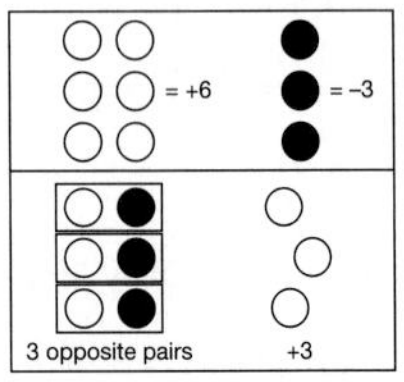

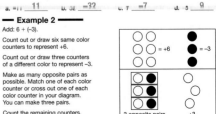

Try It Add. Use counters or draw diagrams to help.

e. −5 + (−4) −9 f. 5 + 3 8 g. −2 + 7 5 h. 8 + (−9) −1
i. −7 + 2 −5 j. −3 + (−7) −10 k. 6 + −8 −2 l. 4 + (−1) 3

Sam wanted to buy a video game system. He recorded the change in price over several months on a line graph.

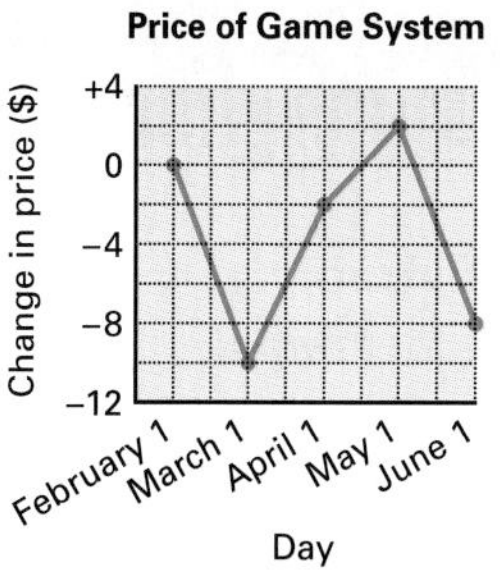

53. How did the original price compare to the final price? Use numbers in your answer.

54. In what month did the price go up the most? March

55. **Test Prep** For their booth at the Spring Fair, Mrs. Alvarado's class had expenses of \$4, \$2, and \$1. The sales at the end of each of the shifts were \$2, \$5, \$6, and \$4. What was their total profit? B

Ⓐ Lost \$10 Ⓑ Earned \$10

Ⓒ Lost \$12 Ⓓ Earned \$12

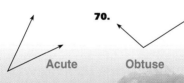

Problem Solving and Reasoning

56. Critical Thinking Jamie earns money by conducting nature hikes. She earned and spent the following dollar amounts: –3, +4, –3, +6, –2, +5, +12. How could you use estimation to determine if Jamie made money or lost money?

57. Critical Thinking GPS Leon had the following test scores to average: 87, 91, 88, 95, and 89. He said, "I guess my average is about 90. My scores are off that by −3, +1, −2, +5, and −1. When I add those numbers, they add to zero. So I must be right." Do you agree with Leon? Explain.

58. Journal Does −5 + 3 equal 3 + (−5)? Use number lines to explain your answer.

Mixed Review

Simplify. *[Lesson 7-2]*

59. $5\frac{3}{4} \times 6$ $34\frac{1}{2}$ **60.** $\frac{3}{7} \times 7$ 3 **61.** $2 \times \frac{1}{2}$ 1 **62.** $10 \times \frac{17}{19}$ $8\frac{18}{19}$

63. $\frac{5}{6} \times 8$ $6\frac{2}{3}$ **64.** $3\frac{2}{3} \times 6$ 22 **65.** $8 \times 6\frac{1}{4}$ 50 **66.** $6 \times \frac{5}{6}$ 5

Classify each angle as acute, right, obtuse, or straight. *[Lesson 8-2]*

67.

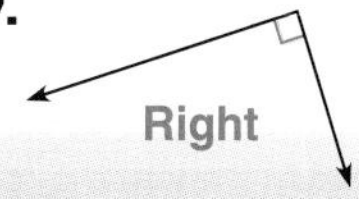

Right

68.

Obtuse

69.

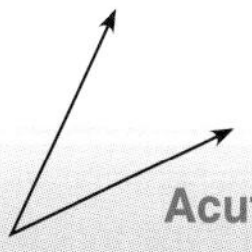

Acute

70.

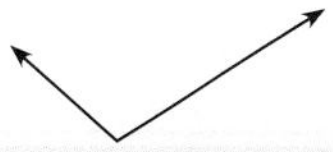

Obtuse

PROBLEM SOLVING 9-2

PROBLEM SOLVING

Name ______________________

Guided Problem Solving 9-2

GPS **PROBLEM 57, PAGE 475**

Leon had the following test scores to average: 87, 91, 88, 95, and 89. He said, "I guess my average is about 90. My scores are off that by −3, +1, −2, +5, and −1. When I add those numbers, they add to zero. So I must be right." Do you agree with Leon? Explain.

Understand

1. Underline the test scores.
2. Circle the integers that describe how far each test score is from 90.
3. What did Leon state? That the difference between his scores and 90 have a sum of zero, so his average score is 90.

Plan

4. What is the sum of Leon's test scores? 450
5. Divide the sum of the test scores by the number of tests to find the average (mean) test score. 90

Solve

6. Add zero to the sum you calculated in Item 4.
   a. What is the new sum? 450 b. The new average? 90
7. Why doesn't your answer change? Adding zero to a number does not change its value.
8. Is the average of Leon's test scores 90? Do you agree with Leon? Yes; Yes.

Look Back

9. Why might this *not* be a useful way to find an average? Could be time consuming if you started with an incorrect average guess.

SOLVE ANOTHER PROBLEM

Ana bowled these scores: 122, 125, 131, and 118. She said, "I guess my average is about 124." Use Leon's method to see if you agree.

(−2) + 1 + 7 + (−6) = 0; so the average is 124; agree.

ENRICHMENT

Name ______________________

Extend Your Thinking 9-2

Patterns in Algebra

The absolute value of a number is the number of units the number is from zero. The absolute value of zero is zero. The absolute value of −3 can be written |−3|.

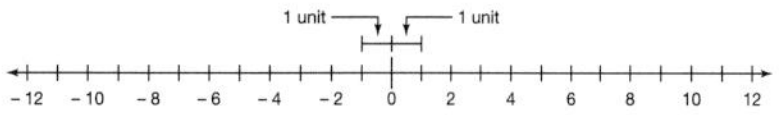

On the number line, −1 is 1 unit from zero, so the absolute value of −1 is 1. This is written as |−1| = 1.

On the number line, +1 is 1 unit from zero, so the absolute value of +1 is 1. This is written as |−1| = 1.

1. Find the absolute value of each number.

a. |−4| 4	b. |+5| 5	c. |−2| 2
d. |+4| 4	e. |−5| 5	f. |+2| 2
g. |−9| 9	h. |+7| 7	i. |−10| 10
j. |+9| 9	k. |−7| 7	l. |+10| 10

2. What two numbers have an absolute value of 8? +8, −8
3. What two numbers have an absolute value of 12? +12, −12
4. What two numbers have an absolute value of 20? +20, −20
5. What pattern do you see in the numbers that have the same absolute value? Possible answer: They are opposites.

Write the next three integers in each pattern. Use absolute value notation.

6. |−8|, |+10|, |−12|, |+14| |−16|, |+18|, |−20|
7. |−1|, |−3|, |−5|, |−7| |−9|, |−11|, |−13|
8. |+1|, |−2|, |+3|, |−4| |+5|, |−6|, |+7|
9. |−5|, |−10|, |−15|, |−20| |−25|, |−30|, |−35|

Exercise Notes

■ Exercises 67–70

Estimation Have students estimate the measure of each angle.

Exercise Answers

53. His original price was \$8 more than the final price.

56. Possible answer: Form zero pairs with a combination of numbers, then mentally add the remaining numbers.

57. Yes; The differences in the scores from their average will always add to zero.

58. Yes; Adding 3 to −5 means starting at −5 and moving 3 to the right, result −2. Adding −5 to 3 means starting at 3 and moving 5 to the left, result −2.

Alternate Assessment

Portfolio Have students cut out ads from magazines or newspapers that illustrate use of integers and make a portfolio entry by creating word problems that correspond to situations depicted by the ads.

▶ Quick Quiz

State if the sum is positive, negative, or zero.

1. 8 + (−9) negative
2. 7 + (−7) zero
3. 10 + (−6) positive

Add.

4. 3 + (−5) −2
5. −5 + (−4) −9
6. −12 + 18 6

Available on Daily Transparency 9-2

9-3 Lesson Organizer

Objective

- Subtract integers.

Materials

- Explore: 2-Color Counters

NCTM Standards

- 1–7

Review

Add.

1. 2 + (−5) −3
2. −8 + (−3) −11
3. 9 + (−4) 5
4. 15 + (−15) 0

Available on Daily Transparency 9-3

Lesson Link

Point out to students that subtraction of integers is related to addition of integers. Since they already know how to add integers, they will extend their understanding to include subtraction.

1 Introduce

Explore

You may wish to use Teaching Tool Transparencies 5: Number Lines and 15: 2-Color Counters with this lesson.

The Point
Students model subtraction of integers by using 2-color counters.

Ongoing Assessment
Watch for students who compare numbers by looking at the numerical parts of the numbers without regard to the signs.

For Groups That Finish Early
When you subtract one number from another and get zero, what must be true? Both numbers must be equal.

9-3 Subtracting Integers

You'll Learn ...

- to subtract integers

... How It's Used

Bank customers add and subtract integers when updating their checkbooks.

Lesson Link In the last lesson, you added integers. Now you'll subtract them. ◄

Explore Subtracting Integers

They Have Nothing to Lose

Materials: 2-color counters

Subtracting Integers

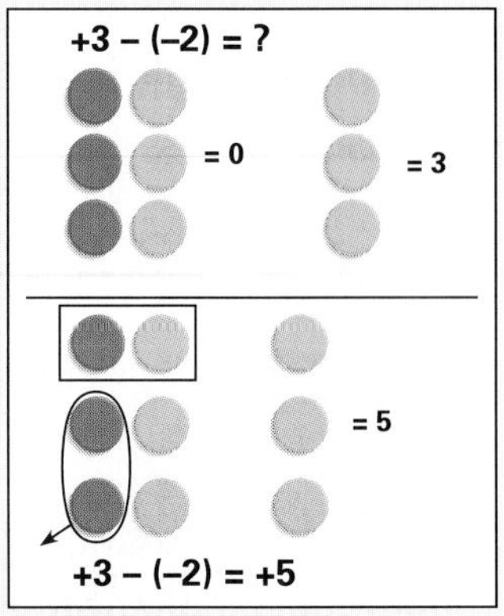

- Count out several zero pairs. There should be as many pairs as the numerical value of the largest number in the problem.
- Count out counters to represent the first number. If the number is positive, put the yellow sides up. If negative, put the red sides up.
- Take away enough counters to represent the second number.
- Remove any zero pairs.
- Describe the number and color of the counters left over.

1. Model each problem, and state the answer.

   a. +4 − (−1) **b.** −5 − (+3) **c.** −4 − (−1) **d.** +5 − (+3)
   e. +2 − (−2) **f.** 0 − (−5) **g.** −7 − (−7) **h.** −7 − (+7)

2. When you subtract a positive number, is the difference smaller or larger than the original number?
3. When you subtract a negative number, is the difference less or more than the original number?

Learn Subtracting Integers

Addition and subtraction are opposite operations. When you take a number and add a negative number to it, the result gets smaller. So when you take a number and *subtract* a negative number, the result gets *bigger.*

MEETING INDIVIDUAL NEEDS

Resources

9-3 Practice
9-3 Reteaching
9-3 Problem Solving
9-3 Enrichment
9-3 Daily Transparency
Problem of the Day
Review
Quick Quiz
Teaching Tool Transparencies 2, 3, 5, 15
Technology Master 46

Learning Modalities

Logical Have students describe various cases in subtracting integers such as *positive integer minus negative integer*. Then have them give examples to show how to find each type of difference.

Kinesthetic Have students make up several pairs of high and low temperatures, some involving negative temperatures. Then have them use a thermometer to locate both temperatures and find the difference between the two temperatures.

Social Students could work with a partner in both preceding activities.

Inclusion

Some students with learning disabilities may have difficulty subtracting integers. Models such as thermometers, number lines, and manipulatives should be used often because they can be very useful in helping students succeed.

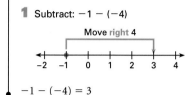

You can subtract integers on a number line by reversing the procedure you used for addition. Find the first number on the line. Move *left* to subtract positive numbers. Move *right* to subtract negative numbers.

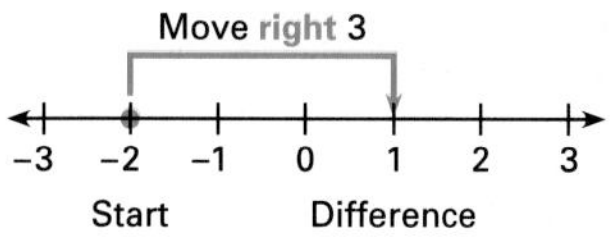

> **Remember**
>
> The opposite of a number is the same number with the opposite sign, as in 4 and −4. The sum of two opposites is always 0.
>
> [Page 473]

Examples

1 Subtract: −1 − (−4)

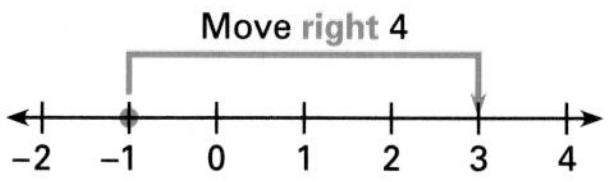

−1 − (−4) = 3

2 Subtract: 1 − 3

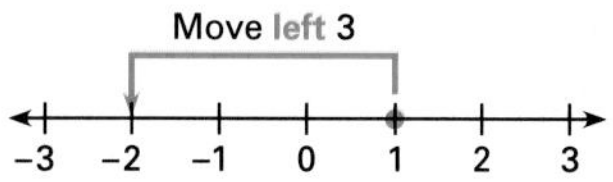

1 − 3 = −2

Try It

Subtract.

a. 5 − 7 −2 **b.** −2 − 6 −8 **c.** 3 − (−1) 4 **d.** −4 − (−3) −1

If you subtract 12 − 20, the result will be −8. If you add 12 + (−20), the result will also be −8. This shows that you can subtract an integer by *adding its opposite.*

12 − (+20) = 12 + (−20)

Example 3

Jennifer earned $14 working in a hydroponics garden. She spent $16 buying shoes and gloves for the job. Find the amount of money she earned or lost.

14 − 16 Write an expression.

14 + (−16) Rewrite the expression by adding the opposite.

−2 Add.

She had a $2 loss.

Try It

Subtract.

a. 5 − (−12) 17 **b.** −8 − (−13) 5 **c.** 10 − (−16) 26 **d.** −24 − (−13) −11

> **Science Link**
>
> Hydroponics is the study of growing plants without soil. Hydroponic methods can be used to grow crops in places without soil, such as deserts or on ships at sea.

MATH EVERY DAY

Problem of the Day

In one roll of Life Savers® there are 4 red, 3 green, 3 orange, 2 white, and 2 yellow candies. If you split open a package at random, what are the chances that you get a red candy? An orange candy? A blue candy? 4 out of 14 or 2 out of 7; 3 out of 14; 0 out of 14 or zero

Available on Daily Transparency 9-3

An Extension is provided in the transparency package.

Fact of the Day

The lowest elevation under the sea is the Mariana trench, the deepest trench in the ocean floor. It is 35,840 feet deep.

Mental Math

Find each product mentally.

1. 5 × 100 500
2. 18 × 10 180
3. 23 × 1000 23,000
4. 670 × 100 67,000

Follow Up

Have students make up other problems to model subtraction of integers.

Answers for Explore

1. a. 5; b. −8; c. −3; d. 2; e. 4; f. 5; g. 0; h. −14
2. Smaller
3. More

2 Teach

Learn

Be sure students understand the procedure for subtracting integers on a number line. Stress that subtraction is the opposite of addition, so they must move left to subtract positive integers and right to subtract negative integers.

Alternate Examples

1. Subtract: −3 − (−7)

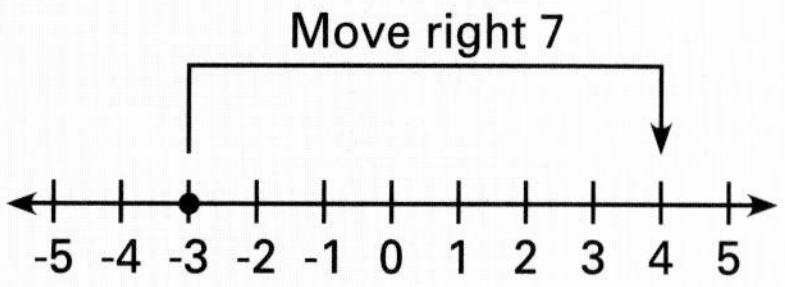

−3 − (−7) = 4

2. Subtract: 2 − 5

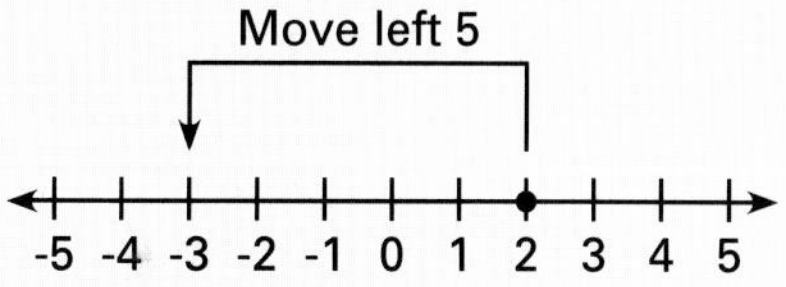

2 − 5 = −3

3. At noon the temperature was 8°F. During the day the temperature dropped 12°. What was the temperature at the end of the day?

8 − 12
8 + (−12) = −4

The temperature was −4°F at the end of the day.

WHAT DO YOU THINK?

Students see two methods of solving a problem. One involves addition of a positive number and a negative number. The other involves subtraction of two whole numbers. Students can decide which of the two correct methods is easier for them.

Answers for What Do You Think?

1–2. Answers may vary.

3 Practice and Assess

Check

Remind students that they can check a subtraction problem by adding their answer to the number they are subtracting. The result should equal the original number they were subtracting from.

Answers for Check Your Understanding

1. Possible answer: Subtraction is the same as adding the opposite.
2. Subtracting a negative number is the same as adding a positive number.

WHAT DO YOU THINK?

Van and Maritess operate a bicycle messenger service. They have one bicycle and $153 in profit. They want to buy a second bicycle from Van's brother. Van's brother is selling the bike for $210, but he's willing to take part of the money as an I.O.U. If Van and Maritess agree to purchase the bike, how much will they owe?

Maritess thinks ...

I'll take our $153 and add a $210 debt.

$153 + (-210) = -57$

We will still owe $57 for the bicycle.

Van thinks ...

I'll take the $210 debt and subtract the $153 that we have. The difference will be the amount we owe.

$210 - 153 = 57$

We will still owe $57 for the bicycle.

What do you think?

1. If you were solving the problem using pencil and paper, which method would be easier?
2. If you were solving the problem with a calculator, which method would be easier?

Check Your Understanding

1. How is subtraction of integers like addition of integers?
2. When you subtract a negative number, why is the result greater than the original number?

MEETING MIDDLE SCHOOL CLASSROOM NEEDS

Tips from Middle School Teachers

I find that the almanac is a useful source for situations that involve integers. I have students find the highest and lowest elevations for various states and then have them find the difference.

Team Teaching

Work with a science teacher to discuss average atmospheric temperatures for the outer planets, namely Jupiter, Saturn, Uranus, Neptune, and Pluto. Have students find the differences between temperatures for various pairs of planets.

Science Connection

In winter, the average temperature on Mars is −125°C. In summer, the temperature sometimes gets as high as 0°C. Temperatures on Mars are colder at the poles just as they are on Earth.

9-3 Exercises and Applications

Practice and Apply

Getting Started State each equation that is modeled.

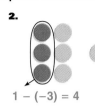

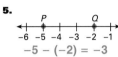

1. 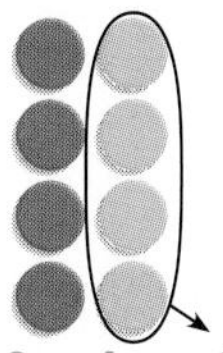

−2 − 4 = −6

2. 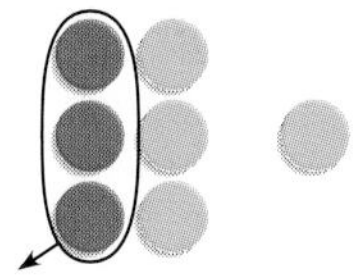

1 − (−3) = 4

3. 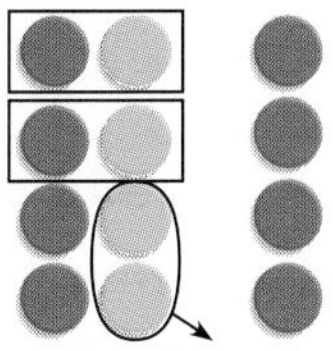

−4 − 2 = −6

Write a subtraction equation that shows the difference between *P* and *Q* on each number line.

4. 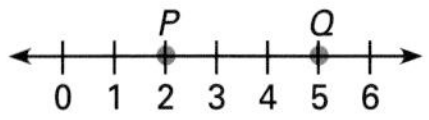

2 − 5 = −3

5. 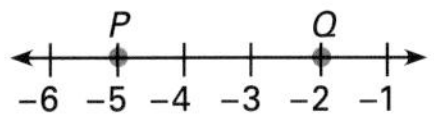

−5 − (−2) = −3

6. 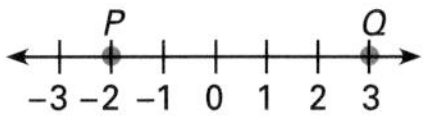

−2 − 3 = −5

Subtract.

7. −7 − 2 −9 **8.** −7 − (−2) −5 **9.** 7 − (−2) 9 **10.** −9 − 11 −20 **11.** 4 − (−8) 12

12. 6 − (−3) 9 **13.** −3 − (−5) 2 **14.** 7 − (−4) 11 **15.** −8 − 3 −11 **16.** −9 − 7 −16

17. 14 − (−5) 19 **18.** 10 − (−9) 19 **19.** −8 − 12 −20 **20.** 16 − (−1) 17 **21.** −13 − (−2) −11

22. −2 − 1 −3 **23.** −5 − 3 −8 **24.** −4 − (−6) 2 **25.** 8 − (−5) 13 **26.** 6 − (−12) 18

27. −9 − (−4) −5 **28.** 0 − (−8) 8 **29.** 9 − (−11) 20 **30.** −17 − (−2) −15 **31.** −5 − 8 −13

32. −9 − 0 −9 **33.** 16 − (−6) 22 **34.** −3 − 1 −4 **35.** 2 − (−9) 11 **36.** 8 − (−9) 17

37. Estimation The lowest elevation on Earth is on the shore of the Dead Sea, 1,310 feet below sea level. The highest elevation on Earth is Mt. Everest in the Himalayas at 29,028 feet. Estimate the difference. 30,300 ft

38. **Test Prep** The temperature outside is −2°C. It drops 5° at night. What is the new temperature? A

Ⓐ −7°C Ⓑ −3°C

Ⓒ 3°C Ⓓ 7°C

Swimmers floating in the Dead Sea

PRACTICE 9-3

PRACTICE

Name ________________

Practice 9-3

Subtracting Integers

Write a subtraction equation that shows the distance between *P* and *Q* on each number line.

1. 0 − (−3) = 3

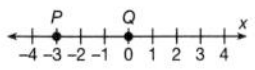

2. 1 − (−4) = 5

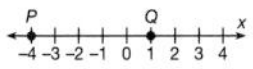

3. −1 − (−3) = 2

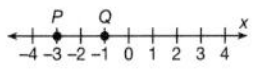

4. 4 − (−1) = 5

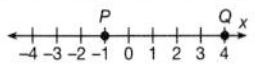

5. 4 − 1 = 3

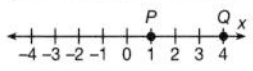

6. 2 − (−2) = 4

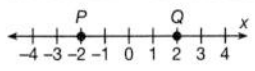

Subtract.

7. −1 − (−15) 14 **8.** 20 − 3 17 **9.** 11 − (−5) 16

10. 20 − 2 18 **11.** −12 − (−12) 0 **12.** −2 − (−4) 2

13. 7 − 13 −6 **14.** 3 − 5 −2 **15.** −6 − 11 −17

16. 9 − 16 −7 **17.** 0 − (−7) 7 **18.** −4 − (−1) −3

19. 5 − (−3) 8 **20.** −9 − 25 −34 **21.** −18 − 10 −28

22. −11 − (−8) −3 **23.** −16 − 9 −25 **24.** 10 − (−9) 19

25. −25 − (−40) 15 **26.** −48 − 0 −48 **27.** −8 − 7 −15

28. 50 − (−8) 58 **29.** −66 − (−10) −56 **30.** 30 − (−42) 72

31. 12 − (−6) 18 **32.** 8 − 18 −10 **33.** 15 − (−8) 23

34. −5 − 1 −6 **35.** 4 − (−22) 26 **36.** −10 − 35 −45

37. 1 − (−2) 3 **38.** 2 − 6 −4 **39.** 6 − 21 −15

40. −3 − 17 −20 **41.** −7 − 4 −11 **42.** 40 − (−12) 52

43. Geography The elevation of New Orleans, Louisiana, is 8 feet below sea level. The elevation of Lake Champlain, Vermont, is 95 feet above sea level. How much higher is Lake Champlain than New Orleans? 103 ft

44. In Fairbanks, Alaska, a typical January temperature is −13°F and a typical April temperature is 30°F. What is the difference between these temperatures? 43°F

RETEACHING

Name ________________

Alternative Lesson 9-3

Subtracting Integers

When you take a number and *subtract* a negative number, the result gets *bigger.* You can subtract a number by *adding its opposite.* For example, 5 − 3 = 5 + (−3) = 2

You can use different color counters to help you subtract.

Example

Subtract: 4 − (−3)

Count out or draw six same color counters to represent +4.

You need to remove three counters of another color. Since there are not any counters of the second color, you need to add opposite *pairs* until there are three counters. Adding an opposite pair is like adding zero.

Once the opposite pair are added, you can remove the three counters.

Count the remaining counters. There are seven positive counters left, so 4 − (−3) = 7.

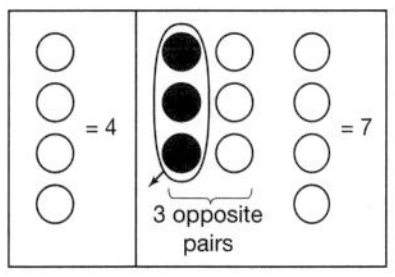

Try It Add. Use the diagram to help.

a. −2 − 5 −7 **b.** 1 − 3 −2

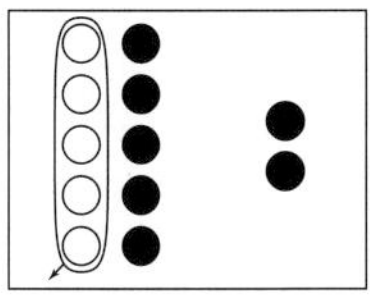

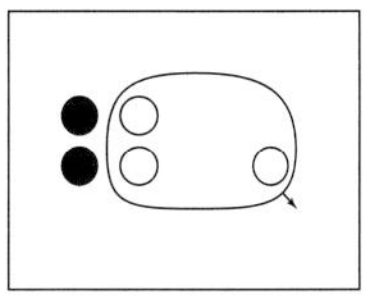

Add. Use counters or draw diagrams to help.

c. −4 − (−6) 2 **d.** 7 − (−2) 9 **e.** −6 − 4 −10 **f.** −2 − (−6) 4

g. 9 − (−8) 17 **h.** 4 − 1 3 **i.** −5 − 2 −7 **j.** 4 − (−1) 5

k. −7 − (−7) 0 **l.** −3 − 1 −4 **m.** 2 − (−3) 5 **n.** +1 − 6 −5

9-3 Exercises and Applications

Assignment Guide

- **Basic**
  1–6, 8–38 evens, 42–50 evens
- **Average**
  2–50 evens
- **Enriched**
  12–36 evens, 37–43, 45–51 odds

Exercise Notes

Exercises 7–36

Error Prevention Some students will add the integers instead of subtracting them. Remind them that when they use a number line to subtract integers, they must reverse the procedure used in adding integers.

Exercise 37

Geography The Dead Sea is a salt lake on the border between Israel and Jordan. Mount Everest is located on the border between Nepal and Tibet.

Exercise 38

Test Prep If students selected C, they added −2 and 5, instead of subtracting 5 from −2.

Reteaching

Activity

Materials: Index cards

- Work in groups of three.
- On index cards write the integers from −10 through 10, one integer per card. Shuffle the cards.
- Write a subtraction sign on an index card.
- One person draws 2 cards and forms a subtraction problem, such as −3 − 8.
- Another person tells a story about money which illustrates the subtraction problem.
- For example, "Tom owes $3 and someone asks him for $8. How much money will Tom owe?"
- Take turns drawing pairs of cards and telling an appropriate money story.
- Record the results so that all types of subtraction problems are recorded, such as 3 − 8, −3 − 8, 3 − (−8), −3 −(−8).

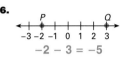

Exercise Notes

■ Exercise 41

Science Besides Earth and Mars, there are two other terrestrial planets, Mercury and Venus. Their surface temperatures are much hotter than on Earth and Mars. On Mercury, the average surface temperature is 167°C and on Venus the average temperature is 457°C.

■ Exercise 43

Problem-Solving Tip You may wish to use Teaching Tool Transparencies 2 and 3: Guided Problem Solving, pages 1–2.

Exercise Answers

40. 6 ft; 10 ft

43. a. +3, −4; Room 12 can have 3 more, Room 13 has 4 too many.

b. 33, 26; Room 14 has 3 too many and Room 15 can have 4 more.

Alternate Assessment

Self Assessment Have students describe what they find most difficult about subtracting integers.

► Quick Quiz

Subtract.

1. 8 − (−2) 10
2. −8 − 2 −10
3. 8 − 2 6
4. −8 − (−2) −6

Available on Daily Transparency 9-3

Use the diagram for Exercises 39–40.

39. What is the distance from the bottom of the ship to the deck? 16 feet

40. How many feet of the ship are under water?

41. Science In a magazine, John read that the average temperature on the surface of Earth is 15°C. The average temperature on the surface of Mars is −50°C. What is the difference between the two temperatures? 65°

Problem Solving and Reasoning

42. Critical Thinking Nicki visited her dad at work and got lost in the building. She started on the first floor. She rode the elevator up 4 floors, then down 2 floors, then up 6 more floors, then down another floor.

a. Write an expression to represent this situation. 1 + 4 − 2 + 6 − 1

b. If Nicki started on the first floor, which floor did she end up on? 8

Problem Solving TIP

Draw a diagram.

43. Choose a Strategy At Kent Junior High, only 30 students can be in each room. Some classes have more than 30 students, and some have less. The principal used a spreadsheet to determine how many students had to be moved.

a. How many students need to be moved in Rooms 12 and 13? What integers should be in the Adjustment column? Explain.

b. How many students are currently in Rooms 14 and 15? Explain.

	A	B	C
	Room No.	Students	Adjustment
1	10	31	− 1
2	11	25	+5
3	12	27	
4	13	34	
5	14		−3
6	15		+4

Problem Solving STRATEGIES

- Look for a Pattern
- Make an Organized List
- Make a Table
- Guess and Check
- Work Backward
- Use Logical Reasoning
- Draw a Diagram
- Solve a Simpler Problem

PROBLEM SOLVING 9-3

Mixed Review

Estimate the measure of each angle. Then measure each with a protractor. *[Lesson 8-3]*

44.
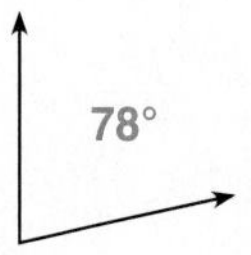

45.
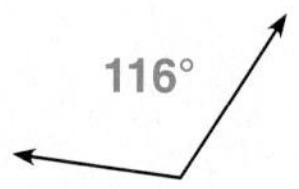

46.

47.
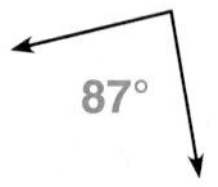

Multiply. *[Lesson 7-3]*

48. $4\frac{1}{3} \times 7\frac{9}{10}$ $34\frac{7}{30}$ **49.** $\frac{4}{5} \times 5\frac{3}{4}$ $4\frac{3}{5}$ **50.** $1\frac{2}{7} \times 3\frac{4}{7}$ $4\frac{29}{49}$ **51.** $10\frac{3}{8} \times \frac{1}{5}$ $2\frac{3}{40}$

PROBLEM SOLVING

Name ______________________

Guided Problem Solving 9-3

GPS **PROBLEM 42, PAGE 480**

Nicki visited her dad at work and got lost in the building. She started on the first floor. She rode the elevator up 4 floors, then down 2 floors, then up 6 more floors, then down another floor.

a. Write an expression to represent this situation.

b. If Nicki started on the bottom floor, which floor did she end up on?

— Understand — Possible answers: Items 6 and 8.

1. Underline the sentence that describes the floors at which Nicki's elevator stopped.

— Plan —

2. Draw a diagram of the building. You may wish to use a vertical number line with zero representing the bottom floor.

Possible Answer:

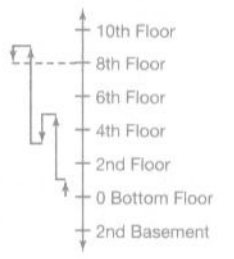

3. Will you use a positive or a negative number to indicate that Nicki rode the elevator *down*? Negative number.

4. Write the integer that represents each part of Nicki's elevator ride.

a. From bottom floor to the first floor +1 b. Up 4 floors +4

c. down 2 floors −2 d. Up 6 floors +6 e. Down 1 floor −1

— Solve —

5. Use the integers in Item 4 to write an expression. +1 + 4 − 2 + 6 − 1

6. Simplify your expression to find which floor Nicki ended up on. 8th floor.

— Look Back —

7. Why was it helpful to draw a diagram? To visualize and keep track of various floors where the elevator stopped.

SOLVE ANOTHER PROBLEM

Ty climbed one flight of stairs. He then rode the elevator down 2 floors, then up 5 floors, then down 3 more floors, then up another floor.

a. Write an expression to represent this situation. +1 − 2 + 5 − 3 + 1

b. If Ty started on the bottom floor, which floor did he end up on? 2nd floor.

ENRICHMENT

Name ______________________

Extend Your Thinking 9-3

Decision Making

Many household and credit card bills come with a *balance due.* This is the amount that needs to be paid. A balance due of $25.00 means that $25.00 is owed to the company.

Last month Ira overpaid his telephone bill. When he received this month's bill, it showed that the monthly charges were $14.95. The balance due was –$15.00.

1. What does it mean that the a negative balance was due? Possible answer: The phone company owes Ira $15.00.

2. Will Ira have to send the phone company a check? No.

3. What will be the balance due next month if Ira's phone charges for the month are $14.95? −$0.05

4. Ira deliberately overpaid his bill. What advantages does he gain by doing this? Possible answer: He saves time because he doesn't need to write and mail the check, and he saves postage.

5. What are the disadvantages in Ira's method? Possible answer: Less money for current expenses, could lose track of which bills are due, loses interest on money.

6. Would you advise Ira to use his method if the bill averaged $1,050 per month instead of $14.95? Explain. Possible answer: No, since the amount is so much greater, he may need the money for other expenses.

7. Would you use Ira's method to pay bills? Why or why not? Possible answer: Yes, for some smaller bills to save time and money.

Multiplying and Dividing Integers

9-4

▶ **Lesson Link** You've added and subtracted integers. Now you'll multiply and divide integers. ◀

You'll Learn ...

■ to multiply and divide integers

... How It's Used

Artisans multiply and divide integers when keeping track of the money they've earned and the expenses they've paid for.

Explore Multiplying and Dividing Integers

What's Your Sign?

Materials: Spreadsheet software

1. You can use a spreadsheet to create a multiplication table for positive and negative numbers. On a blank spreadsheet, enter the following information.

	A	B	C	D	E	F	G	H	I	J
1		−4	−3	−2	−1	0	1	2	3	4
2	−4									
3	−3									
4	−2									
5	−1									
6	0									
7	1									
8	2									
9	3									
10	4									

2. In cell B2, enter the formula **=A2*B1**. Copy the formula across to column J. Then, in each column, copy the formula down to row 10.

3. Study the signs of the products in the spreadsheet. Describe any patterns that you see.

4. Predict the sign of the product of two integers having the following signs.

a. Positive, positive **b.** Positive, negative

c. Negative, positive **d.** Negative, negative

5. Do you think the product of $(-3) \times (-3) \times (-3)$ will be a positive number or a negative number? Explain your reasoning.

MEETING INDIVIDUAL NEEDS

Resources

- 9-4 Practice
- 9-4 Reteaching
- 9-4 Problem Solving
- 9-4 Enrichment
- 9-4 Daily Transparency
  - Problem of the Day
  - Review
  - Quick Quiz
- Teaching Tool Transparency 5
- Lesson Enhancement Transparency 44
- Technology Master 47
- Chapter 9 Project Master
- *Interactive CD-ROM Spreadsheet/ Grapher Tool*

Learning Modalities

Logical Have students make a chart showing the various cases for multiplying and dividing integers, for example, *the product of a negative integer and a positive integer.* Then have them include examples for each case. If students have difficulty, refer them to the patterns seen in **Explore**.

Individual Have students look in magazines or newspapers for examples of items that could be reported using negative numbers. For example, XYZ Corporation lost $27 million last year.

Challenge

Have students answer the following questions:

Name two integers whose product is 10 and whose sum is −7. −5 and −2

Name two integers whose product is −24 and whose sum is 2. −4 and 6

Name two integers whose product is −36 and whose sum is 0. −6 and 6

9-4 Lesson Organizer

Objective

■ Multiply and divide integers.

Materials

■ Explore: Spreadsheet software

NCTM Standards

■ 1–8

▶ Review

Add.

1. $(-10) + (-10)$ −20
2. $(-3) + (-3) + (-3)$ −9
3. $(-4) + (-4) + (-4) + (-4)$ −16

Use repeated addition to write each product as a sum.

4. 3×4 4 + 4 + 4
5. 5×2 2 + 2 + 2 + 2 + 2

Available on Daily Transparency 9-4

1 Introduce

Explore

You may wish to use Teaching Tool Transparency 5: Number Lines and Lesson Enhancement Transparency 44 with this lesson.

The Point

Students use spreadsheet software to look for patterns in integer products and quotients.

Ongoing Assessment

For the formula = A2*B1, some students may not realize that * stands for multiplication.

For Groups That Finish Early

Consider two negative integers. Determine if the following are always positive, sometimes positive, or never positive.

a. The sum never positive

b. The difference sometimes positive

c. The product always positive

Answers for Explore on next page.

Answers for Explore

1. Check student's spreadsheets.
2. See page C2.
3. Possible answer: If the signs are the same, the product is positive. If the signs are different, the product is negative.
4. a. Positive; b. Negative; c. Negative; d. Positive
5. A negative number; The product of the first two numbers gives a positive number, which leaves you with a positive times a negative.

2 Teach

Learn

Alternate Examples

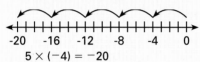

1. Multiply: 5 × (−4)

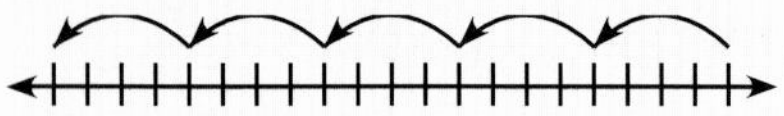

   5 × (−4) = −20

2. Multiply: −6 × (−9)

   The signs are alike, so the product is positive.

   −6 × (−9) = 54

3. Divide: −36 ÷ 9

   The signs are different, so the quotient is negative.

   −36 ÷ 9 = −4.

4. The temperature dropped from 0°C to −12°C in 6 hours. If the temperature dropped the same amount each hour, how much did the temperature change each hour?

   −12 ÷ 6 = −2

   The temperature dropped 2 degrees each hour.

3 Practice and Assess

Check

Answers for Check Your Understanding

1. The signs are the same; The signs are different.
2. Answers may vary.

Learn Multiplying and Dividing Integers

Remember

Division can also be thought of as repeated subtraction. **[Previous course]**

Recall that multiplication is repeated addition. $2 \times 3 = 2 + 2 + 2$

This can help you find the product of a positive integer and a negative integer.

$(-2) \times 3 = (-2) + (-2) + (-2) = -6$

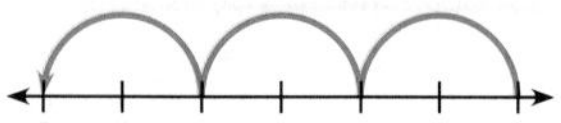

Example 1

Multiply: 3 × (−3)

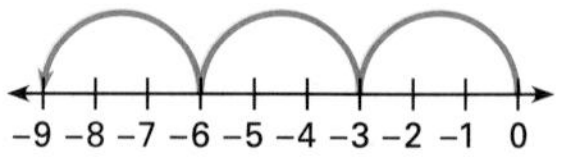

When two integers have *like* signs, the product or quotient will be positive.	$3 \times 4 = 12$ $-20 \div (-4) = 5$
When two integers have *unlike* signs, the product or quotient will be negative.	$-3 \times 4 = -12$ $20 \div (-4) = -5$

Examples

2 Multiply: −7 × (−9)

The signs are alike, so the product is positive.

$-7 \times (-9) = 63$

3 Divide: 72 ÷ (−9)

The signs are different, so the quotient is negative.

$72 \div (-9) = -8$

Study TIP

When solving a word problem, reread the problem and check to see that you answered the question being asked.

4 Over four consecutive hours, the temperature dropped from 0°F to −56°F. If the temperature dropped the same amount each hour, how much did the temperature change each hour?

$-56 \div 4$	Write an expression.
$-56 \div 4 =$ [?] 14	Determine the numerical value of the quotient.
$-56 \div 4 = -14$	Determine the sign of the quotient.

The temperature dropped 14 degrees each hour.

Try It

Multiply. **a.** 4 × (−9) −36 **b.** −15 × (−6) 90 **c.** 12 × 5 60 **d.** −10 × 1 −10

Divide. **e.** −12 ÷ 3 −4 **f.** 24 ÷ 8 3 **g.** 30 ÷ (−6) −5 **h.** −9 ÷ (−3) 3

MATH EVERY DAY

Problem of the Day

At the first annual pet parade, four people marched. Match each owner with his or her pet and give the order in which they marched.

- Bernie's pet was neither first nor second.
- Angelic's pet bird was last.
- Carlotta's pet marched ahead of Bernie's pet, but behind Jake's dog.
- The gerbil marched right behind the cat.

Marching order: Jake's dog; Carlotta's cat; Bernie's gerbil; Angelic's bird

Available on Daily Transparency 9-4

An Extension is provided in the transparency package.

Fact of the Day

The lowest recorded temperature in the United States was −62°C (−80°F) in Prospect Creek, Alaska, on January 23, 1971.

Estimation

Estimate each product.

1. 8 × 39 320
2. 4 × 89 360
3. 3 × 51 150
4. 9 × 73 630

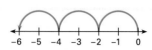

Check Your Understanding

1. What do you know about the signs of two integers if their product is positive? If their quotient is negative?
2. Give a real-world example of multiplication involving a negative integer; of division involving a negative integer.

9-4 Exercises and Applications

Practice and Apply

Getting Started State the sign of the product or quotient.

1. 798 × (−42) Negative **2.** −24 × (−875) Positive **3.** −67 ÷ 46 Negative **4.** −189 ÷ (−63) Positive **5.** −51 × 49 Negative

Multiply.

6. 5 × (−4) −20 **7.** −9 × (−1) 9 **8.** −6 × (−7) 42 **9.** −20 × (−5) 100 **10.** −5 × 8 −40

11. 4 × (−3) −12 **12.** −9 × 9 −81 **13.** −2 × (−9) 18 **14.** 6 × (−12) −72 **15.** −10 × 2 −20

16. −7 × 10 −70 **17.** 8 × (−6) −48 **18.** 5 × (−3) −15 **19.** −8 × 4 −32 **20.** 20 × (−3) −60

Divide.

21. −6 ÷ 3 −2 **22.** 12 ÷ (−4) −3 **23.** 8 ÷ (−2) −4 **24.** −16 ÷ (−4) 4 **25.** −21 ÷ 3 −7

26. −14 ÷ (−2) 7 **27.** −60 ÷ 3 −20 **28.** 9 ÷ (−3) −3 **29.** 4 ÷ (−2) −2 **30.** −18 ÷ (−9) 2

31. 21 ÷ (−3) −7 **32.** −24 ÷ (−6) 4 **33.** −72 ÷ 9 −8 **34.** −30 ÷ 10 −3 **35.** −9 ÷ (−3) 3

Patterns Complete each pattern.

36.	**37.**	**38.**	**39.**
6 ÷ (−2) = −3	−4 × 3 = □ −12	$(-2)^1 = -2$	−9 ÷ 3 = −3
4 ÷ □ = −2 −2	−4 × □ = −8 2	$(-2)^2 = 4$	−6 ÷ 3 = □ −2
2 ÷ (−2) = □ −1	−4 × 1 = −4	$(-2)^3 = -8$	□ ÷ 3 = −1 −3
0 ÷ (−2) = □ 0	−4 × 0 = □ 0	$(-2)^4 =$ □ 16	□ ÷ 3 = 0 0
−2 ÷ □ = 1 −2	□ × −1 = 4 −4	$(-2)^5 =$ □ −32	□ ÷ □ = 1 3, 3
−4 ÷ □ = □ −2, 2	−4 × □ = 8 −2	$(-2)^6 =$ □ 64	6 ÷ □ = □ 3, 2
□ ÷ □ = □ −6, −2, 3	□ × □ = □ −4, −3, 12	$(-2)^7 =$ □ −128	□ ÷ □ = □ 9, 3, 3

40. Sal's business currently has expenses of $4 million and sales of $9 million. Sal wants to triple the size of his business. Express the new expenses, sales, and profit as integers. $−12 million, $27 million, $15 million

GPS

PRACTICE 9-4

PRACTICE

Name ______________________

Practice 9-4

Multiplying and Dividing Integers

Multiply.

1. −2 × 4 −8 **2.** −5 × 6 −30 **3.** 4 × (−5) −20

4. −1 × (−13) 13 **5.** 2 × (−8) −16 **6.** 5 × 19 95

7. −3 × (−6) 18 **8.** 7 × (−4) −28 **9.** −8 × 11 −88

10. −6 × 20 −120 **11.** −3 × (−12) 36 **12.** −4 × 5 −20

13. −7 × 7 −49 **14.** 6 × (−10) −60 **15.** −8 × (−15) 120

Divide.

16. −8 ÷ (−4) 2 **17.** −20 ÷ 4 −5 **18.** −6 ÷ 2 −3

19. −12 ÷ 3 −4 **20.** −5 ÷ 5 −1 **21.** −18 ÷ (−3) 6

22. −45 ÷ (−5) 9 **23.** −4 ÷ (−1) 4 **24.** −48 ÷ 6 −8

25. −6 ÷ (−2) 3 **26.** 0 ÷ (−5) 0 **27.** 12 ÷ (−6) −2

28. 56 ÷ 8 7 **29.** −35 ÷ (−7) 5 **30.** 48 ÷ (−8) −6

Complete each pattern.

31.	**32.**	**33.**	**34.**
−15 ÷ 5 = −3	$(-3)^1 = -3$	−7 × (−3) = 21	−12 ÷ (−4) = 3
−10 ÷ 5 = −2	$(-3)^2 = 9$	−7 × (−2) = 14	−8 ÷ (−4) = 2
−5 ÷ 5 = −1	$(-3)^3 = -27$	−7 × (−1) = 7	−4 ÷ (−4) = 1
0 ÷ 5 = 0	$(-3)^4 =$ 81	−7 × 0 = 0	0 ÷ (−4) = 0
5 ÷ 5 = 1	$(-3)^5 =$ −243	−7 × 1 = −7	4 ÷ (−4) = −1

35. The average daily high temperature in Rome, Italy, typically drops 15°F over the 3 months from July to October. Assuming that it drops the same amount every month, how many degrees does it drop in one month? 5°F

36. Ricky is playing a game in which blue chips are worth 8 points each and red chips are worth −5 points each. Ricky has 7 blue chips and 11 red chips. Find the value of the blue chips and the red chips.

Blue 56 Red −55

RETEACHING

Name ______________________

Alternative Lesson 9-4

Multiplying and Dividing Integers

Use these rules to multiply and divide integers.

When two integers have *like* signs, the product or quotient will be positive.

Both integers are positive:	2 × 3 = 6	6 ÷ 2 = 3
Both integers are negative:	−2 × (−3) = 6	−6 ÷ (−2) = 3

When two integers have *unlike* signs, the product or quotient will be negative.

One integer is negative, the other positive:	−2 × 3 = −6	(−6) ÷ 2 = −3
One integer is positive, the other negative:	2 × (−3) = −6	6 ÷ (−2) = −3

— Example 1 —

Multiply: −8 × 6.

Determine the numerical value of the product. 8 × 6 = 48

Determine the sign of the product. Since one factor is positive and the other is negative, the product is negative. −8 × 6 = −48

So, −8 × 6 = −48.

Try It Multiply.

a. Will the product of −3 × (−5) be positive or negative. Positive.

b. Write the product of −3 × (−5). 15

c. 7 × 2 14 **d.** 4 × (−1) −4 **e.** −2 × (−2) 4 **f.** −2 × 3 −6

— Example 2 —

Divide: −25 ÷ −5.

Determine the numerical value of the quotient. 25 ÷ 5 = 5

Determine the sign of the quotient. Since both integers are negative, the quotient is positive. −25 ÷ −5 = 5

So, −25 ÷ −5 = 5.

Try It Divide.

g. Will the quotient of 72 ÷ (−8) be positive or negative. Negative.

h. Write the quotient of 72 ÷ (−8). −9

i. −32 ÷ 8 −4 **j.** 64 ÷ 8 8

k. −10 ÷ (−10) 1 **l.** −18 ÷ 3 −6

9-4 Exercises and Applications

Assignment Guide

- **Basic**
  2–40 evens, 42–43, 45–55 odds
- **Average**
  8–42 evens, 43–55 odds
- **Enriched**
  12–42 evens, 43–44, 46–56 evens

Exercise Notes

Exercises 6–35

Error Prevention Some students may give answers in which the sign is incorrect. Be sure they realize that the rules for determining signs in the answers are different for multiplication and division than for addition and subtraction of integers.

Reteaching

Activity

Materials: Masking tape

- Using masking tape, make a number line across the floor of the classroom.
- Think of multiplication as "repeated addition."
- Use four related multiplication or division problems, such as 3 × 4, 3 × (−4), −3 × 4, −3 × (−4).
- Walk along the giant number line and show the repeated "jumps" in either the positive or negative direction.
- For example using 3 × 4, start at the origin and make 3 jumps of 4 units to the right or in the positive direction.
- Repeat the process using multiplication and other problems.

Exercise Notes

■ Exercise 42

Test Prep If students selected A, B, or C, they did not realize that all the equations are correct.

Project Progress

You may want to have students use Chapter 9 Project Master.

Exercise Answers

43. −2; Guess −5, actual −3; −5 − (−3) = −2

44. Yes; Possible answer: −6 × 4 is 4 groups of 6 to the left of zero, or −24; 4 × (−6) is also 4 groups of 6 to the left of zero, or −24.

Alternate Assessment

Interview Ask students to state the sign of the product or quotient of each of the following:

8 × 2 positive
−8 × 2 negative
8 × (−2) negative
−8 × (−2) positive
8 ÷ 2 positive
−8 ÷ 2 negative
8 ÷ (−2) negative
−8 ÷ (−2) positive

Quick Quiz

Multiply.

1. 8 × (−5) −40
2. (−6) × (−7) 42
3. −8 × 7 −56

Divide.

4. 18 ÷ (−3) −6
5. (−63) ÷ (−7) 9
6. −48 ÷ 6 −8

Available on Daily Transparency 9-4

41. In 4 hours, the temperature dropped steadily from 0°C to −20°C. Using at least one negative integer, write an equation that shows how much the temperature dropped in 1 hour. −20 ÷ 4 = −5

42. **Test Prep** Which equations are correct? D

I. −10 × −5 = 50
II. −10 ÷ −5 = 2
III. 10 × −5 = −50
IV. −10 ÷ 5 = −2

Ⓐ Only I
Ⓑ Only II and III
Ⓒ Only II, III, and IV
Ⓓ I, II, III, and IV

Problem Solving and Reasoning

43. **Critical Thinking** Toby's game scores were −5, −10, 5, −20, and 15. Toby guessed his average score to be −5. State the difference between his guessed average and his actual average. Explain your reasoning.

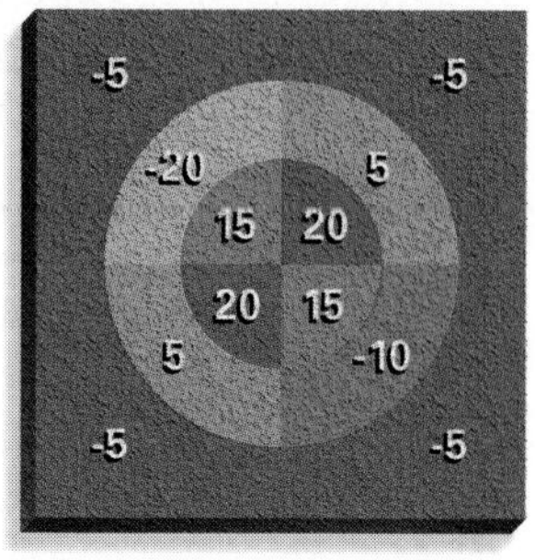

44. Journal Does −6 × 4 equal 4 × (−6)? Use number lines to explain your answer.

Mixed Review

Divide. *[Lesson 7-4]*

45. $4 \div \frac{6}{7}$ $4\frac{2}{3}$ **46.** $1 \div 10\frac{1}{2}$ $\frac{2}{21}$ **47.** $7 \div \frac{3}{4}$ $9\frac{1}{3}$ **48.** $9 \div 4\frac{3}{5}$ $1\frac{22}{23}$

49. $8 \div \frac{2}{7}$ 28 **50.** $3 \div \frac{7}{8}$ $3\frac{3}{7}$ **51.** $5 \div 2\frac{4}{9}$ $2\frac{1}{22}$ **52.** $6 \div \frac{5}{8}$ $9\frac{3}{5}$

Find the measure of the missing angle in each triangle. *[Lesson 8-4]*

53. $m\angle S = 35°$, $m\angle D = 72°$, $m\angle F = \square°$ 73° **54.** $m\angle J = 90°$, $m\angle C = 45°$, $m\angle M = \square°$ 45°

55. $m\angle D = 117°$, $m\angle G = 52°$, $m\angle H = \square°$ 11° **56.** $m\angle B = 19°$, $m\angle N = 24°$, $m\angle M = \square°$ 137°

Project Progress

Gather information about the place you've chosen and list it in a facts chart. Present some information as integers. You might average monthly temperatures, elevations of mountains or depths of lakes, and degrees of latitude.

Problem Solving
Understand
Plan
Solve
Look Back

PROBLEM SOLVING 9-4

PROBLEM SOLVING

Name ______________________

Guided Problem Solving 9-4

GPS PROBLEM 40, PAGE 483

Sal's business currently has expenses of $4 million and sales of $9 million. Sal wants to triple the size of his business. Express the new expenses, sales, and profit as integers.

— Understand —

1. What are the current expenses of Sal's business? $4 million.
2. What are the current sales of Sal's business? $9 million.
3. What does triple mean? Become 3 times larger.

— Plan —

4. Tell whether each number will be positive or negative.
   a. Expenses Negative number. b. Sales Positive number.
5. Which operation will you use to triple each amount? Multiplication.

— Solve —

6. What is triple Sal's current expenses? −$12 million.
7. What is triple Sal's current sales? $27 million.
8. Profit is the amount remaining after expenses are deducted from sales. Write an equation showing how to find the profit in Sal's business. 27 + (−12) = 15

— Look Back —

9. Could you determine if the profit would be a positive or a negative number without doing any calculations? Explain.
   Yes, if sales > expenses, profit is positive and vice versa.

SOLVE ANOTHER PROBLEM

Marky's business currently has expenses of $6 million and sales of $8 million. Marky wants to double the size of her business. Express the new expenses, sales, and profit as integers.
Expenses: −$12 million; Sales: +$16 million; Profit: +$4 million.

ENRICHMENT

Name ______________________

Extend Your Thinking 9-4

Patterns in Numbers

When you multiply two integers with the same sign the product is positive. When you multiply two integers with different signs, the product is negative. What if you multiply more than two integers?

Possible answers: Items 2, 3, 4, and 5

1. Multiply three integers with the same sign.
   a. 3 × 3 × 3 = (3 × 3) × 3 = 9 × 3 = 27
   b. −3 × −3 × −3 = (−3 × −3) × −3 = 9 × −3 = −27
   c. 2 × 5 × 4 = 40 d. −6 × −1 × −9 = −54
   e. 6 × 3 × 4 = 72 f. −2 × −4 × −4 = −32
2. What pattern do you notice in the sign of the product when you multiply three positive numbers?
   It is always positive.
3. What pattern do you notice in the sign of the product when you multiply three negative numbers?
   It is always negative.
4. Predict the sign of the product when you multiply an even number of negative integers. Explain. It will always be positive since each factor can be paired with another and the product of two negative numbers is always positive.
5. Predict the sign of the product when you multiply an odd number of negative integers. Explain. It will always be negative since all factors except one can be paired. The unpaired factor causes the product to be negative.
6. Test your prediction by finding each product.
   a. −2 × −2 × −2 × −2 × −2 = −32
   b. −2 × −2 × −2 × −2 × −2 × −2 × −2 = −128
   c. −2 × −2 × −2 × −2 = 16
   d. −2 × −2 × −2 × −2 × −2 × −2 = 64

Section 9A Connect

In this section, you've seen how earth scientists use positive and negative numbers to study the earth. Now you'll use positive and negative numbers to record information about an earth science experiment.

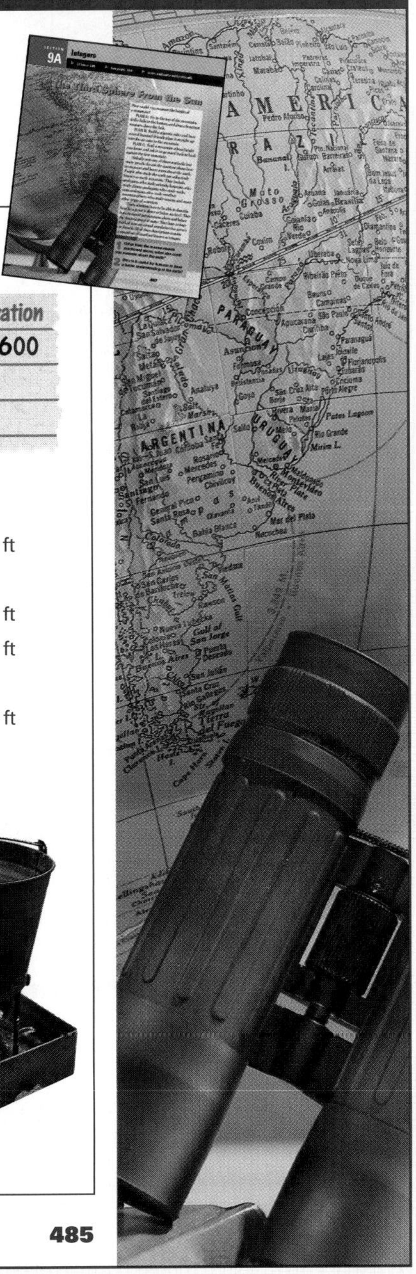

The Third Sphere From the Sun

Becky's family took a two-week hiking vacation. On March 13, they hiked 320 feet up from an elevation of 5280 feet. During the vacation, Becky recorded how much the family's elevation changed.

Date	Change	Elevation
March 13	+320	5600
March 14	-500	
March 15		

1. Copy and complete Becky's chart, using the data below.

a.	March 13	up 320 ft	**b.**	March 14	down 500 ft
c.	March 15	up 460 ft	**d.**	March 16	up 120 ft
e.	March 17	down 240 ft	**f.**	March 18	down 170 ft
g.	March 19	up 570 ft	**h.**	March 20	down 400 ft
i.	March 21	down 130 ft	**j.**	March 22	up 220 ft
k.	March 23	up 40 ft	**l.**	March 24	down 290 ft
m.	March 25	up 200 ft			

2. Becky's family started at an elevation of 5280 ft. On the last day, how many feet up or down must Becky's family hike to return to their starting elevation?

3. Did Becky's family ever hike above 6000 ft? 7000 ft? 8000 ft? Explain.

4. Create a data set of your own that shows a 7-day hike starting and ending at –1000 ft. Explain how you decided what numbers to choose to return to exactly –1000 ft.

Answers for Connect

1.

Date	Change in Elevation (ft)	Elevation at End of Day (ft)
3/13	+320	5600
3/14	–500	5100
3/15	+460	5560
3/16	+120	5680
3/17	–240	5440
3/18	–170	5270
3/19	+570	5840
3/20	–400	5440
3/21	–130	5310
3/22	+220	5530
3/23	+40	5570
3/24	–290	5280
3/25	+200	5480

2. Down 200 feet

3. They never hiked above 6000, 7000, or 8000 feet.

4.

Date	Change in Elevation (ft)	Elevation at End of Day (ft)
Day 0		–1000
Day 1	+300	–700
Day 2	–500	–1200
Day 3	+200	–1000
Day 4	+400	–600
Day 5	–600	–1200
Day 6	+300	–900
Day 7	–100	–1000

Choose easy numbers for the first six days. Determine the elevation on the sixth day, and use that to determine what the change in elevation needs to be to return to 1000 feet on the seventh day.

The Third Sphere From the Sun

The Point

In *The Third Sphere From the Sun* on page 467, students learned about the work of earth scientists. Now they will use positive and negative numbers to record information about an earth science experiment.

About the Page

- The boiling point of water is 100°C (212°F) at sea level. For every 550 feet of altitude the boiling point of water goes down 1°F. Ask students if they think Becky will find any differences in the time it takes to boil water as they hike on the mountain.
- Discuss with students how they will determine the changes in elevation each day.
- Ask students to determine the altitude at the end of one day if they started a hike at ⁻700 feet and walked up 200 feet, or if they walked down 200 feet. ⁻500 feet; ⁻900 feet

Ongoing Assessment

Check that students have created a reasonable set of data and computed the changes correctly for their 7-day hike.

Extension

High altitudes affect recipes and cooking time. Cake and brownie mixes suggest ways to change the recipe to compensate for baking at altitudes above 3500 feet. Ask students to read the cake and brownie mix boxes they have in their homes and report the changes recommended for baking these products at high altitudes. Possible answers: Add extra flour and increase water; Adjust baking time.

Section 9A Review

Review Correlation

Item(s)	Lesson(s)
1, 2	9-4
3	9-3
4	9-2
5	9-4
6	9-2
7	9-3
8–11	9-4
12	9-3
13	9-2
14	9-3
15	9-4
16	9-2
17	9-3
18	9-2
19	9-3
20	9-2
21–25	9-4
26	9-1
27, 28	9-2
29, 30	9-4
31	9-1

Test Prep

Test-Taking Tip

Tell students that problems may be written in order of difficulty, from easiest to hardest. They may consider this question more difficult because they must first determine the correct answer(s) and then select one of the four choices based on their analysis.

Answers for Review

26. Possible answer: She buys 4 books and returns 4 books.
27. Spent $4; Addition, $-12 + 8 = -4$.
28. Lost 12 yards; Subtraction, the sum of 2 and a negative integer must be -10.
29. $-4°C$; Division, $-12 \div 3 = -4$.
30. 30 points; Multiplication, $5 \times 6 = 30$.

Simplify.

1. -9×7 **−63**
2. $25 \times (-4)$ **−100**
3. $-6 - (-5)$ **−1**
4. $12 + (-3)$ **9**
5. $16 \div (-4)$ **−4**
6. $-7 + 2$ **−5**
7. $-2 - (-4)$ **2**
8. $-2 \times (-1)$ **2**
9. $45 \div (-5)$ **−9**
10. $-32 \div (-2)$ **16**
11. $7 \times (-6)$ **−42**
12. $7 - (-6)$ **13**
13. $-7 + 6$ **−1**
14. $-7 - (-6)$ **−1**
15. $-16 \div 8$ **−2**
16. $-8 + (-4)$ **−12**
17. $-8 - (-2)$ **−6**
18. $8 + (-2)$ **6**
19. $8 - (-2)$ **10**
20. $-5 + 9$ **4**
21. $8 \times (-5)$ **−40**
22. $40 \div (-5)$ **−8**
23. $-6 \times (-4)$ **24**
24. $24 \div (-4)$ **−6**
25. $23 \div (-1)$ **−23**
26. Whenever Jill buys new books, she sells back old ones. For each book returned, Jill gets a $2 refund. She pays $3 for every book she buys. How many books could Jill have bought if her bill was $4 after the refund?

Operation Sense For Exercises 27–30, solve each problem, state the operation you used, and explain your answer.

27. Ryan spent 12 dollars to go to a baseball game. He earned 8 the next day. What was the overall change in money for the two days?
28. On 4 plays, the Cardinals lost 10 yards. If they gained 2 yards on the first play, how many did they gain or lose on the other 3 plays?
29. In 3 hours, the temperature dropped steadily from 0°C to −12°C. How much did the temperature drop in one hour?
30. The Board of Directors reported that company stock gained 5 points each year for 6 years. What was the overall change in points for the stock?

Test Prep

Numbers other than zero that have neither a positive nor a negative sign are always positive.

31. On the second day of her descent, a mountain climber started at 12,500 feet above sea level. By the end of the day, she had gone down 2,500 feet. How far above sea level was she at the end of the day? Choose the correct answer(s). **D**

I. −10,000 II. 10,000 III. +10,000 IV. −15,000

Ⓐ Only I Ⓑ Only IV Ⓒ Only I, II, and III Ⓓ Only II and III

REVIEW 9A

Resources

Practice Masters
Section 9A Review

Assessment Sourcebook
Quiz 9A

TestWorks
Test and Practice Software

PRACTICE

Name ________________ **Practice**

Section 9A Review

Simplify.

1. $-3 + 15$ **12**
2. $3 \times (-7)$ **−21**
3. $4 - (-9)$ **13**
4. $28 \div (-7)$ **−4**
5. $10 + (-4)$ **6**
6. -10×4 **−40**
7. $15 - (-6)$ **21**
8. $-100 \div (-10)$ **10**
9. $-6 + (-12)$ **−18**
10. $-6 \times (-4)$ **24**
11. $8 - 21$ **−13**
12. $-63 \div 9$ **−7**
13. $7 + (-11)$ **−4**
14. $12 \times (-3)$ **−36**
15. $-7 - 5$ **−12**
16. The CD Recyclery sells used CDs for $10 each and buys them for $6 each. Bob paid $20 when he bought and sold the same number of CDs. How many CDs did he buy? **5 CDs**

For Exercises 17–20, solve each problem and state the operation you used.

17. Raymond lost $800 on the stock market each month for 5 months in a row. What was the overall change in the value of his stock account? **−$4000; Multiplication**
18. Shelly tossed a ball from the top of a cliff. The ball rose 16 feet, and then fell 40 feet to the bottom of the cliff. How tall was the cliff? **24 ft; Addition**
19. Taylor wrote a check for $18 on the same day his bank paid interest to his account. If his account balance changed $13 that day, how much interest did he earn? **$5; Subtraction**
20. A feather fell 10 feet in 5 seconds. How far did it fall in 1 second? **2 ft; Division**
21. A recipe for bread includes $\frac{1}{4}$ cup of oil, $\frac{1}{2}$ cup of sugar, and $\frac{2}{3}$ cup of milk. Write each measurement as a decimal. *[Lesson 5-7]*

Oil **0.25 cup** Sugar **0.5 cup** Milk **$0.\overline{6}$ cup**

22. The flag of Finland is shown. Does this flag have line symmetry? If so, draw the line or lines of symmetry. *[Lesson 8-8]*

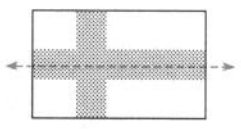

Yes

Section 9B

Graphing on the Coordinate Plane

Visit www.teacher.mathsurf.com for links to lesson plans from teachers and other professionals, NCTM information, and other sites.

LESSON PLANNING GUIDE

Student Edition / **Ancillaries•**

LESSON		MATERIALS	VOCABULARY	DAILY*	OTHER
	Section 9B Opener				
9-5	**The Coordinate Plane**	graph paper	coordinate plane, *x*-axis, *y*-axis, origin, quadrant, ordered pair, coordinate	9-5	Teaching Tool Trans. 7, 8 Lesson Enhancement Trans. 45 Technology Master 48 *WW Math*–Middle School
	Technology	World Wide Web Browser software			
9-6	**Graphing Slides and Flips**	graph paper		9-6	Teaching Tool Trans. 2, 3, 7, 8 Lesson Enhancement Trans. 46 Technology Master 49
9-7	**Graphing Equations**	graph paper	T-table	9-7	Teaching Tool Trans. 7, 8 Lesson Enhancement Trans. 47 Technology Master 50 Ch. 9 Project Master
	Connect	graph paper			Teaching Tool Trans. 7 Interdisc. Team Teaching 9B
	Review				Practice 9B; Quiz 9B; *TestWorks*
	Extend Key Ideas				
	Chapter 9 Summary and Review	graph paper			
	Chapter 9 Assessment	graph paper			Ch. 9 Tests Forms A–F *TestWorks*; Ch. 9 Letter Home
	Cumulative Review, Chapters 1–9	graph paper			Cumulative Review Ch. 1–9 Quarterly Test Ch. 1–9

* Daily Ancillaries include Practice, Reteaching, Problem Solving, Enrichment, and Daily Transparency. Teaching Tool Transparencies are in *Teacher's Toolkits*. Lesson Enhancement Transparencies are in *Overhead Transparency Package*.

SKILLS TRACE

LESSON	SKILL	FIRST INTRODUCED GR. 4	GR. 5	GR. 6	DEVELOP	PRACTICE/ APPLY	REVIEW
9-5	**Plotting and identifying points in the coordinate plane.**			✗ p. 488	pp. 488–489	pp. 490–491	pp. 504, 507, 553
9-6	**Graphing translations and reflections.**			✗ p. 493	pp. 493–495	pp. 496–497	pp. 504, 507, 557
9-7	**Graphing equations.**			✗ p. 498	pp. 498–500	pp. 501–502	pp. 504, 507, 562

CONNECTED MATHEMATICS

Investigation 4 in the unit *Data About Us (Statistics)*, from the **Connected Mathematics** series, can be used with Section 9B.

INTERDISCIPLINARY TEAM TEACHING

Math and Science/Technology

(Worksheet pages 45–46: Teacher pages T45–T46)

In this lesson, students will use a coordinate plane to explore Web page programming.

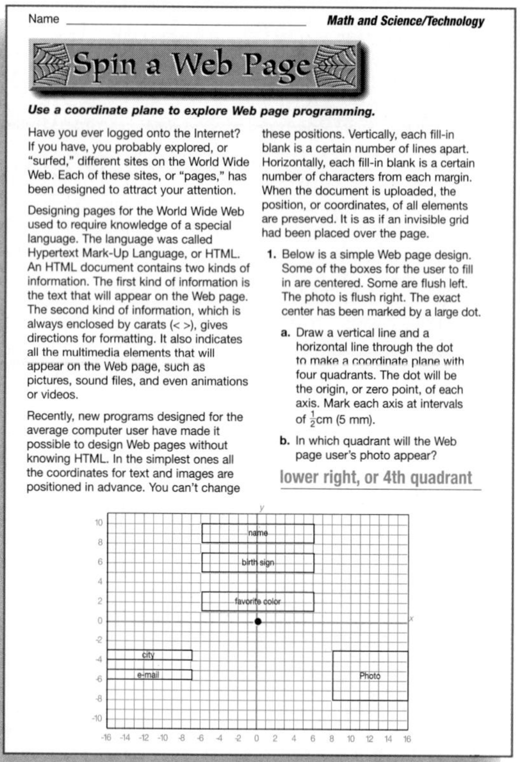

Name ______________________ **Math and Science/Technology**

Spin a Web Page

Use a coordinate plane to explore Web page programming.

Have you ever logged onto the Internet? If you have, you probably explored, or "surfed," different sites on the World Wide Web. Each of these sites, or "pages," has been designed to attract your attention.

Designing pages for the World Wide Web used to require knowledge of a special language. The language was called Hypertext Mark-Up Language, or HTML. An HTML document contains two kinds of information. The first kind of information is the text that will appear on the Web page. The second kind of information, which is always enclosed by carats (< >), gives directions for formatting. It also indicates all the multimedia elements that will appear on the Web page, such as pictures, sound files, and even animations or videos.

Recently, new programs designed for the average computer user have made it possible to design Web pages without knowing HTML. In the simplest ones all the coordinates for text and images are positioned in advance. You can't change these positions. Vertically, each fill-in blank is a certain number of lines apart. Horizontally, each fill-in blank is a certain number of characters from each margin. When the document is uploaded, the position, or coordinates, of all elements are preserved. It is as if an invisible grid had been placed over the page.

1. Below is a simple Web page design. Some of the boxes for the user to fill in are centered. Some are flush left. The photo is flush right. The exact center has been marked by a large dot.

a. Draw a vertical line and a horizontal line through the dot to make a coordinate plane with four quadrants. The dot will be the origin, or zero point, of each axis. Mark each axis at intervals of $\frac{1}{2}$cm (5 mm).

b. In which quadrant will the Web page user's photo appear?

lower right, or 4th quadrant

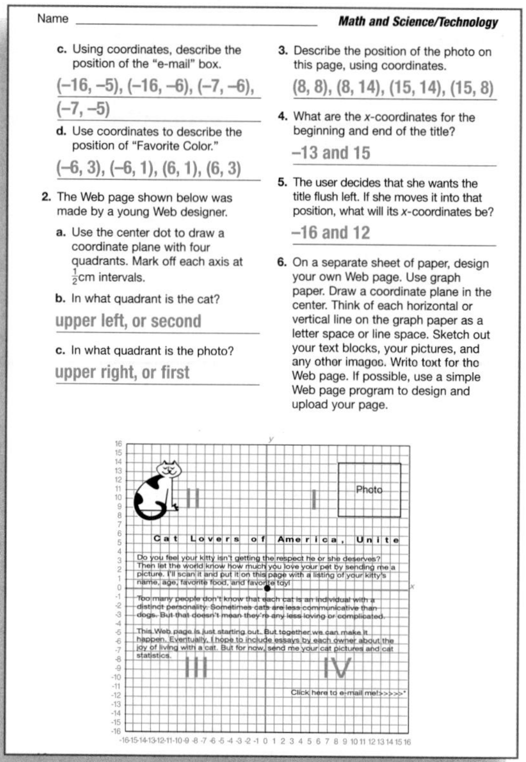

Name ______________________ **Math and Science/Technology**

c. Using coordinates, describe the position of the "e-mail" box.

(–16, –5), (–16, –6), (–7, –6), (–7, –5)

d. Use coordinates to describe the position of "Favorite Color."

(–6, 3), (–6, 1), (6, 1), (6, 3)

2. The Web page shown below was made by a young Web designer.

a. Use the center dot to draw a coordinate plane with four quadrants. Mark off each axis at $\frac{1}{2}$cm intervals.

b. In what quadrant is the cat?

upper left, or second

c. In what quadrant is the photo?

upper right, or first

3. Describe the position of the photo on this page, using coordinates.

(8, 8), (8, 14), (15, 14), (15, 8)

4. What are the *x*-coordinates for the beginning and end of the title?

–13 and 15

5. The user decides that she wants the title flush left. If she moves it into that position, what will its *x*-coordinates be?

–16 and 12

6. On a separate sheet of paper, design your own Web page. Use graph paper. Draw a coordinate plane in the center. Think of each horizontal or vertical line on the graph paper as a letter space or line space. Sketch out your text blocks, your pictures, and any other images. Write text for the Web page. If possible, use a simple Web page program to design and upload your page.

BIBLIOGRAPHY

FOR TEACHERS

Burton, Maurice and Robert, ed. *The Marshall Cavendish International Wildlife Encyclopedia.* New York, NY: Marshall Cavendish, 1990.

Few, Roger. *Animal Encyclopedia for Children.* New York, NY: Macmillan Publications, 1991.

McLeish, John, Ph.D. *Number.* New York, NY: Fawcett Columbine, 1992.

FOR STUDENTS

Bureau of the Census. "Statistical Abstract of the United States." Washington, DC: The National Data Book, 1995.

Knapp, Brian. *Measuring.* Danbury, CT: Grolier, 1994.

Pasley, Sally Grimes. *Finding Your Way.* Belmont, CA: Fearon Education, 1988.

SECTION
9B

Graphing on the Coordinate Plane

▶ History Link ▶ Geography Link ▶ www.mathsurf.com/6/ch9/treasure

A Hunting We Will Go...

In 1795, a teenager named Daniel McGinnis rowed out to Oak Island, off the coast of Nova Scotia. He knew the island had been a hideout for pirates in the 16th and 17th centuries. He noticed a sawed-off tree limb with rope burns and an old ship's tackle above a shallow hole. Two words came to his mind: "Pirate treasure!"

Daniel and a group of friends dug at the spot. They hit platforms of logs every 10 feet. At 90 feet, they uncovered a message saying they would find treasure in 40 more feet. Before they could dig that far, an underground tunnel filled their hole with water—too much to pump out. They abandoned their search.

Since then, other people have spent millions of dollars trying to find the treasure. So far, nobody has found it. Is there a treasure? If so, will it ever be found?

1 **Other than the money itself, why do people search for buried treasure?**

2 **How can you use mathematics to describe the location of something like a buried treasure?**

3 **In what real-world situations is it important to describe a location exactly?**

487

Theme: Treasure Maps

World Wide Web

If your class has access to the World Wide Web, you might want to use the information found at the Web site address given. These interdisciplinary links relate to topics discussed in this section.

About the Page

This page introduces the theme of the section, treasure maps, and discusses searching for buried treasure.

Ask ...

- If you were going to search for buried treasure, what kind of directions would you like to have?

Extensions

The following activities do not require access to the World Wide Web.

History
Piracy was related to times of intense commercial rivalry or bitter religious hostility among nations. Ask students to research the history of piracy.

Geography
Nova Scotia is one of the four Atlantic Provinces of Canada. Ask students to locate Nova Scotia on a map. Have them identify other islands off its coast.

Answers for Questions

1. Possible answers: For publicity, for fun.
2. Possible answer: Use measurements and directions such as north, south, left, right.
3. Possible answers: Locations of accidents, disasters, or dangerous spots to stay away from.

Connect

On page 503, students learn how line graphs can help locate a buried treasure.

Where are we now?

In Section 9A, students graphed and ordered integers and used integers to solve problems.

They learned how to

- order integers.
- add and subtract integers.
- multiply and divide integers.

Where are we going?

In Section 9B, students will

- locate points on a coordinate plane.
- graph translations and reflections on the coordinate plane.
- graph equations on the coordinate plane.

9-5 Lesson Organizer

Objectives

- Plot points on a coordinate plane.
- Read the coordinates of points on a coordinate plane.

Vocabulary

- Coordinate plane, *x*-axis, *y*-axis, origin, quadrant, ordered pair, coordinate

Materials

- Explore: Graph paper

NCTM Standards

- 1–5, 12

Review

Answer the following questions.

1. A friend asks for directions to the mall so you tell them it is 3 blocks away. Is this enough information? Explain. No, they don't know what direction to go.
2. If point *A* is two units from the origin on a number line, where might point *A* be located? −2 or 2

Available on Daily Transparency 9-5

1 Introduce

Explore

You may wish to use Teaching Tool Transparencies 7: $\frac{1}{4}$-Inch Graph Paper, 8: Coordinate Grids, and Lesson Enhancement Transparency 45 with this lesson.

The Point
Students use a treasure map and describe how to locate various treasures by using an informal coordinate system.

Ongoing Assessment
Students may give directions based on moving from treasure to treasure rather than starting at the apple tree in each case.

9-5 The Coordinate Plane

You'll Learn ...
- to plot points on a coordinate plane
- to read the coordinates of points on a coordinate plane

... How It's Used
Forest rangers use coordinates to describe the locations of forest fires.

Vocabulary
coordinate plane
x-axis
y-axis
origin
quadrant
ordered pair
coordinate

▶ Lesson Link You know how to locate points on a number line. Now you'll locate points using two number lines. ◀

Explore Locating Points on a Plane

How Many Muldoons to the Green Monkey?

Materials: Graph paper

You have a map to the 9 treasures of Apple Island. You're at the apple tree in the middle of the island.

Apple Island

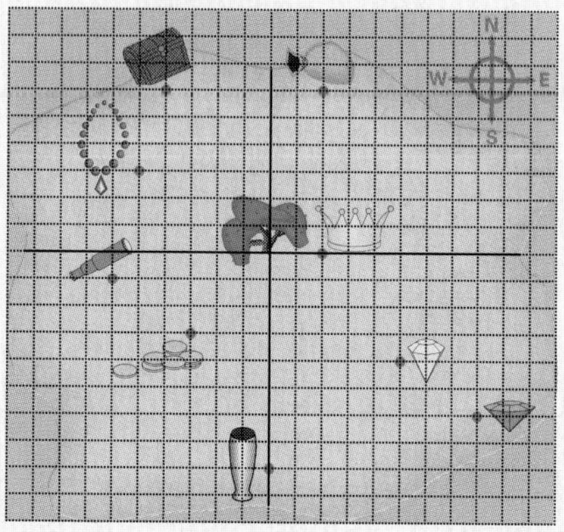

1. Write directions telling how to find each treasure, starting at the apple tree. You may use directions like up, down, left, and right, or compass directions such as north, south, east, and west, or other directions of your choosing. Each unit on the map equals 1 "muldoon."
2. Draw two perpendicular lines on grid paper. Note the location of four treasures of your own on your grid. When connected with lines, the four points should form a rectangle.
3. Write directions for three of the treasures and trade them with a partner. Try to locate your partner's fourth treasure. Describe its location, and explain your method.

MEETING INDIVIDUAL NEEDS

Resources

- 9-5 Practice
- 9-5 Reteaching
- 9-5 Problem Solving
- 9-5 Enrichment
- 9-5 Daily Transparency
  - Problem of the Day
  - Review
  - Quick Quiz
- Teaching Tool Transparencies 7, 8
- Lesson Enhancement Transparency 45
- Technology Master 48
- *Wide World of Mathematics* Middle School: Balancing the Budget

Learning Modalities

Visual Have students bring maps to class and discuss how points are located on the map.

Kinesthetic Have students move their index finger along the *x*-axis and parallel to the *y*-axis to locate a specific point. Also, students could make a coordinate grid on the floor using masking tape to indicate the *x*-axis and the *y*-axis. Then have students walk out the points, walking first left or right, then forward or back for the number of spaces indicated by the coordinates.

Inclusion

Some students may have difficulty graphing in the coordinate plane because they keep reversing the coordinates. Suggest that these students use two fingers to locate the points.

Have students add new vocabulary with examples to their reference books.

Learn The Coordinate Plane

You can use a **coordinate plane** to locate points on the plane. The **x-axis** and the **y-axis** are number lines. They intersect at right angles at their zero points, the **origin**.

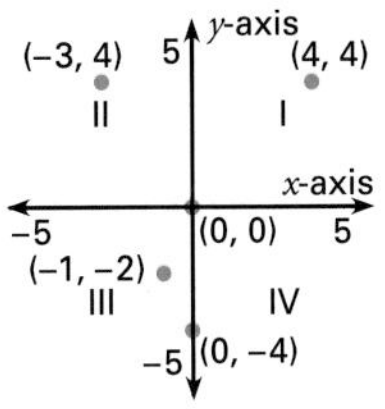

The two axes divide the plane into 4 **quadrants**, numbered I, II, III, and IV.

Any point can be located using an **ordered pair**.
The first **coordinate** tells you how far to move on the x-axis from the origin.
The second coordinate tells you how far to move on the y-axis from the origin.

▶ History Link

The coordinate plane is also called the *Cartesian coordinate plane.* It is named after René Descartes, a 17th-century French philosopher and mathematician.

Examples

1 Give the coordinates of the points.

Starting at the origin, go right (+) or left (−) along the x-axis until you're above or below the point. Then, go up (+) or down (−) to the point.

Coordinates: $A(4, 1)$, $B(1, 4)$, $C(-3, -5)$, $D(0, -2)$, $E(-3, 0)$, $F(2, -4)$

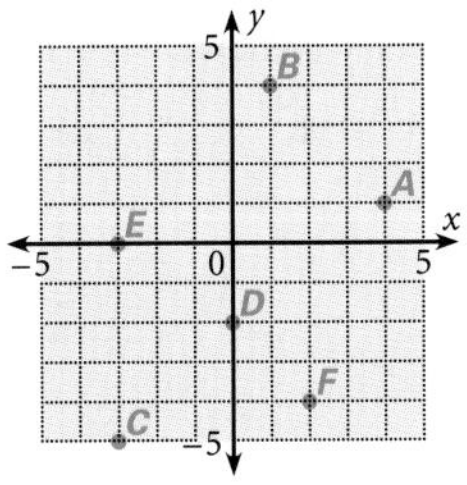

2 On the map, plot the points $M(-2, 5)$ and $N(3, -3)$.

For M, start at the origin. Go left (−) 2 units. Go up (+) 5 units. Mark the point.

For N, start at the origin. Go right (+) 3 units. Go down (−) 3 units. Mark the point.

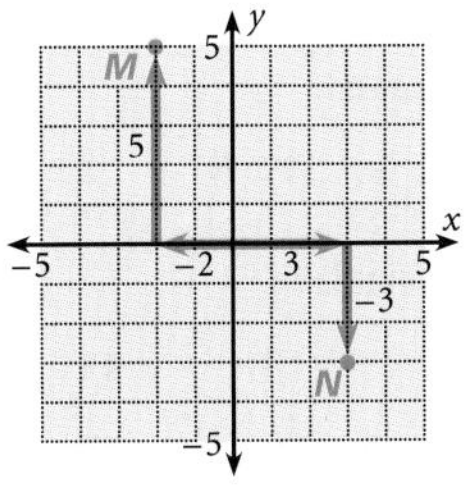

Try It

a. Give the coordinates of the points.

b. Plot and label each point on graph paper.

$H(-2, 2)$	$I(5, 3)$	$J(4, -3)$
$K(0, 1)$	$L(-1, -5)$	$M(5, 0)$

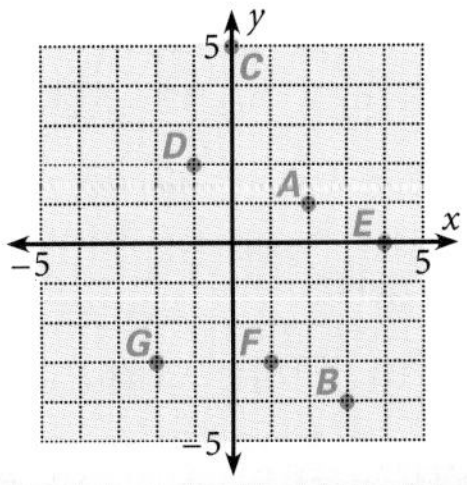

Study TIP

You can remember that the second coordinate in an ordered pair is the y- coordinate by remembering that, in the alphabet, y comes after x.

MATH EVERY DAY

▶ Problem of the Day

Rudy drew two right triangles on a grid. Two points for one triangle were: (2, 0) and (2, −2). Two points for another triangle were (0, 3) and (4, 0). Name at least two points that could be the third vertex of each right triangle. 1st triangle: Any number of the form $(x, 0)$ if $x \neq 2$ or $(x, -2)$ if $x \neq 2$; 2nd triangle: (0, 0) and (4, 3)

Available on Daily Transparency 9-5

An Extension is provided in the transparency package.

Fact of the Day

The grid of parallel east-west and north-south lines that pinpoint places on a map was established about 500 years ago.

Mental Math

Find each product mentally.

1. 8×90 720
2. 30×40 1200
3. 40×500 20,000
4. 700×900 630,000

Answers for Explore

1. Treasure chest: 4 muldoons west, 6 muldoons north.
   Bag: 2 muldoons east, 6 muldoons north.
   Necklace: 5 muldoons west, 3 muldoons north.
   Crown: 2 muldoons east.
   Telescope: 6 muldoons west, 1 muldoon south.
   Coins: 3 muldoons west, 3 muldoons south.
   Vase: 8 muldoons south.
   Diamond: 5 muldoons east, 4 muldoons south.
   Ruby: 8 muldoons east, 6 muldoons south.
2. Answers may vary. Lines should form a rectangle.
3. Answers may vary. Directions to the fourth treasure should be based on the locations of the other three.

2 Teach

Learn

Alternate Examples

1. Give the coordinates of the points.

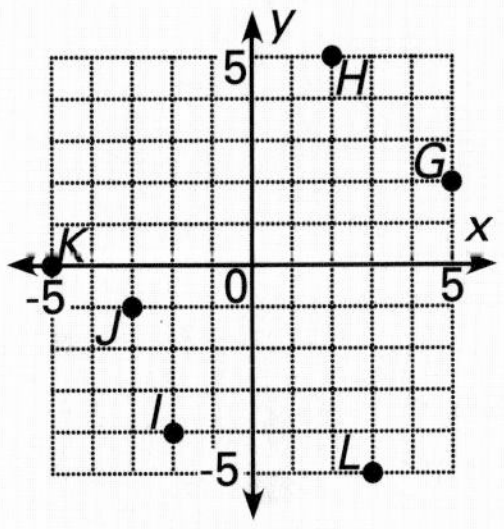

Coordinates: $G(5, 2)$, $H(2, 5)$, $I(-2, -4)$, $J(-3, -1)$, $K(-5, 0)$, $L(3, -5)$.

2. On the map, plot the points $C(-3,2)$ and $D(4, -5)$.

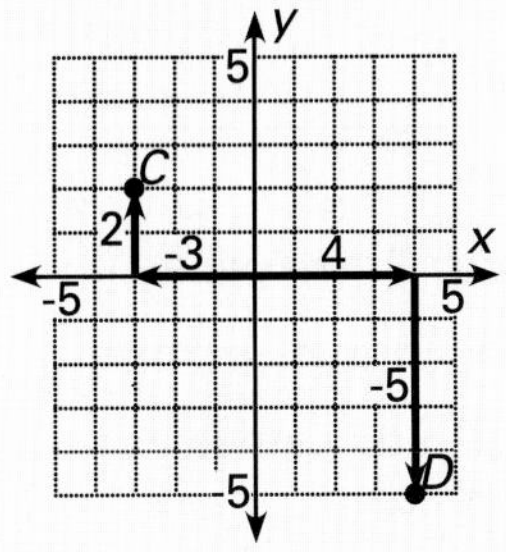

For C, start at the origin. Go left (−) 3 units. Go up (+) 2 units. Mark the point.

For D, start at the origin. Go right (+) 4 units. Go down (−) 5 units. Mark the point.

Answers for Try It on page C2.

9-5 Exercises and Applications

Assignment Guide

- **Basic**
  1–24, 26–32 evens, 35, 37–43 odds
- **Average**
  4–24, 25–29 odds, 31–35, 37–43 odds
- **Enriched**
  9–29 odds, 31–36, 38–42 evens

3 Practice and Assess

Check

Answers for Check Your Understanding

1. I(+, +); II (−, +); III (−, −); IV(+, −).
2. Possible answer: You need to know how far to move horizontally and how far to move vertically.
3. No; (2, 3) is 2 units to the right and 3 units up; (3, 2) is 3 units to the right and 2 units up.

Exercise Answers

15–24.

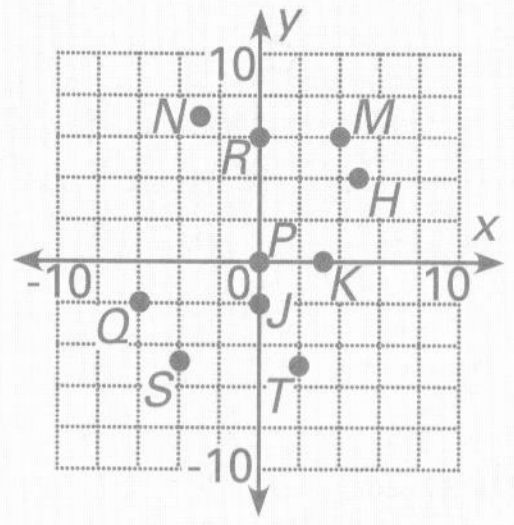

Check Your Understanding

1. How can you use the signs of the coordinates of a point to predict which quadrant the point is in?
2. Why do you need two coordinates to locate a point in the plane?
3. Are the points (2, 3) and (3, 2) the same? Explain.

9-5 Exercises and Applications

Practice and Apply

Getting Started State which quadrant each point lies in.

1. I

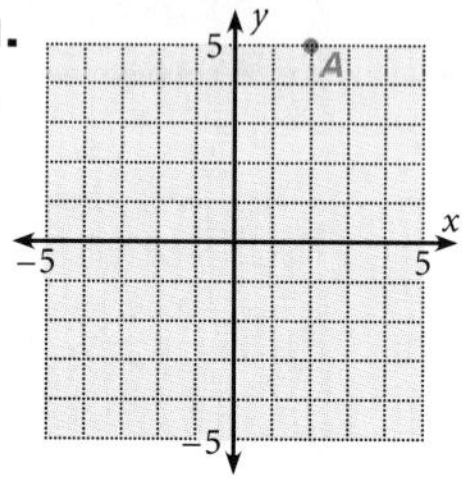

2. III

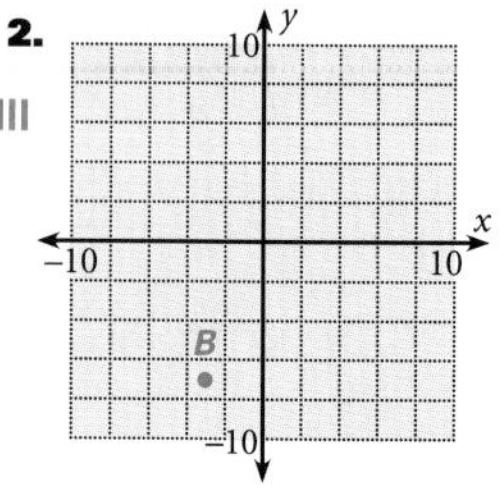

3. III

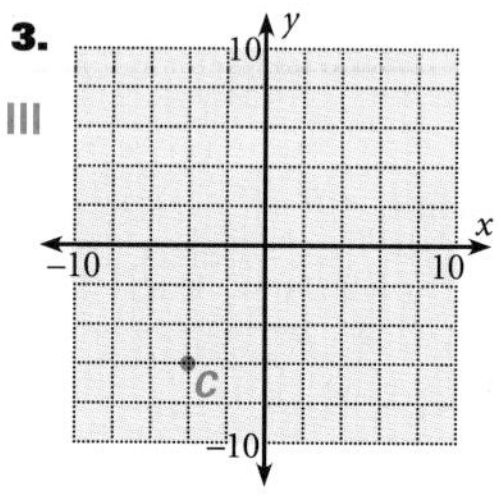

Give the coordinates of each point.

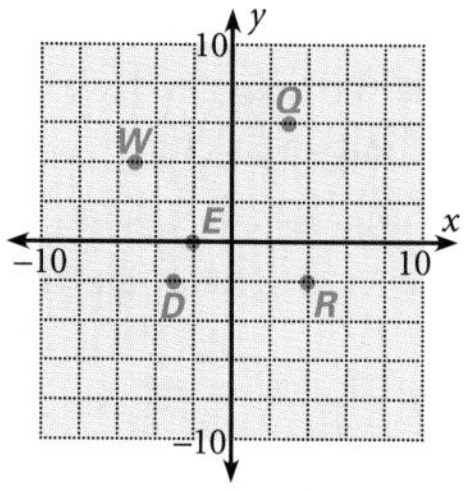

4. *Q* (3, 6) 5. *W* (−5, 4) 6. *E* (−2, 0) 7. *D* (−3, −2) 8. *R* (4, −2)

State which quadrant each point is in.

9. (4, 10) I
10. (−7, 18) II
11. (32, −18) IV
12. (−52, −48) III
13. (6, −45) IV
14. (−13, 17) II

Plot and label each point.

15. *M*(4, 6)
16. *R*(0, 6)
17. *K*(3, 0)
18. *N*(−3, 7)
19. *T*(2, −5)
20. *S*(−4, −5)
21. *J*(0, −2)
22. *Q*(−6, −2)
23. *P*(0, 0)
24. *H*(5, 4)

Describe how to locate each point.

25. (−35, −18)
26. (0, −3)
27. (4, 10)
28. (−52, 63)
29. (88, −23)
30. (8, 0)

PRACTICE 9-5

PRACTICE

Name ______________________

Practice 9-5

The Coordinate Plane

Give the coordinates of each point.

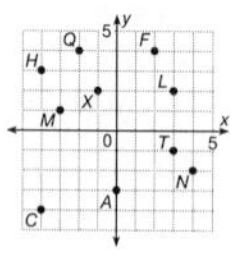

1. *H* (−4, 3) 2. *Q* (−2, 4)
3. *A* (0, −3) 4. *L* (3, 2)
5. *T* (3, −1) 6. *C* (−4, −4)
7. *M* (−3, 1) 8. *X* (−1, 2)
9. *F* (2, 4) 10. *N* (4, −2)

State which quadrant each point is in.

11. (3, −21) IV 12. (−15, −42) III 13. (18, 10) I
14. (−24, 29) II 15. (35, 11) I 16. (−6, 17) II

Plot and label each point.

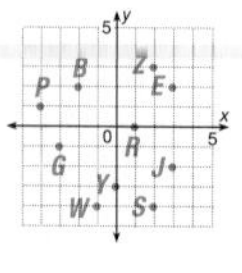

17. *J*(3, −2) 18. *E*(3, 2)
19. *W*(−1, −4) 20. *R*(1, 0)
21. *B*(−2, 2) 22. *Z*(2, 3)
23. *P*(−4, 1) 24. *G*(−3, −1)
25. *Y*(0, −3) 26. *S*(2, −4)

Describe how to locate each point.

27. (21, −36) Go right 21 units and down 36 units from the origin.
28. (−14, −25) Go left 14 units and down 25 units from the origin.
29. **Geometry** Plot these points: (−1, 1), (2, 5), (5, 1), (2, −3).
    a. Connect the points to form a quadrilateral.
    b. Classify the quadrilateral in as many ways as possible.
    Quadrilateral, parallelogram, rhombus

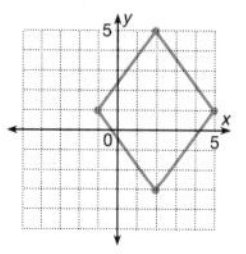

RETEACHING

Name ______________________

Alternative Lesson 9-5

The Coordinate Plane

You can use a **coordinate plane** to locate points on the plane. The **x-axis** and the **y-axis** are number lines. They intersect at right angles at their zero points, the **origin.**

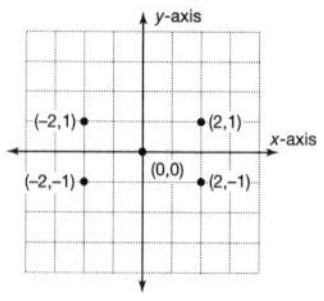

Any point can be located using an **ordered pair.** The first **coordinate** tells you how far to move on the *x*-axis from the origin. Coordinates of points to the right of the origin are *positive* numbers. Coordinates of points to the left are *negative* numbers. The second coordinate tells you how far to move on the *y*-axis from the origin. Coordinates of points up from the origin are *positive* numbers. Coordinates of points down from the origin have coordinates that are *negative* numbers.

Example 1

Give the coordinates of Point *A*.

Start at the origin. Go right along the *x*-axis until you are above Point *A*. You move 3 units *right*, so the first coordinate is +3, or 3.

Then go down to Point *A*. You move 2 units *down*, so the second coordinate is −2.

The coordinates of Point *A* are (3, −2).

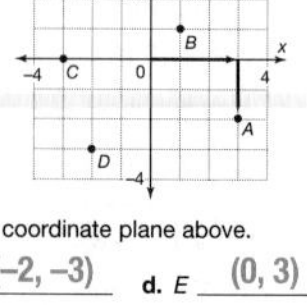

Try It Give the coordinates of each point. Use the coordinate plane above.

a. *B* (1, 1) b. *C* (−3, 0) c. *D* (−2, −3) d. *E* (0, 3)

Example 2

Plot and label Point *G*(−4,3)

Start at the origin. Since the first coordinate is negative, go *left* along the *x*-axis 4 units.

Then, since the second coordinate is positive, go *up* 3 units.

Label the point as *G*.

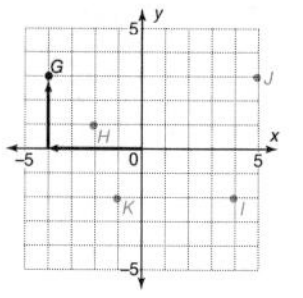

Try It Plot and label each point on the coordinate plane in Example 2.

e. *H*(−2, 1) f. *I*(4, −2)
g. *J*(5, 3) h. *K*(−1,−2)

Reteaching

Activity

Materials: Graph paper

- Work in groups of four.
- One person names an ordered pair.
- The second person graphs the ordered pair.
- The third person plots another point on the graph.
- The fourth person names the ordered pair for that point.
- Repeat the process so that each person has a chance to perform all the steps above.

31. Career Dan is a field geologist surveying drill holes in the Australian desert. He's mapped the location of the holes so that his truck is parked at the origin. 1 (300, 100); 2 (400, 300); 3 (0, 400)

a. What are the coordinates of the three drill holes?

b. Estimate which drill hole is farthest away from Dan's truck. 2

c. How far away from Dan's truck is the third drill hole? 400 units

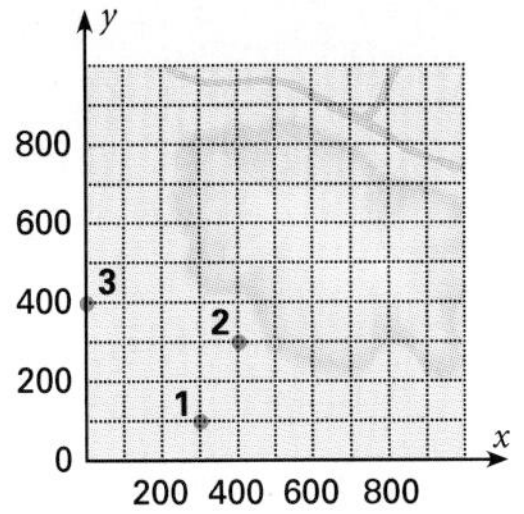

32. **Test Prep** Choose the ordered pair for point *J*. C

Ⓐ (8, −6) Ⓑ (6, 8) Ⓒ (−6, 8) Ⓓ (−6, −8)

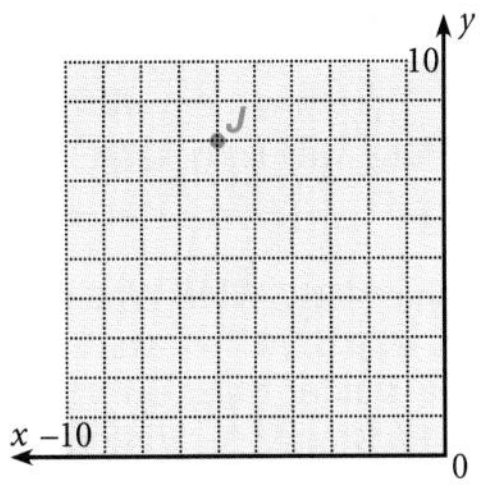

33. Geometry Plot these points: (4, 3), (−2, 3), (6, −2), and (−4, −2).

a. Connect the points to form a quadrilateral.

b. Classify the quadrilateral in as many ways as possible.

Problem Solving and Reasoning

34. Journal What are the signs of each of the coordinates of any point in the first quadrant? The second quadrant? The third quadrant? The fourth quadrant? Explain.

35. Critical Thinking Use the map and the directions given to find the coordinates of the Smallville School.

GPS

The school and the marketplace have the same *y*-coordinate. The *x*-coordinate of the school is twice the difference between the *y*-coordinate of the marketplace and the *y*-coordinate of the gas station. (10, 8)

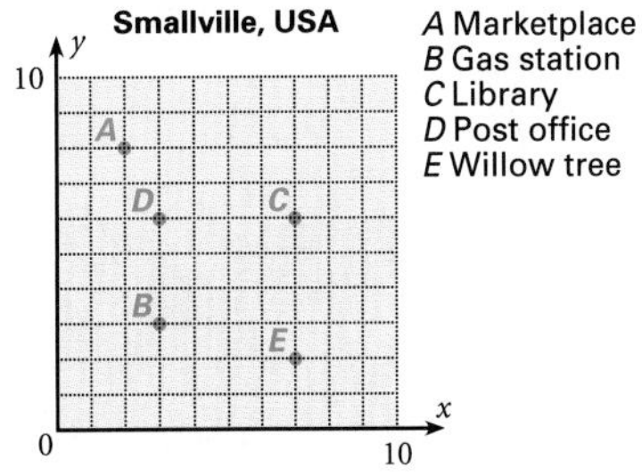

36. Communicate When plotting an ordered pair, why is it important to always use the *first* number to describe the left/right location of the point and the *second* number to describe the up/down location of the point?

Mixed Review

Simplify. *[Lesson 7-5]*

37. $\frac{7}{16} \div \frac{16}{21}$ $\frac{147}{256}$ **38.** $\frac{3}{4} \div \frac{3}{4}$ 1 **39.** $4\frac{7}{9} \div 2\frac{2}{7}$ $2\frac{13}{144}$ **40.** $\frac{4}{7} \div \frac{21}{28}$ $\frac{16}{21}$

State whether the given lengths can form a triangle. *[Lesson 8-5]*

41. 7 m, 8 m, 14 m Yes **42.** 12 cm, 12 cm, 36 cm No **43.** 3 yd, 4 yd, 5 yd Yes

PROBLEM SOLVING 9-5

Exercise Answers

25. Start at the origin. Go left 35 units and down 18 units.
26. Start at the origin. Go down 3 units.
27. Start at the origin. Go right 4 units and up 10 units.
28. Start at the origin. Go left 52 units and up 63 units.
29. Start at the origin. Go right 88 units and down 23 units.
30. Start at the origin. Go right 8 units.
33. a.

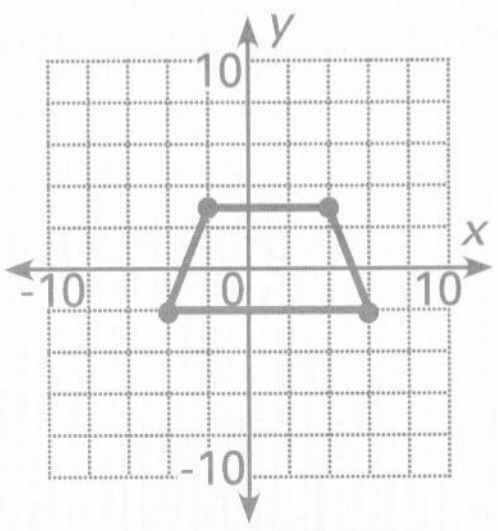

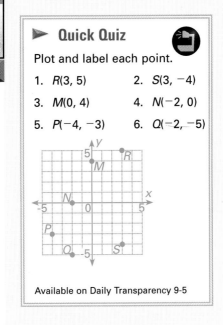

b. Trapezoid, quadrilateral, irregular polygon.

34. (+, +) in I; (−, +) in II; (−, −) in III; (+, −) in IV.

36. Everyone must follow the same order or an ordered pair would not describe only one point.

Alternate Assessment

Performance Have students draw a 4-quadrant grid with all quadrants labeled. Then have them pick two points in each quadrant and label them with the correct ordered pairs.

PROBLEM SOLVING

Name ______________________

Guided Problem Solving 9-5

GPS **PROBLEM 34, PAGE 491**

Use the map and the directions given to find the coordinates of the Smallville School.

The school and the marketplace have the same *y*-coordinate. The *x*-coordinate of the school is twice the difference between the *y*-coordinate of the marketplace and the *y*-coordinate of the gas station.

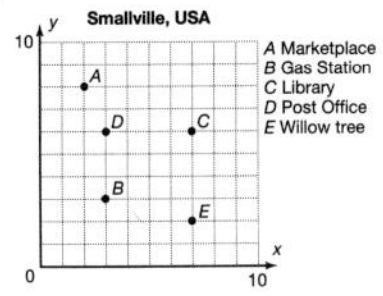

Understand

1. Circle the phrase that tells how to find the *y*-coordinate of the school.
2. Underline the phrase that tells how to find the *x*-coordinate of the school.

Plan

3. Which operations will you use to find the *x*-coordinate of the school? b
   a. Multiplication, then subtraction b. Subtraction, then multiplication
4. The coordinates of the point for the marketplace are (2, 8)
5. The coordinates of the points for gas station are (3, 3)

Solve

6. What is the *y*-coordinate of the ordered pair in Item 4? 8
7. Use the *y*-coordinates of the ordered pairs you wrote in Items 4 and 5 to write an equation for the *x*-coordinate of the school. 2 (8 − 3) = 10
8. What are the coordinates of the school? (10, 8)

Look Back

9. Would it have been easier to find the answer by only writing the value of the *y*-coordinate for each building? Explain. Possible answer: No, it would be more difficult to keep the data organized.

SOLVE ANOTHER PROBLEM

Use the map above and these directions to find the coordinates of the park.

The park and the library have the same *x*-coordinate. The *y*-coordinate of the park is one half the sum of the *x*-coordinate of the post office and the *x*-coordinate of the library. (7, 5)

ENRICHMENT

Name ______________________

Extend Your Thinking 9-5

Visual Thinking

Circle the letter of the figure on the right that completes the pattern shown on the left.

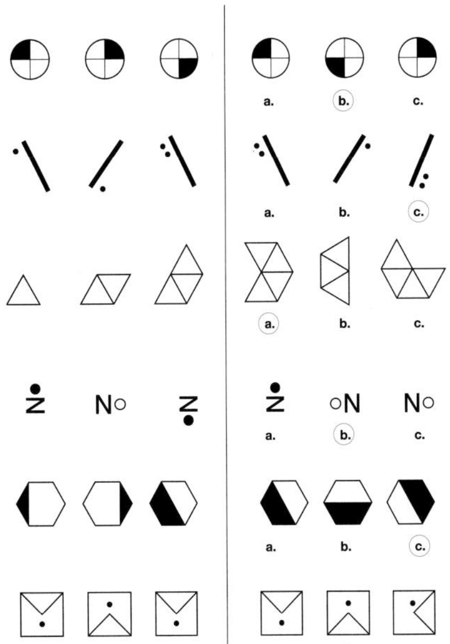

Quick Quiz

Plot and label each point.

1. *R*(3, 5) 2. *S*(3, −4)
3. *M*(0, 4) 4. *N*(−2, 0)
5. *P*(−4, −3) 6. *Q*(−2, −5)

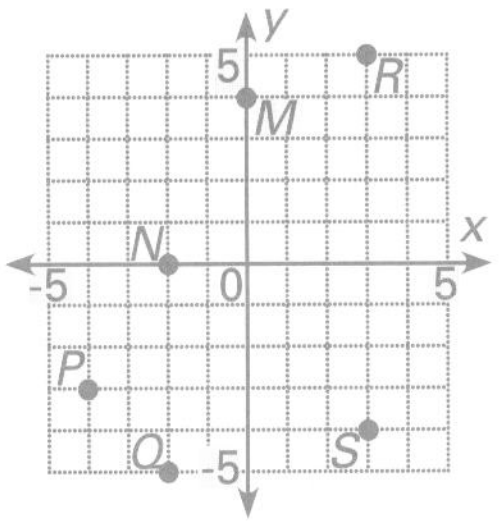

Available on Daily Transparency 9-5

Using Browser Software • Research on the World Wide Web

The Point
Students learn to access the World Wide Web using a URL address or a search engine.

Materials
Computer with access to the World Wide Web.

About the Page

Many computers do not come with built-in access to the World Wide Web. Access to the Web is generally through an on-line company. Be sure your computer has access before using this lesson.

Ask ...

- Have you searched the Web before?
- Describe your experiences and purposes for using the Web.

On Your Own
For the first question, students may generate many thousands of connections. You might want to show them how to narrow their search by adding a second or third word.

TECHNOLOGY

Using Browser Software • Research on the World Wide Web

Problem: How can you find information about buried treasure?

There are many different ways of conducting research to learn more about a particular topic. One way is to search for information on the World Wide Web.

The World Wide Web is a series of web pages. A web page has words and pictures about a particular topic. Every page has a URL address. URL stands for Uniform Resource Locator.

1. **If you know the URL address for the page you want to reach, you can type it into your browser software and press the return key.**

   The software will try to connect you to that page. Sometimes, a page cannot be reached because the computer connected to that page isn't working, or the page no longer exists.

2. **You can also use a *search engine.* The search engine will ask you for a key word you want to research, such as *treasure.* It will list descriptions of the pages related to the key word. You can click on a description to go to the page it describes.**

3. **Many pages have *links* to other pages with related information. A link appears as an underlined word or phrase, and it is usually in a different color. You can go to these pages by clicking on the link.**

ON YOUR OWN

- Try to find information about one of the following topics: pirates, explorers, archaeology, Antarctica.
- Use the World Wide Web to research a topic of your own choice.

Graphing Slides and Flips

9-6

▶ Lesson Link In the last chapter, you learned about translations and reflections. Now you'll graph translations and reflections on the coordinate plane. ◀

Explore Slides and Flips

The Temple of the Trapezoids

Materials: Graph paper

A team of treasure hunters knows the size, shape, and orientation of the ancient Temple of the Trapezoids. Unfortunately, they do not know where on Polygon's Island the temple is located.

1. The map shows the temple floor in one possible location. Copy the sketch onto graph paper and give the coordinates of its four corners.

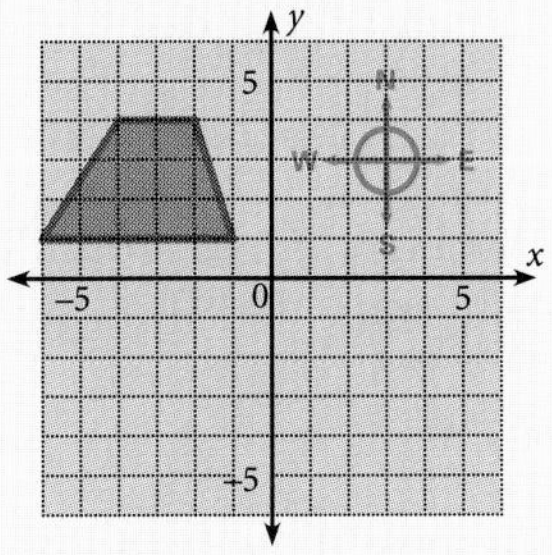

2. Another possible location for the temple is where every point from the first location is moved 6 units east and 3 units south. Graph the temple at this possible location and give the coordinates of its corners.

3. The corners of the north wall of the actual Temple of the Trapezoids are located at (18, 23) and (20, 23). How can you find the coordinates of the other two corners without graphing the temple? What are they?

Learn Graphing Slides and Flips

Recall that a *translation* slides a figure to a new position without rotating the figure. You can graph translations on a coordinate grid. To translate $\triangle ABC$, move each vertex right 4 units and up 4 units. The new triangle is $\triangle A'B'C'$, read as "triangle A prime B prime C prime."

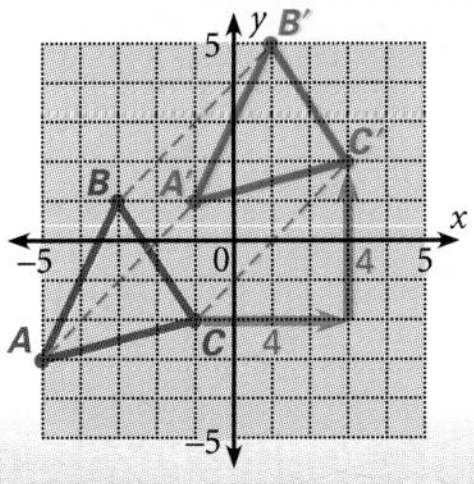

You'll Learn ...

■ to graph translations and reflections on the coordinate plane

... How It's Used

Computer animators slide and flip images on a coordinate plane when creating an animated sequence.

9-6 Lesson Organizer

Objective

- Graph translations and reflections on the coordinate plane.

Materials

- Explore: Graph paper

NCTM Standards

- 1–5, 7, 12

▶ Review

Answer these questions.

1. If the point at (−4, 2) is shifted 3 units to the right and 4 units up, what is the new location? (−1, 6)
2. What point is directly across the *y*-axis from (−4, 2) and the same distance from the *y*-axis? (4, 2)
3. What point is directly across the *x*-axis from (−4, 2) and the same distance from the *x*-axis? (−4, −2)

Available on Daily Transparency 9-6

1 Introduce

Explore

You may wish to use Teaching Tool Transparencies 7: $\frac{1}{4}$-Inch Graph Paper, 8: Coordinate Grids, and Lesson Enhancement Transparency 46 with this lesson.

The Point

Students know the size, shape, and orientation of a trapezoid, but not the location. Using clues, they discover the exact location.

Ongoing Assessment

Students may not recall the definition of a trapezoid. Point out that one pair of sides must be parallel.

For Groups That Finish Early

The corners of the north wall of the temple are at (0, 0) and (2, 0). Find the coordinates of the other corners? (−2, −3) and (3, −3)

Answers for Explore on next page

MEETING INDIVIDUAL NEEDS

Resources

9-6 Practice
9-6 Reteaching
9-6 Problem Solving
9-6 Enrichment
9-6 Daily Transparency
  Problem of the Day
  Review
  Quick Quiz
Teaching Tool Transparencies 2, 3, 7, 8
Lesson Enhancement Transparency 46
Technology Master 49

Learning Modalities

Visual Have students find photos in newspapers or magazines to illustrate translations and reflections of figures.

Kinesthetic Have students use cut-out geometric figures such as squares, triangles, or rectangles and then place them on a coordinate grid. Next have them write coordinates for the vertices of the figures and then slide the figures to a new position and write the coordinates for the image.

Challenge

Have students research the art of M.C. Escher and create their own Escher-like drawing.

Answers for Explore

1. (−6, 1), (−4, 4), (−2, 4), (−1, 1)
2. (0, −2), (2, 1), (4, 1), (5, −2)
3. Add 22 units to the original x-coordinates and add 19 units to the original y-coordinates; (16, 20) and (21, 20).

2 Teach

Learn

Students may need to review earlier lessons in which translations and reflections were discussed.

Alternate Examples

1. Create $\Delta D'E'F'$ by translating ΔDEF 4 units right and 3 units down. Give the coordinates of D', E', and F'. Describe any patterns you find.

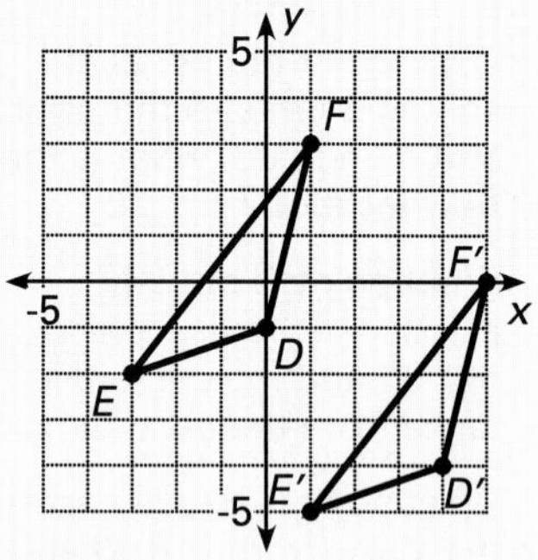

$D(0, -1) \rightarrow D'(0 + 4, -1 - 3) = D'(4, -4)$

$E(-3, -2) \rightarrow E'(-3 + 4, -2 - 3) = E'(1, -5)$

$F(1, 3) \rightarrow F'(1 + 4, 3 - 3) = F'(5, 0)$

ΔDEF has coordinates $D(0, -1)$, $E(-3, -2)$, and $F(1, 3)$. $\Delta D'E'F'$ has coordinates $D'(4, -4)$, $E'(1, -5)$, and $F'(5, 0)$.

The x-coordinates of $\Delta D'E'F'$ are 4 greater than the x-coordinates of ΔDEF. The y-coordinates of $\Delta D'E'F'$ are 3 less than the y-coordinates of ΔDEF.

Example 1

Create $\triangle A'B'C'$ by translating $\triangle ABC$ 5 units left and 3 units up. Give the coordinates of A', B', and C'. Describe any patterns you find.

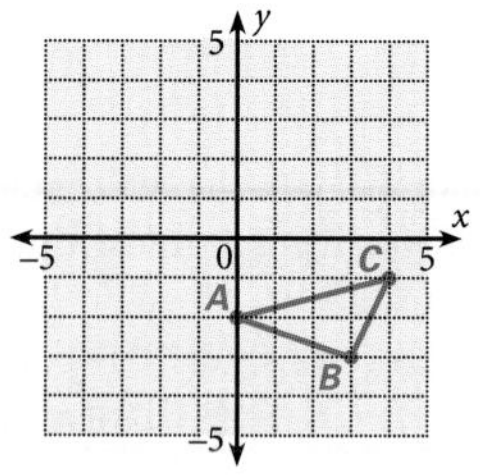

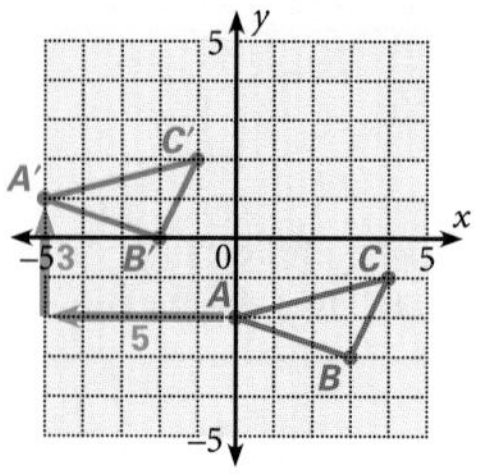

$\triangle ABC$ has coordinates $A(0, -2)$, $B(3, -3)$, and $C(4, -1)$.

$\triangle A'B'C'$ has coordinates $A'(-5, 1)$, $B'(-2, 0)$, and $C'(-1, 2)$.

Notice that the x-coordinates of $\triangle A'B'C'$ are 5 *less than* the x-coordinates of $\triangle ABC$. That's because $\triangle ABC$ was translated 5 units *left* (−).

The y-coordinates of $\triangle A'B'C'$ are 3 *more than* the y-coordinates of $\triangle ABC$. That's because $\triangle ABC$ was translated 3 units *up* (+).

left 5 up 3

↓ ↓

$A(0, -2) \rightarrow A'(0 - 5, -2 + 3) = A'(-5, 1)$

$B(3, -3) \rightarrow B'(3 - 5, -3 + 3) = B'(-2, 0)$

$C(4, -1) \rightarrow C'(4 - 5, -1 + 3) = C'(-1, 2)$

Try It

On the map, create $\triangle L'M'N'$ by translating $\triangle LMN$ 6 units right and 4 units down. Give the coordinates of L', M', and N'. Describe any patterns you find.
$L'(1, -2)$; $M'(2, 0)$; $N'(6, -3)$

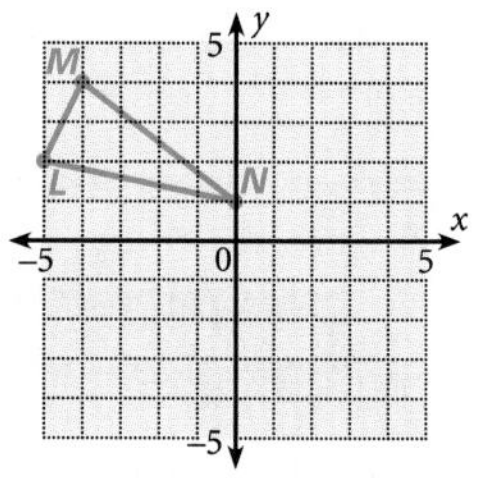

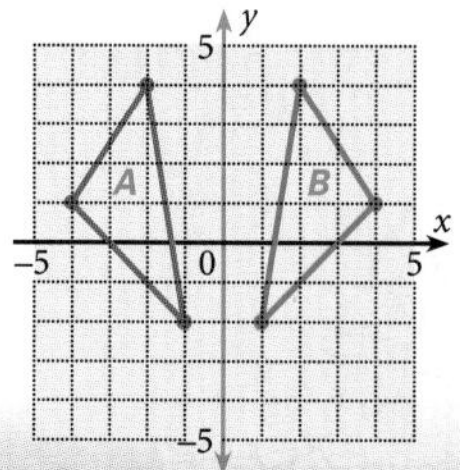

Recall that a *reflection* "flips" a shape over a line of symmetry. $\triangle A$ in the figure has been reflected across the y-axis to give $\triangle B$. The y-axis is the line of symmetry. $\triangle A$ and $\triangle B$ are reflections of each other.

▶ History Link

Early mapmakers in medieval Europe put mistakes on their maps on purpose. That way, if the map ever fell into enemy hands, the enemy would be misinformed about the lay of the land.

MATH EVERY DAY

▶ Problem of the Day

On Tuesday, the temperature outside rose 20° between noon and 4 P.M. At 5 P.M. the temperature was 8° colder than at 4 P.M. Each hour, between 5 P.M. and 9 P.M. the temperature dropped 3°. If the temperature at 9 P.M. was −12° F, what was the temperature at noon? 12° F

Available on Daily Transparency 9-6

An Extension is provided in the transparency package.

Fact of the Day

Satellite photographs are now often used to make maps. A person who makes or studies maps is called a cartographer.

Estimation

Estimate each quotient.

1. 729 ÷ 8 90
2. 3210 ÷ 4 800
3. 562 ÷ 71 8
4. 4902 ÷ 701 7

Example 2

Create $\triangle R'S'T'$ by reflecting $\triangle RST$ across the x-axis. Give the coordinates of R', S', and T'. Describe any patterns you find.

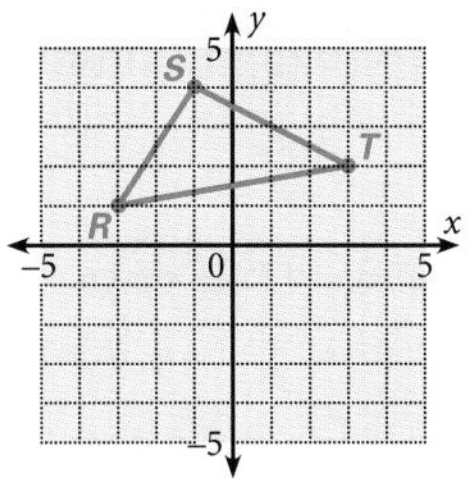

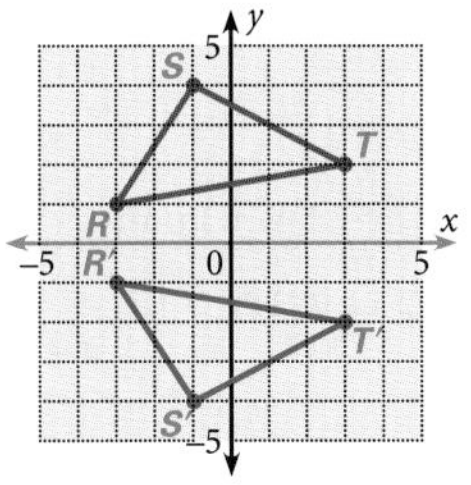

$\triangle RST$ has coordinates $R(-3, 1)$, $S(-1, 4)$, and $T(3, 2)$.

$\triangle R'S'T'$ has coordinates $R'(-3, -1)$, $S'(-1, -4)$, and $T'(3, -2)$.

Notice that the x-coordinates of $\triangle RST$ are the same as the x-coordinates of $\triangle R'S'T'$. That's because a reflection across the x-axis does not move the triangle left or right.

Reflections across the x-axis change each y-coordinate into its *opposite.*

$R(-3, \mathbf{1}) \rightarrow R'(-3, \mathbf{-1})$ $\quad S(-1, \mathbf{4}) \rightarrow S'(-1, \mathbf{-4})$ $\quad T(3, \mathbf{2}) \rightarrow T'(3, \mathbf{-2})$

↑ ↑ ↑ ↑ ↑ ↑

opposite **opposite** **opposite**

Try It

Create $\triangle X'Y'Z'$ by reflecting $\triangle XYZ$ across the y-axis. Give the coordinates of X', Y', and Z'. Describe any patterns you find.
$X'(-1, -1)$; $Y'(-3, 4)$; $Z'(-5, 1)$

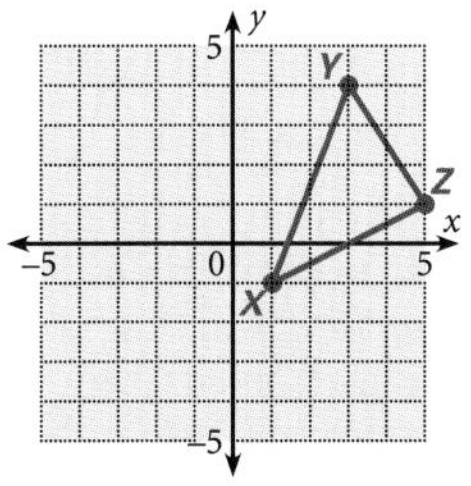

Remember

In transformational geometry, there are three types of movement for a shape: reflection, rotation, and translation.

[Pages 444–456]

Check Your Understanding

1. How are the coordinates of a point changed if the point is translated up or down? Right or left?
2. How are the coordinates of a point changed if the point is reflected across the x-axis? Across the y-axis?

Alternate Examples

2. Create $\Delta P'Q'R'$ by reflecting ΔPQR over the y-axis. Give the coordinates of P', Q', and R'. Describe any patterns you find.

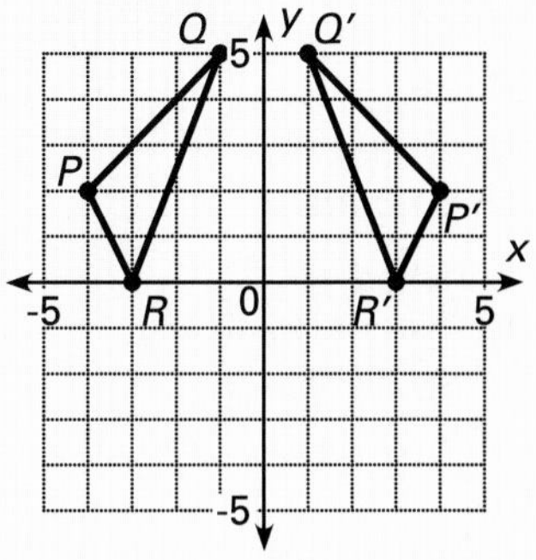

$P(-4, 2) \rightarrow P'(4, 2)$

$Q(-1, 5) \rightarrow Q'(1, 5)$

$R(-3, 0) \rightarrow R'(3, 0)$

ΔPQR has coordinates $P(-4, 2)$, $Q(-1, 5)$, and $R(-3, 0)$. $\Delta P'Q'R'$ has coordinates $P'(4, 2)$, $Q'(1, 5)$, and $R'(3, 0)$.

The y-coordinates of $\Delta P'Q'R'$ are the same as the y-coordinates of ΔPQR.

3 Practice and Assess

Check

Answers for Check Your Understanding

1. An up or down translation changes the y-value. A right or left translation changes the x-value.
2. Reflection across the x-axis changes the sign of the y-coordinate. Reflection across the y-axis changes the sign of the x-coordinate.

MEETING MIDDLE SCHOOL CLASSROOM NEEDS

Tips from Middle School Teachers

Students enjoy looking for letters in the alphabet that look the same when reflected in a mirror. I have them try to find entire words that look the same, for example, MOM or TOOT.

Team Teaching

Work with an art teacher. Show examples of wallpaper designs that illustrate translations and reflections.

Social Studies Connection

Transferring the grid lines from a globe onto a flat piece of paper is called *projection.* The method of projecting a map causes different distortions. The commonly used Mercator projection makes areas near the poles look larger than they really are.

9-6 Exercises and Applications

Assignment Guide

- **Basic** 1–15 odds, 17–18, 20–22, 25–31 odds
- **Average** 5–15 odds, 17–22, 25–31 odds
- **Enriched** 9–15 odds, 17–23, 24–30 evens

Exercise Notes

Exercise 17

Extension Have students reflect $\Delta R'S'T'$ across the *x*-axis.

Exercise 19

Extension Have students reflect $\Delta X'Y'Z'$ across the *y*-axis.

Exercise Answers

13–17. See page C2.

19. See page C3.

9-6 Exercises and Applications

Practice and Apply

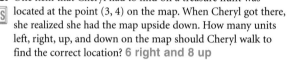

Getting Started **State the coordinates of the image of the point translated 1 unit up.**

1. (4, 5) (4, 6) **2.** (2, 8) (2, 9) **3.** (7, 3) (7, 4) **4.** (0, 0) (0, 1) **5.** (−3, 5) (−3, 6) **6.** (−7, −4) (−7, −3)

For Exercises 7–12, use the point *P* (2, 3) to plot and label *P′*.

7. Slide *P* to the right 3 units *P′*(5, 3)

8. Reflect *P* across the *y*-axis *P′*(−2, 3)

9. Slide *P* 1 unit right and 2 units up *P′*(3, 5)

10. Slide *P* to the left 2 units and down 3 units *P′*(0, 0)

11. Slide *P* 2 units down and 1 unit up *P′*(2, 2)

12. Slide *P* 3 units right and 3 units left *P′*(2, 3)

For Exercises 13–16, plot the image of quadrilateral *GHIJ*.

13. Translate *GHIJ* 3 units up, 4 units right

14. Slide *GHIJ* 2 units left, 5 units up

15. Slide *GHIJ* 2 units right, 3 units down

16. Translate *GHIJ* 5 units down

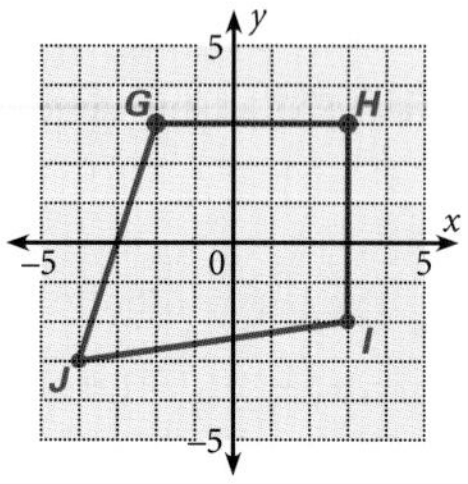

17. Geometry $\triangle RST$ has vertices at *R*(−1, 1), *S*(1, 3), and *T*(4, −1).

a. Draw the graph of $\triangle RST$.

b. Create $\triangle R'S'T'$ by translating $\triangle RST$ 3 units right and 2 units up.

c. State the coordinates of the vertices of $\triangle R'S'T'$. *R′* (2, 3), *S′* (4, 5), *T′* (7, 1)

18. GPS One item that Cheryl had to find on a treasure hunt was located at the point (3, 4) on the map. When Cheryl got there, she realized she had the map upside down. How many units left, right, up, and down on the map should Cheryl walk to find the correct location? 6 right and 8 up

19. Geometry $\triangle XYZ$ has vertices at *X*(−4, 2), *Y*(4, 3), and *Z*(2, 1).

a. Draw the graph of $\triangle XYZ$.

b. Create $\triangle X'Y'Z'$ by reflecting $\triangle XYZ$ across the *x*-axis.

c. Give the coordinates of the vertices of $\triangle X'Y'Z'$.
X′ (−4, −2), *Y′* (4, −3), *Z′* (2, −1)

PRACTICE 9-6

Reteaching

Activity

Materials: Graph paper

- Work in groups of four, use graph paper and follow these steps.
- One person draws a triangle on a coordinate plane.
- The second person translates the triangle 4 units to the right and 3 units up.
- The third person draws a new triangle on another coordinate plane.
- The fourth person reflects the triangle across the *y*-axis.

PRACTICE

Name ______________________

Practice 9-6

Graphing Slides and Flips

For Exercises 1–2, use the point *P*(2, −1) to plot and label *P′*.

1. Slide *P* 2 units left and 3 units up.

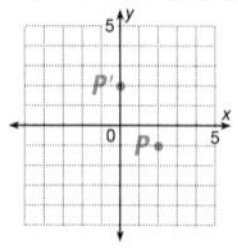

2. Reflect *P* across the *x*-axis.

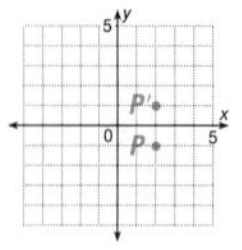

For Exercises 3–4, plot the image of quadrilateral *GHIJ*.

3. Translate *GHIJ* 2 units right and 2 units down.

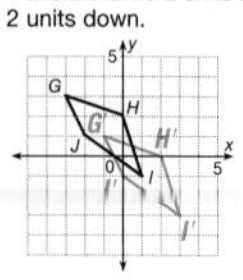

4. Slide *GHIJ* 4 units right and 2 units up.

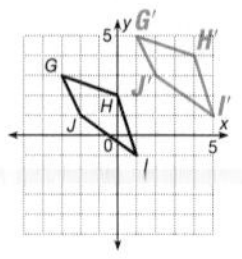

5. $\triangle ABC$ has vertices at *A*(−3, 4), *B*(1, 3), and *C*(−2, 0).

a. Draw the graph of $\triangle ABC$.

b. Create $\triangle A'B'C'$ by translating $\triangle ABC$ 3 units right and 4 units down.

c. Give the coordinates of the vertices of $\triangle A'B'C'$.

A′ (0, 0) *B′* (4, −1) *C′* (1, −4)

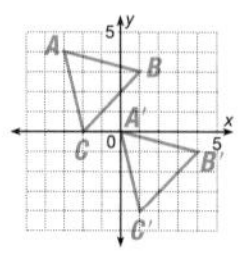

6. $\triangle LMN$ has vertices at *L*(−2, 4), *M*(1, 2), and *N*(−4, −1).

a. Draw the graph of $\triangle LMN$.

b. Create $\triangle L'M'N'$ by reflecting $\triangle LMN$ across the *y*-axis.

c. Give the coordinates of the vertices of $\triangle L'M'N'$.

L′ (2, 4) *M′* (−1, 2) *N′* (4, −1)

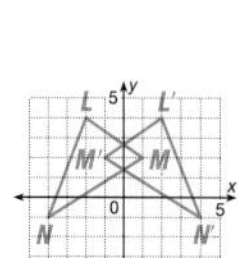

RETEACHING

Name ______________________

Alternative Lesson 9-6

Graphing Slides and Flips

A *translation* slides a figure to a new position without rotating the figure. You can graph translations on a coordinate grid. Changes in the *x*-coordinate indicates movement to the right (+) or left (−). Changes in the *y*-coordinate indicates movement up (+) or down (−).

Translated figures have a specific notation. The translation of $\triangle XYZ$ is $\triangle X'Y'Z'$, which is read as "triangle X prime Y prime Z prime."

Example 1

The coordinates of *P* are (2, 1). State the coordinates of the image of Point *P* translated 2 units down.

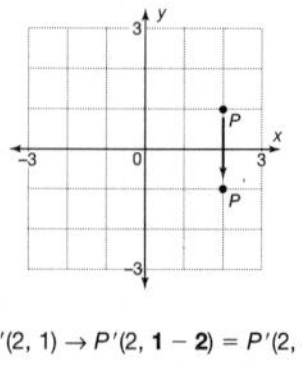

Since the slide is down, the values of the *y*-coordinate will change. To show movement *down*, *subtract* 2 from the value of the *y*-coordinate.

P′(2, 1) → *P′*(2, **1** − **2**) = *P′*(2, **−1**)

So *P′* has the coordinates (2, −1).

Try It State the coordinates of the image of each point translated 1 unit left.

a. (2, 3) (1, 3) **b.** (−1, 0) (−2, 0) **c.** (4, −3) (3, −3)

Example 2

Plot the image of $\triangle RST$ by translating the figure 3 units right.

$\triangle RST$ has coordinates *R* (−2, 3), *S* (0, 4), and *T* (2, −1)

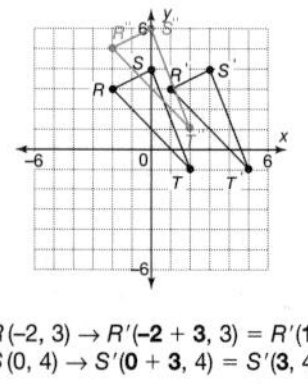

Since the triangle is to be translated to the right, the values of the *x*-coordinates will change. There is no movement up or down, so the value of the *y*-coordinates will not change.

To show the movement to the *right*, *add* 3 to the value of each *x*-coordinate.

R(−2, 3) → *R′*(**−2** + **3**, 3) = *R′*(**1**, 3)
S(0, 4) → *S′*(**0** + **3**, 4) = *S′*(**3**, 4)

Then plot the coordinates of $\triangle R'S'T'$.

T(2, −1) → *T′*(**2** + **3**, −1) = *T′*(**5**, −1)

Try It Plot the image of $\triangle RST$ on the coordinate plane in Example 2 by translating it 2 units up. Label your point *R″ S″* and *T″*.

d. What are the coordinates of *R″*? (−2, 5) Of *S″*? (0, 6) Of *T″*? (2, 1)

20. **Test Prep** Choose the graph that shows $\overrightarrow{KL}$ translated 3 units right and 1 unit down. B

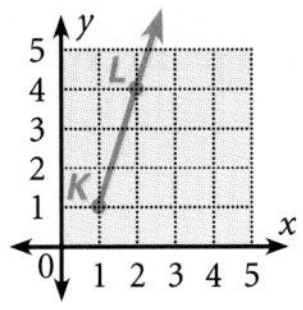

Ⓐ
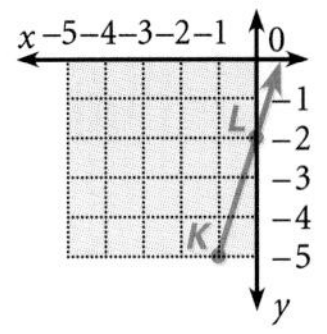

Ⓑ
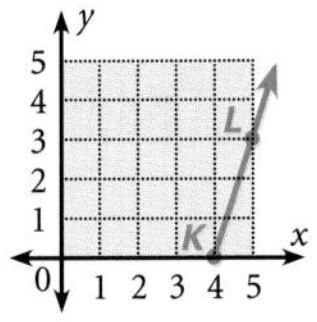

Ⓒ
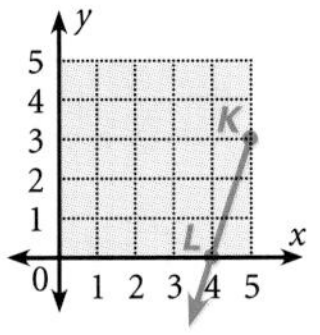

Problem Solving and Reasoning

21. **Critical Thinking** A polygon has vertices at $A(2, 5)$, $B(5, 5)$, $C(5, -1)$, and $D(2, -1)$. Reflect the polygon across the y-axis. Then translate the image 4 units to the right and 2 units down. Give the coordinates of the vertices of the new image. Explain your reasoning.

23. **Communicate** If the coordinates of the vertices of a figure are integers, will the translation or reflection always have integers as coordinates of the vertices?

22. **Choose a Strategy** Can a reflection of a figure and a translation of the same figure be the same shape and have the same coordinates on a coordinate grid? Explain.

Problem Solving STRATEGIES

- Look for a Pattern
- Make an Organized List
- Make a Table
- Guess and Check
- Work Backward
- Use Logical Reasoning
- Draw a Diagram
- Solve a Simpler Problem

Mixed Review

Solve. *[Lesson 7-6]*

24. $t \div \frac{2}{3} = \frac{9}{16}$ $t = \frac{3}{8}$ 25. $\frac{1}{2}p = 2\frac{1}{5}$ $p = 4\frac{2}{5}$ 26. $\frac{12}{15} \div j = \frac{4}{5}$ $j = \frac{3}{3}$ 27. $\frac{8}{9}e = 1$ $e = \frac{9}{8}$

Name each polygon and tell if it is regular or irregular. *[Lesson 8-6]*

28.
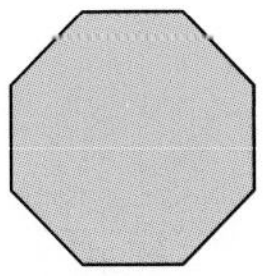
Regular octagon

29.
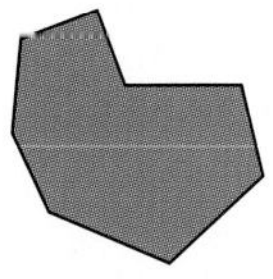
Octagon

30.
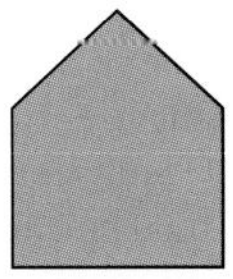
Irregular pentagon

31.
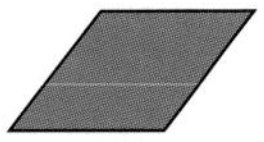
Irregular quadrilateral

PROBLEM SOLVING 9-6

PROBLEM SOLVING

Name ______________________ **Guided Problem Solving 9-6**

GPS PROBLEM 19, PAGE 496

One item that Cheryl had to find on a treasure hunt was located at the point (3, 4) on the map. When Cheryl got there, she realized she had the map upside down. How many units left, right, up, and down on the map should Cheryl walk to find the correct location?

Possible answers: Items 5, 8, and 9

— Understand —

1. Underline what you are asked to find.
2. Why was Cheryl not at those coordinates? She read map upside down.

— Plan —

3. Mark (3, 4) on the coordinate plane. Label it *A*.
4. Turn this page upside down. Imagine that the graph was scaled in the usual way. Then mark (3, 4). Label it *B*.
5. Turn your page to original position. Follow the grid lines to mark the shortest path between the *B* and *A*.

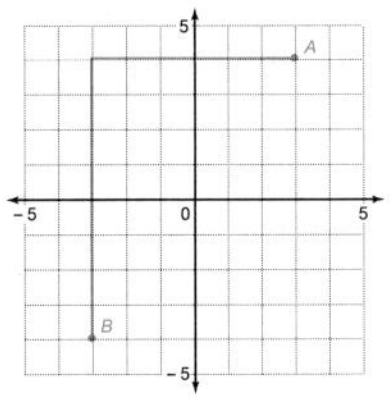

— Solve —

6. Does your path go up or down? How many units? Up; 8 units.
7. Does your path go left or right? How many units? Right; 6 units.

— Look Back —

8. Are there other paths that you could choose? Explain. Yes, for example, one path could start out going right, then up.
9. What is the relationship between the of number of units the path takes and the original coordinates? The path is two times the value of each coordinate.

SOLVE ANOTHER PROBLEM

One item that Norm had to find on a treasure hunt was located at the point (-2, 5) on the map. When Norm got there, he realized he had the map upside down. How many units left, right, up, and down on the map should Norm walk to find the correct location? Up 10, Left 4.

ENRICHMENT

Name ______________________ **Extend Your Thinking 9-6**

Visual Thinking

Count the blocks in each picture. There are no hidden spaces and each block sits on another block unless shown otherwise.

1.
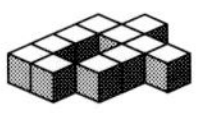
11

2.
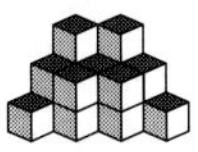
18

3.
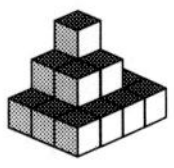
17

4.

34

5.
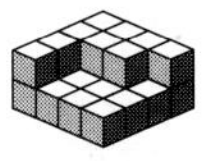
25

6.
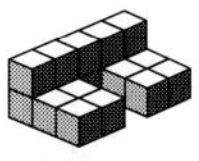
18

7.
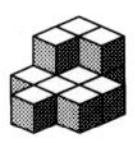
12

8.

16

9.

36

Exercise Notes

■ Exercise 22

Problem-Solving Tip You may wish to use Teaching Tool Transparencies 2 and 3: Guided Problem Solving, pages 1–2.

Exercise Answers

21. $A'(2, 3)$, $B'(-1, 3)$, $C'(-1, -3)$, $D'(2, -3)$; First, reflect the figure, which changes the sign of all of the x-coordinates. Then, translate the resulting image, which adds 4 to each x-coordinate and subtracts 2 from each y-coordinate.

22. Yes; A regular polygon such as a square can be reflected or translated to the same new position.

23. A reflection will have integers as coordinates of the vertices, but a translation may not.

Alternate Assessment

You may want to use the *Interactive CD-ROM Journal* with this assessment.

Journal Have students write a paragraph telling how graphing a translation is different from graphing a reflection.

► Quick Quiz

1. Draw ΔABC with $A(-1, 2)$, $B(-3, 4)$, and $C(-2, 0)$. Then translate it 3 units to the right and 1 unit down.

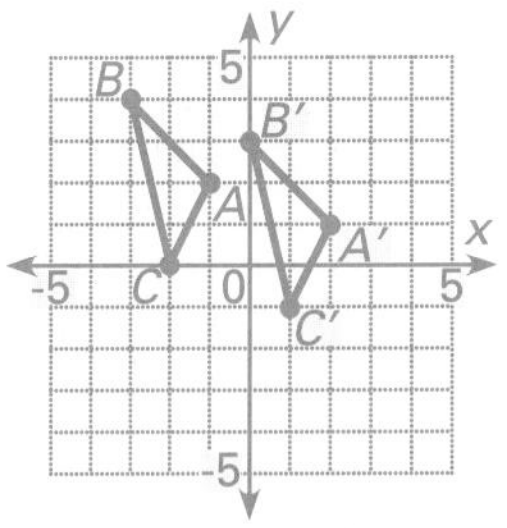

2. Draw ΔHJK with $H(-3, 2)$, $J(-2, 4)$, and $K(-1, 1)$. Then reflect it across the y-axis.

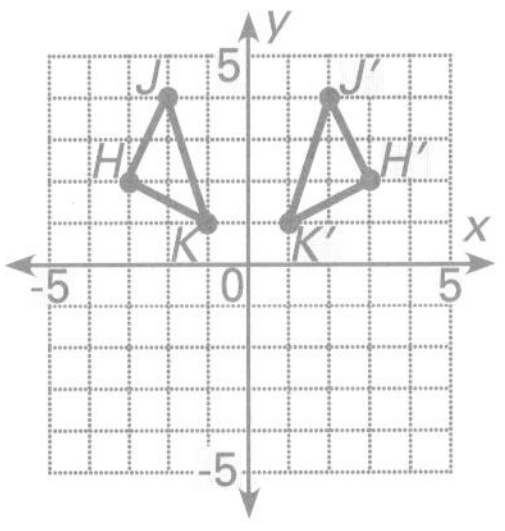

Available on Daily Transparency 9-6

9-7 Lesson Organizer

Objective

- Draw the graph of an equation.

Materials

- Explore: Graph paper

Vocabulary

- T-table

NCTM Standards

- 1–5, 8, 9, 12

Review

Refer to the equation $y = x - 4$.

1. If $x = 0$, what is y? -4
2. If $x = 4$, what is y? 0
3. If $x = 2$, what is y? -2

Refer to the equation $y = 4x$.

4. If $x = 0$, what is y? 0
5. If $x = 2$, what is y? 8

Available on Daily Transparency 9-7

1 Introduce

Explore

You may wish to use Teaching Tool Transparencies 7: $\frac{1}{4}$-Inch Graph Paper, 8: Coordinate Grids, and Lesson Enhancement Transparency 47 with this lesson.

The Point
Students explore drawing graphs of equations by plotting points based on rules written with words.

Ongoing Assessment
For Step 3 some students may try to multiply the original coordinates by $1\frac{1}{2}$.

For Groups That Finish Early
Name the coordinates of the location four years after the ship sank. $(-1, -1)$

9-7 Graphing Equations

You'll Learn ...

- to draw the graph of an equation

... How It's Used

Sound engineers graph equations when developing sound effects with computers.

Vocabulary

T-table

Lesson Link You've learned how to graph translations and reflections on the coordinate plane. Now you'll learn how to graph equations on the plane.

Explore Graphing Equations

Catch My Drift

Materials: Graph paper

In 1705, the pirate ship Silver Legend sank in the Atlantic Ocean at the point $(-5, -9)$ on the map. Every year, the Gulf Stream current moves the ship 1 unit east and 2 units north.

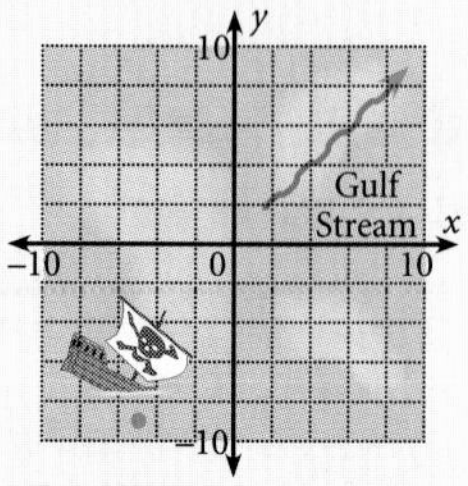

1. Draw an x-y coordinate system. Mark where the ship sank.
2. Draw the ship's location one year later, two years later, and three years later. Explain how you determined the location for each year.
3. Draw the ship's location $1\frac{1}{2}$ years after it sank. Explain how you determined the ship's location at that time.
4. Draw a line indicating the path the ship will travel over the years. Explain how you can determine where this line should be.
5. The year 2005 is 300 years after the sinking. Estimate the coordinates of the ship's location in 2005. Explain how you could determine the exact coordinates of the ship's location in 2005.

Learn Graphing Equations

The algebraic equations you have seen so far have had one variable, as in $x + 3 = 7$. The coordinate plane uses two variables, x for the first coordinate and y for the second. You can use the coordinate plane to draw a picture of an equation.

graph of $y = -x$

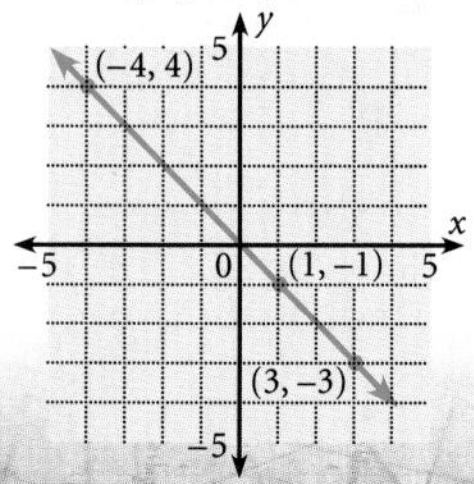

MEETING INDIVIDUAL NEEDS

Resources

- 9-7 Practice
- 9-7 Reteaching
- 9-7 Problem Solving
- 9-7 Enrichment
- 9-7 Daily Transparency
  - Problem of the Day
  - Review
  - Quick Quiz
- Teaching Tool Transparencies 7, 8
- Lesson Enhancement Transparency 47
- Technology Master 50
- Chapter 9 Project Master

Learning Modalities

Visual Have students pick at least six different equations from the exercises and then make a bulletin board to display the graphs on the same coordinate grid.

Kinesthetic If classroom chairs are not already set up in rows and columns, have students rearrange them in that manner. Have students assign ordered pairs to each chair in their classroom as follows: (column, row). Then have students name different equations such as $y = x - 2$. Students sitting in chairs whose ordered pairs satisfy that equation must stand up.

Challenge

Have students graph the equations $y = x + 2$ and $y = 3x$ on the same coordinate axes. Then have them determine the ordered pair of the point where the two graphs intersect. (1, 3)

To draw the graph of an equation

1. Make a **T-table** like the one here. List three or four values for x. Choose easy numbers to work with, such as -1, 0 and 1.
2. For each value of x, use the equation to determine a value for y.
3. Plot the point for each pair of (x, y) values on a coordinate plane.
4. Draw a line connecting the points. This line represents all the other values you could have chosen for x, and the matching y values.

$y = x + 1$

x	y
–1	0
0	1
1	2
2	3

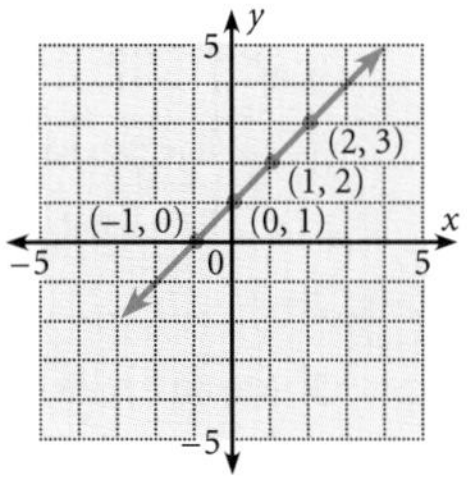

Examples

1 Graph the equation $y = x - 4$.

$y = x - 4$

x	y
–1	–5
0	–4
1	–3
2	–2

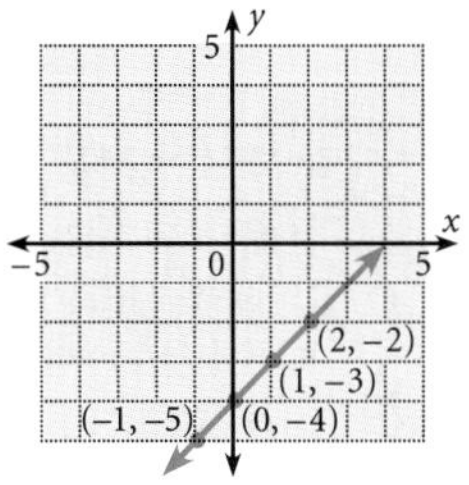

Problem Solving TIP

Look for a pattern in the y values.

2 Graph the equation $y = -2x$

$y = -2x$

x	y
–1	2
0	0
1	–2
2	–4

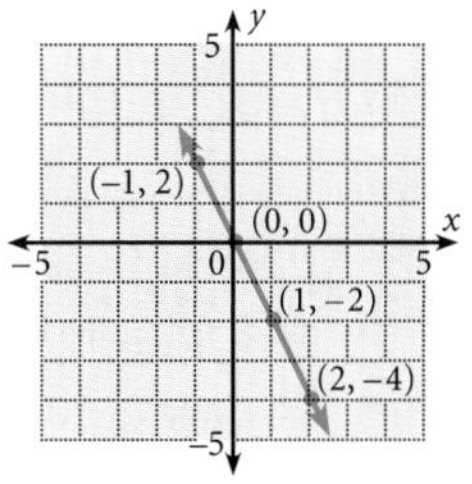

Remember

When multiplying integers, if the factors have like signs, the product will be positive. If they have unlike signs, the product will be negative.

[Page 482]

Try It

Graph each equation.

a. $y = x + 5$ **b.** $y = 2x$ **c.** $y = 8 - x$ **d.** $y = -1x$

MATH EVERY DAY

Problem of the Day

Six students stood under an umbrella. Two left and then three more came. Finally, six more students came. No students got wet. How can that be? It is not raining.

Available on Daily Transparency 9-7

An Extension is provided in the transparency package.

Fact of the Day

The Gulf Stream is about 50 feet wide and almost 2000 feet deep. It flows 70 miles a day at its fastest rate.

Mental Math

Do these mentally.

1. $\frac{1}{4}$ of 12 3
2. $\frac{1}{2}$ of 10 5
3. $\frac{1}{3}$ of 15 5
4. $\frac{1}{10}$ of 20 2

Answers for Explore

1–4.

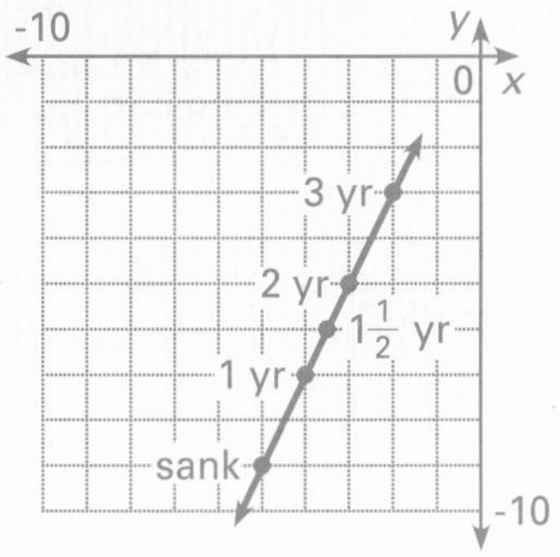

1 yr (–4, –7), 2 yrs (–3, –5), 3 yrs (–2, –3); For every additional year after the ship sank, move its position 1 unit right and 2 units up. For the $\frac{1}{2}$ year, move it 0.5. units right and 1 unit up. The line should connect the points and extend upwards.

5. Exact: (295, 591); The ship will have moved 300 units east and 600 units north. Add these values to the x- and y-coordinates.

2 Teach

Learn

Alternate Examples

1. Graph the equation $y = x - 3$.

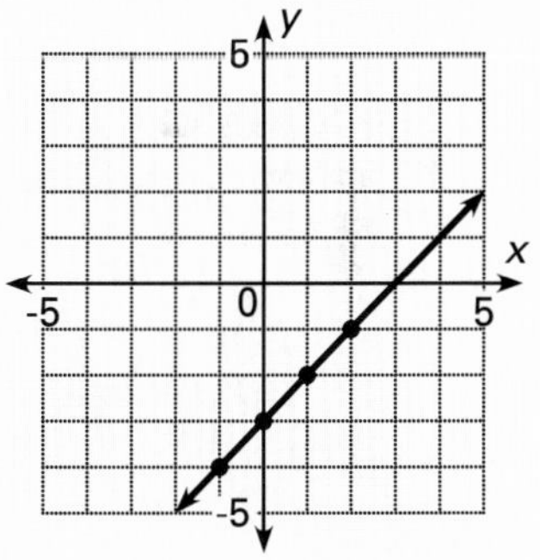

2. Graph the equation $y = -3x$.

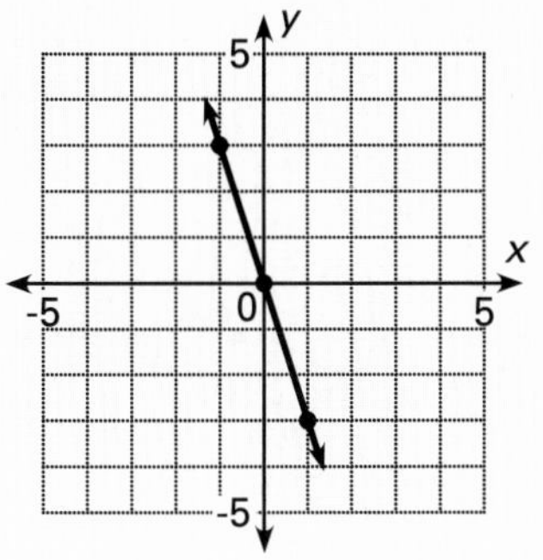

Answers for Try It on page C3.

Students see two methods of solving a problem. One method uses a T-table to determine the recommended maximum pulse rate for a 15-year-old person. The other method uses a graph. Students can decide which of the two correct methods is easier for them.

Answers for What Do You Think?

1. Larry's; It's easier to find 32 years on the graph than it is to figure it out with the table.
2. Possible answers: Used a number line, used mental math.
3. He found the *y*-coordinate that was paired with the *x*-value of 15.

3 Practice and Assess

Check

Be sure students remember that the first number in an ordered pair is the *x*-value, even if *x* does not appear first in a given equation.

Answers for Check Your Understanding

1. Find the point on the graph that has the *x*-value you are given and read the *y*-value at that point. Find the point on the graph that has the *y*-value you are given and read the *x*-value at that point.
2. No; You can draw the graph and see that (1, 3) is not on it, or you can substitute 1 and 3 for *x* and *y*, and see that the equation is false.

WHAT DO YOU THINK?

A T-table and graph in a doctor's office give recommended maximum pulse rates during exercise, according to age.

Susana and Larry are 15 years old. What is their recommended pulse rate?

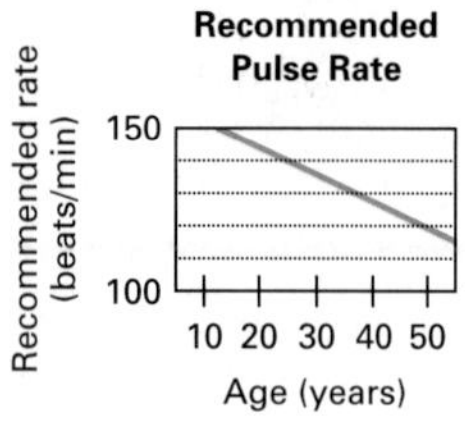

Age (years)	10	20	30	40	50
Rate (beats/min)	152	144	136	128	120

Susana thinks . . .

I'll use the T-table. 15 is halfway between 10 and 20. 148 is halfway between 144 and 152.

So, 148 beats per minute is my recommended rate.

Larry thinks . . .

I'll use the graph. The graph of the equation looks like it passes through (15, 148).

So, 148 beats per minute is my recommended rate.

What do you think?

1. Which method would you use to find the recommended rate for age 32? Explain.
2. How did Susana find the number halfway between 144 and 152?
3. How did Larry know that the graph passed through (15, 148)?

Check Your Understanding

1. How can you use the graph of an equation to find a *y*-value if you know the *x*-value? To find an *x*-value if you know the *y*-value?
2. Is the point (1, 3) on the graph of $y = x + 3$? Explain.

MEETING MIDDLE SCHOOL CLASSROOM NEEDS

Tips from Middle School Teachers

I find that students who are having trouble with graphing can benefit by using a graphing calculator. I still require them to learn basic graphing techniques, but I allow them to use the graphing calculator as a check.

Team Teaching

Work with a physical education instructor. Give students the opportunity to volunteer and see if their pulse rates during exercise are close to the recommended pulse rates given in the table on page 500.

Science Connection

Every time the heart beats, it pushes blood through the arteries. The pulse is felt when the artery walls expand with each beat. To find the pulse, place the fingers on the inside of the wrist or on the throat next to the Adam's apple.

9-7 Exercises and Applications

Practice and Apply

1. **Getting Started** Graph each equation on the same coordinate grid. Describe any patterns you see.

   a. $y = x + 0$ **b.** $y = x + 1$ **c.** $y = x + 2$ **d.** $y = x + 3$

For Exercises 2–6, make a T-table with five (*x*,*y*) pairs for each.

2. $y = x - 53$ **3.** $y = x + 27$ **4.** $y = x - 106$ **5.** $y = -50x$ **6.** $y = 12x$

Graph each equation.

7. $y = x + 1$ **8.** $y = 1 + x$ **9.** $y = -5x$ **10.** $y = 3x$ **11.** $y = 3 + x$

12. $y = x$ **13.** $y = -1x$ **14.** $y = x - 3$ **15.** $y = 2 + x$ **16.** $y = 2x$

17. $y = x + 6$ **18.** $y = -2x$ **19.** $y = x - 4$ **20.** $y = 0x$ **21.** $y = 9$

22. $y = 6$ **23.** $y = 4 - x$ **24.** $y = 10 - x$ **25.** $y = 4 + x$ **26.** $y = -3$

Find the value of *y* when *x* = 4.

27. $y = 47 - x$ **43** **28.** $y = 1 - x$ **−3** **29.** $y = -3 - x$ **−7** **30.** $y = x + 33$ **37** **31.** $y = -2$ **−2**

32. Pamela is a clerk in the receiving department of a company. When an order of computer paper comes in, she gives a ream to each of the four department administrators. The equation $y = x - 4$ gives the number of reams she has left after the distribution. Graph this equation.

33. Consumer A book at the Read It Again bookstore costs \$3. Therefore, the equation for the cost of multiple books is $y = 3x$. Graph this equation.

34. **Test Prep** Choose the graph of $y = x - 3$. **A**

Ⓐ

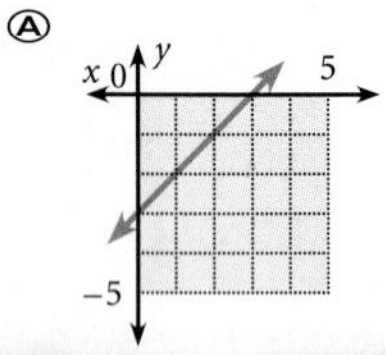

Ⓑ

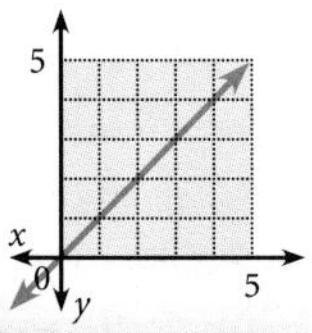

Ⓒ

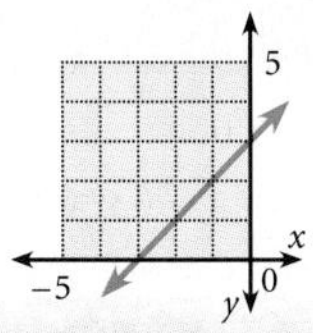

PRACTICE 9-7

PRACTICE

Name ______________________ **Practice 9-7**

Graphing Equations

For Exercises 1–4, make a T-table with five (*x*, *y*) pairs for each. **Possible answers:**

1. $y = x + 12$

x	y
−1	11
0	12
1	13
2	14
3	15

2. $y = -8x$

x	y
−1	8
0	0
1	−8
2	−16
3	−24

3. $y = x - 20$

x	y
−1	−21
0	−20
1	−19
2	−18
3	−17

4. $y = 15x$

x	y
−1	−15
0	0
1	15
2	30
3	45

Graph each equation.

5. $y = x - 1$

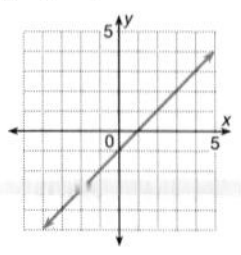

6. $y = x + 5$

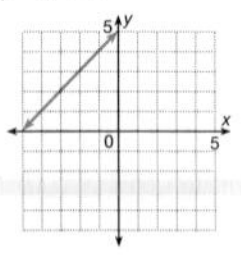

7. $y = -2$

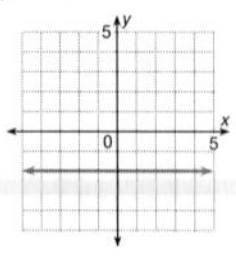

8. $y = -3x$

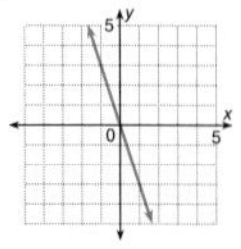

9. $y = x - 2$

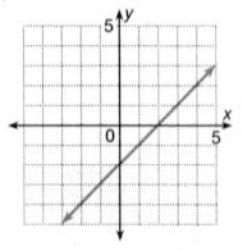

10. $y = 2 - x$

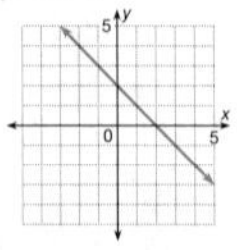

11. The Mystery Music Company sells "grab bag" cassettes for \$1 each. There is a shipping charge of \$4 per order. The equation for the cost of an order is $y = x + 4$. Graph this equation.

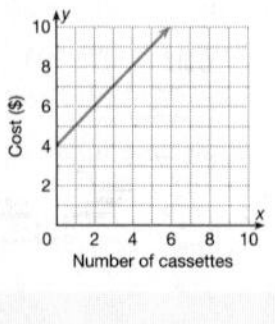

RETEACHING

Name ______________________ **Alternative Lesson 9-7**

Graphing Equations

You can use the coordinate plane to graph equations with two variables. A **T-table** can show various solutions to an equation.

— Example —

Graph the equation $y = x + 5$.

Step 1: Make a T-table for four values of and *y* that will solve the equation.

x	y
−2	3
−1	4
0	5
1	6

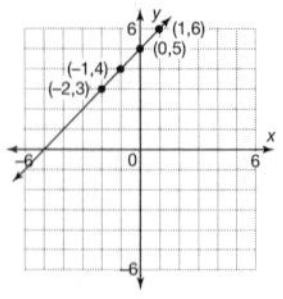

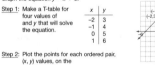

Step 2: Plot the points for each ordered pair, (*x*, *y*) values, on the coordinate plane.

Step 3: Draw a line connecting the points to represent all the other values for *x*, and the matching *y* values.

Try It Graph the equation $y = 3x$.

a. Make a T-table for four values of *x*.

x	y
−1	−3
0	0
1	3
2	6

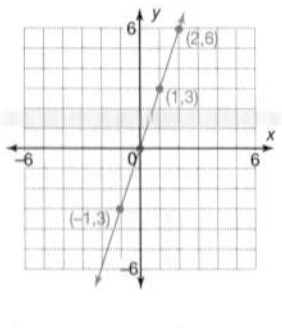

b. Plot the points on the coordinate plane.

c. Draw a line to connect the points.

Graph the equation $y = x - 5$.

x	y
0	−5
1	−4
3	−2
5	0

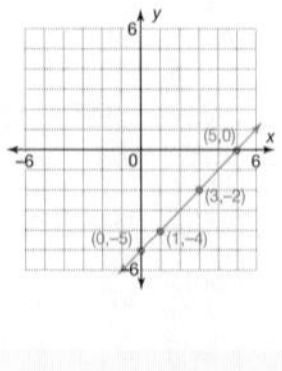

9-7 Exercises and Applications

Assignment Guide

- **Basic** 1–27 odds, 34–35, 37–51 odds
- **Average** 1–33 odds, 34–37, 39–51 odds
- **Enriched** 6–34 evens, 35–38, 40–52 evens

Exercise Notes

Exercises 21–22

Error Prevention Some students will graph the equations $y = 9x$ and $y = 6x$, rather than $y = 9$ and $y = 6$. Remind them that in the equation $y = 9$, there is no mention of *x*. So *x* can be any number.

Exercise 32

Consumer Packages of paper are often sold by the ream. In the past a ream might have been either 480 or 516 sheets, but the standard ream today is 500 sheets.

Exercise Answers

1. a–d.

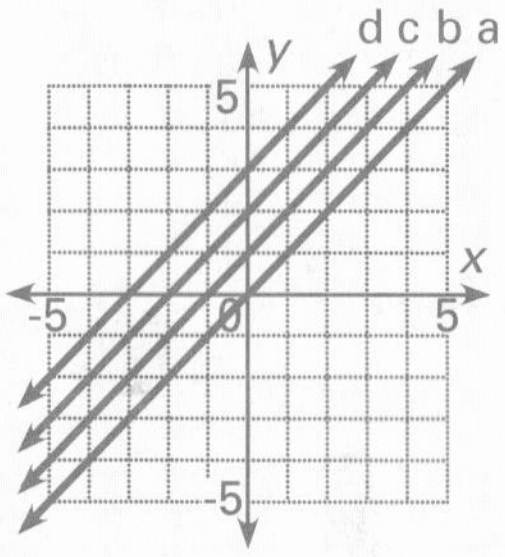

The lines are parallel.

2–26. See pages C3–C4.

32–33. See page C4.

Reteaching

Activity

Materials: Graph paper

- Work in groups of three or four. Use graph paper and take turns completing the following steps.
- Write a simple equation involving *x* and *y*, for example, $y = x - 1$.
- Graph two points satisfying the equation.
- Connect the points with a line.
- Pick a third point on the line and determine its coordinates. Check to see if the coordinates satisfy the equation.

Project Progress

You may want to have students use Chapter 9 Project Master.

Exercise Answers

35. b.

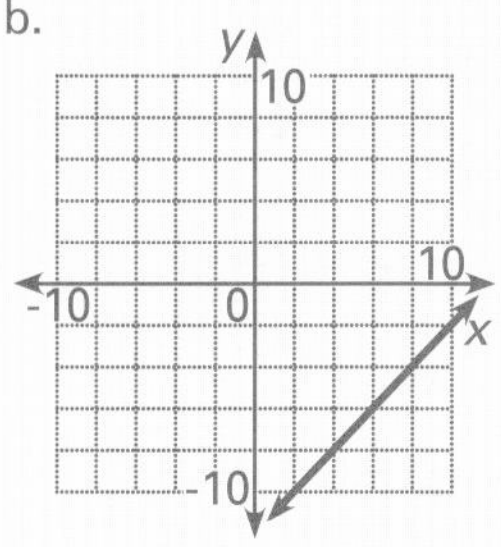

36. $y = 5x$; For each x-value, the y-value is five times greater, whereas for $y = 3x$, the y-value is only three times greater.

37. They are parallel.

38. If you put in 0 for x and the equation simplifies to $y = 0$, then the graph will pass through (0, 0).

45–52. See page C4.

Alternate Assessment

You may want to use the *Interactive CD-ROM Journal* with this assessment.

Journal Have students write a paragraph telling the steps they use in graphing an equation.

Quick Quiz

Graph each equation.

1. $y = x - 2$

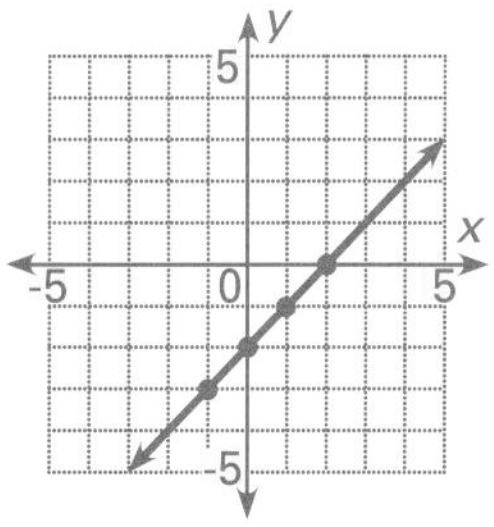

2. $y = -4x$

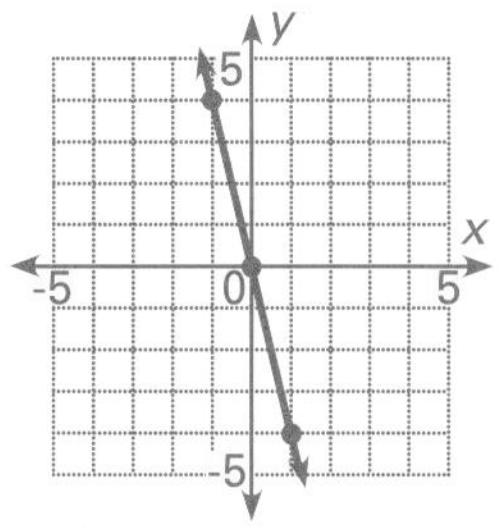

Find the value of y when $x = 4$.

3. $y = 25 - x$ 21

Available on Daily Transparency 9-7

Problem Solving and Reasoning

35. Critical Thinking Shelley earns money bathing dogs. This month, her expenses were only $12. She collected x dollars from her customers.

a. Write an equation for Shelley's profit. Use y for the money she made and x for the money she collected from her customers. $y = x - 12$

b. Graph the equation.

c. Using the graph, how could you predict what Shelley's profit would be if she collected $25 from her customers?

d. Using the equation, how could you predict what Shelley's profit would be if she collected $25 from her customers? Put 25 in for x and solve the equation for y.

36. Critical Thinking Graph the equations $y = 3x$ and $y = 5x$. Which line is steeper? Explain why you think this happens.

37. Critical Thinking Graph the equations $y = x + 3$ and $y = x + (-3)$ on the same coordinate plane. Describe the relationship between the lines.

38. Journal Explain how you can determine from an equation if the line will pass through the origin.

35. c. Find the y-coordinate of the point on the line which has an x-coordinate of 25.

Mixed Review

Convert. *[Lesson 4-3]*

39. 72 feet = □ inches 864 **40.** 94 inches = □ feet $7\frac{5}{6}$ **41.** 3 feet = □ inches 36

42. 52 inches = □ feet $4\frac{1}{3}$ **43.** 0.75 feet = □ inches 9 **44.** 0.5 feet = □ inches 6

Draw an example of each. *[Lesson 8-7]*

45. Rhombus **46.** Parallelogram **47.** Trapezoid **48.** Square

Classify each figure in as many ways as possible. *[Lesson 8-7]*

49. 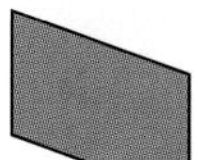 **50.**  **51.** 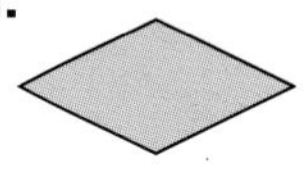 **52.** 

Project Progress

Make a tracing of the shape of your country. Then, transfer the tracing onto graph paper. Draw an x and y axis with the origin in the middle of the country's shape. Start to determine the coordinates for the points that trace out the shape of the country.

Problem Solving
Understand
Plan
Solve
Look Back

PROBLEM SOLVING 9-7

PROBLEM SOLVING

Name ______________________

Guided Problem Solving 9-7

GPS PROBLEM 37, PAGE 502

Graph the equations $y = x + 3$ and $y = x + (-3)$ on the same coordinate plane. Describe the relationship between the lines.

Possible answers: Items 5 and 6

— Understand —

1. Will you graph the equations on one or two coordinates planes? One.
2. What are you asked to describe? The relationship between two lines.

— Plan —

3. Complete the T-tables to find some values of x and y for each equation.

$y = x + 3$

x	y
–1	2
0	3
1	4
2	5

$y = x + (-3)$

x	y
–1	–4
0	–3
1	–2
2	–1

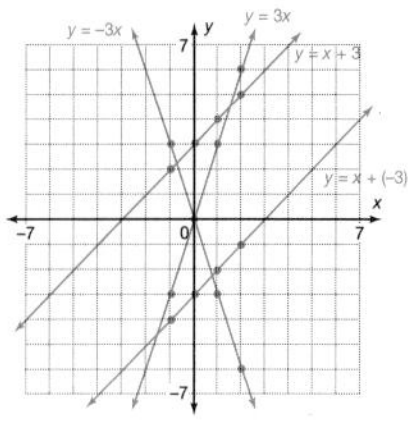

— Solve —

4. Graph each equation. Label each line.
5. What is the relationship between the lines? They are parallel.

— Look Back —

6. Do you think you would get the same result for the equations $y = x - 3$ and $y = x - (-3)$? Explain. Yes, these are the opposites of the two equations graphed.

SOLVE ANOTHER PROBLEM

Graph the equations $y = 3x$ and $y = -3x$ on the coordinate plane above. Label each line. Describe the relationship between the lines.
Possible answer: They intersect at the origin, have an "X" shape, are symmetrical.

ENRICHMENT

Name ______________________

Extend Your Thinking 9-7

Critical Thinking

You can graph two equations on one grid to solve problems such as this one: The sum of two numbers is 3. Their difference is 5. What are the numbers?

Write two equations. Let x = one number and y = other number
The sum of the numbers: $x + y = 3$
The difference of the numbers: $x - y = 5$

1. Make a T-table for each equation.

$x + y = 3$

x	y
–1	4
0	3
1	2
2	1

$x - y = 5$

x	y
–1	–6
0	–5
1	–4
2	–3

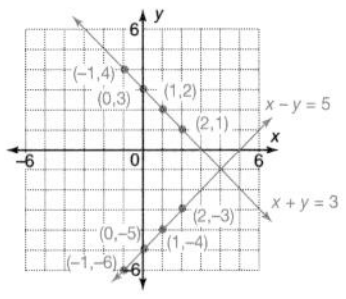

2. Graph each set of ordered pairs on the coordinate plane. Connect the points for each equation and draw a line.
3. What is the ordered pair where the two lines intersect? (4, –1)
4. Substitute the coordinates of the ordered pair in Question 3 into each equation. Show your equations.
$4 + (-1) = 3$; $4 - (-1) = 5$
5. What is the solution to the problem?
One number is 4, other is –1.
6. Solve this problem: The sum of two numbers is 4. Their difference is –2. What are the numbers?
7. Write equations for each condition.
$x + y = 4$; $x - y = -2$
8. Graph each equation. What are the numbers?
One number is 1, other is 3.

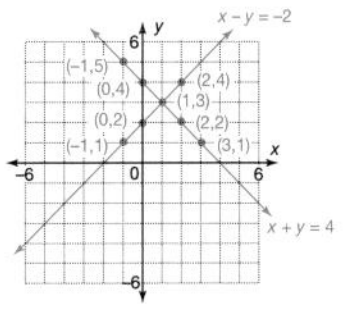

Section 9B Connect

At the beginning of this section, you learned that pirates may have buried treasure on Nova Scotia's Oak Island. Now you'll investigate how line graphs can be used to unscramble a system of tunnels and pinpoint the location of buried treasure.

A Hunting We Will Go ...

Materials: Graph paper

Pearl Island is shaped roughly like a square 10 leagues long and 10 leagues wide. The sides of the island run north-south and east-west. A 300-year-old treasure map gives the following instructions:

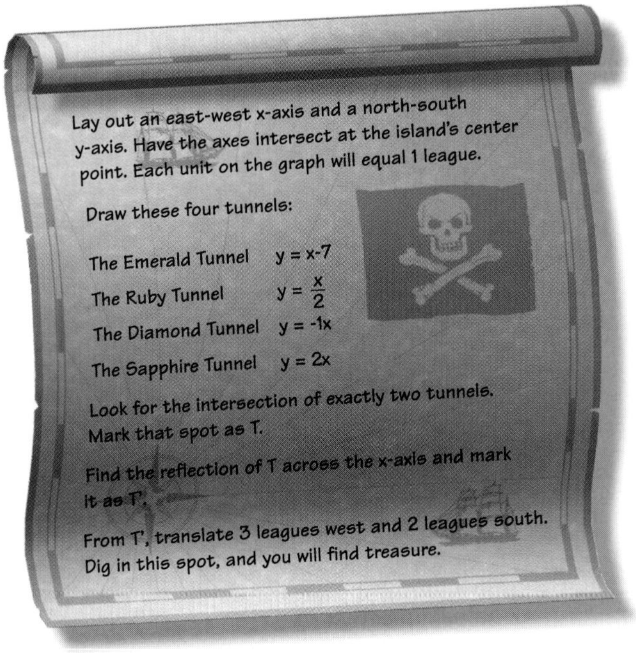
Lay out an east-west x-axis and a north-south y-axis. Have the axes intersect at the island's center point. Each unit on the graph will equal 1 league.
Draw these four tunnels:
The Emerald Tunnel $y = x-7$
The Ruby Tunnel $y = \frac{x}{2}$
The Diamond Tunnel $y = -1x$
The Sapphire Tunnel $y = 2x$
Look for the intersection of exactly two tunnels. Mark that spot as T.
Find the reflection of T across the x-axis and mark it as T'.
From T', translate 3 leagues west and 2 leagues south. Dig in this spot, and you will find treasure.

Where was the intersection of exactly two tunnels? Where is the treasure? Explain your method.

503

9B Connect

A Hunting We Will Go ...

The Point

In *A Hunting We Will Go ...* on page 487, students learned that pirates may have buried treasure on Nova Scotia's Oak Island. Now, students will use line graphs to pinpoint the location of buried treasure.

Materials

Graph paper

Resources

Teaching Tool Transparency 7: $\frac{1}{4}$-Inch Graph Paper

About the Page

- Students should make a T-table for each equation given. Remind students that the *x*-value is written on the left side of the table and the *y*-value is written on the right.
- Discuss with students the values they will assign to *x*.
- Remind them that the T is the intersection of 2 tunnels. (There is an intersection of 3 lines at (0, 0)).
- Ask students to state the location of the buried treasure as an ordered pair.

Ongoing Assessment

Check that students have located the intersection of the two tunnels correctly and "found the treasure" in the correct location.

Extension

Ask students to create a buried treasure map on a coordinate grid. Have them write a story about their treasure and give clues to its location as a set of ordered pairs.

Answers for Connect

Intersection of exactly two tunnels is at (3.5, −3.5); Reflection of (3.5, −3.5) across the *x*-axis is (3.5, 3.5); Translation of (3.5, 3.5) 3 leagues west and 2 leagues south is (0.5, 1.5). Therefore, the treasure is buried at (0.5, 1.5).

Section 9B Review

Review Correlation

Item(s)	Lesson(s)
1, 9	9-2
2, 8	9-3
3–10	9-4
11	9-5
12–15	9-6
16–20	9-7
21	9-5, 9-6
22	9-7
23, 24	9-5

Test Prep

Test-Taking Tip

Tell students that tracing the drawing and marking the number scales on it may help them choose the correct answer.

Answers for Review

16.

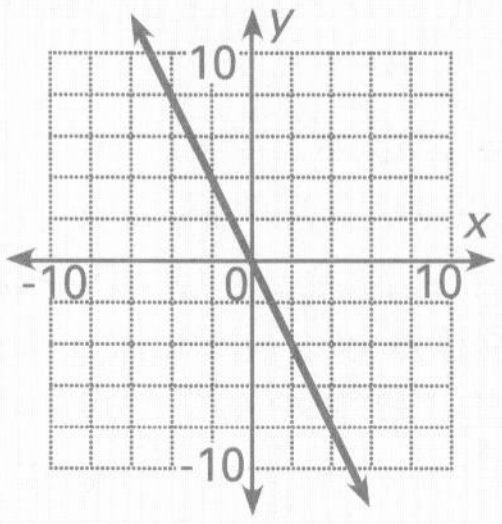

17.

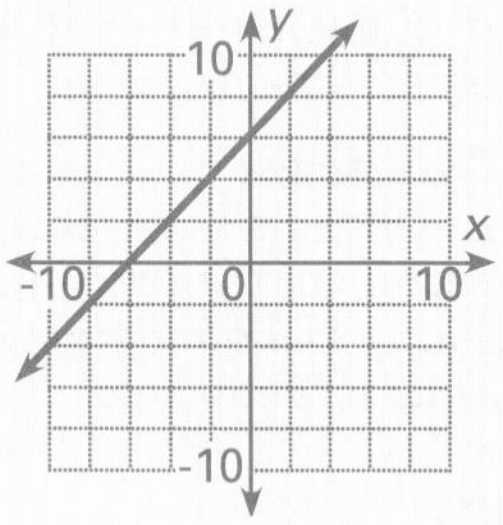

18.

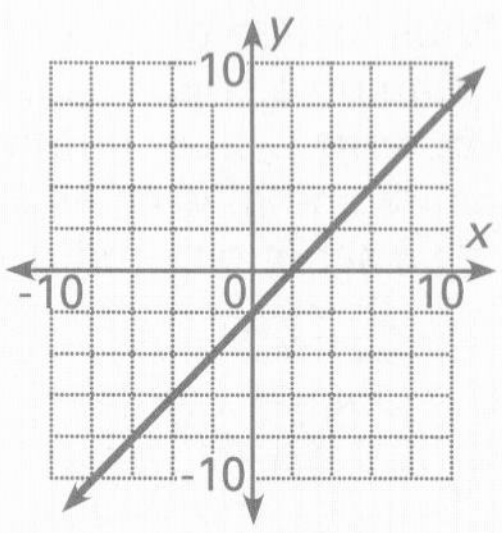

19–22. See page C4.

Simplify.

1. $12 + (-4)$ 8 **2.** $-5 - (-9)$ 4 **3.** $6 \times (-2)$ -12 **4.** $-99 \div (-9)$ 11 **5.** $50 \div (-5)$ -10

6. $4 \times (-10)$ -40 **7.** $-7 \times (-5)$ 35 **8.** $-9 - (-3)$ -6 **9.** $15 + (-10)$ 5 **10.** $8 \div (-1)$ -8

For Exercises 11–15, use the coordinate grid.

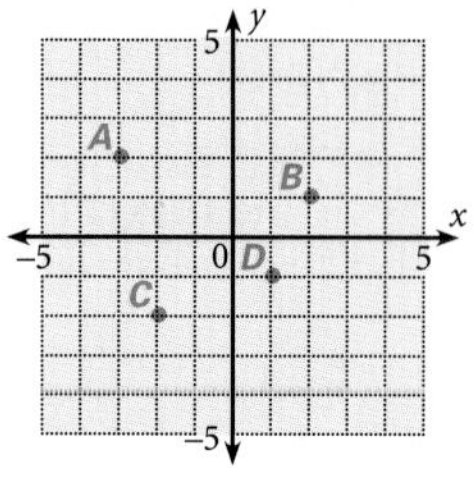

11. What are the coordinates of each point? $A(-3, 2)$, $B(2, 1)$, $C(-2, -2)$, $D(1, -1)$

12. If Point A were translated left 1 space and up 3 spaces, what would be the coordinates of A'? $(-4, 5)$

13. If Point B were reflected across the y-axis, what would be the coordinates of B'? $(-2, 1)$

14. If Point C were reflected across the y-axis and translated 3 points to the right and 2 points down, what would be the coordinates of its image? $(5, -4)$

15. If Point D were translated 3 spaces to the right and 5 spaces up, what would be the coordinates of its image? $(4, 4)$

Graph each equation.

16. $y = -2x$ **17.** $y = 6 + x$ **18.** $y = x - 2$ **19.** $y = x + (-2)$ **20.** $y = 7$

21. Geometry The coordinates of two opposite vertices of a square are $(4, -4)$ and $(2, -2)$. If the square is reflected across the x-axis, what are the coordinates of the four vertices of its image?

22. Graph the equations $y = x + 1$ and $y = x - 1$. Do the lines have a point in common? Explain.

REVIEW 9B

Test Prep

On the coordinate plane, numbers above the x-axis and numbers to the right of the y-axis are always positive.

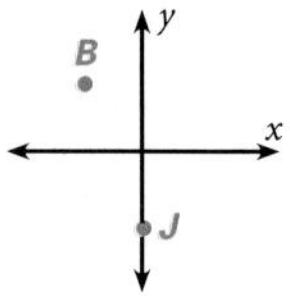

23. Choose the possible ordered pair for point B. A

Ⓐ $(-2, 2)$ Ⓑ $(2, -2)$ Ⓒ $(2, 2)$ Ⓓ $(-2, -2)$

24. Choose the possible ordered pair for point J. A

Ⓐ $(0, -3)$ Ⓑ $(-3, 0)$ Ⓒ $(0, 3)$ Ⓓ $(3, 0)$

Resources

Practice Masters
Section 9B Review

Assessment Sourcebook
Quiz 9B

TestWorks
Test and Practice Software

PRACTICE

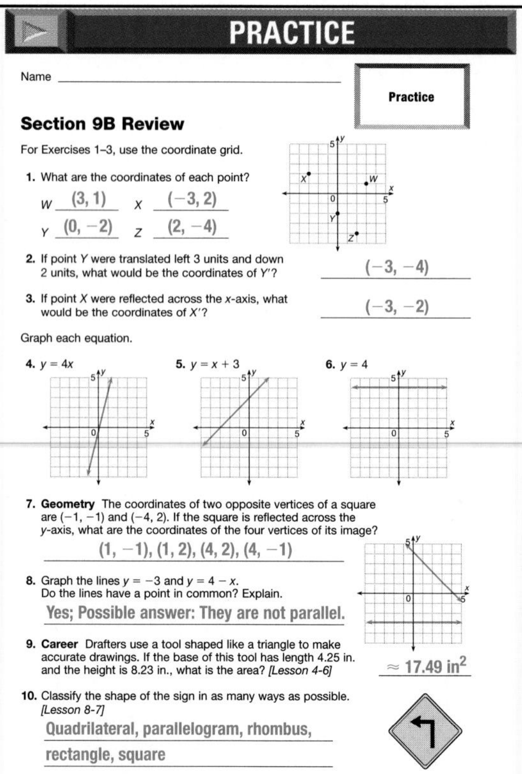

Name ____________ Practice

Section 9B Review

For Exercises 1–3, use the coordinate grid.

1. What are the coordinates of each point?
W (3, 1) X (−3, 2)
Y (0, −2) Z (2, −4)

2. If point Y were translated left 3 units and down 2 units, what would be the coordinates of Y′? (−3, −4)

3. If point X were reflected across the x-axis, what would be the coordinates of X′? (−3, −2)

Graph each equation.

4. y = 4x 5. y = x + 3 6. y = 4

7. **Geometry** The coordinates of two opposite vertices of a square are (−1, −1) and (−4, 2). If the square is reflected across the y-axis, what are the coordinates of the four vertices of its image? (1, −1), (1, 2), (4, 2), (4, −1)

8. Graph the lines y = −3 and y = 4 − x. Do the lines have a point in common? Explain. Yes; Possible answer: They are not parallel.

9. **Career** Drafters use a tool shaped like a triangle to make accurate drawings. If the base of this tool has length 4.25 in. and the height is 8.23 in., what is the area? *[Lesson 4-6]* ≈ 17.49 in²

10. Classify the shape of the sign in as many ways as possible. *[Lesson 8-7]* Quadrilateral, parallelogram, rhombus, rectangle, square

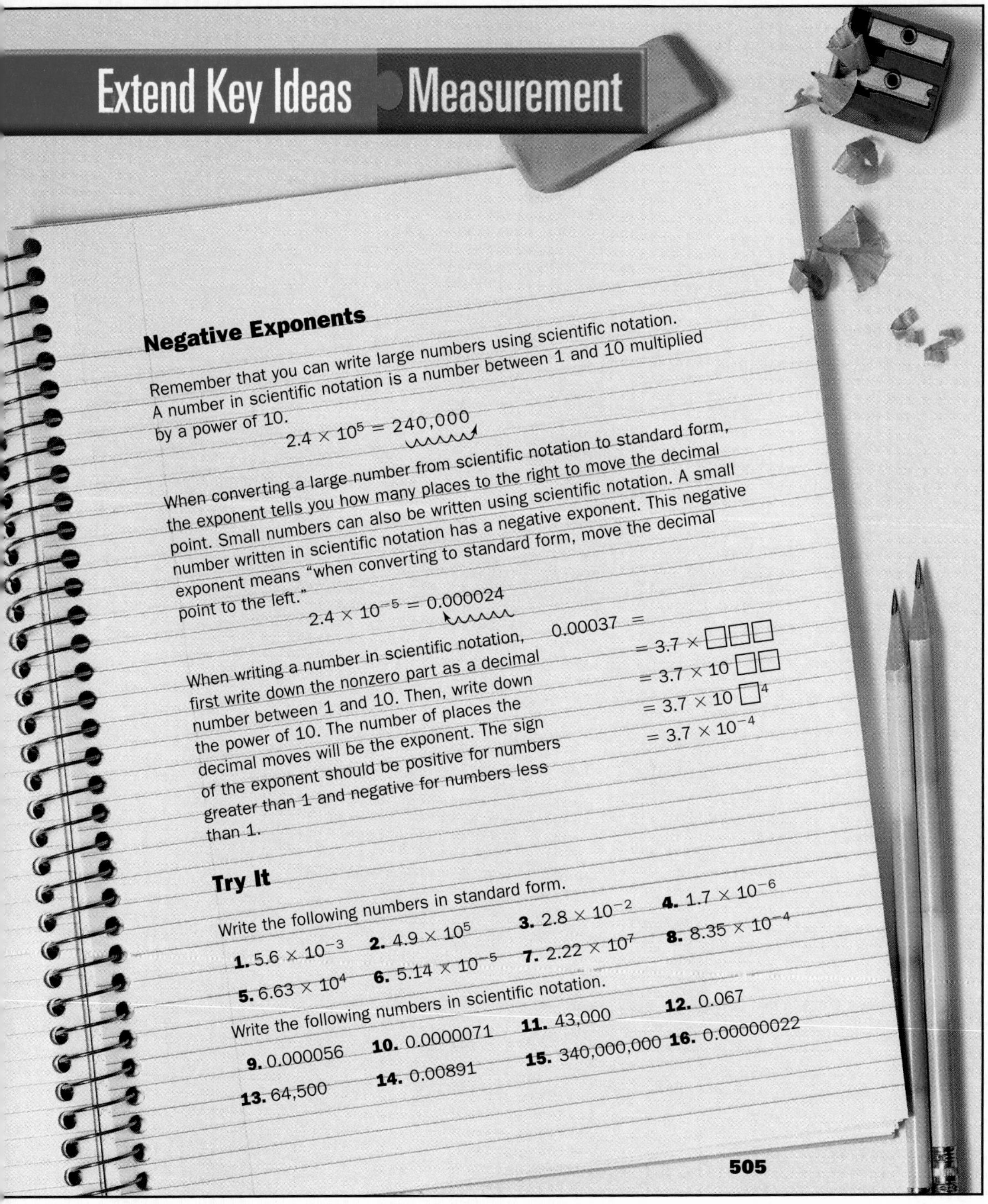

Extend Key Ideas Measurement

Negative Exponents

Remember that you can write large numbers using scientific notation. A number in scientific notation is a number between 1 and 10 multiplied by a power of 10.

$2.4 \times 10^5 = 240,000$

When converting a large number from scientific notation to standard form, the exponent tells you how many places to the right to move the decimal point. Small numbers can also be written using scientific notation. A small number written in scientific notation has a negative exponent. This negative exponent means "when converting to standard form, move the decimal point to the left."

$2.4 \times 10^{-5} = 0.000024$

When writing a number in scientific notation, first write down the nonzero part as a decimal number between 1 and 10. Then, write down the power of 10. The number of places the decimal moves will be the exponent. The sign of the exponent should be positive for numbers greater than 1 and negative for numbers less than 1.

$0.00037 =$
$= 3.7 \times \square\square\square$
$= 3.7 \times 10\,\square\square$
$= 3.7 \times 10\,\square^{4}$
$= 3.7 \times 10^{-4}$

Try It

Write the following numbers in standard form.

1. 5.6×10^{-3} **2.** 4.9×10^5 **3.** 2.8×10^{-2} **4.** 1.7×10^{-6}

5. 6.63×10^4 **6.** 5.14×10^{-5} **7.** 2.22×10^7 **8.** 8.35×10^{-4}

Write the following numbers in scientific notation.

9. 0.000056 **10.** 0.0000071 **11.** 43,000 **12.** 0.067

13. 64,500 **14.** 0.00891 **15.** 340,000,000 **16.** 0.00000022

505

Extend Key Ideas

Negative Exponents

The Point

Students write small numbers in scientific notation, using negative exponents.

About the Page

- You might review briefly how scientific notation is written for large numbers. Some of the exercises review this concept.
- You might ask what operation takes place on the 2.4 when converting 2.4×10^{-5} to 0.000024. Point out that division by 100,000, or 10^5, is the same as multiplying by $\frac{1}{10^5}$. So, if multiplying by 10^{-5} is the same as multiplying by $\frac{1}{10^5}$, what does the negative exponent mean? Division by 100,000; Reciprocal.

Ask …

- For the number 5.2×10^{-6}, how should the decimal point be moved to write the number in standard form? Six places to the left.
- For the number 2.8×10^4, how should the decimal point be moved to write the number in standard form? Four places to the right.

Extension

Find five samples of very large or very small numbers in a science book. Write the numbers in scientific notation, or in standard form.

Answers for Try It

1. 0.0056	9. 5.6×10^{-5}
2. 490,000	10. 7.1×10^{-6}
3. 0.028	11. 4.3×10^4
4. 0.0000017	12. 6.7×10^{-2}
5. 66,300	13. 6.45×10^4
6. 0.0000514	14. 8.91×10^{-3}
7. 22,200,000	15. 3.4×10^8
8. 0.000835	16. 2.2×10^{-7}

Chapter 9 Summary and Review

Review Correlation

Item(s)	Lesson(s)
1, 2	9-1
3	9-2
4	9-4
5, 6	9-2, 9-3
7–10	9-2
11–14	9-3
15–18	9-4
19–21	9-5
22, 23	9-6
24	9-7

For additional review, see page 670.

Answers for Review

1.

Chapter 9 Summary and Review

Graphic Organizer

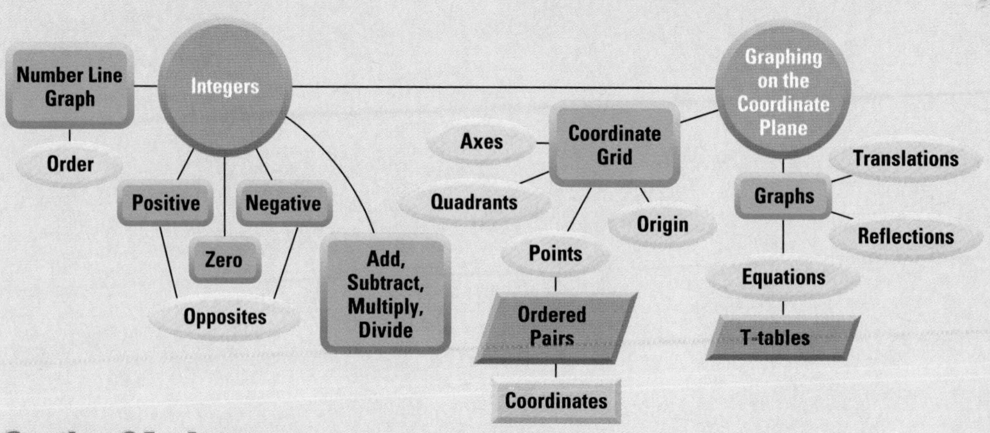

Section 9A Integers

Summary

- **Integers** include positive and negative whole numbers and zero.
- Integers can be graphed as points on a number line.
- Every integer has an **opposite**. The sum of an integer and its opposite is zero.
- You can add, subtract, multiply, or divide any combination of positive and negative integers.

Review

1. Locate the integers $-4, 3, -2, -6, 1$, and 0 on a number line.
2. What is the closest integer to the left of $-2\frac{1}{2}$ on a number line? -3
3. Is the sum of two negative numbers positive or negative? Negative
4. Is the product of two negative numbers positive or negative? Positive

Write a problem that is shown by each model.

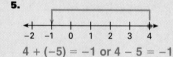

5.

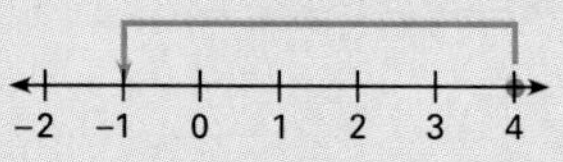

$4 + (-5) = -1$ or $4 - 5 = -1$

6.

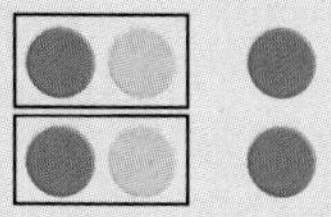

$2 + (-4) = -2$ or $2 - 4 = -2$

Resources

Practice Masters
Cumulative Review Chapters 1–9

Assessment Sourcebook
Quarterly Test Chapters 1–9

PRACTICE

Name ____________

Practice

Cumulative Review Chapters 1–9

Find the circumference C and the area A of each circle where r = radius and d = diameter. Use 3.14 for π. *[Lessons 4-7, 4-8]*

1. $r = 7$ cm, $C \approx$ 43.96 cm, $A \approx$ 153.86 cm^2
2. $d = 10$ ft, $C \approx$ 31.4 ft, $A \approx$ 78.5 ft^2
3. $r = 11$ in., $C \approx$ 69.08 in., $A \approx$ 379.94 in^2
4. $r = 7.3$ m, $C \approx$ 45.844 m, $A \approx$ 167.3306 m^2

Subtract. Write the answer as a whole or mixed number in lowest terms. *[Lesson 6-6]*

5. $9\frac{1}{4} - 6\frac{1}{8}$ $3\frac{1}{8}$
6. $3\frac{1}{2} - 1\frac{1}{3}$ $2\frac{1}{6}$
7. $4\frac{1}{5} - 3\frac{1}{4}$ $\frac{19}{20}$
8. $7\frac{5}{8} - 5\frac{1}{2}$ $2\frac{1}{8}$
9. $6\frac{1}{3} - 2\frac{3}{4}$ $3\frac{7}{12}$
10. $7\frac{2}{3} - 4\frac{1}{6}$ $3\frac{1}{2}$
11. $4\frac{3}{5} - 4\frac{1}{10}$ $\frac{1}{2}$
12. $3\frac{1}{3} - \frac{1}{5}$ $3\frac{2}{15}$
13. $8\frac{1}{4} - 5\frac{4}{5}$ $2\frac{9}{20}$

Classify each figure in as many ways as possible. *[Lesson 8-7]*

14. Quadrilateral, trapezoid

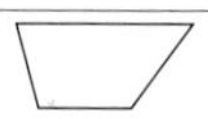

15. Quadrilateral, parallelogram, rectangle

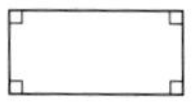

Simplify. *[Lessons 9-2, 9-3, 9-4]*

16. $-7 \times (-4)$ 28
17. $10 - 17$ -7
18. $21 \div (-7)$ -3
19. $-12 + (-11)$ -23
20. $3 \times (-8)$ -24
21. $8 - (-9)$ 17
22. $-48 \div (-6)$ 8
23. $-4 + 22$ 18
24. -5×8 -40

Plot and label each point. *[Lesson 9-5]*

25. $W(-3, -2)$
26. $H(1, -3)$
27. $L(2, -5)$
28. $M(3, 2)$
29. $B(-2, 4)$
30. $D(-4, 0)$
31. $G(4, 3)$
32. $Q(-1, 1)$
33. $Z(4, -3)$

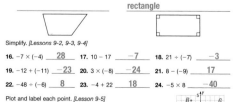

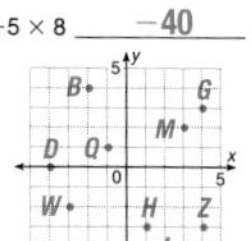

Section 9A Integers *continued*

Simplify.

7. $-3 + 7$ 4 **8.** $-1 + (-5)$ -6 **9.** $8 + (-6)$ 2 **10.** $-6 + 6$ 0

11. $-4 - 2$ -6 **12.** $-5 - 5$ -10 **13.** $-3 - (-3)$ 0 **14.** $7 - (-21)$ 28

15. $3 \times (-7)$ -21 **16.** $-4 \times (-9)$ 36 **17.** $-16 \div 2$ -8 **18.** $-27 \div (-9)$ 3

Section 9B Graphing on the Coordinate Plane

Summary

- You can use a **coordinate grid** with ***x*-** and ***y*-axes** to divide a plane into four **quadrants.**
- You can locate any point on the grid using two **coordinates.** A pair of coordinates is also called an **ordered pair.**
- The axes intersect at right angles at the point (0, 0), called the **origin.**
- A figure can be translated or reflected on a coordinate grid.
- When a figure is reflected across the *x*-axis, only the *y*-coordinates of the image points change. When it is reflected across the *y*-axis, only the *x*-coordinates change.
- To graph an equation, you can first find pairs of values that are true for the equation using a **T-table.** Then, you can graph the points corresponding to these pairs on a coordinate grid.

Review

19. Name the ordered pair for the point 6 units left of the origin along the *x*-axis and 5 units down. $(-6, -5)$

20. Name the quadrant where the point $(-3, 2)$ is located. Quadrant II

21. Name a point the same *distance* from the origin as $(-5, 0)$

a. On the *x*-axis (5, 0) **b.** On the *y*-axis

22. $\triangle RST$ has coordinates $R(-4, 2)$, $S(-3, 4)$, and $T(-2, 2)$. If $\triangle RST$ is reflected across the *x*-axis, name the coordinates of R', S', and T'.

23. Create $A'B'C'D'$ by translating the rectangle $ABCD$ 1 unit to the left and 3 units up. Give the coordinates of A', B', C', and D'.

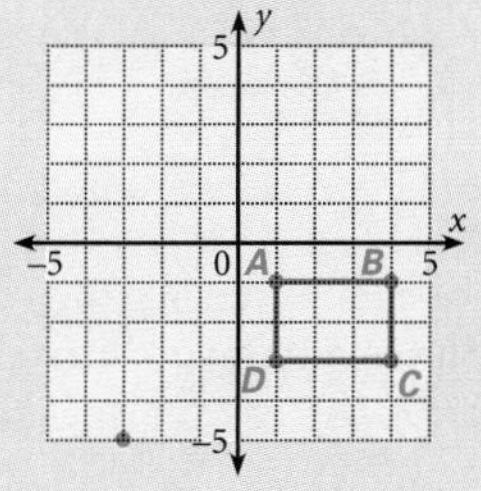

24. a. Graph the equation $y = x + 2$ and the equation $y = x - 1$ on the same coordinate grid.

b. Explain why one of the graphs is a translation of the other.

Answers for Review

22. $R'(-4, -2)$; $S'(-3, -4)$; and $T'(-2, -2)$.

23.

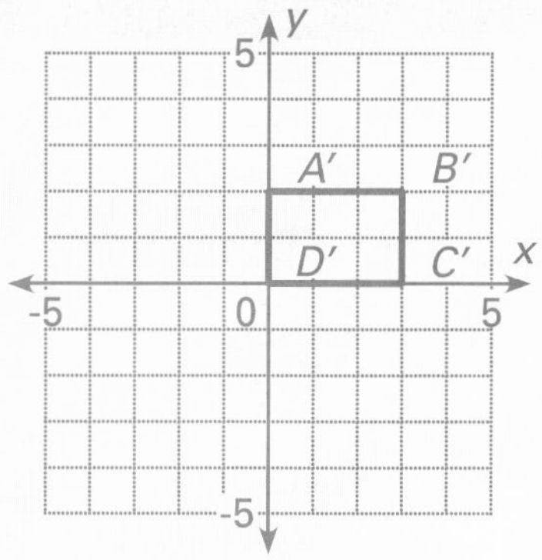

$A'(0, 2)$; $B'(3, 2)$; $C'(3, 0)$; $D'(0, 0)$.

24. a.

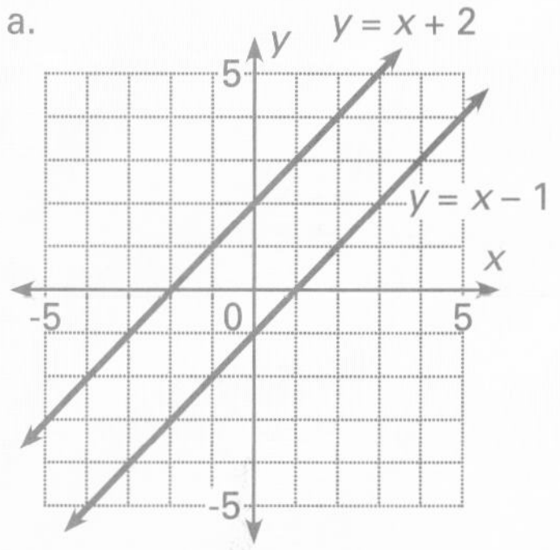

b. Each point on the upper line has been translated down 3 units and over 0 units, to create the lower line.

Chapter 9 Assessment

Chapter 9 Assessment

Fill in each blank with the correct word.

1. The sum of an integer and its ____ is zero. **Opposite**

2. Numbers less than 0 are called ____ numbers. **Negative**

3. You can subtract an integer by adding its ____. **Opposite**

4. The *x*- and *y*-axes of a coordinate grid divide a plane into four ____. **Quadrants**

5. The point (0, 0) on a coordinate grid is called the ____. **Origin**

6. The number −6 is the first ____ of the ordered pair (−6, 7). **Coordinate**

7. It was 36°F at noon in Des Moines. Over the next 7 hours the temperature fell 48°. What integer would you use to represent the new temperature? **−12**

Simplify.

8. $-10 + 7$ **−3** **9.** $4 - (-6)$ **10** **10.** $8 \times (-6)$ **−48** **11.** $-6 \div 6$ **−1**

12. $-4 \times (-2)$ **8** **13.** $-5 + 5$ **0** **14.** $-5 - (-5)$ **0** **15.** $-21 \div (-21)$ **1**

16. Create $\triangle D'E'F'$ by reflecting $\triangle DEF$ across the *y*-axis. Give the coordinates of *D'*, *E'*, and *F'*.

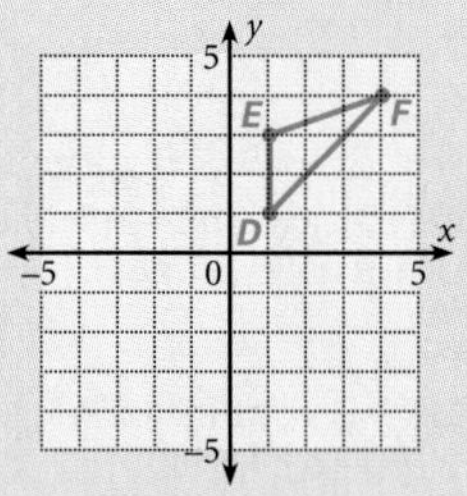

17. Create $\triangle R'S'T'$ by translating $\triangle RST$ 3 units to the right and 4 units down. Give the coordinates of *R'*, *S'*, and *T'*.

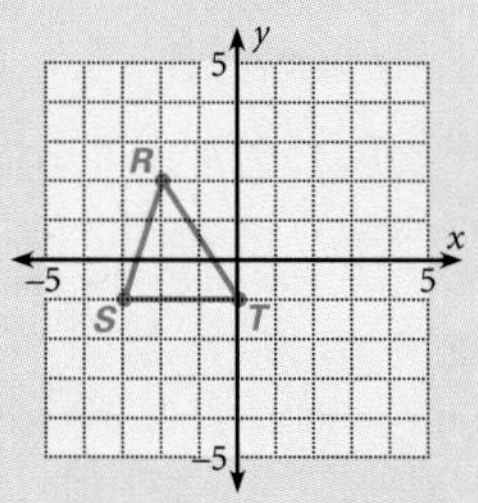

18. Use a T-table and graph the equation $y = -2x$.

Performance Task

Two players, A and B, started a dart game with 0 points. Player A threw three darts, and added the score in each section to his total. His final score was −5. Player B threw three darts, but she subtracted the score in each section from her total. Her final score was −1. On the dart board shown, which three darts belong to Player A, and which three to Player B?

Assessment Correlation

Item(s)	Lesson(s)
1	9-2
2	9-1
3	9-3
4–6	9-5
7	9-3
8, 13	9-2
9, 14	9-3
10–12, 15	9-4
16, 17	9-6
18	9-7

Answers for Assessment

16. $D'(-1, 1)$; $E'(-1, 3)$; $F'(-4, 4)$

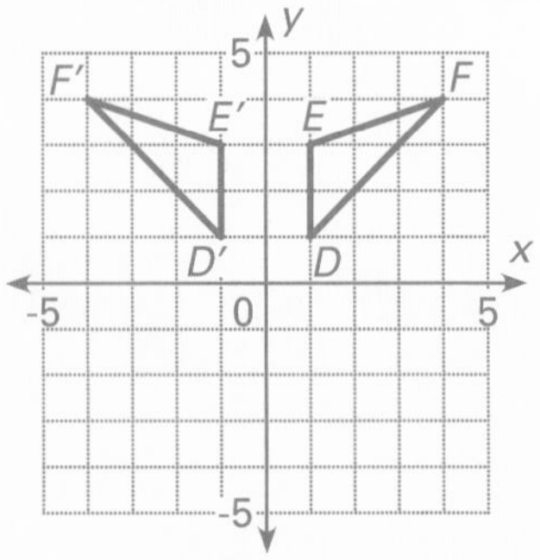

17. $R'(1, -2)$; $S'(0, -5)$; $T'(3, -5)$

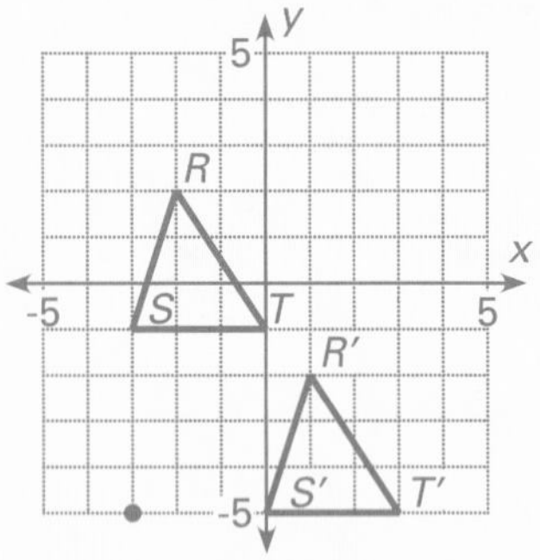

18.

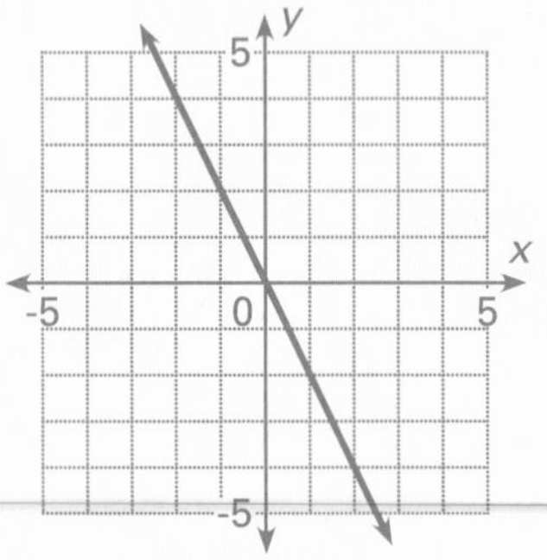

Answer for Performance Task

Player A's darts landed on the rings with values of −2, −4, and 1. Player B's darts landed on the rings with values of −2, −4, and 5.

Resources

Assessment Sourcebook

Chapter 9 Tests
- Forms A and B (free response)
- Form C (multiple choice)
- Form D (performance assessment)
- Form E (mixed response)
- Form F (cumulative chapter test)

TestWorks
Test and Practice Software

Home and Community Connections
- Letter Home for Chapter 9 in English and Spanish

Cumulative Review Test Prep

Cumulative Review Chapters 1–9 — Test Prep

Performance Assessment

Choose one problem.

Ups and Downs

Bar graphs may show negative as well as positive values.

Stock Prices

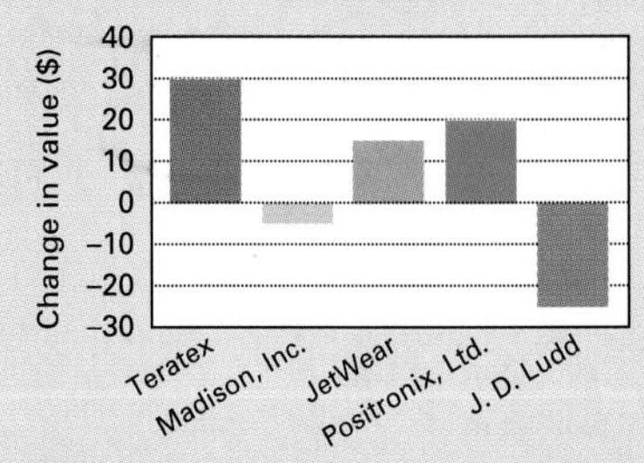

Read the weather page in your newspaper or search the Internet and find the temperatures for five cities for the same date. At least two must be positive, and at least two must be negative. Graph the five temperatures on a bar graph. What was the median temperature for the cities?

The Powers of Negative Numbers

Write out a table showing the values of 2^2, 2^3, 2^4, ..., 2^{10}. In another table, show the values for $(-2)^2$, $(-2)^3$, $(-2)^4$, ..., $(-2)^{10}$. Describe any patterns you see.

DECIMAL DELIGHTS

An ice cream store specializes in making very long sundaes for large groups. A plain, 1-scoop sundae with chocolate topping costs $1.40. Each additional scoop costs an additional $1.40. Write an equation that represents the situation and graph it. How much would a 25-scoop sundae cost? A 40-scoop sundae?

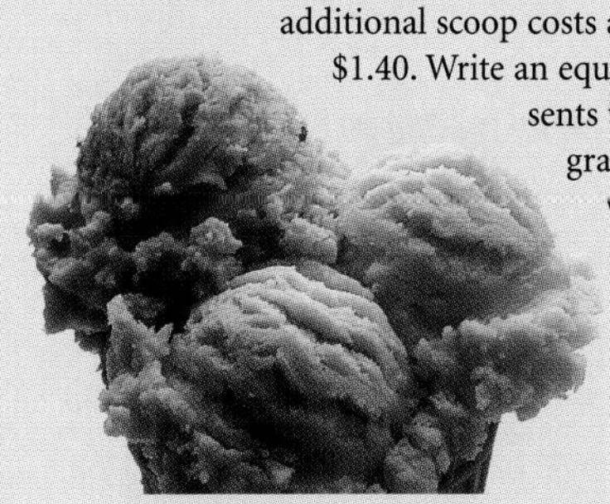

Point Me in the Right Direction

Graph the points (4, 3) and (4, −2) on a coordinate grid. Then state the coordinates of two points which could be connected to (4, 3) and (4, −2) to form each figure.

a. Trapezoid

b. Nonrectangular parallelogram

c. Rectangle

d. Quadrilateral that cannot be classified as a trapezoid or parallelogram

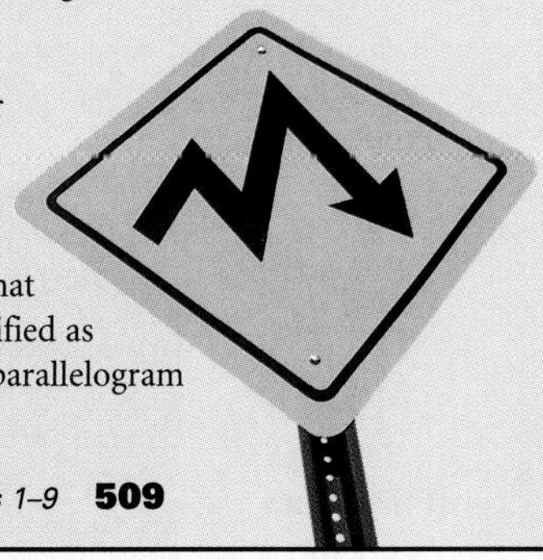

About Performance Assessment

The Performance Assessment options ...

- provide teachers with an alternate means of assessing students.
- address different learning modalities.
- allow students to choose one problem.

Teachers may encourage students to choose the most challenging problem.

Learning Modalities
Ups and Downs **Visual** Students display collected data in a bar graph.
The Powers of Negative Numbers **Logical** Students identify patterns generated by raising a whole number and its inverse to the same power.
Decimal Delights **Individual** Students write an equation and then graph the equation.
Point Me in the Right Direction **Social** Students work in groups to identify the correct coordinates.

Suggested Scoring Rubric

See key on page 465.

Ups and Downs

4	• Graphs all data on a bar graph. • Correctly identifies median temperature.
3	• Graphs most data on a bar graph. • Correctly identifies median temperature.
2	• Graphs some data on a bar graph. • Attempts to identify median temperature.
1	• Graphs little data on a bar graph. • Fails to identify median temperature.

Answers for Assessment

• Decimal Delights

$y = 1.40x$; (25, $35), (40, $56)

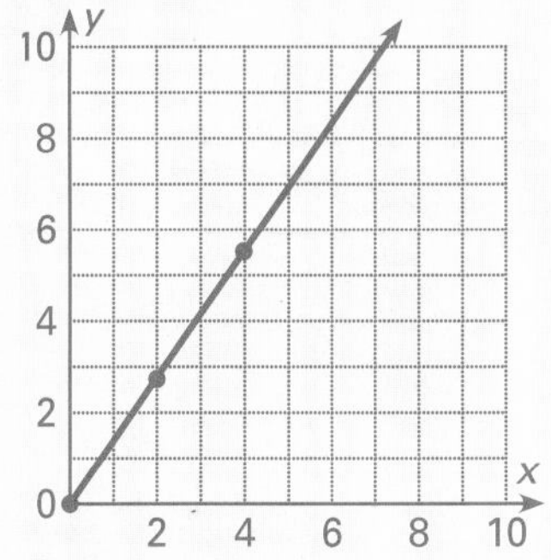

• The Powers of Negative Numbers

For 2^x: 4, 8, 16, 32, 64, 128, 256, 512, 1024

For $(-2)^x$: 4, −8, 16, −32, 64, −128, 256, −512, 1024

Possible description of patterns: If the base is positive, the answer is positive. If the base is negative, and the exponent is odd, the sign of the answer is negative. If the base is negative and the exponent is even, the sign of the answer is positive.

• Point Me in the Right Direction

Possible answers: a. (−2, −2), (−1, 3); b. (−1, 3), (−1, −2); c. (−5, 3), (−5, −2); d. (2, −3), (6, 0).

Chapter 10

Ratio, Proportion, and Percent

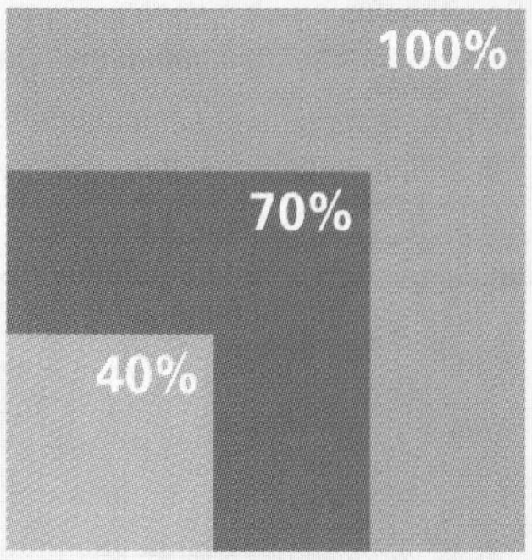

▶ OVERVIEW

Section 10A

Ratios and Rates: Students learn to use ratios to compare quantities.

10-1 What Is a Ratio?

10-2 Equal Ratios

10-3 What Is a Rate?

Section 10B

Proportions: Students learn to express equal ratios as a proportion and to solve proportions.

10-4 What Is a Proportion?

10-5 Solving Proportions Using Cross Products

10-6 Solving Proportions Using Unit Rates

10-7 Similar Figures

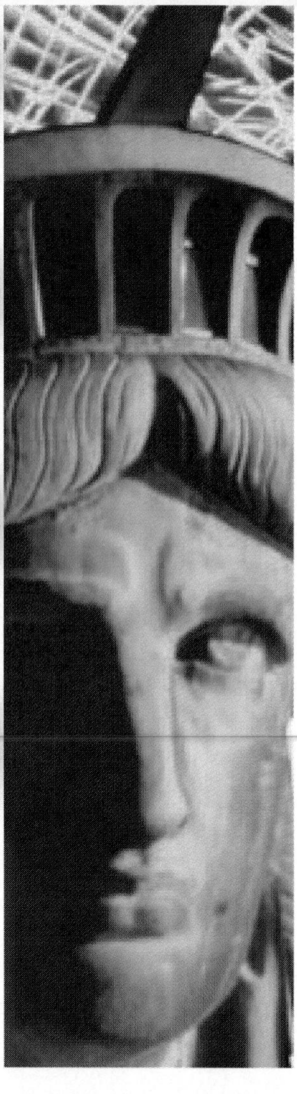

Section 10C

Percents: Students learn to express ratios as percents. They also learn to relate fractions, decimals, and percents.

10-8 What Is a Percent?

10-9 Estimating Percents

10-10 Connecting Percents to Fractions and Decimals

10-11 Finding a Percent of a Number

Meeting NCTM Standards

Curriculum Standards

	Standard		pages
1	**Problem Solving**	Skills and Strategies	512, 519, 522, 533, 537, 544, 546, 555, 567
		Applications	516–517, 521–522, 525–526, 527, 532–533, 536–537, 541–542, 545–546, 547, 552–553, 556–557, 561–562, 566–567, 569
		Exploration	514, 518, 523, 530, 534, 538, 543, 550, 554, 558, 563
2	**Communication**	Oral	513, 516, 521, 524, *526*, 529, 532, 535, 540, 544, 549, 552, 555, 561, 565
		Written	517, 526, 533, 537, 542, *546*, 553, 557, 562, 567
		Cooperative Learning	*514, 518, 523, 530, 534, 538, 543, 550, 554, 558, 563, 565*
3	**Reasoning**	Critical Thinking	517, 522, 526, 533, 537, 542, 546, 553, 557, 562, 567
4	**Connections**	Mathematical	See Standards 5, 7, 12, 13 below.
		Interdisciplinary	Language 564; Literature 542; Health 562; Social Studies 510; Arts & Literature 510; Entertainment 511; Industry *513*, 516, 525, 566; History 516, *520*, 524, *529*, 536, 564; Fine Arts 529, 532; Consumer 533, 566; Geography 537, 541, 548, *549*, 552, 554, 556, *557*, *560*, 567; Science 511, *513*, 522, *525*, *540*, 541, *549*, 551, 559, 565; Health 562
		Technology	539, 564, 568
		Cultural	510, 547
5	**Number and Number Relationships**		514–570
7	**Computation and Estimation**		*519*, 521, 525, *531*, *539*, 541, *544*, 550–568
12	**Geometry**		516, 541, 543–546, 553
13	**Measurement**		536, 538–542

STANDARD

Italic type indicates Teacher Edition reference.

Teaching Standards

Focus on Analysis of Teaching

Teachers should constantly analyze what they and their students are doing, and how that is affecting what students learn. Teachers should

- select some simple ways of maintaining a record of classroom activities.
- describe and comment on each student's progress to parents, administrators, and to the student.

Assessment Standards

Focus on Coherence

Interviews The inclusion of activities that give students the opportunity to demonstrate the knowledge to be assessed is a characteristic of a coherent assessment system. Students' understanding of concepts can be implied by their ability to apply those ideas on a skill-based assessment tool. An interview is one method of gaining such information. In Chapter 10, students are given an opportunity to

- explain *rate*.
- differentiate between ratio and rate.

TECHNOLOGY

For the Teacher

- **Teacher Resource Planner CD-ROM**
  Use the teacher planning CD-ROM to view resources available for Chapter 10. You can prepare custom lesson plans or use the default lesson plans provided.

- **World Wide Web**
  Visit **www.teacher.mathsurf.com** for links to lesson plans from teachers and other professionals, NCTM information, and other sites.

- **TestWorks**
  TestWorks provides ready-made tests and can create custom tests and practice worksheets.

For the Parent

- **World Wide Web**
  Parents can use the Web site at **www.parent.mathsurf.com.**

For the Student

- **Interactive CD-ROM**
  Lesson 10-8 has an *Interactive CD-ROM Lesson*. The *Interactive CD-ROM Journal* and *Interactive CD-ROM Spreadsheet/Grapher Tool* are also used in Chapter 10.

- **Wide World of Mathematics**
  Lesson 10-3 Middle School: New York City Marathon

- **World Wide Web**
  Use with Chapter and Section Openers; Students can go online to the Scott Foresman-Addison Wesley Web site at **www.mathsurf.com/6/ch10** to collect information about chapter themes.

- **Jasper Woodbury Videodisc**
  Lesson 10-3: Get Out the Vote
  Lesson 10-6: Bridging the Gap

STANDARDIZED - TEST CORRELATION

SECTION 10A

LESSON	OBJECTIVE	ITBS Form M	CTBS 4th Ed.	CAT 5th Ed.	SAT 9th Ed.	MAT 7th Ed.	Your Form
10-1	• Express two quantities as a ratio.	✘	✘	✘	✘	✘	
10-2	• Find ratios equal to a given ratio.	✘	✘	✘		✘	
10-3	• Express two quantities with different units as a rate.	✘		✘		✘	

SECTION 10B

LESSON	OBJECTIVE	ITBS Form M	CTBS 4th Ed.	CAT 5th Ed.	SAT 9th Ed.	MAT 7th Ed.	Your Form
10-4	• Learn what a proportion is. • Test to see if two ratios form a proportion.	✘	✘	✘		✘	
10-5	• Solve proportions using cross products.						
10-6	• Solve proportions using unit rates.	✘	✘	✘		✘	
10-7	• Learn what similar figures are. • Use proportions to find lengths in a similar figure.		✘	✘	✘ ✘		

SECTION 10C

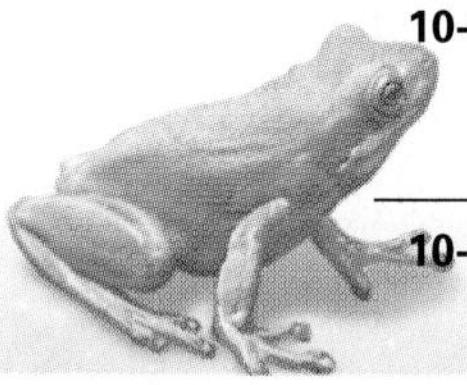

LESSON	OBJECTIVE	ITBS Form M	CTBS 4th Ed.	CAT 5th Ed.	SAT 9th Ed.	MAT 7th Ed.	Your Form
10-8	• Express a quantity as a percent.	✘	✘	✘	✘	✘	
10-9	• Estimate percents.						
10-10	• Express percents as fractions and decimals. • Express fractions and decimals as percents.	✘ ✘	✘ ✘	✘ ✘	✘ ✘	✘ ✘	
10-11	• Find a percent of a number. • Find a whole when given a percent and a part.	✘	✘	✘	✘		

Key: ITBS - Iowa Test of Basic Skills; CTBS - Comprehensive Test of Basic Skills; CAT - California Achievement Test; SAT - Stanford Achievement Test; MAT - Metropolitan Achievement Test

ASSESSMENT PROGRAM

Traditional Assessment

QUICK QUIZZES	SECTION REVIEW	CHAPTER REVIEW	CHAPTER ASSESSMENT FREE RESPONSE	CHAPTER ASSESSMENT MULTIPLE CHOICE	CUMULATIVE REVIEW
TE: pp. 517, 522, 526, 533, 537, 542, 546, 553, 557, 562, 567	SE: pp. 528, 548, 570 *Quiz 10A, 10B, 10C	SE: pp. 572–573	SE: p. 574 *Ch. 10 Tests Forms A, B, E	*Ch. 10 Tests Forms C, E	SE: p. 575 *Ch. 10 Test Form F

Alternate Assessment

INTERVIEW	JOURNAL	ONGOING	PERFORMANCE	PORTFOLIO	PROJECT	SELF
TE: p. 526	SE: pp. 517, 526, 533, 537, 542, 557, 562 TE: pp. 512, 522, 546, 567	TE: pp. 514, 518, 523, 530, 534, 538, 543, 550, 554, 558, 563	SE: p. 574 TE: pp. 517, 537, 553, 557 *Ch. 10 Tests Forms D, E	TE: pp. 533, 542	SE: pp. 511, 526, 546, 562 TE: p. 511	TE: p. 562

*Tests and quizzes are in *Assessment Sourcebook*. Test Form E is a mixed response test.
Forms for Alternate Assessment are also available in *Assessment Sourcebook*.

TestWorks: Test and Practice Software

MIDDLE SCHOOL PACING CHART

REGULAR PACING

Day	5 classes per week
1	Chapter 10 Opener; Problem Solving Focus
2	Section **10A** Opener; Lesson **10-1**
3	Lesson **10-2**
4	Lesson **10-3**
5	**10A** Connect; **10A** Review
6	Section **10B** Opener; Lesson **10-4**
7	Lesson **10-5**
8	Lesson **10-6**
9	Lesson **10-7**
10	**10B** Connect; **10B** Review
11	Section **10C** Opener; Lesson **10-8**
12	Lesson **10-9**
13	Lesson **10-10**
14	Lesson **10-11**; Technology
15	**10C** Connect; **10C** Review; Extend Key Ideas
16	Chapter 10 Summary and Review
17	Chapter 10 Assessment Cumulative Review, Chapter 1–10

BLOCK SCHEDULING OPTIONS

Block Scheduling for Complete Course

Chapter 10 may be presented in

- eleven 90-minute blocks
- fourteen 75-minute blocks

Each block consists of a combination of

- Chapter and Section Openers
- Explores
- Lesson Development
- Problem Solving Focus
- Technology
- Extend Key Ideas
- Connect
- Review
- Assessment

For details, see *Block Scheduling Handbook.*

Block Scheduling for Interdisciplinary Course

Each block integrates math with another subject area.

In Chapter 10, interdisciplinary topics include

- Fire Prevention
- Statues
- Rain Forests

Themes for Interdisciplinary Team Teaching 10A, 10B, and 10C are

- Life on Earth
- Scale Models of Buildings
- Electrical Power Usage

For details, see *Block Scheduling Handbook.*

Block Scheduling for Lab-Based Course

In each block, 30–40 minutes is devoted to lab activities including

- Explores in the Student Edition
- Connect pages in the Student Edition
- Technology options in the Student Edition
- Reteaching Activities in the Teacher Edition

For details, see *Block Scheduling Handbook.*

Block Scheduling for Course with *Connected Mathematics*

In each block, investigations from **Connected Mathematics** replace or enhance the lessons in Chapter 10.

Connected Mathematics topics for Chapter 10 can be found in

- *Bits and Pieces II*
- *Bits and Pieces I*

For details, see *Block Scheduling Handbook.*

INTERDISCIPLINARY BULLETIN BOARD

Set Up

Suggest that students research the top speeds of famous transportation modes of the past and present. Examples include the Rocket (1829), Clermont (1807), French TGV train (1980), Cadillac® coupe (1958), DC-3 (1935), and Concorde (1976).

Procedure

- Have groups choose a transportation mode to research.
- Groups should draw pictures of their topic, label them with names and dates of production, and indicate their speed.

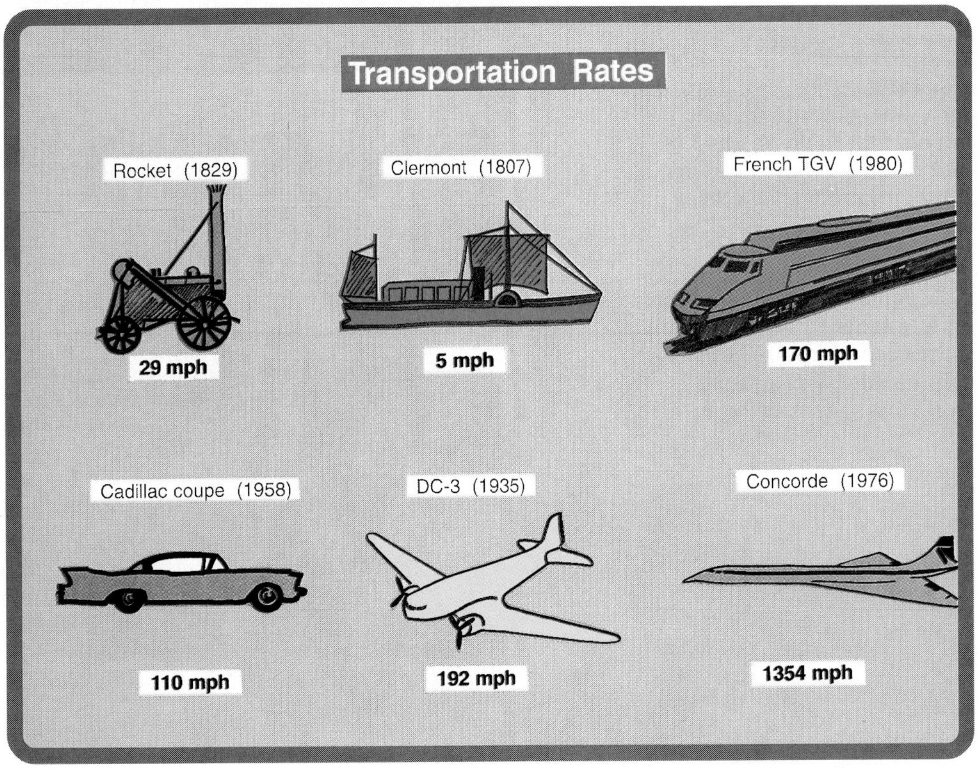

Chapter 10

The information on these pages shows how ratios, proportions, and percents are used in real-life situations.

World Wide Web

If your class has access to the World Wide Web, you might want to use the information found at the Web site addresses given.

Extensions

The following activities do not require access to the World Wide Web.

People of the World
Ask students to investigate the "Golden Ratio" and to find examples of other structures and art forms that use this ratio.

Social Studies
Have students investigate the population density of their state and determine the population density of the United States. In 1990, the population density of the United States was 70.3 people per square mile.

Arts & Literature
Talk about how the lengths of strings on musical instruments are changed by the person playing the instrument and how this change affects the notes. Students who play violins or guitars may be able to share their experiences.

Entertainment
Suggest that students investigate the impact that radio has had on people's lives and how the programming of radio shows has changed since 1930.

Science
Have students investigate revolutions per minute (rpm) or revolutions per second (rps). They may include machinery or motors which record speeds using rpm or rps.

10 Ratio, Proportion, and Percent

Cultural Link
www.mathsurf.com/6/ch10/people

Arts & Literature Link
www.mathsurf.com/6/ch10/arts

People of the World

The Parthenon, built in Athens in the 400s B.C., incorporated the Greeks' ideal "Golden Ratio," which is approximately 0.618 to 1.

Arts & Literature

If one harp string is twice as long as another, the longer one will play the same note one octave lower. If one string is half as long as another, it will play the same note one octave higher.

Social Studies

Population density measures how many people there are for each square mile. New Jersey has a population density of 1042 people per square mile. Alaska has a population density of 1 person per square mile.

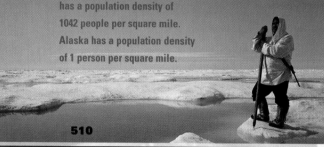

510

TEACHER TALK

Meet Jim Foley

Champlin Park High School
Champlin, Minnesota

When I teach this chapter, I integrate ratio and proportion with many other subjects. I show students how an understanding of ratio and proportion can help them solve problems related to science, sports, shopping, and art.

I use M & M's® to teach ratio and proportion. I ask students to compare the different colors of M & M's in a bag and see if the ratio of different colors is the same. Students' results will not all be the same. Some will eat a few candies. Students are willing to talk and write about their findings during these activities. I introduce proportion by asking the students if they think all bags of M & M's will have the same color ratios, or if the ratios vary depending on the size of the bag.

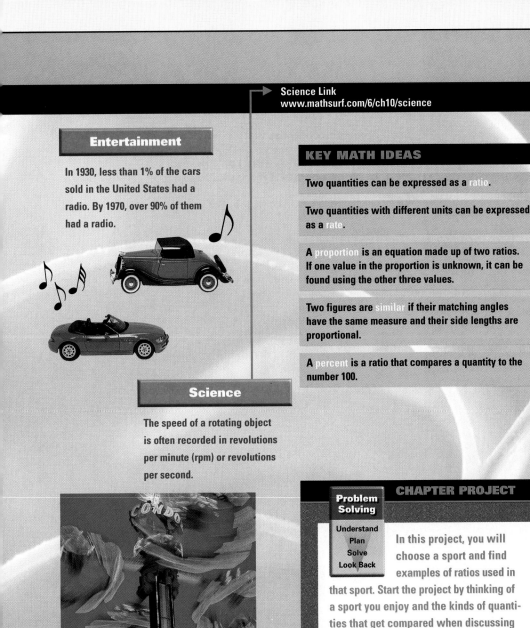

Science Link
www.mathsurf.com/6/ch10/science

Entertainment

In 1930, less than 1% of the cars sold in the United States had a radio. By 1970, over 90% of them had a radio.

Science

The speed of a rotating object is often recorded in revolutions per minute (rpm) or revolutions per second.

KEY MATH IDEAS

Two quantities can be expressed as a **ratio**.

Two quantities with different units can be expressed as a **rate**.

A **proportion** is an equation made up of two ratios. If one value in the proportion is unknown, it can be found using the other three values.

Two figures are **similar** if their matching angles have the same measure and their side lengths are proportional.

A **percent** is a ratio that compares a quantity to the number 100.

CHAPTER PROJECT

Problem Solving
Understand
Plan
Solve
Look Back

In this project, you will choose a sport and find examples of ratios used in that sport. Start the project by thinking of a sport you enjoy and the kinds of quantities that get compared when discussing the sport.

511

Chapter Project

Students investigate ratios used in their favorite sports.

Resources
Chapter 10 Project Master

Introduce the Project

- Begin by discussing students' favorite sports and how they are played.
- Talk about the kinds of information collected about various sports.
- Discuss where students might find information about sports records, such as in almanacs, newspapers, and the Internet.

Project Progress

Section A, page 526 Students identify ratios used in the sport they have chosen and explain the significance of each ratio.

Section B, page 546 Students research or invent proportions related to a person or team playing the chosen sport.

Section C, page 562 Students convert all ratios to a percent and a decimal.

Community Project

A community project for Chapter 10 is available in *Home and Community Connections.*

Cooperative Learning

You may want to use Teaching Tool Transparency 1: Cooperative Learning Checklist with **Explore** and other group activities in this chapter.

PROJECT ASESSMENT

You may choose to use this project as a performance assessment for the chapter.

Performance Assessment Key

Level 4 Full Accomplishment

Level 3 Substantial Accomplishment

Level 2 Partial Accomplishment

Level 1 Little Accomplishment

Suggested Scoring Rubric

4
- Ratios have direct applications to chosen sport.
- All conversions are correct.

3
- Ratios are logical applications to chosen sport.
- Most conversions are correct.

2
- Ratios have a remote application to chosen sport.
- Some conversions are correct.

1
- Ratios have no application to chosen sport.
- Few conversions are correct.

Problem Solving Focus

Checking for a Reasonable Answer

The Point
Students focus on looking back at the problem to determine if their answer is reasonable.

Resources
Teaching Tool Transparency 18: Problem-Solving Guidelines

Interactive CD-ROM Journal

About the Page

Using the Problem-Solving Process
There are two parts to verifying an answer: checking the computation itself and checking to see if the answer is reasonable and makes sense. Discuss the following suggestions for looking back at a problem:

- Review the process for finding the answer.
- Estimate the answer and determine if your calculated answer is reasonable.

Ask ...
- How did you solve Problem 1? How can you decide if your answer is reasonable? Possible answer: Find the product of 127 and 160. Multiply 100 by 160. Because of rounding down, the answer should be slightly larger than 16,000.
- Describe a quick way to determine if the answer to Problem 2 is reasonable. Possible answer: The perimeter is $2 \times 160 + 2 \times 127$; Since 2×160 is close to 385, 385 is probably too small.

Answers for Problems
1. Close enough; The area is 20,320 ft^2.
2. Too low; The perimeter is 574 ft.
3. Too high; $\frac{1}{4}$ of 144 is 36.
4. Close enough; The perimeter of the hexagon is 33 ft, so a few more tiles are needed to go around the perimeter.

Journal

Have students write a paragraph describing the purpose of the *Look Back* step in problem solving.

Problem Solving
Understand
Plan
Solve
Look Back

Checking for a Reasonable Answer

Once you have solved a problem, it is a good idea to look back at your work to verify that you have done it correctly. One way to do this is to check your answer against the original situation to see if your answer is reasonable.

Problem Solving Focus

Each of these problems has an answer, but the answer is not exactly right. State if the answer is too low, too high, or close enough, and explain why.

1. A community garden is being designed for a vacant lot. The entire lot measures 127 feet by 160 feet. What is the area of the lot? *20,000 ft^2*
2. The garden committee will build a fence around the lot. They will plant ivy to grow along the sides of the fence. How much fencing will they need for the 127- by 160-foot lot? *385 feet*
3. On the first day of planting, 144 people volunteered to help with the planting. One-fourth of the volunteers tilled the soil. How many volunteers tilled the soil? *45*
4. A space in the shape of a hexagon is set aside to be planted with marigolds. The perimeter of the hexagon will have a border of square tiles. Each side of the hexagon is $5\frac{1}{2}$ feet. Each tile is 1 square foot. How many tiles will the committee need? *36*

Additional Problem

The population of Prineville is 788. In a recent election, 45% of the population voted. How many of Prineville's residents voted?

1. How would you solve this problem? Possible answer: Write 45% as a decimal and multiply that number by 788.
2. Is an estimate of 200 too high, too low, or about right? Too low; The estimate has to be at least half of 700, or 350.
3. Is an estimate of 500 too high, too low, or about right? Too high; The number will be less than 50% of 800, or 400.
4. What is a reasonable estimate? Possible answer: 400

Section 10A

Ratios and Rates

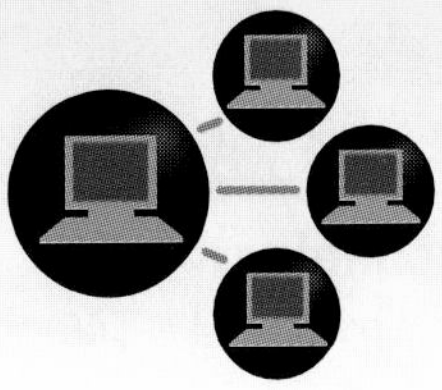

Visit **www.teacher.mathsurf.com** for links to lesson plans from teachers and other professionals, NCTM information, and other sites.

LESSON PLANNING GUIDE

Student Edition / **Ancillaries***

LESSON	MATERIALS	VOCABULARY	DAILY	OTHER
Chapter 10 Opener				Ch. 10 Project Master Ch. 10 Community Project Teaching Tool Trans. 1
Problem Solving Focus				Teaching Tool Trans. 18 *Interactive CD-ROM Journal*
Section 10A Opener				
10-1 **What Is a Ratio?**		ratio	10-1	Lesson Enhancement Trans. 48
10-2 **Equal Ratios**			10-2	Teaching Tool Trans. 2, 3 Lesson Enhancement Trans. 49 Technology Master 51
10-3 **What Is a Rate?**		rate, unit rate	10-3	Technology Master 52 Ch. 10 Project Master *WW Math*–Middle School
Connect	watch with second hand, yardstick or meter stick			Interdisc. Team Teaching 10A
Review				Practice 10A; Quiz 10A; *TestWorks*

* Daily Ancillaries include Practice, Reteaching, Problem Solving, Enrichment, and Daily Transparency. Teaching Tool Transparencies are in *Teacher's Toolkits*. Lesson Enhancement Transparencies are in *Overhead Transparency Package*.

SKILLS TRACE

LESSON	SKILL	FIRST INTRODUCED GR. 4	GR. 5	GR. 6	DEVELOP	PRACTICE/ APPLY	REVIEW
10-1	**Expressing two quantities as a ratio.**		✘		pp. 514–515	pp. 516–517	pp. 528, 548, 570, 572, 583
10-2	**Finding equal ratios.**			✘ p. 518	pp. 518–520	pp. 521–522	pp. 528, 548, 570, 572, 587
10-3	**Expressing two quantities as a rate.**			✘ p. 523	pp. 523–524	pp. 525–526	pp. 528, 548, 570, 572, 592

CONNECTED MATHEMATICS

Investigation 1 in the unit *Bits and Pieces II (Using Rational Numbers)*, from the **Connected Mathematics** series, can be used with Section 10A.

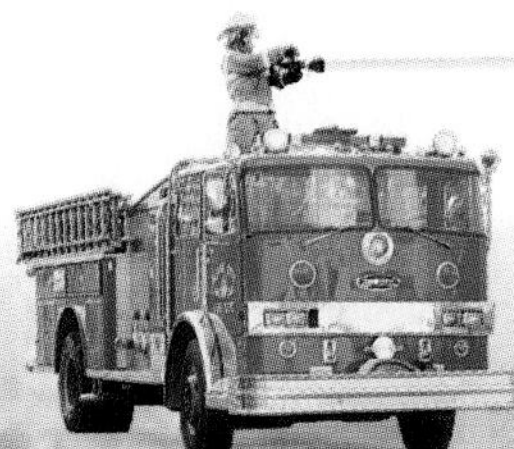

INTERDISCIPLINARY TEAM TEACHING

Math and Science/Technology

(Worksheet pages 47–48: Teacher pages T47–T48)

In this lesson, students investigate how the ratio of daytime to nighttime hours affects life on Earth.

Name ______________________ ***Math and Science/Technology***

Investigate how the ratio of daytime to nighttime hours affects life on Earth.

As the Earth travels around the Sun, different parts of it are tilted toward or away from the Sun. On the first day of summer in the Northern Hemisphere, which occurs in June, the northern half of the Earth tilts toward the Sun, and the southern half tilts away from it. At this time, the Sun is "up" longer in the north than in the south; the reverse is true around December 21st, the first day of winter in the north. On the first day of fall and spring, however, the Earth tilts neither toward nor away from the Sun, and the Sun is "up" and "down" for equal twelve-hour periods of time.

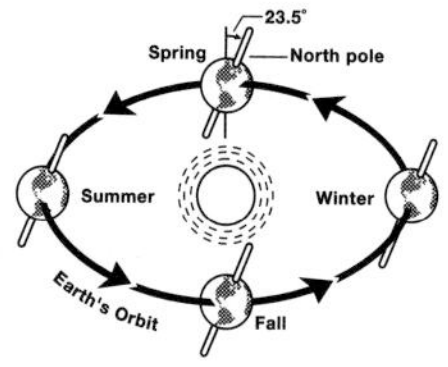

Two things determine how long the Sun is up or down at any given time or location: the time of the year and the latitude of the location. Latitude is the distance north or south of the equator. The Sun is up longest in summer, shortest in winter. But the daytime-nighttime ratio changes with latitude. For example, the farther you are from the equator in the summer, the more daytime and the less nighttime you will have. Therefore, someone living in Alaska, New York, or Canada will have more daylight in June than someone living in California, Texas, or Florida. In winter, the ratio reverses. The farther from the equator you are, the less daytime you will have compared to nighttime. Places that are near the equator have almost equal amounts of daytime and nighttime throughout the year.

Daylight affects the lives of most living things. Flowering plants blossom and develop as daylight and temperatures increase, then wither as daylight and temperatures decrease. That's why farmers plant crops in spring, rather than in fall. As grasses, shrubs, and trees sprout leaves and flowers, many insects and other animals become active. The land warms and people begin new activities, too. Think of ways in which changes in daylight affect your life.

1. a. Use a map or globe to determine the hemisphere in which you live.

The United States is in the Northern Hemisphere.

b. Use a map or globe to determine your latitude.

Students' responses will vary.

c. When does the area in which you live experience the most daylight? The least daylight?

See below.

Name ______________________ ***Math and Science/Technology***

2. Complete the chart below by calculating the ratios of daylight hours to nighttime hours. An example has been provided to help you get started. Then answer the questions that follow the table.

a. What causes the changes in ratios from January to August in most of the cities listed in the table?

the tilt of the Earth's axis relative to the Sun

b. Locate Nairobi on a map or globe. Why do you think its ratio of daytime to nighttime is the same in January and August?

Nairobi is close to the equator.

c. Study a map of the world. Why do you think Los Angeles and Rio de Janeiro have almost opposite ratios of daylight to nighttime?

See below.

3. a. List economic activities that day-night ratios affect.

See below.

b. Select one activity you listed in item 3a. Explain how the day-night ratio affects this activity.

Students' responses will vary.

c. Finland is a country that has a very short growing season because frosts that stunt plant development come early in the fall and last until late in the spring. Finland's latitude, however, gives it much daylight in the summer. How might long hours of daylight make up for short growing seasons?

Plants can grow faster since there is more light each day.

4. Why would airline pilots traveling from Europe to Africa be good subjects in a study about the effects of day-night ratios on the human body?

See below.

5. Check with a local weather service to find out the time of sunset and sunrise for various times of the year in your area. Create a table of ratios of daylight hours to nighttime hours for your area.

Place	Hours of Daylight in January	Ratio of Daytime Hours to Nighttime Hours in January	Hours of Daylight in August	Ratio of Daytime Hours to Nighttime Hours in August
Bangkok, Thailand	11	11:13	13	13:11
Los Angeles, United States	10	10:14	13	13:11
London, Great Britain	8	8:16	15	15:9
Montreal, Canada	9	9:15	14	14:10
Rio de Janeiro, Brazil	13	13:11	11	11:13
Nairobi, Kenya	12	12:12	12	12:12

Answers

1. c. The Northern Hemisphere experiences the most daylight around June 21 and the least around December 21.
2. c. Los Angeles is in the Northern Hemisphere, Rio de Janeiro is in the Southern Hemisphere, and they are about the same distance from the equator.
3. a. Students' responses will vary. Examples include influences upon agriculture, farming, hunting, fishing, manufacturing, and tourism.
4. Airline pilots traveling along such routes would experience dramatic changes in day-to-night ratios.

BIBLIOGRAPHY

FOR TEACHERS

Cooney, Thomas J. *Teaching and Learning Mathematics in the 1990s.* Reston, VA: NCTM, 1990.

Edwards, Edgar L., ed. *Algebra for Everyone.* Reston, VA: NCTM, 1990.

Miller, Ross. *American Apocalypse: The Great Fire and the Myth of Chicago.* Chicago, IL: University of Chicago Press, 1990.

Zawojewski, Judith S., et al. *Dealing with Data and Chance: Addenda Series, Grades 5–8.* Reston, VA: NCTM, 1991.

FOR STUDENTS

Gallant, Roy A. *The Peopling of Planet Earth: Human Population Growth Through the Ages.* New York, NY: Macmillan, 1990.

Macdonald, Fiona. *A Greek Temple.* New York, NY: P. Bedrick Books, 1992.

Moffett, George D. *Global Population Growth: 21st Century Challenges.* Ithaca, NY: Foreign Policy Association, 1994.

Phelan, Mary Kay. *The Story of the Great Chicago Fire,* 1871. New York, NY: Crowell, 1971.

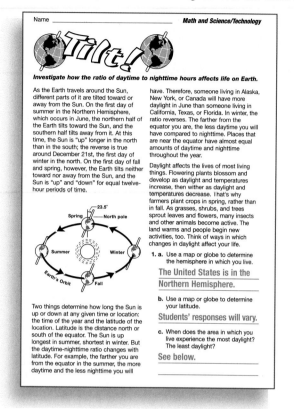

SECTION **10A**

Ratios and Rates

▶ Industry Link ▶ Science Link ▶ www.mathsurf.com/6/ch10/fires

Fire Alarm
October 8, 1871

8:30 p.m. According to one source, Catherine O'Leary milks her cow in her small barn. The cow knocks over her lantern, and the barn catches fire. Mrs. O'Leary starts a bucket brigade, but doesn't think to call the fire department.

9:05 p.m. William Lee goes to fire box 296 and pulls the lever, signaling a fire. The box is faulty, and the alarm does not get through.

9:10 p.m. Fire dispatcher William Brown ignores a red glow in the distance, assuming it is the rekindling of an earlier fire already under control.

9:21 p.m. Brown receives an alarm from fire box 342, a mile south of the fire. He sends seven fire-fighting vehicles to the wrong location.

By the time the fire crew arrived at the correct location, it was too late. The Great Fire of Chicago eventually destroyed over 17,000 homes, and over 300 people lost their lives. Every year, fire stations across the country remember this event by conducting Fire Prevention Week during the week of October 8.

1 The Great Fire of Chicago started out as a small fire. Why did it become so huge and devastating?

2 Do you think the Great Fire of Chicago could have been prevented? Why or why not?

3 How can mathematics help when trying to prevent fires?

Currier, N. and Ives, J. "The Great Chicago Fire"

513

Where are we now?

In Grade 5, students explored ratio, proportion, and percent.

They learned how to

- use grids to draw ratios.
- graph ratios.
- connect ratio and percent.
- estimate percent of a number.

Where are we going?

In Grade 6, Section 10A, students will

- express two quantities as a ratio.
- find ratios equal to a given ratio.
- express two quantities with different units as a rate.

Theme: Fire Prevention

World Wide Web

If your class has access to the World Wide Web, you might want to use the information found at the Web site address given. The interdisciplinary links relate to topics discussed in this section.

About the Page

This page introduces the theme of the section, fire prevention, and discusses the Great Fire of Chicago.

Ask ...

- What is a fire box? A signal box that was placed on street corners and used to send an alarm to the fire department.

Extensions

The following activities do not require access to the World Wide Web.

Industry
The Great Fire of Chicago destroyed the business district of the city. Have students research the rebuilding of Chicago after the fire.

Science
Experts say it is more important to keep fires from starting than to develop ways of putting them out. Have students research the fire-prevention programs in their community.

Answers for Questions

1. A lot of precautions were overlooked. There were very dry conditions and high winds, and the firefighters did not arrive soon enough.
2. Possible answer: Yes; The faulty alarm box should have been maintained better.
3. Possible answers: Mathematics can be used to find locations, to determine how much water to spray on a fire, or to help make evacuation plans.

Connect

On page 527, students investigate how quickly their school can be evacuated.

10-1 Lesson Organizer

Objective

- Express two quantities as a ratio.

Vocabulary

- Ratio

NCTM Standards

- 1–5, 12

► Review

Write each fraction in lowest terms.

1. $\frac{6}{12}$ $\frac{1}{2}$
2. $\frac{4}{10}$ $\frac{2}{5}$
3. $\frac{6}{15}$ $\frac{2}{5}$
4. $\frac{8}{12}$ $\frac{2}{3}$

Available on Daily Transparency 10-1

► Lesson Link

Discuss ratios with the class by having students give examples of comparisons of quantities. Classroom examples might be the number of girls to the number of boys or the number of manipulative sets to the number of students.

1 Introduce

Explore

You may wish to use Lesson Enhancement Transparency 48 with **Explore**.

The Point
Students explore ratios by deciding which statements that describe ratios are true. Students use pictures that show different quantities to decide.

Ongoing Assessment
Check to see that students are writing reasons for why each statement is either true or false. To help students write the reasons, encourage students to describe to one another how they know that a statement is true or false.

10-1 What Is a Ratio?

You'll Learn ...

■ to express two quantities as a ratio

... How It's Used

Caterers use ratios to determine how much food to prepare for an event.

Vocabulary

ratio

► Lesson Link You've learned how to work with fractions. Now you will work with a special kind of fraction called a ratio. ◄

Explore Ratios

What Happened at the Party?

Dear Joleen,

It's too bad you weren't in town for Rebecca's 12th birthday party. It was really great, except that there wasn't enough pizza. (There were only 2 slices for each kid.) She had an angelfood cake topped by 2 candles for each year of her age.

The guest list favored girls—3 out of every 5 guests were girls. Rebecca asked for jeans and got what she wanted—out of every 7 presents, 4 were jeans.

I hope you can make it to Rebecca's party next year!

Your friend,

Stephanie

Which of the underlined statements are true? Which are false? Give reasons for your answers.

MEETING INDIVIDUAL NEEDS

Resources

- **10-1** Practice
- **10-1** Reteaching
- **10-1** Problem Solving
- **10-1** Enrichment
- **10-1** Daily Transparency
  - Problem of the Day
  - Review
  - Quick Quiz

Lesson Enhancement Transparency 48

Learning Modalities

Kinesthetic Give groups of students two different quantities of colored counters. Have each group write as many ratios comparing the different-colored objects as possible.

Verbal Have students describe all the ways of reading a ratio out loud. Possible answers: "3 is to 5," "3 divided by 5," "3 for each 5," "3 to 5."

English Language Development

Students would benefit greatly from using a wide variety of manipulatives and visuals to develop the concept of a ratio.

Learn — What Is a Ratio?

A **ratio** is a comparison of two quantities. The ratio of erasers to pencils can be written as 5 to 3, 5:3, or $\frac{5}{3}$.

Example 1

Give a ratio comparing the number of cats and dogs that can be adopted at the animal shelter.

The ratio is 2 to 7, 2:7, or $\frac{2}{7}$.

Like fractions, ratios can sometimes be rewritten in lowest terms.

Examples

2 Six out of ten fire deaths occur in homes without fire detectors. Write this ratio in lowest terms.

$$\frac{6}{10} = \frac{6 \div 2}{10 \div 2}$$ Divide numerator and denominator by the same number.

$$= \frac{3}{5}$$ Simplify.

In lowest terms, the ratio is 3 to 5, 3:5, or $\frac{3}{5}$.

3 Give a ratio comparing the number of male soccer players and the total number of players in lowest terms.

$$\frac{\text{number of male players}}{\text{number of players}} = \frac{2}{6} = \frac{1}{3}$$

Try It

Give a ratio comparing the quantities in lowest terms.

a. Number of triangles and number of squares 2:5

b. Number of squares and number of figures 1:2

DID YOU KNOW?

It is recommended that the batteries in a smoke detector should be tested once a month, and replaced at least once a year.

MATH EVERY DAY

Problem of the Day

Volumes 1 through 9 of a set of books were on a shelf. One book was removed. The sum of the numbers of the volumes that remained on the shelf is divisible by both 4 and 9. Which volume was removed? Volume 9; The sums of the remaining volumes range from 36 to 44, depending upon the volume removed. 36 is the only sum divisible by 4 and 9.

Available on Daily Transparency 10-1

An Extension is provided in the transparency package.

Fact of the Day

In the Great Fire of Chicago in 1871, about 100,000 people were left homeless out of a population of approximately 300,000.

Mental Math

Find each sum mentally.

1. 20 + 5 + 10 35
2. 40 + 30 + 6 76
3. 70 + 2 + 10 + 4 86

For Groups That Finish Early

Write 3 more true statements by filling in the blanks in 3 different ways.

There were ______ for every ______.

Follow Up

Have students discuss which statements are true and which are false. Have students give the correct ratio for false statements and the ratio shown by the pictures for the true statements.

Answers for Explore

True: 3 out of every 5 guests were girls. The picture shows 6 girls and 10 guests.

False: 2 slices of pizza for each kid. The picture shows 10 guests and 18 pieces of pizza or 1.8 slices for each guest.

False: 2 candles for each year of her age. The picture shows 1 candle for every 2 years of her age.

False: Out of every 7 presents, 4 were jeans. The picture shows 14 presents and only 6 jeans.

2 Teach

Learn

Alternate Examples

Use the information given in Examples 1 and 3 on the student page for Alternate Examples 1 and 3.

1. Give a ratio comparing the number of cats and the total number of animals that can be adopted at the animal shelter.

   The ratio is 2 to 9, 2:9, or $\frac{2}{9}$.

2. About 4 out of 10 lbs of garbage are paper products. Write this ratio in simplest form.

   $$\frac{4}{10} = \frac{4 \div 2}{10 \div 2} = \frac{2}{5}$$

   In lowest terms, the ratio is 2 to 5, 2:5, or $\frac{2}{5}$.

3. Give a ratio comparing the number of female soccer players and the total number of players.

   $$\frac{\text{number of female players}}{\text{number of players}} = \frac{4}{6} = \frac{2}{3}$$

10-1 Exercises and Applications

Assignment Guide

- **Basic**
  1–14, 17, 19–22, 25–30
- **Average**
  1–11 odds, 12–23, 25–31 odds
- **Enriched**
  1–11 odds, 12–24, 25–31 odds

3 Practice and Assess

Check

Answers for Check Your Understanding

1. Possible answer: Ratios can look like fractions when written with a numerator and denominator. Ratios cannot be written as decimals. Ratios compare two different quantities whereas fractions show parts of a whole.
2. Possible answer: 3 red blocks to 10 blocks; 3 red blocks to 7 blue blocks.

Reteaching

Activity

Materials: Counters

- Use 6 blue counters, 3 red counters, and 4 green counters (or counters of 3 other colors).
- Place the blue counters next to the red counters. The ratio of blue counters to red counters is 6:3, or 2:1.
- Write the ratio of blue counters to green counters. 6:4, or 3:2
- Write the ratio of red counters to green counters. 3:4
- Write the ratio of green counters to all counters. 4:13

PRACTICE 10-1

Check Your Understanding

1. How is a ratio like a fraction? How is it different?
2. Give an example of a ratio that compares a part to the whole. Give an example of a ratio that compares a part to a part.

10-1 Exercises and Applications

Practice and Apply

Getting Started State if each is a ratio.

1. 6:13 Yes 2. 6 × 13 No 3. $\frac{6}{13}$ Yes 4. 13 to 6 Yes 5. 6 + 13 No 6. 6 − 13 No

Geometry For Exercises 7–10, use the shapes pictured.

7. What is the ratio of squares to hexagons? 3:2
8. Give the ratio of hexagons to squares. 2:3
9. What is the ratio of triangles to circles? 2:3
10. Give the ratio of hexagons to the whole group. 2:15
11. **Industry** Fire engines carry fire hoses. Fire trucks carry mainly ladders and fire-fighting equipment other than hoses. At one point, the city of San Francisco had 40 fire engines and 18 fire trucks.
    GPS
    a. Give the ratio of fire engines to fire trucks in lowest terms. 20:9
    b. Give the ratio of fire trucks to total fire vehicles in lowest terms. 9:29

12. **Test Prep** Which of the following compares the number of pennies to the number of quarters? D
    Ⓐ 3:9 Ⓑ 9:4 Ⓒ 2:3 Ⓓ 9:3

PRACTICE

Name ______

Practice 10-1

What is a Ratio?

For Exercises 1–4, use the shapes pictured. Possible answers:

1. What is the ratio of triangles to circles? 4 to 5
2. What is the ratio of triangles to stars? 2 : 1
3. Give the ratio of circles to squares. 5 to 1
4. What is the ratio of triangles to the whole group? $\frac{1}{3}$

A box contains 6 green chips, 10 blue chips, and 7 white chips. Give each ratio in three ways. Possible answers:

5. Green chips to blue chips 3 to 5, 3 : 5, $\frac{3}{5}$
6. Blue chips to white chips 10 to 7, 10 : 7, $\frac{10}{7}$
7. White chips to green chips 7 to 6, 7 : 6, $\frac{7}{6}$
8. Green chips to white chips 6 to 7, 6 : 7, $\frac{6}{7}$

For Exercises 9–11, refer to the animals pictured.

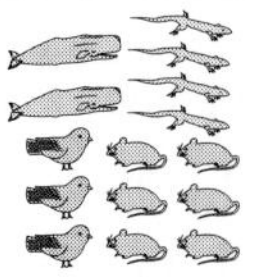

9. The ratio of which animal to the whole group is 4 : 15? Lizard
10. The ratio of which animal to the whole group is 1 : 5? Bird
11. Which two animals are compared in a ratio of $\frac{4}{3}$? Lizard, bird
12. **Social Science** In 1995, the U.S. Senate consisted of 46 Democrats and 54 Republicans.
    a. Give the ratio of Democrats to Republicans in lowest terms. 23 to 27, 23 : 27, or $\frac{23}{27}$
    b. Give the ratio of Republicans to all Senators in lowest terms. 27 to 50, 27 : 50, or $\frac{27}{50}$
13. At Jackson High School, 14 out of 35 students in the marching band are sophomores. Write this as a ratio in lowest terms. 2 to 5, 2 : 5, or $\frac{2}{5}$

RETEACHING

Name ______

Alternative Lesson 10-1

What is a Ratio?

A **ratio** is a comparison of two quantities. The ratio of Xs to Os in the box can be written as 4 to 3, 4:3, or $\frac{4}{3}$. Like fractions, ratios can be rewritten in lowest terms.

X	X	X	X
O	O	O	

Example 1

Give a ratio comparing the number of shaded squares to white squares.

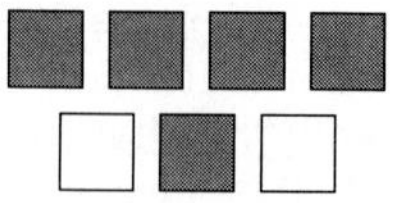

There are five shaded squares and two white squares.

The ratio of shaded squares to white squares can be written as 5 to 2, 5:2, or $\frac{5}{2}$.

Try It Use the letters in the box.

A	C	C	C	L	L	L	L	L
O	O	O	R	R	R	R	R

a. How many letters in all? 17 letters.
b. How many letters are Rs? 5 Rs
c. How many letters are Os? 3 Os
d. Give the ratio of Rs to Os. 5:3
e. Give the ratio of Os to all letters. 3:17

Example 2

Give a ratio comparing the number of obtuse angles to acute angles. Write this ratio in lowest terms.

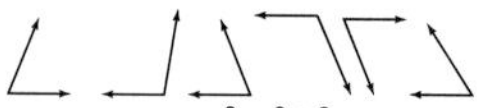

There are two obtuse angles and four acute angles.

Write the ratio. To rewrite in lowest terms, divide numerator and denominator by the same number. $\frac{2}{4} = \frac{2 \div 2}{4 \div 2}$

Simplify. $= \frac{1}{2}$

In lowest terms, the ratio can be written as 1 to 2, 1:2, or $\frac{1}{2}$.

Try It Use the circles pictured. Write each ratio in lowest terms.

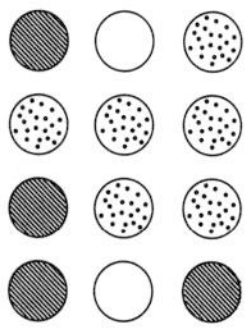

f. Give the ratio of dotted figures to striped figures. 3:2
g. Give the ratio of all figures to white figures. 6:1
h. Give the ratio of striped figures to all figures. 1:3
i. Give the ratio of striped figures to white figures. 2:1

A bag contains 3 red marbles, 8 blue marbles, and 10 yellow marbles. Give each ratio in three ways.

13. Red marbles to blue marbles

14. Yellow marbles to blue marbles

15. Red marbles to all marbles

16. Blue marbles to all marbles

17. At Midtown School, 24 out of the 49 sixth graders are in one of Ms. Campbell's classes. Write this as a ratio. 24:49

18. Mrs. Ng has 12 boys and 15 girls in her science class. Give each ratio.

a. Boys to girls 4:5 **b.** Girls to boys 5:4 **c.** Boys to students 4:9 **d.** Girls to students 5:9

For Exercises 19–21, refer to the animals pictured.

19. The ratio of which animal to the whole group is 3:14? Turtles

20. The ratio of which animal to the whole group is 2:7? Dogs

21. Which two animals are compared in a ratio of 3:4? Turtles to dogs

PROBLEM SOLVING 10-1

Problem Solving and Reasoning

22. Critical Thinking Using ratios, three students described a cabinet containing 8 plates and 11 bowls. Helga used 8 to 11. Kendra used 11:8. Ka-fei used $\frac{8}{19}$. Explain how all three students could be correct.

23. Critical Thinking At the corner drug store, 32 out of 60 toothbrushes are red. How many are blue? Explain.

24. Journal How is writing a ratio in lowest terms like writing a fraction in lowest terms?

Mixed Review

Tell if the line is a line of symmetry. *[Lesson 8-8]*

25.

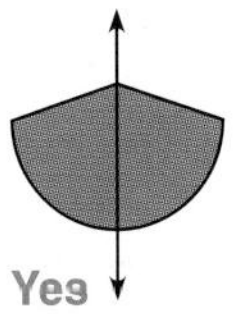

Yes

26.

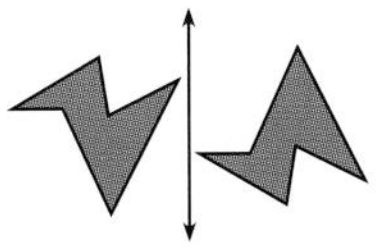

No

27.

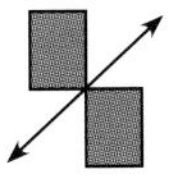

No

28.

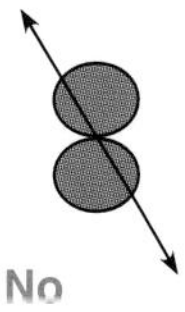

No

Find the missing measurement for each rectangle. *[Lesson 4-4]*

29. Area = 72 in^2
Base = 8 in.
Height = ☐
9 in.

30. Area = ☐
Base = 6.4 mm
Height = 2.3 mm
14.72 mm^2

31. Area = 27.2 km^2
Base = ☐
Height = 13.6 km
2 km

32. Area = ☐
Base = 3 ft
Height = 12 ft
36 ft^2

Exercise Notes

Exercise 20

Error Prevention You might want to suggest to some students that they write a ratio equivalent to 2:7 to help them. Ask them how the total number of animals, 14, might be used to write this ratio.

Exercise Answers

13. 3 to 8; 3:8; $\frac{3}{8}$
14. 5 to 4; 5:4; $\frac{5}{4}$
15. 1 to 7; 1:7; $\frac{1}{7}$
16. 8 to 21; 8:21; $\frac{8}{21}$
22. Each ratio compares the quantities in a different way. Helga gave the ratio of plates to bowls; Kendra gave the ratio of bowls to plates; Ka-fei gave the ratio of plates to the total number of plates and bowls.
23. Do not know; The colors of the other 28 toothbrushes are not known.
24. The process is exactly the same: factor out the greatest common factor.

Alternate Assessment

Performance Have each student write a ratio for the number of consonants to the number of vowels in his or her first name and another ratio using his or her last name. Then have each student write a ratio for the number of consonants in his or her first and last names to the total number of letters in his or her first and last names. Repeat this step using the number of vowels.

PROBLEM SOLVING

Name ______________________

Guided Problem Solving 10-1

GPS PROBLEM 11, PAGE 516

Fire engines carry fire hoses. Fire trucks carry mainly ladders and fire-fighting equipment other than hoses. At one point, the city of San Francisco had 40 fire engines and 18 fire trucks.

a. Give the ratio of fire engines to fire trucks in lowest terms.

b. Give the ratio of fire trucks to total fire vehicles in lowest terms.

— Understand —

1. How many fire *engines* did the city of San Francisco have? 40 engines.
2. How many fire *trucks* did the city of San Francisco have? 18 trucks.

— Plan —

3. How will you find the total number of fire vehicles in San Francisco? Add number of fire engines and number of fire trucks.
4. What is the total number of fire vehicles in San Francisco? 58 vehicles.

— Solve —

5. What is the ratio of fire engines to fire trucks? 40:18
6. Write your ratio in Item 5 in lowest terms, if possible. 20:9
7. What is the ratio of fire trucks to total fire vehicles? 18:58
8. Write your ratio in Item 7 in lowest terms, if possible. 9:29

— Look Back —

9. How can you tell if the ratio is in lowest terms? Possible answer: Numerator and denominator have no common factor.

SOLVE ANOTHER PROBLEM

Use the fire vehicle data above to write each ratio in lowest terms.

a. What is the ratio of fire trucks to fire engines? 9:20

b. What is the ratio of fire vehicles to fire engines? 29:20

ENRICHMENT

Name ______________________

Extend Your Thinking 10-1

Visual Thinking

Each of the nine squares in the "spreadsheet" should contain all of the lines and symbols from both the labeled square above it and the one to its left.

For example, if square A contained a circle and square 1 contained a dot, then the square A1 would contain both a circle and a dot in their respective positions.

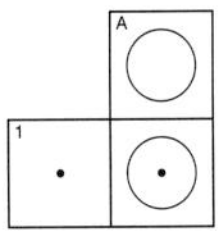

1. Draw the shape that is needed to correctly complete each row and column.

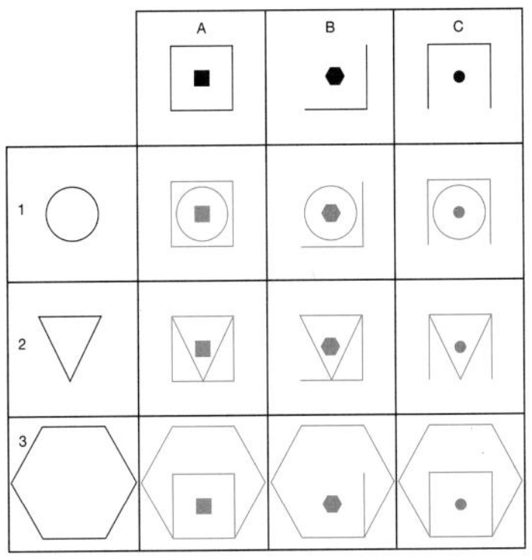

Quick Quiz

In a pencil box, there are 3 blue pencils, 4 red pencils, and 2 black pencils. Write each ratio.

1. Blue pencils to red pencils
   3:4
2. Blue pencils to all pencils
   3:9 or 1:3
3. Red pencils to all pencils
   4:9

Available on Daily Transparency 10-1

10-2 Lesson Organizer

Objective

- Find ratios equal to a given ratio.

NCTM Standards

- 1–4, 7

▶ Review

Write two fractions equal to each fraction. Possible answers are given.

1. $\frac{2}{3}$ $\frac{4}{6}, \frac{6}{9}$
2. $\frac{4}{10}$ $\frac{2}{5}, \frac{8}{20}$
3. $\frac{6}{12}$ $\frac{3}{6}, \frac{2}{4}$

▶ Lesson Link

Have students discuss situations where different ratios are known to be equal. Students might suggest recipe quantities, such as 3 cups of flour for 2 dozen cookies and 6 cups for 4 dozen cookies, or batting averages, such as 1 hit out of 3 times at bat and 2 hits out of 6 times at bat.

1 Introduce

Explore

You may wish to use Lesson Enhancement Transparency 49 with **Explore**.

The Point
Students explore ratios by recording the number of different items in their classroom and writing ratios comparing these items. Ratios that are approximately equal are introduced by finding ratios about equal to 2:1.

Ongoing Assessment
As students work on Step 4, check to see that they recognize that they are looking for two items where there are approximately twice as many of one as the other.

10-2 Equal Ratios

You'll Learn ...

- to find ratios equal to a given ratio

... How It's Used

Advertisers use equal ratios to explain how many out of a given number of people choose to use their product or service.

▶ Lesson Link You've used ratios to compare quantities. Now you will learn how to use tables to find equal ratios. ◀

Explore Ratios

You Can Count On It

1. Copy and complete the table based on your own classroom. For the last two lines, choose your own items and count them.

Item	Number	Item	Number
Boys		Doors	
Girls		Windows	
Teachers		Pencil sharpeners	
Desks		Your choice #1	
Chairs		Your choice #2	

2. Write the following ratios.
   - **a.** Boys to girls
   - **b.** Teachers to students
   - **c.** Desks to chairs
   - **d.** Doors to windows
   - **e.** Doors to people
   - **f.** People to pencil sharpeners
3. Write three ratios of your own. State the items being compared.
4. Find two quantities in your classroom whose ratio is about 2:1. How do you know the ratio is about 2:1? Repeat using 5:1 and 10:1.
5. Which ratios in Step 2 are important to people outside your class? Who might want to know these ratios? Why?

Learn Equal Ratios

Sometimes you need to find ratios that are equal to a known ratio. You can create equal ratios by multiplying both quantities of the ratio by the same amount. A table can help organize the information.

MEETING INDIVIDUAL NEEDS

Resources

- **10-2** Practice
- **10-2** Reteaching
- **10-2** Problem Solving
- **10-2** Enrichment
- **10-2** Daily Transparency
  - Problem of the Day
  - Review
  - Quick Quiz
- Teaching Tool Transparencies 2, 3
- Lesson Enhancement Transparency 49
- Technology Master 51

Learning Modalities

Social Have students work in groups of three or four. Have each student write a ratio on a sheet of paper. Then ask students to pass their paper to the person on their right. Write a ratio equal to the ratio they have received. Have students rotate papers again and continue.

Kinesthetic Have students use sheets of paper of two different colors to represent a ratio. Have them show and write the ratio of 2 blue sheets to 3 yellow sheets. Have students tear each sheet in half and record the new ratio. Have them tear each sheet again to show a third equal ratio.

Inclusion

Some students may have difficulty visualizing equal ratios. Allow these students to draw pictures or use manipulatives to represent equal ratios. As students continue to work with these concepts, encourage them to try problems without using the manipulatives.

Example 1

The city of San Francisco has 2 fire hydrants for every 3 city blocks. Find four ratios equal to this ratio.

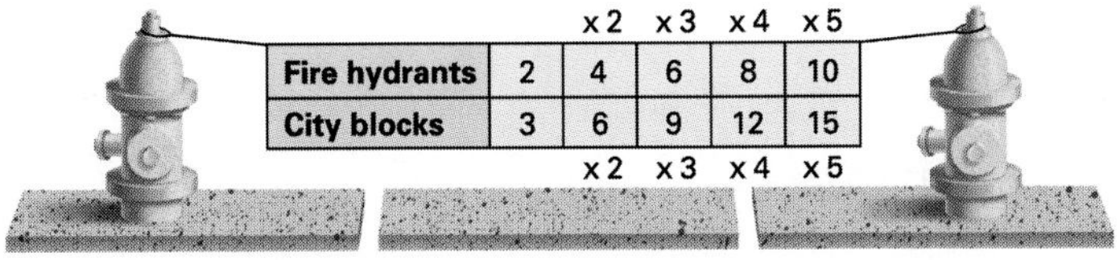

		x2	x3	x4	x5
Fire hydrants	2	4	6	8	10
City blocks	3	6	9	12	15
		x2	x3	x4	x5

San Francisco's ratio of fire hydrants to city blocks is equal to 4:6, 6:9, 8:12, and 10:15. Other answers are possible.

Division can also be used to find equal ratios. You can use any number, but numbers that go evenly into both quantities are the easiest to use.

Example 2

Using division, find three ratios that equal 40 to 60.

40			
60			

Set up a table.

	÷ 2	÷ 5	÷ 10
40	20	8	4
60	30	12	6
	÷ 2	÷ 5	÷ 10

Use division to find equal ratios.

Three ratios that equal 40 to 60 include 20 to 30, 8 to 12, and 4 to 6.

Try It

For each ratio, state another ratio equal to it.

a. 5:9 **b.** $\frac{3}{8}$ **c.** 60 to 100 **d.** 1:13

e. For every 12 pie slices sold at the Circus Cafe, 4 are cherry. Find one equal ratio using multiplication, and one equal ratio using division.

Remember

You can also use either multiplication or division to find fractions equal to a given fraction.

[Page 294]

Problem Solving TIP

When using division, try to choose numbers that are easy to divide by. Every whole number that ends in a zero is divisible by 2, 5, and 10.

MATH EVERY DAY

Problem of the Day

Which of the squares below is surrounded entirely by different digits?

1	5	2	1	0	2	3
3	6	5	2	9	1	4
2	4	1	3	8	5	0
5	7	0	6	4	2	7
4	1	2	3	5	1	8

1	5	2	1	0	2	3
3	6	5	2	9	1	4
2	4	1	**3**	8	5	0
5	7	0	6	4	2	7
4	1	2	3	5	1	8

Available on Daily Transparency 10-2

An Extension is provided in the transparency package.

Fact of the Day

On October 8, 1871, a forest fire in Peshtigo, Wisconsin, killed 1182 people. No other forest fire recorded has caused so many human deaths.

Estimation

Estimate each product.

1. 21 × 83 1600
2. 43 × 19 800
3. 51 × 32 1500

For Groups That Finish Early

Double the number of boys and girls in Step 2a. Write the ratio of boys to girls. Is this ratio equal to the ratio that you wrote in 2a? Yes

Triple the number of boys and girls in Step 2a. Write the ratio of boys to girls. Is this ratio equal to the other two ratios? Yes

Follow Up

Have volunteers share their answers for Step 3. Discuss the ratios that students wrote in Step 4 and how they determined that these ratios were about 2:1. Discuss the reasons students wrote as answers for Step 5.

Answers for Explore

1–5. Answers may vary.

2 Teach

Learn

Alternate Examples

1. At Hickory Middle School, 3 out of 5 students chose pizza as their favorite food. Find four ratios equal to this ratio.

		×2	×3	×4	×5
Students choosing pizza	3	6	9	12	15
All students	5	10	15	20	25
		×2	×3	×4	×5

Hickory Middle School's ratio of students choosing pizza to all students is equal to 6:10, 9:15, 12:20, and 15:25. Other answers are possible.

2. Using division, find three ratios that equal 36 to 48.

	÷2	÷3	÷4
36	18	12	9
48	24	16	12
	÷2	÷3	÷4

Three ratios that equal 36 to 48 include 18 to 24, 12 to 16, and 9 to 12.

Answers for Try It

Possible Answers:

a. 10:18 b. $\frac{6}{16}$

c. 3 to 5 d. 2:26

e. 24 to 8; 3 to 1

WHAT DO YOU THINK?

Students see two methods of finding equal ratios. Students can compare these ratios to see which ratio is the most meaningful in this situation.

Answers for What Do You Think?

1. Erica and Jamar are both correct; The answers are all proportional to each other.
2. Numbers that divide both 24 and 32 evenly.

3 Practice and Assess

Check

Answers for Check Your Understanding

1. Infinitely many.
2. Yes; Multiply both quantities by the same amount.

WHAT DO YOU THINK?

In Erica and Jamar's homeroom, 24 out of the 32 students want to go to Hillsdale Park for the school picnic. Erica and Jamar want to convince the teachers to choose Hillsdale Park. They plan to show three different ratios equal to $\frac{24}{32}$ in their presentation.

Erica thinks ...

I'll use a table, multiplying numerator and denominator by 2, 3, and 4.

		×2	×3	×4
Numerator	24	48	72	96
Denominator	32	64	96	128
		×2	×3	×4

Three equivalent ratios are $\frac{48}{64}$, $\frac{72}{96}$, and $\frac{96}{128}$.

Jamar thinks ...

I'll use a table, dividing the numerator and denominator by convenient numbers.

		÷2	÷4	÷8
Numerator	24	12	6	3
Denominator	32	16	8	4
		÷2	÷4	÷8

Three equivalent ratios are $\frac{12}{16}$, $\frac{6}{8}$, and $\frac{3}{4}$.

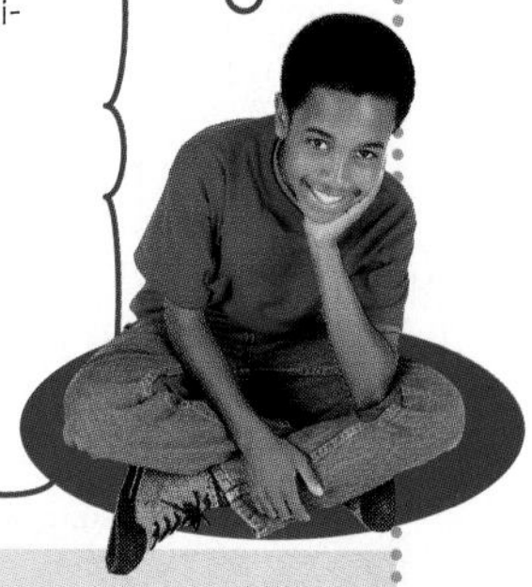

What do you think?

1. Erica and Jamar got different answers. Is each answer correct? Explain.
2. What does Jamar mean by "convenient numbers"?

MEETING MIDDLE SCHOOL CLASSROOM NEEDS

Tips from Middle School Teachers

I find that my students enjoy solving problems that relate to their own lives. I like to have my students make up word problems of their own, based on facts, numbers, and situations in their own lives.

Team Teaching

Work with a foods teacher to demonstrate how equal ratios are used in doubling and tripling a recipe.

History Connection

In the early 1800s, most firefighters were volunteers. Water-pumping contests were an important part of the periodic *fireman's musters,* when volunteer firefighters from a wide area would get together for competitions, entertainment, and learning.

Check Your Understanding

1. For a given ratio, how many equal ratios can you create?
2. Is it possible to find a ratio that is equal to $\frac{2}{5}$, 2:5, and 2 to 5? Explain.

10-2 Exercises and Applications

PRACTICE 10-2

Practice and Apply

Getting Started State if each ratio is in lowest terms.

1. $\frac{5}{6}$ Yes **2.** 2:10 No **3.** 7 to 18 Yes **4.** 4:3 Yes **5.** $\frac{9}{3}$ No **6.** 6 to 2 No

Give two ratios equal to the given ratio.

7. 4 to 5 **8.** $\frac{10}{20}$ **9.** 12:8 **10.** $\frac{25}{40}$ **11.** $\frac{4}{6}$ **12.** 3:7

13. $\frac{4}{8}$ **14.** 7 to 1 **15.** $\frac{1}{8}$ **16.** 5:10 **17.** $\frac{3}{4}$ **18.** 2.1 to 4.2

State if the ratios are equal.

19. 7 to 21; 1 to 3 Yes **20.** 6:9; 3:2 No **21.** $\frac{5}{4}$; 10:8 Yes **22.** 1 to 10; $\frac{2}{5}$ No

23. The circle graph shows the number of colored beads used in a hand-beaded bracelet. Carole wants to make a smaller bracelet using the same ratios of colors. Draw a circle graph that shows how many beads of each color Carole could use.

GPS

Colored Beads

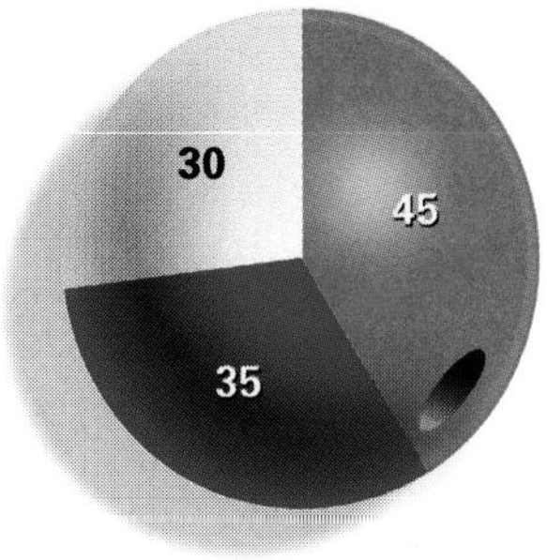

24. Estimation Mary jogs 5 laps in 7 minutes. Rikki jogs 11 laps in 15 minutes. Do Mary and Rikki jog at about the same speed? Yes

25. **Test Prep** In order to control fires, some cities and counties require an indoor sprinkler system in each newly built house. If a sprinkler system goes on, 7 out of 10 times the fire will be controlled. How many fires out of 20 will be controlled? A

Ⓐ 14 Ⓑ 17 Ⓒ 20 Ⓓ 70

10-2 Exercises and Applications

Assignment Guide

- **Basic** 1–12, 19–25, 27–32, 34–42 evens
- **Average** 1–17 odds, 19–25, 27–30, 32–42 evens
- **Enriched** 1–23 odds, 24–26, 29–32, 33–43 odds

Exercise Notes

Exercise 18

Error Prevention If students are confused by the decimals, suggest that they multiply both numbers by 10.

Exercise Answers

Possible answers for 7–18:

7. 8 to 10; 12 to 15
8. $\frac{1}{2}$, $\frac{5}{10}$
9. 6:4; 3:2
10. $\frac{5}{8}$; $\frac{10}{16}$
11. $\frac{2}{3}$; $\frac{16}{24}$
12. 6:14; 9:21
13. $\frac{1}{2}$; $\frac{2}{4}$
14. 14 to 2; 21 to 3
15. $\frac{2}{16}$; $\frac{3}{24}$
16. 1:2; 15:30
17. $\frac{6}{8}$; $\frac{12}{16}$
18. 1 to 2; 4.2 to 8.4

23.

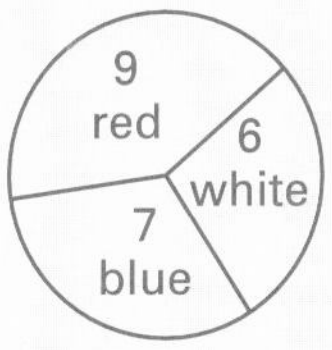

PRACTICE

Name ______________________

Practice 10-2

Equal Ratios

Give two ratios equal to the given ratio. Possible answers:

1. 8 to 12 2 to 3, 16 to 24
2. $\frac{3}{5}$ $\frac{6}{10}$, $\frac{9}{15}$
3. 9 to 3 3 to 1, 18 to 6
4. 15 : 35 3 : 7, 30 : 70
5. $\frac{8}{10}$ $\frac{4}{5}$, $\frac{16}{20}$
6. $\frac{7}{8}$ $\frac{14}{16}$, $\frac{21}{24}$

State if the ratios are equal.

7. 4 : 8; 1 : 2 Yes
8. $\frac{3}{6}$, $\frac{5}{8}$ No
9. 12 to 15, 4 to 5 Yes
10. $\frac{10}{12}$, $\frac{15}{18}$ Yes
11. 15 : 20, 20 : 25 No
12. 10 to 8, 20 to 15 No
13. $\frac{5}{9}$, 8 to 13 No
14. 8 : 14, $\frac{4}{7}$ Yes
15. 12 to 28, 18 : 42 Yes

For exercises 16–19, give three equal ratios. Possible answers:

16. A third grade class has 4 boys for every 3 girls. 4 to 3, 8 to 6, 12 to 9
17. A pet store has 5 cat collars for every 8 dog collars. $\frac{5}{8}$, $\frac{10}{16}$, $\frac{15}{24}$
18. A corporation has 2 secretaries for every executive. 2 : 1, 4 : 2, 8 : 4
19. A carnival game has 2 winners for every 7 losers. 2 : 7, 4 : 14, 8 : 28

Complete each table of equal ratios.

20. 8 snakes for every 3 turtles

Snakes	8	16	24	32
Turtles	3	6	9	12

21. 7 dogs out of 12 pets

Dogs	7	14	21	28
Pets	12	24	36	48

22. 12 pizzas to 9 lasagnas

Pizzas	4	8	12	16
Lasagnas	3	6	9	12

23. 16 cars to 20 trucks

Cars	4	8	12	16
Trucks	5	10	15	20

24. **Social Science** The ratio of Delaware residents to Maine residents was about 55 : 100 in 1970 and about 66 : 120 in 1990. Are these ratios equal? Yes

RETEACHING

Name ______________________

Alternative Lesson 10-2

Equal Ratios

You can find ratios that are equal to a known ratio by multiplying or dividing both quantities of the ratio by the same amount.

Example 1

Using multiplication, find four ratios equal to $\frac{1}{5}$.

Set up a table.

	×2	×3	×4	×5
1	2	3	4	5
5	10	15	20	25

Four ratios equal to 1:5 are 2:10, 3:15, 4:20, and 5:25. Other answers are possible.

Try It Find four ratios equal to each ratio by using multiplication to complete the tables. Then write the ratios to the right of the table.

a.

3	6	9	12	15
8	16	24	32	40

Possible answers: 6:16, 9:24, 12:32, 15:40

b.

1	2	3	4	5
6	12	18	24	30

2:12, 3:18, 4:24, 5:30

Example 2

Using division, find four ratios equal to $\frac{48}{72}$.

Set up a table.

	÷2	÷3	÷4	÷6
48	24	16	12	8
72	36	24	18	12

Four ratios equal to 48:72 are 24:36, 16:24, 12:18, and 8:12. Other answers are possible.

Try It Find four ratios equal to each ratio by using division to complete the tables. Then write the ratios to the right of the table.

a.

80	40	20	16	8
100	50	25	20	10

Possible answers: 40:50, 20:25, 16:20, 8:10

b.

75	25	15	5	1
150	50	30	10	2

25:50, 15:30, 5:10, 1:2

Reteaching

Activity

Materials: Counters

- Use 6 red counters and 9 blue counters (or counters of two other colors).
- Write the ratio of red counters to all counters. 6:15
- Write two ratios equal to the ratio above. Possible answer: 12:30, 2:5.
- Write the ratio of blue counters to all counters. 9:15
- Write two ratios equal to the ratio above. Possible answer: 18:30, 3:5.
- Repeat the process with different-colored counters.

Exercise Notes

■ Exercise 32

Problem-Solving Tip You may wish to use Teaching Tool Transparencies 2 and 3: Guided Problem Solving, pages 1–2.

Exercise Answers

Possible answers for 26–28:

26. 2:6; 3:9; 4:12

27. 14:20; 28:40; 21:30

28. 14:4; 21:6; 28:8

32. 19; Begin with the simplest ratio, 2:5, and multiply both quantities by the numbers 2–19. The answers will be the same as if you were to divide by a series of whole numbers and fractions.

33. a–b.

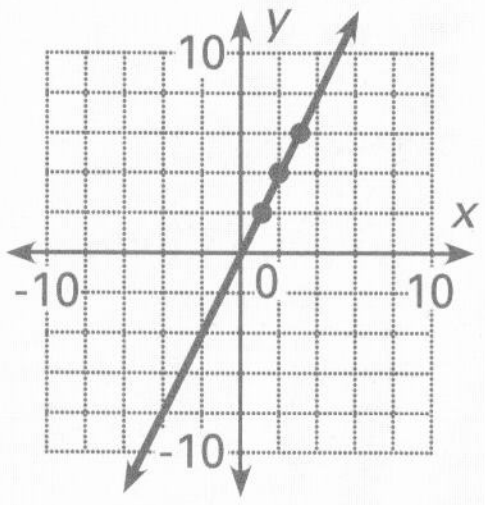

c.

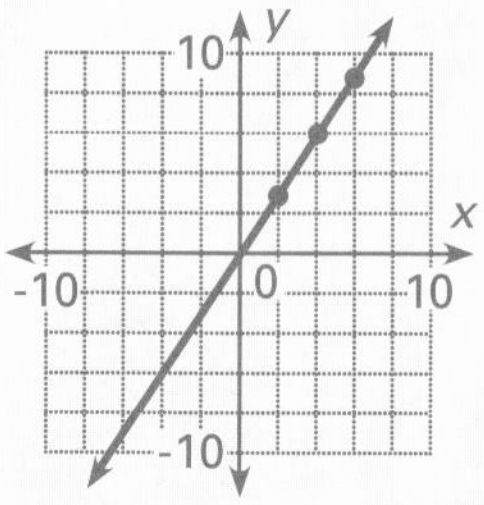

d. Yes; Explanations may vary.

Alternate Assessment

You may want to use the *Interactive CD-ROM Journal* with this assessment.

Journal Have students write a paragraph about how they can find different ratios equal to a given ratio. Encourage students to use drawings of materials or situations that illustrate their thinking.

➤ Quick Quiz

Give two ratios equal to each.

Possible answers are given.

1. 2 to 3 4 to 6; 8 to 12
2. $\frac{4}{10}$ $\frac{2}{5}$, $\frac{8}{20}$
3. 4:5 8:10; 12:15

Available on Daily Transparency 10-2

PROBLEM SOLVING 10-2

For Exercises 26–28, give three equal ratios.

26. Science In Oregon in 1995, for every forest fire caused by lightning, about 3 forest fires were caused by humans.

27. Seven out of ten calls to the fire department are for medical purposes.

28. A college residence hall has 7 students for every 2 bathrooms.

Complete each table of equal ratios.

29. 8 men to 10 women

Men	4			16
Women		10	15	

Men: 8, 12; Women: 5; 20

30. 5 fire fighters for each truck

Fire fighters				
Trucks	1	2	3	4

Fire fighters: 5, 10, 15, 20

31. 6 triangles out of 15 figures

Triangles	2	4	6	8
Figures				

Figures: 5, 10, 15, 20

Problem Solving and Reasoning

32. Choose a Strategy How many whole-number ratios equal to 40:100 can you find using division? Explain your method.

33. Critical Thinking The ratios 1 to 2, 2 to 4, and 3 to 6 are equal ratios.

a. Graph the ratios on the same coordinate grid. Use the first number in the ratio as the *x*-coordinate and the second as the *y*-coordinate

b. Draw a straight line that connects the points.

c. Repeat steps **a** and **b** using the ratios 2 to 3, 4 to 6, and 6 to 9.

d. Do you think every set of equal ratios can be graphed as a straight line? Explain.

Problem Solving STRATEGIES

- Look for a Pattern
- Make an Organized List
- Make a Table
- Guess and Check
- Work Backward
- Use Logical Reasoning
- Draw a Diagram
- Solve a Simpler Problem

Mixed Review

What is the least rotation that will land the figure on top of itself? *[Lesson 8-9]*

34.  180°

35. 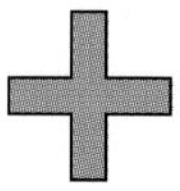 90°

36. 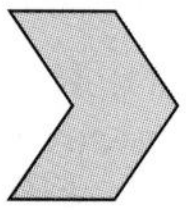 360°

37.  90°

Find the area if *b* is the base and *h* is the height of a parallelogram. *[Lesson 4-5]*

38. $b = 4, h = 5$ 20 unit²

39. $b = 6$ in., $h = 3$ in. 18 in²

40. $h = 12$ cm, $b = 3$ cm 36 cm²

41. $h = 10$ ft, $b = 88$ ft 880 ft²

42. $h = 10.5$ m, $b = 1.5$ m 15.75 m²

43. $b = 67$ mm, $h = 100$ mm 6700 mm²

PROBLEM SOLVING

Name ______

Guided Problem Solving 10-2

GPS PROBLEM 23, PAGE 521

The circle graph shows the number of colored beads used in a hand-beaded bracelet. Carole wants to make a smaller bracelet using the same ratios of colors. Draw a circle graph that shows how many beads of each color Carole could use.

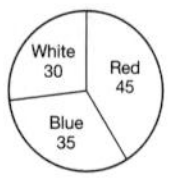

— Understand —

1. In the circle graph above, how many beads are **a.** white? 30 beads. **b.** blue? 35 beads. **c.** red? 45 beads. **d.** there in all? 110 beads.

— Plan —

2. Equal ratios can help find the number of beads in the smaller bracelet. Will you multiply or divide to find the equal ratios? Divide.
3. Write the ratio of blue beads to total beads. Then write an equal ratio. $\frac{35}{110} = \frac{7}{22}$
4. Write each ratio. Then write an equal ratio that has the same number of total beads as the ratio in Item 3.
   a. white beads:total beads $\frac{30}{110}, \frac{6}{22}$ **b.** red beads:total beads $\frac{45}{110}, \frac{9}{22}$

— Solve —

5. In the smaller bracelet, how many beads are
   a. there in all? 22 beads. **b.** white? 6 beads.
   c. red? 9 beads. **d.** blue? 7 beads.
6. Use your answers to Item 5 to draw a circle graph.

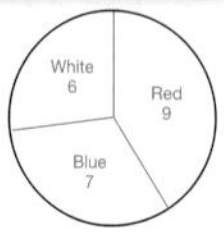

— Look Back —

7. Did the size of each section in your circle graph change from the size in the graph at the top of the page? Explain. No, because the proportion of each color to the total did not change.

SOLVE ANOTHER PROBLEM

Carole wants to make a larger bracelet using the same ratios of colors as in the circle graph at the top of the page. Draw a circle graph that shows how many beads of each color Carole could use.

Possible answer:

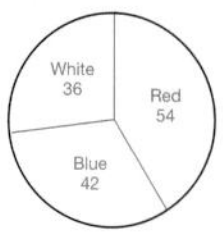

ENRICHMENT

Name ______

Extend Your Thinking 10-2

Critical Thinking

The ratios below describe a set of polygons. Use the ratios to find the number of polygons in the set. All ratios are written in lowest terms.

Equilateral triangles to isosceles triangles is 2 to 3.

Isosceles triangles to scalene triangles is 6:5.

Triangles to rectangles is $\frac{5}{4}$.

Rhombuses to trapezoids is 3:5.

Quadrilaterals to triangles is $\frac{4}{3}$. Possible answer: Items 1 and 3

1. List the order in which you will find the number of polygons in the set. Explain.
   a. First Equilateral triangle. **b.** Second Isosceles triangle.
   c. Third Scalene triangle. **d.** Fourth Rectangle.
   e. Fifth Rhombus. **f.** Sixth Trapezoid.
   It is easiest to find how many of each type of triangle, then use those quantities to find number of rectangles and other quadrilaterals.

2. What is the fewest number of polygons that can be in the set?
   a. Equilateral triangles 4 **b.** Isosceles triangles 6
   c. Scalene triangles 5 **d.** Triangles 15
   e. Rectangles 12 **f.** Rhombuses 3
   g. Trapezoids 5 **h.** Quadrilaterals 20

3. Show the number of polygons in another set that has the same ratios.
   a. Equilateral triangles 8 **b.** Isosceles triangles 12
   c. Scalene triangles 10 **d.** Triangles 30
   e. Rectangles 24 **f.** Rhombuses 6
   g. Trapezoids 10 **h.** Quadrilaterals 40

What Is a Rate?

10-3

▶ Lesson Link You've learned about ratios, and you've learned to find equal ratios. In this lesson you will use a special type of ratio called a rate. ◀

You'll Learn ...

■ to express two quantities with different units as a rate

... How It's Used

Tug boat captains use rates to determine how long it will take to sail to a particular destination.

Vocabulary

rate

unit rate

Explore Rates

Doing It by the Book

Four students are in the Bookworm Club.

- Kevin reads 2 books every week.
- Joanna reads 7 books a month.
- Carlo reads 113 books a year.
- Noriko reads $\frac{1}{4}$ of a book each day.

1. Estimate how many books each student reads in a year. Explain how you made your estimates.

2. Estimate the number of books each student reads in a month.

3. There are approximately 4 weeks in a month. Estimate the number of books each student reads in a week.

4. Is it possible to find the number of books read per day? Per decade? Per any length of time? Explain.

5. Rank the students from the fewest books read to the most books read. Which set of estimates did you choose? Why?

Learn What Is a Rate?

Some ratios are known as **rates**. A rate is a comparison of two quantities with different units of measure.

The average Dalmatian can run 15,400 feet in 5 minutes. The rate $\frac{15,400 \text{ feet}}{5 \text{ minutes}}$ compares the number of *feet* to the number of *minutes*. This can be read "15,400 feet *per* 5 minutes."

DID YOU KNOW?

Dalmatians were first used by firemen because the dogs developed a strong attachment to the firemen's horses. The dogs would bark if any thieves tried to steal the horses.

MEETING INDIVIDUAL NEEDS

Resources

10-3 Practice
10-3 Reteaching
10-3 Problem Solving
10-3 Enrichment
10-3 Daily Transparency
Problem of the Day
Review
Quick Quiz
Technology Master 52
Chapter 10 Project Master
Wide World of Mathematics Middle School: New York City Marathon

Learning Modalities

Verbal Have students make a table or poster that organizes the estimates they found in **Explore**. The students could label the rows with the names of the students and label the columns with the different periods of time.

Social Have students work in groups to create a list of as many rates as they can which are used in everyday situations.

Inclusion

To make rates more concrete, have students perform activities for a given length of time. Have students work in pairs, timing each other to see how many times they can jump rope, for example, in 1 minute. Then have them write the rate. Help students create tables and graphs with the results of their activities. This will encourage the students to see a relationship between rates and ratios.

10-3 Lesson Organizer

Objective

- Express two quantities with different units as a rate.

Vocabulary

- Rate, unit rate

NCTM Standards

- 1–4, 7

▶ Review

Find each product or quotient.

1. $5 \times (-3)$ -15
2. $-7 \times (-6)$ 42
3. -10×4 -40
4. $-6 \times (-9)$ 54

Available on Daily Transparency 10-3

1 Introduce

Explore

The Point

Students explore rates by working with ratios of a number of books read during various lengths of time. They estimate equivalent ratios with the same time frame so that the ratios can be compared.

Ongoing Assessment

As students are working, encourage them to check their answers for reasonableness. Have students check to see that their estimates for books read in a year are consistent with their estimates for books read in a month.

Answers for Explore

1. Kevin: 104; Joanna: 84; Carlo: 113; Noriko: 91; Estimate equivalent ratios using the numbers given and conversion factors.
2. Kevin: 8; Joanna: 7; Carlo: 9; Noriko: 8.

Answers for Explore continue on next page.

Answers for Explore

3. Kevin: 2; Joanna: 2; Carlo: 2; Noriko: 2.
4. Yes; Yes; Yes; Multiply or divide the given rate by the appropriate conversion factor.
5. Joanna, Noriko, Kevin, Carlo; Possible answers: Use estimates for books per year because the differences are more obvious.

2 Teach

Learn

Alternate Examples

1. Ladder trucks have power-operated aerial ladders. If the ladder can be extended 30 feet in 10 seconds, what is the rate of feet per second?

   The rate that compares 30 feet with 10 seconds is $\frac{\text{30 feet}}{\text{10 seconds}}$. If you divide both numbers by 10, you get the unit rate of $\frac{\text{3 feet}}{\text{1 second}}$.

2. Every 2 weeks, Jacob watches 3 movies. Use a table to find four rates describing this situation.

×2 ×3 ×4

Number of Movies	3	6	9	12
Number of Weeks	2	4	6	8

×2 ×3 ×4

Four rates that describes this situation are $\frac{\text{3 movies}}{\text{2 weeks}}$, $\frac{\text{6 movies}}{\text{4 weeks}}$, $\frac{\text{9 movies}}{\text{6 weeks}}$, and $\frac{\text{12 movies}}{\text{8 weeks}}$.

Answers for Try It

Possible answers: $\frac{\text{72 mi}}{\text{164 min}}$, $\frac{\text{108 mi}}{\text{246 min}}$, $\frac{\text{144 mi}}{\text{328 min}}$, $\frac{\text{180 mi}}{\text{410 min}}$

3 Practice and Assess

Check

Answers for Check Your Understanding

1. Possible answer: 1 ft to 10 ft; Any ratio in which the two quantities being compared have the same unit is not a rate.
2. The numerical value of the second quantity in the rate is 1.
3. Yes; Yes

If the comparison is to 1 unit, the rate is called a **unit rate**.

$$\frac{\text{15,400 feet} \div 5}{\text{5 minutes} \div 5} = \frac{\text{3080 feet}}{\text{1 minute}} \leftarrow \text{1 unit}$$

The unit rate is **3080** feet per minute.

Examples

▶ History Link

The first fire engines were pumped by hand. They were replaced by steam-powered pumps, and finally by internal combustion engines, which use gasoline and diesel fuel.

1 A typical fire engine can hold 500 gallons of water. This water is used up in 10 minutes of continuous spraying. What is the rate of gallons per minute?

The rate that compares 500 gallons with 10 minutes is $\frac{\text{500 gallons}}{\text{10 minutes.}}$ If you divide both numbers by 10, you get the unit rate of $\frac{\text{50 gallons}}{\text{1 minute}}$.

2 Every 3 hours, Henry's hamster eats 4 ounces of food. Use a table to find four rates describing this situation.

Since a rate is a ratio, you can find equal rates the same way you found equal ratios. Multiply or divide both quantities by the same number.

× 2 × 3 × 4

Ounces of food	4	8	12	16
Number of hours	3	6	9	12

× 2 × 3 × 4

Four rates that describe this situation are $\frac{\text{4 oz}}{\text{3 hr}}$, $\frac{\text{8 oz}}{\text{6 hr}}$, $\frac{\text{12 oz}}{\text{9 hr}}$, and $\frac{\text{16 oz}}{\text{12 hr}}$.

Try It

In 1987, Australian Greg Mutton paddled a bathtub 36 miles in 82 minutes, a world record. Use a table to find four rates describing this situation.

Check Your Understanding

1. Give an example of a ratio that is not a rate. Why isn't it a rate?
2. How can you tell if a rate is a unit rate?
3. A race car went 200 miles an hour. Is this a ratio? Is it a rate?

MATH EVERY DAY

▶ Problem of the Day

Androcas wants three different stamps that are joined together. The stamps are on a sheet of 24. There are 6 designs, A through F, as shown below. Androcas wants one of the stamps to be design A. How many different combinations of three stamps can he get?

A	B	C	D	E	F
G	H	A	B	C	D
E	F	G	H	A	B
C	D	E	F	G	H

12; ABC, ABD, ABG, ABH, ACD, ACE, ACG, ACH, AFG, AFH, AGE, AGH

Available on Daily Transparency 10-3

An Extension is provided in the transparency package.

Fact of the Day

In 1871, Chicago had 17 horse-drawn steam fire engines, 23 hose carts, and 4 hook-and-ladder wagons.

Mental Math

Find each product mentally.

1. 10 × 0.9 9
2. 10 × 0.09 0.9
3. 100 × 0.09 9
4. 1000 × 0.9 900
5. 1000 × 0.09 90

10-3 Exercises and Applications

Practice and Apply

Getting Started **State if the ratio is a rate.**

1. 5 flowers in every square foot Yes **2.** $\frac{\text{15 minutes}}{\text{1 car wash}}$ Yes **3.** 12 clips to 2 clips No **4.** 7:1 No

State if the ratio is a unit rate.

5. $\frac{\text{3 in.}}{\text{1 year}}$ Yes **6.** $\frac{\text{5 apples}}{\text{7 oranges}}$ No **7.** $\frac{\text{3 inches}}{\text{1 inch}}$ No **8.** $\frac{\text{5 dollars}}{\text{1 pound}}$ Yes

For each situation, give two equal rates.

9. Margaret rode her bicycle 14 miles in 2 hours.

10. Randy bought fabric with a pattern of 5 shapes in every 3 feet.

11. Justen did 30 jumping jacks in 40 seconds.

For Exercises 12–14, use the bar graph.

12. Give three different rates that describe the speed of the cheetah.

13. Give a rate that uses the number 10.

14. Give a rate that compares a distance to $\frac{1}{2}$ hour.

15. Estimation Jo drove her car 98 miles and used 4 gallons of gas. Estimate how many miles she can go on 1 gallon of gas. About 25 mi

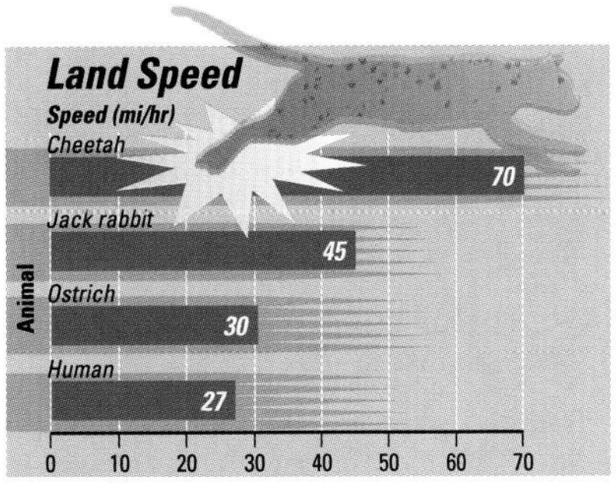

Use the table for Exercises 16–17.

16. Industry The table shows the maximum rate of water flow from fire hydrants of different colors. The rates are written in liters per minute. How many liters of water flow from each fire hydrant in five minutes?

17. Industry If a fire hydrant pumped 227,040 liters in 60 minutes, what color would the fire hydrant be? Orange

Color	Rate (L/min)
Green	5677
Orange	3784
Red	1892

PRACTICE

Name ______________________

Practice 10-3

What is a Rate?

State if the ratio is a unit rate.

1. $\frac{\text{3 cats}}{\text{5 dogs}}$ No 2. $\frac{\text{1 ounce}}{\$0.15}$ No 3. $\frac{\text{12 inches}}{\text{1 foot}}$ Yes 4. $\frac{\text{20 miles}}{\text{1 hour}}$ Yes
5. $\frac{\text{6 pounds}}{\text{1 dollar}}$ Yes 6. $\frac{\text{125 miles}}{\text{5 hours}}$ No 7. $\frac{\text{1 table}}{\text{6 chairs}}$ No 8. $\frac{\text{1 dollar}}{\text{3 oranges}}$ No
9. $\frac{\text{2 cups}}{\text{1 pint}}$ Yes 10. $\frac{\text{3 quarts}}{\text{2 pounds}}$ No 11. $\frac{\text{4 books}}{\text{1 dollar}}$ Yes 12. $\frac{\text{13 feet}}{\text{1 foot}}$ No

For each situation, give two equal rates. **Possible answers:**

13. Robert drove 20 miles in 30 minutes. $\frac{\text{20 mi}}{\text{30 min}}, \frac{\text{2 mi}}{\text{3 min}}$

14. Helen earned $18 for working 3 hours. $\frac{\$18}{\text{3 hr}}, \frac{\$6}{\text{1 hr}}$

15. A radio station played 15 songs in 1 hour. $\frac{\text{15 songs}}{\text{1 hr}}, \frac{\text{30 songs}}{\text{2 hr}}$

16. A breakfast cereal contains 75 raisins in every pound. $\frac{\text{75 raisins}}{\text{1 lb}}, \frac{\text{150 raisins}}{\text{2 lb}}$

17. Becky ran 2 miles in 14 minutes. $\frac{\text{2 mi}}{\text{14 min}}, \frac{\text{1 mi}}{\text{7 min}}$

18. June bought 3 pounds of asparagus for $2. $\frac{\text{3 lb}}{\$2}, \frac{\text{6 lb}}{\$4}$

For Exercises 19–21, use the bar graph.
Possible answers:

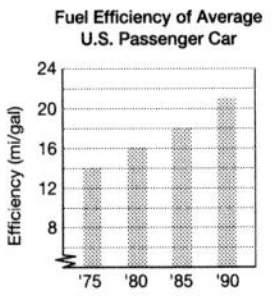

19. Give a rate that uses the number 28.

Year: 1975 Rate: $\frac{\text{28 mi}}{\text{2 gal}}$

20. Give three different rates that describe the average fuel efficiency in 1985.
$\frac{\text{18 mi}}{\text{1 gal}}, \frac{\text{36 mi}}{\text{2 gal}}, \frac{\text{54 mi}}{\text{3 gal}}$

21. Use the average fuel efficiency in 1990 to give a rate that compares a distance to $\frac{1}{3}$ gallon of gasoline. $\frac{\text{7 mi}}{\frac{1}{3}\text{ gal}}$

22. Rhoda has 4 hours to type a 12-page report. How much time can she spend typing each page? $\frac{1}{3}$ hr or 20 min

23. Helga did 3 math problems in 5 minutes. If there are 45 similar problems in her homework assignment, how long will it take her to complete the assignment? 75 min or $1\frac{1}{4}$ hr

RETEACHING

Name ______________________

Alternative Lesson 10-3

What Is a Rate?

Some ratios are know as **rates.** A rate is a comparison of two quantities with different units of measure, such as $\frac{\text{60 mi}}{\text{1 hr}}$. If the comparison is to 1 unit, the rate is called a **unit rate.** Find equal rates by multiplying or dividing both quantities by the same number.

Example 1

State if the ratio $\frac{\text{3 apples}}{\$5}$ is a rate.

The ratio is a rate because the measures are in different units.

Try It If the ratio is a rate, write *rate.* If it is not, write *ratio.*

a. 5 circles to 2 circles Ratio. b. 24 packages per carton Rate.

c. 5 dogs:8 cats Rate. d. 3 teaspoons to 1 teaspoon Ratio.

Example 2

State if the rate 45 students in two classrooms is a unit rate.

The ratio is a *not* a unit rate because the comparison is to 2 classrooms. To be a unit rate the comparison must be to one unit.

Try It If the ratio is a unit rate, write *unit rate.* If it is not, write *rate.*

e. 36 inches to 3 feet Rate. f. 20 quarters in $5 Rate.

g. 12 eggs in a dozen Unit rate. h. 25 miles per gallon Unit rate.

Example 3

Ingrid runs 15 miles every 7 days. Use a table to find three more rates describing this situation.

		×2	×3	×4
Miles Run	15	30	45	60
Days	7	14	21	28

Three rates are $\frac{\text{30 miles}}{\text{14 days}}, \frac{\text{45 miles}}{\text{21 days}}, \frac{\text{60 miles}}{\text{28 days}}$.

Try It Miguel has 90 minutes of softball practice every 3 days. Use a table to find three more rates describing this situation.

Minutes	90	180	270	360
Days	3	6	9	12

Possible answers:

i. $\frac{\text{180 minutes}}{\text{6 days}}, \frac{\text{270 minutes}}{\text{9 days}}, \frac{\text{360 minutes}}{\text{12 days}}$

Assignment Guide

- **Basic**
  1–12, 16, 19–21, 25–33 odds
- **Average**
  1–6, 10–13, 15–21, 24–32 evens
- **Enriched**
  2–12 evens, 13–23, 24–32 evens

Exercise Notes

Exercise 12

Science Although cheetahs are capable of running at a top speed of 70 miles per hour, they can only maintain this speed for a few hundred yards.

Exercise 15

Extension Ask students to find out how many miles per gallon the car of a family member or friend gets.

Exercise Answers

Possible answers for 9–14:

9. $\frac{\text{7 mi}}{\text{1 hr}}, \frac{\text{21 mi}}{\text{3 hr}}$

10. $\frac{\text{10 shapes}}{\text{6 ft}}, \frac{\text{25 shapes}}{\text{15 ft}}$

11. $\frac{\text{15 jj}}{\text{20 sec}}, \frac{\text{3 jj}}{\text{4 sec}}$

12. $\frac{\text{70 mi}}{\text{1 hr}}, \frac{\text{140 mi}}{\text{2 hr}}, \frac{\text{210 mi}}{\text{3 hr}}$

13. An ostrich runs 300 miles in 10 hours.

14. Cheetah runs 35 miles in $\frac{1}{2}$ hour.

16. Green: 28,385 L; Orange: 18,920 L; Red: 9,460 L

Reteaching

Activity

Materials: Ruler, counters

- Draw a 3-inch line and place 2 counters above it. This illustrates the rate $\frac{\text{2 counters}}{\text{3 inches}}$.
- Extend the line 3 inches and place 2 counters above the new 3-inch part. Write a rate for the total line length and total number of counters. $\frac{\text{4 counters}}{\text{6 inches}}$
- Repeat the process described above two more times. Write two more rates which describe the situation. Possible answers: $\frac{\text{6 counters}}{\text{9 inches}}, \frac{\text{8 counters}}{\text{12 inches}}$

Exercise Notes

■ Exercise 18

Extension Have students check their pulse to find the number of beats in 10 seconds. Then students could use this rate to find the number of beats in 30 seconds.

Project Progress

You may want to have students use Chapter 10 Project Master.

Exercise Answers

21. 2.5 hours; Divide 5 by 2.

22. Ratios compare two quantities. Rates are ratios that compare quantities with different units.

23. Multiply the rate by $\frac{60 \text{ seconds}}{1 \text{ minute}}$.

24. Yes;

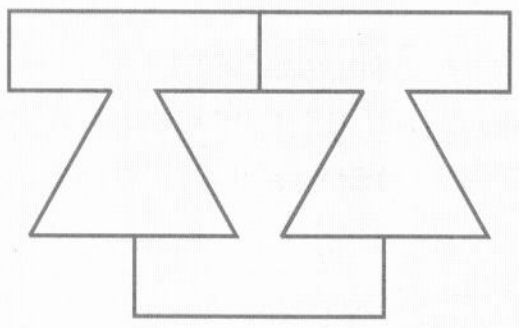

25. Yes;

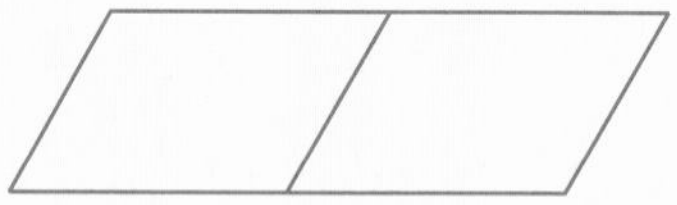

26. No

27. No

Alternate Assessment

Interview Have students explain what a rate is. Have them give an example of a rate and an example of a ratio that is not a rate.

► Quick Quiz

For each situation, give two equal rates.

1. 4 quarters in 1 dollar.
   Possible answer: $\frac{8 \text{ quarters}}{2 \text{ dollars}}, \frac{12 \text{ quarters}}{3 \text{ dollars}}$
2. 60 miles in 2 hours.
   Possible answer: $\frac{120 \text{ miles}}{4 \text{ hours}}, \frac{30 \text{ miles}}{1 \text{ hour}}$

Available on Daily Transparency 10-3

PROBLEM SOLVING 10-3

18. Raul checked his pulse, and counted 27 beats in 15 seconds. At that rate, how many beats would he have counted in 45 seconds? **81**

19. **Test Prep** Doug needs 800 tiles for a new bathroom floor. The tiles cost $16 per 100. At that rate, how much will Doug spend on tiles? **D**

Ⓐ $20 Ⓑ $50 Ⓒ $100 Ⓓ $128

20. A grocery store checker can total the purchases for about 3 average customers in 10 minutes. At this rate, how many customers can the checker serve in one hour? **18**

Problem Solving and Reasoning

21. **Critical Thinking** GPS Cameron is making decorations for "Back to School Night." He can make 2 posters in an hour. At this rate, how long will it take him to make 5 posters? Explain.

22. Journal Describe the similarities and differences between ratios and rates.

23. **Communicate** Describe how you could change a rate of meters per second to meters per minute.

Mixed Review

State if each figure will tessellate. If it tessellates, make a sketch to show how. *[Lesson 8-10]*

24. 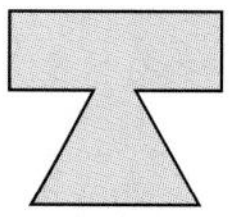
25. 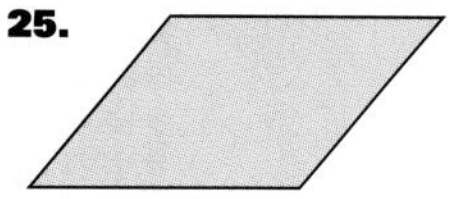
26. 
27. 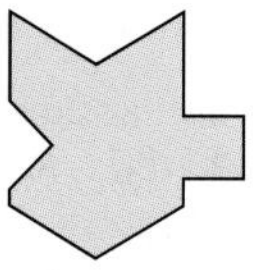

Find the area of the triangle if *b* is the base and *h* is the height. *[Lesson 4-6]*

28. $b = 7$ ft, $h = 6$ ft **21 ft²**
29. $b = 1.6$ m, $h = 3$ m **2.4 m²**
30. $h = 5$ in., $b = 50$ in. **125 in²**
31. $h = 0.3$ cm, $b = 0.8$ cm **0.12 cm²**
32. $h = 12$ yd, $b = 3$ yd **18 yd²**
33. $b = 600$ mi, $h = 400$ mi **120,000 mi²**

Project Progress

List some ways that ratios can be used in the sport you've chosen. Here are some examples: number of hits compared to times at bat, number of games won compared to number of games played; number of people on a team compared to number on the field. Explain the meaning of each ratio.

Problem Solving: Understand, Plan, Solve, Look Back

526 *Chapter 10 • Ratio, Proportion, and Percent*

PROBLEM SOLVING

Name ____________________

Guided Problem Solving 10-3

GPS PROBLEM 21, PAGE 526

Cameron is making decorations for "Back to School Night." He can make 2 posters in an hour. At this rate, how long will it take him to make 5 posters? Explain.

— Understand —

1. Circle how many posters Cameron can make in one hour.
2. Underline what you are asked to find.

— Plan —

3. What is the unit rate to make the posters? **2 posters:1 hour.**
4. How many minutes in one hour? **60 minutes.**
5. Write the rate as posters to minutes. **2 posters: 60 minutes.**
6. Complete the table to find an equal rate.

Posters	1	2	3	4	5
Minutes	30	60	90	120	150

— Solve —

7. How long will it take Cameron to make 5 posters? **150 minutes.**
8. How many *hours* will it take Cameron to make 5 posters? **$2\frac{1}{2}$ hours.**
9. Explain how you found your answer. **Possible answer: Convert hours to minutes, then find equal rates.**

— Look Back —

10. What is another way to find how long it would take Cameron to make 5 posters? **Possible answer: Multiply the unit rate $\frac{2 \text{ posters}}{1 \text{ hour}}$ by $\frac{2.5}{2.5}$.**

SOLVE ANOTHER PROBLEM

Morgan can make 48 cookies in an hour. At this rate, how long will it take her to make 60 cookies? **$1\frac{1}{4}$ hours.**

ENRICHMENT

Name ____________________

Extend Your Thinking 10-3

Decision Making

Glynnis wants to take dance lessons during her summer break. School ends May 29. She has called three dance schools to see when classes start, the days and times they are offered, how much they cost, and whether the school charges by class or by session.

	Clodagh's Dance	New Steps	Stepping High
Start Date	No specific time, can start at any time	June 15	May 17
Class Times	Mon., Wed., or Fri. 3:00 – 4:00 P.M.	Tues. 4:00 – 5:30 P.M.	Sat. 9:00 – 10:15 A.M.
Minimum Number of Classes	One class	Ten classes	Eight classes
Cost	$6 per class	$75 for ten classes	$52 for eight classes

1. What is the unit rate for each class?
   a. Clodagh's Dance **$\frac{\$6}{\text{class}}$** b. New Steps **$\frac{\$7.50}{\text{class}}$**
   c. Stepping High **$\frac{\$6.50}{\text{class}}$**
2. How would your answers to Question 1 change if you were to write the unit rate in cost per *hour*?

	Total hours for each payment	Cost per hour
a. Clodagh's Dance	**1 hour**	**$\frac{\$6}{\text{hour}}$**
b. New Steps	**15 hours**	**$\frac{\$5}{\text{hour}}$**
c. Stepping High	**10 hours**	**$\frac{\$5.20}{\text{hour}}$**

3. What other things should Glynnis consider when making her choice? **Possible answer: Location of school, times of her other activities, how to get to the school.**
4. Which dance school would you advise Glynnis to attend? Explain the advantage of taking these classes. **Possible answer: Clodagh's Dance because the classes are shorter and she can pay by the class.**

At the beginning of this section, you learned how important it is to be prepared for fires. Now you will investigate to see how quickly your classroom and school cafeteria can be evacuated.

Fire Alarm

Materials: Watch with second hand, Yardstick or Meter stick

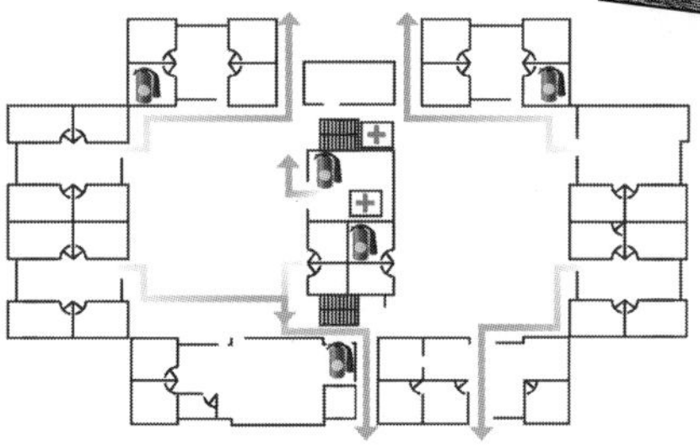

1. Have everyone in your class exit through one classroom door in an orderly fashion as if evacuating for an emergency. Time how long this takes.
2. Write a rate giving the number of people that can exit through the door per minute.
3. Compare the width of a classroom door with the width of a single cafeteria door. Then estimate the rate at which people can exit the cafeteria through the door.
4. Check the number and size of the other cafeteria doors. Then estimate the rate at which people can exit the cafeteria through all its doors.
5. The "maximum occupancy" of a room is the number of people that can be evacuated in 1 minute. Estimate the maximum occupancy of your cafeteria.
6. Write a report to the principal evaluating the cafeteria design in terms of emergency evacuation. Is the maximum occupancy you calculated in Step 5 a good recommendation? How could the cafeteria be improved to allow for a faster and safer evacuation?

MAX OCCUPANCY 150

USE STAIRS IN CASE OF EMERGENCY

EXIT

Fire Alarm

The Point

In *Fire Alarm* on page 513, students read about how the Great Chicago Fire began and spread so quickly. Now students will time the emergency evacuation of their classroom and cafeteria.

Materials

Watch with second hand, yardstick or meter stick

About the Page

- Show students how to use a watch with second hand correctly so they can time the evacuations accurately.
- Assign two students to keep track of the amount of time it takes for students to evacuate your classroom.
- Discuss with students how they can determine the rate of exit. If students do not do their own timing, suggest a number for the evacuation time.
- If the width of the classroom door differs from the width of the cafeteria door, discuss how this could affect the evacuation time.
- Discuss the variables that could affect the rate of exit from the cafeteria, such as placement of tables, chairs, and trash cans, width of the door, location of the food line, and so on.

Ongoing Assessment

Check that students have timed the evacuation and measured the doorways accurately. Check that their estimate of the people who can exit the cafeteria in one minute is reasonable.

Extension

The fire department probably has determined the amount of time it should take for students to clear your school in an emergency. Most schools are required to have fire drills. Ask your principal if your class could receive the evacuation times from the classrooms and other areas of the school during one of the fire drills. Compare the fire drill results with your results.

Answers for Connect

Answers may vary.

10A Review

Review Correlation

Item(s)	Lesson(s)
1–3	10-1
4–9	10-2
10, 11	10-3

Test Prep

Test-Taking Tip

When a question involves units, it is necessary to include the correct units in the answer. If students chose C, they did not consider units. They may have just recognized that 27 is 3×9 and 12 is 3×4.

Answers for Review

3. Possible answers:

$\frac{3 \text{ red}}{5 \text{ blue}}$, $\frac{3 \text{ red}}{4 \text{ green}}$, $\frac{5 \text{ blue}}{4 \text{ green}}$, $\frac{4 \text{ green}}{3 \text{ red}}$, $\frac{1 \text{ red}}{4 \text{ total}}$

5. Possible answers: 3:8, 12:32, 18:48

9. Answers may vary.

Section 10A Review

REVIEW 10A

1. 23,000 of the 30,000 fire departments in the United States are staffed by volunteers. Write this ratio in lowest terms. 23:30

2. Last month the County Fire Department responded to 8 home fires and 6 brush fires. Give each ratio in lowest terms.

a. Home fires to brush fires 4:3 **b.** Brush fires to home fires 3:4

c. Home fires to all fires 4:7 **d.** Brush fires to all fires 3:7

3. Tamara has 3 red marbles, 5 blue marbles, and 4 green marbles. Give 5 ratios in lowest terms to describe the situation.

4. Complete each table of equal ratios. Squares: 9; Circles: 10, 20; Books: 2, 6, 200

Squares	3	6		12
Circles	5		15	

Binders	3	9	27	300
Books			18	

5. Give three ratios equal to 6:16.

6. There are 6 dogs and 5 cats. Write the ratio of dogs to cats in three ways. 6:5, $\frac{6}{5}$, 6 to 5

For Exercises 7–9, use the stones pictured.

7. Give the ratio of metallic stones to red stones. 1:3

8. What is the ratio of purple and blue stones to green stones? 9:7

9. Write a ratio which compares something to the total number of stones.

10. Alex made 24 phone calls in 18 days. Write this as a rate in lowest terms. $\frac{4 \text{ calls}}{3 \text{ days}}$

Test Prep

When asked to find an equal rate, make sure the units are correct.

11. Which rate is equivalent to 9 pounds in 4 hours? D

Ⓐ $\frac{8 \text{ pounds}}{18 \text{ hours}}$ Ⓑ $\frac{8 \text{ hours}}{18 \text{ minutes}}$ Ⓒ $\frac{27 \text{ ounces}}{12 \text{ minutes}}$ Ⓓ $\frac{27 \text{ pounds}}{12 \text{ hours}}$

Resources

Practice Masters
Section 10A Review

Assessment Sourcebook
Quiz 10A

TestWorks
Test and Practice Software

PRACTICE

Name ______________________

Practice

Section 10A Review

1. About 160,000 of Rhode Island's 1,000,000 residents live in Providence. Write this ratio in lowest terms. $\frac{4}{25}$

2. Last week a local humane society rescued 14 dogs and 10 cats.Give each ratio in lowest terms. Possible answers:

   a. Dogs to cats 7 : 5 b. Cats to dogs $\frac{5}{7}$

   c. Dogs to all animals $\frac{7}{12}$ d. Cats to all animals 5 to 12

3. Lucy has 5 quarters, 3 dimes, and 2 nickels. Give 5 ratios in lowest terms to describe the situation. Possible answers:
   quarters to dimes: $\frac{5}{3}$, dimes to nickels: $\frac{3}{2}$, nickels to quarters: $\frac{2}{5}$, quarters to all coins: $\frac{1}{2}$, nickels to all coins: $\frac{1}{5}$

4. Complete each table of equal ratios.

Men	7	21	49	70
Women	9	27	63	90

Telephones	5	10	15	20
Fax Machines	6	12	18	24

5. Give three ratios equal to 45 : 65. 9 : 13, 18 : 26, 27 : 39

6. There are 8 magazines and 15 books. Write the ratio of magazines to books in three ways. $\frac{8}{15}$, 8 : 15, 8 to 15

For Exercises 7–8, use the figures pictured. Possible answers:

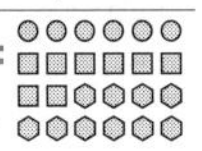

7. Give the ratio of circles to hexagons. 3 : 5

8. What is the ratio of hexagons and squares to circles? 3 to 1

9. Martin watched 10 movies in 25 hours. Write this as a rate in lowest terms. $\frac{2 \text{ movies}}{5 \text{ hours}}$

10. The Peachy King Beverage Company advertises that its product contains "$\frac{2}{5}$ real fruit juice!" How much fruit juice is in a 16 ounce container of this drink? *[Lesson 7-2]* $6\frac{2}{5}$ oz

11. **Science** An emperor penguin has been observed diving to a depth of 1584 feet below sea level. Write an integer to describe the penguin's height during its dive. *[Lesson 9-1]* −1584 ft

Section 10B

Proportions

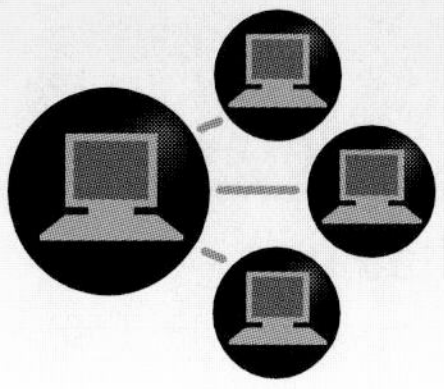

Visit www.teacher.mathsurf.com for links to lesson plans from teachers and other professionals, NCTM information, and other sites.

LESSON PLANNING GUIDE

Student Edition / Ancillaries*

LESSON		MATERIALS	VOCABULARY	DAILY	OTHER
	Section 10B Opener				
10-4	**What Is a Proportion?**		cross product, proportion	10-4	Technology Master 53
10-5	**Solving Proportions Using Cross Products**			10-5	
10-6	**Solving Proportions Using Unit Rates**			10-6	
10-7	**Similar Figures**	centimeter ruler, protractor	similar	10-7	Teaching Tool Trans. 2, 3, 6, 16, 17 Technology Master 54 Ch. 10 Project Master
	Connect	centimeter ruler, protractor			Interdisc. Team Teaching 10B Teaching Tool Trans. 6, 16, 17
	Review				Practice 10B; Quiz 10B; *TestWorks*

* Daily Ancillaries include Practice, Reteaching, Problem Solving, Enrichment, and Daily Transparency. Teaching Tool Transparencies are in *Teacher's Toolkits*. Lesson Enhancement Transparencies are in *Overhead Transparency Package*.

SKILLS TRACE

LESSON	SKILL	FIRST INTRODUCED GR. 4	GR. 5	GR. 6	DEVELOP	PRACTICE/ APPLY	REVIEW
10-4	**Identifying proportions.**		✗		pp. 530–531	pp. 532–533	pp. 548, 570, 573, 597
10-5	**Solving proportions using cross products.**			✗ p. 534	pp. 534–535	pp. 536–537	pp. 548, 570, 573, 605
10-6	**Solving proportions using unit rates.**			✗ p. 538	pp. 538–540	pp. 541–542	pp. 548, 573, 609
10-7	**Identifying similar figures and finding missing lengths.**		✗		pp. 543–544	pp. 545–546	pp. 548, 570, 573, 614

CONNECTED MATHEMATICS

Investigation 1 in the unit *Bits and Pieces II (Using Rational Numbers)*, from the **Connected Mathematics** series, can be used with Section 10B.

INTERDISCIPLINARY TEAM TEACHING

Math and Social Studies

(Worksheet pages 49–50: Teacher pages T49–T50)

In this lesson, students use proportions to build scale models of buildings.

Name ______________________ ***Math and Social Studies***

SCRAPING THE SKY

Use proportions to build scale models of buildings.

Skyscrapers are the world's tallest buildings. They are mainly built for office space, but they can also be used for apartments, stores, hotels, restaurants, athletic clubs, and other facilities. Skyscrapers symbolize a city's growth and prosperity. In a developing city, space for buildings becomes harder and harder to find. Land also becomes very expensive. For these reasons, buildings must be built taller, rather than wider. The result is the skyscraper.

By the 1920s, New York City was the skyscraper capital of the world. Almost 200 skyscrapers were built in the city between 1902 and 1929. One of the oldest and most famous skyscrapers in New York is the Flatiron Building. It got its name because it is shaped like a clothes iron. Completed in 1903, it is 21 stories tall, short by today's standards but tall for its time.

Three developments made the construction of skyscrapers possible: (1) the quality of steel improved. Steel is a hard, rust-resistant metal made of iron combined with other substances. (2) The structural steel frame was designed. Steel frames support the walls and floors of buildings much as your skeleton supports your body. (3) The development of the elevator increased access to the tall buildings. Before the elevator, buildings could not be taller than the number of stairs people could climb.

Competition among builders produced taller and taller skyscrapers. New York's Empire State Building was finished in 1931 and was the world's tallest skyscraper. It has 102 stories and measures 1,250 feet from the sidewalk to the roof. The Empire State Building kept its title until the 1970s when it was replaced by the World Trade Center in New York City. Today the tallest building in the world is the Petronas Towers in Kuala Lumpur, Malayasia.

Architects often create scale models of skyscrapers. A scale model is a small version of an object. The model's dimensions are proportional to the full-size object. One reason scale models are made is to see how the finished building will look. Architects may also create scale models of a section of a city to determine how a new skyscraper will fit in. At other times, architects build a scale model and then test it to see how the building will respond to such things as wind. Before the construction of the Worldwide Plaza, a 45-story skyscraper in New York City, a scale model was built to test its strength. The model was placed in a wind tunnel at the University of Western Ontario. A wind tunnel is a device in which air is made to move at various speeds, as wind does. Winds hit the model just as they would hit the skyscraper on the New York street on which it was to be built. By studying the results of the test, architects could modify the design to produce a building that moved neither too much nor too little when winds blew on it.

In addition to using proportions to build scale models, architects use proportions to draw building plans, or blueprints. For example, $\frac{1}{4}$ inch on a blueprint might represent 1 foot of an actual building. So an 8-foot-tall door would appear as a 2-inch-tall drawing on the blueprint.

Name ______________________ ***Math and Social Studies***

1. What advances in technology made the skyscraper possible?
   Possible answers: The invention of high-quality steel, the development of steel frame construction, and the elevator.

2. a. The scale model of Worldwide Plaza was 1:500. What does this ratio mean?
   The model was $\frac{1}{500\text{th}}$ the size of the actual building.

   b. If the building was 800 feet tall, including structures built on the roof, how tall was the scale model?
   1.6 feet

3. Complete the following table. Round all decimals to the tenths place. An example has been provided to help you get started.

4. Make a scale model of a building. You might choose a famous building or a building in your community. Working in small groups, find the dimensions. The building can be any size, from a shed to an office building. Using the dimensions, set up proportions for making a scale model of the building. Use a scale that will allow you to build a model that will fit on a table and will not be too tall for you to reach its top. Use materials of your choice for the model, but try to make the model look as much like the real building as possible.

5. a. Who, besides architects, must understand proportions so buildings can be constructed correctly? Explain your answer.
   See below.

   b. What kinds of scale models have you played with or constructed? About what was the scale of each model?
   See below.

Name and Location of Skyscraper	Height from Sidewalk to Roof (feet)	Total Height of Building Including *Structures Built on Roof (feet)	Ratio of Height of Structures on Roof to Height of Building from Sidewalk to Roof	Total Height of a 1:500 Model (feet)
Sears Tower, Chicago, Illinois	1454	1707	253:1454	3.4
Empire State Building, New York, New York	1250	1454	204:1250	2.9
John Hancock Center, Chicago, Illinois	1127	1476	349:1127	3.0
Bank of China, Hong Kong	1001	1309	308:1001	2.6

*Structures include such objects as television antennas, spires, and statues.

Answers

5. a. Builders. They must follow the dimensions shown on the blueprints so the building is proportional to the plans.

5. b. Possible answers: Students may suggest scale models of airplanes, statues, cars, and boats. Scales will vary. Literature that accompanies the models usually describes the scale. In some cases, students may have to estimate or calculate the scale, such as that of a souvenir Statue of Liberty or other famous structure.

BIBLIOGRAPHY

FOR TEACHERS

Cooney, Thomas J. *Teaching and Learning Mathematics in the 1990s.* Reston, VA: NCTM, 1990.

Edwards, Edgar L., ed. *Algebra for Everyone.* Reston, VA: NCTM, 1990.

Miller, Ross. *American Apocalypse: The Great Fire and the Myth of Chicago.* Chicago, IL: University of Chicago Press, 1990.

Zawojewski, Judith S., et al. *Dealing with Data and Chance: Addenda Series, Grades 5–8.* Reston, VA: NCTM, 1991.

FOR STUDENTS

Doherty, Craig A. *The Golden Gate Bridge.* Woodridge, CT: Blackbirch Press, 1995.

Jensen, Vickie. *Carving a Totem Pole.* New York, NY: H. Holt, 1996.

Sorensen, Lynda. *The Statue of Liberty.* Vero Beach, FL: Rourke Books, 1994.

Stewart, Hilary. *Looking at Totem Poles.* Seattle, WA: University of Washington Press, 1993.

SECTION **10B**

Proportions

▶ Fine Arts Link ▶ History Link ▶ www.mathsurf.com/6/ch10/statues

A MONUMENTAL STORY

"I was born in Paris in 1884. I made my first and only overseas trip to New York City, that same year. In 1903, poet Emma Lazarus called me the 'Mother of Exiles.' I stand at 151 feet and 1 inch, and I haven't sat down for over 100 years. Who am I?"

The paragraph above describes none other than the Statue of Liberty. The designer, Frédéric Bartholdi, spent over 13 years planning this monument to freedom and hope. He started with a small clay model. Then he built three plaster models, each one larger than the one before. These models became the "blueprint" for the statue's construction.

When designing a statue, artists must pay careful attention to scale. If the nose is too big for the face, or the shoulders too narrow for the height, then the effect of the statue can be altered. A statue with the intended proportions is not only a work of art … it is a work of mathematics.

1 Statues can cost thousands of dollars and take years to construct. Why do people spend the time and money to build them?

2 Other than the Statue of Liberty, what are some examples of things with humanlike features that are not human-sized?

3 How could an artist use mathematics when designing a statue? Give three examples.

529

Where are we now?

In Section 10A, students learned to express quantities as ratios.

They learned how to

- express two quantities as a ratio.
- find ratios equal to a given ratio.
- express two quantities with different units as a rate.

Where are we going?

In Section 10B, students will

- test to see if two ratios form a proportion.
- solve proportions using cross products.
- solve proportions using unit rates.
- identify similar figures.
- use proportions to find the length of a similar figure.

Theme: Statues

World Wide Web

If your class has access to the World Wide Web, you might want to use the information found at the Web site address given. The interdisciplinary links relate to topics discussed in this section.

About the Page

This page introduces the theme of the section, statues, and discusses the mathematics used in designing a statue.

Ask …

- Why do artists make models before they actually construct a statue?

Extensions

The following activities do not require access to the World Wide Web.

Fine Arts

Sculpture is one of the oldest forms of art. Ask students to research and identify other forms of art that use mathematics.

History

"Give me your tired, your poor, your huddled masses yearning to breathe free," is part of the poem, *The New Colossus*, inscribed on the pedestal of the Statue of Liberty. Have students research the connection of this poem to the Statue of Liberty.

Answers for Questions

1. Possible answer: In order to honor people and ideals.
2. Possible answers: Trophies, sculptures of humans, cameo pins.
3. Possible answers: To find proportions, measurements, angles, and areas.

Connect

On page 547, students create a blueprint for a model of a totem pole.

10-4 Lesson Organizer

Objectives

- Learn what a proportion is.
- Test to see if two ratios form a proportion.

Vocabulary

- Cross product, proportion

NCTM Standards

- 1–4, 7

► Review

Are the ratios in each pair equal?

1. $\frac{3}{4}, \frac{6}{8}$ Yes
2. $\frac{4}{5}, \frac{12}{15}$ Yes
3. $\frac{2}{5}, \frac{6}{10}$ No
4. $\frac{2}{3}, \frac{5}{15}$ No

Available on Daily Transparency 10-4

1 Introduce

Explore

The Point
Students explore the pattern of the units in equal ratios by examining and completing arrangements of shapes. These arrangements illustrate equal ratios and the structure of proportions.

Ongoing Assessment
Students who are having difficulty might be asked to complete sentences like: "One triangle is to 2 triangles as 1 circle is to ..."

For Groups That Finish Early
Create another four-square pattern on your own, leaving out the shapes in one of the top squares. Exchange patterns with your partner and fill in the missing square.

10-4 What Is a Proportion?

You'll Learn ...

- what a proportion is
- to test to see if two ratios form a proportion

... How It's Used

Clothing designers use proportions when designing clothes to fit people comfortably.

Vocabulary

cross product

proportion

► Lesson Link You've used tables to create equal ratios. Now you'll learn an easy way to check whether two ratios are equal. ◄

Explore Equal Ratios

Four Square

Each "four-square" below represents an equal ratio using four sets of shapes arranged in a particular order. One set of shapes in each four-square is missing.

A.

▲	●
▲▲	? ?

B.

▲▲	▲▲▲▲
●●	? ?

C.

●	▲▲
●●●	? ?

D.

●●	●●●●
▲▲▲▲	? ?

1. These are the missing shapes from the four-squares. Determine where each set of shapes belongs. Explain your answers.
   a. ▲▲▲▲▲▲ **b.** ●● **c.** ▲▲▲▲▲▲▲▲ **d.** ●●●●
2. For the four-squares above, can the shape in the upper left corner match the shape below it? Can it match the shape to the right of it? Can it match the shape diagonal to it? Explain.
3. Create three four-square patterns of your own like the ones above.

Learn What Is a Proportion?

For two ratios, a **cross product** is the result of multiplying the top value in one ratio by the bottom value in the other.

$\frac{2}{5}$ $\frac{3}{10}$ $5 \times 3 = 15$ $2 \times 10 = 20$

MEETING INDIVIDUAL NEEDS

Resources

10-4 Practice
10-4 Reteaching
10-4 Problem Solving
10-4 Enrichment
10-4 Daily Transparency
 Problem of the Day
 Review
 Quick Quiz
Technology Master 53

Learning Modalities

Social Have students work together in groups of three or four. Have two students each give a ratio and the other students determine whether or not these two ratios form a proportion.

Visual Have students draw loops to set up cross-product equations. This will help them focus on the numbers that they are to multiply.

Verbal Have students write a description of how they can use cross products to determine if two ratios form a proportion.

Inclusion

Materials: 2-color counters

Have students use counters to solve proportions. Write a proportion, such as $\frac{3 \text{ red}}{4 \text{ blue}} = \frac{?}{8 \text{ blue}}$, on a sheet of paper. Have students place counters on a second sheet of paper to show the ratio given. Then they find the number of red counters that would form a proportion.

A **proportion** is a pair of equal ratios. In a proportion, the cross products of the two ratios are equal.

$$\frac{2}{5} = \frac{6}{15} \qquad 5 \times 6 = 30 \qquad 2 \times 15 = 30$$

Proportions often include different units of measurement. Units must be the same across the top and bottom *or* down the left and right sides. If the units only match diagonally, then the ratios do not form a proportion.

Examples

1 Decide if the ratios form a proportion.

a. $\frac{6 \text{ ft}}{10 \text{ sec}} \stackrel{?}{=} \frac{9 \text{ ft}}{15 \text{ sec}}$

The units are the same across the top and bottom. The cross products are equal.

$6 \times 15 = 90.$
$10 \times 9 = 90.$

It is a proportion.

b. $\frac{4 \text{ ft}}{6 \text{ ft}} \stackrel{?}{=} \frac{12 \text{ sec}}{18 \text{ sec}}$

The units are the same down the left and right sides. The cross products are equal.

$4 \times 18 = 72.$
$6 \times 12 = 72.$

It is a proportion.

c. $\frac{5 \text{ ft}}{10 \text{ sec}} \stackrel{?}{=} \frac{4 \text{ sec}}{8 \text{ ft}}$

The units are not the same across or down.

It is not a proportion.

2 The Golden Gate Bridge is 6480 ft long, with 756 ft tall towers. The model of the bridge used in *Superman* was 60 ft long with 7 ft tall towers. Was the model proportional to the actual bridge?

$\frac{60}{7} \stackrel{?}{=} \frac{6480}{756}$ ← bridge length ← tower height   Write terms of the ratios in the same order.

$60 \times 756 = 45{,}360$

$7 \times 6{,}480 = 45{,}360$ Determine the cross products.

The cross products are equal, so the ratios form a proportion. The model was proportional.

Try It

Decide if the ratios form a proportion.

a. $\frac{6}{8} \stackrel{?}{=} \frac{9}{12}$ Yes **b.** $\frac{2}{3} \stackrel{?}{=} \frac{7}{10}$ No **c.** $\frac{5 \text{ mi}}{2 \text{ hr}} \stackrel{?}{=} \frac{15 \text{ hr}}{6 \text{ mi}}$ No **d.** $\frac{\$12}{32 \text{ min}} \stackrel{?}{=} \frac{\$3}{8 \text{ min}}$ Yes

DID YOU KNOW?

The color of paint used for the Golden Gate Bridge is called international orange. The bridge is constantly repainted to restore the damage done by the weather. It takes approximately one year to repaint the bridge.

MATH EVERY DAY

Problem of the Day

The number 9 can be written as a fraction using all ten digits 0 through 9. One way is shown below. Try to find at least one more way. (Zero cannot be the first digit of either number.)

$9 = \frac{95{,}823}{10{,}647}$ $\frac{97{,}524}{10{,}836}$ or $\frac{95{,}742}{10{,}638}$

Available on Daily Transparency 10-4

An Extension is provided in the transparency package.

Fact of the Day

The main span of the Golden Gate Bridge measures 4,200 feet from tower to tower. It cost $35,000,000 when it was built.

Estimation

Estimate each sum.

1. $3\frac{3}{8} + 4\frac{3}{4}$ 8
2. $8\frac{1}{6} + 1\frac{1}{3}$ 9
3. $6 + 2\frac{2}{3}$ 9
4. $4\frac{1}{2} + 5\frac{2}{3}$ 11

Follow Up

Have students discuss their answers for Steps 1 and 2. Have volunteers share some of the patterns that they created in Step 3.

Answers for Explore

1. a. C; b. A; c. D; d. B
2. Up and down: yes; Left and right: yes; Diagonal: no.
3. Answers may vary.

2 Teach

Learn

Alternate Examples

1. Decide if the ratios form a proportion.

a. $\frac{200 \text{ mi}}{4 \text{ hr}} \stackrel{?}{=} \frac{600 \text{ mi}}{8 \text{ hr}}$

The units are the same across the top and bottom. The cross products are not equal.

$200 \times 8 = 1600$

$4 \times 600 = 2400$

It is not a proportion.

b. $\frac{8 \text{ ft}}{12 \text{ ft}} \stackrel{?}{=} \frac{2 \text{ min}}{3 \text{ min}}$

The units are the same down the left and right sides. The cross products are equal.

$8 \times 3 = 24$

$12 \times 2 = 24$

It is a proportion.

c. $\frac{9 \text{ ft}}{3 \text{ sec}} \stackrel{?}{=} \frac{5 \text{ sec}}{15 \text{ ft}}$

The units are not the same across or down.

It is not a proportion.

2. A 1973 Corvette is about 184.8 inches long and 48 inches high. A model of this car is 7.7 inches long and 2 inches high. Is the model proportional to the actual car?

$\frac{7.7}{2} \stackrel{?}{=} \frac{184.8}{48}$ car length / car height

$7.7 \times 48 = 369.6$

$2 \times 184.8 = 369.6$

The cross products are equal, so the ratios form a proportion. The model is proportional.

Assignment Guide

- **Basic** 1, 2–14 evens, 18–20, 22–25, 30–38 evens
- **Average** 1, 8–16 evens, 18–26, 29–39 odds
- **Enriched** 8–18 evens, 19–27, 30–38 evens

3 Practice and Assess

Check

Answers for Check Your Understanding

1. The cross products must be equal and the units up and down or right and left must be the same. Examples may vary.
2. Possible answer: They have the same ratio.

Reteaching

Activity

Materials: Play money or slips of paper with \$10 and \$5 written on them

- At work, Terry and her friends made \$75 in 5 hours on Saturday and \$45 in 3 hours on Sunday.
- Use play money to determine if the two pay rates are proportional.
- Divide \$75 into 5 piles to show how much they made each hour on Saturday.
- Divide \$45 into 3 piles to show how much they made each hour on Sunday.
- During those two days, did they make the same amount of money each hour? Yes
- Write the rate for Saturday and the rate for Sunday. $\frac{\$75}{5}, \frac{\$45}{3}$
- Determine the cross products. $75 \times 3 = 225$ and $45 \times 5 = 225$
- Do these rates form a proportion? Yes

PRACTICE 10-4

Check Your Understanding

1. How can you tell if two ratios form a proportion? Give an example.
2. What does it mean to say that quantities are "proportional"?

10-4 Exercises and Applications

Practice and Apply

1. **Getting Started** Match the ratio pairs to their cross products.

   a. $\frac{3}{4}$ and $\frac{30}{40}$ II b. $\frac{5}{6}$ and $\frac{3}{5}$ III **I.** 14 and 8 **II.** 120 and 120

   c. $\frac{1}{2}$ and $\frac{7}{8}$ I d. $\frac{2}{3}$ and $\frac{6}{9}$ IV **III.** 18 and 25 **IV.** 18 and 18

State whether or not each pair of ratios forms a proportion.

2. $\frac{4}{3}$ □ $\frac{12}{9}$ Yes 3. $\frac{8}{5}$ □ $\frac{11}{7}$ No 4. $\frac{8}{3}$ □ $\frac{32}{12}$ Yes 5. $\frac{27}{4}$ □ $\frac{20}{3}$ No 6. $\frac{45}{81}$ □ $\frac{5}{9}$ Yes

7. $\frac{6}{25}$ □ $\frac{4}{117}$ No 8. $\frac{7}{2}$ □ $\frac{21}{6}$ Yes 9. $\frac{3}{23}$ □ $\frac{6}{50}$ No 10. $\frac{3}{16}$ □ $\frac{5}{30}$ No 11. $\frac{29}{4}$ □ $\frac{24}{6}$ No

12. $\frac{2\text{ tsp}}{1\text{ oz}}$ □ $\frac{4\text{ oz}}{8\text{ tsp}}$ No 13. $\frac{75\text{ mi}}{3\text{ hr}}$ □ $\frac{125\text{ mi}}{5\text{ hr}}$ Yes 14. $\frac{6\text{ acres}}{10\text{ acres}}$ □ $\frac{15\text{ ft}}{25\text{ ft}}$ Yes

For Exercises 15 and 16, choose the proportion that is written correctly.

15. a. $\frac{1\text{ cat}}{2\text{ dogs}} = \frac{4\text{ dogs}}{8\text{ cats}}$ b. $\frac{1\text{ cat}}{2\text{ dogs}} = \frac{4\text{ cats}}{8\text{ dogs}}$ c. $\frac{1\text{ cat}}{8\text{ cats}} = \frac{4\text{ dogs}}{2\text{ dogs}}$ b

16. a. $\frac{24\text{ inches}}{2\text{ feet}} = \frac{48\text{ inches}}{4\text{ feet}}$ b. $\frac{24\text{ inches}}{2\text{ feet}} = \frac{48\text{ feet}}{4\text{ inches}}$ c. $\frac{24\text{ inches}}{2\text{ feet}} = \frac{4\text{ feet}}{48\text{ inches}}$ a

17. **Fine Arts** Here is a picture of the *Motherland* in Volgograd, Russia. In the photo, 1 cm is about 49 feet. How tall is the actual statue? 269.5 ft

18. Cedrick earned \$209 for 38 hours of work last week. This week he earned \$176 for 32 hours of work. Do these rates form a proportion? Yes

19. **Test Prep** Which of the following is a proportion? A

    Ⓐ $\frac{25}{15} = \frac{15}{9}$ Ⓑ $\frac{6}{10} = \frac{7}{12}$ Ⓒ $\frac{18}{5} = \frac{9}{3}$ Ⓓ $\frac{10}{3} = \frac{16}{6}$

PRACTICE

Name ____________

Practice 10-4

What is a Proportion?

State whether or not each pair of ratios forms a proportion.

1. $\frac{6}{12} \overset{?}{=} \frac{12}{14}$ No 2. $\frac{3}{20} \overset{?}{=} \frac{2}{10}$ No 3. $\frac{20}{12} \overset{?}{=} \frac{25}{15}$ Yes
4. $\frac{27}{6} \overset{?}{=} \frac{36}{8}$ Yes 5. $\frac{13}{11} \overset{?}{=} \frac{24}{20}$ No 6. $\frac{3}{4} \overset{?}{=} \frac{15}{20}$ Yes
7. $\frac{10}{4} \overset{?}{=} \frac{45}{20}$ No 8. $\frac{15}{10} \overset{?}{=} \frac{3}{2}$ Yes 9. $\frac{12}{21} \overset{?}{=} \frac{16}{28}$ Yes
10. $\frac{3}{24} \overset{?}{=} \frac{4}{32}$ Yes 11. $\frac{12}{20} \overset{?}{=} \frac{4}{7}$ No 12. $\frac{2}{9} \overset{?}{=} \frac{5}{22}$ No
13. $\frac{6}{15} \overset{?}{=} \frac{4}{12}$ No 14. $\frac{15}{18} \overset{?}{=} \frac{20}{24}$ Yes 15. $\frac{17}{12} \overset{?}{=} \frac{10}{7}$ No
16. $\frac{25}{35} \overset{?}{=} \frac{15}{21}$ Yes 17. $\frac{10}{9} \overset{?}{=} \frac{16}{14}$ No 18. $\frac{32}{36} \overset{?}{=} \frac{40}{45}$ Yes
19. $\frac{2\text{ tsp}}{7\text{ gal}} \overset{?}{=} \frac{6\text{ tsp}}{21\text{ gal}}$ Yes 20. $\frac{12\text{ cm}}{20\text{ g}} \overset{?}{=} \frac{15\text{ g}}{25\text{ cm}}$ No 21. $\frac{\$14}{3\text{ hr}} \overset{?}{=} \frac{\$84}{18\text{ hr}}$ Yes
22. $\frac{27\text{ lb}}{\$21} \overset{?}{=} \frac{14\text{ lb}}{\$18}$ No 23. $\frac{15\text{ sec}}{21\text{ sec}} \overset{?}{=} \frac{10\text{ in.}}{15\text{ in.}}$ No 24. $\frac{6\text{ ft}}{13\text{ gal}} \overset{?}{=} \frac{7\text{ ft}}{14\text{ gal}}$ No

For Exercises 25–30, choose the proportion that is written correctly.

25. a. $\frac{20\text{ men}}{25\text{ women}} = \frac{5\text{ men}}{4\text{ women}}$ (b.) $\frac{20\text{ men}}{25\text{ women}} = \frac{4\text{ men}}{5\text{ women}}$ c. $\frac{4\text{ men}}{5\text{ women}} = \frac{25\text{ women}}{20\text{ men}}$
26. a. $\frac{27\text{ acres}}{\$15} = \frac{\$25}{45\text{ acres}}$ b. $\frac{\$27}{15\text{ acres}} = \frac{\$25}{45\text{ acres}}$ (c.) $\frac{45\text{ acres}}{\$25} = \frac{27\text{ acres}}{\$15}$
27. a. $\frac{12\text{ pies}}{4\text{ cakes}} = \frac{6\text{ cakes}}{18\text{ pies}}$ (b.) $\frac{4\text{ cakes}}{12\text{ pies}} = \frac{6\text{ cakes}}{18\text{ pies}}$ c. $\frac{12\text{ pies}}{4\text{ cakes}} = \frac{6\text{ pies}}{18\text{ cakes}}$
28. (a.) $\frac{6\text{ gal}}{15\text{ gal}} = \frac{2\text{ min}}{5\text{ min}}$ b. $\frac{5\text{ min}}{15\text{ gal}} = \frac{6\text{ gal}}{2\text{ min}}$ c. $\frac{6\text{ gal}}{2\text{ min}} = \frac{5\text{ gal}}{15\text{ min}}$
29. a. $\frac{25\text{ chairs}}{5\text{ tables}} = \frac{10\text{ tables}}{2\text{ chairs}}$ b. $\frac{25\text{ chairs}}{5\text{ tables}} = \frac{2\text{ tables}}{10\text{ chairs}}$ (c.) $\frac{25\text{ chairs}}{5\text{ tables}} = \frac{10\text{ chairs}}{2\text{ tables}}$
30. (a.) $\frac{36\text{ lb}}{28\text{ ft}} = \frac{18\text{ lb}}{14\text{ ft}}$ b. $\frac{18\text{ lb}}{14\text{ ft}} = \frac{28\text{ lb}}{36\text{ ft}}$ c $\frac{36\text{ ft}}{28\text{ lb}} = \frac{18\text{ lb}}{14\text{ ft}}$
31. During the butterfly stroke competitions at the 1972 Summer Olympic Games, Mayumi Aoki swam 100 meters in 64 seconds, and Karen Moe swam 200 meters in 136 seconds. Do these rates form a proportion? No
32. At Deliah's Hardware, you can buy 5 feet of PVC pipe for \$1.10, or 8 feet for \$1.76. Are these prices proportional? Yes

RETEACHING

Name ____________

Alternative Lesson 10-4

What Is a Proportion?

For two ratios, a **cross product** is the result of multiplying the top value in one ratio by the bottom value in the other.

A **proportion** is a pair of equal ratios. Units of measurement must be the same across the top and bottom *or* down the left and right sides. In a proportion the cross products of the two ratios are equal.

Example 1

Find the cross products for the ratios $\frac{3\text{ ft}}{5\text{ sec}}$ and $\frac{12\text{ ft}}{20\text{ sec}}$.

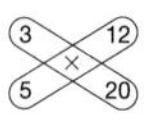

Multiply the top value of the first ratio and the bottom value of the second ratio. $3 \times 20 = 60$

Multiply the bottom value of the first ratio and the top value of the second ratio. $5 \times 12 = 60$

The cross products are 60 and 60.

Try It Find the cross products for each pair of ratios.

a. $\frac{3}{9}$ and $\frac{4}{12}$ $3 \times$ 12 = 36; $9 \times$ 4 = 36
b. $\frac{5}{8}$ and $\frac{3}{5}$ 5 × 5 = 25; $8 \times$ 3 = 24
c. $\frac{4}{10}$ and $\frac{6}{15}$ 4 × 15 = 60; 10 × 6 = 60

Example 2

State whether or not the ratios form a proportion.

Find the cross products for the ratios $\frac{6\text{ minutes}}{3\text{ minutes}}$ and $\frac{12\text{ feet}}{6\text{ feet}}$.

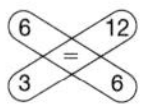

The cross products are equal, so the ratios form a proportion.

Try It Find the cross products. Then state whether or not the ratios form a proportion. Write *yes* or *no.*

d. $\frac{4}{5} \overset{?}{=} \frac{2}{3}$ $4 \times$ 3 = 12; $5 \times$ 2 = 10; No.
e. $\frac{10}{50} \overset{?}{=} \frac{2}{10}$ 10 × 10 = 100; $50 \times$ 2 = 100; Yes.
f. $\frac{9}{12} \overset{?}{=} \frac{6}{8}$ 9 × 8 = 72; 12 × 6 = 72; Yes.

20. **Test Prep** Which of the following is proportional to $\frac{3}{5}$? D

Ⓐ $\frac{4}{6}$ Ⓑ $\frac{10}{6}$ Ⓒ $\frac{5}{3}$ Ⓓ $\frac{12}{20}$

21. For which two classes are the ratios of boys to girls proportional? Ms. Lee and Mrs. Nieto

22. For which two classes are the ratios of girls to total students proportional? Ms. Lee and Mrs. Nieto

23. **Consumer** A 16 oz drink at Tito's Sandwich Shop costs 99¢. A 20 oz drink costs $1.19. Are these prices proportional? No

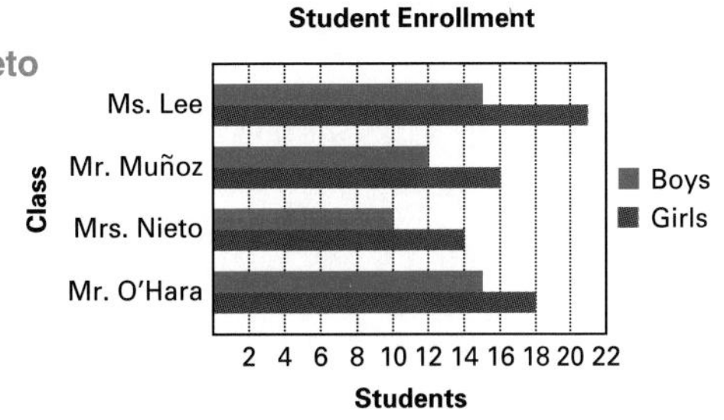

Problem Solving and Reasoning

24. **Communicate** How do you use multiplication to determine if two ratios are proportional?

25. **Choose a Strategy** Janice can run 100 meters in 12 seconds. Carl can run 500 meters in 48 seconds. Susan runs at a rate of 10 meters per second. Phillip can run 200 meters in 24 seconds. Which two students run at the same rate? Explain how you found your answer.

Problem Solving STRATEGIES

- Look for a Pattern
- Make an Organized List
- Make a Table
- Guess and Check
- Work Backward
- Use Logical Reasoning
- Draw a Diagram
- Solve a Simpler Problem

26. **Critical Thinking** The following ratios do not form a proportion: $\frac{3}{8}$ and $\frac{6}{9.5}$. How can you determine this without actually finding the cross products?

27. Journal Explain why the following is not a proportion.

$\frac{\$0.25}{\text{1 lb of apples}}$ and $\frac{\text{3 lb of apples}}{\$0.75}$

Mixed Review

Order from greatest to least. *[Lesson 9-1]*

28. 4, −7, −2, −9 — 4, −2, −7, −9

29. 31, −55, 55, −13 — 55, 31, −13, −55

30. 2, 22, −22, −222 — 22, 2, −22, −222

31. −17, −53, −31, −9 — −9, −17, −31, −53

32. 18, 0, −5, 22 — 22, 18, 0, −5

33. 41, −14, −41, 44 — 44, 41, −14, −41

34. 26, −6, −2, 62 — 62, 26, −2, −6

35. −178, 133, 0, −100 — 133, 0, −100, −178

Find the missing measurement(s) for each circle, where r = radius, d = diameter, and c = circumference. Use 3.14 for π. *[Lesson 4-7]*

36. $r \approx 4$ mm, $d = 8$ mm, $c \approx$ ☐ 25.12 mm

37. $r = 2.1$, $d =$ ☐, $c \approx 13.188$ 4.2

38. $r \approx 1.1$ in, $d =$ ☐, $c \approx$ ☐ d = 2.2 in., $c \approx$ 6.908 in.

39. $r =$ ☐, $d =$ ☐, $c \approx 27.632$ yd r = 4.4 yd; d = 8.8 yd

Exercise Notes

■ Exercise 21

Extension Have students determine if the ratio of boys to girls is proportional in their own class.

Exercise Answers

24. Use multiplication to find the cross products. If the cross products are equal, the ratios are proportional.

25. Janice and Phillip. Possible answer: Convert all rates to equal rates with 48 seconds as the denominator.

26. Possible answer: $3 \times 2 = 6$, but $8 \times 2 \neq 9.5$.

27. The units are not the same across or down.

Alternate Assessment

Portfolio Have students select examples of pairs of ratios that form a proportion and pairs of ratios that do not. Students should then add examples of both to their portfolios.

Quick Quiz

State whether or not each pair of ratios forms a proportion.

1. $\frac{4}{5}, \frac{5}{6}$ No
2. $\frac{7}{12}, \frac{14}{24}$ Yes
3. $\frac{3\text{ ft}}{10\text{ sec}}, \frac{6\text{ sec}}{20\text{ ft}}$ No

Available on Daily Transparency 10-4

PROBLEM SOLVING

Name ____________

Guided Problem Solving 10-4

GPS **PROBLEM 25, PAGE 533**

Janice can run 100 meters in 12 seconds. Carl can run 500 meters in 48 seconds. Susan runs at a rate of 10 meters per second. Phillip can run 200 meters in 24 seconds. Which two students run at the same rate? Explain how you found your answer.

— Understand — Possible answer: Item 6

1. Underline the question.
2. Write the rate that each student runs in meters per seconds.
   a. Janice $\frac{100}{12}$ b. Carl $\frac{500}{48}$ c. Susan $\frac{10}{1}$ d. Phillip $\frac{200}{24}$

— Plan —

3. Make an organized list to compare the pairs of rates.
   a. Janice and Carl $\frac{100}{12} \stackrel{?}{=} \frac{500}{48}$
   b. Janice and Susan $\frac{100}{12} \stackrel{?}{=} \frac{10}{1}$
   c. Janice and Phillip $\frac{100}{12} \stackrel{?}{=} \frac{200}{24}$
   d. Carl and Susan $\frac{500}{48} \stackrel{?}{=} \frac{10}{1}$
   e. Carl and Phillip $\frac{500}{48} \stackrel{?}{=} \frac{200}{24}$
   f. Susan and Phillip $\frac{10}{1} \stackrel{?}{=} \frac{200}{24}$

— Solve —

4. Which of the pairs of rates in Item 3 form a proportion? $\frac{100}{12} = \frac{200}{24}$
5. Which students run at the same rate? Explain. Possible answer: Janice and Phillip, since they have equal rates.

— Look Back —

6. How could you find which students run at the same rate by writing each rate in lowest terms. Equal rates will be the same when written in lowest terms.

SOLVE ANOTHER PROBLEM

Guillermo made $15 for baby-sitting 5 hours. Megan made $28 in 8 hours. Thomas earned $2.50 in 1 hour, and Della earned $14 in 4 hours. Which two students were paid the same rate? Explain. Megan and Della; They were each paid $3.50 per hour.

ENRICHMENT

Name ____________

Extend Your Thinking 10-4

Patterns in Numbers

Find the sum and product of the numbers below.

Possible answers: Items 10–13

	Sum	Product
1. 3 and $\frac{3}{2}$	$4\frac{1}{2}$	$4\frac{1}{2}$
2. 4 and $\frac{4}{3}$	$5\frac{1}{3}$	$5\frac{1}{3}$
3. 5 and $\frac{5}{4}$	$6\frac{1}{4}$	$6\frac{1}{4}$
4. 6 and $\frac{6}{5}$	$7\frac{1}{5}$	$7\frac{1}{5}$
5. 7 and $\frac{7}{6}$	$8\frac{1}{6}$	$8\frac{1}{6}$
6. 8 and $\frac{8}{7}$	$9\frac{1}{7}$	$9\frac{1}{7}$
7. 9 and $\frac{9}{8}$	$10\frac{1}{8}$	$10\frac{1}{8}$
8. 10 and $\frac{10}{9}$	$11\frac{1}{9}$	$11\frac{1}{9}$
9. 11 and $\frac{11}{10}$	$12\frac{1}{10}$	$12\frac{1}{10}$

10. How is the sum and product of each pair of numbers related? Sums and products are equal.

11. What pattern do you see in the sums and products as you look down the column? Whole number part increases by 1. Denominator of fraction part also increases by 1. Numerators are all 1.

12. Compare the first and second number in each pair. What pattern do you see? Numerator of the second number is the same as the first number. Denominator is one less than numerator.

13. Write two equations using another other pair of numbers that have the same sum and product. $12 + \frac{12}{11} = 13\frac{1}{11}$; $12 \times \frac{12}{11} = 13\frac{1}{11}$

10-5 Lesson Organizer

Objective

- Solve proportions using cross products.

NCTM Standards

- 1–4, 13

Review

Solve each equation.

1. $4x = 20$ $x = 5$
2. $6x = 48$ $x = 8$
3. $7x = 28$ $x = 4$
4. $3x = 36$ $x = 12$

Available on Daily Transparency 10-5

Lesson Link

Have students discuss how they determined in the last lesson whether or not two ratios formed a proportion.

1 Introduce

Explore

The Point
Students explore solving proportions by using number sense to estimate the value of a missing number in a proportion.

Ongoing Assessment
As students are working, check to see that both students are involved in explaining why the statements are true or false.

For Groups That Finish Early
Find the value of x that would complete the proportion in Step 2. Use this method to find the value of y in Step 3.

Follow Up
Have students give their answers and explain how they found them.

10-5 Solving Proportions Using Cross Products

You'll Learn ...

- to solve proportions using cross products

... How It's Used

Special-effects artists use cross products when determining how large or small something should be on a model to look realistic when filmed.

Lesson Link In the last lesson, you learned what a proportion is. Now you will find a missing number in a proportion. ◄

Explore Solving Proportions

Truth or Dare Revisited

Each proportion is followed by two statements. Only one of the statements is true. For each problem, use your number sense to choose the correct statement, and explain how you know it's true.

1. Proportion: $\frac{6}{10} = \frac{w}{5}$

a. If w is replaced with 3, the proportion will be true.

b. If w is replaced with 3, the proportion will be false.

2. Proportion: $\frac{5}{7} = \frac{x}{8}$

a. The value of x cannot be 6 because 6 is too large.

b. The value of x cannot be 6 because 6 is too small.

3. Proportion: $\frac{3}{4} = \frac{y}{3}$

a. The value of y is a whole number.

b. The value of y is a decimal number.

Learn Solving Proportions Using Cross Products

People use proportions to determine the value of an unknown measurement. If you know one measurement and the ratio that the known and unknown measurement should have, you can use a proportion to determine the unknown measure.

MEETING INDIVIDUAL NEEDS

Resources

- **10-5** Practice
- **10-5** Reteaching
- **10-5** Problem Solving
- **10-5** Enrichment
- **10-5** Daily Transparency
  - Problem of the Day
  - Review
  - Quick Quiz

Learning Modalities

Verbal Have students write a description of how proportions can be solved using cross products.

Social Have students work in groups of three. One student writes a ratio and one student writes another ratio with the numerator or denominator as a variable. The third student solves the proportion to find the value of the variable. Students should switch roles and repeat the process.

Challenge

Have students go to the grocery store to find an item which is sold in 3 different sizes and bring the prices to class. Then have them determine which is the best buy. The largest package is usually the best buy. Challenge students to find a product for which the smaller package is the better buy. Possible answer: A 20 lb bag of rice may cost less per oz than a 2 lb bag, but if only a small amount of rice is needed, the rest will be unused. Inexpensive products that are not necessary to buy are not bargains.

Example 1

Use cross products to solve the proportion $\frac{x}{15} = \frac{3}{5}$.

$5x = 15 \times 3$ Write the cross products.

$5x = 45$ Multiply.

$x = 9$ Think: What number times 5 equals 45?

If the numbers in a proportion are so complex that you can't use mental math to determine the value of a variable, you can use division. Division is the opposite of multiplication, and can be used to undo multiplication.

Example 2

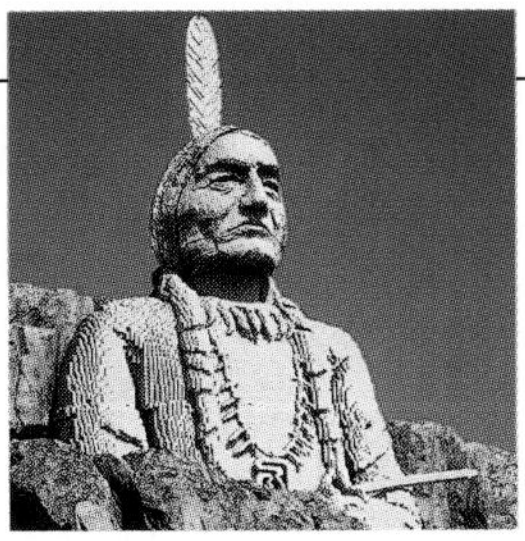

A 24 ft tall statue of the Sioux Indian chief Sitting Bull, in Denmark, is made entirely of Lego blocks. If the real Sitting Bull stood 6 ft and his head was 0.875 ft tall, find the height of the statue's head.

Let h be the height of the statue's head.

$\frac{\text{head height}}{\text{total height}} \begin{matrix}\rightarrow \\ \rightarrow\end{matrix} \frac{h}{24} = \frac{0.875}{6}$ Write a proportion.

$6h = 24 \times 0.875$ Write the cross products.

$6 \times h = 21$ Think: What number times 6 equals 21?

$h = 21 \div 6$ Use **division** to undo **multiplication**.

$h = 3.5$

The statue's head is 3.5 ft tall.

Try It

Solve each proportion.

a. $\frac{8}{12} = \frac{6}{x}$ 9 **b.** $\frac{4}{x} = \frac{6}{15}$ 10 **c.** $\frac{5}{20} = \frac{x}{6}$ 1.5 **d.** $\frac{4}{x} = \frac{10}{18}$ 7.2

MENTAL MATH

Since the denominator in the first fraction is three times bigger than the denominator in the second fraction, the numerator must also be three times bigger.

Remember

For decimal multiplication, the number of digits after the decimal point in the product should be the same as the total number of digits after the decimal points in the factors.

[Page 182]

Check Your Understanding

1. If all the numbers are different, how many numbers do you need in a proportion to be able to solve the proportion using cross products? Why?

2. Can you solve a proportion without using cross products? Explain.

Answers for Explore

1. a; The cross products will be equal to 30.
2. a; Use the cross products: $5 \times 8 = 7 \times x$. If x was 6, $40 < 42$.
3. b; Use the cross products: 3×3 is 9, and there is no whole number that can be multiplied by 4 to equal 9.

2 Teach

Learn

Alternate Examples

1. Use cross products to solve the proportion $\frac{x}{12} = \frac{5}{6}$.

   $6x = 12 \times 5$

   $6x = 60$

   $x - 10$

2. The sculpted head of George Washington on Mount Rushmore is about 60 feet high. George Washington was 74 inches tall. If the actual height of his head was 10 inches, how tall would the sculpture be if Mount Rushmore showed his entire body?

   Let h be the height of the sculpture.

   $\frac{60}{h} = \frac{10}{74}$

   $10h = 60 \times 74$

   $10 \times h = 4440$

   $h = 4440 \div 10$

   $h = 444$

   The height of the sculpture would be 444 feet.

3 Practice and Assess

Check

Answers for Check Your Understanding

1. 3; An equation where the cross products are set equal to each other can be solved for the unknown variable.
2. Yes; Possible answers: Divide or multiply across; Find an equivalent fraction to the fraction that is known.

MATH EVERY DAY

Problem of the Day

How many squares are shown below?

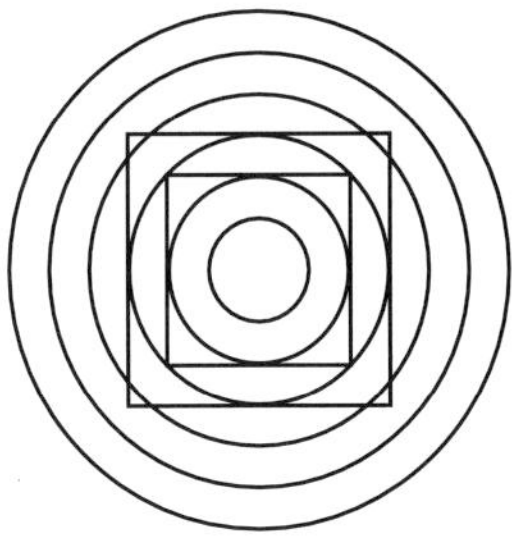

Two

Available on Daily Transparency 10-5

An Extension is provided in the transparency package.

Fact of the Day

The Statue of Liberty personifies Liberty as a woman who has just won her freedom. The burning torch symbolizes that her freedom enlightens the world.

Mental Math

Find each quotient mentally.

1. $600 \div 60$ 10
2. $360 \div 40$ 9
3. $8000 \div 20$ 400
4. $5400 \div 90$ 60
5. $7000 \div 70$ 100

10-5 Exercises and Applications

Assignment Guide

- Basic
  1–5, 7–33 odds, 37–47 odds
- Average
  1–31 odds, 32–33, 36–48 evens
- Enriched
  8–26 evens, 27–35, 36–48 evens

Exercise Notes

Exercise 28

Error Prevention To avoid setting up the proportion incorrectly, have students determine if their answer is reasonable. Ask them if more or less than 1820 pounds of copper was used.

Exercise 29

History Gustave Eiffel, who also built the Eiffel Tower in Paris, made the framework of the Statue of Liberty. The framework consists of iron and is supported by steel columns.

Reteaching

Activity

Materials: Index cards

- Make number cards by writing a number from 1 to 9 on each card. Make at least two cards for each number.
- Form a ratio by placing one card above the other.
- Form an equal ratio by multiplying each number in the ratio by the same third number. The cards might look like this:

$$\frac{\boxed{2}}{\boxed{3}} = \frac{\boxed{2}\times\boxed{4}}{\boxed{3}\times\boxed{4}}$$

- Rearrange the cards to show cross products. The cards above would be rearranged like this:

$$\boxed{2}\times\boxed{3}\times\boxed{4} = \boxed{3}\times\boxed{2}\times\boxed{4}$$

- Notice that the factors in each cross product are the same, so the products will be the same.
- Make other pairs of equal ratios with the number cards and rearrange the cards to show the cross products.

10-5 Exercises and Applications

PRACTICE 10-5

Practice and Apply

Getting Started Use the cross products to write an equation.

1. $\frac{9}{12} = \frac{3}{x}$ $9x = 36$ **2.** $\frac{78}{3} = \frac{26}{d}$ $78d = 78$ **3.** $\frac{j}{5} = \frac{55}{44}$ $44j = 275$ **4.** $\frac{6}{g} = \frac{42}{36}$ $42g = 216$ **5.** $\frac{7}{16} = \frac{s}{8}$ $16s = 56$

Solve each proportion.

6. $\frac{6}{8} = \frac{x}{12}$ 9 **7.** $\frac{x}{8} = \frac{21}{14}$ 12 **8.** $\frac{45}{m} = \frac{5}{3}$ 27 **9.** $\frac{10}{14} = \frac{c}{35}$ 25 **10.** $\frac{15}{14} = \frac{210}{l}$ 196

11. $\frac{6}{11} = \frac{9}{x}$ 16.5 **12.** $\frac{a}{7} = \frac{5}{3}$ $11.\overline{6}$ **13.** $\frac{2.4}{4.5} = \frac{u}{1.8}$ 0.96 **14.** $\frac{8.4}{y} = \frac{11.2}{6.8}$ 5.1 **15.** $\frac{m}{3} = \frac{10}{5}$ 6

16. $\frac{16}{c} = \frac{24}{3}$ 2 **17.** $\frac{y}{7} = \frac{9}{21}$ 3 **18.** $\frac{7}{10} = \frac{v}{20}$ 14 **19.** $\frac{10}{g} = \frac{15}{4}$ $2.\overline{6}$ **20.** $\frac{18}{k} = \frac{14}{3}$ $3\frac{6}{7}$

21. $\frac{5}{6} = \frac{3}{a}$ 3.6 **22.** $\frac{6}{16} = \frac{w}{12}$ 4.5 **23.** $\frac{5}{22} = \frac{35}{m}$ 154 **24.** $\frac{p}{12} = \frac{5}{15}$ 4 **25.** $\frac{12}{20} = \frac{14}{x}$ $23.\overline{3}$

26. Yesterday Stu earned \$31.50 for 5 hours of work. Today he worked for 7 hours at the same pay rate. How much did he earn today? \$44.10

27. Measurement If the rectangles shown are proportional to each other, what are the lengths of the unknown sides? 12

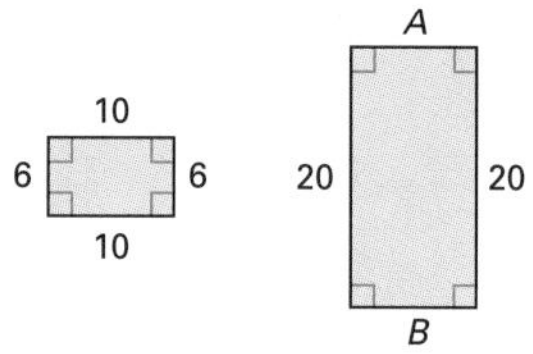

28. A factory uses 25 pounds of steel for every 37 pounds of copper. Last week the factory used 1820 pounds of steel. How much copper was used? 2693.6 lb

29. History In 1885, U.S. citizens living in Paris gave France a model of the Statue of Liberty. The model now stands on an island in the Seine River in Paris. The Statue of Liberty is about 150 feet tall, and the model in Paris is about 40 feet tall. If the torch of the taller statue measures about 20 feet and the statues are proportional to each other, how tall is the model's torch? $5\frac{1}{3}$ ft

PRACTICE

Name ____________

Practice 10-5

Solving Proportions Using Cross Products

Solve each proportion.

1. $\frac{12}{a} = \frac{16}{20}$ $a =$ 15	2. $\frac{2}{8} = \frac{t}{20}$ $t =$ 5	3. $\frac{30}{a} = \frac{20}{18}$ $a =$ 27	4. $\frac{45}{x} = \frac{18}{8}$ $x =$ 20
5. $\frac{u}{5} = \frac{6}{3}$ $u =$ 10	6. $\frac{15}{5} = \frac{6}{a}$ $a =$ 2	7. $\frac{m}{8} = \frac{12}{16}$ $m =$ 6	8. $\frac{40}{y} = \frac{16}{2}$ $y =$ 5
9. $\frac{16}{36} = \frac{g}{45}$ $g =$ 20	10. $\frac{s}{28} = \frac{30}{21}$ $s =$ 40	11. $\frac{4}{5} = \frac{8}{d}$ $d =$ 10	12. $\frac{15}{5} = \frac{12}{c}$ $c =$ 4
13. $\frac{16}{28} = \frac{h}{7}$ $h =$ 4	14. $\frac{2}{k} = \frac{3}{6}$ $k =$ 4	15. $\frac{30}{3} = \frac{j}{2}$ $j =$ 20	16. $\frac{3}{r} = \frac{2}{8}$ $r =$ 12
17. $\frac{20}{8} = \frac{f}{2}$ $f =$ 5	18. $\frac{2}{20} = \frac{z}{10}$ $z =$ 1	19. $\frac{20}{d} = \frac{4}{5}$ $d =$ 25	20. $\frac{4}{q} = \frac{2}{7}$ $q =$ 14
21. $\frac{z}{15} = \frac{2}{6}$ $z =$ 5	22. $\frac{2}{3} = \frac{b}{6}$ $b =$ 4	23. $\frac{y}{2} = \frac{6}{4}$ $y =$ 3	24. $\frac{2}{5} = \frac{4}{n}$ $n =$ 10
25. $\frac{10}{m} = \frac{8}{4}$ $m =$ 5	26. $\frac{27}{6} = \frac{j}{8}$ $j =$ 36	27. $\frac{g}{3.5} = \frac{1.6}{1.4}$ $g =$ 4	28. $\frac{8}{36} = \frac{p}{9}$ $p =$ 2
29. $\frac{14}{16} = \frac{28}{p}$ $p =$ 32	30. $\frac{t}{24} = \frac{10}{16}$ $t =$ 15	31. $\frac{45}{u} = \frac{27}{12}$ $u =$ 20	32. $\frac{10}{45} = \frac{2}{x}$ $x =$ 9
33. $\frac{25}{q} = \frac{15}{12}$ $q =$ 20	34. $\frac{15}{20} = \frac{v}{4}$ $v =$ 3	35. $\frac{p}{6} = \frac{3}{2}$ $p =$ 9	36. $\frac{3}{7} = \frac{12}{a}$ $a =$ 28

37. Measurement If 5 pints of water weigh 80 oz, find the weight of 12 pints of water. 192 oz

38. In 1967, a minimum wage worker would receive \$84 for 60 hours of work. How much would the worker receive for 75 hours of work? \$105

RETEACHING

Name ____________

Alternative Lesson 10-5

Solving Proportions Using Cross Products

If you know one measurement and the ratio that the known and unknown measurement should have, you can write a proportion. Then you can use mental math or division to find the value of the unknown measure.

— Example 1 —

Use mental math to solve the proportion $\frac{4}{8} = \frac{3}{a}$.

Write the cross products as an equation.	$4a = 8 \times 3$
Multiply.	$4a = 24$
Think: What number times 4 equals 24?	$a = 6$

So, the proportion is $\frac{4}{8} = \frac{3}{6}$.

Try It Write an equation for each proportion. Then use mental math to solve.

a. $\frac{1}{4} = \frac{b}{12}$ 12 = 4b, $b =$ 3 **b.** $\frac{5}{c} = \frac{35}{49}$ 245 = 35c, $c =$ 7 **c.** $\frac{d}{3} = \frac{18}{27}$ 27d = 54, $d =$ 2

— Example 2 —

Use division to solve the proportion $\frac{2}{6} = \frac{1.5}{e}$.

Write the cross products as an equation.	$2e = 6 \times 1.5$
Multiply.	$2e = 9$
Use division to undo the multiplication.	$e = 9 \div 2$
Simplify.	$e = 4.5$

So, the proportion is $\frac{2}{6} = \frac{1.5}{4.5}$.

Try It Write an equation for each proportion. Then use division to solve.

d. $\frac{6}{10} = \frac{f}{12}$ 72 = 10f, $f =$ 7.2 **e.** $\frac{5}{g} = \frac{6}{36}$ 180 = 6g, $g =$ 30 **f.** $\frac{h}{9} = \frac{7}{12}$ 12h = 63, $h =$ 5.25

30. **Geography** One stone statue on Easter Island is 12 meters high. The nose of the statue is 3.3 meters long. If a proportional statue is only 10 meters high, how long would the nose be? 2.75 m

31. **Test Prep** Maria designs flags and banners. She always makes a flag proportional to the flagpole it hangs from. If one flag is 6 feet wide and its pole is 24 feet long, how wide would a flag with a 20-foot pole be? A

Ⓐ 5 feet Ⓑ 8 feet

Ⓒ 50 feet Ⓓ 80 feet

32. The pictographs show the number of students playing a sport in the fall, and what sport they played. In the spring, 400 students played a sport. If the proportion of students playing soccer to students playing sports was the same in the fall and in the spring, how many students played soccer in the spring? 320

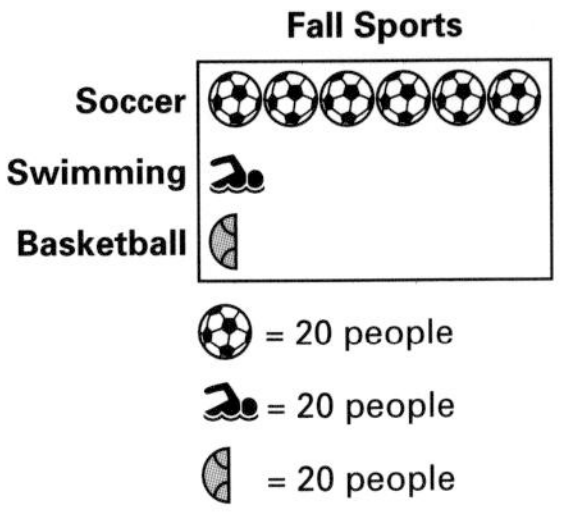

PROBLEM SOLVING 10-5

Problem Solving and Reasoning

33. **Choose a Strategy** Darius thought that you could solve proportions only when three of the values are given, and one value is missing. Then he saw the proportion $\frac{4}{x} = \frac{x}{9}$, where two values are given and two are missing. Darius was able to solve the problem. What is the value of x? Explain your method.

34. Journal Explain how to use cross products to find the missing value in a proportion.

35. **Critical Thinking** In the proportion $\frac{-4}{10} = \frac{z}{-20}$, will the value of z be greater than or less than 0? Explain.

Problem Solving STRATEGIES

- Look for a Pattern
- Make an Organized List
- Make a Table
- Guess and Check
- Work Backward
- Use Logical Reasoning
- Draw a Diagram
- Solve a Simpler Problem

Mixed Review

Add. *[Lesson 9-2]*

36. $4 + (-7)$ -3 **37.** $-8 + (-10)$ -18 **38.** $-12 + 11$ -1 **39.** $3 + (-9)$ -6 **40.** $6 + (-2)$ 4

Find the area of each circle, where r = radius and d = diameter. Use 3.14 for π. Round to the nearest hundredth. *[Lesson 4-8]*

41. $r = 2$ cm 12.56 cm² **42.** $d = 6.6$ feet 34.19 ft² **43.** $d = 14$ cm 153.86 cm² **44.** $r = 11$ feet 379.94 ft²

45. $r = 12$ inches 452.16 in² **46.** $r = 40$ mm 5024 mm² **47.** $d = 9.1$ yards 65 yd² **48.** $r = 0.4$ miles 0.50 mi²

Exercise Notes

■ Exercise 31

Test Prep If students selected D, suggest that they write out what is being compared so that they correctly set up the proportion.

Exercise Answers

33. 6; Use cross products: $x \times x = 36$, so x must be 6.

34. Possible answer: Set the cross products equal to each other. Solve the equation for the unknown variable.

35. Greater than 0; The cross product of 2 negative numbers is positive. A positive number will have to be multiplied by 10 in the cross product to also have a positive result.

Alternate Assessment

Performance Have each student write a problem by filling in the blanks.

Sam worked for ______ hours and earned ______. The next day he worked for ______ hours at the same pay rate. How much did he make on the second day?

Have students exchange problems with another student and write a proportion to solve their problem.

▶ Quick Quiz

Solve each proportion.

1. $\frac{4}{6} = \frac{x}{9}$ $x = 6$
2. $\frac{m}{8} = \frac{12}{32}$ $m = 3$
3. $\frac{6}{10} = \frac{y}{15}$ $y = 9$
4. $\frac{7}{w} = \frac{2}{3}$ $w = 10.5$

Available on Daily Transparency 10-5

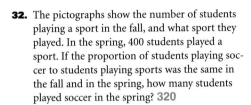

PROBLEM SOLVING

Name ______________________ **Guided Problem Solving 10-5**

GPS PROBLEM 33, PAGE 537

Darius thought that you could solve proportions only when three of the values are given, and one value is missing. Then he saw the proportion $\frac{4}{x} = \frac{x}{9}$, where two values are given and two are missing. Darius was able to solve the problem. What is the value of x? Explain your method.

Possible answers: Items 5 and 6.

— Understand —

1. Write the proportion. $\frac{4}{x} = \frac{x}{9}$
2. What are you asked to find? Value of x.

— Plan —

3. Use the cross products to write an equation. $36 = x \cdot x$

— Solve —

4. Use mental math to find the value of x. $x = 6$
5. Explain your method. Use cross products to write an equation. Then use mental math to solve.

— Look Back —

6. What other strategy could you use to find the value of x? Guess and Check.

SOLVE ANOTHER PROBLEM

Lorraine saw the proportion $\frac{x}{x} = \frac{x}{9}$, where one value is given and three are missing. Lorraine was able to solve the problem. What is the value of x? How can you use this to give the value of x for any similar proportions. Explain.

Possible answer: $x = 9$; Since $\frac{x}{x}$ is equal to 1, then $\frac{x}{9}$ must also equal 1. So, x must equal 9. The value of x in similar proportions will equal the value of the known value.

ENRICHMENT

Name ______________________ **Extend Your Thinking 10-5**

Critical Thinking

You can write proportions using numbers other than whole numbers. These proportions are solved in the same way as other proportions. Find the cross products and solve for the variable.

$$\frac{\frac{1}{2}}{\frac{1}{4}} = \frac{6}{a}$$

Find the cross products.	$\frac{1}{2} \times a = \frac{1}{4} \times 6$
Multiply.	$\frac{1}{2}a = \frac{6}{4}$
Divide by $\frac{1}{2}$.	$a = \frac{6}{4} \div \frac{1}{2}$
Multiply by the reciprocal.	$a = \frac{6}{4} \times \frac{2}{1}$
Solve for a.	$a = 3$

Solve each proportion. Show your work.

1. $\frac{\frac{1}{6}}{\frac{3}{4}} = \frac{6}{b}$ $b =$ 27
2. $\frac{\frac{1}{8}}{\frac{3}{4}} = \frac{10}{c}$ $c =$ 60
3. $\frac{\frac{2}{5}}{\frac{1}{4}} = \frac{d}{15}$ $d =$ 24
4. $\frac{e}{8} = \frac{\frac{1}{16}}{\frac{1}{10}}$ $e =$ 5
5. $\frac{f}{1\frac{2}{5}} = \frac{8}{\frac{4}{5}}$ $f =$ 14
6. $\frac{7\frac{1}{2}}{2\frac{1}{2}} = \frac{g}{6}$ $g =$ 18
7. $\frac{\frac{8}{10}}{3h} = \frac{6}{25}$ $h =$ $\frac{10}{9}$ or $1\frac{1}{9}$
8. $\frac{\frac{3}{10}f}{9} = \frac{40}{15}$ $j =$ 80

10-6 Lesson Organizer

Objective

- Solve proportions using unit rates.

NCTM Standards

- 1–4, 7, 12, 13

▶ Review

Answer the following questions.

1. If Ted makes $56 for 8 hours of work, what does he earn each hour? $7
2. If 3 pounds of carrots cost $1.50, what is the cost per pound? $0.50
3. If a seven-day cruise costs $1155, what is the cost per day? $165

Available on Daily Transparency 10-6

1 Introduce

Explore

The Point
Students explore solving problems using unit rates by determining the price per ounce of several types of cereal.

Ongoing Assessment
Check students' work to make sure that their estimates are close enough so that the prices of the cereal can be sequenced.

For Groups That Finish Early

1. According to your estimates, which cereal is less expensive, Nuts 'n Flakes or Raisin Wheats? Nuts 'n Flakes
2. Find the exact price per ounce of Raisin Wheats. $0.30
3. At this rate, what would be the price of a 20-oz box of Nuts 'n Flakes? $6.00

10-6 Solving Proportions Using Unit Rates

You'll Learn ...

- to solve proportions using unit rates

... How It's Used

Divers use unit rates when determining the water pressure at a given depth.

▶ Lesson Link You've learned how to solve proportions using cross products. Now you will learn another method for solving proportions. ◀

Explore Unit Rates

Food for Thought

Brand	Price	Size
Nuts 'n Flakes	$4.60	20 oz
Mighty Pops	$3.84	16 oz
Toastie Oaties	$4.05	15 oz
Nature's Finest	$4.00	16 oz
Cornies	$3.00	12 oz
Raisin Wheats	$4.20	14 oz

1. Rank the cereals from least expensive to most expensive in terms of total price.
2. For each brand of cereal, estimate the price for 1 ounce.
3. Rank the cereals from least expensive per ounce to most expensive per ounce.
4. If you're looking for the "best buy," is it more important to look at the price per box or price per ounce? Explain.
5. List three reasons why you might buy a cereal that's not the best buy.

MEETING INDIVIDUAL NEEDS

Resources

- **10-6** Practice
- **10-6** Reteaching
- **10-6** Problem Solving
- **10-6** Enrichment
- **10-6** Daily Transparency
  - Problem of the Day
  - Review
  - Quick Quiz

Learning Modalities

Kinesthetic Have students act out unit rates by rearranging themselves to show rates such as 4 students in a row or 5 students at each table.

Individual Ask students to think of all the rates they use in their daily lives and make a list.

English Language Development

Help students relate rates to real life by bringing in grocery newspaper ads showing a price for several of one item. Have students determine how much it would cost to buy fewer of these items if the ad allows. For example, if an item is selling at 4 for $1.00, how much would 3 of the items cost? $0.75 Challenge students to find additional examples of how rates apply to their own lives.

Learn Solving Proportions Using Unit Rates

Recall that a unit rate is a ratio where one quantity is compared to exactly one unit of another quantity. You can find the unit rate by using division.

Example 1

Market Supreme sells granola by the pound. Tammy's granola weighed 8 pounds. The cashier charged her \$12. What was the price per pound?

$$\frac{\$12}{8 \text{ pounds}} = \frac{\$12 \div 8}{8 \text{ pounds} \div 8}$$ Write a ratio. Divide by the unit quantity.

$$= \frac{\$1.50}{1 \text{ pound}}$$

The price of granola is \$1.50 per pound.

HINT

You can also use a calculator to find a unit rate by entering numerator [÷] denominator [=].

Unit rates can be used to solve proportions. Find the unit rate of the given proportion, and use multiplication to find the unknown value.

Example 2

The *Tian Tan* (Temple of Heaven) *Buddha* on Lantau Island, Hong Kong, weighs 275 tons and cost \$9,000,000 to build. If the cost of the statue is proportional to the weight, about how much would the statue have cost if it weighed 300 tons?

DID YOU KNOW?

At 112 feet tall, the *Tian Tan Buddha* is one of the ten tallest free-standing statues in the world.

$$\frac{\$9{,}000{,}000 \div 275 \text{ tons}}{275 \text{ tons} \div 275 \text{ tons}} \approx \frac{\$32{,}727}{1 \text{ ton}}$$ Find the unit rate.

The statue cost about \$32,727 per ton. Now, multiply by the new number of tons.

300 tons × \$32,727 per ton = \$9,818,100

It would have cost about \$9,818,100.

Try It

a. A zebra can run 420 ft in 7 seconds. Find the zebra's rate per minute. 3600 ft/min

b. Veronica bought 20 pencils for \$1.60. At that rate, how much would 35 pencils cost? \$2.80

MATH EVERY DAY

Problem of the Day

Which description fits this graph?

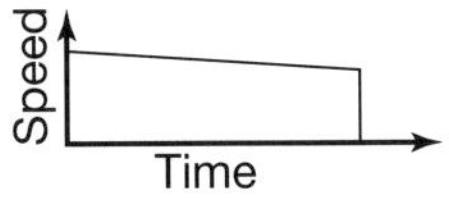

a. A car is traveling down a street, then stops at a stop light.
b. A snowball is thrown and hits a building.
c. A bicyclist is riding down the street and stops at a corner.
d. A golf ball is hit onto the green and rolls to a stop.

b.

Available on Daily Transparency 10-6

An Extension is provided in the transparency package.

Fact of the Day

The number of cheetahs in the world has been decreasing. It has been exiled from its home as the wild lands have been converted for farming and manufacturing.

Estimation

Estimate each product.

1. 6.25 × 8.7 54
2. 3.07 × 1.85 6
3. 300 × 6.6 2100
4. 21.2 × 5.9 120

Follow Up

Have volunteers share their answers for Steps 1–5.

Answers for Explore

1. Cornies, Mighty Pops, Nature's Finest, Toastie Oaties, Raisin Wheats, Nuts 'n Flakes.
2. Nuts 'n Flakes: \$0.23; Mighty Pops: \$0.24; Toastie Oaties: \$0.27; Nature's Finest: \$0.25; Cornies: \$0.25; Raisin Wheats: \$0.30.
3. Nuts 'n Flakes, Mighty Pops, Nature's Finest = Cornies, Toastie Oaties, Raisin Wheats.
4. Price per ounce; The amount per box may vary.
5. Possible answers: The cereal tastes better; The best buy doesn't come in the size you want; The best buy isn't available.

2 Teach

Learn

Alternate Examples

1. Juan bought 6 yards of ribbon for a craft project. The total cost was \$ 6.90. What was the price per yard?

   $$\frac{\$6.90}{6 \text{ yards}} = \frac{\$6.90 \div 6}{6 \text{ yards} \div 6} = \frac{\$1.15}{1 \text{ yard}}$$

   The price of ribbon was \$1.15 per yard.

2. Sarah bought 3 pounds of apples for \$4.50. At this price, how much would she have to pay for 5 pounds?

   $$\frac{\$4.50 \div 3}{3 \text{ pounds} \div 3} = \frac{\$1.50}{1 \text{ pound}}$$

   The apples cost \$1.50 per pound. Now, multiply this by the new number of pounds.

   5 pounds × \$1.50 per pound = \$7.50

   Five pounds of apples would cost \$7.50.

WHAT DO YOU THINK?

Students see two methods of solving proportions. One method uses cross products, and the other method uses a unit rate. Students can decide which method they prefer.

Answers for What Do You Think?

1. Answers may vary.
2. Aaron and Lauren both used multiplication and division because every method of finding a missing value in a proportion requires both multiplication and division.

3 Practice and Assess

Check

Answers for Check Your Understanding

1. Possible answer: When using unit rates, you first divide and then multiply. When using cross products, you first multiply and then divide.
2. Possible answer: Some shoppers carry a calculator to quickly calculate the unit rate on similar products in order to find the best buy.

WHAT DO YOU THINK?

Aaron and Lauren want to read *The Lion, The Witch, and The Wardrobe*. The book is 216 pages long. Yesterday, they each read the first 12 pages in about 18 minutes. How long will it take to read the entire book?

Aaron thinks ...

I'll use cross products.

$$\frac{18 \text{ minutes}}{12 \text{ pages}} = \frac{x \text{ minutes}}{216 \text{ pages}}$$

The cross products are 3888 and 12x.

If 12x equals 3888, then x is 3888 divided by 12, or 324.

It will take 324 minutes, or about $5\frac{1}{2}$ hours, to read the book.

Lauren thinks ...

I'll use unit rates.

$$\frac{18 \text{ minutes}}{12 \text{ pages}} = \frac{18 \text{ minutes} \div 12}{12 \text{ pages} \div 12}, \text{ or 1.5 minutes per page}$$

216 pages × 1.5 minutes per page = 324 minutes

It will take 324 minutes, or about $5\frac{1}{2}$ hours, to read the book.

What do you think?

1. Whose method do you prefer? Why?
2. Did both Aaron and Lauren have to use multiplication? Did they both have to use division? Explain.

Check Your Understanding

1. How does solving a proportion by unit rates differ from solving by cross products?
2. Give an example of how shoppers use unit rates.

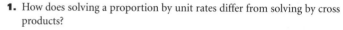

MEETING MIDDLE SCHOOL CLASSROOM NEEDS

Tips from Middle School Teachers

I find that students understand unit rates better when they find real-life examples. Therefore, I have them bring newspapers and magazines to class and we look for examples of unit rates.

Team Teaching

Work with a social studies teacher to explain how the number of members in the House of Representatives from each state are determined. Use proportions to estimate the number of representatives from a given state.

Science Connection

Sound travels through different kinds of matter at different speeds. Sound travels faster through liquids than through gases, and fastest through solids. The speed of sound through air is about 340 meters per second. Through glass, it is 4,540 meters per second.

10-6 Exercises and Applications

Practice and Apply

Getting Started State what number you should divide the numerator and denominator by to find the unit rate.

1. $\frac{16 \text{ miles}}{3 \text{ hours}}$ 3 **2.** $\frac{17 \text{ cats}}{4 \text{ square feet}}$ 4 **3.** $\frac{9 \text{ holes}}{7 \text{ inches}}$ 7 **4.** $\frac{5 \text{ feet}}{12 \text{ seconds}}$ 12 **5.** $\frac{2 \text{ minutes}}{8 \text{ problems}}$ 8

Find the unit rate for each.

6. $\frac{6 \text{ mi}}{12 \text{ sec}}$ $\frac{1}{2}$ mi/sec **7.** $\frac{10 \text{ houses}}{5 \text{ mi}}$ 2 houses/mi **8.** $\frac{12 \text{ pencils}}{3 \text{ boxes}}$ 4 pencils/box **9.** $\frac{62 \text{ holes}}{12 \text{ in}^2}$ $5\frac{1}{6}$ holes/in²

10. $\frac{\$18}{4 \text{ lb}}$ \$4.50/lb **11.** $\frac{6 \text{ waves}}{10 \text{ sec}}$ 0.6 waves/sec **12.** $\frac{17 \text{ people}}{37 \text{ ft}^2}$ ≈ 0.46 people/ft² **13.** $\frac{9 \text{ slices}}{3 \text{ people}}$ 3 slices/person

14. $\frac{7 \text{ in. rain}}{3 \text{ days}}$ $2\frac{1}{3}$ in. rain/day **15.** $\frac{6 \text{ m}}{18 \text{ hr}}$ $\frac{1}{3}$ m/hr **16.** $\frac{14 \text{ kg}}{3 \text{ bags}}$ $4\frac{2}{3}$ kg/bag **17.** $\frac{11 \text{ cups}}{22 \text{ servings}}$ 0.5 cup/serving

18. $\frac{16 \text{ shapes}}{5 \text{ boxes}}$ 3.2 shapes/box **19.** $\frac{3 \text{ turtles}}{2 \text{ mi}^2}$ 1.5 turtles/mi² **20.** $\frac{62 \text{ lines}}{1 \text{ sheet}}$ 62 lines/sheet **21.** $\frac{15 \text{ m}}{2 \text{ sec}}$ 7.5 m/sec

Solve each proportion using unit rates.

22. $\frac{24 \text{ lb}}{12 \text{ ft}} = \frac{?}{28 \text{ ft}}$ 56 lb **23.** $\frac{?}{6 \text{ hr}} = \frac{210 \text{ mi}}{5 \text{ hr}}$ 252 mi **24.** $\frac{?}{3 \text{ lb}} = \frac{\$3.50}{7 \text{ lb}}$ \$1.50 **25.** $\frac{6.6 \text{ points}}{3 \text{ games}} = \frac{?}{1 \text{ game}}$ 2.2 points

26. $\frac{62 \text{ m}}{20 \text{ sec}} = \frac{?}{32 \text{ sec}}$ 99.2 m **27.** $\frac{?}{3 \text{ sec}} = \frac{21 \text{ drips}}{7 \text{ sec}}$ 9 drips **28.** $\frac{?}{9 \text{ m}} = \frac{16 \text{ kites}}{0.25 \text{ m}}$ 576 kites **29.** $\frac{3 \text{ apples}}{5 \text{ lunches}} = \frac{?}{2 \text{ lunches}}$ 1.2 apples

30. Geography The *Colossi of Memnon* in Karnak, Egypt, are 21 meters tall. They also measure 70 feet tall. Using these measurements, find the number of meters in a foot. 0.3 meters per foot

GPS

31. Estimation Emma estimates that she collected about 70 apples from the orchard and put an equal number of apples into each of 6 baskets. Mrs. Sanders wants 3 baskets of apples. Set up and solve a proportion to determine about how many apples Mrs. Sanders would receive.

32. Science The speed of sound through water is 1460 m/sec. Is this a unit rate? How far does sound travel through water in 2 seconds? Yes; 2920 m

33. Number Sense Which is a better value, 2 pounds of bananas for 50¢ or 3 pounds of bananas for 72¢? 3 pounds for 72¢

PRACTICE 10-6

PRACTICE

Name ____________________

Practice 10-6

Solving Proportions Using Unit Rates

Find the unit rate for each.

1. $\frac{12 \text{ books}}{3 \text{ shelves}}$ $\frac{4 \text{ books}}{1 \text{ shelf}}$ 2. $\frac{14 \text{ tsp}}{7 \text{ gal}}$ $\frac{2 \text{ tsp}}{1 \text{ gal}}$ 3. $\frac{108 \text{ pages}}{9 \text{ hours}}$ $\frac{12 \text{ pages}}{1 \text{ hr}}$

4. $\frac{6 \text{ gal}}{2 \text{ min}}$ $\frac{3 \text{ gal}}{1 \text{ min}}$ 5. $\frac{30.48 \text{ cm}}{12 \text{ in.}}$ $\frac{2.54 \text{ cm}}{1 \text{ in.}}$ 6. $\frac{40 \text{ mice}}{8 \text{ rats}}$ $\frac{5 \text{ mice}}{1 \text{ rat}}$

7. $\frac{28 \text{ cats}}{4 \text{ dogs}}$ $\frac{7 \text{ cats}}{1 \text{ dog}}$ 8. $\frac{\$315}{35 \text{ hr}}$ $\frac{\$9}{1 \text{ hr}}$ 9. $\frac{10 \text{ CDs}}{5 \text{ tapes}}$ $\frac{2 \text{ CDs}}{1 \text{ tape}}$

10. $\frac{90 \text{ cars}}{15 \text{ trucks}}$ $\frac{6 \text{ cars}}{1 \text{ truck}}$ 11. $\frac{14 \text{ cups}}{42 \text{ sec}}$ $\frac{\frac{1}{3} \text{ cup}}{1 \text{ sec}}$ 12. $\frac{18 \text{ boys}}{18 \text{ girls}}$ $\frac{1 \text{ boy}}{1 \text{ girl}}$

13. $\frac{576 \text{ pt}}{72 \text{ gal}}$ $\frac{8 \text{ pt}}{1 \text{ gal}}$ 14. $\frac{120 \text{ mi}}{3 \text{ hr}}$ $\frac{40 \text{ mi}}{1 \text{ hr}}$ 15. $\frac{35 \text{ carrots}}{10 \text{ potatoes}}$ $\frac{3\frac{1}{2} \text{ carrots}}{1 \text{ potato}}$

16. $\frac{36 \text{ cups}}{18 \text{ bowls}}$ $\frac{2 \text{ cups}}{1 \text{ bowl}}$ 17. $\frac{68 \text{ men}}{17 \text{ women}}$ $\frac{4 \text{ men}}{1 \text{ woman}}$ 18. $\frac{375 \text{ ft}^2}{25 \text{ people}}$ $\frac{15 \text{ ft}^2}{1 \text{ person}}$

Solve each proportion using unit rates.

19. $\frac{28 \text{ cows}}{20 \text{ moose}} = \frac{14 \text{ cows}}{10 \text{ moose}}$ 20. $\frac{25 \text{ pt}}{10 \text{ ft}^2} = \frac{20 \text{ pt}}{8 \text{ ft}^2}$ 21. $\frac{7 \text{ hits}}{2 \text{ innings}} = \frac{21 \text{ hits}}{6 \text{ innings}}$

22. $\frac{4 \text{ ft}}{12 \text{ sec}} = \frac{2 \text{ ft}}{6 \text{ sec}}$ 23. $\frac{\$15}{9 \text{ lb}} = \frac{\$5}{3 \text{ lb}}$ 24. $\frac{15 \text{ meals}}{3 \text{ days}} = \frac{25 \text{ meals}}{5 \text{ days}}$

25. $\frac{5 \text{ drops}}{50 \text{ gal}} = \frac{3 \text{ drops}}{30 \text{ gal}}$ 26. $\frac{10°}{2 \text{ hr}} = \frac{15°}{3 \text{ hr}}$ 27. $\frac{32 \text{ gal}}{4 \text{ hr}} = \frac{16 \text{ gal}}{2 \text{ hr}}$

28. $\frac{45 \text{ in.}}{5 \text{ lb}} = \frac{18 \text{ in.}}{2 \text{ lb}}$ 29. $\frac{12 \text{ lb}}{4 \text{ sec}} = \frac{3 \text{ lb}}{1 \text{ sec}}$ 30. $\frac{\$6}{2 \text{ hr}} = \frac{\$9}{3 \text{ hr}}$

31. $\frac{35 \text{ mi}}{10 \text{ L}} = \frac{28 \text{ mi}}{8 \text{ L}}$ 32. $\frac{14 \text{ oz}}{4 \text{ in}^3} = \frac{21 \text{ oz}}{6 \text{ in}^3}$ 33. $\frac{27 \text{ min}}{24 \text{ ft}} = \frac{9 \text{ min}}{8 \text{ ft}}$

34. In 1909, French workmen removed a white stork's nest weighing 660 kilograms from the top of a cathedral. The nest also weighed 1452 pounds. Using these measurements, find the number of pounds in a kilogram. 2.2 lb

35. **History** The Northrop XB–35 aircraft used in World War II had a wingspan of 172 feet. Melba's model of this aircraft has a wingspan of $21\frac{1}{2}$ inches. How many feet does one inch of the model represent? 8 ft

RETEACHING

Name ____________________

Alternative Lesson 10-6

Solving Proportions Using Unit Rates

A unit rate is a ratio where one quantity is compared to exactly one unit of another quantity. You can use division to find the unit rate.

Unit rates can be used to solve proportions. Find the unit rate of the given proportion, and use multiplication to find the unknown value.

Example 1

Find the unit rate of $\frac{\$24}{10 \text{ paintbrushes}}$.

Divide by the unit quantity. $\frac{\$24 \div 10}{10 \text{ paintbrushes} \div 10}$

Simplify. $= \frac{\$2.40}{1 \text{ paintbrush}}$

So, the unit rate is \$2.40 for one paintbrush.

Try It Find the unit rate for each.

a. $\frac{\$45}{9 \text{ hours}} = \frac{45 \div 9}{9 \text{ hours} \div 9} = \frac{\$5}{1 \text{ hour}}$

b. $\frac{300 \text{ miles}}{15 \text{ gallons}}$ $\frac{20 \text{ miles}}{1 \text{ gallon}}$ c. $\frac{48 \text{ cars}}{4 \text{ trailers}}$ $\frac{12 \text{ cars}}{1 \text{ trailer}}$

Example 2

Use unit rates to solve the proportion $\frac{\$60}{12 \text{ pounds}} = \frac{?}{15 \text{ pounds}}$.

Divide to find the unit rate. $\frac{\$60 \div 12}{12 \text{ pounds} \div 12} = \frac{\$5}{1 \text{ pound}}$

Multiply the unit rate by the number of pounds. \$5 per pound × 15 pounds = \$75

So, it would cost \$75 for 15 pounds.

Try It Use unit rates to solve each proportion.

d. $\frac{6\ c}{3 \text{ gal}} = \frac{?\ c}{25 \text{ gal}}$

$\frac{6\ c \div 3}{3 \text{ gal} \div 3} = \frac{2c}{1 \text{ gal}}$

2 c per gal × 25 = 50 gal

So, $\frac{6\ c}{3 \text{ gal}} = \frac{50\ c}{25 \text{ gal}}$

e. $\frac{360 \text{ mi}}{12 \text{ wk}} = \frac{? \text{ mi}}{5 \text{ wk}}$

$\frac{360 \text{ mi} \div 12}{12 \text{ wk} \div 12} = \frac{30 \text{ mi}}{1 \text{ wk}}$

30 mi per wk × 5 wk= 150 mi

So, $\frac{360 \text{ mi}}{12 \text{ wk}} = \frac{150 \text{ mi}}{5 \text{ wk}}$

10-6 Exercises and Applications

Assignment Guide

- **Basic**
  1–13, 22–25, 30–34 evens, 37, 41–51 odds
- **Average**
  2–30 evens, 31–34, 36–37, 40–50 evens
- **Enriched**
  18–30 evens, 32–39, 40–50 evens

Exercise Notes

Exercises 6–21

Error Prevention Students may think that their answers are wrong if they end up with decimals or fractions. Remind them that this will happen when the denominator is larger than the numerator.

Exercise 31

Estimation Some students might use unit rates to solve this problem. They might estimate 11 apples per basket and, therefore, about 33 apples in 3 baskets. You might have students who used equivalent fractions or cross products discuss their methods.

Exercise Answers

31. $\frac{70 \text{ apples}}{6 \text{ baskets}} = \frac{x}{3 \text{ baskets}}$; $x = 35$ apples.

Reteaching

Activity

Materials: Counters, containers

- Use counters and small containers to find unit rates.
- Place the same number of counters in each container.
- If there are 24 counters in 4 containers, how many counters would be in 7 such containers? 42 counters
- If there are 27 counters in 3 containers. How many counters would be in 6 such containers? 54 counters

Exercise Notes

■ Exercise 35

Literature Artemis was known as both the goddess of the hunt and the goddess of wild animals. She is often portrayed as a young, beautiful hunter carrying a bow and an arrow with a deer or another wild animal at her side.

■ Exercise 39

Extension Have students look in newspapers and magazines to find examples of unit rates.

Exercise Answers

36. Possible answer: When the numerator is divisible by the denominator, as in 100 apples for $5.

37. Find the unit rate for square feet per dollar:

$\frac{7\text{ ft}^2 \div 4.50}{\$4.50 \div 4.50} = \frac{1\frac{5}{9}\text{ft}^2}{\$1.00}$; Find the unit rate for dollars per square foot:

$\frac{\$4.50 \div 7}{7\text{ ft}^2 \div 7} = \frac{\text{about }\$0.64}{1\text{ ft}^2}$; Dollars per square foot.

38. a. 160 ft; Solve the proportion $\frac{6\text{ in.}}{48\text{ ft}} = \frac{20\text{ in.}}{x}$.

b. 7 sec; $\frac{1\text{ sec}}{5\text{ in.}} = \frac{x}{35\text{ in.}}$

c. No; Everything is used.

39. Possible answers:

$\frac{4\text{ quarters}}{1\text{ dollar}}, \frac{16\text{ ounces}}{1\text{ pound}}, \frac{12\text{ months}}{1\text{ year}}, \frac{7\text{ days}}{1\text{ week}}, \frac{24\text{ hours}}{1\text{ day}}$.

Alternate Assessment

Portfolio Have students select work illustrating different methods of solving proportions and add them to their portfolios. They might include problems they have solved using equivalent fractions, cross products, and unit rates.

▶ Quick Quiz

Solve each proportion using unit rates.

1. $\frac{24\text{ inches}}{2\text{ feet}} = \frac{?}{5\text{ feet}}$ 60 inches
2. $\frac{\$4.20}{3\text{ pounds}} = \frac{?}{7\text{ pounds}}$ $9.80
3. $\frac{60\text{ feet}}{4\text{ seconds}} = \frac{?}{6\text{ seconds}}$ 90 feet

Available on Daily Transparency 10-6

PROBLEM SOLVING 10-6

34. **Test Prep** Which animal is moving the fastest? C

Ⓐ A cat at 660 ft per 15 sec. Ⓑ A greyhound at 616 ft per 12 sec.

Ⓒ A zebra at 645 ft per 11 sec. Ⓓ An elephant at 1100 ft per 30 sec.

35. **Literature** Janet wants to make a wooden carving of Artemis, Greek goddess of the hunt. She imagines that Artemis is 7 feet tall. If her carving is 12 inches tall, how many feet does 1 inch represent? About 0.583 ft, or $\frac{7}{12}$ ft

Problem Solving and Reasoning

36. **Journal** Describe a situation where you could use mental math to find the unit rate of a ratio.

37. **Communicate** If 7 square feet of carpet cost $4.50, how can you find the rate of square feet per dollar? How can you find the rate of dollars per square foot? If you were carpeting a room, which rate would be the most sensible rate to use?

38. **Critical Thinking** Fiona is filming a 6-inch lizard to represent a 48-foot monster. The lizard moves at a rate of 5 inches per second.

a. If Fiona films a 20-inch-tall movie set, how tall does the set look in the movie? Explain.

b. How long will it take for the small lizard to move 35 inches? Explain how you found your answer.

c. Is there any numerical information in the problem that isn't needed to answer the first two questions? Explain.

39. **Communicate** Name five unit rates that people use every day. For example, there are 60 minutes in 1 hour.

Mixed Review

Find the area of the irregular shape. *[Lesson 4-9]*

40. 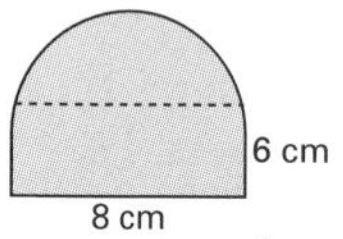

≈ 73.12 cm²

41. 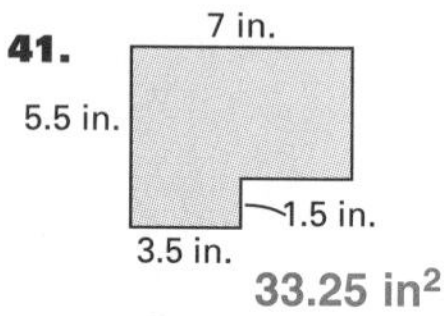

33.25 in²

42. 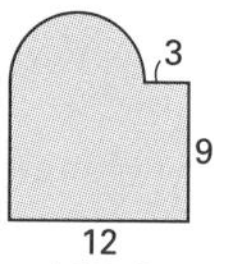

139.8

43. 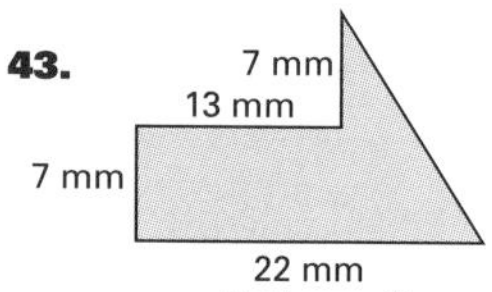

154 mm²

Subtract. *[Lesson 9-3]*

44. 12 − (−7) 19 45. −8 − 9 −17 46. −16 − 10 −26 47. 11 − (−3) 14

48. −5 − (−9) 4 49. −4 − (−1) −3 50. 0 − (−13) 13 51. 2 − (−4) 6

PROBLEM SOLVING

Name ______

Guided Problem Solving 10-6

GPS PROBLEM 30, PAGE 541

The *Colossi of Memnon* in Karnak, Egypt, are 21 meters tall. They also measure 70 feet tall. Using these measurements, find the number of meters in a foot.

— Understand —

1. How tall is the *Colossi of Memnon*, in meters? 21 meters.
2. How tall is the *Colossi of Memnon*, in feet? 70 feet.
3. It takes more feet than meters to measure the height. Is a meter longer or shorter than a foot? Longer.
4. What are you asked to find? Number of meters in a foot.

— Plan —

5. Write the heights as a ratio of meters to feet. $\frac{21}{70}$
6. Complete the equation to find the unit rate.

$\frac{21\text{ meters} \div 70}{70\text{ feet} \div 70} = \frac{0.3\text{ meters}}{1\text{ foot}}$

— Solve —

7. Write a sentence giving how many meters are in one foot.
Possible answer: There are 0.3 meters in 1 foot.

— Look Back —

8. Let *m* be the number of meters. Use the measurement of the *Colossi* to write a proportion. Then find cross products to solve.
$\frac{21}{70} = \frac{m}{1}$; $21 = 70m$; $m = \frac{21}{70} = 0.3$

SOLVE ANOTHER PROBLEM

A Jamaican pumpkin soup recipe uses 160 milliliters of light cream. This is equal to 32 teaspoons of light cream. Using these measurements, find the number of milliliters in one teaspoon. 5 milliliters.

ENRICHMENT

Name ______

Extend Your Thinking 10-6

Decision Making

Possible answers: Items 2–5

Alfonso, Bryan, and four of their friends are going to the lake. They want to rent a canoe and have a picnic lunch on the island.

1. Alfonso wants to make potato salad. His recipe will serve 8 people. Use unit ratios to rewrite the recipe to serve 6 people.

$\frac{1}{3}$ cup Italian dressing	5 medium potatoes
1 cup chopped celery	4 hard boiled eggs
1 teaspoon salt	$\frac{1}{2}$ cup salad dressing or mayonnaise
$\frac{1}{4}$ cup Italian dressing	$3\frac{3}{4}$ medium potatoes
$\frac{3}{4}$ cup chopped celery	3 hard boiled eggs
$\frac{3}{4}$ teaspoon salt	$\frac{3}{8}$ cup salad dressing or mayo

2. They stop at the deli to buy ham for their sandwiches. One package of ham sells for 0.5 pound for $2.50. There are about 8 slices in each package. How much ham should they buy? How much will it cost? Each person can eat about 2 slices, so they need 12 slices, or 0.75 pound. It will cost $3.75.

3. Each canoe can hold 4 people. It will cost them $16 to rent one canoe for 4 hours or $25 for the day. It takes 15 minutes to row to the island. How can they rent only one canoe? Four people row to the island, one or two row back to pick up the others.

4. How many canoes should they rent and for how long? Explain. Two canoes for 4 hours each. That will allow them to go to places other than the island as a group.

5. They need to tell their families about when they should be home. It takes about 10 minutes to get to the park. About how long will they be on the outing? Explain. About 5 hours. It takes about 1 hour to travel round trip to the park and the island. That leaves about 4 hours to eat and have fun.

Similar Figures

10-7

▶ Lesson Link You've learned about geometric figures. Now you'll explore a class of figures whose dimensions are proportional. ◀

You'll Learn ...

- what similar figures are
- to use proportions to find lengths in a similar figure

... How It's Used

Drivers use similar figures when calculating the actual distance between two locations on a road map.

Vocabulary

similar

Explore Similar Figures

The Same ... But Different!

Materials: Centimeter ruler, Protractor

1. Draw a large triangle, $\triangle A$, with three unequal sides. Measure and label the length of each side and the width of each angle.
2. Draw a smaller triangle whose angles have the same measures as the angles of $\triangle A$. Call the new triangle $\triangle B$. Measure and label the length of each side.
3. Find these ratios:

   a. $\frac{\text{longest side of } \triangle A}{\text{longest side of } \triangle B}$ b. $\frac{\text{mid-length side of } \triangle A}{\text{mid-length side of } \triangle B}$

   c. $\frac{\text{shortest side of } \triangle A}{\text{shortest side of } \triangle B}$
4. Are the longest sides proportional to the shortest sides? Explain.
5. Are the longest sides proportional to the mid-length sides? Explain.
6. Are the mid-length sides proportional to the shortest sides? Explain.

Learn Similar Figures

Recall that figures with the same size and shape are *congruent*. The symbol ≅ means "is congruent to."

Figures that have the same shape but not necessarily the same size are **similar** figures. The symbol ~ means "is similar to."

The objects pictured are similar because their shapes are the same, even though their sizes are different.

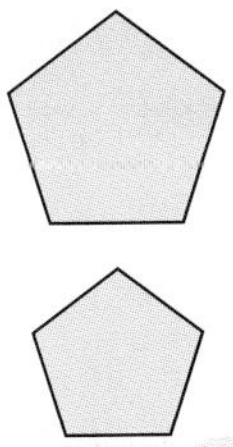

MEETING INDIVIDUAL NEEDS

Resources

10-7 Practice
10-7 Reteaching
10-7 Problem Solving
10-7 Enrichment
10-7 Daily Transparency
- Problem of the Day
- Review
- Quick Quiz

Teaching Tool Transparencies 2, 3, 6, 16, 17
Technology Master 54
Chapter 10 Project Master

Learning Modalities

Visual Have students draw diagrams to illustrate a variety of similar shapes.

Social Have students work together to decide which of several shapes are similar.

Challenge

Have students find the values of x and y if $A \sim B$.
$x = 15$, $y = 8$

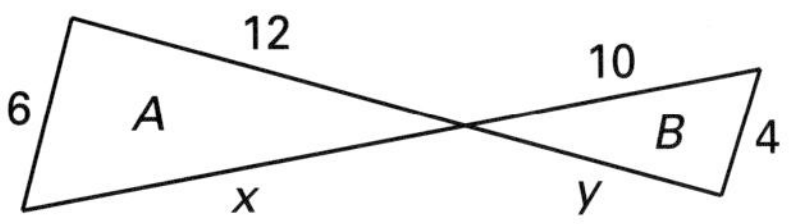

10-7 Lesson Organizer

Objectives

- Learn what similar figures are.
- Use proportions to find lengths in a similar figure.

Vocabulary

- Similar

Materials

- Explore: Centimeter ruler, protractor

NCTM Standards

- 1–4, 7, 12

▶ Review

Add.

1. −7 + (−3) −10
2. −8 + 2 −6
3. 12 + (−5) 7
4. −20 + (−4) −24

Available on Daily Transparency 10-7

1 Introduce

Explore

You may wish to use Teaching Tool Transparencies 6: Cuisenaire Angle Ruler, 16: Rulers, and 17: Protractor with **Explore**.

The Point
Students explore similar figures by drawing two triangles with angles of the same size. They discover that the corresponding sides of the two triangles are proportional.

Ongoing Assessment
Check that students are using protractors correctly. Also make sure that they are measuring angles and side lengths accurately so that when they compare the side lengths, they will appear to be proportional.

Answers for Explore
1–2. Answers may vary.
3. The ratios should be equal.
4–6. Yes; The ratios are equal.

2 Teach

Learn

Alternate Examples

1. State whether the polygons are congruent, similar, or neither.

a.

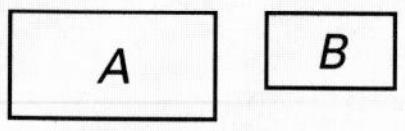

The figures are the same shape but different sizes. $A \sim B$.

b.

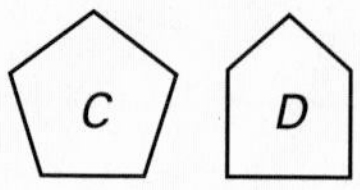

The figures are not the same shape or size. They are neither congruent nor similar.

c.

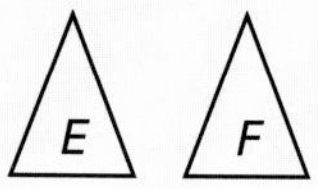

The figures are the same shape and size. $E \cong F$.

2. $\Delta C \sim \Delta D$. Find the length of the side labeled m.

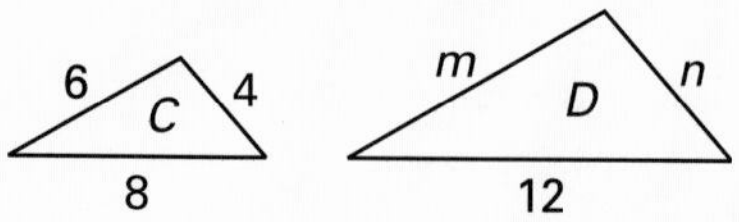

The triangles are similar, so the matching sides are proportional.

$\frac{6}{m} = \frac{8}{12}$

$8m = 6 \times 12$

$8m = 72$

$m = 9$

Remember

Congruent figures have the same shape and the same size. **[Page 444]**

Example 1

State whether the polygons appear to be congruent, similar, or neither.

a.

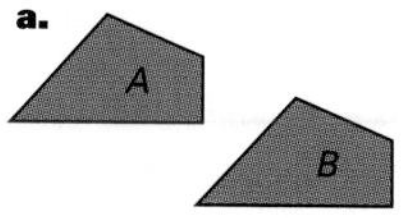

The figures are the same shape and size. $A \cong B$.

b.

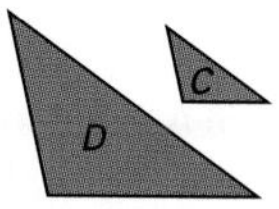

The figures are the same shape but different sizes. $C \sim D$.

c.

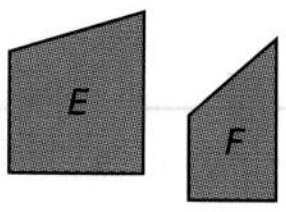

The figures are not the same shape or size. They are neither congruent nor similar.

If two figures are similar, their matching angles have the same measure and their matching sides are proportional.

Problem Solving TIP

Some problems give you information that isn't needed to solve the problem. In this example, you don't need to know that the length of the right side of $\triangle A$ is 18.

Example 2

$\triangle A \sim \triangle B$. Find the length of the side labeled x.

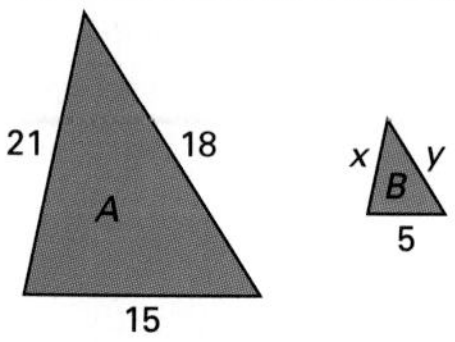

The triangles are similar, so the matching sides are proportional.

$\frac{21}{x} = \frac{15}{5}$ Write a proportion using the sides that match each other.

$15x = 21 \times 5$ Write the cross products.

$15 \times x = 105$ Multiply. Think: What number times 15 equals 105?

$x = 105 \div 15$ Use division to undo **multiplication**.

$x = 7$

Try It

Find the length of the side labeled y in Example 2. 6

Check Your Understanding

1. How are similar figures and congruent figures alike? How are they different?
2. If two figures are congruent, are they similar? Explain.
3. Give an example of similar figures you see in everyday life.

3 Practice and Assess

Check

Answers for Check Your Understanding

1. Possible answer: Similar figures and congruent figures are alike because both have the same shape. They are different because congruent figures are the same size, but similar figures do not have to be the same size.
2. Yes; Corresponding angles are congruent and the sides are proportional.
3. Possible answer: Real people and people in photographs.

MATH EVERY DAY

Problem of the Day

The date September 8, 1998 can be written as 9/8/98. Notice that the month/day designation is the same as the last two digits of the year. How many times in a year can this happen? Explain. None or once. For example, in years between 2000 and 2010, it will not be possible. In years without a zero as either the ones or tens digit, it happens once a year.

Available on Daily Transparency 10-7

An Extension is provided in the transparency package.

Fact of the Day

A blueprint is made on paper coated with special chemicals. The chemicals make the paper turn blue when the paper is exposed to light.

Estimation

Estimate.

1. $\frac{1}{4}$ of 95 25
2. $\frac{1}{6}$ of 117 20
3. $\frac{1}{3}$ of 62 20
4. $\frac{1}{8}$ of 98 12

10-7 Exercises and Applications

Practice and Apply

Getting Started State whether the polygons are congruent, similar, or neither.

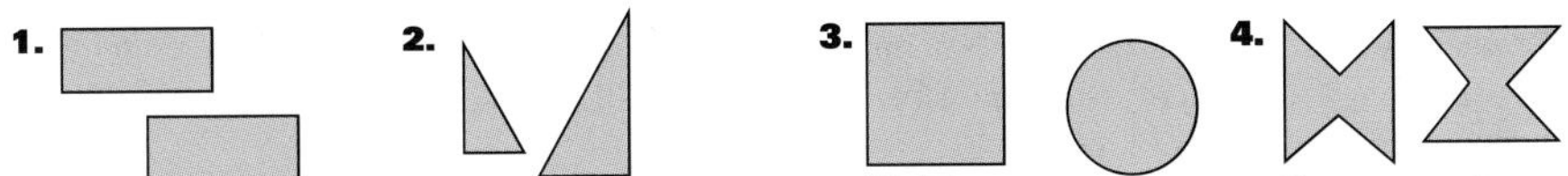

1. Congruent
2. Similar
3. Neither
4. Congruent

For Exercises 5–10, find the missing side lengths.

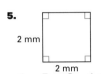

5. 2 mm, 2 mm; 1 mm, *C*, *A*, *B*
A = B = C = 1 mm

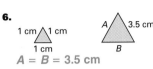

6. 1 cm, 1 cm, 1 cm; *A*, 3.5 cm, *B*
A = B = 3.5 cm

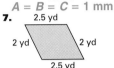

7. 2.5 yd, 2 yd, 2 yd, 2.5 yd; *A*, *B*, 0.5 yd, *C*
A = C = 0.625 yd, B = 0.5 yd

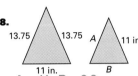

8. 13.75, 13.75, 11 in.; *A*, 11 in., *B*
A = 11, B = 8.8

9.

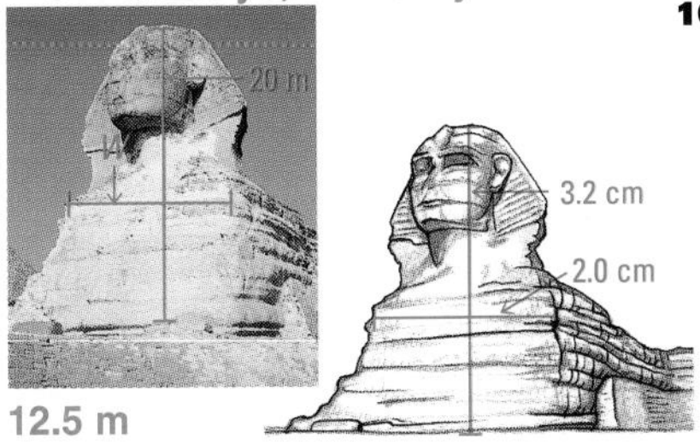

12.5 m

10.

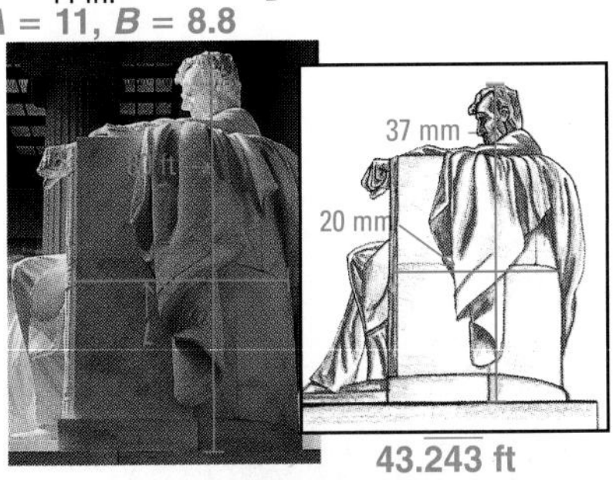

43.243 ft

11. **Geography** On the map, 1 inch equals 250 actual miles.
    a. Estimate the actual distances of the triangular flight plan indicated on the map. 1000 mi; 675 mi; 1667.5 mi
    b. Are the triangle shown on the map and the life-size triangle similar figures? Yes

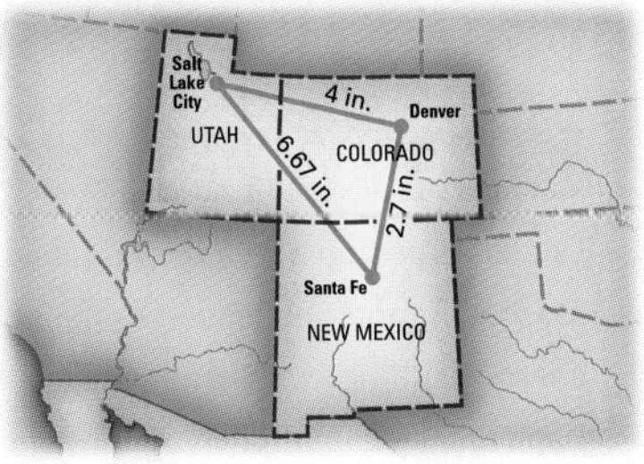

PRACTICE

Name ______________

Practice 10-7

Similar Figures

Find the missing side lengths.

1. $A =$ 16 in. $B =$ 12 in. $C =$ 16 in. (9 in., 12 in.; 12 in.)
2. $A =$ 18 cm $B =$ 13.5 cm (22.5 cm; 14 cm, 17.5 cm, 10.5 cm)
3. $A =$ 3 m $B =$ 3 m $C =$ 3 m (3 m; 4 m, 4 m, 4 m, 4 m)
4. $A =$ 12 in. $B =$ $7\frac{1}{2}$ in. $C =$ 12 in. (4 in., $2\frac{1}{2}$ in., $2\frac{1}{2}$ in., 4 in.; $7\frac{1}{2}$ in.)
5. $A =$ 5 ft $B =$ 7 ft (9 ft; 10 ft, 18 ft, 14 ft)
6. $A =$ 7.8 cm $B =$ 3 cm $C =$ 7.2 cm (2.5 cm, 6.5 cm, 6 cm, 5 cm; 6 cm)
7. On the map, 1 inch equals 850 actual miles.
   a. What are the actual distances between the cities?
   New York to New Orleans ≈ 1174 mi
   New Orleans to Miami ≈ 670 mi
   Miami to New York ≈ 1094 mi

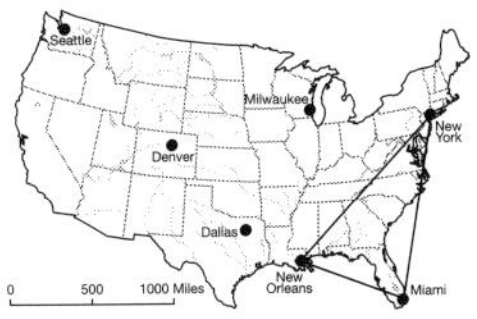

   b. Is the triangle shown on the map similar to the life-size triangle? Explain.
   Possible answer: No; Earth's surface is curved.
8. The lengths of the sides of a triangle are 45 cm, 55 cm, and 70 cm. The shortest side of a similar triangle has length 27 cm. What are the lengths of the other two sides of the similar triangle? 33 cm; 42 cm

RETEACHING

Name ______________

Alternative Lesson 10-7

Similar Figures

Figures with the same size and shape are *congruent.* The symbol ≅ means "is congruent to."

Figures that have the same shape but not necessarily the same size are **similar** figures. The symbol ~ means "is similar to."

If two figures are similar, their matching angles have the same measure and their matching sides are proportional.

Example 1

State whether the polygons appear to be congruent, similar, or neither.

The figures are the same shape and size.

So, they are congruent.

Try It State whether the polygons appear to be congruent, similar, or neither.

a. Neither.

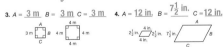

b. Similar.

Example 2

$\triangle ABC \sim \triangle DEF$. Find the length of the side labeled *k*.

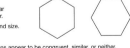

The triangles are similar, so the matching sides are proportional.

Write a proportion using the sides that match each other. $\frac{k}{3} = \frac{2}{1}$

Write the cross products. $k = 3 \times 2$

Multiply to solve for *k*. $k = 6$

So, the side labeled *k* measures 6 cm.

Try It $\triangle GHI \sim \triangle JKL$. Find the missing side lengths.

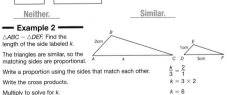

d. Write a proportion using sides that match. $\frac{20}{12} = \frac{s}{15}$

e. Solve for *s*. 25

f. Solve for *t*. 15

(G, H, I, s, t, 20 m; J, K, L, 15 m, 9 m, 12 m)

10-7 Exercises and Applications

Assignment Guide

- **Basic** 1–14, 18–38 evens
- **Average** 1–15, 18–38 evens
- **Enriched** 5–16, 17–37 odds

Exercise Notes

Exercise 11

Geography The amount of detail that can be shown in a map is relative to the scale chosen. A *large-scale* map would be used to show an area in great detail. A *small-scale* map would leave out a lot of detail.

Reteaching

Activity

Materials: Graph paper, scissors, protractor or angle ruler

- Draw a triangle on graph paper so that at least one side lies along a grid line.
- Measure the angles and the lengths of the sides.
- Make the triangle smaller by cutting along one of the grid lines of the graph paper that is parallel to a side of the triangle.
- Measure the angles of the new triangle.
- How do the angles of the new triangle compare to the angles of the original triangle? They are the same.
- Measure the lengths of the sides.
- Find the ratio of the longest sides of the two triangles, the shortest sides, and the mid-length sides.
- Are the ratios equal? Yes

Exercise Notes

■ Exercise 14

Problem-Solving Tip You may wish to use Teaching Tool Transparencies 2 and 3: Guided Problem Solving, pages 1–2.

■ Exercises 27–38

Error Prevention If students have difficulty with these exercises, suggest that they review the rules for divisibility.

Project Progress

You may want to have students use Chapter 10 Project Master.

Exercise Answers

14. 180 ft; Solve the proportion $\frac{4 \text{ in.}}{40 \text{ ft}} = \frac{5 \text{ in.}}{x \text{ ft}}$ to find that $x = 50$ ft is the other length of the house and then find the perimeter.

15. No; Similar figures need to be the same shape, but not the same size. Yes; Congruent figures are not only the same shape, but also the same size.

16. Yes; All equilateral triangles have 60° angles and the three sides are the same length.

Alternate Assessment

You may want to use the *Interactive CD-ROM Journal* with this assessment.

Journal Have students write a paragraph describing congruent and similar figures and include the relationship between corresponding sides and angles. The written explanation should be supported by drawings of several pairs of figures, clearly labeled, to show the relationships described.

► Quick Quiz

Find the missing sides of the triangle.

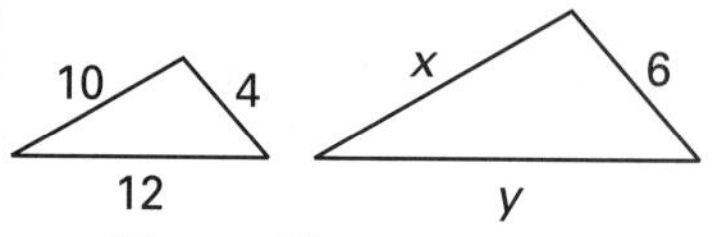

$x = 15$, $y = 18$

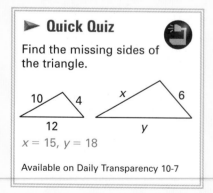

Available on Daily Transparency 10-7

PROBLEM SOLVING 10-7

12. **Test Prep** Which triangles are similar? **A**

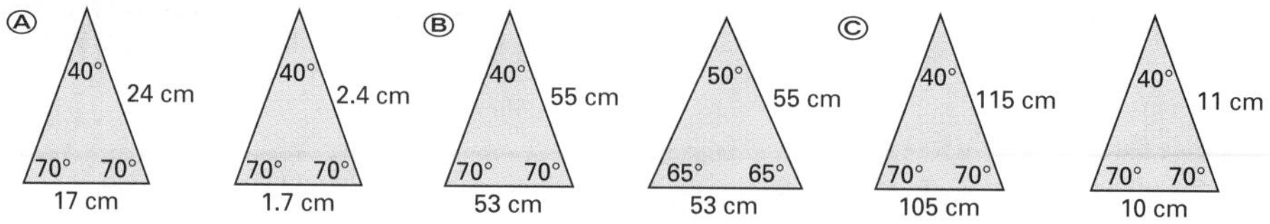

13. **Geometry** A rectangle has sides of 5 ft and 8 ft. A similar rectangle has two sides of 40 feet. There are two possible answers for the length of the other side of the larger rectangle. What are they? **25 ft or 64 ft**

GPS

Problem Solving and Reasoning

14. **Choose a Strategy** Gigi's house and the blueprint for her house are similar figures. Her house is shaped like a rectangle. On the blueprint, the base and height of the rectangle are 4 inches and 5 inches. If the shorter side of her house is 40 feet, what is the perimeter? Explain.

15. **Critical Thinking** Is every pair of similar figures congruent? Is every pair of congruent figures similar? Explain.

16. **Critical Thinking** If two triangles are equilateral, are they similar? Explain.

Problem Solving STRATEGIES

- Look for a Pattern
- Make an Organized List
- Make a Table
- Guess and Check
- Work Backward
- Use Logical Reasoning
- Draw a Diagram
- Solve a Simpler Problem

Mixed Review

Simplify. *[Lesson 9-4]*

17. $7 \times (-3)$ **−21** **18.** $18 \div (-9)$ **−2** **19.** $-8 \times (-2)$ **16** **20.** $-22 \div 11$ **−2** **21.** -10×7 **−70**

22. $-14 \div 7$ **−2** **23.** $-2 \times (-13)$ **26** **24.** $6 \div (-3)$ **−2** **25.** $-36 \div (-3)$ **12** **26.** $-25 \times (-4)$ **100**

Tell whether the first number is divisible by the second. *[Lesson 5-1]*

27. 65, 5 **Yes** **28.** 33, 11 **Yes** **29.** 57, 6 **No** **30.** 106, 10 **No** **31.** 882, 9 **Yes** **32.** 116, 2 **Yes**

33. 36, 4 **Yes** **34.** 59, 3 **No** **35.** 49, 7 **Yes** **36.** 81, 8 **No** **37.** 100, 25 **Yes** **38.** 1265, 5 **Yes**

Project Progress

Choose a person or team who plays the sport you selected. Research or invent several proportions related to the number of your player or team's wins. For example: number of home games/number of wins; attendance/number of wins. Explain the proportions you have written.

Problem Solving: Understand, Plan, Solve, Look Back

PROBLEM SOLVING

Name ____________________

Guided Problem Solving 10-7

GPS **PROBLEM 13, PAGE 546**

A rectangle has sides of 5 ft and 8 ft. A similar rectangle has two sides of 40 feet. There are two possible answers for the length of the other side of the larger rectangle. What are they?

Possible answer: Item 11

— Understand —

1. What are the dimensions of the smaller rectangle? **5 ft and 8 ft.**
2. What is one dimension of a similar rectangle? **40 feet.**
3. Underline the number of possible answers.

Check students' work for Items 5, 6, and 8.

— Plan —

4. What is true about matching sides of similar figures? **Sides proportional.**
5. Draw the smaller rectangle. Label the sides.
6. Draw another rectangle. Label the sides so that the 40 ft side matches the 5 ft side.
7. Which other side could the 40 ft side match in the smaller rectangle? **8 ft side.**
8. Draw the larger rectangle. Label the sides another way.

— Solve —

9. Write a proportion to find the missing side of the rectangle drawn
   a. in Item 6. $\frac{5}{40} = \frac{8}{x}$ b. in Item 8. $\frac{8}{40} = \frac{5}{x}$
10. What is the length of the missing side for the rectangle drawn
    a. in Item 6. **64 ft** b. in Item 8. **25 ft**

— Look Back —

11. Why did the two sides measuring 40 feet have to be the parallel sides in the rectangle? **If sides are not parallel, figure would be a square, and not similar to rectangle.**

SOLVE ANOTHER PROBLEM

A parallelogram has sides of 2 m and 3 m. A similar parallelogram has two sides of 6 m. There are two possible answers for the length of the other sides of the larger parallelogram. What are they? **9 m, 4 m**

ENRICHMENT

Name ____________________

Extend Your Thinking 10-7

Patterns in Geometry

Part of the first drawing is shown in the second drawing.

Possible answers: Items 1-3, and 5

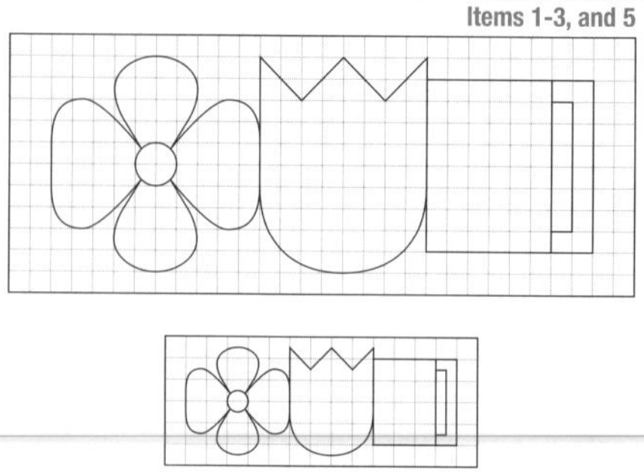

1. How are the drawings alike? **They are drawings of the same things.**
2. How are the drawings different? **They are different sizes.**
3. What pattern relate the two drawings? **Smaller drawing is $\frac{1}{2}$ size of larger drawing. Proportionately, each line that takes 2 units in larger drawing, takes 1 unit in smaller drawings.**
4. Use the pattern to continue the drawing. **Check students' drawings.**
5. What might the pattern be if you wanted to enlarge the drawing? Explain. **2 to 1. Proportionately, each line that takes 1 unit in smaller drawing will take more than one unit in larger drawing.**

Section 10B Connect

In this section, you've seen how artists use proportions to convert actual measurements to model measurements. Now you'll use that process to create a blueprint for a model of a totem pole.

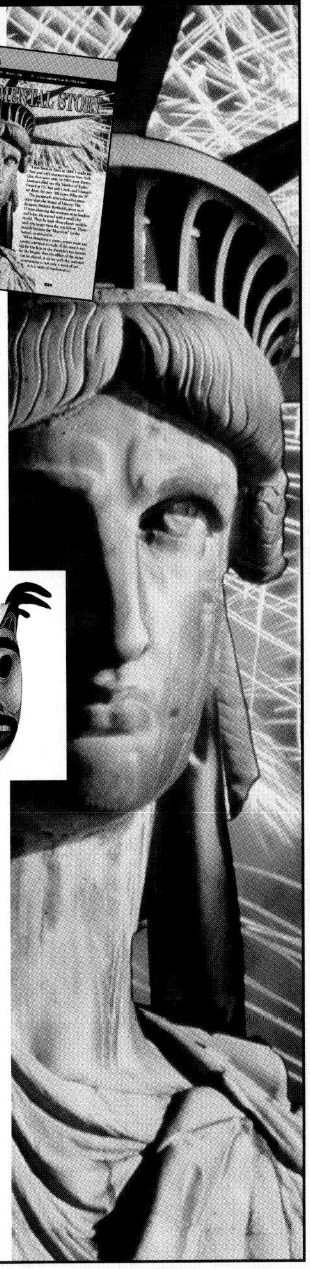

A Monumental Story

Materials: Centimeter ruler, Protractor

America's Northwest Coast Native Americans live along the Pacific coast from northern Oregon to southern Alaska. They include the Tlingit, Haida, and Bella Coola tribes. They use cedar wood to carve totem poles, some as tall as 7-story buildings. The poles are carved with fantastic figures relating to the family histories of the Native Americans.

You will design a proportional sketch for a totem pole. Here are the specifications for the totem pole:

1. The totem pole will be 15 m tall.
2. The totem pole will have 5 geometrically-shaped sections.
   a. A rectangle, 5 m tall
   b. A square, 3 m tall
   c. A trapezoid, 3 m tall
   d. A circle, 2 m in diameter
   e. A triangle, 2 m tall
3. The totem pole will have enough artistic detail so that the sections tell a story.

Your sketch should be a rectangle 24 cm tall and 4 cm wide. It should list all the "sketch lengths" in one color and the "actual totem pole lengths" they correspond to in another color.

You should also attach a paragraph explaining the story told by your totem pole.

A Monumental Story

The Point

In *A Monumental Story* on page 529, students learned that the designer of the Statue of Liberty created several clay and plaster models before the statue's construction. Now students will use proportions to convert actual measurements to model measurements and create a blueprint of a totem pole.

Materials

Centimeter ruler, protractor

Resources

Teaching Tool Transparencies
6: Cuisenaire Angle Ruler
16: Rulers
17: Protractor

About the Page

- Discuss the scale students will use for their blueprint. Ask students how they will determine the scale if the sketch is 24 cm tall and the totem is going to be 15 m tall.

  $\frac{24 \text{ cm}}{15 \text{ m}} = \frac{8 \text{ cm}}{5 \text{ m}} = \frac{1 \text{ cm}}{0.625 \text{ m}}$

- Remind students that their totem pole must contain the 5 geometric shapes described.
- Ask students how wide the actual totem pole will be.
  250 cm or 2.5 m

Ongoing Assessment

Check that students have drawn an accurate sketch containing the required geometric shapes and have correctly determined the sketch lengths and actual totem pole lengths.

Extension

Have students research totem poles. Ask them to choose one that they like and share a picture of it and the story it tells with the class. Display the totem pole pictures in your classroom.

Answers for Connect
Answers may vary.

10B Review

Review Correlation

Item(s)	Lesson(s)
1	10-2
2–5	10-3
6–10	10-5
11	10-6
12, 13	10-7
14, 15	10-5

Test Prep

Test-Taking Tip

Remind students that there is often more than one approach to solving a problem. For example, to solve these problems, students may use cross multiplication or they may first recognize that they are solving equivalent fractions.

Answers for Review

1. Possible answers: $\frac{5\text{ cm}}{2\text{ sec}}, \frac{50\text{ cm}}{20\text{ sec}}, \frac{75\text{ cm}}{30\text{ sec}}$

Section 10B Review

REVIEW 10B

1. Use a table to find three rates equal to $\frac{25\text{ cm}}{10\text{ sec}}$.

Find the unit rate for each ratio.

2. $\frac{51\text{ people}}{142\text{ ft}^2}$ $\approx$ 0.36 people/ft^2

3. $\frac{\$39}{60\text{ min}}$ \$0.65/min

4. $\frac{59\text{ pretzels}}{10\text{ servings}}$ 5.9 pretzels/serving

5. $\frac{18\text{ commercials}}{30\text{ min}}$ 0.6 commercials/min

Solve each proportion.

6. $\frac{32}{15} = \frac{?}{33}$ 70.4

7. $\frac{42}{?} = \frac{20}{24}$ 50.4

8. $\frac{7\text{ lb}}{18\text{ hr}} = \frac{?}{24\text{ hr}}$ $9.\overline{3}$ lb

9. $\frac{\$6}{20\text{ oz}} = \frac{?}{1\text{ oz}}$ \$0.30

10. Geography The statue shown is a 14-ft statue of King Kamehameha. It stands outside Aliiolani Hale, the state supreme court building, in Honolulu, Hawaii. The base of the statue is 6 feet tall, and the body is 8 feet tall. If the entire statue was 20 feet tall, how tall would the base and body be? Round your answers to the nearest tenth of a foot. base = 8.6 feet; body = 11.4 feet

11. If Danielle can wash 2 cars in 24 minutes, how many cars could she wash in an hour? 5

In each pair of similar figures, find the missing side lengths.

12.

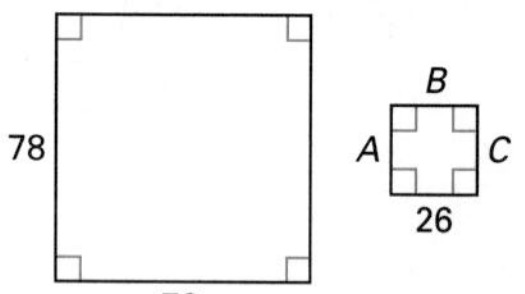

$A = B = C = 26$

13.

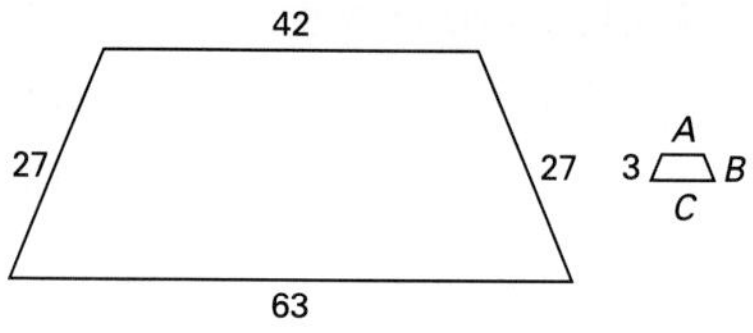

$A = 4.6, B = 3, C = 7$

Test Prep

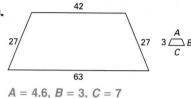

When solving a proportion on a multiple choice test, you can find the cross products for each choice. The correct answer will give equal cross products.

14. Solve: $\frac{2}{65} = \frac{6}{x}$ B

Ⓐ 390 Ⓑ 195 Ⓒ 780 Ⓓ 290

15. Solve: $\frac{4}{5} = \frac{6}{x}$ B

Ⓐ 9 Ⓑ 7.5 Ⓒ 9.5 Ⓓ 7

Resources

Practice Masters
Section 10B Review

Assessment Sourcebook
Quiz 10B

TestWorks
Test and Practice Software

PRACTICE

Name ______________________

Practice

Section 10B Review

Find the unit rate for each ratio.

1. $\frac{45\text{ kg}}{15\text{ m}}$ $\frac{3\text{ kg}}{1\text{ m}}$
2. $\frac{48\text{ lemons}}{\$8}$ $\frac{6\text{ lemons}}{\$1}$
3. $\frac{105\text{ mi}}{3\text{ hr}}$ $\frac{35\text{ mi}}{1\text{ hr}}$
4. $\frac{108\text{ cows}}{6\text{ acres}}$ $\frac{18\text{ cows}}{1\text{ acre}}$
5. $\frac{20\text{ windows}}{4\text{ doors}}$ $\frac{5\text{ windows}}{1\text{ door}}$
6. $\frac{100\text{ cars}}{25\text{ min}}$ $\frac{4\text{ cars}}{1\text{ min}}$

Solve each proportion.

7. $\frac{15}{50} = \frac{3}{10}$
8. $\frac{3}{18} = \frac{2}{12}$
9. $\frac{14}{12} = \frac{21}{18}$
10. $\frac{4\text{ dogs}}{9\text{ cats}} = \frac{8\text{ dogs}}{18\text{ cats}}$
11. $\frac{18\text{ rings}}{\$20} = \frac{27\text{ rings}}{\$30}$
12. $\frac{25\text{ gal}}{5\text{ min}} = \frac{20\text{ gal}}{4\text{ min}}$

13. In 1996, a chocolate chip cookie with an area of 5240 square feet was made by Cookie Time of New Zealand. It contained about 5600 pounds of chocolate. This equals how many pounds of chocolate per square foot of cookie? About 1.07 lb/ft^2

14. If Chester can type 75 words in 100 seconds, how many words could he type in 5 minutes? 225 words

In each pair of similar figures, find the missing side lengths.

15. $A =$ 35 in. $B =$ 21 in. $C =$ 35 in.

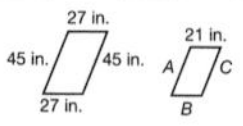

16. $A =$ 13.6 cm $B =$ 6.4 cm

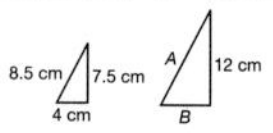

17. An instant pasta dinner package contains a packet of plain pasta plus a flavor packet weighing $\frac{1}{8}$ pound. If the entire package weighs $\frac{7}{16}$ pound, what is the weight of the plain pasta? *[Lesson 6-3]* $\frac{5}{16}$ lb

18. Mildred always has \$200 of her monthly salary transferred automatically to a savings account. The equation $y = x - 200$ gives the amount of her paycheck, where x is her after-tax income. Graph this equation. *[Lesson 9-7]*

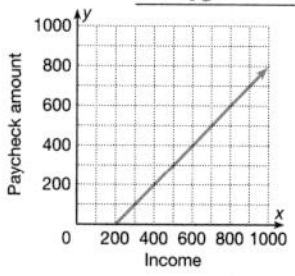

Section 10C

Percents

Visit www.teacher.mathsurf.com for links to lesson plans from teachers and other professionals, NCTM information, and other sites.

LESSON PLANNING GUIDE

Student Edition / Ancillaries

LESSON	MATERIALS	VOCABULARY	DAILY	OTHER
Section 10C Opener				
10-8 What Is a Percent?		percent	10-8	Teaching Tool Trans. 11 Lesson Enhancement Trans. 50 *Interactive CD-ROM Lesson*
10-9 Estimating Percents			10-9	Teaching Tool Trans. 22 Lesson Enhancement Trans. 51
10-10 Connecting Percents to Fractions and Decimals	10 x 10 grids, colored pencils or markers		10-10	Teaching Tool Trans. 11 Lesson Enhancement Trans. 52 Technology Master 55 Ch. 10 Project Master
10-11 Finding a Percent of a Number			10-11	Teaching Tool Trans. 23 Technology Master 56
Technology	spreadsheet software			*Interactive CD-ROM Spreadsheet/Grapher Tool*
Connect				Interdisc. Team Teaching 10C
Review				Practice 10C; Quiz 10C; *TestWorks*
Chapter 10 Summary and Review				
Chapter 10 Assessment				Ch. 10 Tests Forms A–F *TestWorks*; Ch. 10 Letter Home
Cumulative Review Chapters 1–10				Cumulative Review, Ch. 1–10

SKILLS TRACE

LESSON	SKILL	FIRST INTRODUCED GR. 4	GR. 5	GR. 6	DEVELOP	PRACTICE/APPLY	REVIEW
10-8	Expressing a quantity as a percent.		✗		pp. 550–551	pp. 552–553	pp. 570, 573, 614
10-9	Estimating percents.		✗		pp. 554–555	pp. 556–557	pp. 570, 573, 609
10-10	Expressing percents as fractions and decimals and vice versa.		✗		pp. 558–560	pp. 561–562	pp. 570, 573, 605
10-11	Finding a percent of a whole number.		✗		pp. 563–565	pp. 566–567	pp. 570, 573, 597

CONNECTED MATHEMATICS

Investigations 4–6 from the unit *Bits and Pieces I (Understanding Rational Numbers) and* the unit *Bits and Pieces II (Using Rational Numbers)*, from the **Connected Mathematics** series, can be used with Section 10C.

INTERDISCIPLINARY TEAM TEACHING

Math and Science/Technology

(Worksheet pages 51–52: Teacher pages T51–T52)

In this lesson, students use percentages to compare electrical power usage in homes.

Name ______________________ ***Math and Science/Technology***

Watch Those Watts!

Use percentages to compare electrical power usage in homes.

Most of humankind's energy needs, except transportation, are supplied by electrical power. Electricity is produced in big power plants and sent to homes through wires.

Electricity is used to make household appliances work. The amount of electrical power used by an appliance is measured in *watts.* For example, the wattage of a light bulb may be 60 watts. A brighter light bulb may use 100 watts of electrical power. One thousand watts of electrical power equals one *kilowatt. Kilo* comes from a Greek word for "thousand." In the United States, people who use electrical power pay for electricity according to the number of kilowatt hours (kWh) used in one month. One kWh means that 1000 watts of electricity were used for one hour. The average cost of one kWh in the United States is 8.6 cents.

A typical radio uses 71 watts of electricity. The average use of a radio is three hours per day, or 213 watts. In a 31-day month, this would come to 6,603 watts or 6.6 kWh. So the average monthly cost of using such a radio would be about 57 cents. (6.6 kWh × 8.6 cents/kWh = 56.8 cents)

The average home in the U.S. has about 30 appliances. Some appliances are used more than others. For example, a survey taken in Ohio during the 1980s showed that a large percentage of owners of deep-fat fryers, warming trays, and toaster ovens did not use them very often. The same survey showed that people frequently used other appliances, such as hand-held hair dryers, steam irons, coffeemakers, and vacuum cleaners.

The total energy usage of an appliance depends on three things:

1. The number of watts the appliance uses.
2. The length of time an appliance is used.
3. The number of times per month or year that the appliance is used.

When people buy appliances, they often see energy labels on the appliances. This is especially true on large appliances, such as washing machines, water heaters, and air conditioners. Energy labels make it easy to compare the efficiency of similar appliances. For example, two dishwashers may be the same size and have similar features, but one requires less energy to run. Customers are likely to choose the one that uses less energy and will save them money on their electricity bills.

1. Electricity bills from your utility company usually vary from month to month. What might cause these variations?

See below.

Name ______________________ ***Math and Science/Technology***

Appliance	Used	Did Not Use
toaster	100%	0%
hard-top hair dryer	64%	36%
deep-fat fryer	67%	33%
can opener	93%	7%
vacuum cleaner	98%	2%
toaster oven	70%	30%
coffeemaker	89%	11%
warming tray	67%	33%
slow cooker	96%	4%
hair setter	66%	34%

2. The table above shows the results of a survey in which people were asked whether they used an appliance they had purchased. Complete the table by calculating the missing percentages. Then answer the questions that follow.

a. Which appliance was used by everyone who bought it?

toaster

b. How many appliances were used by more than half the people?

all of them

c. Which appliance was used by the fewest people?

hard-top hair dryer

d. How does appliance usage in your home compare with the data in this table? Explain your answer.

See below.

e. Who would benefit from knowing percentages such as these? How might they use this information?

See below.

3. a. When might a person be willing to pay more for one dishwasher than another with the same features?

See below.

b. How can consumers convince manufacturing companies to produce appliances that use the least amount of energy?

See below.

4. Make a list of ten appliances that you think are frequently used by young people. Then, survey your class to determine the number and percentage of students who use each appliance. Round all percentages to the nearest percentage. (An example, based on an imaginary class of 25 students, is provided to help you understand how to complete this activity.)

Number of students in your class: ______________

Appliance	Number of Students Who Use the Appliance	Percentage of Students Who Use the Appliance
radio	23	92

Answers

1. The major cause would be variations in outside temperature, which causes people to increase use of energy for heating when temperatures are low, and for cooling when temperatures are high.

2. d. Students' responses will vary, based on their families' appliance ownership and usage.

2. e. Power companies might use this information. If several high-wattage appliances are used by a large number of people in an area, more power will be needed in that area. Also, appliance manufacturing companies may use this information to decide which appliances to manufacture and which ones not to manufacture.

3. a. When a more expensive dishwasher uses less energy and the owner may save money in the long run

   b. By purchasing only those appliances that use the least amount of energy

BIBLIOGRAPHY

FOR TEACHERS

Cooney, Thomas J. *Teaching and Learning Mathematics in the 1990s.* Reston, VA: NCTM, 1990.

Edwards, Edgar L., ed. *Algebra for Everyone.* Reston, VA: NCTM, 1990.

Miller, Ross. *American Apocalypse: The Great Fire and the Myth of Chicago.* Chicago, IL: University of Chicago Press, 1990.

Zawojewski, Judith S., et al. *Dealing with Data and Chance: Addenda Series, Grades 5–8.* Reston, VA: NCTM, 1991.

FOR STUDENTS

Dorros, Arthur. *Rain Forest Secrets.* New York, NY: Scholastic, 1990.

LeVert, Suzanne. *Yukon.* New York, NY: Chelsea House, 1992.

Palazzo-Craig, Janet. *Wonders of the Rain Forest.* Mahwah, NJ: Troll Associates, 1990.

Sherrow, Victoria. *The Gecko.* Minneapolis, MN: Dillon Press, 1990.

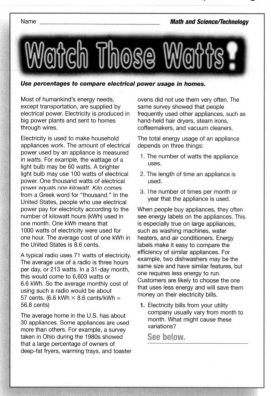

SECTION **10C**

Percents

▶ Science Link ▶ Geography Link ▶ www.mathsurf.com/6/ch10/rain_forest

Touring the Rain Forest

"Good morning, everyone. I'll be your guide for today's tour through the rain forest.

"That sound you're hearing is a howler monkey. They call most often in the morning, when the air is cool and sound travels better. Birds at different forest levels use different kinds of chirps to communicate. Butterflies communicate using their own perfumes.

"Have you seen any animals yet? They are there. Many look like plants to help them hide. That vine up there is really a snake. That flower is an orchid mantis. And those leaves on the tree … they're butterflies.

"Oh, be careful! Don't disturb that poison dart frog. It has enough poison to paralyze a monkey. Some frog poisons are strong enough to kill six people.

"I hope you've enjoyed the tour. Yes, I know I didn't get to everything. But there is such diverse animal life here that we could never describe it all in one tour. Please come back soon! There's still so much to learn!"

1 What sorts of things can people hope to learn by studying the rain forest?

2 How can mathematics be used when learning about the rain forest?

549

Where are we now?

In Section 10B, students learned to solve proportions. They explored the properties of similar figures.

They learned how to

- test to see if two ratios form a proportion.
- solve proportions using cross products.
- solve proportions using unit rates.
- identify similar figures.
- use proportions to find the length of a similar figure.

Where are we going?

In Section 10C, students will

- express a quantity as a percent.
- estimate percents.
- express percents as fractions and decimals.
- express fractions and decimals as percents.
- find the percent of a whole number.
- find a whole number when given the percent and the parts.

Theme: Rain Forests

World Wide Web

If your class has access to the World Wide Web, you might want to use the information found at the Web site address given. The interdisciplinary links relate to topics discussed in this section.

About the Page

This page introduces the theme of the section, rain forests, and discusses things seen on a tour of the rain forest.

Ask …

- What is the rain forest? A dense evergreen forest occupying a tropical region with an annual rainfall of at least 100 inches.

Extensions

The following activities do not require access to the World Wide Web.

Science
Unusual plants and animals live in the high humidity of the tropical rain forest. Ask students to research the plant and animal life in the rain forest and report their findings.

Geography
Where is the rain forest? Ask students to research the areas of the world where the rain forest exists.

Answers for Questions

1. Possible answers: Learn about animals and plants that don't live anywhere else. Learn what kinds of medicines can be made from things living or growing in rain forests.
2. Possible answers: Mathematics is used to tell about size and growth rates or to describe how many types of plants or animals there are in rain forests.

Connect

On page 569, students use percents to analyze facts about the rain forest.

INTERACTIVE LESSON 10-8

Lesson Organizer

Objective

- Express a quantity as a percent.

Vocabulary

- Percent

NCTM Standards

- 1–4, 7, 12

Review

Write an equal ratio with 100 as the second term.

1. $\frac{1}{2}$ $\frac{50}{100}$
2. $\frac{1}{4}$ $\frac{25}{100}$
3. $\frac{3}{10}$ $\frac{30}{100}$
4. $\frac{3}{5}$ $\frac{60}{100}$

Available on Daily Transparency 10-8

1 Introduce

Explore

You may wish to use Teaching Tool Transparency 11: 10 × 10 Grids and Lesson Enhancement Transparency 50 with this lesson.

The Point
Students explore the meaning of percents by deciding if statements involving percents are reasonable.

Ongoing Assessment
Students might be encouraged to think of specific examples to help them determine whether or not the statements are reasonable.

Answers for Explore
Possible answers:

1. Yes; They would have to win every time they play.
2. Yes; There's a 50% chance of being born a male.
3. Yes; It is more likely that it will rain than that it will not rain.

10-8 What Is a Percent?

You'll Learn ...

■ to express a quantity as a percent

... How It's Used

Accountants use percents in circle graphs to represent sources of a company's income.

Vocabulary

percent

▶ Lesson Link You've used ratios throughout this chapter. Now you will compare the ratio of a number to 100. ◀

Explore Percents

Just Be Reasonable!

Read each statement and answer the question that follows. Explain your reasoning.

1. Mrs. Roberts says her favorite football team wins 100% of the time. Do you think she is exaggerating?
2. Kevin says that about 50% of the students in his school are males. Does Kevin's estimate seem reasonable?
3. The weather report predicts a 90% chance of rain. Would it be a good idea to take an umbrella?
4. Donna read 20% of a book last night. Randall read 30% of a magazine last night. Did Randall read more pages than Donna?
5. A local store's sale ad says, "Everything Must Go—Prices Slashed By 2%." Do you think you would find good bargains at this sale?
6. Write three percent statements like the ones above.

Learn What is a Percent?

A **percent** is a ratio that compares a part to a whole using the number 100. The percent is the number of hundredths that the part is equal to.

MEETING INDIVIDUAL NEEDS

Resources

- **10-8** Practice
- **10-8** Reteaching
- **10-8** Problem Solving
- **10-8** Enrichment
- **10-8** Daily Transparency
  - Problem of the Day
  - Review
  - Quick Quiz
- Teaching Tool Transparency 11
- Lesson Enhancement Transparency 50
- *Interactive CD-ROM Lesson*

Learning Modalities

Visual Have students shade parts of a 10 × 10 grid to show different percents.

Social Have students work with a partner. Have one student shade a certain percent of a grid and then have the other student tell what percent is shaded. Then have students switch roles and repeat the process.

Verbal Have students locate data which is expressed in percents, such as survery results. Then have the students represent the percents of the data with bar graphs, shaded grids, or some other format.

Inclusion

Materials: Counters

Give students exactly 100 counters of various colors. Have them make tallies of each color and then find the percent that each is of the total.

Examples

Give the percent for the portion of each figure that is shaded.

1

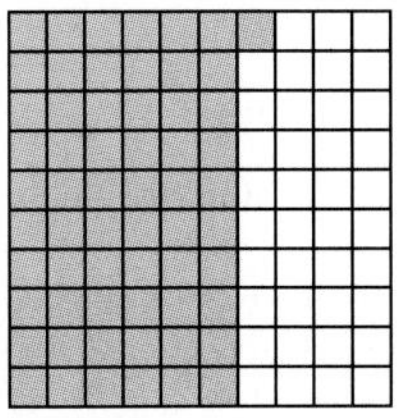

61 of the 100 squares are shaded.

$\frac{61}{100} = 61\%$

2

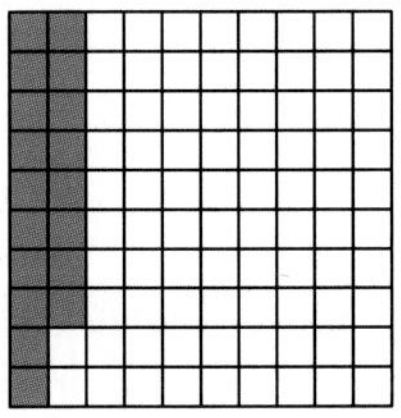

18 of the 100 squares are shaded.

$\frac{18}{100} = 18\%$

If a quantity is broken into 100 pieces, it is easy to describe using percents. It is also easy to use percents when working with fourths or tenths.

$\frac{1}{10} = \frac{10}{100}$, or 10% $\frac{1}{4} = \frac{25}{100}$, or 25% $\frac{1}{2} = \frac{50}{100}$, or 50% $\frac{3}{4} = \frac{75}{100}$, or 75%

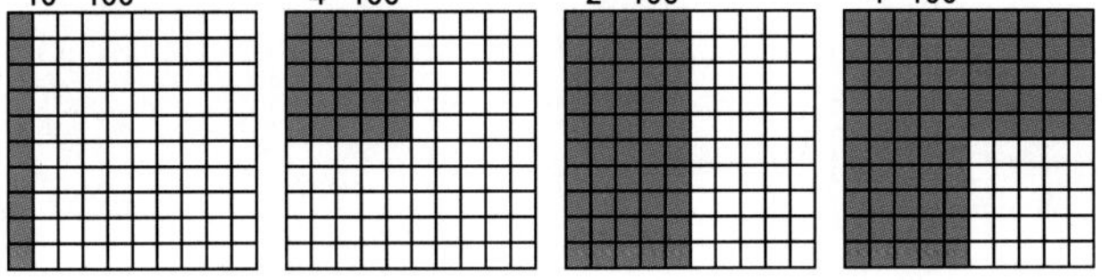

> **▶ Science Link**
>
> The toucan is one of the best-known bird species from the rain forest. Each toucan's beak is colored in a slightly different way, allowing toucans to recognize one another.

Example 3

The shaded portion of the figure represents the portion of the world's bird species that live in rain forests. What percent of the bird species live in rain forests?

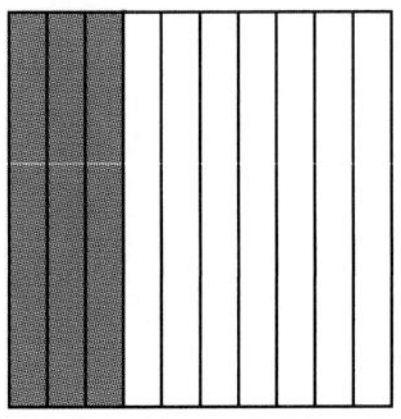

Each shaded section is $\frac{1}{10}$, or 10%, of the figure. Three sections are shaded, so the percent is $3 \times 10\%$, or 30%.

30% of the world's bird species live in rain forests.

Try It

Give the percent of each figure that is shaded.

a. 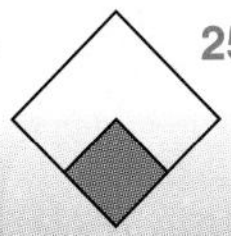 25%

b. 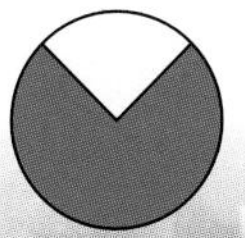 75%

Answers for Explore

4. Probably not; It depends on how many pages were in the book and in the magazine.
5. No; 2% is not much of a discount.
6. Answers may vary.

2 Teach

Learn

Alternate Examples

Give the percent of each figure that is shaded.

1. 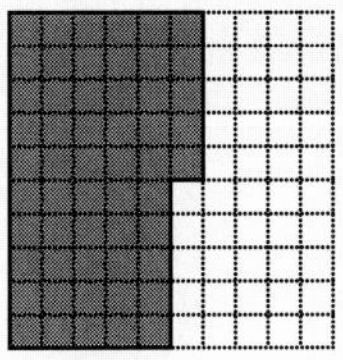

   55 of the 100 squares are shaded.

   $\frac{55}{100} = 55\%$

2. 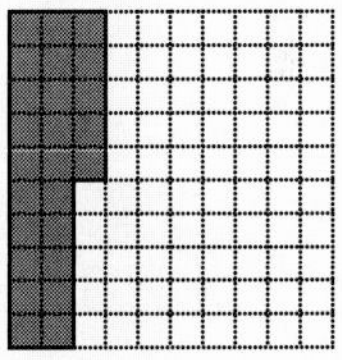

   25 of the 100 squares are shaded.

   $\frac{25}{100} = 25\%$

3. The shaded portion of the figure represents the percent of the world's population that lives along a coastline or within 100 miles of one. What percent of the population lives along a coast?

   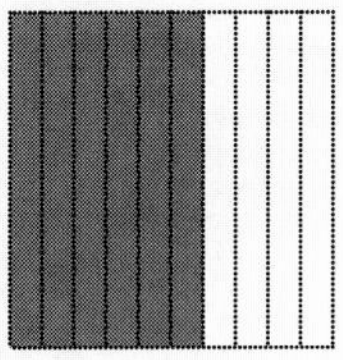

   Each shaded section is $\frac{1}{10}$, or 10%, of the figure. Six sections are shaded, so the percent is $6 \times 10\%$, or 60%.

   60% of the world's population lives along a coast.

MATH EVERY DAY

▶ Problem of the Day

Mary Joyce, a 27-year-old Alaskan woman, left her home near Juneau on December 22, 1935. On March 26, 1936, she and her dog team arrived at Fairbanks—a trip of 1000 miles. Assuming she started and ended her trip at noon, what was her average rate in miles per day? Round your answer to the nearest tenth. 10.5 miles per day (1000 ÷ 95 = 10.5; 1936 is a leap year.)

Available on Daily Transparency 10-8

An Extension is provided in the transparency package.

Fact of the Day

In the tropical rain forest, rain may occur more than 200 days a year. In a year, the average rainfall can be 50 to 260 inches.

Mental Math

Find each quotient mentally.

1. 200 ÷ 25 8
2. 300 ÷ 50 6
3. 600 ÷ 30 20
4. 400 ÷ 40 10

10-8 Exercises and Applications

Assignment Guide

- **Basic** 1–16, 18, 20, 22, 27–43 odds
- **Average** 5–20, 22–24, 27–43 odds
- **Enriched** 5–17 odds, 18–26, 28–42 evens

3 Practice and Assess

Check

Answers for Check Your Understanding

1. 100% is the entire quantity; 0% is nothing.
2. Yes; A 150% markup on a dress from wholesale price to retail price could be \$100 wholesale to \$250 retail. The retail price is 150% of the wholesale price.
3. Yes; It depends on the initial quantities. For example, 25% of 8 is 2 whereas 50% of 2 is 1, $2 > 1$.

Exercise Notes

Exercises 7–14

Error Prevention If students are confused by the variety of shapes, remind them that they are still comparing the amount shaded to the total number of parts.

Reteaching

Activity

Materials: 10×10 grids

- Use a 10×10 grid and shade 10 small squares.
- Write the ratio of shaded squares to total squares and write the percent. $\frac{10}{100}$, 10%
- Shade in more small squares so that half of the large square is shaded.
- How many small squares are shaded? 50
- Write the ratio of shaded squares to total squares. $\frac{50}{100}$ Write the percent. 50%

PRACTICE 10-8

Check Your Understanding

1. What is 100% of something? What is 0% of something?
2. Can a quantity be *more than* 100% of another quantity?
3. Can 25% of something be bigger than 50% of something else? Explain.

10-8 Exercises and Applications

Practice and Apply

Getting Started Tell if each ratio is greater than or less than 50%.

1. $\frac{56}{100}$ Greater
2. $\frac{23}{100}$ Less
3. $\frac{5}{100}$ Less
4. $\frac{80}{100}$ Greater
5. $\frac{45}{100}$ Less
6. $\frac{98}{100}$ Greater

Give the percent of each figure that is shaded.

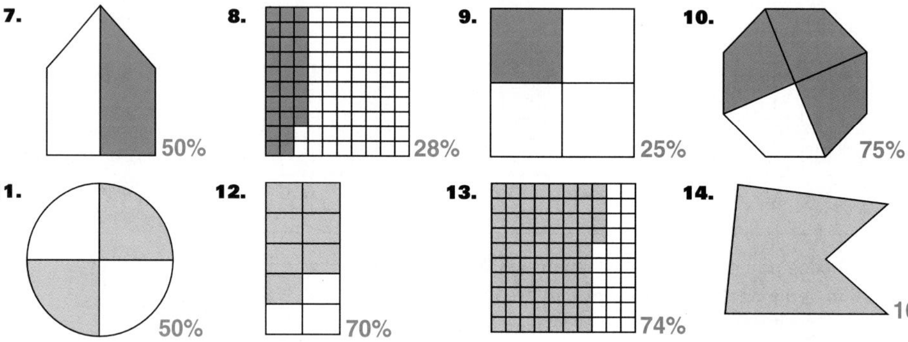

7. 50%
8. 28%
9. 25%
10. 75%
11. 50%
12. 70%
13. 74%
14. 100%

Geography The circle graph shows the percent of Asia's rain forest that is located in each country. Use the graph for Exercises 15–17.

15. About what percent of Asia's rain forest is located in Myanmar? Outside of Myanmar? About 12%; About 88%
16. Which country has the highest percent of Asia's rain forest? Estimate the percent. Indonesia, 40%
17. What three parts of the graph combined account for 50% of Asia's rain forest? India, Myanmar, Other

Asia's Rain Forests

PRACTICE

Name ____________

Practice 10-8

The Meaning of Percent

Give the percent of each figure that is shaded.

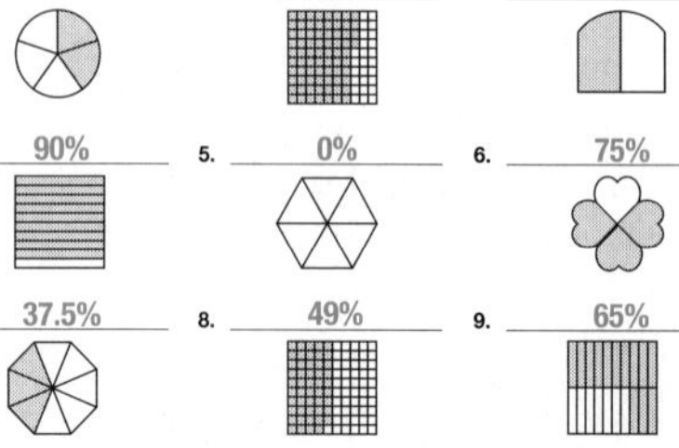

1. 40%
2. 74%
3. 50%
4. 90%
5. 0%
6. 75%
7. 37.5%
8. 49%
9. 65%

The circle graph shows the educational attainment of Americans over 25 years old in 1994. Use the graph for Exercises 10–12.

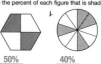

Educational Attainment of Americans

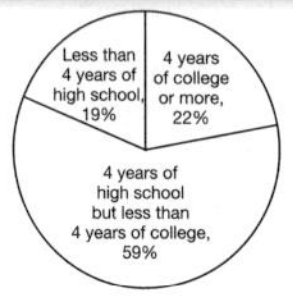

10. What percent of the population has completed
    less than 4 years of high school? 19%
    4 years of high school or more? 81%
11. Which category includes the highest percent of Americans over 25? 4 yrs h.s. but < 4 yrs college
    What is the percent? 59%
12. Which two categories combined amount for 41% of Americans over 25? < 4 yrs h.s., ≥ 4 yrs college
13. **Geography** 22% of the land in Vietnam is arable (suitable for farming). What percent is not arable? 78%

RETEACHING

Name ____________

Alternative Lesson 10-8

What Is a Percent?

A **percent** is a ratio that compares a part to a whole using the number 100. The percent is the number of hundredths that the part is equal to.

Example 1

Give the percent of the figure that is shaded.

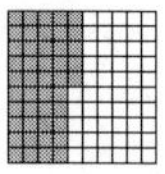

45 of the 100 squares are shaded. $\frac{45}{100} = 45\%$

So, 45% of the figure is shaded.

Try It Give the percent of each figure that is shaded.

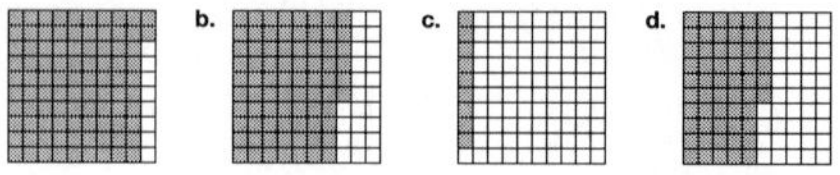

a. 92%
b. 76%
c. 9%
d. 56%

Example 2

Give the percent of the figure that is shaded.

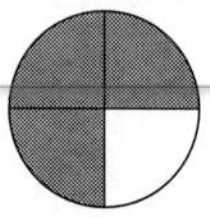

Each shaded section is $\frac{1}{4}$, or 25%, of the figure. Three sections are shaded, so the percent is $3 \times 25\%$, or 75%.

So, 75% of the figure is shaded.

Try It Give the percent of the figure that is shaded.

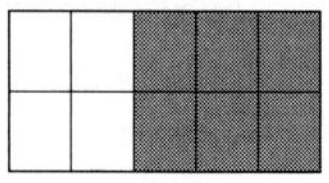

e. What fraction describes each section? $\frac{1}{10}$
f. What percent describes each section? 10%
g. How many sections are shaded? 6 sections.
h. What percent is shaded? 60%

Give the percent of each figure that is shaded.

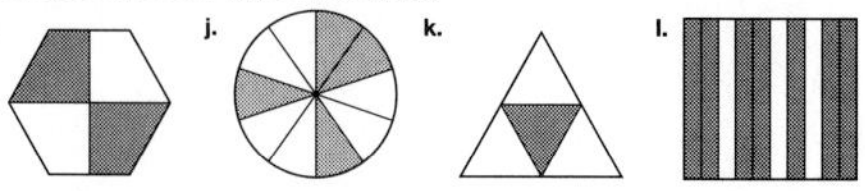

i. 50%
j. 40%
k. 25%
l. 70%

18. Geometry What percent of the shapes are quadrilaterals? 50%

GPS

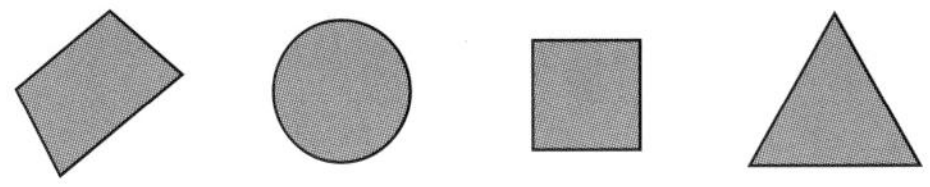

19. Number Sense Kwi and Park are building a model out of sugar cubes. Each has half of a box. If Kwi has used half of his sugar cubes, what percent of the box has he used? 25%

20. **Test Prep** What percent of the figure is shaded? C

Ⓐ 15% Ⓑ 17%

Ⓒ 85% Ⓓ 170%

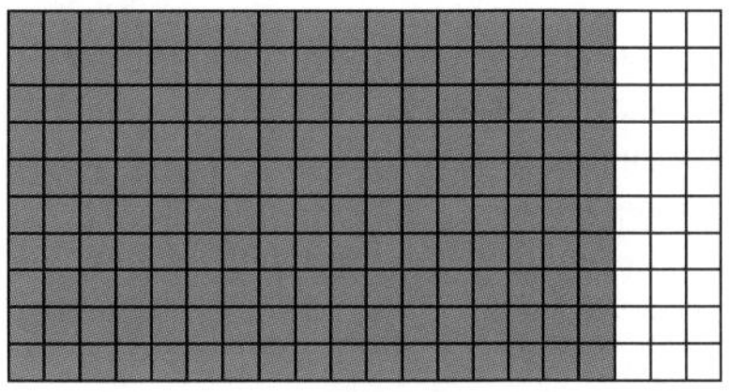

21. Crista's end-of-the-year math test had 100 problems.

a. If she got 89 of them correct, what percent of the problems did she get correct? 89%

b. Is it possible for her to get 113% of the problems correct? No

Problem Solving and Reasoning

22. Communicate A corporation says that its 1997 earnings were 120% of its 1996 earnings. Explain how this percent can be greater than 100%.

23. Communicate Do you think every ratio can be written as a percent? Explain your reasoning.

Critical Thinking Tell if the situations in Exercises 24–26 are possible or not. Explain your reasoning.

24. 62% of the students in Mrs. Chen's class are boys, and 48% are girls.

25. 48% of the students in Mr. Davis' class are wearing blue jeans, and 27% are wearing T-shirts.

26. Students in Mr. O'Malley's class showed an improvement in their test scores of 110%.

Mixed Review

On a coordinate grid, plot and label each point. *[Lesson 9-5]*

27. $Y(-5, 2)$ **28.** $K(3, 9)$ **29.** $A(6, -2)$ **30.** $M(-4, -5)$ **31.** $P(-3, 4)$

Find the prime factorization. [Lesson 5-2]

32. 58 2×29 **33.** 25 5^2 **34.** 26 2×13 **35.** 95 5×19 **36.** 405 $3^4 \times 5$ **37.** 125 5^3

38. 56 $2^3 \times 7$ **39.** 6 2×3 **40.** 288 $2^5 \times 3^2$ **41.** 88 $2^3 \times 11$ **42.** 87 3×29 **43.** 72 $2^3 \times 3^2$

Exercise Notes

■ Exercise 26

Error Prevention If students have difficulty with this problem, have them first determine what would be meant by 100% improvement.

Exercise Answers

22. They exceeded their 1996 earnings by 20%.

23. Yes; Divide the numerator by the denominator and multiply by 100. Some percents will be approximates.

24. No; The total is more than 100%.

25. Yes; These two percents do not need to add to 100%. Some of the students wearing blue jeans may also be wearing T-shirts, or none may be wearing T-shirts.

26. Yes; The students improved a great deal. For example, their tests scores could have been 40% and their new test scores 84%, which is an improvement of 110%.

27–31.

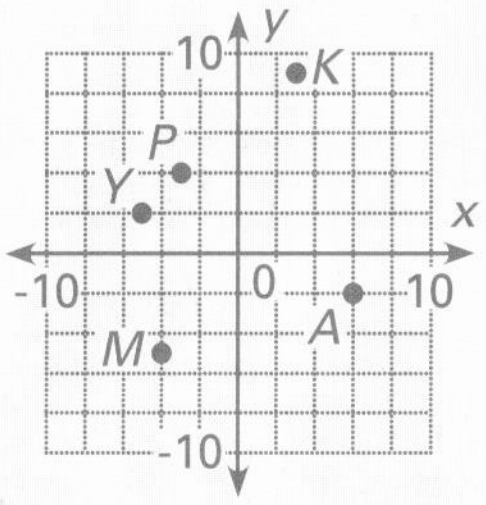

Alternate Assessment

Performance Have students draw four diagrams which show 40%. Have them describe how they determined that 40% of each figure is shown.

PROBLEM SOLVING

Name ______________

Guided Problem Solving 10-8

GPS **PROBLEM 18, PAGE 553**

What percent of the shapes are quadrilaterals?

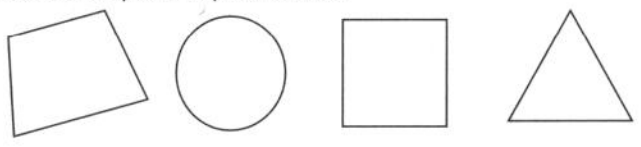

Understand Possible answer: Item 8

1. What is the name of the

   a. first figure? Trapezoid. b. second figure? Circle.

   c. third figure? Square. d. fourth figure? Triangle.

2. What is the definition of a quadrilateral? A polygon with four sides.

Plan

3. Which of the shapes are quadrilaterals? Trapezoid and square.

4. Write a ratio of the number of quadrilaterals to the total number of figures. $\frac{2}{4}$

5. A percent compares a part to a whole. What number represents the whole in a percent? 100

Solve

6. Write an equal ratio to the ratio you wrote in Item 4. Use the "whole" you named in Item 5 as the denominator. $\frac{50}{100}$

7. Write the percent of the figures that are quadrilaterals. 50%

Look Back

8. What is another way you could find the percent of figures that are quadrilaterals?
   Each figure is $\frac{1}{4}$, or 25%, of the total; $2 \times 25\% = 50\%$.

SOLVE ANOTHER PROBLEM

What percent of the shapes are polygons? 75%

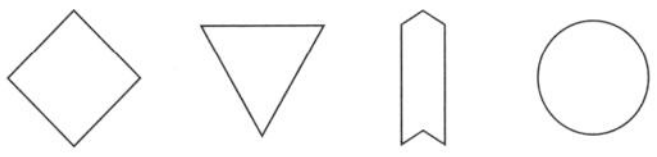

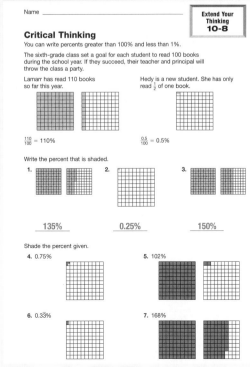

ENRICHMENT

Name ______________

Extend Your Thinking 10-8

Critical Thinking

You can write percents greater than 100% and less than 1%.

The sixth-grade class set a goal for each student to read 100 books during the school year. If they succeed, their teacher and principal will throw the class a party.

Lamarr has read 110 books so far this year.

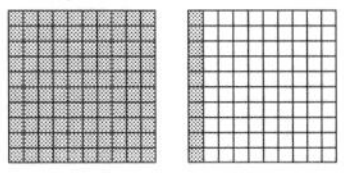

$\frac{110}{100} = 110\%$

Hedy is a new student. She has only read $\frac{1}{2}$ of one book.

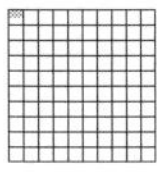

$\frac{0.5}{100} = 0.5\%$

Write the percent that is shaded.

1. 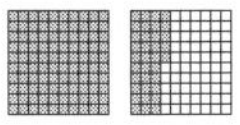
   135%

2. 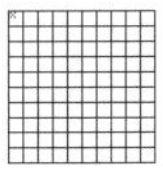
   0.25%

3. 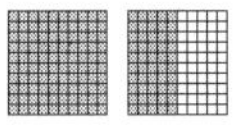
   150%

Shade the percent given.

4. 0.75%
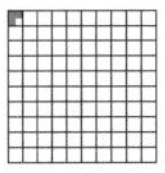

5. 102%
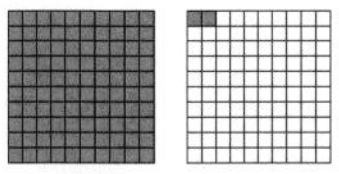

6. $0.3\overline{3}\%$
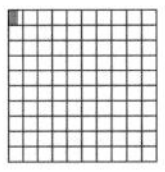

7. 168%
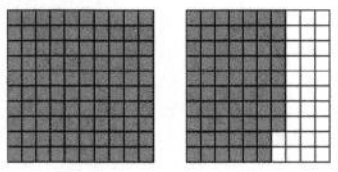

▶ Quick Quiz

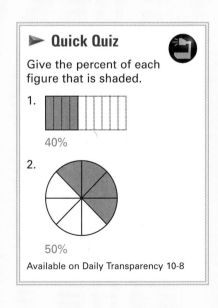

Give the percent of each figure that is shaded.

1. 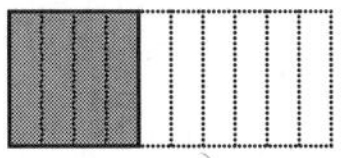
   40%

2. 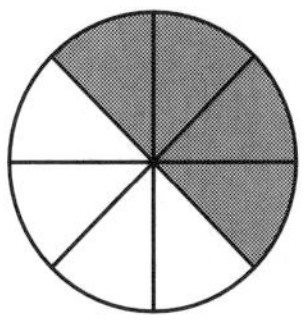
   50%

Available on Daily Transparency 10-8

10-9 Lesson Organizer

Objective

- Estimate percents.

NCTM Standards

- 1–4, 7

Review

Draw each of the following:

1. Two congruent triangles.
2. Two similar triangles.
3. Two similar quadrilaterals.

Check students' drawings.

Available on Daily Transparency 10-9

1 Introduce

Explore

You may wish to use Lesson Enhancement Transparency 51 with this lesson.

The Point
Students explore estimating percents by finding examples of ratios that are approximately equal to various percents.

Ongoing Assessment
As students are working, check to see that they are trying to find quantities that show approximate, not exact, percents.

For Groups That Finish Early
Describe a ratio in your classroom that is not equal to a percent listed in Step 2. Trade papers with other students in you group and estimate the percent.

Answers for Explore

1–2. Answers may vary.

3. Possible answers: Overestimate: The percent of people for whom you need to bring food, so no one is left out; Underestimate: The percent of students who might attend a school play, so that expenses are not allowed to exceed income; Exact: Figuring out sales tax.

10-9 Estimating Percents

You'll Learn ...

- to estimate percents

... How It's Used

Emergency planners work with percent estimates when preparing for earthquakes, floods, and tornadoes.

Lesson Link In the last lesson, you learned the meaning of percent. Now you will estimate percents.

Explore Estimating Percents

The Percent Scavenger Hunt

1. Find a ratio or comparison in your classroom that is equal to about 10%. For example, about 10% of the students may be left-handed. Explain why you think the percent is about 10%.
2. Repeat Step 1 for the following percents.

   a. 25% **b.** 50% **c.** 60% **d.** 75% **e.** 90% **f.** 100%
3. Describe circumstances where it would be best to overestimate or underestimate a percent. Describe a circumstance where it would be best to get an exact percent.

Learn Estimating Percents

Geography Link

Nearly all of the earth's rain forests are located between the Tropic of Cancer (latitude 23° 26′ north) and the Tropic of Capricorn (latitude 23° 26′ south). Every continent except for Europe and Antarctica has a significant amount of land covered by rain forests.

Recall that $\frac{1}{2}$ of something is 50%, $\frac{1}{4}$ is 25%, and $\frac{1}{10}$ is 10%. When estimating a percent, think of a fraction close to the given value that uses halves, fourths, or tenths. These fractions can easily be expressed as percents.

Example 1

The map shows the rain forest in Indonesia. Estimate the percent of Indonesia that is made up of rain forest.

The shaded part of the map is more than $\frac{3}{4}$, but less than $\frac{4}{4}$. It is about $\frac{8}{10}$.

Your estimate should be more than 75% but less than 100%. You might estimate 80%.

About 80% of Indonesia's land is made up of rain forest.

MEETING INDIVIDUAL NEEDS

Resources

- **10-9** Practice
- **10-9** Reteaching
- **10-9** Problem Solving
- **10-9** Enrichment
- **10-9** Daily Transparency
  - Problem of the Day
  - Review
  - Quick Quiz
- Teaching Tool Transparency 22
- Lesson Enhancement Tranparency 51

Learning Modalities

Verbal Have students work together to find newspaper articles where estimated percents are involved.

Kinesthetic Have students work in pairs to fold a circle in half. Have them shade one part to represent 50%. Ask students to fold two circles in fourths and shade one section to represent 25% and three sections to represent 75%. Have students use additional circles to estimate other percents such as 30% or 70% by comparing them to the circles they shaded first.

Challenge

Materials: Almanac

Have students use what they have learned about percents to guess what percent of the total population of the United States lives in each state. Then have them use an almanac to verify their guesses.

Examples

2 Estimate the percent of the figure that is shaded.

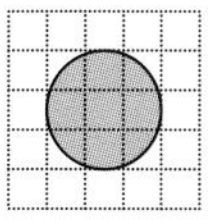

The circle covers 5 squares completely or almost completely. It covers about $\frac{1}{2}$ of 4 more squares. The combined number of covered squares is about

$5 + \frac{1}{2} + \frac{1}{2} + \frac{1}{2} + \frac{1}{2}$, or 7.

The total number of squares is 5×5, or 25.

The part shaded is about $\frac{7}{25}$, which is about $\frac{1}{4}$, or 25%.

About 25% of the figure is shaded.

3 Of Mr. Niemeyer's 80 students, 71 wore Halloween costumes. Estimate the percent of Mr. Niemeyer's students who did *not* wear costumes.

$80 - 71 = 9$, so 9 students did *not* wear costumes.

9 is about $\frac{1}{10}$ of 80, or about 10% of 80. About 10% did *not* wear costumes.

Problem Solving TIP

When estimating area on a grid, a shaded part sometimes fills up part of a square, but not all of it. One way to estimate the area is to count a square with more than half shaded as 1 and to count a square with less than half shaded as 0.

Try It

a. Estimate the percent of the figure that is shaded. 20%

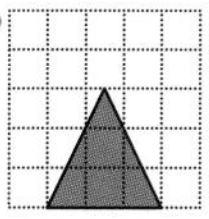

b. 32 out of the 45 dentists surveyed recommend GlowBrite Toothpaste. Approximately what percent recommend GlowBrite? 70%

Check Your Understanding

1. If you know 10% of a number, how can you use estimation to find 5% of the number? 20% of the number? 80% of the number?
2. Describe a situation where you could use mental math to find a percent exactly, instead of having to estimate.
3. If you are describing a pizza that's been partially eaten, is it easier to estimate the fraction not eaten, or the percent not eaten? Explain.

MATH EVERY DAY

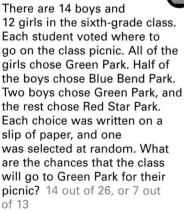

Problem of the Day

There are 14 boys and 12 girls in the sixth-grade class. Each student voted where to go on the class picnic. All of the girls chose Green Park. Half of the boys chose Blue Bend Park. Two boys chose Green Park, and the rest chose Red Star Park. Each choice was written on a slip of paper, and one was selected at random. What are the chances that the class will go to Green Park for their picnic? 14 out of 26, or 7 out of 13

Available on Daily Transparency 10-9

An Extension is provided in the transparency package.

Fact of the Day

Of all the Earth's species, 50% live in rain forests. Up to 200 different kinds of trees can live in a 2.5-acre plot of land.

Estimation

Estimate each sum.

1. $21.5 + 43.7$ 66
2. $68.9 + 24.5$ 95
3. $55.2 + 13.4$ 68

2 Teach

Learn

You may wish to use Teaching Tool Transparency 22: Map of the United States with Alternate Example 1.

Alternate Examples

1. Estimate the percent of the area of the U.S. that is west of the Mississippi River.

   The area west of the Mississippi River is more than 50%, but less than 75%. It is about 60%.

   About 60% of the U.S. area is west of the Mississippi River.

2. Estimate the percent of the figure that is shaded.

   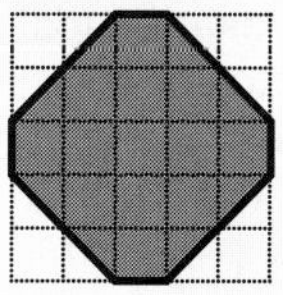

   The figure covers 13 whole squares and 8 half-squares.

   $13 + \frac{1}{2} + \frac{1}{2} + \frac{1}{2} + \frac{1}{2} + \frac{1}{2} + \frac{1}{2} + \frac{1}{2} + \frac{1}{2}$ or 17.

   There is a total of 25 squares.

   The part shaded is $\frac{17}{25}$, which is about $\frac{3}{4}$ or 75%.

   About 75% of the figure is shaded.

3. Of 96 sixth-grade students, 73 ride the bus to school. Estimate the percent of students who do not ride the bus.

   $96 - 73 = 23$. 23 is about $\frac{1}{4}$ of 96, or about 25% of 96.

   About 25% do not ride the bus to school.

3 Practice and Assess

Check

Answers for Check Your Understanding

1. Half of 10% is 5%; Twice 10% is 20%; 8 times 10% is 80%.
2. Possible answer: When the percent is a multiple of 5 or 10.
3. Fraction not eaten; The number of slices missing can be compared to the total number of slices.

10-9 Exercises and Applications

Assignment Guide

- **Basic**
  1–4, 5–27 odds, 30, 33–47 odds
- **Average**
  3–25 odds, 26–30, 33–47 odds
- **Enriched**
  4–24 evens, 25–32, 34–48 evens

Exercise Notes

Exercises 1–4

Error Prevention If students' estimates are not correct, remind them that they should be comparing shaded squares to total squares, *not* shaded squares to unshaded squares.

Exercise 23

Geography Rain forests almost all lie near the equator. The Amazonian rain forest is the largest tropical rain forest. It covers about a third of South America.

Reteaching

Activity

Materials: 10 × 10 grids

- On a 10 × 10 grid, shade 10 small squares, or 10%, of the squares.
- Using a different 10 × 10 grid for each, shade 25%, 50%, 75%, and 100% of the squares.
- On another 10 × 10 grid, shade any number of small squares.
- Estimate the percent that you shaded by comparing this area to the other five areas. Which percent is it closest to? Answers may vary.

10-9 Exercises and Applications

PRACTICE 10-9

Practice and Apply

Getting Started Estimate what percent of each grid is shaded.

1. 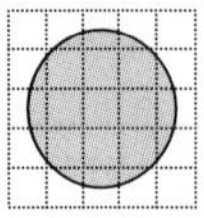 50%

2. 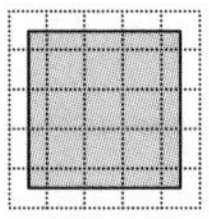 64%

3. 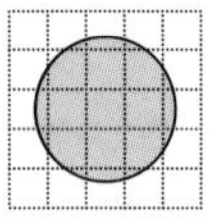 40%

4. 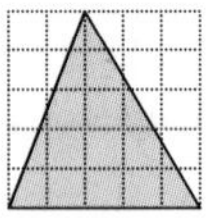 50%

Estimate what percent of each figure is shaded.

5. 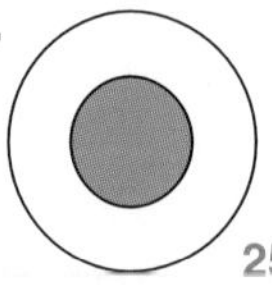 25%

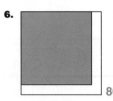

6.  80%

7. 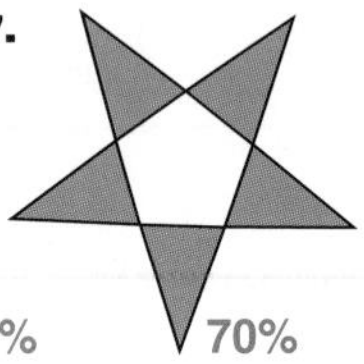 70%

8. 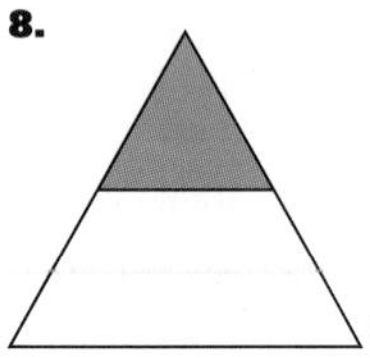 25%

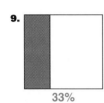

9.  33%

10. 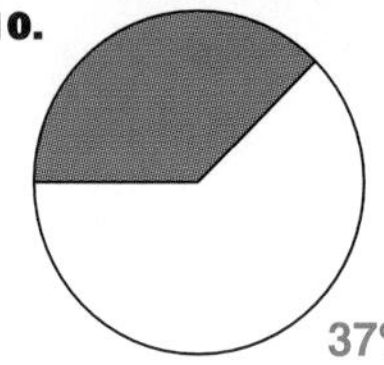 37%

11. 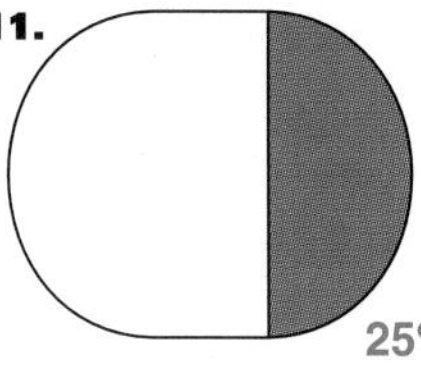 25%

12. 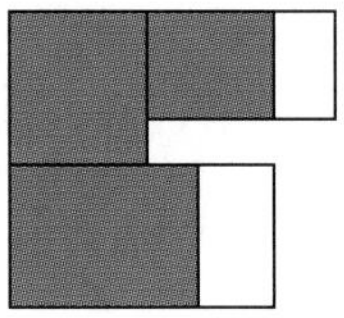 85%

Estimate the percent.

13. 8 out of 72 10% **14.** 12 out of 77 15% **15.** 93 out of 187 75% **16.** 318 out of 965 32% **17.** 12 out of 16 75%

18. $\frac{39}{150}$ 25% **19.** $\frac{57}{90}$ 60% **20.** $\frac{14}{109}$ 13% **21.** $\frac{6}{657}$ 1% **22.** $\frac{474}{489}$ 97%

23. Estimation One researcher estimates that rain forests cover about 3,536,342 square miles of the earth's 50,500,000 square miles of land. About what percent of the earth's land is covered by rain forests? 7%

24. Estimation Of the 7800 known species of birds, about 2600 live in rain forests. What percent of bird species live in rain forests? About 33%

PRACTICE

Name ______________________

Practice 10-9

Estimating Percents

Estimate what percent of each figure is shaded.

1. ≈ 60% 
2. ≈ 40% 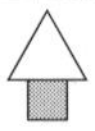
3. ≈ 60% 
4. ≈ 40% 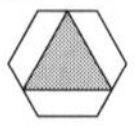
5. ≈ 40% 
6. ≈ 60% 
7. ≈ 50% 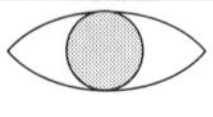
8. ≈ 50% 
9. ≈ 80% 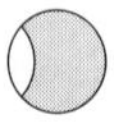

Estimate the percent.

10. 13 out of 66 ≈ 20% **11.** 31 out of 118 ≈ 25% **12.** 18 out of 21 ≈ 90%

13. 73 out of 80 ≈ 90% **14.** 47 out of 77 ≈ 60% **15.** 93 out of 190 ≈ 50%

16. $\frac{312}{420}$ ≈ 75% **17.** $\frac{59}{84}$ ≈ 70% **18.** $\frac{25}{240}$ ≈ 10% **19.** $\frac{45}{148}$ ≈ 30%

20. $\frac{59}{74}$ ≈ 80% **21.** $\frac{88}{116}$ ≈ 75% **22.** $\frac{41}{47}$ ≈ 90% **23.** $\frac{61}{99}$ ≈ 60%

24. In 1989, the EarthGrains Bakery in Fort Payne, Alabama, set a world record by baking a cake weighing 128,000 lb. The cake included 16,000 lb of icing. About what percent of the cake was icing? About 10%

25. Patents are issued to inventors to prevent others from stealing their ideas. In 1965, 37,000 out of 63,000 patents were issued to U.S. corporations. About what percent is this? About 60%

RETEACHING

Name ______________________

Alternative Lesson 10-9

Estimating Percents

When estimating a percent, think of a fraction close to the given value that uses halves, fourths, or tenths. These fractions can easily be expressed as percents: $\frac{1}{2}$ is 50%, $\frac{1}{4}$ is 25%, and $\frac{1}{10}$ is 10%.

Example 1

Estimate what percent of the grid is shaded.

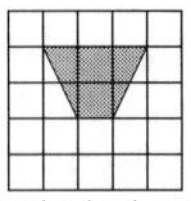

The trapezoid covers 2 squares completely. It covers about $\frac{1}{2}$ of 4 more squares. Add to estimate the total number of shaded squares. $2 + \frac{1}{2} + \frac{1}{2} + \frac{1}{2} + \frac{1}{2}$, or 4 squares.

The total number of squares is 5 × 5, or 25.

The shaded part is about $\frac{4}{25}$, which is about $\frac{1}{5}$, or 20%.

About 20% of the figure is shaded.

Try It Estimate what percent of each grid is shaded. Estimates may vary.

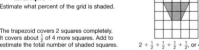

a. 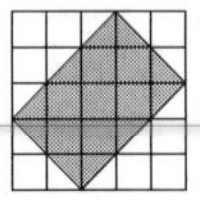 50%

b. 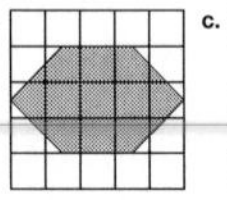 40%

c. 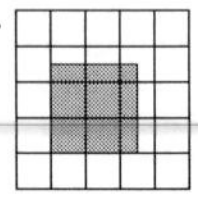 25%

d. 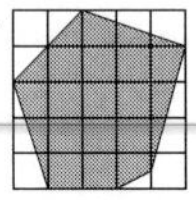 70%

Example 2

Estimate the percent: 32 out of 40.

32 is a little more than $\frac{3}{4}$ of 40.

So, 32 out of 40 is about 75%.

Try It Estimate the percent.

e. 9 out of 91 is about what fraction? $\frac{1}{10}$ What percent? 10%

f. 140 out of 300 is about what fraction? $\frac{1}{2}$ What percent? 50%

g. 2 out of 206 is about what fraction? $\frac{1}{100}$ What percent? 1%

h. 15 out of 45 33%. i. 23 out of 98 25%. j. 83 out of 105 80%.

k. 298 out of 500 60%. l. 71 out of 97 70%. m. 4 out of 422 1%.

25. **Test Prep** Estimate what percent of the figure is shaded. C

Ⓐ 45% Ⓑ 50%

Ⓒ 65% Ⓓ 95%

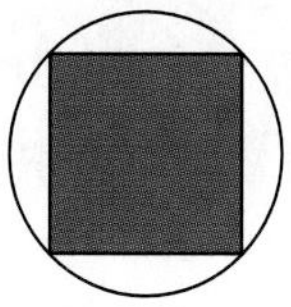

Geography **A rain forest is an example of a *biome*, or a particular type of environment. Use the map showing the major biomes of South America for Exercises 26–28.**

26. About what percent of South America is desert? 10%

27. About what percent of South America is rain forest? 33%

28. About what percent of the South American rain forest is above the equator? 33%

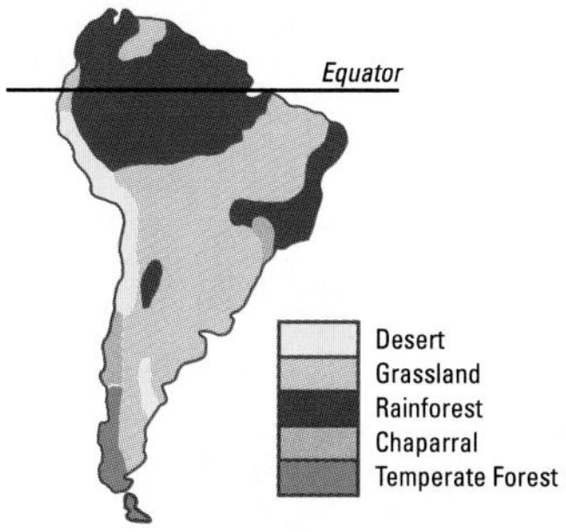

Problem Solving and Reasoning

29. **Communicate** Is it easier to estimate the percent for $\frac{7}{200}$ or $\frac{7}{310}$? Explain.

30. **Critical Thinking** If a shirt was originally \$20, went on sale for 15% off, and then was put on clearance with an additional 45% off, estimate the clearance price of the shirt. Explain your reasoning.

31. **Critical Thinking** In a right triangle, estimate the percent of the number of angles that are **not** right angles. Explain your reasoning.

32. Journal Explain two different ways you can estimate what percent 75 is of 200.

Mixed Review

For Exercises 33–36, plot the image of trapezoid *JKLM*. *[Lesson 9-6]*

33. Translate *JKLM* 2 units down, 6 units right

34. Slide *JKLM* 5 units right, 1 unit down

35. Slide *JKLM* 3 units up, 4 units left

36. Translate *JKLM* 2 units down

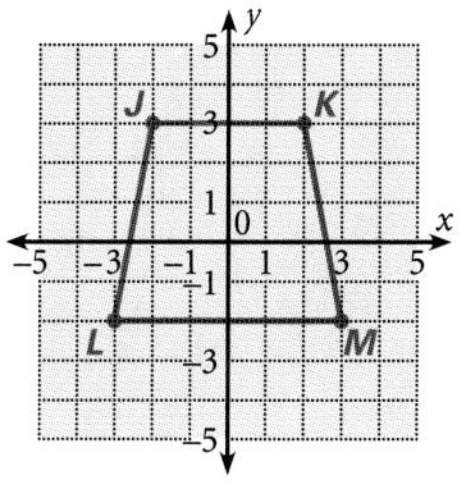

Find the LCM of each pair. *[Lesson 5-3]*

37. 1, 6 6 **38.** 10, 12 60 **39.** 6, 4 12 **40.** 8, 8 8 **41.** 5, 10 10 **42.** 25, 75 75

43. 5, 6 30 **44.** 12, 8 24 **45.** 14, 3 42 **46.** 12, 14 84 **47.** 3, 2 6 **48.** 13, 1 13

Exercise Notes

■ Exercises 26–28

Geography A biome is a plant and animal community that covers a large geographical area. The boundaries of a biome are determined primarily by differences in climate. Ecologists and biologists have recognized that plants and animals have special features which make them well-adapted for survival in their particular biomes.

■ Exercise 30

Extension Discuss why the clearance price is not 60% off the original price. Students should recognize that the discount is not found by finding 45% of \$20, but rather 45% of the sale price.

Exercise Answers

29. $\frac{7}{200}$; Because it is easy to divide the numerator and denominator by 2 and then calculate the percent.

30 About \$9.00; The first discount reduced the price to \$17.00, and then it was reduced nearly by half.

31. 67% are not right angles; 2 out of 3 are not, so multiply both parts of the ratio by 33 to get a fraction close to $\frac{66}{100}$.

32. Possible answers: Divide both parts of the ratio by 2; Draw a picture.

33–36. See page C4.

Alternate Assessment

Performance Have students draw 9-by-9 squares on graph paper, estimate different percents of the area, and shade them. Have students explain how they decided how much of the square to shade.

PROBLEM SOLVING

Name ____________________

Guided Problem Solving 10-9

GPS PROBLEM 30, PAGE 557

If a shirt was originally \$20, went on sale for 15% off, and then was put on clearance with an additional 45% off, estimate the clearance price of the shirt. Explain your reasoning.

— Understand — Possible answers: Items 9 and 10

1. What was the original price of the shirt? \$20

2. What was the first discount? 15% The second discount? 45%

— Plan —

3. Is 15% closer to $\frac{1}{10}$, $\frac{2}{10}$, or $\frac{1}{4}$? $\frac{2}{10}$

4. Is 45% closer to $\frac{1}{4}$, $\frac{4}{10}$, or $\frac{1}{2}$? $\frac{1}{2}$

— Solve —

5. Use the fraction in Item 3 to estimate 15% of \$20. \$4

6. Subtract the discount to find the first clearance price. \$16

7. Use the fraction in Item 4 to estimate 45% of the first clearance price. \$8

8. Subtract the discount to find the second clearance price. \$8

9. Explain your reasoning. Estimated the first clearance price, then used that price to estimate the second clearance price.

— Look Back —

10. Do you think your estimated clearance price is higher or lower than the actual clearance price. Explain. Lower than; Estimated fractions are greater than actual percents.

SOLVE ANOTHER PROBLEM

If a jacket was originally \$90, went on sale for 30% off, and then was put on clearance with an additional 15% off, estimate the clearance price of the jacket. Explain your reasoning. Possible answer: \$48

30% of 90 ≈ \$30; 15% of \$60 ≈ \$12; \$60 – \$12 = \$48

ENRICHMENT

Name ____________________

Extend Your Thinking 10-9

Visual Thinking

Circle the letter of the figure that does not belong. Then write the reason why in the blanks at the right.

Possible answers:

Example: Reason:

a. b. c. ⓓ Not a triangle.

1. 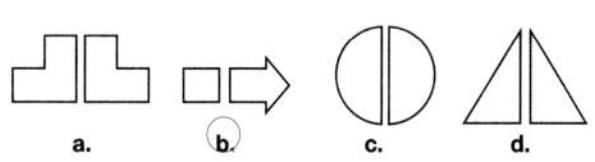

a. ⓑ c. d. Not a reflection.

2. 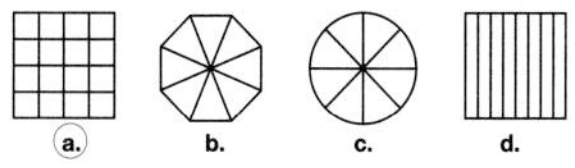

ⓐ b. c. d. Not divided into eighths.

3. 

a. b. ⓒ d. Not divided in half.

4. 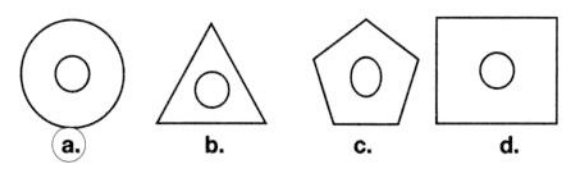

ⓐ b. c. d. Not a circle inside a polygon.

5. 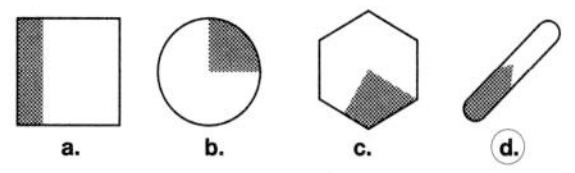

a. b. c. ⓓ Shaded part is not one fourth.

➤ Quick Quiz

Estimate the percent.

1. 33 out of 68
 Possible answer: 50%

2. $\frac{7}{72}$ Possible answer: 10%

3. 5 out of 28
 Possible answer: 20%

Available on Daily Transparency 10-9

10-10 Lesson Organizer

Objectives

- Express percents as fractions and decimals.
- Express fractions and decimals as percents.

Materials

- Explore: 10 x 10 grids, colored pencils (or markers)

NCTM Standards

- 1–4, 7

Review

Fill in the blanks.

1. 5 × ______ = 100 20
2. 25 × ______ = 100 4
3. 20 × ______ = 100 5

Available on Daily Transparency 10-10

1 Introduce

Explore

You may wish to use Teaching Tool Transparency 11: 10 × 10 Grids and Lesson Enhancement Transparency 52 with this lesson.

The Point
Students explore relating fractions, decimals, and percents by coloring in parts of a square to model a percent, decimal, or fraction and by naming some parts in more than one way.

Ongoing Assessment
As students are working, have them explain to each other and to you how they know that the areas shaded represent the percents, decimals, or fractions given.

For Groups That Finish Early
Look at the grids that you colored. Can you describe the number of squares colored using a different name? Try to describe each area in at least one other way.

10-10 Connecting Percents to Fractions and Decimals

You'll Learn ...

- to express percents as fractions and decimals
- to express fractions and decimals as percents

... How It's Used

Travel agents use percents to compare the costs of different travel packages.

▶ **Lesson Link** You've seen that a percent compares a number to 100. Now you'll use this relationship to rewrite percents as fractions and decimals. ◀

Explore Percents as Fractions and Decimals

Grid-dle Me This

Materials: 10 x 10 grids, Colored pencils (or markers)

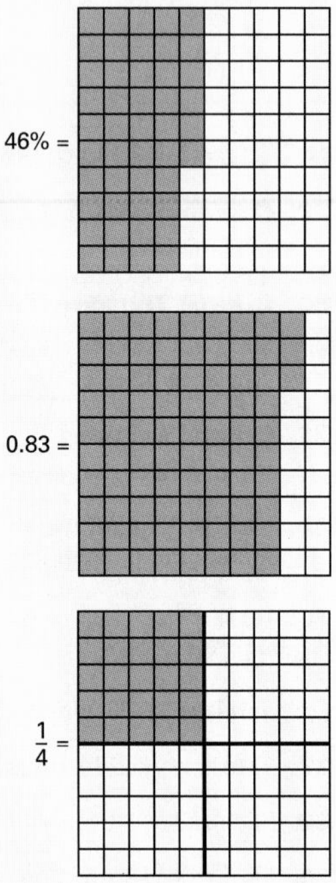

Modeling a Percent

- Color in a number of squares equal to the percent.

1. Model these percents:

a. 21% **b.** 55% **c.** 4% **d.** 75%

Modeling a Decimal

- Color in one column for each tenth.
- Color in one square for each hundredth.

2. Model these decimals:

a. 0.66 **b.** 0.75 **c.** 0.02 **d.** 0.49

Modeling a Fraction

- Divide the grid into groups of equal size. The number of groups should equal the denominator.
- Color in as many groups as the numerator.

3. Model these fractions:

a. $\frac{3}{4}$ **b.** $\frac{3}{5}$ **c.** $\frac{7}{10}$ **d.** $\frac{1}{2}$

4. Rank the 12 values from steps 1–3 from least squares colored to most squares colored.

5. For a given grid, can you describe the number of squares colored using either a percent or a decimal? Explain.

6. For a given grid, can you describe the number of squares colored using either a percent or a fraction? Explain.

MEETING INDIVIDUAL NEEDS

Resources

- 10-10 Practice
- 10-10 Reteaching
- 10-10 Problem Solving
- 10-10 Enrichment
- 10-10 Daily Transparency
  - Problem of the Day
  - Review
  - Quick Quiz
- Teaching Tool Transparency 11
- Lesson Enhancement Transparency 52
- Technology Master 55
- Chapter 10 Project Master

Learning Modalities

Verbal Have students write a procedure for changing a percent to a decimal and to a fraction. They can write the procedure on an index card for easy reference.

Social Have students work in groups of three or four to prepare posters showing percent, decimal, and fraction equivalences.

English Language Development

Some students may have trouble relating the concepts to the forms for fractions, decimals, and percents. To make it easier for them to understand, use pictures linking idea and symbol together.

Learn Connecting Percents to Fractions and Decimals

Fractions, percents, and decimals all describe parts of a whole. To convert a percent into a fraction or decimal, rewrite the percent as a fraction over 100.

Examples

1 Write 53% as a fraction.

$53\% = \frac{53}{100}$

2 Write 91% as a decimal.

$91\% = \frac{91}{100} = 0.91$

If you want to convert a fraction into a percent, you can do so with a proportion.

$\frac{\text{part}}{\text{whole}} = \frac{\text{percent value}}{100}$

Example 3

The White's tree frog is $\frac{5}{8}$ the length of the flying gecko. Rewrite this fraction as a percent.

$\frac{5}{8} = \frac{x}{100}$ Write a proportion using the fraction and 100.

$8x = 500$ Find the cross products.

$x = 500 \div 8$ Use division to undo multiplication.

$x = 62.5$ Divide.

The White's tree frog is 62.5% of the length of the flying gecko.

Try It

Write the following as fractions and decimals:

a. 83% $\frac{83}{100}$; 0.83 **b.** 7% $\frac{7}{100}$; 0.07 **c.** Write $\frac{3}{8}$ as a percent. 37.5%

Remember

If a fraction does not have a power of 10 as a denominator, you can still convert it to a decimal by dividing the numerator by the denominator. **[Page 303]**

▶ Science Link

The flying gecko does not actually fly, but it can glide from tree to tree by spreading its webbed feet apart as much as possible.

A table of common percents and their equivalents is given below.

Percent	10%	20%	25%	30%	$33\frac{1}{3}\%$	40%	50%	60%	$66\frac{2}{3}\%$	70%	75%	80%	90%	100%
Decimal	0.1	0.2	0.25	0.3	$0.\overline{3}$	0.4	0.5	0.6	$0.\overline{6}$	0.7	0.75	0.8	0.9	1.0
Fraction	$\frac{1}{10}$	$\frac{1}{5}$	$\frac{1}{4}$	$\frac{3}{10}$	$\frac{1}{3}$	$\frac{2}{5}$	$\frac{1}{2}$	$\frac{3}{5}$	$\frac{2}{3}$	$\frac{7}{10}$	$\frac{3}{4}$	$\frac{4}{5}$	$\frac{9}{10}$	1

MATH EVERY DAY

▶ Problem of the Day

There are some red, white, and black marbles in a bag. The chances of drawing a red marble are 1 out of 2. The chances of drawing a black marble are 1 out of 3. The chances of drawing a white marble are 1 out of 4. There are 6 white marbles in the bag. How many red marbles are in the bag?

12 red marbles

Available on Daily Transparency 10-10

An Extension is provided in the transparency package.

Fact of the Day

Alaska is America's largest state. Its land area measures 570,374 square miles.

Mental Math

Find each product mentally.

1. 102×3 306
2. 214×2 428
3. 122×4 488

Answers for Explore

1. a. b. c. d.

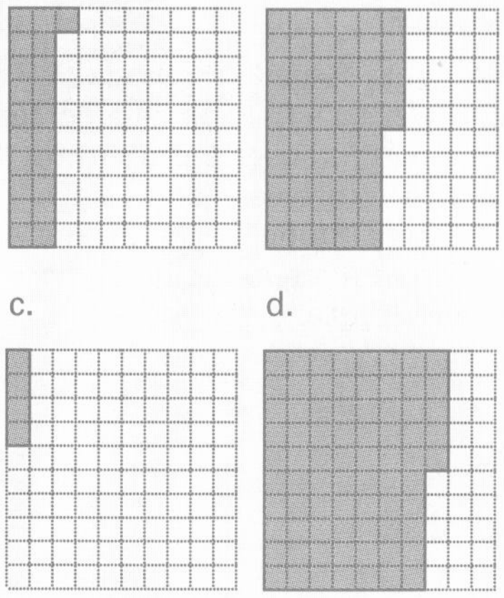

2. a. b. c. d.

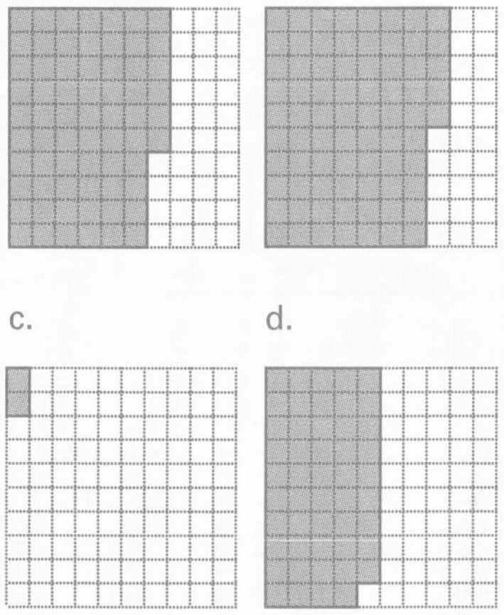

3. a–d. See page C4.
4. 0.02, 4%, 21%, 0.49, $\frac{1}{2}$, 55%, $\frac{3}{5}$, 0.66, $\frac{7}{10}$, and $\frac{3}{4}$ = 0.75 = 75%.
5. Yes; Percents can be converted to decimals and vice versa.
6. Yes; Percents and fractions both can be used to represent parts of a whole.

2 Teach

Learn

Alternate Examples

1. Write 37% as a fraction.

   $37\% = \frac{37}{100}$

2. Write 86% as a decimal.

   $86\% = \frac{86}{100} = 0.86$

3. $\frac{4}{5}$ of the sixth-grade class will attend the play. Rewrite this fraction as a percent.

   $\frac{4}{5} = \frac{x}{100}$

   $5x = 400$

   $x = 400 \div 5$

   $x = 80$

   80% of the sixth-grade class will attend the play.

WHAT DO YOU THINK?

Students see two methods of expressing a fraction as a percent. One method uses a proportion and the other uses equivalent fractions. Students can decide which of the two methods they prefer to use.

Answers for What Do You Think?

1. Answers may vary.
2. Percents are expressed as parts of 100.
3. In order to find an equivalent ratio with 100 in the denominator of the new fraction.

3 Practice and Assess

Check

Answers for Check Your Understanding

1. Possible answer: Converting a percent to a fraction is usually easier because it requires no arithmetic. One simply removes the percent sign and writes the numerical value over 100.
2. Possible answer: The actual numbers may be large and therefore confusing. It is often more informative to summarize with a percent or fraction.

WHAT DO YOU THINK?

Alaska, our largest state, has just $\frac{6}{25}$ the area of the South American rain forest. For their social studies report, Jamar and Susana want to express this fraction as a percent.

Jamar thinks ...

I'll find the value of n in the proportion $\frac{6}{25} = \frac{n}{100}$.

The cross products are equal, so $6 \times 100 = 25n$. This means $600 = 25n$.

I can find n by using division to undo multiplication.

$600 \div 25 = 24$

Alaska is 24% of the size of the South American rain forest.

Susana thinks ...

I'll use equivalent fractions.

Since $25 \times 4 = 100$, I can multiply the numerator and the denominator by 4 to get an equivalent fraction with a denominator of 100.

$$\frac{6}{25} = \frac{6 \times 4}{25 \times 4} = \frac{24}{100}$$

Alaska is 24% of the size of the South American rain forest.

What do you think?

1. Which method do you prefer? Why?
2. Why did Jamar use the proportion $\frac{6}{25} = \frac{n}{100}$?
3. Why did Susana multiply both 6 and 25 by 4?

MEETING MIDDLE SCHOOL CLASSROOM NEEDS

Tips from Middle School Teachers

I find that students have a much easier time with the conversions between fractions, decimals, and percents if they have several benchmark numbers whose equivalent forms are known. For example, students usually understand $\frac{1}{2} = 0.5 = 50\%$. When working with other numbers, they find it helpful to go back to the example they clearly understand.

Team Teaching

Inform the science teacher that your classes are studying percents, decimals, and fractions. Suggest that students be encouraged to use the most convenient form when working with percents in science class.

Geography Connection

In 1950, rain forests covered about 12% of the Earth's land. Today, nearly half have been cut. About 75 acres of rain forest are destroyed every minute, meaning that between 32,500,000 and 37,500,000 acres are destroyed every year. Half of the remaining rain forests may be gone by the year 2000.

Check Your Understanding

1. Which is easier, converting a fraction to a percent or converting a percent to a fraction? Explain.
2. Newspaper articles sometimes express relationships as percents and sometimes as fractions. Why?

10-10 Exercises and Applications

Practice and Apply

Getting Started Convert to a decimal.

1. 37% 0.37 **2.** 87.2% 0.872 **3.** 100% 1.0 **4.** 3% 0.03 **5.** 10% 0.1 **6.** 112% 1.12
7. 234% 2.34 **8.** 678% 6.78 **9.** 67.3% 0.673 **10.** 5% 0.05 **11.** 88.87% 0.8887 **12.** 13.8% 0.138

Convert to a fraction in lowest terms.

13. 56% $\frac{14}{25}$ **14.** 15% $\frac{3}{20}$ **15.** 75% $\frac{3}{4}$ **16.** 66% $\frac{33}{50}$ **17.** 150% $1\frac{1}{2}$ **18.** 125% $1\frac{1}{4}$
19. 89% $\frac{89}{100}$ **20.** 136% $1\frac{9}{25}$ **21.** 90% $\frac{9}{10}$ **22.** 43% $\frac{43}{100}$ **23.** 234% $2\frac{17}{50}$ **24.** 78% $\frac{39}{50}$

Convert to a percent.

25. 0.84 84% **26.** 0.95 95% **27.** 0.04 4% **28.** 0.9 90% **29.** $\frac{55}{50}$ 110% **30.** $\frac{14}{200}$ 7%
31. $\frac{17}{20}$ 85% **32.** $\frac{39}{100}$ 39% **33.** 0.53 53% **34.** $\frac{4}{5}$ 80% **35.** $\frac{3}{10}$ 30% **36.** 0.453 45.3%
37. 0.56 56% **38.** 0.32 32% **39.** $\frac{12}{25}$ 48% **40.** $\frac{98}{100}$ 98% **41.** 0.75 75% **42.** 0.23 23%
43. 0.675 67.5% **44.** $\frac{5}{100}$ 5% **45.** 0.333 33.3% **46.** $\frac{3}{5}$ 60% **47.** $\frac{76}{200}$ 38% **48.** 0.01 1%

Give the shaded part of each figure as a percent, fraction, and decimal.

49.
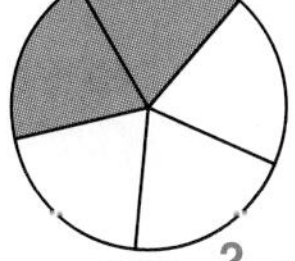
40%, $\frac{2}{5}$, 0.4

50.
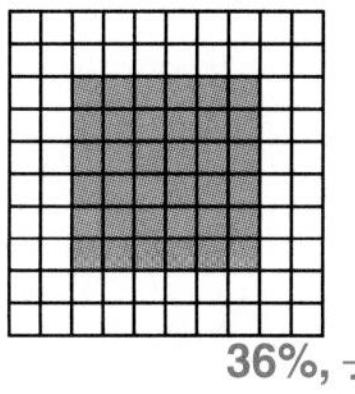
36%, $\frac{36}{100}$, 0.36

51.
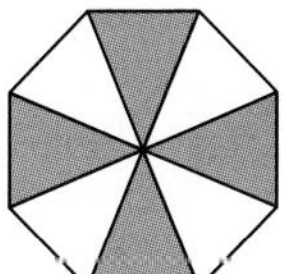
50%, $\frac{4}{8}$, 0.5

52.
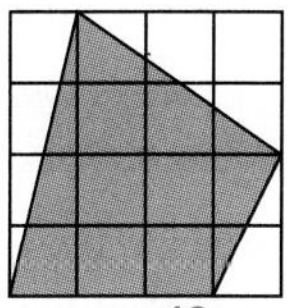
62.5%, $\frac{10}{16}$, 0.625

53. Two-thirds of the students at the Liberty Academy use the bus on the weekends. Convert this value to a percent. $66.\overline{6}\%$

PRACTICE 10-10

10-10 Exercises and Applications

Assignment Guide

- **Basic** 1–41 odds, 49–51, 55, 57, 61–71 odds
- **Average** 1–35 odds, 49–53, 55–77 odds
- **Enriched** 10–54 evens, 55, 57–60, 62–76 evens

Exercise Notes

Exercises 13–48

Error Prevention If students have difficulty with these exercises, suggest that they review the conversions from fractions to decimals to percents, and vice versa.

PRACTICE

Name ______________________

Practice 10-10

Converting Percents to Fractions and Decimals

Convert to a fraction in lowest terms.

1. 80% $\frac{4}{5}$ 2. 25% $\frac{1}{4}$ 3. 78% $\frac{39}{50}$ 4. 98% $\frac{49}{50}$
5. 32% $\frac{8}{25}$ 6. 30% $\frac{3}{10}$ 7. 45% $\frac{9}{20}$ 8. 118% $\frac{59}{50}$
9. 65% $\frac{13}{20}$ 10. 185% $\frac{37}{20}$ 11. 63% $\frac{63}{100}$ 12. 28% $\frac{7}{25}$
13. 275% $\frac{11}{4}$ 14. 84% $\frac{21}{25}$ 15. 104% $\frac{26}{25}$ 16. 18% $\frac{9}{50}$

Convert to a percent.

17. $\frac{7}{10}$ 70% 18. $\frac{37}{50}$ 74% 19. $\frac{1}{2}$ 50% 20. $\frac{18}{25}$ 72%
21. 0.41 41% 22. 0.03 3% 23. 0.74 74% 24. 0.92 92%
25. $\frac{123}{300}$ 41% 26. $\frac{15}{20}$ 75% 27. $\frac{31}{20}$ 155% 28. $\frac{1}{10}$ 10%
29. 0.67 67% 30. 4.10 410% 31. 0.8 80% 32. 0.137 13.7%

Give the shaded part of each figure as a percent, fraction, and decimal.

33.
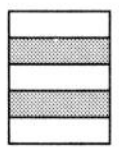
percent: 40% fraction: $\frac{2}{5}$ decimal: 0.4

34.
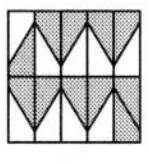
percent: 55% fraction: $\frac{11}{20}$ decimal: 0.55

35.

percent: 60% fraction: $\frac{3}{5}$ decimal: 0.6

36.
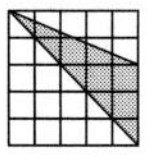
percent: 30% fraction: $\frac{3}{10}$ decimal: 0.3

37. In 1993, about $\frac{1}{50}$ of American children lived with relatives other than their parents. Convert this value to a percent. 2%

38. In 1950, $\frac{2}{25}$ of the American population was at least 65 years old. What percent is this? 8%

RETEACHING

Name ______________________

Alternative Lesson 10-10

Connecting Percents to Fractions and Decimals

Fractions, percents, and decimals all describe parts of a whole. To convert a percent into a fraction or decimal, rewrite the percent as a fraction over 100.

You can use a proportion to convert a fraction into a percent. $\frac{\text{part}}{\text{whole}} = \frac{\text{percent value}}{100}$

Example 1

Convert 15% to a fraction in lowest terms and to a decimal.

	To convert to a fraction.	To convert to a decimal.
Write the percent as a fraction with a denominator of 100.	$15\% = \frac{15}{100}$	$15\% = \frac{15}{100}$
Then rewrite in requested form.	$= \frac{15 \div 5}{100 \div 5} = \frac{3}{20}$	$= 0.15$

So, $15\% = \frac{3}{20} = 0.15$.

Try It Convert to a fraction in lowest terms and to a decimal.

a. $67\% = \frac{67}{100} = \frac{67}{100} = 0.67$ b. $48\% = \frac{48}{100} = \frac{12}{25} = 0.48$
c. $82\% = \frac{82}{100} = \frac{41}{50} = 0.82$ d. $35\% = \frac{35}{100} = \frac{7}{20} = 0.35$

Example 2

Convert $\frac{1}{3}$ to a percent.

Write a proportion using the fraction and 100. $\frac{\text{part}}{\text{whole}} \begin{matrix}\to 1\\ \to 3\end{matrix} = \begin{matrix}x \leftarrow\\ 100 \leftarrow\end{matrix} \frac{\text{percent value}}{100}$

Find the cross products. $100 = 3x$

Use division to undo multiplication. $100 \div 3 = x$

Divide. Solve for x. $33\frac{1}{3} = x$

So, $\frac{1}{3} = 33\frac{1}{3}\%$.

Try It Convert to a percent.

e. Write a proportion. $\frac{4}{5} = \frac{x}{100}$ f. Find the cross products. $5x = 400$
g. Write $\frac{4}{5}$ as a percent. 80% h. $\frac{12}{100} =$ 12%
i. $\frac{30}{50} =$ 60% j. $\frac{26}{40} =$ 65%

Reteaching

Activity

Materials: 10 × 10 grids

- Using a separate 10 × 10 grid for each, shade $\frac{1}{2}$, 40%, 50%, $\frac{2}{5}$, 0.40, and 0.50.
- Identify the squares that show the same amount of shading.
- Which values are equal?
  $\frac{1}{2} = 0.50 = 50\%$
  $\frac{2}{5} = 0.40 = 40\%$

Exercise Notes

■ Exercise 54

Health Only 5,000 of the 250,000 species of plants in the rain forests have been studied for medicinal purposes.

■ Exercise 55

Test Prep If students selected A, they failed to realize that the denominator of the fraction was 50, not 100.

Project Progress

You may want to have students use Chapter 10 Project Master.

Exercise Answers

59. If a decimal is less than 0.1, it is less than 10%; If a decimal is greater than 1.0, it is greater than 100%.

60. Answers may vary.

61.

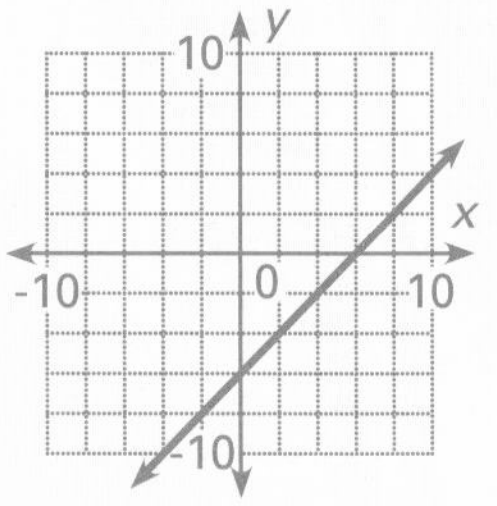

62.

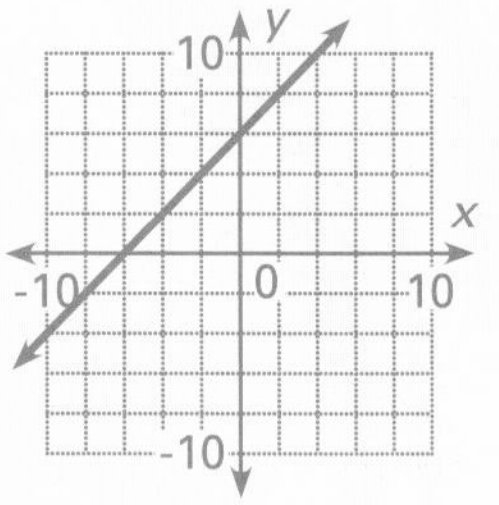

63–65. See page C4.

Alternate Assessment

Self Assessment Have students describe what they feel is most difficult about converting between decimals, fractions, and percents.

▶ Quick Quiz

Convert to a decimal and a fraction.

1. 60% 0.60, $\frac{3}{5}$

Convert to a percent.

2. $\frac{45}{50}$ 90%
3. 0.33 33%

Available on Daily Transparency 10-10

PROBLEM SOLVING 10-10

54. Health 25% of all medicines in use today come from plant sources, many of which are found in rain forests. Convert this value to a decimal. 0.25

55. **Test Prep** Which of the following is equal to $\frac{23}{50}$? C

Ⓐ 23% Ⓑ 50% Ⓒ 46% Ⓓ 217%

56. Number Sense Chandra has $\frac{1}{3}$ of the marbles, and Liu has 30%. Who has more? Can you tell how many each person has? Chandra; No

Problem Solving and Reasoning

57. Critical Thinking 45% of the students at Suburban High School are boys. 30% of the boys at Suburban High School have curly hair. What fraction of the students at Suburban High School are boys with curly hair? $\frac{27}{200}$

58. Critical Thinking Fanny's Fashion Center is advertising a sale. Everything is $\frac{1}{5}$ off. What percent of full price should you expect to pay? 80%

59. Communicate How can you determine without converting to a percent if a decimal is less than 10%? Greater than 100%?

60. Journal In what situations would it be easier to work with fractions? With decimals? With percents? Explain.

Mixed Review

Graph each equation. *[Lesson 9-7]*

61. $y = x - 6$ **62.** $y = 6 + x$ **63.** $y = 8x$ **64.** $y = -2x$ **65.** $y = -5 + x$

Name an equivalent fraction. *[Lesson 5-4]* Possible answers:

66. $\frac{5}{6}$ $\frac{10}{12}$ **67.** $\frac{14}{20}$ $\frac{7}{10}$ **68.** $\frac{10}{32}$ $\frac{5}{16}$ **69.** $\frac{19}{50}$ $\frac{38}{100}$ **70.** $\frac{2}{7}$ $\frac{4}{14}$ **71.** $\frac{6}{10}$ $\frac{3}{5}$

72. $\frac{7}{29}$ $\frac{21}{87}$ **73.** $\frac{6}{24}$ $\frac{1}{4}$ **74.** $\frac{12}{96}$ $\frac{6}{48}$ **75.** $\frac{50}{75}$ $\frac{2}{3}$ **76.** $\frac{150}{200}$ $\frac{15}{20}$ **77.** $\frac{10}{80}$ $\frac{1}{8}$

Project Progress

For each ratio you have written so far, express the ratio as a percent and also as a decimal. Explain how you can use proportions to do this.

Problem Solving
Understand
Plan
Solve
Look Back

PROBLEM SOLVING

Name ______________

Guided Problem Solving 10-10

GPS PROBLEM 57, PAGE 562

45% of the students at Suburban High School are boys. 30% of the boys at Suburban High School have curly hair. What fraction of the students at Suburban High School are boys with curly hair?

— Understand —

1. What percent of the students at Suburban High are boys? 45%
2. What percent of the boys at Suburban High have curly hair? 30%
3. Are you going to write your answer as a percent, a decimal, or a fraction? A fraction.

— Plan —

4. Suppose you were given the number of boys at Suburban High. How would you find how many boys have curly hair? Multiply the number of boys by the fraction of boys with curly hair.
5. You know the fraction of boys in the school rather than the number of boys. Which operation will you use to find what fraction of students are boys with curly hair? Multiplication.
6. Write the number of students that are boys as a fraction. Then rewrite the fraction in lowest terms. $\frac{45}{100}$; $\frac{9}{20}$
7. Write the number of boys that have curly hair as a fraction. Then rewrite the fraction in lowest terms. $\frac{30}{100}$; $\frac{3}{10}$

— Solve —

8. Write an expression to find the fraction of students that are boys with curly hair. $\frac{9}{20} \times \frac{3}{10}$
9. What fraction of the students at Suburban High are boys with curly hair? $\frac{27}{200}$

— Look Back —

10. Show how to estimate to see if your answer is reasonable. 45% is about $\frac{1}{2}$; 30% is about $\frac{1}{4}$; $\frac{1}{2} \times \frac{1}{4} = \frac{1}{8}$; $\frac{1}{8} = \frac{25}{200}$ which is about $\frac{27}{200}$.

SOLVE ANOTHER PROBLEM

20% of the houses on the block are white. 65% of the white houses have blue trim. What fraction of these houses are white with blue trim? $\frac{13}{100}$

ENRICHMENT

Name ______________

Extend Your Thinking 10-10

Patterns in Numbers

Write each percent as a decimal.

1. 45% 0.45 2. 91% 0.91 3. 88% 0.88
4. 8% 0.08 5. 27% 0.27 6. 100% 1.00

7. Compare the digits in the percent and the decimal. How are they alike?
Possible answer: Digits are the same.

8. What pattern do you see in the placement of the decimal point when writing the percent as a decimal?
Possible answer: The decimal point moves two places to the left.

9. Use the pattern to write each percent as a decimal.
a. 56% 0.56 b. 70% 0.7 or 0.70 c. 42% 0.42
d. 13% 0.13 e. 3% 0.03 f. 29% 0.29

Write each decimal as a percent.

10. 0.9 90% 11. 0.68 68% 12. 0.24 24%
13. 0.67 67% 14. 0.07 7% 15. 0.71 71%

16. What pattern do you see in the placement of the decimal point when writing the decimal as a percent?
Possible answer: The digits stay the same and the decimal point moves two places to the right.

17. Use the pattern to write each percent as a decimal.
a. 0.55 55% b. 0.04 4% c. 0.36 36%
d. 0.82 82% e. 0.5 50% f. 0.251 25.1%

Finding a Percent of a Number

10-11

▶ Lesson Link You've learned to find percents by working with fractions. Now you'll work with percents by using decimals. ◀

You'll Learn ...

- to find a percent of a number
- to find a whole when given a percent and a part

... How It's Used

Community pool managers estimate percents to determine the right amount of chlorine to add to a pool.

Explore Finding Percents

What's for Sale?

Donna's Discount World is having a sale.

Item	Regular Price	Discount
Blouse	$30	20% off
Jeans	$50	1/3 off
Belt	$15	10% off
Skirt	$40	1/4 off
Dress	$60	2/3 off
Jacket	$80	25% off
Shoes	$70	1/2 off

1. Estimate the amount discounted from each item.
2. Estimate the sale price of each item.
3. Rank the items from least expensive to most expensive both before and after discount. Are both rankings the same? Explain.
4. Why might a store manager want to represent a discount as a percent? Why might he or she want to represent it as a fraction?

Learn Finding a Percent of a Number

Recall that you can use proportions to convert fractions into percents. You can also use proportions when looking for a percent of a whole number.

$$\frac{\text{part}}{\text{whole}} = \frac{\text{percent value}}{100}$$

MEETING INDIVIDUAL NEEDS

Resources
10-11 Practice
10-11 Reteaching
10-11 Problem Solving
10-11 Enrichment
10-11 Daily Transparency: Problem of the Day; Review; Quick Quiz
Teaching Tool Transparency 23
Technology Master 56

Learning Modalities

Visual Have students draw 20 small circles. Have them shade 10%, 20%, 50%, and 70% of the circles.

Kinesthetic Have students use a geoboard to show different percents of the total area of the geoboard by ringing the part with a rubber band.

Challenge

Have students develop a questionnaire and conduct a survey to see which sports are most popular at different grade levels. Have them represent the results as percents of the total number of students surveyed at each grade and the total number of students surveyed in all. Have them draw conclusions from the results.

10-11 Lesson Organizer

Objectives

- Find a percent of a number.
- Find a whole when given a percent and a part.

NCTM Standards

- 1–4, 7

▶ Review

Find:

1. $\frac{1}{3}$ of 30 10
2. $\frac{1}{4}$ of 60 15
3. $\frac{2}{5}$ of 40 16

Available on Daily Transparency 10-11

1 Introduce

Explore

You may wish to use Teaching Tool Transparency 23: Scientific Calculator with this lesson.

The Point

Students explore finding percents by estimating amounts of discount when the rates are expressed both as percents and as fractions.

Ongoing Assessment

Encourage students to keep their findings well organized so as to not confuse the amount of discount with the sale price. Check to see that students are determining whether or not their estimates are reasonable.

For Groups That Finish Early

Which is the best buy? Does saving the largest amount of money make it the best buy?

Answers for Explore on next page.

Answers for Explore

1. Estimated discounts: Blouse: \$6; Jeans: \$17; Belt: \$1.50; Skirt: \$10; Dress: \$40; Jacket: \$20; Shoes: \$35.
2. Estimated sale prices: Blouse: \$24; Jeans: \$33; Belt: \$13.50; Skirt: \$30; Dress: \$20; Jacket: \$60; Shoes: \$35.
3. Before: Belt, Blouse, Skirt, Jeans, Dress, Shoes, Jacket; After: Belt, Dress, Blouse, Skirt, Jeans, Shoes, Jacket; No; The rankings are different because of the various discounts.
4. Possible answer: Managers want a sale to look and sound really good. In some situations, a percent sounds better but sometimes fractions sound better. For example: "This product has been marked down by 30%" or "We are selling this product at one-third its original cost for a limited time."

2 Teach

Learn

Alternate Examples

1. Find 27% of 38.

   Estimate: $\frac{1}{4} \times 40 = 10$

   $\frac{x}{38} = \frac{27}{100}$

   $100x = 1026$

   $x = 1026 \div 100$

   $x = 10.26$

   10.26 is close to the estimate of 10, so the answer is reasonable.

2. In the United States, 55% of all Americans live and work in counties along the oceans or Great Lakes. How many of the approximately 250 million people live and work in coastal counties?

   55% of 250 = ?

   55% of 250 = 0.55×250

   = 137.5

   137.5 million people live and work in coastal counties.

Language Link

Recall that the word *of* often means multiplication.

History Link

Ynez Mexia, a self-taught plant collector, documented several thousand plant species from North and South America. In one two-year trip, she collected over 65,000 plant specimens from the Amazon rain forest.

HINT

Some calculators have a [%] key that will change the percent into a decimal. You can find 70% of 3000 by entering 70 [%] [×] 3000 [=].

Example 1

Find 53% of 62.

Estimate: $\frac{1}{2} \times 60 = 30$ — 53% is slightly more than $\frac{1}{2}$, and 62 is close to 60.

part → $\frac{x}{62} = \frac{53}{100}$ ← percent value
whole → ← 100 — Write a proportion.

$100x = 3286$ — Find the cross products.

$x = 3286 \div 100$ — Use division to undo multiplication.

$x = 32.86$ — Divide.

32.86 is close to the estimate of 30, so the answer is reasonable.

You can also convert the percent to a decimal and multiply.

Example 2

Pharmacologists have identified about 3000 types of plants that have cancer-fighting properties. 70% of them grow in the rain forest. How many types of cancer-fighting plants grow in the rain forest?

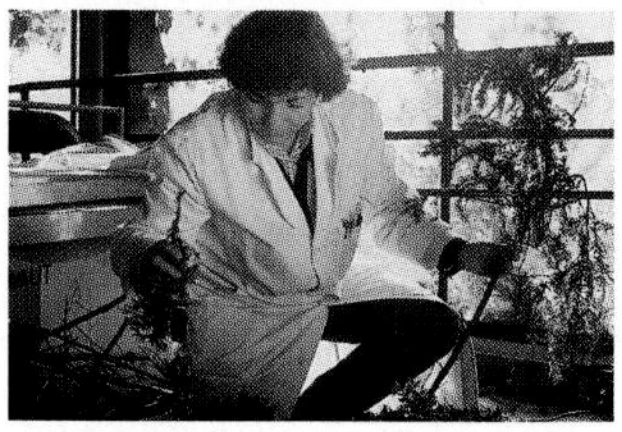

70% of 3000 = ?

70% of 3000 = 0.70×3000 — Rewrite the percent as a decimal.

= 2100 — Multiply.

2100 types of cancer-fighting plants grow in the rain forest.

Try It

a. 65% of the 940 students at Tyler Academy have attended at least one other school. How many students have attended more than one school? 611

b. Winston scored about 83% on a 160-point test. About how many points did he receive credit for? 133

MATH EVERY DAY

Problem of the Day

The Republic of Rwanda has an area about equal to 28% of the size of the state of Indiana. Indiana has an area of about 36,300 square miles. What is the area of Rwanda? Is this more than or less than $\frac{1}{4}$ the size of Indiana?

About 10,164 square miles; slightly more than $\frac{1}{4}$ the size of Indiana

Available on Daily Transparency 10-11

Fact of the Day

The Yukon Territory in Canada covers 186,661 square miles of land.

Estimation

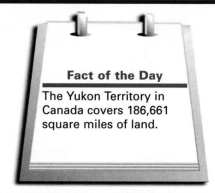

Estimate each product.

1. 3146×3 9000
2. 1798×4 8000
3. 2851×2 6000

In some situations, you know the percent and the value of the percent, but you need to determine how big the "whole" is. You can also solve these problems using a proportion.

Example 3

The sales tax in Pennsylvania is 6%. Reuben had to pay $9 in sales tax on his purchase of a glockenspiel at Pennsylvania Percussion. Find the cost of the glockenspiel.

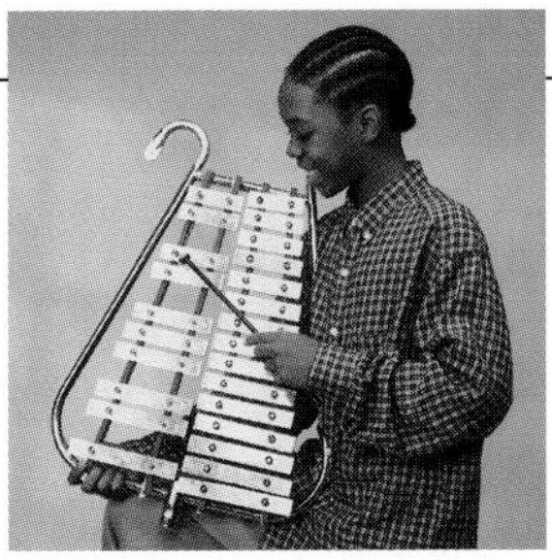

Let x represent the cost of the glockenspiel.

part → **whole** → $\frac{9}{x} = \frac{6}{100}$ ← **percent value** ← **100** Write a proportion.

$6x = 900$ Find the cross products.

$x = 900 \div 6$ Use division to undo multiplication.

$x = 150$ Divide.

The glockenspiel cost $150.

Try It

a. 28 is 40% of what number? 70

b. According to the Yukon Tourism Board in Canada, there are about 30,000 people in the Yukon Territory. That's 60% of the number of moose in the territory. How many moose are there in the Yukon? 50,000

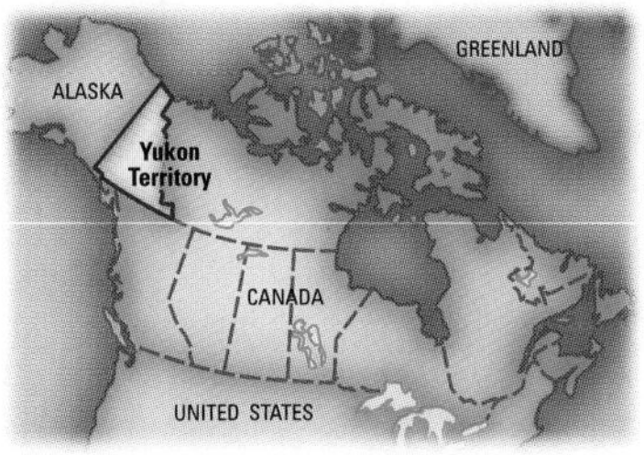

DID YOU KNOW?

Any instrument that creates sound by hitting one object with another is known as a percussion instrument.

▶ Science Link

The male moose sheds his antlers every winter and grows new ones in the spring.

Check Your Understanding

1. What happens to a percent of a whole when the whole increases?

2. Give an example of a percent you might want to find outside of the classroom. Use the word *of* in your example to indicate multiplication.

Alternate Examples

3. Jack saved $10 on a jacket. The discount was 25%. What was the original price of the jacket?

   Let x represent the original price of the jacket.

   $\frac{10}{x} = \frac{25}{100}$

   $25x = 1000$

   $x = 40$

   The original price of the jacket was $40.

3 Practice and Assess

Check

Answers for Check Your Understanding

1. The part increases proportionally.
2. Possible answer: Percent of allowance saved.

MEETING MIDDLE SCHOOL CLASSROOM NEEDS

Tips from Middle School Teachers

I find that the newspaper is an excellent source of problems and activities that can be used to teach percents. I give students calculators and department-store advertisements and have them work in small groups to find the best buys for popular items such as jeans or athletic shoes.

Cooperative Learning

Have students work in groups of three. Give each group a set of problems like the following:

1. Find 20% of 65.
2. 20% of what is 13.
3. What percent of 65 is 13?

Have each student in the group solve one of the problems. Students can then share their solutions and see the relationship among these problems.

Science Connection

Scientists have studied less than 1% of the plants living in the rain forests to see if they can be used as medicines. Today, $\frac{1}{4}$ of our prescription drugs are from rain forest plants. Quinine, a drug used in treating malaria, is from the bark of a rain forest tree.

Assignment Guide

- Basic
  1–12, 26–38 evens, 42, 45–67 odds
- Average
  1–16, 25–31 odds, 33–38, 41–42, 51–67 odds
- Enriched
  20–36, 39–44, 46–68 evens

Exercise Notes

Exercise 34

Consumer In most states, sales tax, a certain percentage of a sale, is levied on the sale of goods and services. Alaska, Delaware, Montana, New Hampshire, and Oregon have no state-wide sales and use taxes.

Exercise 36

Test Prep If students selected B, they did not remember to change 52% into a decimal. Remind them to check their work.

Exercise Answers

34. Dog: \$0.43, \$8.58; Bone: \$0.16, \$3.16; Pillow: \$0.22, \$4.47; Bowl: \$0.29, \$5.79.

Reteaching

Activity

Materials: 10 × 10 grids, colored pencils

- On a 10 × 10 grid, color 50 squares.
- Using a darker color, color 20% of the 50 squares.
- How many squares did you color? 10 squares
- On another 10 × 10 grid, color 40 squares.
- Using a darker color, color 60% of the 40 squares.
- How many squares did you color? 24 squares

10-11 Exercises and Applications

PRACTICE 10-11

Practice and Apply

Getting Started Simplify.

1. 50% of 100 50 **2.** 25% of 100 25 **3.** 20% of 10 2 **4.** 62% of 1000 620

Simplify. Round your answer to the nearest hundredths.

5. 34% of 65 22.1 **6.** 68% of 63.2 42.98 **7.** 22% of 84 18.48 **8.** 25% of 64 16

9. 99% of 106 104.94 **10.** 140% of 50 70 **11.** 100% of 54.3 54.3 **12.** 9% of 525 47.25

13. 33% of 68 22.44 **14.** 19% of 2.34 0.44 **15.** 2% of 18.8 0.38 **16.** 83% of 34 28.22

17. 76% of 20 15.2 **18.** 50% of 66 33 **19.** 25% of \$10.99 \$2.75 **20.** 15% of \$20.13 \$3.02

21. 13.6% of 45 6.12 **22.** 4.5% of \$12.02 \$.54 **23.** 37% of 23 8.51 **24.** 6% of 294 17.64

Find the total amount.

25. 30% of □ is 75 250 **26.** 45% of □ is 90 200 **27.** 4.3% of □ is 8.6 200 **28.** 90% of □ is 63 70

29. 7% of □ is 6.16 88 **30.** 22% of □ is 0.22 1 **31.** 7.5% of □ is 13.2 176 **32.** 115% of □ is \$69 60

33. A test has 24 multiple choice questions. How many do you need to answer correctly to score at least 80%? 20 or more

34. **Consumer** The sales tax on the items shown is 5.25%. For each item, find the sales tax amount and the total price.

35. Shalini earned \$34,000 in 1997. If her 1998 income was 108% of her 1997 income, how much did she earn in 1998? \$36,720

36. **Test Prep** Find 52% of 780. C

Ⓐ 390 Ⓑ 40,560

Ⓒ 405.6 Ⓓ 520

37. Of the estimated 300 species of hummingbirds, 83% can be found in rain forests. About how many species can be found in rain forests? 249

38. **Industry** Argentina produced 11,100 passenger cars in 1991 and 21,000 in 1992. What percent of the number of 1992 cars was the number of 1991 cars?. ≈ 52.9%

PRACTICE

Name ______________________

Practice 10-11

Finding a Percent of a Whole Number

Simplify. Round your answer to the nearest hundredth.

1. 28% of 11 3.08 2. 44% of 46 20.24 3. 66% of 21 13.86
4. 95% of 49 46.55 5. 12% of 8 0.96 6. 14% of 37 5.18
7. 29% of \$16.50 \$4.79 8. 1% of 32 0.32 9. 15% of 60 9
10. 42% of 4 1.68 11. 17% of 2.89 0.49 12. 39% of 83.75 32.66
13. 11% of 18 1.98 14. 3% of 15 0.45 15. 24% of 100 24
16. 20% of 7.63 1.53 17. 19% of \$21.95 \$4.17 18. 6% of 53 3.18
19. 36% of 21 7.56 20. 30% of 69 20.7 21. 35% of 35 12.25
22. 61% of 41 25.01 23. 7% of 12.8 0.90 24. 68% of 84 57.12
25. 9% of 64.88 5.84 26. 56% of 98 54.88 27. 73% of 79 57.67

Find the total amount.

28. 24% of 160 is 38.4 29. 30% of 48 is 14.4 30. 16% of 325 is 52
31. 79% of 510 is 402.9 32. 41% of 60 is 24.6 33. 38% of 300 is 114
34. 5% of 285 is 14.25 35. 84% of \$89 is \$74.76 36. 62% of 1250 is 775
37. 55% of 74 is 40.7 38. 25% of 84 is 21 39. 12% of 86 is 10.32
40. 36% of 175 is 63 41. 8% of 120 is 9.6 42. 68% of \$25 is \$17
43. 65% of 216 is 140.4 44. 32% of 37.5 is 12 45. 88% of 150 is 132

46. **Consumer** Molly bought a video game that was priced at \$24.95. She had to pay 6.5% sales tax. Find the sales tax amount and the total price.

tax: \$1.62 total: \$26.57

47. The population of Chula Vista, California increased from 83,927 in 1980 to 135,163 in 1990. Find the percent increase. About 61%

RETEACHING

Name ______________________

Alternative Lesson 10-11

Finding a Percent of a Number

You can use a proportion to find a percent of a whole number or you can convert the percent to a decimal and multiply. $\frac{\text{part}}{\text{whole}} = \frac{\text{percent value}}{100}$

Example 1

Simplify 22% of 83.

Write a proportion. $\frac{\text{part}}{\text{whole}} \begin{matrix}\rightarrow \\ \rightarrow\end{matrix} \frac{x}{83} = \frac{22}{100} \begin{matrix}\leftarrow \\ \leftarrow\end{matrix} \frac{\text{percent value}}{100}$

Find the cross products. $100x = 1826$

Use division to undo multiplication. $x = 1826 \div 100$

Divide. Solve for *x*. $x = 18.26$

So, 22% of 83 is 18.26.

Try It Simplify 70% of 35.

a. Write 70% as a decimal. 0.7 b. Multiply the decimal and 35. 24.5

Simplify.

c. 55% of 55 30.25 d. 84% of 75 = 63 e. 18% of 9 1.62
f. 26% of 45 11.7 g. 63% of 150 = 94.5 h. 99% of 350 346.5

Example 2

Find the total amount. 25% of □ is 98.

Write a proportion using the fraction and 100. $\frac{\text{part}}{\text{whole}} \begin{matrix}\rightarrow \\ \rightarrow\end{matrix} \frac{98}{x} = \frac{25}{100} \begin{matrix}\leftarrow \\ \leftarrow\end{matrix} \frac{\text{percent value}}{100}$

Find the cross products. $9800 = 25x$

Use division to undo multiplication. $9800 \div 25 = 25x \div 25$

Divide. Solve for *x*. $392 = x$

So, 98 is 25% of 392.

Try It Find the total amount. 16% of □ is 12.

i. Write a proportion. $\frac{12}{x} = \frac{16}{100}$ j. Find cross products. 1200 = 16*x*

k. 46% of what number is 14? 75

l. 80% of □ is 8 10 m. 65% of □ is 13 20 n. 4% of □ is 18 450
o. 24% of □ is 6 25 p. 60% of □ is 54 90 q. 12% of □ is 66 550

39. Geography At the beginning of 1994, Ethiopia had a population of 55,200,000. If the population was growing at a rate of 3% per year, how much did the population increase that year? By 1,656,000

40. Chance Gloria plays a game 100 times, and her chances of winning are 60%. Esmerelda plays the same game 50 times, and her chances of winning are 49%. Who will win more games?
Probably Gloria

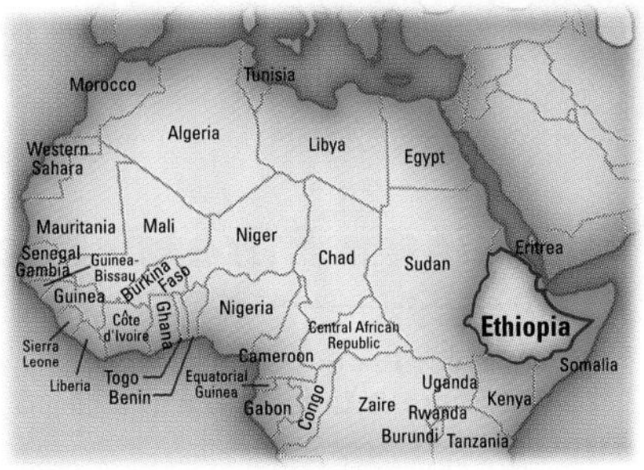

PROBLEM SOLVING 10-11

Problem Solving and Reasoning

41. Critical Thinking Penelope explained how she calculated a 5% discount for a $22 meal. "First, I moved the decimal point over one place, and got $2.20. Then, I took half of that, which was $1.10. The meal is $22 minus $1.10, or $20.90." Do you agree with her answer? Will her method always work? Explain.

42. Choose a Strategy A new student's score on a spelling test was about 72% of Catherine's score. Catherine's score was about 98% of Tom's score. Tom's score was about 94% of Luanna's score. Luanna got 93 out of 100 points. How many points did the new student get?

GPS

43. Critical Thinking Hank bought some stock at $15 per share and later sold it at $30 per share. He told Robin his stock had gone up by 100%. Robin said he sold it for 200% of the original price. Who was right?
They're both correct.

44. Communicate If you know the percent and the part, and you want to know the whole, explain how you can use division instead of proportions.
About 62 points

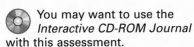

Problem Solving STRATEGIES

- Look for a Pattern
- Make an Organized List
- Make a Table
- Guess and Check
- Work Backward
- Use Logical Reasoning
- Draw a Diagram
- Solve a Simpler Problem

Mixed Review

Write in lowest terms. *[Lesson 5-5]*

45. $\frac{7}{14}$ $\frac{1}{2}$ **46.** $\frac{5}{25}$ $\frac{1}{5}$ **47.** $\frac{20}{30}$ $\frac{2}{3}$ **48.** $\frac{6}{18}$ $\frac{1}{3}$ **49.** $\frac{12}{36}$ $\frac{1}{3}$ **50.** $\frac{8}{10}$ $\frac{4}{5}$

51. $\frac{6}{8}$ $\frac{3}{4}$ **52.** $\frac{9}{15}$ $\frac{3}{5}$ **53.** $\frac{3}{21}$ $\frac{1}{7}$ **54.** $\frac{4}{24}$ $\frac{1}{6}$ **55.** $\frac{21}{35}$ $\frac{3}{5}$ **56.** $\frac{6}{9}$ $\frac{2}{3}$

Write each as an improper fraction or mixed number. *[Lesson 5-6]*

57. $6\frac{4}{5}$ $\frac{34}{5}$ **58.** $\frac{6}{5}$ $1\frac{1}{5}$ **59.** $2\frac{8}{9}$ $\frac{26}{9}$ **60.** $\frac{10}{3}$ $3\frac{1}{3}$ **61.** $5\frac{1}{7}$ $\frac{36}{7}$ **62.** $\frac{16}{7}$ $2\frac{2}{7}$

63. $\frac{21}{2}$ $10\frac{1}{2}$ **64.** $11\frac{3}{4}$ $\frac{47}{4}$ **65.** $3\frac{1}{2}$ $\frac{7}{2}$ **66.** $\frac{65}{8}$ $8\frac{1}{8}$ **67.** $\frac{14}{5}$ $2\frac{4}{5}$ **68.** $9\frac{11}{12}$ $\frac{119}{12}$

PROBLEM SOLVING

Name ______________________

Guided Problem Solving 10-11

GPS PROBLEM 42, PAGE 567

A new student's score on a spelling test was about 72% of Catherine's score. Catherine's score was about 98% of Tom's score. Tom's score was about 94% of Luanna's score. Luanna got 93 out of 100 points. How many points did the new student get? Possible answer: Item 4

— Understand —

1. How many points did Luanna score on the spelling test? 93 points.
2. Underline how each student's score relates to another student's score such as, 72% of Catherine's.

— Plan —

3. Which strategy will you use to find the new student's score? c
   a. Look for a Pattern b. Draw a Diagram c. Work Backward
4. What operation do you use to find a percent of a number? Multiplication.
5. There are no fractional points given for partially correct answers. What should you do if your answer is a decimal? Round to the nearest whole number.

— Solve —

6. How many points did Tom score? 87 points.
7. How many points did Catherine score? 85 points.
8. How many points did the new student score? 61 points.

— Look Back —

9. Order the students scores from least to greatest. Does this correspond with the clues given in the problem? New student, Catherine, Tom, Luanna; Yes.

SOLVE ANOTHER PROBLEM

Eden's bowling score was about 96% of Remy's score. Remy's score was about 75% of Laneesha's score. Laneesha's score was 100% of Martin's score. Martin's bowling score was 150 points. How many points did the Eden score? 108 points.

ENRICHMENT

Name ______________________

Extend Your Thinking 10-11

Decision Making

Nora has just started her first job after graduating from college. She earns $22,000 per year. She has estimated all her expenses in her budget as percents of her annual salary.

1. Write Nora's budget in dollars.

Rent	21%	$4620
Food	12%	$2640
Clothing	10%	$2200
Transportation	9%	$1980
Medical	3%	$660
Recreation	8%	$1760
Federal Taxes	11%	$2420
State Taxes	5%	$1100
Savings	5%	$1100
Miscellaneous	16%	$3520

2. If Nora gets an apartment by herself, her *monthly* rent would be $550. What percent of her salary is that? 30%
3. Subtract 21% from your answer to Question 2 to find the percent change in her rent expense in relation to her total budget. 9%
4. Some things, like Federal taxes, cannot be changed because they are not under Nora's control. What changes *can* she make so that she can move to her own apartment? Possible answer: Decrease the clothing budget by 2%, miscellaneous budget by 5% and recreation budget by 2%.
5. Do you think Nora should get her own apartment? Why or why not? Possible answer: Yes, so she can have her privacy. It is worth having less money to spend on other things.

Exercise Notes

Exercise 39

Geography The population of Ethiopia is primarily rural; about 88% of the people live in rural areas, and about 12% of the people live in urban areas.

Exercise 41

Extension Using the method discussed in this exercise, have students find a 15% and 20% tip on a restaurant bill of $25.
15% tip: $3.75; 20% tip: $5.00.

Exercise Answers

41. Penelope's method will work every time because 5% is equal to half of 10%.
42. About 62 points.
44. Divide the part by the percent expressed as a decimal or fraction.

Alternate Assessment

You may want to use the *Interactive CD-ROM Journal* with this assessment.

Journal Have students write a paragraph describing a method to find a percent of a number. Students should support their explanation with a variety of worked-out examples.

Quick Quiz

Simplify.

1. 24% of 70 16.8
2. 36% of 80 28.8

Find the total amount.

3. 40% of what is 32? 80

Available on Daily Transparency 10-11

Technology

Using a Spreadsheet • Creating a Circle Graph

The Point
Students enter data into a spreadsheet and create a circle graph.

Materials
Spreadsheet software

Resources
Interactive CD-ROM Spreadsheet/Grapher Tool

About the Page
Most spreadsheets can create different graphs from data, such as bar graphs, line graphs, and circle graphs. Find out what other types of graphs your spreadsheet software is capable of creating.

Ask ...
- How are the percents calculated? Divide the number in each cell by the sum of the numbers in the column.
- How does the software know what angle to make each sector? Multiply the percent by 360. This will be the number of degrees in the central angle.
- What goes in column A? The grades on the math test.
- What goes in column B? The number of students earning each grade.

Answers for Try It
a–b. Answers may vary.

On Your Own
For the second question, students' responses may vary, but having the software calculate the percents and the central angles are two advantages in favor of using the spreadsheet.

Answers for On Your Own
- Each section in the graph would be the same size.
- Possible answer: Spreadsheets are easier; Spreadsheet programs automatically determine all of the percents as well as the size of each section in the circle graph.

TECHNOLOGY

Using a Spreadsheet • Creating a Circle Graph

Problem: The data below represents the grades a math class received on a test. What would the data look like in a circle graph?

You can use your spreadsheet to organize the data and draw a circle graph.

C	A	C	B	C	B	A	B	A	D	C	B	A
B	D	C	A	B	A	C	C	B	A	C	B	C
F	A	B	C	C	A	B	C	B	C	A	C	F

1 Enter the data into the spreadsheet as shown.

2 Select cells A2 to B6. These cells contain the grades and the number of students earning each grade.

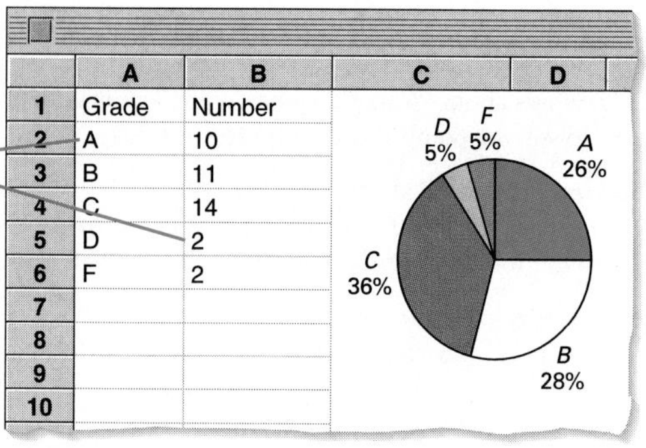

3 Using the graph option, choose a circle graph that shows labels and percents.

TRY IT

a. Collect data from students about their favorite class. Use a spreadsheet to make a circle graph of the data.

b. Collect data from students about the kind of pet they have. Use a spreadsheet to make a circle graph of the data.

ON YOUR OWN

▶ What would a circle graph look like if all the categories in column A had the same number in column B?

▶ Is it easier to create a circle graph by hand or with a spreadsheet? Explain.

Section 10C Connect

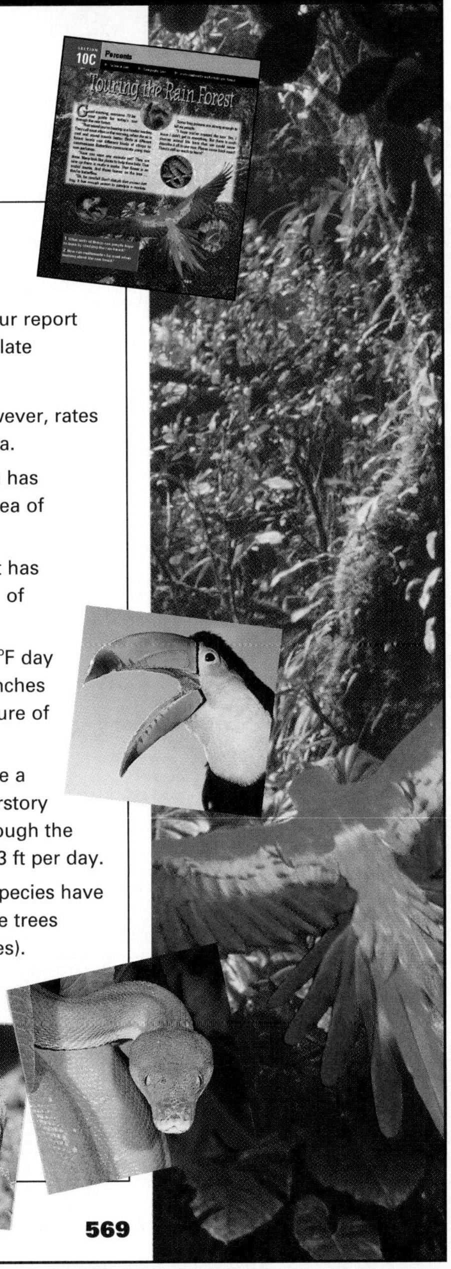

In this section, you've been given many percent facts related to the world's rain forests. Now you'll begin with the facts and use them to create some percents of your own.

Touring the Rain Forest

Write a short report on rain forests, based on some of the following information. Choose information that interests you. Your report should contain at least 5 percents, all of which you must calculate yourself.

A. Tropical rain typically falls at a rate of 1 inch per hour. However, rates as high as 16 inches per hour have been recorded in Liberia.

B. Tropical Costa Rica has an area of 20,000 square miles and has 8,000 species of plants. Nontropical Great Britain has an area of 94,000 square miles and has 1,600 species of plants.

C. A 3-square-mile section of Costa Rica's La Selva rain forest has 394 species of birds. Nontropical Pennsylvania has an area of 45,000 square miles and has 197 species of birds.

D. Tropical temperatures generally vary between 68°F and 85°F day and night year-round. Tropical rain forests get about 200 inches of rain per year. Northern Alaska has an average temperature of 40°F and gets 50 inches of rain each year.

E. The tallest trees are about 150–200 ft tall. Beneath these are a canopy of 60–90 ft vines and trees. Beneath this is an understory of 15–45 ft shrubs. Leaves average 6 inches in length, although the corozo palm has 30 ft leaves. Some bamboo shoots grow 3 ft per day.

F. In the rain forests of the Malay Archipelago, 25,000 plant species have been identified. These include orchids (4,000 species), large trees (2,500 species), heathers (700 species), and figs (500 species).

569

Touring the Rain Forest

The Point

In *Touring the Rain Forest* on page 549, students learned about the diverse animal life that inhabits a rain forest. Now students will determine percents from supplied facts.

About the Page

- Discuss the information given about rain forests. Suggest that students make a list of the different types of information given on the page.
- Discuss examples of the comparisons students can make in their report. Examples could include: Number of species of plants per square mile in Costa Rica compared to number of species of plants in Great Britain per square mile, number of heathers compared to number of orchids in the Malay Archipelago, the percent of change in temperature in the tropics, and so on.

Ongoing Assessment

Check that students have written a reasonable report that includes five percent problems that they solved correctly.

Extension

Ask students to review the information given and write a problem that would yield a percent greater than 100%.

Possible answers: What percent of Costa Rica's land area is the land area of Great Britain? $\frac{94}{20} = 470\%$. Express the number of orchid species compared to fig tree in the Malay Archipelago as a percent. $\frac{4000}{500} = 800\%$

Answers for Connect

Answers may vary.

10C Review

Review Correlation

Item(s)	Lesson(s)
1a	10-1
1b	10-3
1c	10-8
2–6	10-4
7–11	10-5
12–14	10-7
15–18	10-11
19	10-9
20, 21	10-10
22	10-11

Test Prep

Test-Taking Tip

Remind students to check that their answer is reasonable. In the problem, the number in both B and C is greater than 100% of 328 and the number in D is less than 10% of 328. Choice A is the most reasonable answer.

Answers for Review

19. Possible answers:

a. 80%

b. 60%

Section 10C Review

REVIEW 10C

1. For every 4 carrots that Rennie grows, she grows 3 lettuce plants.

a. What is the ratio of lettuce to carrots? 3:4

b. Write this ratio in lowest terms and as a unit rate. $\frac{3}{4}$; 0.75 lettuce/carrot

c. What percent of Rennie's vegetables are carrots? ≈ 57.14%

Tell if each is a proportion. If it is not, explain why.

2. $\frac{5}{9} \square \frac{10}{9}$ No **3.** $\frac{7}{3} \square \frac{21}{9}$ Yes **4.** $\frac{20}{45} \square \frac{4}{9}$ Yes **5.** $\frac{5}{7} \square \frac{5}{7}$ Yes **6.** $\frac{16}{4} \square \frac{60}{15}$ Yes

Solve each proportion.

7. $\frac{2}{7} = \frac{x}{14}$ 4 **8.** $\frac{x}{28} = \frac{3}{6}$ 14 **9.** $\frac{35}{m} = \frac{14}{4}$ 10 **10.** $\frac{63}{27} = \frac{c}{40}$ $93.\overline{3}$ **11.** $\frac{1}{2} = \frac{600}{l}$ 1200

Find the missing side lengths on these similar figures.

12.

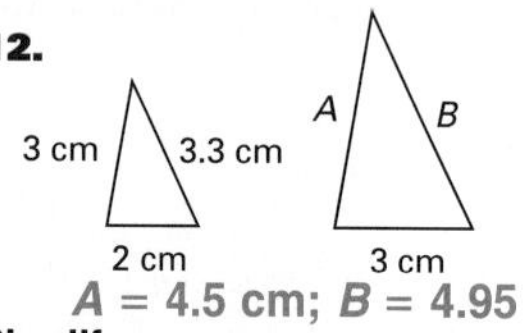

A = 4.5 cm; B = 4.95 cm

13.

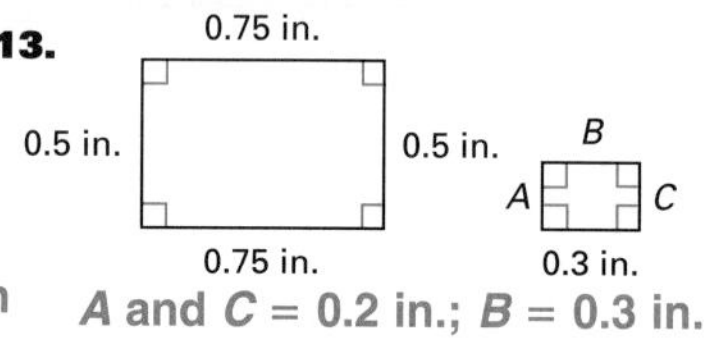

A and C = 0.2 in.; B = 0.3 in.

14.

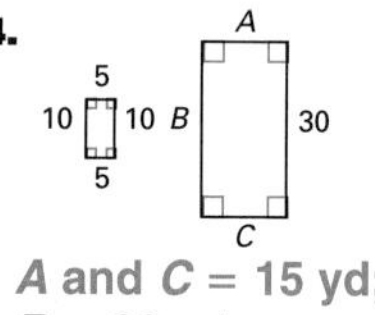

A and C = 15 yd; B = 30 yd

Simplify.

15. 78% of 37 28.86 **16.** 8% of 46.3 3.704 **17.** 12% of 146 17.52 **18.** 230% of 57 131.1

19. Number Sense Estimate the percent of each figure that is shaded.

a.

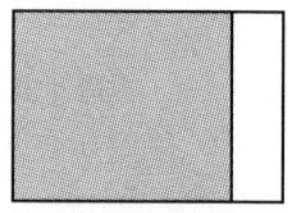

b.

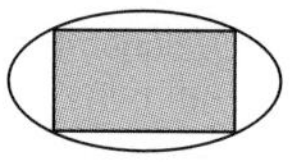

20. Convert 64% to a decimal and a fraction. 0.64; $\frac{64}{100}$ or $\frac{16}{25}$

21. Convert 0.95 and $\frac{3}{5}$ to percents. 95%; 60%

Test Prep

When asked to find a percent of a number, you can sometimes use estimation to eliminate wrong answers.

22. Find 68% of 328. A

Ⓐ 223.04 Ⓑ 22,304 Ⓒ 2230.4 Ⓓ 2.2304

Resources

Practice Masters
Section 10C Review

Assessment Sourcebook
Quiz 10C

TestWorks
Test and Practice Software

PRACTICE

Name ____________________ Practice

Section 10C Review

Estimate the percent of each figure that is shaded.

1. ≈ 30% 2. ≈ 80% 3. ≈ 70%

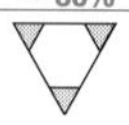

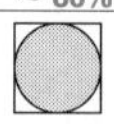

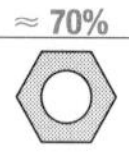

Convert each percent to a decimal and a fraction.

4. 37% 0.37; $\frac{37}{100}$ 5. 40% 0.4; $\frac{2}{5}$ 6. 84% 0.84; $\frac{21}{25}$

7. 35% 0.35; $\frac{7}{20}$ 8. 170% 1.7; $\frac{17}{10}$ 9. 12% 0.12; $\frac{3}{25}$

10. 68% 0.68; $\frac{17}{25}$ 11. 8% 0.08; $\frac{2}{25}$ 12. 38% 0.38; $\frac{19}{50}$

Convert to a percent.

13. 0.47 47% 14. 0.1 10% 15. 0.95 95% 16. 0.74 74%

17. $\frac{7}{10}$ 70% 18. $\frac{19}{25}$ 76% 19. $\frac{14}{40}$ 35% 20. $\frac{27}{50}$ 54%

21. 0.02 2% 22. 2.73 273% 23. 0.462 46.2% 24. 0.87 87%

25. $\frac{11}{2}$ 550% 26. $\frac{8}{5}$ 160% 27. $\frac{9}{10}$ 90% 28. $\frac{8}{25}$ 32%

Simplify.

29. 28% of 64 17.92 30. 70% of 51 35.7 31. 68% of 94 63.92

32. 43% of 83 35.69 33. 4% of 23 0.92 34. 86% of 28.5 24.51

35. 225% of 74 166.5 36. 94% of 46 43.24 37. 63% of 37 23.31

38. **Measurement** One grain is to equal $\frac{1}{20}$ of a scruple. Write and solve an equation to find the number of scruples in 70 grains. *[Lesson 7-6]*

Possible answer: $x \div \frac{1}{20} = 70$; $3\frac{1}{2}$ scruples

39. **Science** Temperatures on Mercury are as high as 510°C and as low as −210°C. Find the difference between these temperatures. *[Lesson 9-3]* 720°C

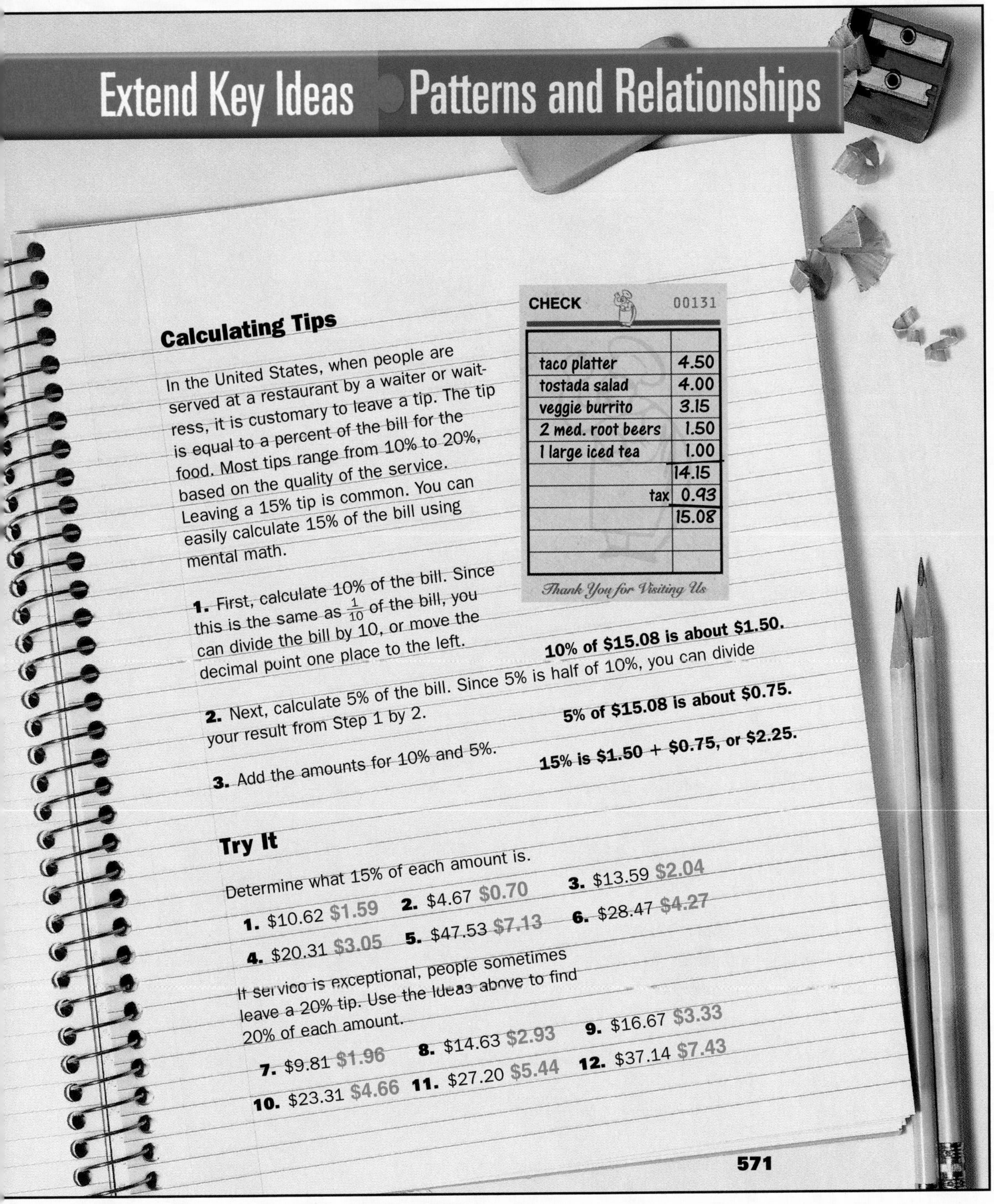

Extend Key Ideas Patterns and Relationships

Calculating Tips

In the United States, when people are served at a restaurant by a waiter or waitress, it is customary to leave a tip. The tip is equal to a percent of the bill for the food. Most tips range from 10% to 20%, based on the quality of the service. Leaving a 15% tip is common. You can easily calculate 15% of the bill using mental math.

CHECK	00131
taco platter	4.50
tostada salad	4.00
veggie burrito	3.15
2 med. root beers	1.50
1 large iced tea	1.00
	14.15
tax	0.93
	15.08

Thank You for Visiting Us

1. First, calculate 10% of the bill. Since this is the same as $\frac{1}{10}$ of the bill, you can divide the bill by 10, or move the decimal point one place to the left. **10% of $15.08 is about $1.50.**

2. Next, calculate 5% of the bill. Since 5% is half of 10%, you can divide your result from Step 1 by 2. **5% of $15.08 is about $0.75.**

3. Add the amounts for 10% and 5%. **15% is $1.50 + $0.75, or $2.25.**

Try It

Determine what 15% of each amount is.

1. $10.62 $1.59 **2.** $4.67 $0.70 **3.** $13.59 $2.04
4. $20.31 $3.05 **5.** $47.53 $7.13 **6.** $28.47 $4.27

If service is exceptional, people sometimes leave a 20% tip. Use the ideas above to find 20% of each amount.

7. $9.81 $1.96 **8.** $14.63 $2.93 **9.** $16.67 $3.33
10. $23.31 $4.66 **11.** $27.20 $5.44 **12.** $37.14 $7.43

571

Extend Key Ideas

Calculating Tips

The Point
Students learn a method to calculate 15% and 20% tips mentally.

About the Page

Point out to students that in this case, because the 10% and the 5% are being calculated from the same amount, the amount of the bill, 10% + 5% = 15%.

Ask ...

- How can you calculate 10% mentally? Move the decimal one place to the left.
- How can you calculate 5% mentally? Take half the amount calculated for 10%.
- How can you calculate 20% mentally? Double the amount calculated for 10%.

Extension

Have students find other percents that they can calculate using mental math. Ask them to explain how they would calculate each.

Chapter 10 Summary and Review

Review Correlation

Item(s)	Lesson(s)
1–4	10-1
5	10-2
6	10-3
7	10-4
8	10-5
9	10-6
10	10-7
11–14	10-10
15	10-11
16, 17	10-3

For additional review, see page 671.

Chapter 10 Summary and Review

Graphic Organizer

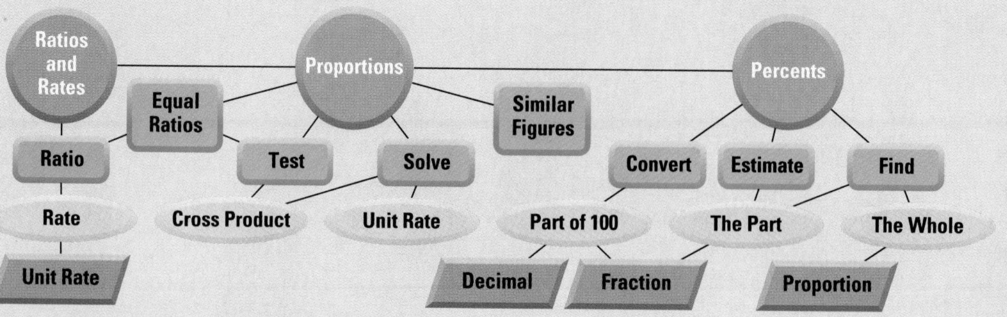

Section 10A Ratios and Rates

Summary

- A **ratio** compares two quantities.
- You can create equal ratios by multiplying or dividing each quantity by the same number.
- A **rate** is a ratio that compares two quantities that have different units. A **unit rate** is a rate that compares a quantity to 1 unit of measure.

Review

1. Show three ways to write the ratio of six yams to eleven potatoes. 6:11, 6 to 11, $\frac{6}{11}$

2. Write the ratio $\frac{12}{16}$ in lowest terms. $\frac{3}{4}$

3. Assume there are 5 fingers on each person's hand. In a group of six people, what is the ratio in simplest form:

a. Of fingers to people? 10 to 1

b. Of people to fingers? 1 to 10

c. Of fingers to hands? 5 to 1

d. Of hands to people? 2 to 1

4. What is the ratio of Elk School students to Rhodes students? Elk School students to total students? 3 to 4; 3 to 7

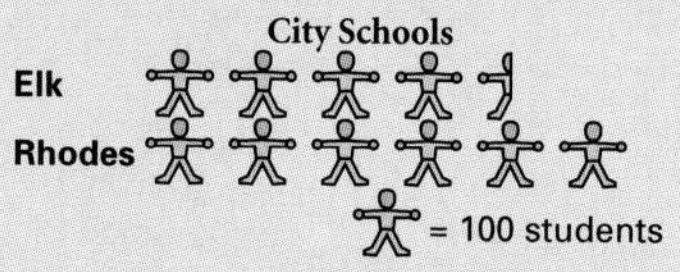

5. Which of the following ratios is *not* equal to the ratio 14 to 21? A

Ⓐ $\frac{3}{2}$ Ⓑ $\frac{2}{3}$ Ⓒ 60:90 Ⓓ $\frac{12}{18}$

6. Which of the following is a rate? B

Ⓐ $\frac{7\text{ hr}}{1\text{ hr}}$ Ⓑ $\frac{3\text{ mi}}{7\text{ hr}}$ Ⓒ $\frac{3\text{ mi}}{1\text{ mi}}$ Ⓓ $\frac{3}{1}$

572 *Chapter 10 • Ratio, Proportion, and Percent*

Resources

Practice Masters
Cumulative Review Chapters 1–10

PRACTICE

Name ______________________

Practice

Cumulative Review Chapters 1–10

Write in lowest terms. *[Lesson 5-5]*

1. $\frac{9}{15}$ $\frac{3}{5}$ **2.** $\frac{20}{25}$ $\frac{4}{5}$ **3.** $\frac{24}{36}$ $\frac{2}{3}$ **4.** $\frac{10}{22}$ $\frac{5}{11}$

5. $\frac{14}{49}$ $\frac{2}{7}$ **6.** $\frac{8}{64}$ $\frac{1}{8}$ **7.** $\frac{6}{21}$ $\frac{2}{7}$ **8.** $\frac{12}{90}$ $\frac{2}{15}$

9. $\frac{35}{75}$ $\frac{7}{15}$ **10.** $\frac{24}{42}$ $\frac{4}{7}$ **11.** $\frac{8}{18}$ $\frac{4}{9}$ **12.** $\frac{33}{57}$ $\frac{11}{19}$

Simplify. *[Lessons 7-3, 7-5]*

13. $3\frac{2}{7} \times 2\frac{2}{3}$ $8\frac{16}{21}$ **14.** $\frac{1}{9} \div 6\frac{2}{3}$ $\frac{1}{60}$ **15.** $4\frac{4}{5} \times 1\frac{1}{5}$ $5\frac{19}{25}$ **16.** $\frac{2}{3} \div \frac{1}{3}$ 2

17. $5\frac{1}{2} \times \frac{1}{4}$ $1\frac{3}{8}$ **18.** $1\frac{5}{6} \div \frac{3}{10}$ $6\frac{1}{9}$ **19.** $1\frac{2}{3} \times 1\frac{1}{4}$ $2\frac{1}{12}$ **20.** $7\frac{1}{2} \div 4$ $1\frac{7}{8}$

21. $\frac{5}{7} \times \frac{14}{15}$ $\frac{2}{3}$ **22.** $\frac{5}{7} \div 2\frac{2}{3}$ $\frac{15}{56}$ **23.** $1\frac{1}{5} \times 4\frac{1}{3}$ $5\frac{1}{5}$ **24.** $4\frac{1}{2} \div 12\frac{1}{2}$ $\frac{9}{25}$

Classify each triangle as acute, right, or obtuse. *[Lesson 8-4]*

25. Obtuse

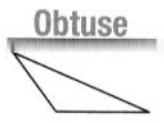

26. Right

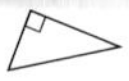

27. Obtuse

28. Acute

Solve each proportion. *[Lesson 10-5]*

29. $\frac{45}{50} = \frac{d}{40}$ $d =$ 36 **30.** $\frac{10}{2} = \frac{j}{5}$ $j =$ 25 **31.** $\frac{15}{12} = \frac{y}{8}$ $y =$ 10 **32.** $\frac{y}{6} = \frac{15}{9}$ $y =$ 10

33. $\frac{12}{16} = \frac{q}{20}$ $q =$ 15 **34.** $\frac{35}{15} = \frac{7}{g}$ $g =$ 3 **35.** $\frac{27}{m} = \frac{9}{7}$ $m =$ 21 **36.** $\frac{8}{12} = \frac{4}{d}$ $d =$ 6

Find the total amount. *[Lesson 10-11]*

37. 18% of 650 is 117 **38.** 35% of 220 is 77 **39.** 70% of 48 is 33.6

40. 75% of 128 is 96 **41.** 62% of 300 is 186 **42.** 44% of 275 is 121

43. 63% of 180 is 113.4 **44.** 120% of 85 is 102 **45.** 185% of 40 is 74

Section 10B Proportions

Summary

- You find a **cross product** by multiplying the top value of one ratio by the bottom value of another ratio.
- If the cross products of two ratios are equal, the two ratios form a **proportion.**
- You can use cross products or a unit rate to solve proportions.
- **Similar figures** have the same shape, but different sizes. Their angles have the same measure, and their sides are proportional.

Review

7. Can the ratios $\frac{7\text{ mi}}{10\text{ hr}}$ and $\frac{21\text{ hr}}{30\text{ mi}}$ form a proportion? Explain.

8. Use cross products to solve the proportion $\frac{9}{m} = \frac{3}{5}$. 15

9. Red ribbon costs $0.96 a foot. Use a unit rate to find out how much 54 in. cost. $4.32

10. Explain why the two triangles are similar.

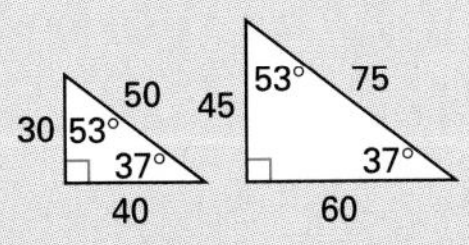

Section 10C Percents

Summary

- A **percent** is a ratio of a number to 100. It is written using the % symbol.
- To estimate a percent, think of a fraction you can easily write as a percent that's roughly equal to the amount being estimated.
- When using a percent to find a part or a whole, use a proportion to find the missing value. To find a part, you can also convert the percent to a decimal and multiply.

Review

Write each percent as a ratio of a number to 100, as a fraction in lowest terms, and as a decimal.

11. 35% (11. $\frac{35}{100}, \frac{7}{20}$, 0.35) **12.** 20% ($\frac{20}{100}, \frac{1}{5}$, 0.2) **13.** 8% ($\frac{8}{100}, \frac{2}{25}$, 0.08) **14.** 75% ($\frac{75}{100}, \frac{3}{4}$, 0.75)

15. In Texas in 1995, about 25% of the population over 5 years old spoke a language other than English at home. If this population was 18,723,991, about how many people spoke a language other than English at home? ≈ 4,680,998 people

16. Use a table to find four equal rates that describe saving $6 for every 4 days of work.

17. What is the unit rate of the firefighters' response time of 7.5 minutes to a fire 5 miles away? $\frac{1.5\text{ min}}{1\text{ mi}}$

Answers for Review

7. No; The units are not the same across or down.

10. Possible answer: Corresponding angles are equal; Corresponding sides form a proportion.

16. Possible answer: $\frac{\$3}{2\text{ days}}, \frac{\$12}{8\text{ days}}, \frac{\$18}{12\text{ days}}, \frac{\$24}{16\text{ days}}$.

Chapter 10 Assessment

Assessment Correlation

Item(s)	Lesson(s)
1–3	10-1
4	10-5, 10-6
5	10-10
6, 7	10-7
8, 9	10-2
10	10-4
11	10-5
12	10-6
13	10-7
14–17	10-10
18, 19	10-11

Answers for Assessment

8. Possible answers: 10:14, 15:21, 20:28, 25:35.

10. The units are not the same across or down. Possible answer: $\frac{8 \text{ mi}}{32 \text{ mi}} = \frac{5 \text{ hr}}{20 \text{ hr}}$

13. Similar; Their matching sides are all in the ratio of $\frac{1}{3}$ and both figures contain the same size angles.

Answer for Performance Task

The final price was $137.20; 56% of the original.

Chapter 10 Assessment

Write the ratio as a fraction in lowest terms.

1. 4 out of 32 dentists $\frac{1}{8}$

2. One chaperone for every 6 students. $\frac{1}{6}$

3. Ninety of the 100 students passed the test. $\frac{9}{10}$

For Exercises 4–7, determine whether the statement is true or false. If it is false, rewrite it as a true statement.

4. Cross products and unit rates are used to solve proportions. True

5. A percent can be written as a fraction and compares a quantity to the number 1. False

6. If two triangles are similar, they are congruent. False

7. Two figures are similar if their shapes are the same and their side lengths are proportional. True

8. Write four equal ratios for the ratio 5:7.

9. Write the ratio of 7 triangles to 8 squares in three ways. 7 to 8, 7:8, $\frac{7}{8}$

10. Why is $\frac{8 \text{ mi}}{5 \text{ hr}} = \frac{20 \text{ hr}}{32 \text{ mi}}$ not a correct proportion? Rewrite it correctly.

11. Fuji apples cost $2.10 for 3 lb. Use a proportion to find how much it would cost to buy 7 lb. $4.90

12. Valencia oranges cost $3.16 for 4 lb. Use a unit rate to find how much it would cost to buy 5 lb. $3.95

13. Are the two figures congruent, similar, or neither? Explain.

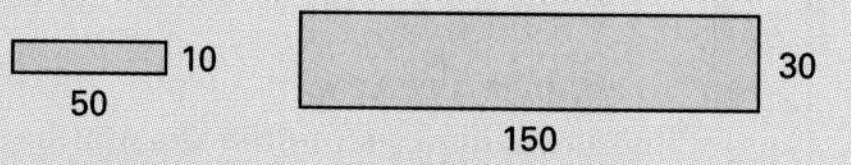

Write the percent as a ratio of a number to 100, as a fraction in lowest terms, and as a decimal.

14. 70% **15.** 27% **16.** 40% **17.** 5%

14. $\frac{70}{100}, \frac{7}{10}$, 0.7 15. $\frac{27}{100}, \frac{27}{100}$, 0.27 16. $\frac{40}{100}, \frac{2}{5}$, 0.4 17. $\frac{5}{100}, \frac{1}{20}$, 0.05

18. Jonah had 84 baseball cards. He threw 25% of them away. How many did he throw away? 21 cards

19. Jessica had 6 Florida Marlin cards, which was 3 percent of her total collection. How many cards did she have in her collection? 200 cards

Performance Task

A bicycle shop advertised a 30% discount on their bikes. After two weeks, they gave an additional 20% off the sale prices. John bought a bike the last day of the sale. Its original price was $245. What did it cost him? What percent of its original price was the final price?

Resources

Assessment Sourcebook
Chapter 10 Tests
- Forms A and B (free response)
- Form C (multiple choice)
- Form D (performance assessment)
- Form E (mixed response)
- Form F (cumulative chapter test)

TestWorks
Test and Practice Software

Home and Community Connections
- Letter Home for Chapter 10 in English and Spanish

Cumulative Review Test Prep

Cumulative Review Chapters 1–10 Test Prep

Multiple Choice

Choose the best answer.

1. A graph that shows separately the tens place values and ones place values of the data is a *[Lesson 1-6]* D

Ⓐ Bar graph Ⓑ Circle graph
Ⓒ Pictograph Ⓓ Stem-and-leaf plot

2. Supply the next three numbers in the number pattern: 15, 25, 23, 33, 31, … *[Lesson 2-9]* B

Ⓐ 29, 39, 37 Ⓑ 41, 39, 49
Ⓒ 41, 51, 49 Ⓓ None of these

3. Find the quotient of 88.88 ÷ 44. *[Lesson 3-10]* A

Ⓐ 2.02 Ⓑ 2.2 Ⓒ 20.2 Ⓓ 22

4. How many millimeters are there in 3 meters? *[Lesson 4-2]* C

Ⓐ 30 Ⓑ 300 Ⓒ 3000 Ⓓ 30,000

5. What is the approximate area of a circle with a diameter of 10 ft? *[Lesson 4-8]* C

Ⓐ 15.7 ft^2 Ⓑ 31.4 ft^2
Ⓒ 78.5 ft^2 Ⓓ 314 ft^2

6. Tell whether 495 is divisible by 2, 3, 5, 9, or 10. *[Lesson 5-1]* B

Ⓐ 5 Ⓑ 3, 5, 9 Ⓒ 3, 5 Ⓓ 2, 3, 5, 9

7. Order from smallest to largest: $\frac{1}{4}, \frac{4}{5}, \frac{2}{3}$ *[Lesson 5-8]* D

Ⓐ $\frac{4}{5}, \frac{1}{4}, \frac{2}{3}$ Ⓑ $\frac{4}{5}, \frac{2}{3}, \frac{1}{4}$,
Ⓒ $\frac{1}{4}, \frac{4}{5}, \frac{2}{3}$ Ⓓ $\frac{1}{4}, \frac{2}{3}, \frac{4}{5}$

8. Solve the equation $x - \frac{3}{5} = \frac{2}{3}$. *[Lesson 6-3]* A

Ⓐ $1\frac{4}{15}$ Ⓑ $\frac{5}{8}$ Ⓒ $\frac{2}{5}$ Ⓓ $\frac{1}{15}$

9. Estimate $5\frac{3}{5} + 7\frac{1}{3}$. *[Lesson 6-4]* B

Ⓐ 12 Ⓑ 13
Ⓒ 14 Ⓓ None of these

10. How many $\frac{2}{3}$-cup servings are contained in 12 cups of juice? *[Lesson 7-4]* C

Ⓐ 6 Ⓑ 8
Ⓒ 18 Ⓓ None of these

11. The sum of two angles of a triangle is 37°. What is the third angle's measure? *[Lesson 8-4]* A

Ⓐ 143° Ⓑ 106° Ⓒ 53° Ⓓ 16°

12. What is the least rotation clockwise that will land the figure on top of itself? *[Lesson 8-9]* D

Ⓐ 360°
Ⓑ 270°
Ⓒ 180°
Ⓓ 90°

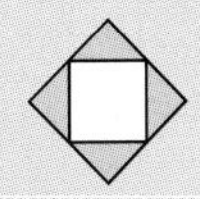

13. Simplify: −3 − (−5). *[Lesson 9-3]* C

Ⓐ −8 Ⓑ −2 Ⓒ 2 Ⓓ 8

14. The cross products for $\frac{m}{7} = \frac{12}{21}$ are *[Lesson 10-5]* A

Ⓐ $21m = 84$ Ⓑ $7m = 252$
Ⓒ $12m = 147$ Ⓓ None of these

About Multiple-Choice Tests

The Cumulative Review found at the end of Chapters 2, 4, 6, 8, 10, and 12 can be used to prepare students for standardized tests.

Students sometimes do not perform as well on standardized tests as they do on other tests. There may be several reasons for this related to the format and content of the test.

- **Format**
Students may have limited experience with multiple-choice tests. For some questions, such tests are harder because having options may confuse the students.

- **Content**
A standardized test may cover a broader range of content than normally covered on a test, and the relative emphasis given to various strands may be different than given in class. Also, some questions may assess general aptitude or thinking skills and not include specific pieces of mathematical content.

It is important not to let the differences between standardized tests and other tests shake your students' confidence.

Chapter 11

Solids and Measurement

▶ OVERVIEW

Section 11A

Solids and Surface Area: Students learn to classify three-dimensional shapes and to find the surface area of a polyhedron.

11-1 Classifying Solids

11-2 Exploring Surface Area

11-3 Surface Area Formulas

11-4 Surface Area of a Cylinder

Section 11B

Volume: Students learn how to draw solid figures and how to find the volume of a rectangular prism.

11-5 Three-Dimensional Figures

11-6 Exploring Volume

11-7 Calculating Volume

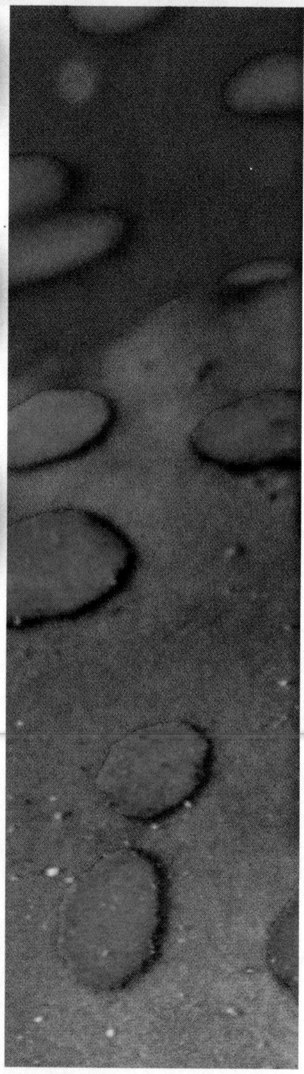

Meeting NCTM Standards

Curriculum Standards

STANDARD

	Standard		pages
1	**Problem Solving**	Skills and Strategies	578, 589, *592*, 597, 604, 609
		Applications	582–583, 586–587, 591–592, 596–597, 599, 604–605, 608–609, 613–614, 615
		Exploration	580, 584, 588, 593, 602, 606, 610
2	**Communication**	Oral	579, 581, *583*, 585, 591, 596, 601, 603, 607, *609*, 612
		Written	*578*, *583*, 587, *592*, 600, 605
		Cooperative Learning	*580*, *584*, *588*, *591*, *593*, *602*, *606*, *610*
3	**Reasoning**	Critical Thinking	583, 587, 592, 597, 605, 609, 614
4	**Connections**	Mathematical	See Standards 8, 12, 13 below.
		Interdisciplinary	Geography *608*, *612*, 613; Arts & Literature 576; Entertainment 576; Science 577, *601*, 607, *608*, 611, *613*, *614*; Social Studies 577; Fine Arts 583, *595*; Industry *579*, 587, 596; Consumer *579*, *583*; Language 603; Health 590
		Technology	585, 590, 598
		Cultural	576
8	**Patterns and Functions**		604
12	**Geometry**		580–617
13	**Measurement**		584–597, 606–617

Italic type indicates Teacher Edition reference.

Teaching Standards

Focus on Student Discourse

The nature of classroom discourse is a major influence on what students learn about mathematics. Students should

- engage in making conjectures.
- explore examples and counterexamples to investigate a conjecture.
- propose approaches and solutions to problems.

Assessment Standards

Focus on Mathematics

Journals The Mathematics Standard encourages teachers to use assessment activities that give rich information about students' mathematical knowledge and thinking processes and dispositions. Journal-writing activities require that students verbalize those thinking processes. In Chapter 11, students are asked to explain

- why a problem's solution should agree with given facts.
- how they identify a prism.
- how they find the surface area of a rectangular prism.

TECHNOLOGY

For the Teacher

- **Teacher Resource Planner CD-ROM**
  Use the teacher planning CD-ROM to view resources available for Chapter 11. You can prepare custom lesson plans or use the default lesson plans provided.
- **World Wide Web**
  Visit **www.teacher.mathsurf.com** for links to lesson plans from teachers and other professionals, NCTM information, and other sites.
- **TestWorks**
  TestWorks provides ready-made tests and can create custom tests and practice worksheets.

For the Parent

- **World Wide Web**
  Parents can use the Web site at **www.parent.mathsurf.com.**

For the Student

- **Interactive CD-ROM**
  Lesson 11-6 has an *Interactive CD-ROM Lesson*. The *Interactive CD-ROM Journal* and *Interactive CD-ROM Spreadsheet/Grapher Tool* are also used in Chapter 11.
- **Wide World of Mathematics**
  Lesson 11-6 Middle School: Chunnel
- **World Wide Web**
  Use with Chapter and Section Openers; Students can go online to the Scott Foresman-Addison Wesley Web site at **www.mathsurf.com/6/ch11** to collect information about chapter themes.
- **Jasper Woodbury Videodisc**
  Lesson 11-6: Blueprint for Success
  Lesson 11-7: The Big Splash

STANDARDIZED - TEST CORRELATION

SECTION 11A

LESSON	OBJECTIVE	ITBS Form M	CTBS 4th Ed.	CAT 5th Ed.	SAT 9th Ed.	MAT 7th Ed.	Your Form
11-1	• Classify different solids.	✘		✘		✘	
11-2	• Find the surface area of a polyhedron by using a net of the solid.						
11-3	• Use surface area formulas.		✘	✘	✘	✘	
11-4	• Find the surface area of a cylinder.						

SECTION 11B

LESSON	OBJECTIVE	ITBS Form M	CTBS 4th Ed.	CAT 5th Ed.	SAT 9th Ed.	MAT 7th Ed.	Your Form
11-5	• Draw the front, side, and top views of a solid.						
11-6	• Calculate the volume of a rectangular prism.	✘	✘	✘		✘	
11-7	• Use the volume formula for rectangular prisms.	✘	✘	✘		✘	

Key: ITBS - Iowa Test of Basic Skills; CTBS - Comprehensive Test of Basic Skills; CAT - California Achievement Test; SAT - Stanford Achievement Test; MAT - Metropolitan Achievement Test

ASSESSMENT PROGRAM

	QUICK QUIZZES	SECTION REVIEW	CHAPTER REVIEW	CHAPTER ASSESSMENT FREE RESPONSE	CHAPTER ASSESSMENT MULTIPLE CHOICE	CUMULATIVE REVIEW	
Traditional Assessment	TE: pp. 583, 587, 592, 597, 605, 609, 614	SE: pp. 600, 616 *Quiz 11A, 11B	SE: pp. 618–619	SE: p. 620 *Ch. 11 Tests Forms A, B, E	*Ch. 11 Tests Forms C, E	SE: p. 621 *Ch. 11 Test Form F	
	INTERVIEW	JOURNAL	ONGOING	PERFORMANCE	PORTFOLIO	PROJECT	SELF
Alternate Assessment	TE: pp. 583, 609	SE: pp. 587, 600 TE: pp. 578, 592	TE: pp. 580, 584, 588, 593, 602, 606, 610	SE: pp. 620, 621 TE: p. 605 *Ch. 11 Tests Forms D, E	TE: pp. 587, 614	SE: pp. 577, 587, 614 TE: p. 577	TE: p. 597

*Tests and quizzes are in *Assessment Sourcebook*. Test Form E is a mixed response test. Forms for Alternate Assessment are also available in *Assessment Sourcebook*.

TestWorks: Test and Practice Software

MIDDLE SCHOOL PACING CHART

REGULAR PACING

Day	5 classes per week
1	Chapter 11 Opener; Problem Solving Focus
2	Section **11A** Opener; Lesson **11-1**
3	Lesson **11-2**
4	Lesson **11-3**
5	Lesson **11-4**; Technology
6	**11A** Connect; **11A** Review
7	Section **11B** Opener; Lesson **11-5**
8	Lesson **11-6**
9	Lesson **11-7**
10	**11B** Connect; **11B** Review; Extend Key Ideas
11	Chapter 11 Summary and Review
12	Chapter 11 Assessment Cumulative Review, Chapters 1–11

BLOCK SCHEDULING OPTIONS

Block Scheduling for
Complete Course

Chapter 11 may be presented in

- seven 90-minute blocks
- nine 75-minute blocks

Each block consists of a combination of

- Chapter and Section Openers
- Explores
- Lesson Development
- Problem Solving Focus
- Technology
- Extend Key Ideas
- Connect
- Review
- Assessment

For details, see *Block Scheduling Handbook.*

Block Scheduling for
Interdisciplinary Course

Each block integrates math with another subject area.

In Chapter 11, interdisciplinary topics include

- Packages
- Aquariums

Themes for Interdisciplinary Team Teaching 11A and 11B are

- Shaping Glass
- Technical Drawings

For details, see *Block Scheduling Handbook.*

Block Scheduling for
Lab-Based Course

In each block, 30–40 minutes is devoted to lab activities including

- Explores in the Student Edition
- Connect pages in the Student Edition
- Technology options in the Student Edition
- Reteaching Activities in the Teacher Edition

For details, see *Block Scheduling Handbook.*

Block Scheduling for
Course with *Connected Mathematics*

In each block, investigations from **Connected Mathematics** replace or enhance the lessons in Chapter 11.

Connected Mathematics topics for Chapter 11 can be found in

- *Ruins of Montarek*

For details, see *Block Scheduling Handbook.*

INTERDISCIPLINARY BULLETIN BOARD

Set Up

Explain that students will be looking at the classroom from different viewpoints. Divide the class into three groups.

Procedure

- The groups will make scale drawings. A suggested scale is 1/8 in.:1 ft.
- The first group should draw a front view of the classroom, the second group a side view, and the third group a top view.
- Groups should assign members responsibility for specific tasks, including: finding the actual area; drawing the area using scale measurements; drawing furniture and other objects as they would appear in the view; drawing people as they would appear in the view.

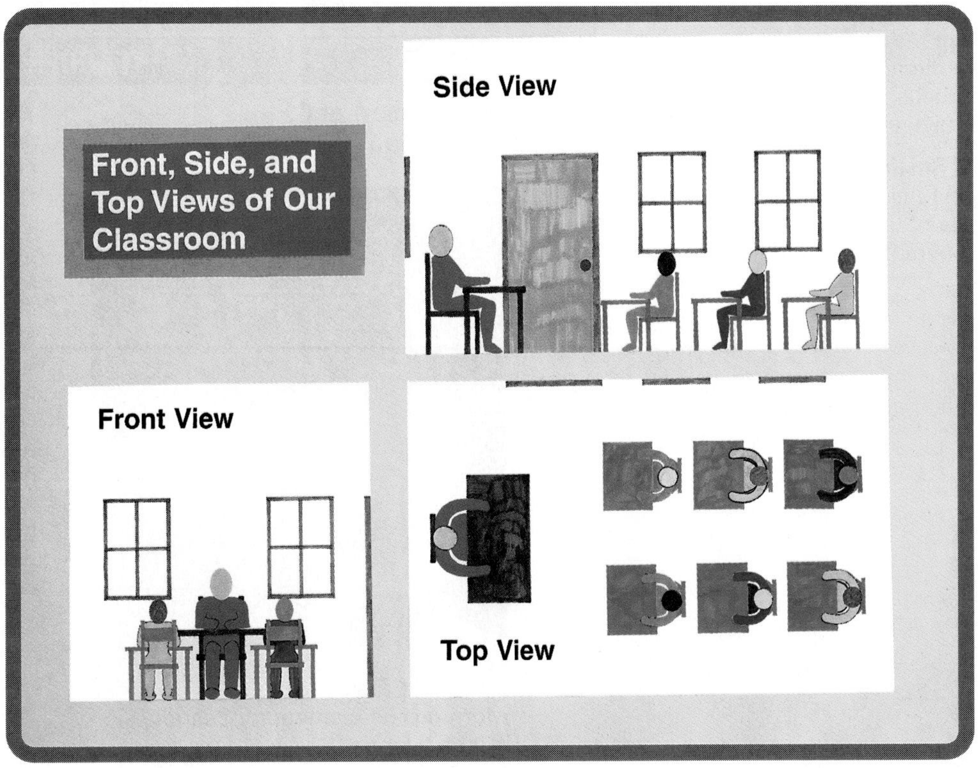

Chapter 11

The information on these pages shows how solids and surface area are used in real-life situations.

World Wide Web

If your class has access to the World Wide Web, you might want to use the information found at the Web site addresses given.

Extensions

The following activities do not require access to the World Wide Web.

People of the World
Have students work with a partner to investigate and report on the unusual shapes of houses built by other cultures.

Arts & Literature
Have students experiment with drawing a box in one-point perspective by drawing a square or rectangle and a vanishing point and then using it to complete the box.

Entertainment
Ask students why a basketball and a bowling ball have such different weights and construction. A bowling ball is solid. It is designed to roll and knock over pins, so it needs to be heavier.

Science
Ask students why they think basketballs, baseballs, and golf balls have a spherical shape.

Social Studies
Suggest that students determine the size of the pyramids as well as when pyramids were built in Egypt.

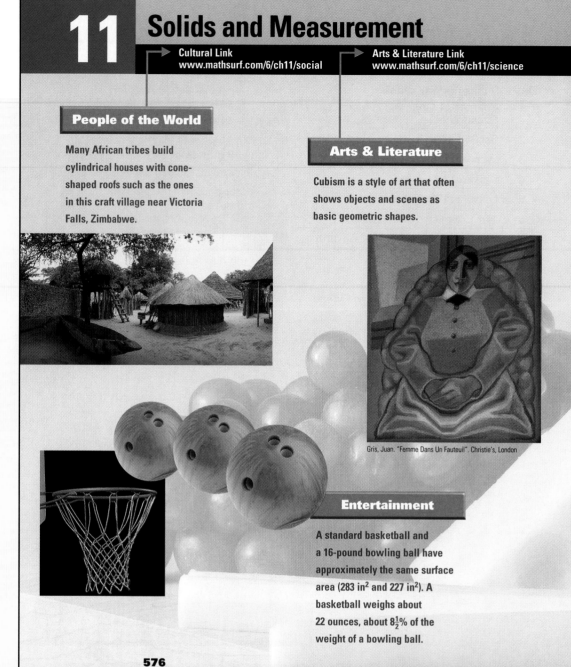

11 Solids and Measurement

Cultural Link
www.mathsurf.com/6/ch11/social

Arts & Literature Link
www.mathsurf.com/6/ch11/science

People of the World

Many African tribes build cylindrical houses with cone-shaped roofs such as the ones in this craft village near Victoria Falls, Zimbabwe.

Arts & Literature

Cubism is a style of art that often shows objects and scenes as basic geometric shapes.

Gris, Juan. "Femme Dans Un Fauteuil". Christie's, London

Entertainment

A standard basketball and a 16-pound bowling ball have approximately the same surface area (283 in^2 and 227 in^2). A basketball weighs about 22 ounces, about $8\frac{1}{2}$% of the weight of a bowling ball.

TEACHER TALK

Meet Robert and Mary Margaret Capraro

Morningside Elementary School
Miami, Florida

North Twin Lakes Elementary School
Hialeah, Florida

When we introduce geometric solids and their measurement, we equip our classroom with boxes, scrap paper, rulers, scissors, and grid paper. We explore the relationship between points and lines on a plane and vertices and edges on geometric solids. Once the connections have been made, we have students take apart a cereal box to begin learning about nets and the two-dimensional shapes which, when combined, make regular solids. We have students transfer the cereal box net to grid paper to explore surface area. Students are challenged to invent nets representing other solids and, with that accomplished, they use centimeter cubes to measure volume.

Science

In zero gravity, water "drops" are shaped like spheres. This is because the water molecules can form the most compact shape possible for their volume, which happens to be a sphere.

Social Studies

The Great Pyramid in Giza, Egypt, is made from over 2,000,000 stones. Each stone weighs 2,500 pounds.

KEY MATH IDEAS

A **solid** is a three-dimensional shape.

A **polyhedron** is a three-dimensional shape whose **faces** are polygons.

You can calculate the **surface area** for a polyhedron by using a **net**, which allows you to see the measures of each face, or sometimes by directly applying a formula.

The amount of space inside a solid is the **volume** of the solid.

Surface area is measured with square units, such as cm^2. Volume is measured with cubic units, such as cm^3.

CHAPTER PROJECT

Problem Solving
Understand
Plan
Solve
Look Back

In this project, you will determine what would be a good size for an aquarium in your classroom. Begin the project by recording how many fish you want in the aquarium. Also record how many inches long you want each fish to be.

577

Chapter Project

Students determine the size of an aquarium on the basis of the number of fish it will hold.

Resources
Chapter 11 Project Master

Introduce the Project

- Discuss the kinds of fish students might be able to have in an aquarium. Distinguish between saltwater and fresh-water fish.
- Talk about the number of fish an aquarium might hold and what other equipment besides the aquarium you might need, such as a heater and a filter.
- Talk about where students might get information about how many fish can go into an aquarium, such as from tropical fish stores, books, and the Internet.

Project Progress
Section A, page 587 Students use the total length of all fish and the area of water surface to determine an appropriate fish tank.

Section B, page 614 Students measure the volume of an aquarium and the volume of their classroom to determine if an aquarium would fit in the classroom.

Community Project

A community project for Chapter 11 is available in *Home and Community Connections.*

Cooperative Learning

You may want to use Teaching Tool Transparency 1: Cooperative Learning Checklist with **Explore** and other group activities in this chapter.

PROJECT ASSESSMENT

You may choose to use this project as a performance assessment for the chapter.

Performance Assessment Key

Level 4 Full Accomplishment

Level 3 Substantial Accomplishment

Level 2 Partial Accomplishment

Level 1 Little Accomplishment

Suggested Scoring Rubric

4
- Number of fish and their total length are accurately calculated.
- Size of aquarium is appropriate for classroom and fish.

3
- Number of fish and their total length are adequately calculated.
- Size of aquarium is adequate for classroom and fish.

2
- Number of fish and their total length are calculated with some degree of error.
- Size of aquarium is appropriate for either classroom or fish.

1
- Number of fish and their total length are inaccurately calculated.
- Size of aquarium is not appropriate.

Problem Solving Focus

Checking the Rules of the Problem

The Point

Students focus on determining if their answer is appropriate.

Resources

Teaching Tool Transparency 18: Problem-Solving Guidelines

Interactive CD-ROM Journal

About the Page

Using the Problem-Solving Process

Once students have completed work on a problem, it is important that they be able to determine if their answer is appropriate. Discuss the following suggestions:

- Check the answer against all the facts.
- Determine if your answer addresses the question posed in the problem.

Ask ...

- What is one fact you would check in Problem 1?
- In Problem 2, did Sid play more or fewer games than Mai? How do you know? More; Julio played $1\frac{1}{2}$ times as many as Mai and Sid played 5 more games than Julio.

Answers for Problems

1. Answer #3 is correct. In Answer #1, Kareem spent \$2 less than Chris and Maggie didn't spend 25% of the other's total. In Answer #2, Kareem spent \$2 less than Chris and Sid spent \$3 more than Kareem.
2. Answer #1 is correct. In Answer #2, Julio played only half as many games as Mai; Mai played 3 more games than Danielle, and all together they played only 50 games. In Answer #3 the numbers are correct, but the names are not with the correct numbers.

Journal

Ask students to write a paragraph explaining why it is important to check that their solution agrees with all the facts in the problem.

Problem Solving

Understand
Plan
Solve
Look Back

Checking the Rules of the Problem

When solving problems, it's important to look back to verify that your answer is appropriate. For example, check the facts in the problem and verify that your solution agrees with all of them.

Problem Solving Focus

Each problem has three answers. State which answer is correct, and which sentences in the problem the other two answers don't agree with.

1. Kareem, Chris, Maggie, and Sid spent \$31.25 at the diner. Kareem spent \$2.00 more than Chris. Sid spent \$3.00 less than Kareem. Maggie spent 25% of the total spent by Kareem, Chris, and Sid. How much did each person pay?

Answer #1	Answer #2	Answer #3
K = \$ 8.00	K = \$12.00	K = \$10.00
C = \$10.00	C = \$14.00	C = \$ 8.00
S = \$ 5.00	S = \$15.00	S = \$ 7.00
M = \$ 8.25	M = \$10.25	M = \$ 6.25

2. After leaving the diner, Sid met Mai, Julio, and Danielle at Videorama to play Pinball Whiz. Every player gets a free turn when he or she scores over 25,000 points on a game. Sid played five more games than Julio. Julio played $1\frac{1}{2}$ times as much as Mai. Mai played three fewer games than Danielle. All together they played 88 games. How many games did each person play?

Answer #1	Answer #2	Answer #3
D = 19	D = 13	D = 24
J = 24	J = 8	J = 19
S = 29	S = 13	S = 16
M = 16	M = 16	M = 29

Additional Problem

Karen, Jei, Alana, and Sean collected aluminum cans for recycling to raise money for classroom books. Jei brought in twice as many pounds of aluminum cans as Karen. Alana brought in as many pounds as Jei and Karen together. Sean collected $\frac{1}{3}$ as many cans as Alana. In total, they collected 175 pounds. How many pounds did each person collect?

1. Is the following solution correct: Karen, 40; Jei, 80; Alana, 120; Sean, 25? Explain. No; The sum is not 175.
2. Is the following solution correct: Karen, 50; Jei, 25; Alana, 75; Sean, 25? Explain. No; Jei collected twice as many pounds as Karen, not half as many as stated in this solution.
3. Is the following solution correct: Karen, 25; Jei, 50; Alana, 75; Sean, 25? Explain. Yes; The solution satisfies all the conditions.

Section 11A

Solids and Surface Area

Visit www.teacher.mathsurf.com for links to lesson plans from teachers and other professionals, NCTM information, and other sites.

LESSON PLANNING GUIDE

Student Edition | **Ancillaries**

LESSON		MATERIALS	VOCABULARY	DAILY	OTHER
	Chapter 11 Opener				Ch. 11 Practice Master Ch. 11 Community Project Teaching Tool Trans. 1
	Problem Solving Focus				Teaching Tool Trans. 18 *Interactive CD-ROM Journal*
	Section 11A Opener				
11-1	**Classifying Solids**	prisms, pyramids, spheres, cones, cylinders	solid, face, edge, polyhedron, prism, base, pyramid, net, cylinder, cone, sphere, cube	11-1	Lesson Enhancement Trans. 53 Technology Master 57
11-2	**Exploring Surface Area**	Cuisenaire rods, centimeter graph paper	surface area	11-2	Ch. 11 Project Master
11-3	**Surface Area Formulas**			11-3	Lesson Enhancement Trans. 54 Technology Master 58
11-4	**Surface Area of a Cylinder**	cans of food, graph paper		11-4	Teaching Tool Trans. 2, 3 Lesson Enhancement Trans. 55
	Technology	spreadsheet software			*Interactive CD-ROM Spreadsheet/Grapher Tool*
	Connect	metric ruler			Teaching Tool Trans. 16 Interdisc. Team Teaching 11A
	Review				Practice 11A; Quiz 11A; *TestWorks*

SKILLS TRACE

LESSON	SKILL	FIRST INTRODUCED GR. 4	GR. 5	GR. 6	DEVELOP	PRACTICE/APPLY	REVIEW
11-1	**Classifying solids.**		✘		pp. 580–581	pp. 582–583	pp. 600, 616, 618, 629
11-2	**Finding surface areas of polyhedron.**		✘		pp. 584–585	pp. 586–587	pp. 600, 619, 629
11-3	**Using formulas to find surface areas.**			✘ p. 588	pp. 588–590	pp. 591–592	pp. 600, 619, 633
11-4	**Finding surface area of cylinders.**			✘ p. 593	pp. 593–595	pp. 596–597	pp. 600, 619, 633

CONNECTED MATHEMATICS

Investigations 1 and 10 from the unit *Ruins of Montarek (Spatial Visualization)*, from the **Connected Mathematics** series, can be used with Section 11A.

INTERDISCIPLINARY TEAM TEACHING

Math and Science/Technology

(Worksheet pages 53–54: Teacher pages T53–T54)

In this lesson, students explore glass-making and the geometric shapes of glass products.

Name ______________________ *Math and Science/Technology*

Explore glass-making and the geometric shapes of glass products.

Glass! It comes in all colors and shapes. It is made into containers, windows, television screens, lenses, inexpensive jewelry, and lots of other things. It can be transparent, a good idea when it's part of a camera or microscope lens. It can also be cloudy, which is useful when it's part of a window in a room that requires privacy. It can be made to melt at very high temperatures, which is true of laboratory glassware. It can also be designed to melt at low temperatures, which is desirable for the manufacture of glass containers found in a supermarket. Since less heat is needed to make such containers, they are cheap to produce.

All the different kinds of glass are made from one basic type of chemical. It's called *silica*, which is the main ingredient of sand. Mixing and heating silica with other chemicals can produce glass with different properties. This fact has been known for a very long time. As a matter of fact, glass was one of the earliest materials manufactured by humans.

Over the centuries, various cultures have learned to shape glass into useful and beautiful objects. At first, glass was shaped while in its cool, solid state. Among the earliest glass objects were beads, made in Egypt around 1500 B.C. An Egyptian artisan began with a solid block of glass, slowly chipped it and sanded it into a smooth shape, then carefully drilled a hole through the bead so it could be strung.

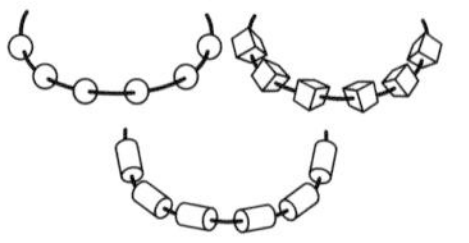

1. Name the shapes of the three kinds of beads shown in the picture.
   sphere, cube, cylinder
2. a. Which of these beads is a polyhedron?
   The cube is a polyhedron.
   b. Which are prisms?
   The cube and the cylinder are prisms.
3. In the first century B.C., people in the Middle East discovered that glass could be heated and blown into hollow shapes. The technique spread throughout the world. Until the nineteenth century most glass containers were made this way. The process begins when a gob of melted glass is gathered at the end of a long, metal pipe. The glassblower blows through the pipe, and the glass forms a bubble. Then tongs are used to pull the glass bubble into other shapes.

Name ______________________ *Math and Science/Technology*

Today's bottles and jars are made by a combination of casting and glass blowing. First, melted glass is dropped into a mold. Then blasts of air shot into the bottom of the mold inflate the glass and push it against the sides of the mold to give the glass its shape.

The drawings below show three designs for glassware. Their basic shapes are combinations of solid figures. Often these basic shapes have been slightly altered to make the object more useful. For example, the Tiffany vase is basically a sphere with a cylinder neck. However, the top edge of the cylinder has been slightly turned out to make a lip and the sphere has been flattened at the bottom slightly so that the vase will stand.

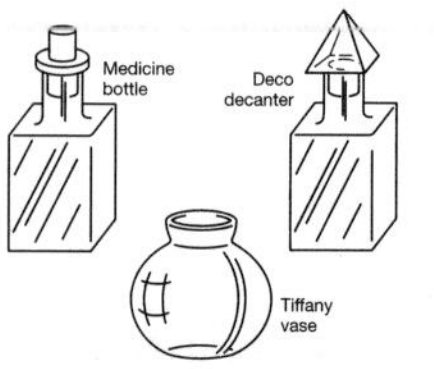

a. Which of these glass containers is basically made up of a prism, a cylinder, and a pyramid?
   deco decanter

b. Describe the basic shapes that make up the nineteenth-century medicine bottle.
   rectangular prism topped by a cylindrical neck

4. Which two objects have rectangular bases?
   deco decanter and medicine bottle
5. Package designers and label-makers have to know the surface area of glass containers so that their packages and labels will fit properly. The rectangular part of the medicine bottle is 6 cm tall, 4 cm wide, and 3 cm deep. Calculate the total surface area of the back, front, sides, top, and bottom. Consider the top is a solid rectangle (without a hole for the neck).
   $108\ cm^2$; $(6 \times 4) \times 2 + (6 \times 3) \times 2 = 84 + (3 \times 4) \times 2 = 108$
6. Design your own glass container. It can have a single shape or a combination of shapes. It can be of one color or a variety of colors. It can be transparent or cloudy. Use only prisms, pyramids, spheres, cones, and cylinders for your shapes. Give the container's dimensions and surface area. Explain the purpose of the container and how your design suits the purpose.
   Designs will vary. The shapes should work together to create a reasonable and attractive container. Other properties should be in harmony with the purpose of the container.

BIBLIOGRAPHY

FOR TEACHERS

Geist, Sidney. *Brancusi; A Study of the Sculpture.* New York, NY: Grossman, 1968.

Kuriam, George Thomas. *The New Book of World Rankings.* New York, NY: Facts on File, 1990.

Nardo, Don. *Gravity: The Universal Force.* San Diego, CA: Lucent Books, 1990.

Smith, Carter. *The Pyramid Builders.* Englewood Cliffs, NJ: Silver Burdett Press, 1991.

Sterba, Gunther, ed. *The Aquarium Encyclopedia.* Cambridge, MA: MIT Press, 1983.

FOR STUDENTS

Millard, Anne. *Pyramids.* New York, NY: Kingfisher, 1996.

Solga, Kim. *Make Sculptures!* Danbury, CT: Grolier Educational Corporation, 1993.

Skurzynski, Gloria. *Zero Gravity.* New York, NY: Bradbury Press, 1994.

SECTION **11A**

Solids and Surface Area

▶ Consumer Link ▶ Industry Link ▶ www.mathsurf.com/6/ch11/packages

The Grapes of Wrap

Which package of grapes would you be most likely to buy?

When you shop, each product competes for your attention. To catch your eye, package designers create containers in a variety of shapes, sizes, designs, and color combinations. But designing a package is not as easy as it sounds.

◆ Consumers notice large containers, but store owners like small containers, so that they can stock as many items as possible.

◆ Consumers notice fancy packaging materials, but they are expensive to manufacture.

◆ Consumers notice unusual shapes, but these are difficult to pack and transport.

Geometry plays a critical role in designing packages with the most appeal for the least money.

1 Why did you choose the package of grapes that you picked?

2 In what ways might a package designer use mathematics?

Where are we now?

In Chapter 10, students explored two-dimensional plane figures.

They learned how to

- find the perimeter of polygons.
- find the area of squares, rectangles, parallelograms, and triangles.
- find the area and circumference of circles.

Where are we going?

In Section 11A, students will

- classify three-dimensional shapes.
- find the surface area of a polyhedron by using a net of the solid.
- use surface area formulas.
- find the surface area of a cylinder.

Theme: Packages

World Wide Web

If your class has access to the World Wide Web, you might want to use the information found at the Web site address given. The interdisciplinary links relate to topics discussed in this section.

About the Page

This page introduces the theme of the section, packages, and discusses package design.

Ask …

- Why are boxes and cans the most common packagings for food products?
- How do food manufacturers attract a customer's attention?

Extensions

The following activities do not require access to the World Wide Web.

Consumer

Food producers are now required by law to list ingredients, calories, grams of fat, and other nutrition information on their packages. Ask students to bring in samples of food packages and discuss the information listed on them.

Industry

How does a business design its packages to help sell its products? Ask students to bring empty cereal boxes or other product packages to school. Have students compare the designs of the packages.

Answers for Questions

1. Answers may vary.
2. Possible answers: To describe the size, shape, contents, and weight of a package.

Connect

On page 599, students design and decorate a package for a new toy.

11-1 Lesson Organizer

Objective

- Classify different solids.

Vocabulary

- Solid, face, edge, polyhedron, prism, base, pyramid, net, cylinder, cone, sphere, cube

Materials

- Explore: Prisms, pyramids, spheres, cones, cylinders

NCTM Standards

- 1–4, 12

▶ Review

Discuss the following questions.

1. Name as many different polygons as you can. Answers may vary.
2. Why is a circle not considered to be a polygon? A polygon cannot have curved edges, so a circle cannot be a polygon.

Available on Daily Transparency 11-1

1 Introduce

Explore

You may wish to use Lesson Enhancement Transparency 53 with this lesson.

The Point
Students compare several different kinds of solid figures and describe them so that someone else would know what they are describing. Then they discuss which of the shapes are familiar in packaging of products.

Ongoing Assessment
Watch for students who give descriptions that might describe more than one type of figure.

For Groups That Finish Early
Which polygons appear most often in the figures? Rectangles and triangles

11-1 Classifying Solids

You'll Learn ...

- to classify different solids

... How It's Used

Art instructors use solid classifications when describing to students how to draw a particular object.

Vocabulary

solid
face
edge
polyhedron
prism
base
pyramid
net
cylinder
cone
sphere
cube

▶ Lesson Link You know how to classify flat figures, like circles and polygons. Now you'll classify three-dimensional shapes. ◀

Explore Solids

Shape Up and Ship Out!

Materials: Prisms, Pyramids, Spheres, Cones, Cylinders

1. Choose several of the available shapes.
2. Describe each shape so that someone reading your description could tell which solid you were describing.
3. Which figures remind you of shapes used to package familiar products? Name some of the products. Why might the manufacturers have chosen those shapes?
4. Which package shapes would be easiest to make and transport? Which would be most difficult? Explain.

Learn Classifying Solids

A **solid** is a three-dimensional figure or a figure that takes up space. The flat surfaces of a solid are called **faces**. The line where two faces come together is an **edge**. The point where several edges come together is a *vertex*.

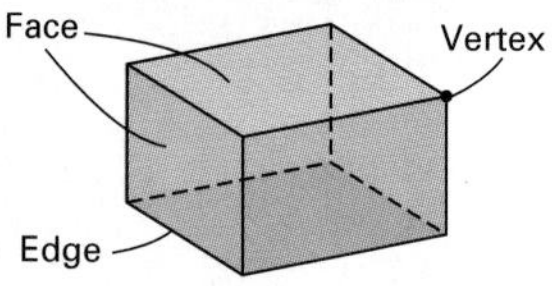

A solid whose faces are polygons is called a **polyhedron**. If two of the faces are parallel and congruent, the polyhedron is a **prism**. The parallel faces of a prism are the **bases**.

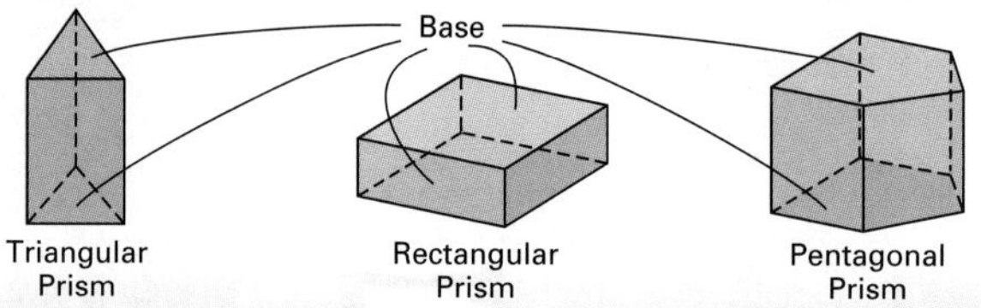

MEETING INDIVIDUAL NEEDS

Resources

- **11-1** Practice
- **11-1** Reteaching
- **11-1** Problem Solving
- **11-1** Enrichment
- **11-1** Daily Transparency
  - Problem of the Day
  - Review
  - Quick Quiz

Lesson Enhancement Transparency 53

Technology Master 57

Learning Modalities

Visual Have students use magazines or newspapers to find illustrations for the various kinds of solid figures. Then have them make a bulletin board display.

Kinesthetic Use the solid figures mentioned in **Explore** and have students point out edges, faces, and vertices of various solid figures.

English Language Development

Many new vocabulary words are introduced in this lesson. It would be helpful to take extra time with students for whom English is a second language. You might have these students make up cards with a drawing to illustrate each new word. Also, have students find out the equivalent terms in their native language. This information can be displayed on a chart.

A **pyramid** is a solid with one base. All the other faces are triangles. Both prisms and pyramids can be named by the shapes of their bases.

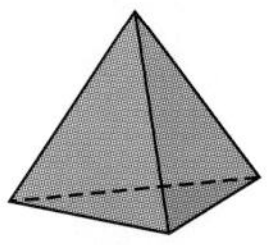
Triangular pyramid

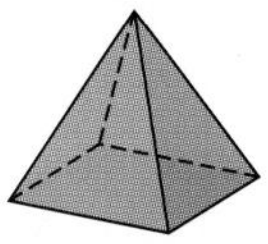
Rectangular pyramid

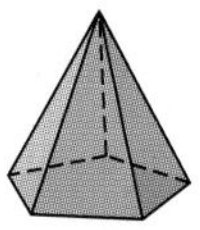
Pentagonal pyramid

Solids with curved surfaces are not polyhedrons.

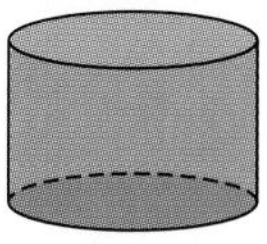
Cylinder

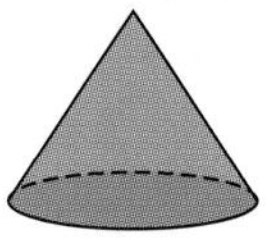
Cone

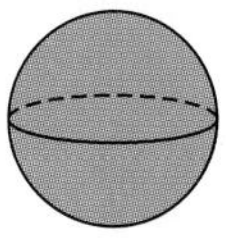
Sphere

DID YOU KNOW?

Products in a grocery store are carefully arranged on the shelves. The more popular an item is, the closer it is placed to eye level. This is done to encourage shoppers to buy the item.

Examples

Classify each solid. If the solid is a polyhedron, tell how many faces, edges, and vertices it has.

1

The solid is a triangular prism with 5 faces, 9 edges, and 6 vertices.

2

The solid is a square (or rectangular) pyramid with 5 faces, 8 edges, and 5 vertices.

3

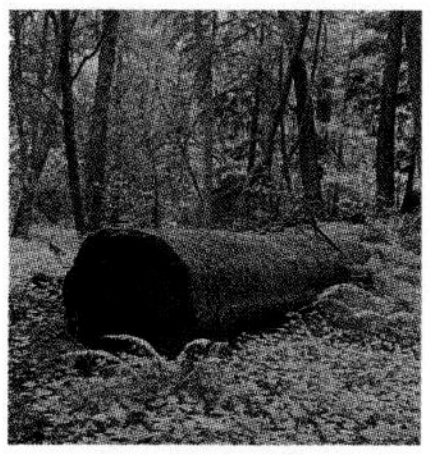

The solid is a cylinder. It is not a polyhedron.

A flat pattern that can be folded into a solid is called a **net**. A solid may have several different nets. Both nets in the figure can be folded to make a **cube** (a square prism).

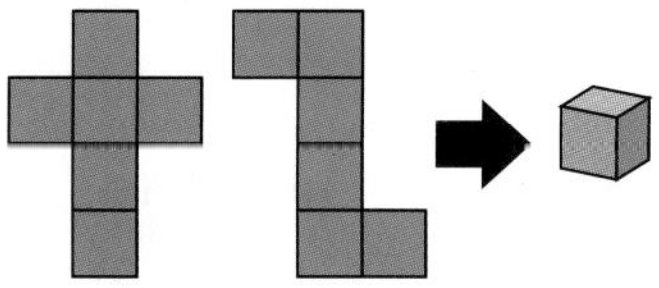

MATH EVERY DAY

Problem of the Day

Australian Thomas Morris liked skipping rope. In 1937 he set a record by skipping a rope for two hours, two seconds. The first hour he averaged $3\frac{1}{3}$ skips per second. The rest of the time he averaged 3 skips per second. How many times did he skip the rope in his record-setting session? 22,806 skips $[(3\frac{1}{3} \times 60 \times 60) + (3 \times 60 \times 60) + (3 \times 2)]$

Available on Daily Transparency 11-1

An Extension is provided in the transparency package.

Fact of the Day

A bee's nest is made of 6-sided cells. The walls, only $\frac{1}{80}$ of an inch thick, can support 30 times their own weight.

Mental Math

Find each sum mentally.

1. $\frac{1}{4} + \frac{1}{4}$ $\frac{1}{2}$
2. $\frac{3}{8} + \frac{3}{8}$ $\frac{3}{4}$
3. $\frac{7}{9} + \frac{1}{9}$ $\frac{8}{9}$
4. $\frac{9}{16} + \frac{3}{16}$ $\frac{3}{4}$

Answers for Explore

1–2. Answers may vary.

3. Possible answer: Prisms, cylinders; These shapes are commonly used for food containers. The shapes are probably chosen because they are the most efficient means of packaging the products.

4. Answers may vary.

2 Teach

Learn

Point out that drawings of three-dimensional figures are flat, even though the figures they represent are not flat. Dashed lines are used to represent hidden edges.

Alternate Examples

Classify each solid. If the solid is a polyhedron, tell how many faces, edges, and vertices it has.

1.

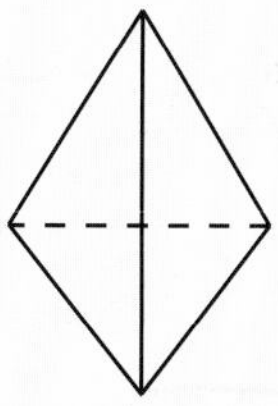

The figure is a triangular pyramid. It has 4 faces, 6 edges, and 4 vertices.

2.

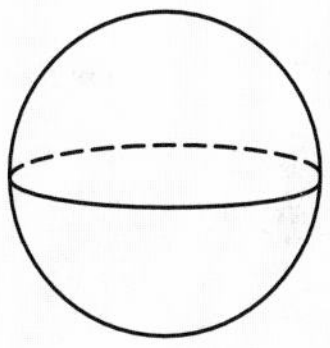

The figure is a sphere.

3.

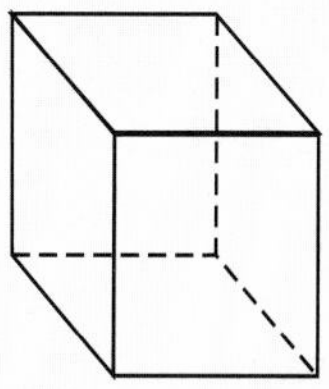

The figure is a rectangular prism. It has 6 faces, 12 edges, and 8 vertices.

11-1 Exercises and Applications

Assignment Guide

- **Basic** 1–20, 23, 26–32 evens
- **Average** 5–24, 26–32 evens
- **Enriched** 7–33

3 Practice and Assess

Check

Answers for Check Your Understanding

1. No; No; A prism has two bases whereas a pyramid has one base. A sphere has a curved surface whereas a polyhedron has faces that are polygons.
2. The bases can be any polygons; The sides are rectangles.

Exercise Answers

7. Triangular prism; 6 vertices, 9 edges, 5 faces.

10. Rectangular prism; 8 vertices, 12 edges, 6 faces.

12. Triangular pyramid; 4 vertices, 6 edges, 4 faces.

13–16. See page C5.

Reteaching

Activity

Materials: Graph paper, scissors

- Use the two nets for cubes on page 581 and a sheet of graph paper to enlarge the nets.
- Choose a convenient size for the squares, and make all squares the same size.
- Cut out the nets and then fold them to make cubes.

Check Your Understanding

1. Is a pyramid a prism? Is a sphere a polyhedron? Explain.
2. In a prism, what shapes appear as the bases?

11-1 Exercises and Applications

PRACTICE 11-1

Practice and Apply

1. Square and triangles
2. Rectangles and triangles

Getting Started For each figure, state the shape of each face.

1. 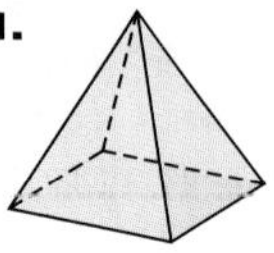
2. 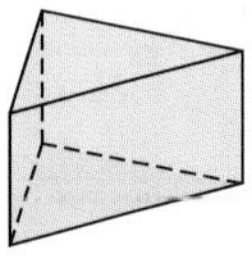
3. 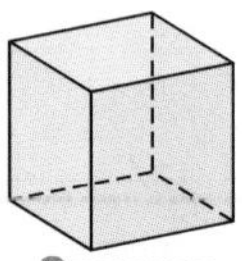 Squares
4. 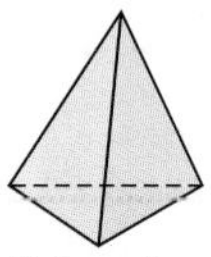 Triangles

Geometry Classify each solid. If it is a polyhedron, tell how many vertices, edges, and faces it has.

5. 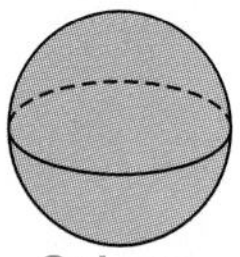 Sphere
6. 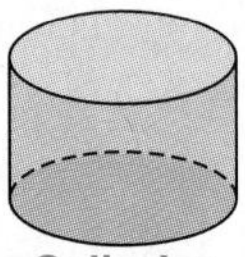 Cylinder
7. 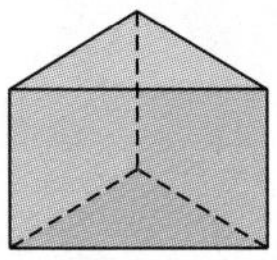
8. 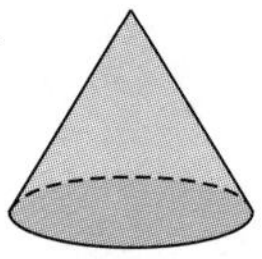 Cone
9. 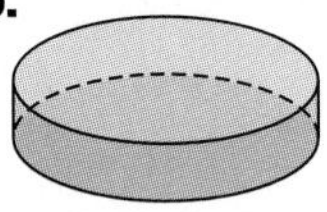 Cylinder
10. 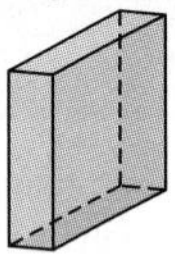
11. 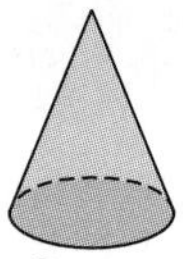 Cone
12. 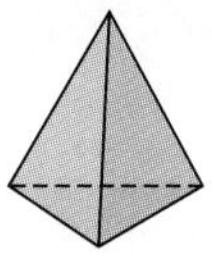

Geometry Draw an example of each.

13. Sphere
14. Triangular prism
15. Cylinder
16. Cone

Classify each group of figures.

17. 

Rectangular prisms

18. 

Cylinders

19. 
Spheres

PRACTICE

Name ____________

Practice 11-1

Classifying Solids

Classify each solid. If it is a polyhedron, tell how many vertices, edges, and faces it has.

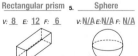

1. Cone — V: N/A E: N/A F: N/A 
2. Cylinder — V: N/A E: N/A F: N/A 
3. Triangular pyramid — V: 4 E: 6 F: 4 
4. Rectangular prism — V: 8 E: 12 F: 6 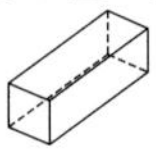
5. Sphere — V: N/A E: N/A F: N/A 
6. Triangular prism — V: 6 E: 9 F: 5 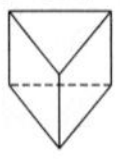

Draw an example of each. Possible answers.

7. Cube 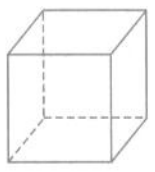
8. Square pyramid 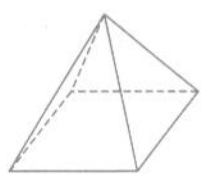
9. Rectangular prism 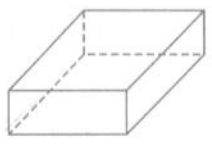

Classify each group of figures.

10. Cones 

11. Triangular prisms 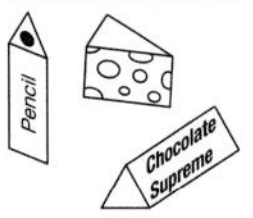

12. Rectangular prisms 

RETEACHING

Name ____________

Alternative Lesson 11-1

Classifying Solids

A **solid** is a three-dimensional figure or a figure that takes up space. The flat surfaces of a solid are called **faces**. The line where two faces come together is an **edge**. The point where several edges come together is a *vertex*.

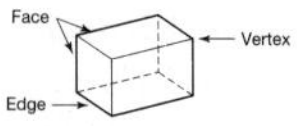

A solid whose faces are polygons is called a **polyhedron**. If two of the faces are parallel and congruent, the polyhedron is a **prism**. The parallel faces of a prism are the **bases**.

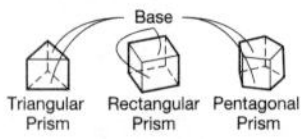

A **pyramid** is a solid with one base. All the other faces are triangles. Both prisms and pyramids can be named by the shapes of their bases.

Example

Classify the solid. If it is a polyhedron, tell how many vertices, edges, and faces it has.

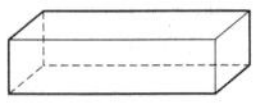

The solid is made up of flat surfaces, so it is a polyhedron.
It has two bases so it is a prism.
The bases are rectangles, so it is a rectangular prism.
There are 8 vertices, 12 edges, and 6 faces.
So, the figure is a rectangular prism with 8 vertices, 12 edges, and 6 faces.

Try It

Complete the table to classify each solid. If it is a polyhedron, tell how many vertices, edges, and faces it has.

	(pyramid)	(sphere)	(prism)
Number of bases	One	None	Two
Shape of base	Triangle	N/A	Pentagon
Figure	Triangular pyramid	Sphere	Pentagonal prism
Vertices	4	N/A	10
Edges	6	N/A	15
Faces	4	N/A	7

20. **Test Prep** How many edges and vertices does the given figure have? **A**

Ⓐ 6 edges and 4 vertices

Ⓑ 7 edges and 6 vertices

Ⓒ 6 edges and 5 vertices

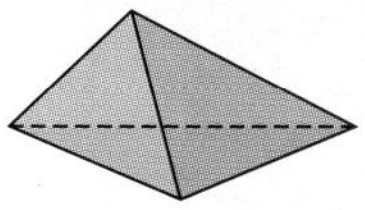

Name the solids in each figure.

21.

22.

Rickey, George. "Cluster of Four Cubes," 1992, stainless steel. National Gallery of Art, Washington D.C. Gift of George Rickey and Patrons Permanent Fund.

Problem Solving and Reasoning

23. Critical Thinking Use what you know about triangular, rectangular, and pentagonal prisms to draw a hexagonal prism. Classify each of the faces and explain your drawing. GPS

24. Critical Thinking Heidi is mailing a set of building blocks to her cousin. She needs to decide which box to use. Most of the blocks are rectangular or triangular prisms, and the types of boxes she can use are shown. Explain to Heidi what shape box she should use and why.

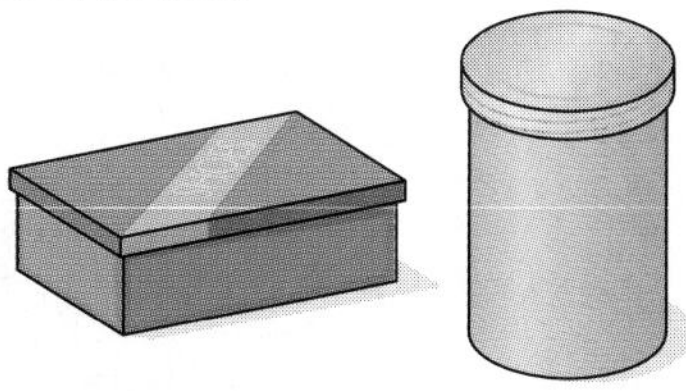

25. Communicate Can you classify a polyhedron if you know only how many edges it has? Vertices? Faces? Explain your reasoning.

Mixed Review

26. What is the ratio of vowels to letters in the alphabet? *[Lesson 10-1]* **5 to 26**

27. Give the ratio of pennies in a dollar to dimes in a dollar. *[Lesson 10-1]* **100 to 10**

Write each as a decimal. *[Lesson 5-7]*

28. $\frac{3}{8}$ **0.375** **29.** $\frac{10}{4}$ **2.5** **30.** $3\frac{1}{2}$ **3.5** **31.** $\frac{3}{4}$ **0.75** **32.** $\frac{24}{12}$ **2.0** **33.** $\frac{5}{6}$ **$0.8\overline{3}$**

PROBLEM SOLVING 11-1

PROBLEM SOLVING

Name ______________________

Guided Problem Solving 11-1

GPS **PROBLEM 23, STUDENT PAGE 583**

Use what you know about triangular, rectangular, and pentagonal prisms to draw a hexagonal prism. Classify each of the faces and explain your drawing.

Understand

1. What are you asked to draw? **Hexagonal prism.**
2. Does a prism have one base or two parallel, congruent bases? **Two bases.**

Plan

3. What polygon makes up the base for each of these prisms?
   a. Triangular **Triangle.** b. Rectangular **Rectangle.**
   c. Pentagonal **Pentagon.**
4. What polygon will make up the base of a hexagonal prism? **Hexagon.**
5. What polygon makes up the sides for each of the three given prisms? **Rectangle.**
6. What polygon will make up the sides of a hexagonal prism? **Rectangle.**

Solve

7. Draw a hexagonal prism. **Possible answer:**

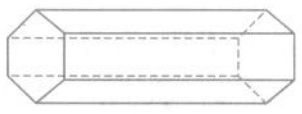

8. Explain your drawing.
   3-D shape; 2 hexagonal bases; 6 rectangular sides.

Look Back

9. What is the pattern in the number of faces in triangular, rectangular, and pentagonal prisms? How many faces will be in a hexagonal prism?
   Possible answer: The pattern of faces increases by 1: 5, 6, 7... so there will be 8 faces in the hexagon.

SOLVE ANOTHER PROBLEM

Draw an octagonal prism. Classify each of the faces and explain your drawing? **Possible answer:**

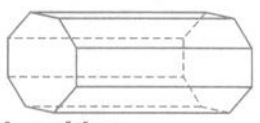

3-D shape; 2 octagonal bases; 8 rectangular sides.

ENRICHMENT

Name ______________________

Extend Your Thinking 11-1

Patterns in Geometry Possible answers: Items 5 and 10

Find the vertices, edges, and faces for each figure.

1. **6** vertices, **9** edges, **5** faces

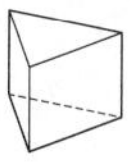

2. **8** vertices, **12** edges, **6** faces

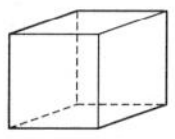

3. **10** vertices, **15** edges, **7** faces

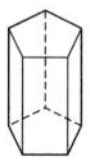

4. **12** vertices, **18** edges, **8** faces

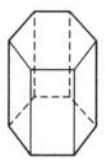

5. What pattern do you see in the number of vertices, edges, and faces of the prisms?
   If n = number of sides, then v (vertices) = $2n$, e (edges) = $3n$, and f (faces) = $n + 2$.

6. **4** vertices, **6** edges, **4** faces

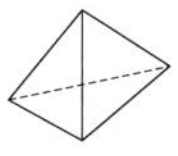

7. **5** vertices, **8** edges, **5** faces

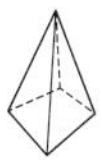

8. **6** vertices, **10** edges, **6** faces

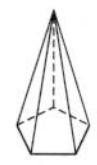

9. **7** vertices, **12** edges, **7** faces

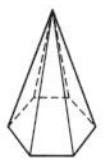

10. What pattern do you see in the number of vertices, edges, and faces of the pyramids?
    If n = number of sides, then v (vertices) = $n + 1$, e (edges) = $2n$, and f (faces) = $n + 1$.

Exercise Notes

■ Exercise 24

Consumer In 1954 a Danish carpenter named Ole KirkChristiansen invented interlocking plastic blocks called Lego®. They became popular as children's toys. The word *Lego* is based on two Danish words meaning "play well."

Exercise Answers

21. cone
22. cubes
23.

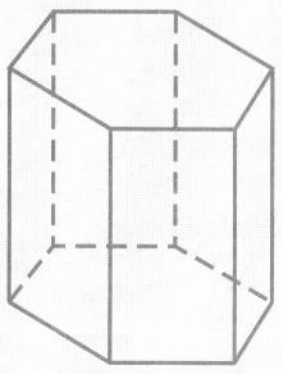

Each base is a hexagon and the 6 faces are rectangles.

24. Possible answer: Most of the blocks have straight edges so she should use a rectangular-prism box in order to minimize wasted space.
25. No; No; No; Possible answer: To classify a polyhedron, you need to know the shapes of the faces. Knowing how many edges, vertices, or faces does not mean that you can determine the shapes of the faces.

Alternate Assessment

Interview Have students explain how they determine if a three-dimensional figure is a prism.

► Quick Quiz

Classify each solid. If it is a polyhedron, state the number of vertices, edges, and faces.

1.

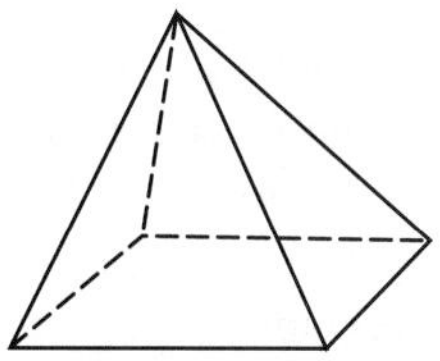

Rectangular pyramid; 5 vertices, 8 edges, 5 faces.

2.

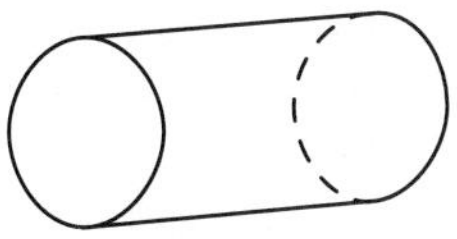

Cylinder

Available on Daily Transparency 11-1

11-2 Lesson Organizer

Objective

- Find the surface area of a polyhedron by using a net of the solid.

Vocabulary

- Surface area (SA)

Materials

- Explore: Cuisenaire rods, centimeter graph paper

NCTM Standards

- 1–4, 12, 13

Review

Find the area of each polygon.

1. Rectangle with base 10 cm and height 5 cm 50 cm^2
2. Square with side 10 yd 100 yd^2
3. Triangle with base 7 mm and height 8 mm 28 mm^2

Available on Daily Transparency 11-2

1 Introduce

Explore

The Point
Students explore how arranging Cuisenaire rods in different ways can affect the surface area of a solid.

Ongoing Assessment
Watch for students who have trouble drawing nets for the prisms. Suggest that students fold their nets around the Cuisenaire rods to ensure that they have constructed the nets properly.

For Groups That Finish Early
Pick one of the prisms you created and draw a different net that would cover the prism.

Answers for Explore
1–3. Answers may vary.
4. Yes; Explanations may vary.

11-2 Exploring Surface Area

You'll Learn ...
- to find the surface area of a polyhedron by using a net of the solid

... How It's Used
Upholsterers use surface area when designing covers for furniture.

Vocabulary
surface area (SA)

▶ Lesson Link In the last lesson you learned how to name solids. Now you'll find the area of the net for a polyhedron. ◀

Explore Areas of Solids

Wrap Artists

Materials: Cuisenaire rods, Centimeter graph paper

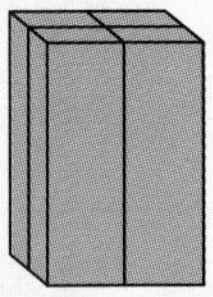

1. Choose four Cuisenaire rods of the same color. Create a rectangular prism by putting the rods together as shown. Draw a net for your rectangular prism. How many squares will it take to cover the prism?
2. Using the same four rods, put them together as shown. Draw a net for this prism. How many squares will it take to cover this prism?
3. Repeat Steps 1 and 2 with a different set of four rods.
4. When you change the way four rods are arranged to make a prism, does that change the number of squares needed to cover the prism? Explain.

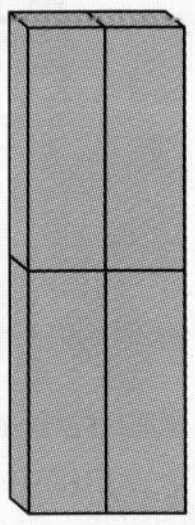

Learn Surface Area

The **surface area (SA)** of a polyhedron is the sum of the areas of all of its faces. To find the surface area of a polyhedron such as this rectangular prism, unfold it into a net of polygons and then add their areas.

Like the area for a single polygon, surface area is measured in square units, such as cm^2.

MEETING INDIVIDUAL NEEDS

Resources

- 11-2 Practice
- 11-2 Reteaching
- 11-2 Problem Solving
- 11-2 Enrichment
- 11-2 Daily Transparency
  - Problem of the Day
  - Review
  - Quick Quiz
- Chapter 11 Project Master

Learning Modalities

Verbal Have students write a paragraph describing how they would determine the surface area of a rectangular prism.

Kinesthetic Have students use graph paper and copy the nets shown in Exercise 14 on page 587. Then have them try folding the nets to see which net actually forms a cube.

Inclusion

Some students will have trouble visualizing solid figures when the nets are given. It is helpful for them to actually cut out nets and fold them to form solid figures. When testing, students may need to make cut-outs and manipulate them.

Examples

1 For the solid, count the number of faces and state the shape of each face.

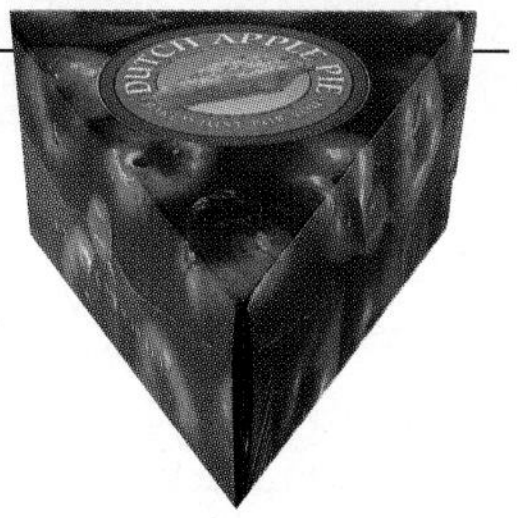

The solid has five faces. The top and the bottom are triangles. The other three faces are rectangles.

2 Find the surface area of the pyramid.

The net consists of a 5-by-5 square and 4 triangles with bases of 5 and heights of 6.

SA = area of square + area of 4 triangles

$$\begin{aligned} SA &= (5 \times 5) + 4 \times (5 \times 6 \div 2) \\ &= 25 + 4 \times (15) \\ &= 25 + 60 \\ &= 85 \end{aligned}$$

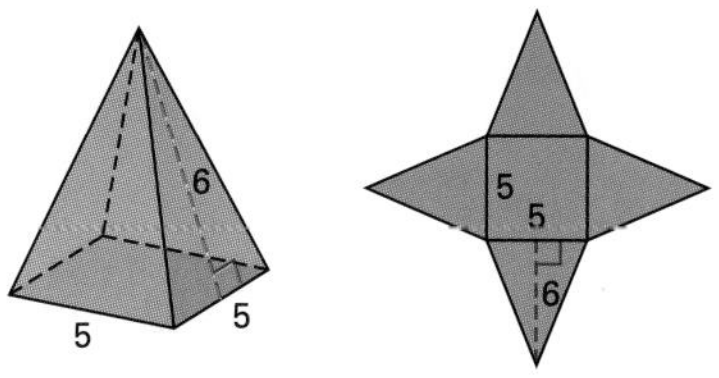

The surface area is 85 square units.

HINT

The STO► button stores numbers in the calculator's memory. Press 5 × 5 = STO► to store the area of the square. When you know the area of the four triangles, press + RCL = to add this to the number in memory.

Try It

a. Count the number of faces, and state the shape of each face. 6 faces: All rectangles

b. Find the surface area. 272 units^2

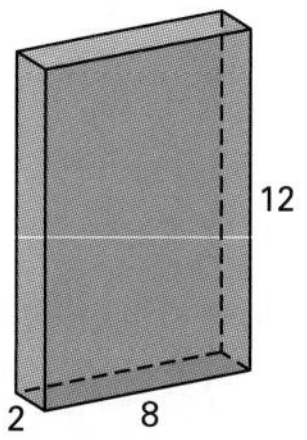

Check Your Understanding

1. Why must you be able to find areas of polygons in order to find surface areas of polyhedrons?

2. Describe a shortcut for finding the surface area of a cube.

MATH EVERY DAY

Problem of the Day

Draw the figure that continues the pattern.

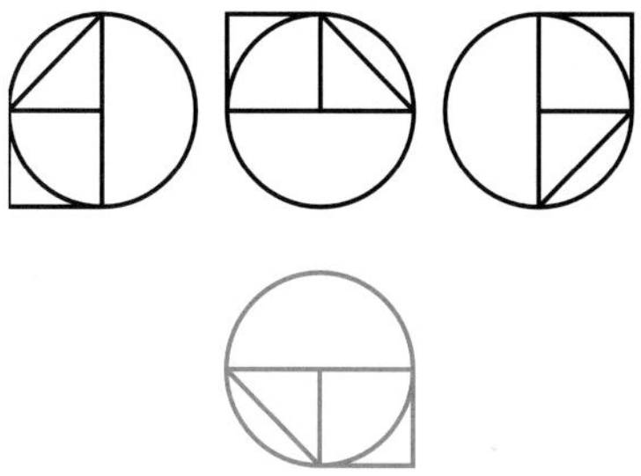

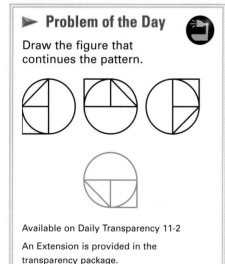

Available on Daily Transparency 11-2

An Extension is provided in the transparency package.

Fact of the Day

The United States Postal Service delivered 177,100,000,000 pieces of mail in 1994.

Estimation

Estimate each product.

1. 27×39 1200
2. 81×41 3200
3. 711×12 8400
4. 998×19 19,000

2 Teach

Learn

Remind students that all faces of a polyhedron are polygons, but not all solid figures are polyhedrons.

Alternate Examples

1. For the solid, count the number of faces and state the shape of each face.

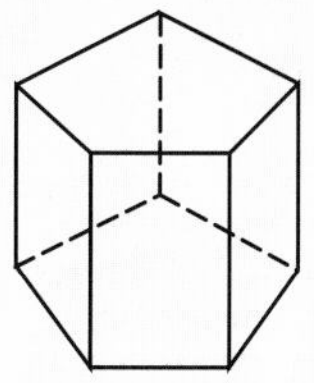

The solid has seven faces. The top and the bottom are pentagons. The other five faces are rectangles.

2. Find the surface area of the pyramid.

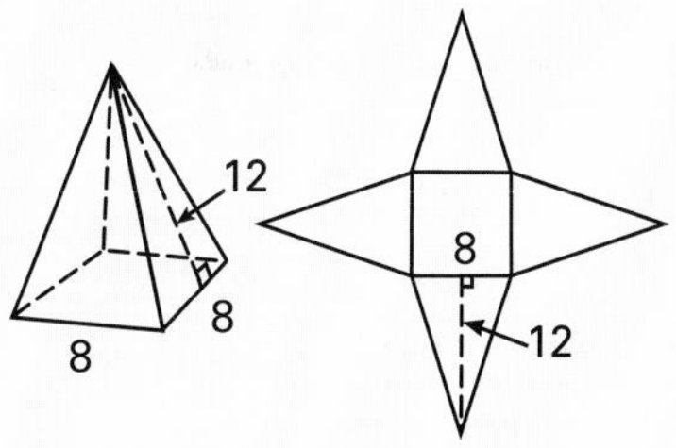

The net consists of an 8-by-8 square and 4 triangles with a base of 8 and height of 12.

SA = area of square + area of 4 triangles

$$\begin{aligned} SA &= (8 \times 8) + 4 \times (8 \times 12 \div 2) \\ &= 64 + 4 \times (48) \\ &= 64 + 192 \\ &= 256 \end{aligned}$$

The surface area is 256 square units.

3 Practice and Assess

Check

Answers for Check Your Understanding

1. The surface area of a polyhedron is the sum of the areas of the faces, which are polygons.
2. SA = $6s^2$, where s is the length of a side.

11-2 Exercises and Applications

Assignment Guide

- **Basic** 1–4, 5–13 odds, 14, 17–27 odds
- **Average** 2–15, 17–27 odds
- **Enriched** 5–18, 20–28 evens

Exercise Answers

5. 24 cm^2; Cube or rectangular prism
6. 22.5 yd^2; Rectangular prism
7. 60 $units^2$; Triangular prism
8. 62.4 in^2; Triangular pyramid
9. 6 faces: All rectangles; 310 ft^2
10. 6 faces: All rectangles; 184 in^2
11. 5 faces: 2 triangles and 3 rectangles; 112.4 in^2

11-2 Exercises and Applications

Practice and Apply

Getting Started Find each area.

1. 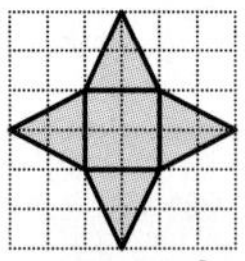
12 $units^2$

2. 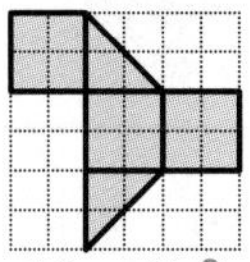
16 $units^2$

3. 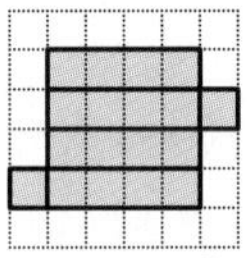
18 $units^2$

4. 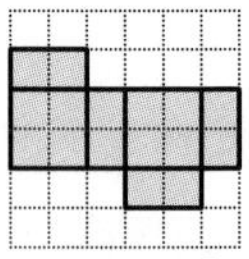
16 $units^2$

Geometry Find the area of each net. Classify the solid.

5. 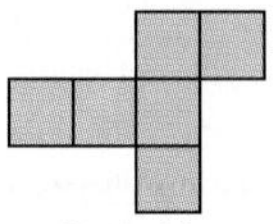
Each side is 2 cm

6. 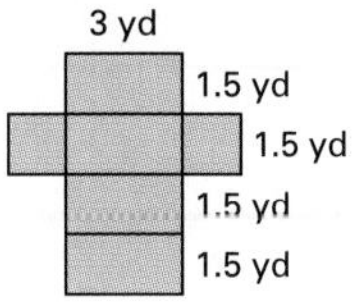

7. 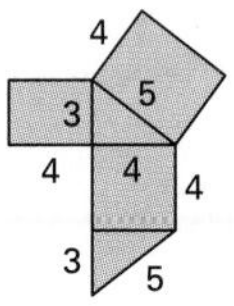

8. 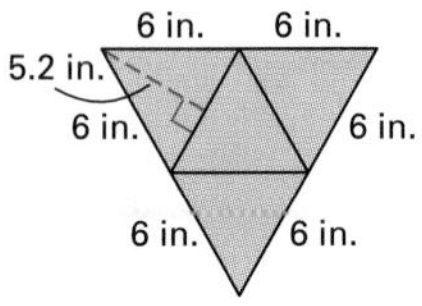

Geometry For exercises 9–11, state the number of faces. Then classify each face and find the total surface area.

9. 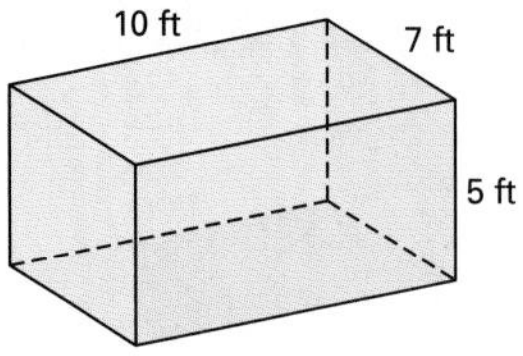

10. 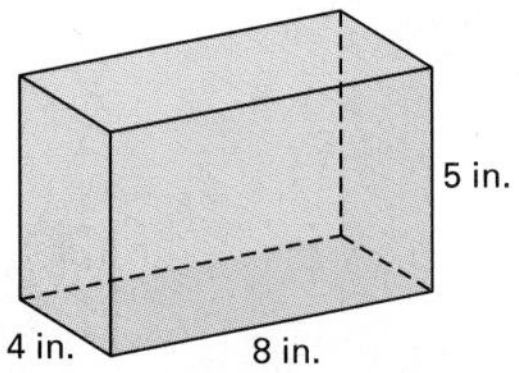

11. 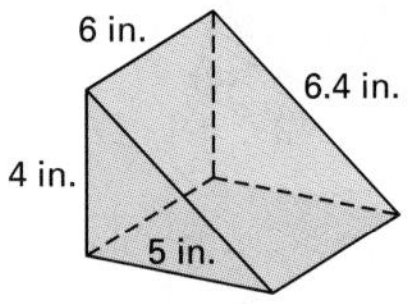

12. A box of spaghetti measures $1\frac{1}{2}$ in. wide, 4 in. long and 12 in. high. What is the total surface area of the package? 144 in^2

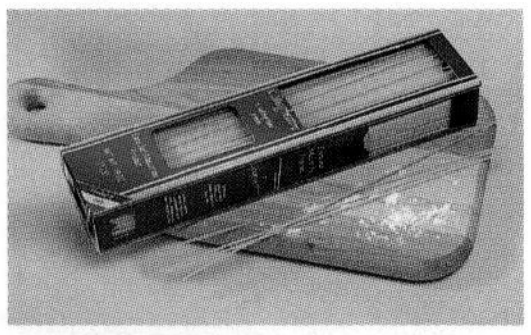

13. GPS If wrapping paper costs $0.29 a square foot, how much would it cost to cover the box shown? $0.93

PRACTICE

Name ____________________

Practice 11-2

Exploring Surface Area

Find the area of each net. Classify the solid.

1. *SA:* 1000 ft^2 Square pyramid
2. *SA:* 121.5 cm^2 Cube
3. *SA:* 920 in^2 Triangular prism

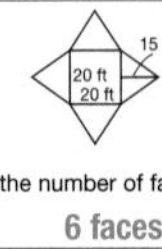

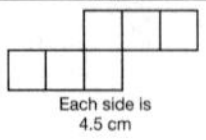
Each side is 4.5 cm

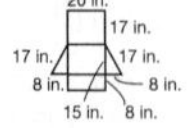

State the number of faces. Then classify each face and find the total surface area.

4. 6 faces: 6 rectangles
   SA: 318 in^2

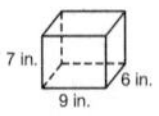

5. 5 faces: 2 triangles, 3 rectangles
   SA: 13,398 cm^2

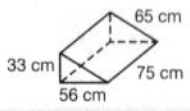

6. 6 faces: 6 squares
   SA: 384 m^2

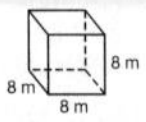

7. 6 faces: 2 trapezoids, 4 rectangles
   SA: 3,610 mm^2

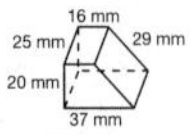

8. 6 faces: 6 rectangles
   SA: 684 ft^2

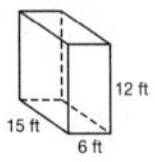

9. 5 faces: 4 triangles, 1 square
   SA: 6.44 cm^2

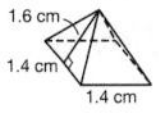

10. A box of shredded wheat cereal measures 7 in. by $9\frac{3}{4}$ in. by $2\frac{1}{4}$ in. How much cardboard was used to make the box? (Assume there is no overlap.) $211\frac{7}{8}$ in^2

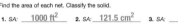

RETEACHING

Name ____________________

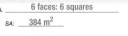

Alternative Lesson 11-2

Exploring Surface Area

The **surface area (*SA*)** of a polyhedron is the sum of the areas of all of its faces. To find the surface area of a polyhedron such as this rectangular prism, unfold it into a net of polygons and then add their areas.

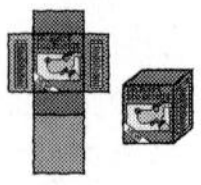

Like the area for a single polygon, surface area is measured in square units, such as cm^2.

Example

Find the surface area of the prism.

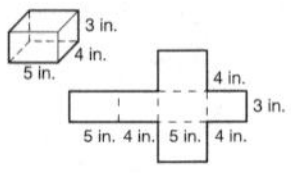

The net consists of 2 rectangles with lengths of 5 in. and widths of 4 in., two 4 in.-by-3 in. rectangles, and two 5 in.-by-3 in. rectangles.

SA = area of 2 rectangles + area of 2 rectangles + area of 2 rectangles

$$\begin{aligned} SA &= 2 \times (5 \times 4) &+ 2 \times (4 \times 3) &+ 2 \times (5 \times 3) \\ &= 2 \times (20) &+ 2 \times (12) &+ 2 \times (15) \\ &= 40 &+ 24 &+ 30 \\ &= 94 \text{ in}^2 \end{aligned}$$

The surface area of the rectangular prism is 94 in^2.

Try It

Find the surface area of each solid.

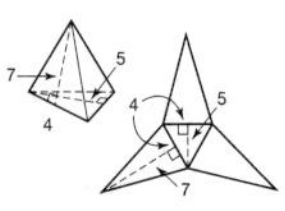

a. Which polygons make up the net? 4 triangles.

b. Write an equation to find the area of the base. $A = \frac{1}{2} \times 4 \times 5 = 10$

c. Write an equation to find the area of each of the other faces. $A = \frac{1}{2} \times 4 \times 7 = 14$

d. What is the area of all the other faces? 42 $units^2$

e. Add to find the surface area. 52 $units^2$

f. 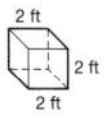

24 ft^2 SA

g. 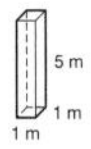

22 m^2 SA

Reteaching

Activity

Materials: Cardboard box

- Work in groups of three or four.
- Use a cardboard box to make a net.
- Cut along several edges so that the box can be laid flat to illustrate its net.
- Find the surface area of the cardboard box. Answers may vary.

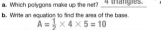

14. **Test Prep** Which net can form a cube? D

Ⓐ Ⓑ Ⓒ Ⓓ

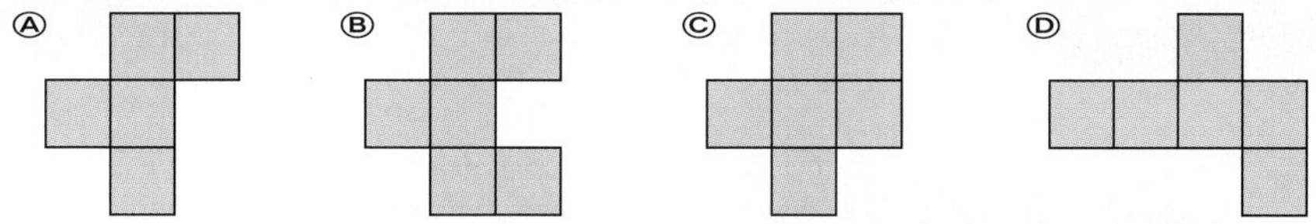

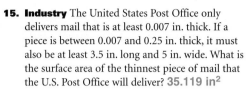

15. **Industry** The United States Post Office only delivers mail that is at least 0.007 in. thick. If a piece is between 0.007 and 0.25 in. thick, it must also be at least 3.5 in. long and 5 in. wide. What is the surface area of the thinnest piece of mail that the U.S. Post Office will deliver? 35.119 in^2

Problem Solving and Reasoning

16. Journal List some differences between the perimeter of a rectangle, the area of a rectangle, and the surface area of a rectangular prism. Can any of the quantities be negative? Explain.

17. **Critical Thinking** Regan has enough foil to cover half of the larger box shown. Since the dimensions of the smaller box are half those of the larger box, she thinks she can completely cover the smaller box instead. Do you agree with Regan? Explain.

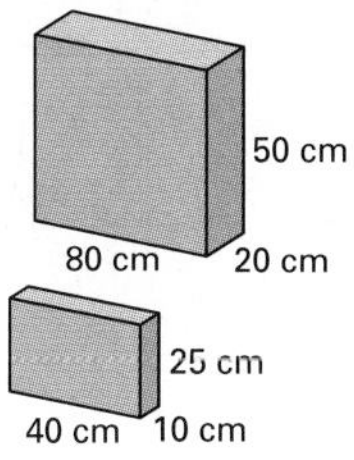

18. **Communicate** Can a polyhedron have more than one net? Can one net form more than one polyhedron? Explain your reasoning.

PROBLEM SOLVING 11-2

Mixed Review

For each ratio, give two equivalent ratios. *[Lesson 10-2]* Possible answers:

19. $\frac{3}{4}$ $\frac{6}{8}$, $\frac{9}{12}$ 20. 6:24 3:12, 2:8 21. $\frac{4}{10}$ $\frac{2}{5}$, $\frac{8}{20}$ 22. 7 to 9 14 to 18, 21 to 27 23. $\frac{11}{12}$ $\frac{22}{24}$, $\frac{33}{36}$ 24. 3:8 6:16, 9:24

Order from smallest to largest. *[Lesson 5-8]*

25. $\frac{1}{2}$, 0.23, 1.23 0.23, $\frac{1}{2}$, 1.23 26. 6.7, $\frac{1}{6}$, $\frac{5}{6}$ $\frac{1}{6}$, $\frac{5}{6}$, 6.7 27. 8.2, $8\frac{1}{4}$, 8.75 8.2, $8\frac{1}{4}$, 8.75 28. $\frac{1}{3}$, $\frac{3}{3}$, 3.3 $\frac{1}{3}$, $\frac{3}{3}$, 3.3

Project Progress

A fish needs at least 20 square inches of water surface on the top of the tank for each inch of body length. Based on the total length of all of your fish, find out what the area of the water surface in your aquarium should be. Use this number to figure out a possible length and width for the tank.

Problem Solving
Understand
Plan
Solve
Look Back

PROBLEM SOLVING

Name ______

Guided Problem Solving 11-2

GPS PROBLEM 13, STUDENT PAGE 586

If wrapping paper costs $0.29 a square foot, how much would it cost to cover the box shown?

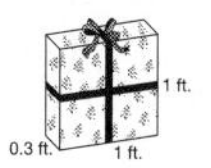

Understand

1. Underline what you are asked to find.
2. How much does the wrapping paper cost? $0.29 per square foot.

Plan

3. How many faces does the box have? 6 faces.
4. What shape is each face? Rectangle.
5. Which net can you use to make the box? b.

a. b.

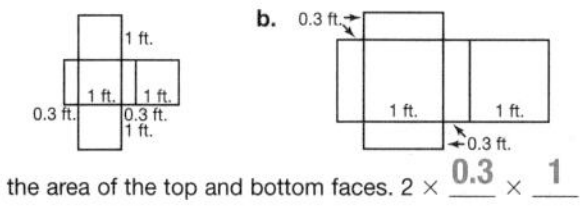

6. Find the area of the top and bottom faces. 2 × 0.3 × 1 = 0.6
7. Find the area of the front and back faces. 2 × 1 × 1 = 2
8. Find the area of the left and right faces. 2 × 0.3 × 1 = 0.6
9. What is the surface area of the box? 3.2 square feet.

Solve

10. Multiply to find the cost of the paper needed to cover the box without overlapping edges. $0.93

Look Back

11. Could you draw a different net for the box? Would it change your answer? Explain.
Yes; no; Dimensions do not change, so neither would answer.

SOLVE ANOTHER PROBLEM

If wrapping paper costs $2.50 a square meter, how much would it cost to cover the box shown? $20

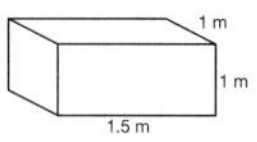

ENRICHMENT

Name ______

Extend Your Thinking 11-2

Visual Thinking

Circle the nets that can be folded to make a cube.

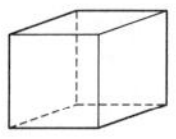

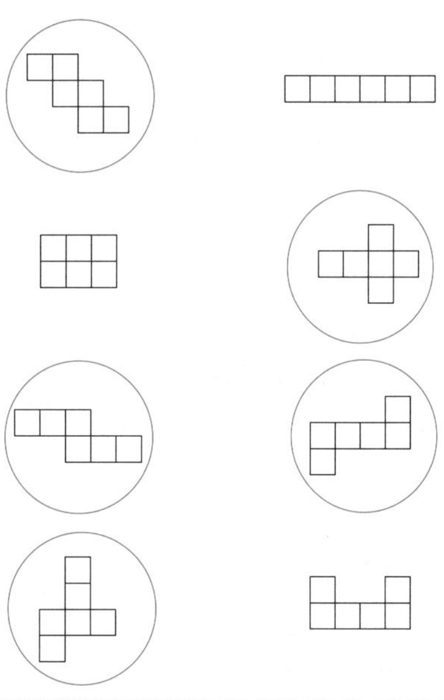

Project Progress

You may want to have students use Chapter 11 Project Master.

Exercise Answers

16. Possible answers: Perimeter is measured in units, but area and surface area are measured in square units. Perimeter is the distance around a two-dimensional figure. Area is the amount of surface a two-dimensional figure covers. Surface area is the sum of the areas of the faces of a three-dimensional figure; No; These quantities are always positive.

17. Yes; The surface area of the larger box is 13,200 cm^2. The surface area of the smaller box is 3,300 cm^2. She could cover the smaller box and more.

18. Sometimes; No; The polygons in the net have to be the same, but sometimes they can be in different places, so two nets for one polyhedron can look different. There is only one way you can fold a net so that all of the edges connect and make a polyhedron.

Alternate Assessment

Portfolio Have students pick several exercises that they think best exemplify the concepts of the lesson.

Quick Quiz

State the number of faces. Then classify each face and find the total surface area.

1.

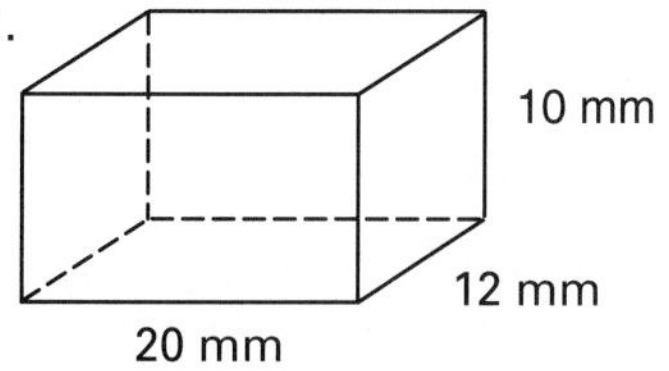

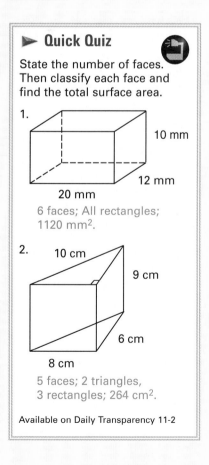

6 faces; All rectangles; 1120 mm^2.

2.

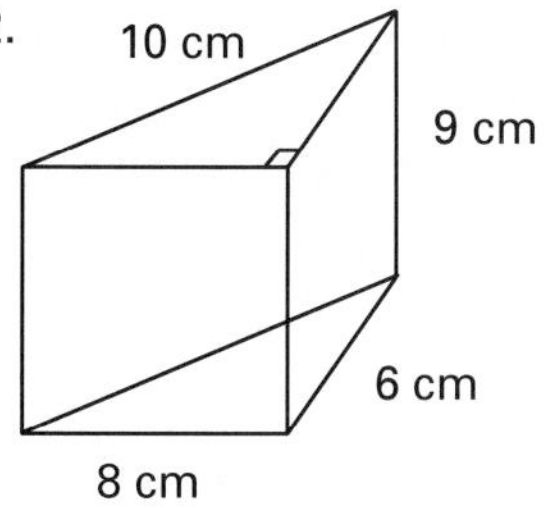

5 faces; 2 triangles, 3 rectangles; 264 cm^2.

Available on Daily Transparency 11-2

11-3 Lesson Organizer

Objective

- **Use surface area formulas.**

NCTM Standards

- **1–4, 12, 13**

▶ Review

Evaluate each expression.

1. $(2 \times 5 \times 7) + (2 \times 5 \times 9) + (2 \times 7 \times 9)$ 286
2. $6(12^2)$ 864
3. $(9 \times 9) + (4 \times (10 \times 8 \div 2))$ 241

Available on Daily Transparency 11-3

▶ Lesson Link

Have students discuss various formulas they have studied for finding areas of polygons.

1 Introduce

Explore

The Point
Students match diagrams of rectangular prisms with the nets for the prisms and then explore how to find the surface area of a rectangular prism.

Ongoing Assessment
Be sure students understand that the numbers shown on the nets represent the areas of the faces, not the lengths of sides. Point out that the art for **Explore** is not drawn to scale.

For Groups That Finish Early
How would the net for a cube differ from the nets in **Explore**? All the polygons would be squares.

Follow Up
For each prism, have students make a drawing of a net different from the one shown.

11-3 Surface Area Formulas

You'll Learn ...

- to use surface area formulas

... How It's Used

Set designers calculate surface area when determining the cost to construct a given set.

▶ Lesson Link You know how to use a net to find the surface area of a polyhedron. Now you will use formulas to find surface areas. ◀

Explore Surface Area

It's All on the Surface

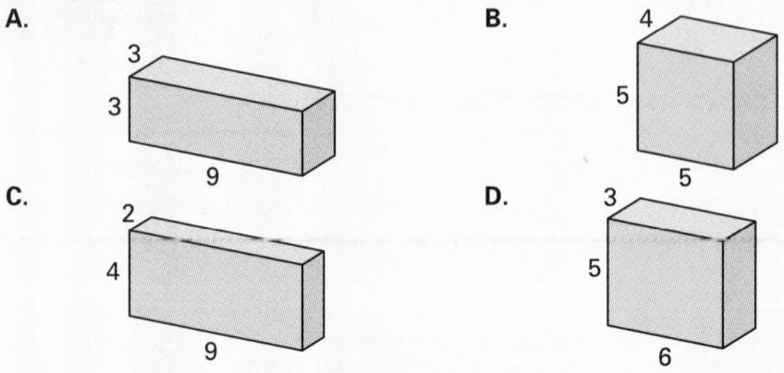

1. Each figure below is a net of one of the prisms above. (Figures not drawn to scale.) The areas of the faces are marked on the nets. Match each prism with its net.

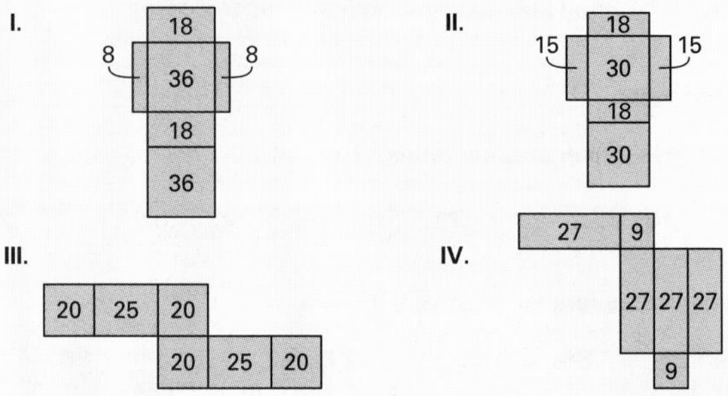

2. Find the surface area of each prism. Describe patterns you see in the areas of the faces.
3. If two prisms have the same surface area, are they the same prism? Explain.
4. Suppose you unfolded one of the above prisms into a net different from the one shown. Would the surface area be different? Explain.

MEETING INDIVIDUAL NEEDS

Resources

11-3 Practice
11-3 Reteaching
11-3 Problem Solving
11-3 Enrichment
11-3 Daily Transparency
- Problem of the Day
- Review
- Quick Quiz

Lesson Enhancement Transparency 54
Technology Master 58

Learning Modalities

Visual Have students make a bulletin board display showing several different cardboard cartons alongside drawings of nets for the cartons.

Social Have students work in groups of three or four to measure the length, width, and height of their classroom and then determine the interior surface area of the classroom, including walls, floor, and ceiling.

Challenge

A set of 27 wooden cubes are glued together to form a $3 \times 3 \times 3$ cube. Then the outside of the cube is painted red. How many of the cubes have paint on 3 sides? 8 On 2 sides? 12 On 1 side? 6 On no sides? 1

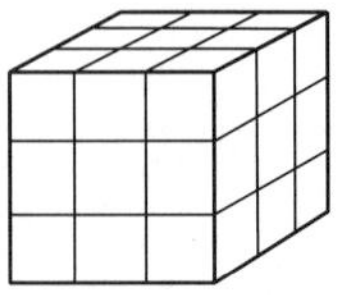

Learn Surface Area Formulas

You've seen that you can find the surface area of any polyhedron by adding the areas of its faces. When a polyhedron is a rectangular prism, you can use a shortcut to find its surface area.

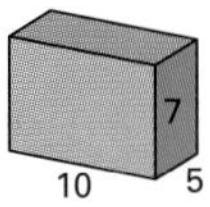

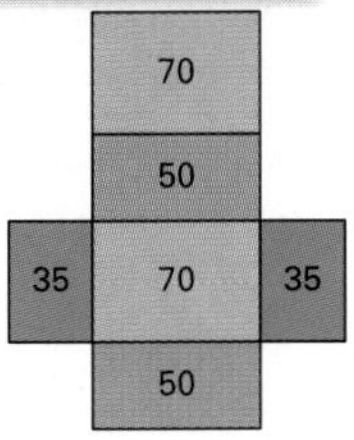

Notice that opposite each face is a "twin" with the same area.

$l \times w \quad l \times w \quad l \times h \quad l \times h \quad w \times h \quad w \times h$

$50 \longleftrightarrow 50 \quad 70 \longleftrightarrow 70 \quad 35 \longleftrightarrow 35$

The total surface area is the sum of the areas of three sets of twins:

$SA = (2 \times 50) + (2 \times 70) + (2 \times 35)$

SA (rectangular prism) = $(2 \times l \times w) + (2 \times l \times h) + (2 \times w \times h)$

Example 1

Find the surface area of the box.

$l = 7, w = 2, h = 6$

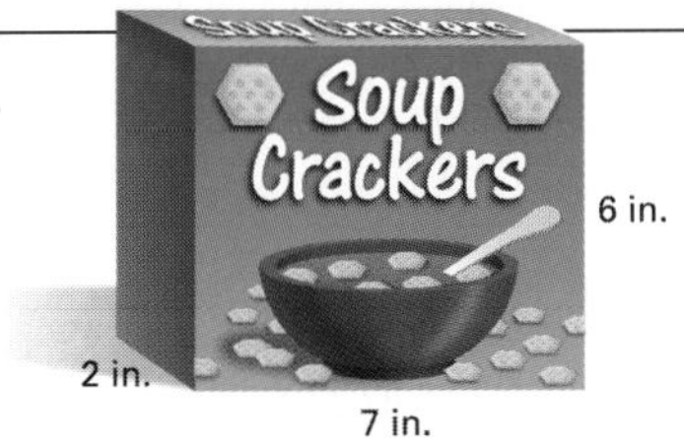

$SA = (2 \times l \times w) + (2 \times l \times h) + (2 \times w \times h)$

$= (2 \times 7 \times 2) + (2 \times 7 \times 6) + (2 \times 2 \times 6)$

$= 28 + 84 + 24$

$= 136$

The surface area is 136 in^2.

Problem Solving TIP

You can also find the area of just the top, front, and side of the box, add these areas together, and then multiply by 2. This method involves less multiplication and may make it easier to spot a mistake in arithmetic.

If a rectangular prism is a cube with side s, the length, width, and height all equal s. This simplifies the surface area formula.

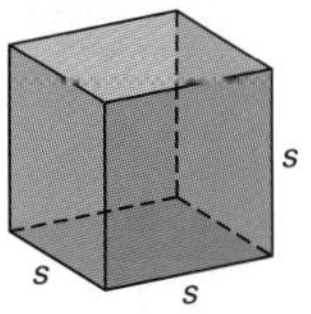

SA (cube) = $6s^2$

Remember

In the formula $6s^2$, the "2" is an exponent. It means that you should multiply the value of s by itself. [Page 78]

Answers for Explore

1. A and IV; B and III; C and I; D and II
2. A 126 units^2; B: 130 units^2; C: 124 units^2; D: 126 units^2. Possible answer: There are always at least two faces of each area.
3. No; See prisms A and D above. They have the same surface area, but are different prisms.
4. No; Since it is still the same figure, the surface area will be the same.

2 Teach

Learn

You may wish to use Lesson Enhancement Transparency 54 with **Try It**.

Alternate Examples

1. Find the surface area of the container.

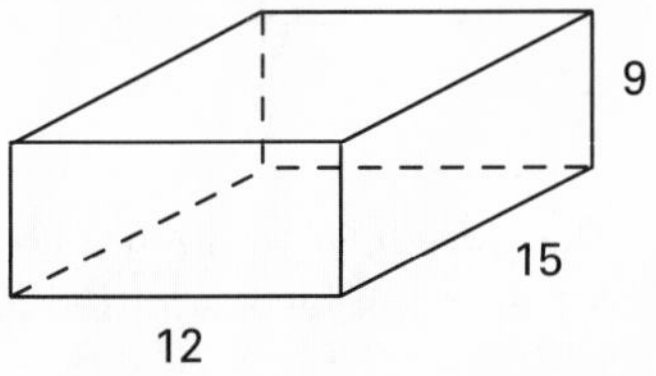

$l = 12$ in., $w = 15$ in., $h = 9$ in.

$SA = (2 \times l \times w) + (2 \times l \times h) + (2 \times w \times h)$

$= (2 \times 12 \times 15) + (2 \times 12 \times 9) + (2 \times 15 \times 9)$

$= 846$

The surface area is 846 in^2.

MATH EVERY DAY

Problem of the Day

Emilio's CD collection contained 2 reggae CDs and 7 country CDs. He has twice as many alternative music CDs as he has country CDs. He has half as many rock CDs as the total of reggae and alternative music. He also has 1 rap CD. If Emilio chooses one of his CDs at random, what are the chances that he will pick a rock CD? 8 out of 32, or 1 out of 4

Available on Daily Transparency 11-3

An Extension is provided in the transparency package.

Fact of the Day

The Great Pyramid of Cheops, a tomb built about 2600 B.C., is 148.2 meters tall and covers 13 acres of land.

Estimation

Estimate each quotient.

1. $710 \div 72$ 10
2. $323 \div 81$ 4
3. $5421 \div 61$ 90
4. $4710 \div 59$ 80

Alternate Examples

2. Find the surface area of the box.

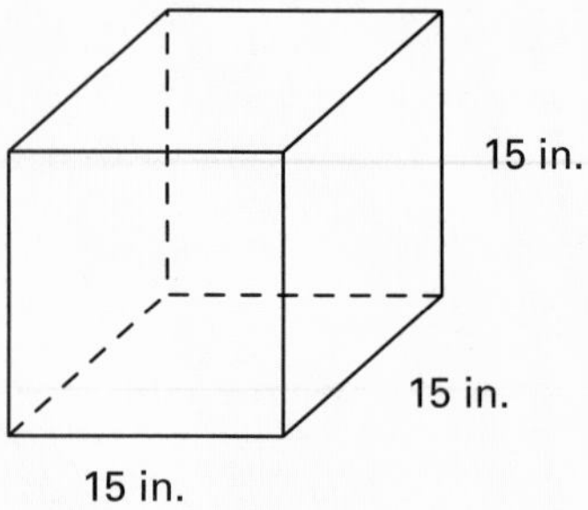

The box is a cube 15 in. on a side.

$SA = 6s^2 = 6 \times 15^2$

$= 6 \times 225$

$= 1350$

The surface area is 1350 in^2.

3. Find the surface area of the pyramid.

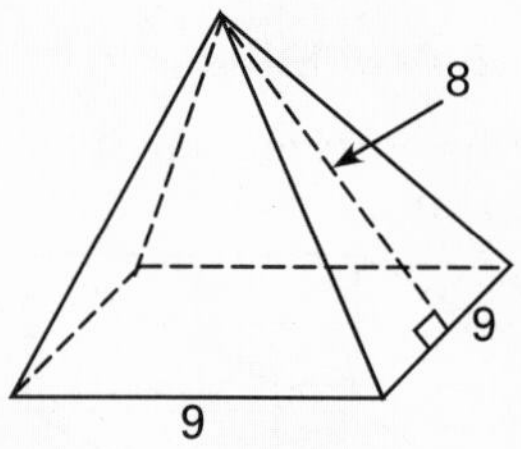

The base is a square 9 units on a side. Each face is a triangle with base 9 and height 8.

$SA = (9 \times 9) + [4 \times (9 \times 8 \div 2)]$

$= 81 + [4 \times 36]$

$= 225$

The surface area is 225 units^2.

Example 2

Remember

According to the order of operations, you should multiply in an expression *before* you add. **[Page 99]**

Find the surface area of the baseball box.

The box is a cube 3 in. on a side.

$SA = 6s^2 = 6 \times 3^2$

$= 6 \times 9$

$= 54$

The surface area is 54 in^2.

If the triangular faces of a pyramid are congruent, you can use this shortcut to find the surface area of the pyramid:

SA = area of base + [(number of triangular faces) × (area of each face)]

Example 3

HINT

The parentheses keys can help you use the order of operations. Enter (8 × 8) + 4 × (8 × 6 ÷ 2) =. The calculator should show the correct answer of 160.

Find the surface area of the pyramid.

The base is a square 8 units on a side. Each face is a triangle with base 8 and height 6.

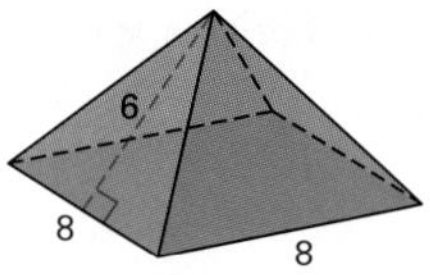

$SA = (8 \times 8) + [4 \times (8 \times 6 \div 2)]$

$= 64 \quad + [4 \times \quad (24) \quad]$

$= 160$

The surface area is 160 units^2.

Try It

Find the surface area of each solid.

a.

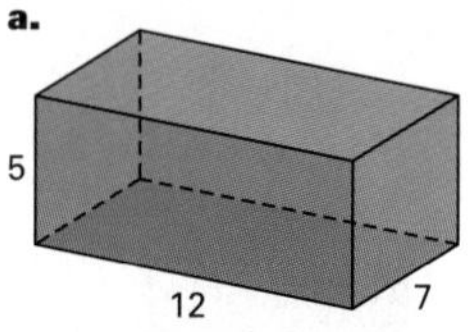

358 units^2

b.

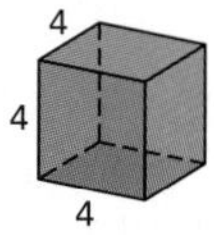

96 units^2

c.

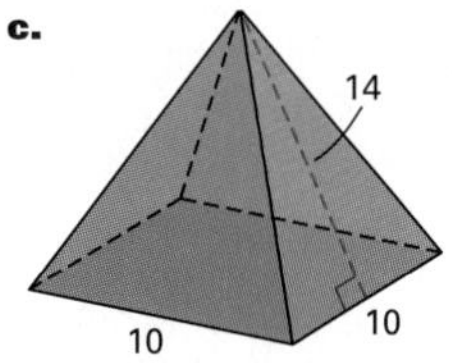

380 units^2

3 Practice and Assess

Check

Answers for Check Your Understanding

1. Yes; A cube is a rectangular prism.
2. Find the area of each face, and add the areas together.

MEETING MIDDLE SCHOOL CLASSROOM NEEDS

Tips from Middle School Teachers

I find that using actual boxes and wrapping paper is a useful technique for helping students understand the concept of surface area.

Team Teaching

Work with a social studies teacher when discussing pyramids. Have students research Egyptian and Mexican pyramids.

Health Connection

The United States Department of Agriculture has developed a Food Guide to help in planning a healthy diet. The Food Guide categorizes breakfast cereals in the bread, cereal, rice, and pasta group. The guide recommends that a person eats 6 to 11 servings a day from this group.

Check Your Understanding

1. Can you use the formula for the surface area of a rectangular prism to find the surface area of a cube? Explain.

2. Suppose you couldn't remember the formula for the surface area of a rectangular prism. What would you do to find the surface area?

11-3 Exercises and Applications

Practice and Apply

Getting Started **Find the surface area of each cube.**

1.

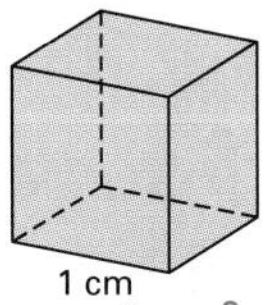

6 cm^2

2.

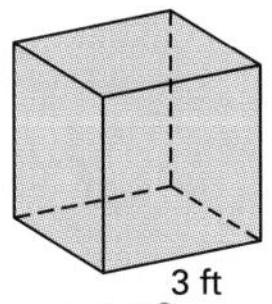

54 ft^2

3.

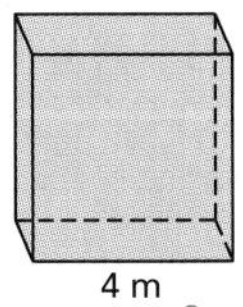

96 m^2

4.

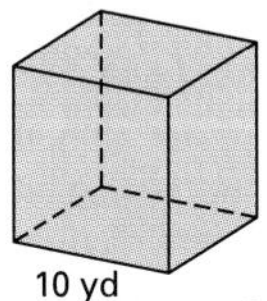

600 yd^2

Find the surface area.

5.

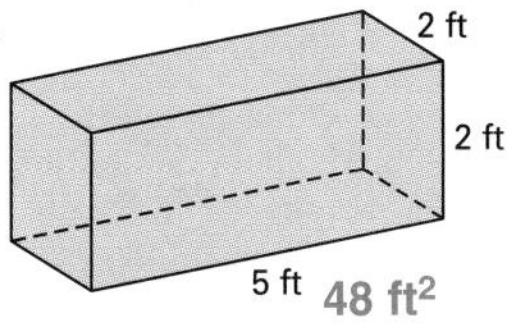

48 ft^2

6.

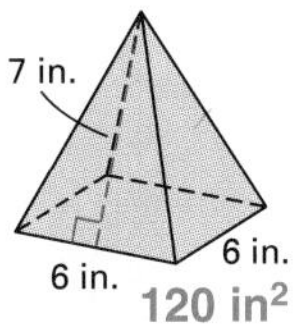

120 in^2

7.

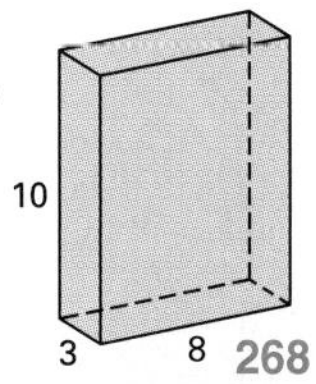

268 units^3

8.

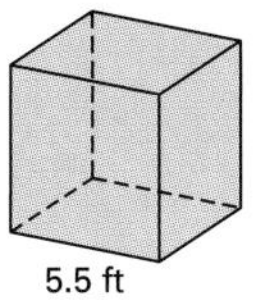

181.5 ft^2

9.

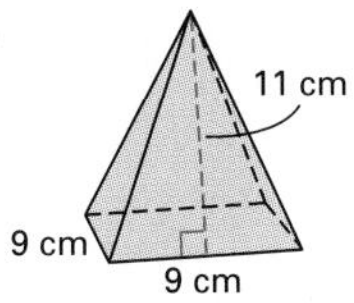

279 cm^2

10.

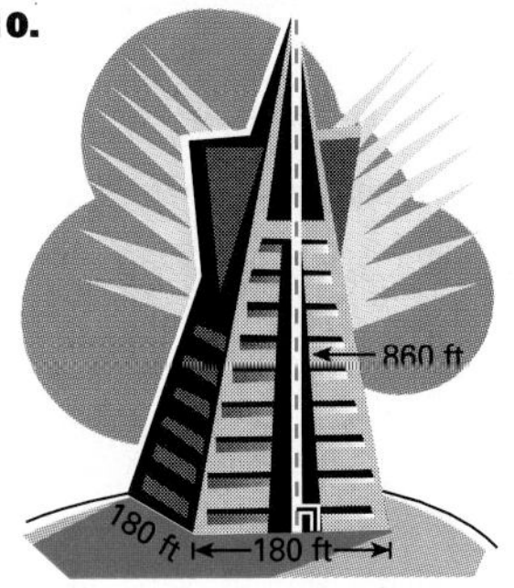

342,000 ft^2

Geometry **Find the surface area of each rectangular prism.**

11. $l = 4.1$ cm, $w = 3$ cm, $h = 6$ cm 109.8 cm^2

12. $l = 10$ in., $w = 15$ in., $h = 12$ in. 900 in^2

13. The side of a number cube measures 1.5 cm. What is its surface area? 13.5 cm^2

11-3 Exercises and Applications

Assignment Guide

- **Basic**
  1–13, 15, 18, 20–26 evens
- **Average**
  4–18, 20–26 evens
- **Enriched**
  5–18, 19–27 odds

Exercise Notes

Exercises 1–4

Error Prevention Watch out for students who apply the formula for the surface area of a cube incorrectly. For example, in Exercise 1, they may write SA = 6(1^2), but incorrectly think that 1^2 is equal to 2 and then write SA = 12, rather than 6. Stress that s^2 means $s \times s$, and $1 \times 1 = 1$.

PRACTICE 11-3

PRACTICE

Name ______________________

Practice 11-3

Surface Area Formulas

Find the surface area.

1. 726 in^2

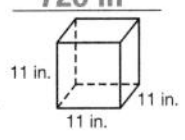

2. 418 cm^2

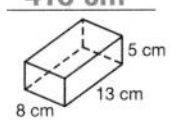

3. 451 yd^2

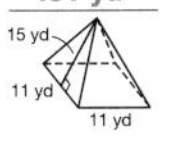

4. 3,174 mm^2

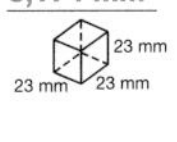

5. 258 ft^2

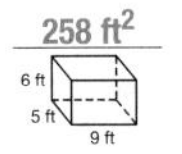

6. 144 m^2

7. $165\frac{3}{8}$ in^2

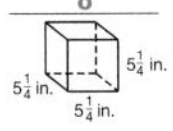

8. 2,250 cm^2

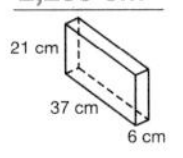

9. 228 yd^2

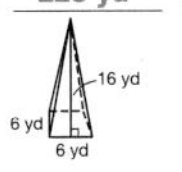

10. 10,584 m^2

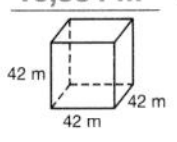

11. 28 ft^2

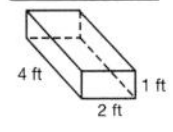

12. 24.15 m^2

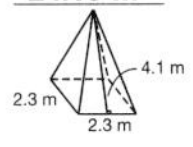

13. 1,014 in^2

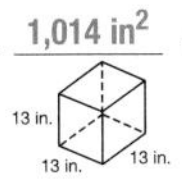

14. 708.6 cm^2

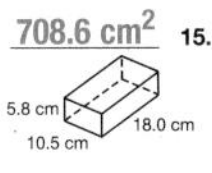

15. $215\frac{11}{16}$ in^2

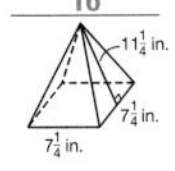

16. 69.36 mm^2

Find the surface area of each rectangular prism.

17. $\ell = 9$ ft, $w = 8$ ft, $h = 2$ ft

$SA =$ 212 ft^2

18. $\ell = 14$ cm, $w = 11$ cm, $h = 19$ cm

$SA =$ 1258 cm^2

19. $\ell = 3\frac{1}{2}$ in., $w = 2\frac{1}{2}$ in., $h = 4\frac{1}{2}$ in.

$SA =$ $71\frac{1}{2}$ in^2

20. $\ell = 6.1$ m, $w = 4.4$ m, $h = 5.5$ m

$SA =$ 169.18 m^2

21. A music company wants to design a cardboard box for mailing a 2-CD set measuring 14.2 cm by 12.4 cm by 2.5 cm. What is the least amount of cardboard that can be used for the box? 485.16 cm^2

RETEACHING

Name ______________________

Alternative Lesson 11-3

Surface Area Formulas

When a polyhedron has congruent faces, you can use shortcuts (formulas) to find the surface area.

Example 1

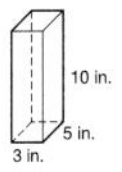

Find the surface area of the prism.
$l = 3$ in. $w = 5$ in. $h = 10$ in.

Substitute the measures into the formula (shortcut) and solve.

$SA = (2 \times l \times w) + (2 \times l \times h) + (2 \times w \times h)$
$= (2 \times 3 \times 5) + (2 \times 3 \times 10) + (2 \times 5 \times 10)$
$= 30 + 60 + 100$
$= 190$

The surface area of the rectangular prism is 190 in^2.

Try It Find the surface area of the prism.
$l = 20$ m $w = 4$ m $h = 9$ m

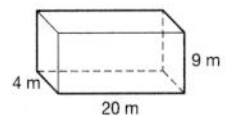

a. Substitute the measures into the formula.
$(2 \times 20 \times 4) + (2 \times 20 \times 9) + (2 \times 4 \times 9)$

b. Solve to find the surface area. 592 m^2

Example 2

Find the surface area of the pyramid.

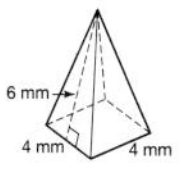

The base of the pyramid is a square measuring 4 mm on a side. Each face is a triangle with a base of 4 mm and a height of 6 mm.

Substitute the measures into the formula (shortcut) and solve.

SA (pyramid) = area of base + [(number of triangular faces) × (area of each face)]
$= (4 \times 4) + [4 \times (4 \times 6 \div 2)]$
$= 16 + [4 \times 12]$
$= 64$

The surface area of the pyramid is 64 mm^2.

Try It Find the surface area of the pyramid.

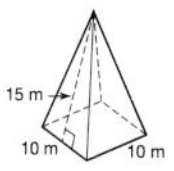

The base of the pyramid is a square measuring 10 m on a side. Each face is a triangle with a base of 10 m and a height of 15 m.

c. Substitute the measures into the shortcut.
$(10 \times 10) + [4 \times (10 \times 15 \div 2)]$

d. Solve to find the surface area. 400 mm^2

Reteaching

Activity

Materials: 2 cardboard boxes or cereal boxes

- Work with a partner.
- Use two different cereal boxes or other types of cardboard boxes.
- Measure the length, width, and height of each box.
- Then use a formula to determine the surface area of each box. Answers may vary.

Exercise Notes

■ Exercise 18

Problem-Solving Tip Remind students to always check that the figures are labeled using the same units. Students need to first change the units so that they are the same for each solid, either both in feet or both in inches.

Exercise Answers

18. **b**; The surface area of **b** is 377.28 in^2. The surface area of **a** is only 314 in^2.

Alternate Assessment

You may want to use the *Interactive CD-ROM Journal* with this assessment.

Journal Have students draw a rectangular prism and label the length, width, and height. Then have them tell how they would use a formula to find the surface area of the prism.

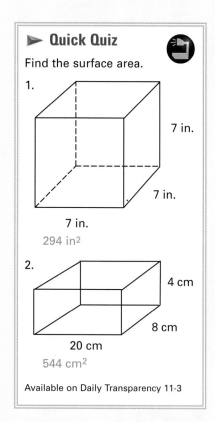

➤ Quick Quiz

Find the surface area.

1.

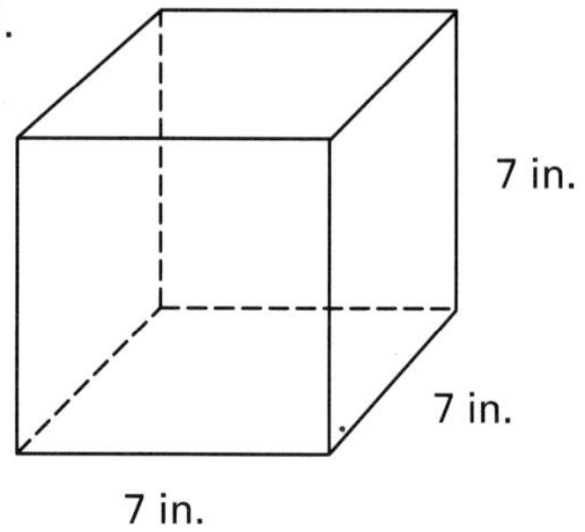

294 in^2

2.

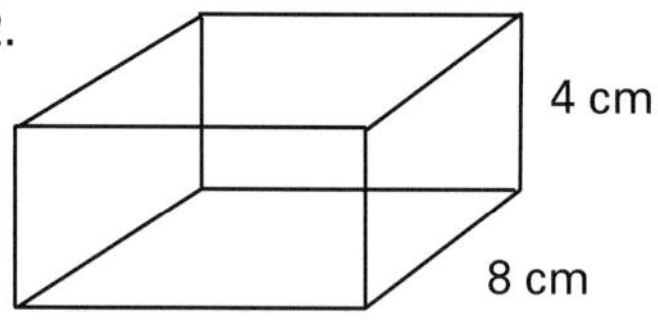

544 cm^2

Available on Daily Transparency 11-3

PROBLEM SOLVING 11-3

14. A trailer is 23 ft by 9 ft by 8 ft. How much aluminum siding is used for the trailer, including the top and the bottom? 926 ft^2

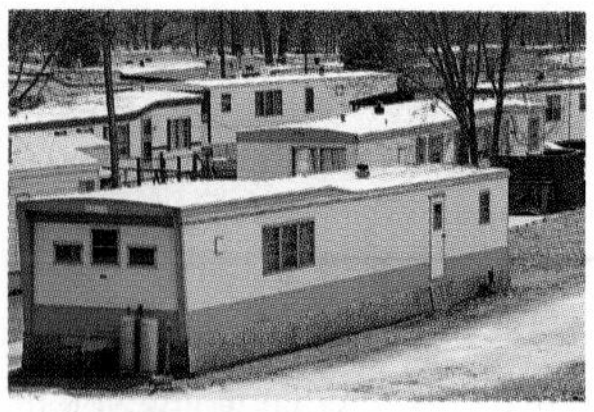

15. **Test Prep** What is the surface area of a cube with 4-in. sides? C

Ⓐ 48 in^2 Ⓑ 64 in^2

Ⓒ 96 in^2 Ⓓ 144 in^2

16. Mariana wants to cover the pyramid shown with gold foil.

a. How many square feet of foil does she need? 224 ft^2

b. If the foil costs \$0.02 per square foot, estimate how much Mariana should plan to spend. \$4.48

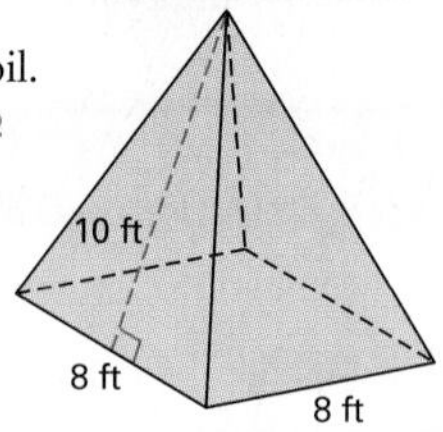

Problem Solving and Reasoning

17. Critical Thinking The Wrap'n'Pack gift wrapping company has three different-sized medium boxes. What is the average surface area for a medium box? 1128 in^2

Medium Boxes (in.)	A	B	C
Length	12	20	8
Width	12	16	6
Height	12	24	2

18. Critical Thinking Which solid has the greater surface area? Explain.

GPS **a.**

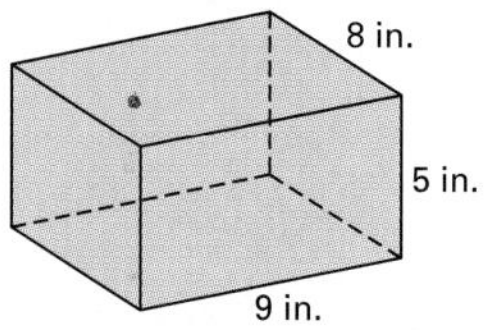

b.

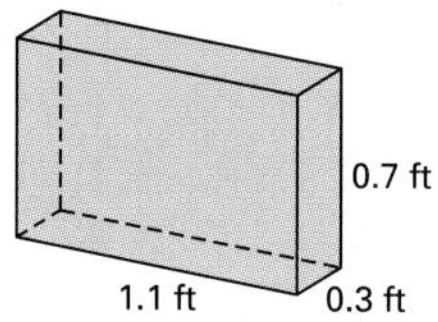

Mixed Review

State if the ratio is a rate. *[Lesson 10-3]*

19. $\frac{6 \text{ mi}}{4 \text{ hr}}$ Yes **20.** $\frac{1 \text{ kitten}}{7 \text{ ounces}}$ Yes **21.** $\frac{6 \text{ in.}}{11 \text{ in.}}$ No **22.** 7:9 No

Simplify. *[Lesson 6-2]*

23. $\frac{5}{6} - \frac{2}{3}$ $\frac{1}{6}$ **24.** $\frac{1}{4} + \frac{7}{11}$ $\frac{39}{44}$ **25.** $\frac{3}{4} - \frac{2}{7}$ $\frac{13}{28}$ **26.** $\frac{10}{12} + \frac{1}{6}$ 1 **27.** $\frac{4}{9} - \frac{2}{7}$ $\frac{10}{63}$

PROBLEM SOLVING

Name ______________________

Guided Problem Solving 11-3

GPS **PROBLEM 18, STUDENT PAGE 592**

Which solid has the greater surface area? Explain.

a.

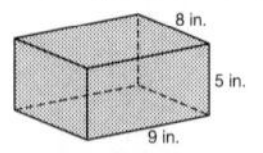

b.

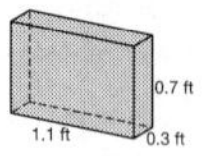

— Understand —

1. What are you asked to compare? Surface area.
2. Are the units of measurement the same or different in each solid? Different.

— Plan —

3. How can you convert feet to inches? Multiply by 12.
4. Convert each measure to inches.
   a. 1.1 ft 13.2 in. **b.** 0.7 ft 8.4 in. **c.** 0.3 ft 3.6 in.
5. What is the formula to find the surface area of each solid? a
   a. $SA = (2 \times l \times w) + (2 \times l \times h) + (2 \times w \times h)$ **b.** $SA = s^2$

— Solve —

6. What is the surface area in square inches of Solid a? 314 in^2
7. What is the surface area in square inches of Solid b? 377.28 in^2
8. Which solid has the greater surface area? Explain.
   Solid b, since 377.28 > 314.

— Look Back —

9. How could you find the answer in another way? Possible answer:
   Convert inches to feet. Then find each surface area.

SOLVE ANOTHER PROBLEM

Which solid has the greater surface area? Explain.

a.

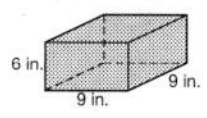

b.

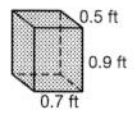

Solid b, since 2.86 ft^2 > 2.625 ft^2.

ENRICHMENT

Name ______________________

Extend Your Thinking 11-3

Decision Making

Suppose you bought a present for a friend's birthday. The present is in a box that has a length of 12 inches, a width of 9 inches and a height of 10 inches. You can either have the gift wrapped at the store where it was purchased or wrap the gift yourself.

The store has complimentary (free) gift wrapping. The paper is silver with the store's name imprinted on it. The bow is white.

You could also have the store wrap the gift in a specialty wrapping paper. It would be decorated with balloons and have a bow with a small teddy bear or boomerang. The cost would be \$4.50.

A roll of wrapping paper that contains 15 square feet costs \$3.25. A package of two wrapping paper sheets costs \$2.25. Each sheet measures 20 in. by $2\frac{1}{2}$ ft. A large bow sells for \$1.50 and a small bow sells for \$1.00.

Possible answers: Items 2, 3, and 5

1. List the choices you have in wrapping the package. List the cost beside the choice. Consider the cost of the whole roll of paper, not just the part of the roll needed to wrap the package.
   Store free; specialty \$4.50; roll/lg bow \$4.75; roll/ sm bow \$4.25; sheets/lg bow \$3.75; sheets/sm bow \$3.25.
2. What is the advantage in having the store wrap the package?
   Looks better, no mess, no excess paper, may be faster.
3. What is the advantage of buying wrapping paper and a bow and wrapping the package yourself?
   Cheaper (use excess paper for another package), can add personal touches.
4. Calculate the surface area of the package. Are the sheets of wrapping paper large enough to cover the package without cutting and pasting?
   No, because SA = 636 in^2 and the area of one sheet is only 600 in^2.
5. Which option do you think is the best? Explain.
   Complimentary wrap since it is free, will look fine, and you can spend more on the gift (it's what inside that counts!).

Surface Area of a Cylinder

11-4

▶ Lesson Link You've found the surface areas of several polyhedrons. Now you'll find surface areas of a type of solid with curved surfaces. ◀

You'll Learn ...

■ to find the surface area of a cylinder

... How It's Used

Aluminum can manufacturers calculate surface area when determining the amount of aluminum needed for a given size can.

Explore Cylinders

Caution: Curves Ahead!

Materials: Cans of food (e.g., soup can, juice can) without labels, Graph paper

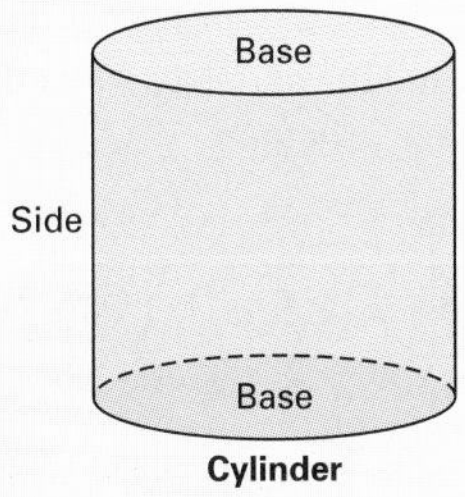

1. What is the shape of a can's label after it has been removed and flattened? Draw a "label" for your can. It should be sized to fit exactly on your can.
2. What is the shape of a can's bases? Add two bases to your label to make a net for your can.
3. Cut your net out and tape it together to form a solid. Does your solid have the same size and shape as the can?
4. Describe the relationship between the circumference of the base of your can and what you drew in Steps 1 and 2.
5. Estimate the surface area of your can.

Learn Surface Area of a Cylinder

A cylinder has two bases. Each base is a circle. The side can be unrolled to form a rectangle. Notice that the length of the rectangle equals the circumference of the circle.

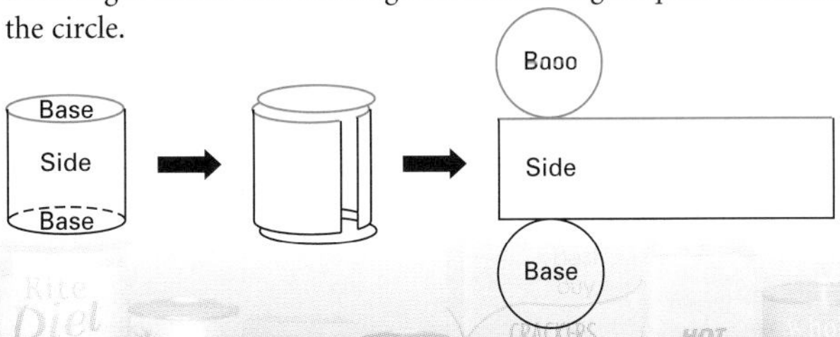

MEETING INDIVIDUAL NEEDS

Resources

- **11-4** Practice
- **11-4** Reteaching
- **11-4** Problem Solving
- **11-4** Enrichment
- **11-4** Daily Transparency
  - Problem of the Day
  - Review
  - Quick Quiz
- Teaching Tool Transparencies 2, 3
- Lesson Enhancement Transparency 55

Learning Modalities

Kinesthetic Have students cut apart a cylindrical cardboard carton, such as a rolled oats container, to show how the net for a cylinder is formed.

Verbal Have students write a paragraph telling how they would go about determining the surface area of a cylindrical object for which they did not know any measurements.

Inclusion

The formula for the surface area of a cylinder is complicated, and some students will have trouble applying it. Break these problems down into small steps which students can follow to help them better understand the process. Create a template of the steps so that students may have a consistent strategy to input the numbers.

11-4 Lesson Organizer

Objective

- Find the surface area of a cylinder.

Materials

- Explore: Cans of food (e.g., soup can, juice can) without labels, graph paper

NCTM Standards

- 1–4, 12, 13

▶ Review

Find the area of each circle. Use 3.14 for π.

1. Circle with radius 21 cm
   1384.74 cm^2
2. Circle with diameter 48 mm
   1808.64 mm^2

Available on Daily Transparency 11-4

1 Introduce

Explore

You may wish to use Lesson Enhancement Transparency 55 with this lesson.

The Point

Students make a net for a cylinder, tape it to form a cylinder, and explore how to find the surface area.

Ongoing Assessment

The fact that each circle in the net touches the rectangle at just one point is confusing to some students. Have them think of opening a can with a can opener. If the opener leaves a small portion of tin joining the top to the sides, the top will not come off.

For Groups That Finish Early

If you double the height of a cylinder but keep the bases the same size as on the original cylinder, how does this affect the net? The height of the rectangle will be twice as high, but the length will be the same and the circles will be the same.

Answers for Explore on next page.

Answers for Explore

1. Rectangle

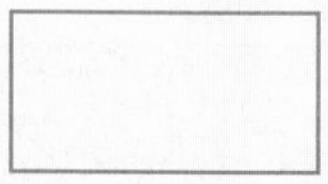

2. Circle

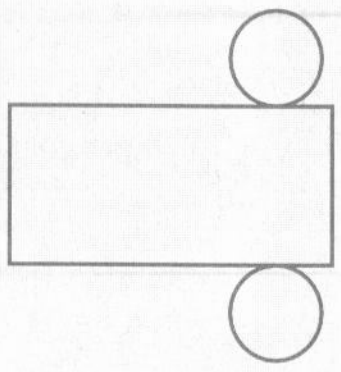

3. Yes; The solid and the can should be the same size.
4. The circumference of the base of the can equals the circumference of the circles on the net and the length of two sides of the rectangle on the net.
5. Answers may vary.

2 Teach

Learn

Alternate Examples

1. Find the surface area of the can. Use 3.14 for π.

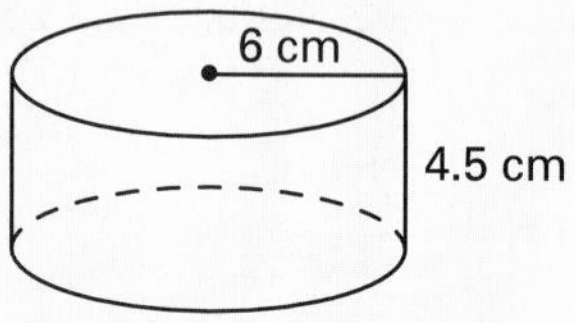

$r = 6$ cm $\quad h = 4.5$ cm

$SA = (2 \times \pi r^2) + (h \times 2\pi r)$

$SA = (2 \times 3.14 \times 6 \times 6) + (4.5 \times 2 \times 3.14 \times 6)$

$= 226.08 + 169.56$

$= 395.64$

The surface area is 395.64 cm^2.

2. Find the surface area of this silo. Use 3.14 for π.

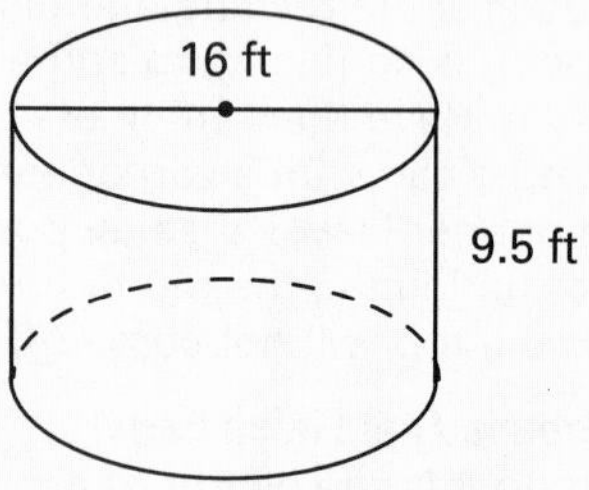

If the diameter is 16, the radius is half of that, or 8.

$SA = (2 \times \pi r^2) + (h \times 2\pi r)$

$SA = (2 \times 3.14 \times 8 \times 8) + (9.5 \times 2 \times 3.14 \times 8)$

$= 401.92 + 477.28$

$= 879.2$

The surface area is 879.2 ft^2.

Remember

The area formula for a circle is $\pi \times radius^2$. You can use 3.14 as an approximation for π.

[Page 252]

You can use these relationships to find the surface area of a cylinder whose height is h and whose bases have a radius of r.

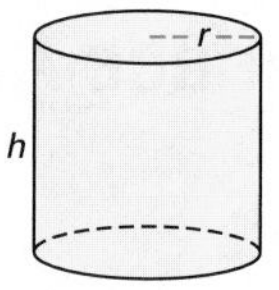

SA = (2 × area of base) + (area of rectangular side)

= (2 × area of base) + (height of side × length of side)

= (2 × area of base) + (height of cylinder × circumference of base)

= $(2 \times \pi r^2) + (h \times 2\pi r)$

$SA = (2 \times \pi r^2) + (h \times 2\pi r)$

Example 1

Find the surface area of the ice cream container. Use 3.14 for π.

$r = 2.5$ in. $\quad h = 6.5$ in.

$SA = (2 \times \pi r^2) + (h \times 2\pi r)$

$SA \approx (2 \times 3.14 \times 2.5 \times 2.5) + (6.5 \times 2 \times 3.14 \times 2.5)$

$\approx 39.25 + 102.05$

≈ 141.3

The surface area is about 141.3 in^2.

If you know the diameter of the base of a cylinder, you can find the radius by dividing the diameter by 2.

Example 2

Find the surface area. Use 3.14 for π.

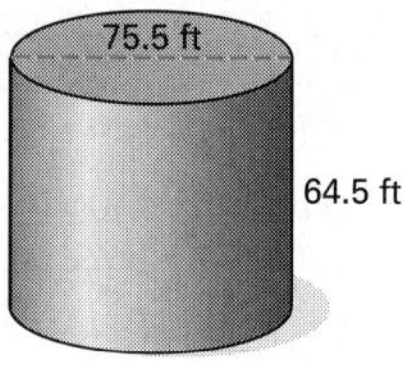

If the diameter is 75.5, the radius is half of that, or 37.75.

$SA = (2 \times \pi r^2) + (h \times 2\pi r)$

$\approx (2 \times 3.14 \times 37.75 \times 37.75) + (64.5 \times 2 \times 3.14 \times 37.75)$

$\approx 8{,}949.4 + 15{,}291$

$\approx 24{,}240.4$

The surface area is about 24,240.4 ft^2.

MATH EVERY DAY

Problem of the Day

For a craft project, you are covering the sides of coffee cans with material. You have a piece of corduroy that is a 48 in.-by-48 in. square. Each coffee can is $6\frac{1}{2}$ in. tall and has a radius of 3 in. You will cover only the side of each can. You can put small pieces of material together to cover the cans. How many cans can you cover with the available material? 18 coffee cans

Available on Daily Transparency 11-4

An Extension is provided in the transparency package.

Fact of the Day

Canned food was not common in the United States until the Civil War. By 1870, 30,000,000 cans of food were produced each year.

Mental Math

Find each product mentally.

1. 7.1 × 10 71
2. 3.3 × 100 330
3. 5.2 × 1000 5,200
4. 8.9 × 10,000 89,000

Chip's Cheesesticks are sold in half-cylinder packages like the one shown. Ricardo and Maritess want to know the surface area of a package.

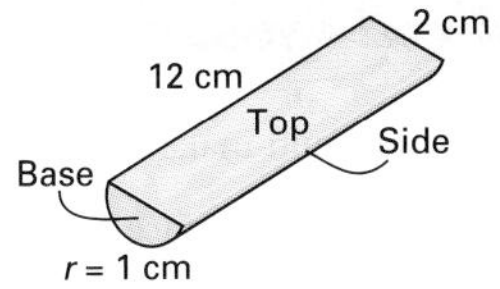

WHAT DO YOU THINK?

Maritess thinks ...

I'll add the areas up one at a time.

The rectangular top is 12×2, or 24 cm^2.

The 2 half-circles can be put together to make one full circle. The full circle is $\pi \times 1^2$, or about 3.14 cm^2.

The curved side is a rectangle with a height of 12 and a base of half the circle's circumference. Half of the circle's circumference is $\pi \times$ diameter $\div 2$, or about $3.14 \times 2 \div 2$, or 3.14. The curved side is 12×3.14, or about 37.68 cm^2.

The total surface area is about $24 + 3.14 + 37.68 = 64.82$.

The surface area is about 65 cm^2.

Ricardo thinks ...

I'll use the formula $SA = (2 \times \pi r^2) + (h \times 2\pi r)$ to find the surface area of a complete cylinder, and then divide by 2.

$$SA \approx [(2 \times 3.14 \times 1^2) + (12 \times 2 \times 3.14 \times 1)] \div 2$$
$$= 81.64 \div 2 = 40.82 \text{ cm}^2.$$

The rectangular top is 12 cm by 2 cm, for an area of 24 cm^2.
I'll add that to the half cylinder. $40.82 \text{ cm}^2 + 24 \text{ cm}^2 = 64.82 \text{ cm}^2$.

The surface area is about 65 cm^2.

What do you think?

1. Which method do you think is easier? Why?

2. How would the solution change if the package had no top?

WHAT DO YOU THINK?

Students see two methods for finding the surface area of a half cylinder. One method involves applying the formula for the surface area of a cylinder, dividing the area by 2, and then adding the area for the rectangular top portion. The other method involves finding the areas of all parts of the package and then adding them to find the total surface area. Students can decide which of the two correct methods is easier for them.

Answers for What Do You Think?

1. Answers may vary.
2. The surface area would be about 41 cm^2.

MEETING MIDDLE SCHOOL CLASSROOM NEEDS

Tips from Middle School Teachers

Some students don't understand how the formula for surface area of a cylinder applies to the net for a cylinder. I first have them draw a net for a cylinder and then label one side of the rectangle as $2\pi r$ and the other side as h. Then I have students label the radius of each circle as r.

Team Teaching

Work with an art teacher to have students design labels that will fit on cylindrical containers of various sizes.

Fine Arts Connection

Columns are used both to support and decorate buildings. Most columns have three parts. The central upright part, the *shaft*, is usually cylindrical. It stands on a support called the *base*. Above the shaft is the decorative *capital*.

Using a Spreadsheet • Finding the Surface Area of a Cylinder

The Point
Students use the formula capabilities of a spreadsheet to calculate the surface area of a cylinder.

Materials
Spreadsheet software

Resources
Interactive CD-ROM Spreadsheet/Grapher Tool

About the Page

To find the surface area of a cylinder, you need to know the area of the two bases, which are the same, and the lateral area. The area of each base is πr^2 and the lateral area is the circumference of the base times the height, which is $2\pi rh$.

Ask ...

- What is calculated by the formula in cell D2? The area of one base.
- Why is there multiplication by 2 in the formula in cell E2? Because cell D2 contains the area of one base, but a cylinder has two bases of equal size.
- In Part b of **Try It,** how might the comparisons be made more easily? Expand the spreadsheet to include more rows and copy the formulas. This way, the information for each set of measurements could be shown at once.

Answers for Try It

a. Cylinder with height of 3 cm and radius of 4 cm.

b. Cylinder with height of 1 unit and radius of 9 units.

On Your Own
For the first question, some spreadsheet software may use "+" rather than "=."

Answers for On Your Own

- The = is used so that the spreadsheet program knows you are entering a formula.
- Possible answer: If the numbers are large or have too many digits to enter into a calculator, it may be more efficient to use a spreadsheet.

TECHNOLOGY

Using a Spreadsheet • Finding the Surface Area of a Cylinder

Problem: Which has more surface area, a cylinder with a height of 5 cm and a radius of 2 cm, or a cylinder with a height of 2 cm and a radius of 5 cm?

You can use spreadsheets to quickly complete the calculations.

	A	B	C	D	E
1	Height	Radius	Lateral SA	Base area	Total SA
2					

1 **Enter the information into the spreadsheet as shown.**

	A	B	C	D	E
1	Height	Radius	Lateral SA	Base area	Total SA
2	5	2	62.8	12.56	87.92
3	2	5	62.8	78.50	219.80

2 **In cell A2, enter** 5. **In cell B2, enter** 2. **In cell C2, enter the formula** =2*3.14*A2*B2. **In cell D2, enter the formula** =3.14*(B2)^2. **In cell E2, enter the formula** =C2+2*D2.

3 **Copy the contents of row 2 down to row 3. Then, change the height value to** 2 **and the radius value to** 5.

Solution: A cylinder with a height of 2 cm and a radius of 5 cm has more surface area than a cylinder with a height of 5 cm and a radius of 2 cm.

TRY IT

a. Which has more surface area, a cylinder with a height of 3 cm and a radius of 4 cm, or a cylinder with a height of 4 cm and a radius of 3 cm?

b. If the height and radius of a cylinder must be whole numbers whose sum is 10, how much should the height and radius be to get the cylinder with the largest surface area?

ON YOUR OWN

- Why do you think it's necessary to type an = at the beginning of each formula?
- Why might a person want to set up a spreadsheet to calculate the surface area of a cylinder instead of using a calculator or pencil and paper?

598

Chip's Cheesesticks are sold in half-cylinder packages like the one shown. Ricardo and Maritess want to know the surface area of a package.

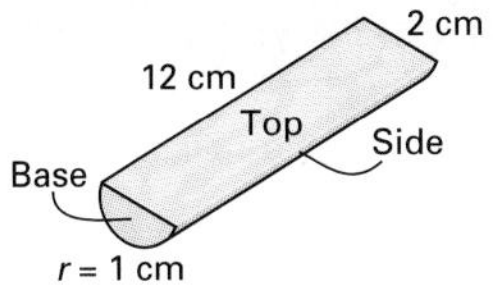

WHAT DO YOU THINK ?

Maritess thinks ...

I'll add the areas up one at a time.

The rectangular top is 12 × 2, or 24 cm^2.

The 2 half-circles can be put together to make one full circle. The full circle is $\pi \times 1^2$, or about 3.14 cm^2.

The curved side is a rectangle with a height of 12 and a base of half the circle's circumference. Half of the circle's circumference is π × diameter ÷ 2, or about 3.14 × 2 ÷ 2, or 3.14. The curved side is 12 × 3.14, or about 37.68 cm^2.

The total surface area is about 24 + 3.14 + 37.68 = 64.82.

The surface area is about 65 cm^2.

Ricardo thinks ...

I'll use the formula $SA = (2 \times \pi r^2) + (h \times 2\pi r)$ to find the surface area of a complete cylinder, and then divide by 2.

$SA \approx [(2 \times 3.14 \times 1^2) + (12 \times 2 \times 3.14 \times 1)] \div 2$

$= 81.64 \div 2 = 40.82$ cm^2.

The rectangular top is 12 cm by 2 cm, for an area of 24 cm^2.
I'll add that to the half cylinder. 40.82 cm^2 + 24 cm^2 = 64.82 cm^2.

The surface area is about 65 cm^2.

What do you think?

1. Which method do you think is easier? Why?
2. How would the solution change if the package had no top?

WHAT DO YOU THINK ?

Students see two methods for finding the surface area of a half cylinder. One method involves applying the formula for the surface area of a cylinder, dividing the area by 2, and then adding the area for the rectangular top portion. The other method involves finding the areas of all parts of the package and then adding them to find the total surface area. Students can decide which of the two correct methods is easier for them.

Answers for What Do You Think?

1. Answers may vary.
2. The surface area would be about 41 cm^2.

MEETING MIDDLE SCHOOL CLASSROOM NEEDS

Tips from Middle School Teachers

Some students don't understand how the formula for surface area of a cylinder applies to the net for a cylinder. I first have them draw a net for a cylinder and then label one side of the rectangle as $2\pi r$ and the other side as h. Then I have students label the radius of each circle as r.

Team Teaching

Work with an art teacher to have students design labels that will fit on cylindrical containers of various sizes.

Fine Arts Connection

Columns are used both to support and decorate buildings. Most columns have three parts. The central upright part, the *shaft*, is usually cylindrical. It stands on a support called the *base*. Above the shaft is the decorative *capital*.

11-4 Exercises and Applications

Assignment Guide

- Basic
  1–13 odds, 14–17, 21–33 odds
- Average
  3–13 odds, 14–18, 20–32 evens
- Enriched
  6–14 evens, 15–20,
  22–32 evens

3 Practice and Assess

Check

Answers for Check Your Understanding

1. Possible answer: Construct a rectangle. Construct 2 circles with a circumference equal to the length of the rectangle. Wrap the rectangle into a tube so the height of the tube is equal to the width of the rectangle. Attach the two circles at each end of the tube.
2. With no top: Find the area of the rectangle and one circle or SA = $(\pi r^2) + (h \times 2\pi r)$; With no bases: Find the area of the rectangle only or SA = $h \times 2\pi r$.

Exercise Notes

Exercises 1–4

Error Prevention Some students might give answers that are twice as large as they should be because students confuse diameter and radius. Remind them that circumference is either $2\pi r$ or πd, where r stands for the radius and d stands for the diameter.

Reteaching

Activity

Materials: Cylindrical objects

- Work with a partner.
- Bring several cylindrical objects to class.
- Measure the objects so that you can determine the surface areas. Answers may vary.

Check Your Understanding

1. Describe how you could make a cylinder.
2. How would you find the surface area of a cylinder with a bottom base but no top base? With no bases?

11-4 Exercises and Applications

PRACTICE 11-4

Practice and Apply

Getting Started Find the circumference of each cylinder. Use 3.14 for π.

1 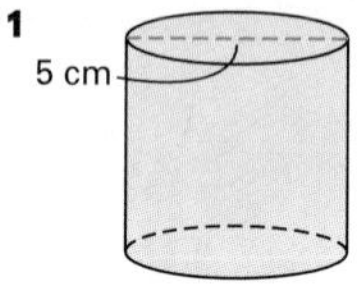

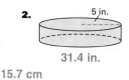

15.7 cm

2. 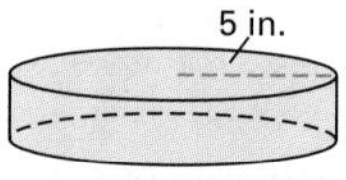

31.4 in.

3. 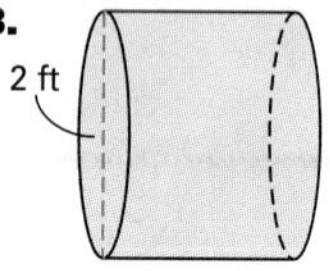

6.28 ft

4. 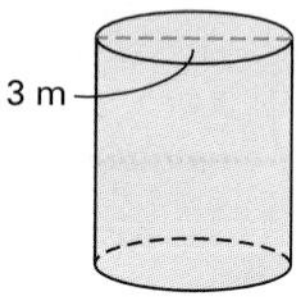

9.42 m

Find the surface area of each cylinder. Use 3.14 for π.

5. 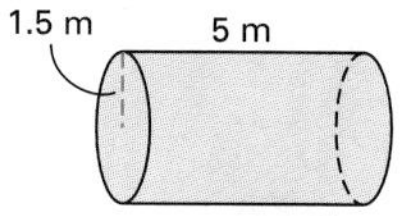

61.23 m²

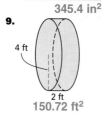

6. 

345.4 in²

7. 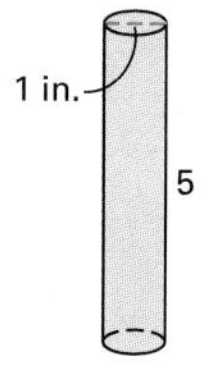

17.27 in²

8. 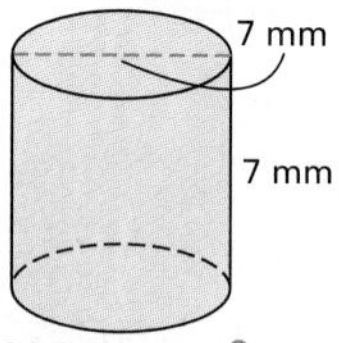

230.79 mm²

9. 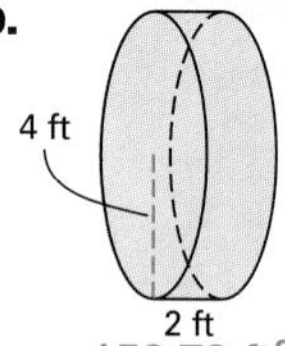

150.72 ft²

Given the radius and the height of each cylinder, find the surface area. Use 3.14 for π.

10. $r = 7, h = 10$ 747.32 units²
11. $r = 1, h = 21$ 138.16 units²
12. $r = 5, h = 3.5$ 266.9 units²
13. $r = 12, h = 16$ 2110.08 units²

14. **Industry** A can of cake frosting is 4.5 inches tall and has a 3 inch diameter.

GPS **a.** If there is no overlap, what is the area of the can's label? 42.39 in²

b. What is the surface area of the entire can? 56.52 in²

PRACTICE

Name ____________________

Practice 11-4

Surface Area of a Cylinder

Find the surface area of each cylinder. Use 3.14 for π.

1. 1,431.84 ft² 2. 1,356.48 in² 3. 138.16 m² 4. 1,055.04 cm²

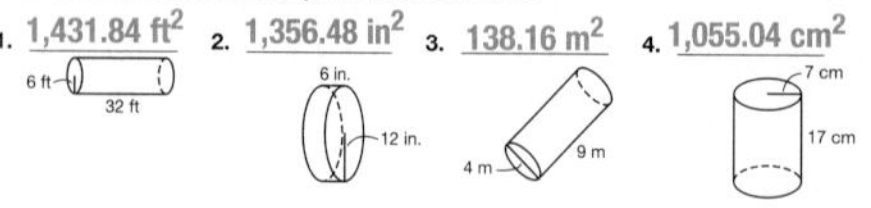

5. 904.32 mm² 6. 131.88 yd² 7. 1,456.96 cm² 8. 123.6375 in²

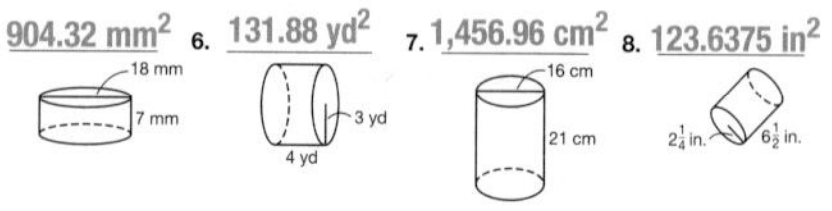

9. 92.8812 cm² 10. 219.8 ft² 11. 4490.2 mm² 12. 1201.05 in²

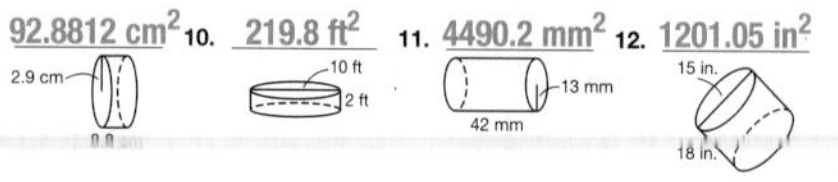

13. 38.4336 m² 14. 571.48 yd² 15. 276.7125 in² 16. 15,255.69 cm²

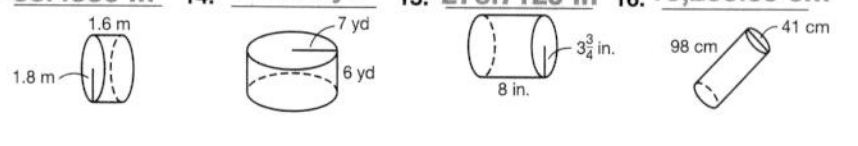

Given the radius and height of each cylinder, find the surface area. Use 3.14 for π.

17. $r = 3.8, h = 15$ SA ≈ 448.6432
18. $r = 21, h = 4$ SA ≈ 3297
19. $r = 12, h = 13$ SA ≈ 1884
20. $r = 2.1, h = 4.9$ SA ≈ 92.316
21. $r = 7.1, h = 40$ SA ≈ 2100.0948
22. $r = 18, h = 11.5$ SA ≈ 3334.68
23. An oatmeal box has the shape of a cylinder with diameter $3\frac{7}{8}$ in. and height 7 in. What is the surface area of the box? About 108.75 in²

RETEACHING

Name ____________________

Alternative Lesson 11-4

Surface Area of a Cylinder

A cylinder has two bases. Each base is a circle. The side can be unrolled to form a rectangle. The length of the rectangle equals the circumference of the circle.

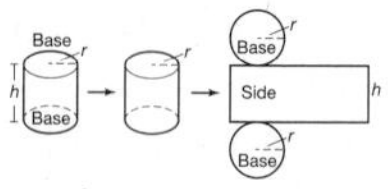

You can use these relationships to find the surface area of a cylinder whose height is h and whose bases have a radius of r.

SA = (2 × area of base) + (area of rectangular side)
= (2 × area of base) + (height of side × length of side)
= (2 × area of base) + (height of cylinder × circumference of base)
= $(2 \times \pi r^2) + (h \times 2\pi r)$

Example

Find the surface area of the cylinder.
Use 3.14 for π. $r = 4$ m $h = 8$ m

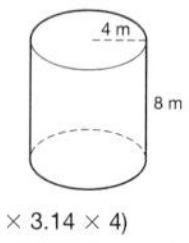

Substitute the measures into the formula (shortcut) and solve

SA = $(2 \times \pi r^2) + (h \times 2\pi r)$
= $(2 \times 3.14 \times 4 \times 4) + (8 \times 2 \times 3.14 \times 4)$
= 100.48 + 200.96
= 301.44

The surface area of the rectangular prism is about 301.44 m².

Try It Find the surface area of the cylinder.
Use 3.14 for π. $r = 1$ cm $h = 4$ cm

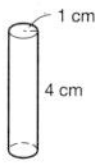

a. Substitute measures into the formula.
$(2 \times 3.14 \times 1 \times 1) + (4 \times 2 \times 3.14 \times 1)$

b. Solve to find the surface area. 31.4 cm²

Find the surface area of the cylinder.
Use 3.14 for π. $d = 6$ in. $h = 3$ in.

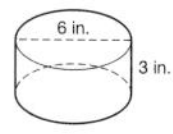

c. Divide the diameter by 2 to find the radius. 3 in.

d. Substitute measures into the formula.
$(2 \times 3.14 \times 3 \times 3) + (3 \times 2 \times 3.14 \times 3)$

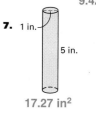

e. Solve to find the surface area. 113.04 in²

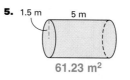

15. If a cylindrical gift box costs $0.01 per square inch to produce, how much does it cost to make each box?

a.

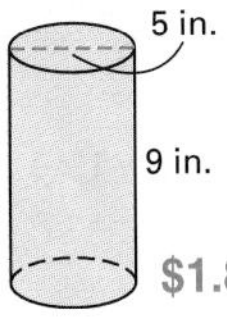

$1.81

b.

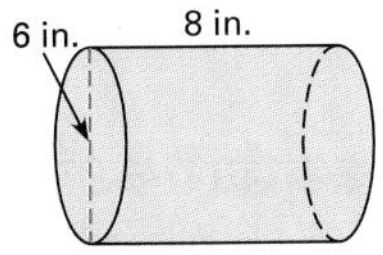

$2.07

16. **Test Prep** Choose the best estimate of the surface area of the cylinder shown. C

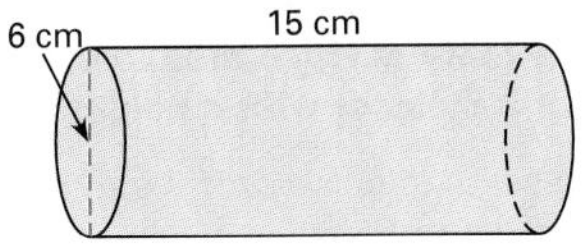

Ⓐ 90 cm^2 Ⓑ 110 cm^2

Ⓒ 360 cm^2 Ⓓ 540 cm^2

Problem Solving and Reasoning

17. Choose a Strategy Tito has found the surface area of 4 cylinders and recorded the data in the bar graph. The surface area of a 5th cylinder is greater than the 2nd but less than the 3rd. Find a possible height and diameter for the 5th cylinder.

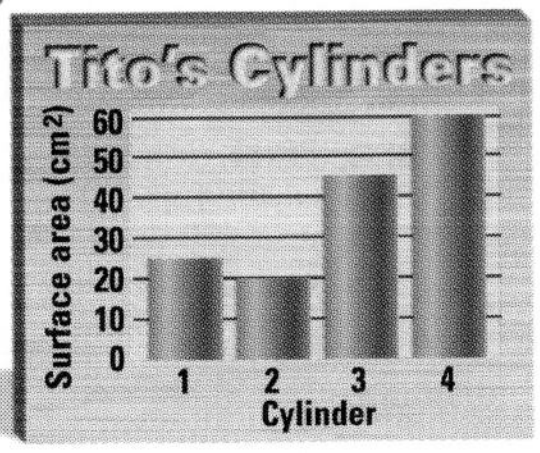

Problem Solving STRATEGIES

- Look for a Pattern
- Make an Organized List
- Make a Table
- Guess and Check
- Work Backward
- Use Logical Reasoning
- Draw a Diagram
- Solve a Simpler Problem

18. Critical Thinking How much advertising space is there on the label of a can with a diameter of 3 in. and a height of 4 in.? Explain.

19. Critical Thinking Some doll collectors display their dolls in cases like the one shown. The back of the case is a 12 in. by 5 in. rectangle. The bottom and top pieces are both half-circles. The front is clear plastic. What is the surface area of the entire case? Describe how you found it and explain your reasoning.

PROBLEM SOLVING 11-4

Mixed Review

State if the pair of ratios form a proportion. *[Lesson 10-4]*

20. $\frac{2}{9}$ and $\frac{9}{2}$ No **21.** $\frac{5}{10}$ and $\frac{1}{2}$ Yes **22.** $\frac{4}{7}$ and $\frac{2}{3}$ No

23. $\frac{7}{27}$ and $\frac{21}{54}$ No **24.** $\frac{4}{10}$ and $\frac{110}{27}$ No

25. $\frac{1}{2}$ and $\frac{32}{16}$ No **26.** $\frac{1}{8}$ and $\frac{3}{24}$ Yes **27.** $\frac{10}{16}$ and $\frac{2}{4}$ No **28.** $\frac{9}{4}$ and $\frac{36}{36}$ No **29.** $\frac{12}{5}$ and $\frac{60}{144}$ No

Simplify. *[Lesson 10-11]*

30. 62% of 200 124 **31.** 30% of 58 17.4 **32.** 78% of 24 18.72 **33.** 12% of 2 0.24

Exercise Notes

Exercise 17

Problem-Solving Tip You may wish to use Teaching Tool Transparencies 2 and 3: Guided Problem Solving, pages 1–2.

Exercises 20–29

Error Prevention If students have difficulty with these exercises, check that they are using the cross products to determine if the ratios form a proportion.

Exercise Answers

17. The surface area of the cylinder must be between 20 cm^2 and 45 cm^2. Possible answer: height = 3 cm and diameter = 2 cm.

18. ≈ 37.68 in^2; Assuming the label is only on the rectangular side, SA = $h \times 2\pi r = 4 \times 2(3.14)(1.5)$.

19. ≈ 173.825 in^2; Find the surface area of the whole cylinder and then divide it by 2. Add the area of the rectangle to this area. SA = $[2\pi(2.5)^2 + 2\pi(2.5)(12)] \div 2 + (12 \times 5)$.

Alternate Assessment

Self Assessment Have students describe what they find most difficult about computing the surface area of a cylinder.

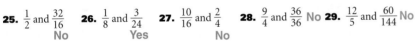

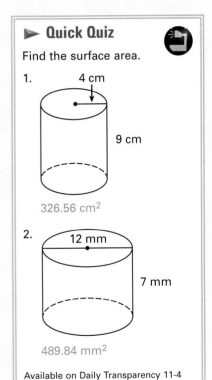

Quick Quiz

Find the surface area.

1.

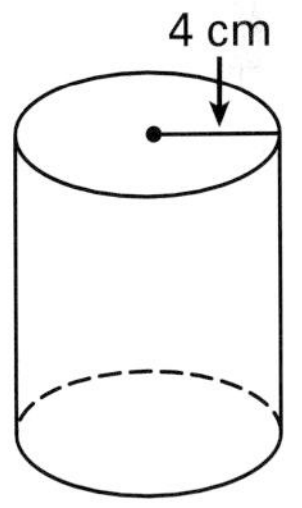

326.56 cm^2

2.

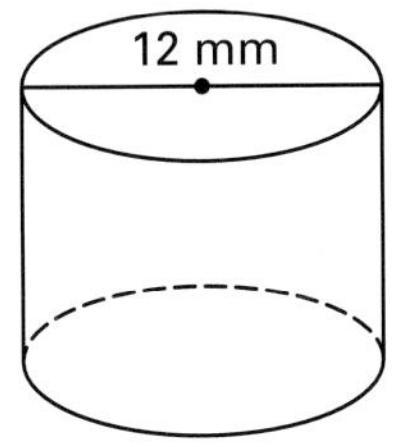

489.84 mm^2

Available on Daily Transparency 11-4

PROBLEM SOLVING

Name ______________________

Guided Problem Solving 11-4

GPS PROBLEM 14, STUDENT PAGE 596

A can of cake frosting is 4.5 inches tall and has a 3 inch diameter.

a. If there is no overlap, what is the area of the can's label?

b. What is the surface area of the entire can?

— Understand —

1. Underline the height and diameter of the can.
2. Does the side or the base of a can contain the label? Side.

— Plan —

3. What shape is the side of a cylinder? Rectangle.
4. What is the formula to find the area of the side of a cylinder? b

   a. $A = 2\pi r^2$ **b.** $A = h \times 2\pi r$ **c.** $A = d\pi$

5. What shape is the base of a cylinder? Circle.
6. What is the formula to find the area of the base of a cylinder? $A = \pi r^2$
7. How can you find the total surface area of the can once you know the areas of the base and the side? Find side + (2×base).
8. What is the radius of the can? 1.5 in.

— Solve —

9. What is the area of the can's label? 42.39 in^2
10. What is the surface area of the entire can? 56.52 in^2

— Look Back —

11. Write the surface area formula. Then use it to check your answer to Item 10.
    $SA = (2 \times \pi r^2) + (h \times 2\pi r) = 56.52$ in^2

SOLVE ANOTHER PROBLEM

A can is 6.5 inches tall and has a 5 inch diameter.

a. If there is no overlap, what is the area of the can's label? 102.05 in^2

b. What is the surface area of the entire can? 141.3 in^2

ENRICHMENT

Name ______________________

Extend Your Thinking 11-4

Critical Thinking

Find each area. Read the description of what you are asked to do very carefully. Use 3.14 for π.

1. The edge of each cube that makes up the "staircase" measures 6 inches. Find the number of square inches of shelf paper that is needed to cover the "staircase." 432 in^2

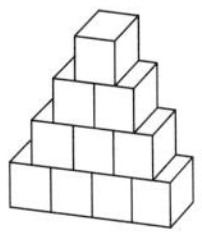

2. Find the surface area of the house sculpture. Remember that there is no top to the rectangular prism. 320 cm^2

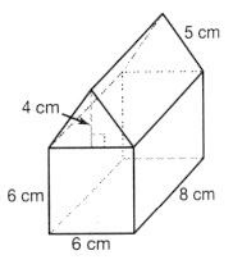

3. Find the surface area of the candle and candle holder. Do not count the area where the candle sits on the holder. 270.04 in^2

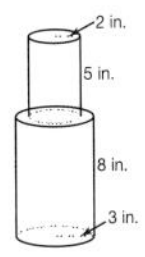

4. The cylinder has an open top. You want to paint the inside and outside of the cylinder. How many square feet of paint will you need to complete the project? 125.6 ft^2

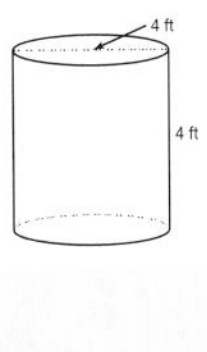

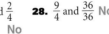

Technology

Using a Spreadsheet • Finding the Surface Area of a Cylinder

The Point
Students use the formula capabilities of a spreadsheet to calculate the surface area of a cylinder.

Materials
Spreadsheet software

Resources
Interactive CD-ROM Spreadsheet/Grapher Tool

About the Page

To find the surface area of a cylinder, you need to know the area of the two bases, which are the same, and the lateral area. The area of each base is πr^2 and the lateral area is the circumference of the base times the height, which is $2\pi rh$.

Ask ...

- What is calculated by the formula in cell D2? The area of one base.
- Why is there multiplication by 2 in the formula in cell E2? Because cell D2 contains the area of one base, but a cylinder has two bases of equal size.
- In Part b of **Try It,** how might the comparisons be made more easily? Expand the spreadsheet to include more rows and copy the formulas. This way, the information for each set of measurements could be shown at once.

Answers for Try It

a. Cylinder with height of 3 cm and radius of 4 cm.

b. Cylinder with height of 1 unit and radius of 9 units.

On Your Own
For the first question, some spreadsheet software may use "+" rather than "=."

Answers for On Your Own

- The = is used so that the spreadsheet program knows you are entering a formula.
- Possible answer: If the numbers are large or have too many digits to enter into a calculator, it may be more efficient to use a spreadsheet.

TECHNOLOGY

Using a Spreadsheet • Finding the Surface Area of a Cylinder

Problem: Which has more surface area, a cylinder with a height of 5 cm and a radius of 2 cm, or a cylinder with a height of 2 cm and a radius of 5 cm?
You can use spreadsheets to quickly complete the calculations.

	A	B	C	D	E
1	Height	Radius	Lateral SA	Base area	Total SA
2					

1 **Enter the information into the spreadsheet as shown.**

	A	B	C	D	E
1	Height	Radius	Lateral SA	Base area	Total SA
2	5	2	62.8	12.56	87.92
3	2	5	62.8	78.50	219.80

2 **In cell A2, enter 5. In cell B2, enter 2. In cell C2, enter the formula** =2*3.14*A2*B2. **In cell D2, enter the formula** =3.14*(B2)^2. **In cell E2, enter the formula** =C2+2*D2.

3 **Copy the contents of row 2 down to row 3. Then, change the height value to** 2 **and the radius value to** 5.

Solution: A cylinder with a height of 2 cm and a radius of 5 cm has more surface area than a cylinder with a height of 5 cm and a radius of 2 cm.

TRY IT

a. Which has more surface area, a cylinder with a height of 3 cm and a radius of 4 cm, or a cylinder with a height of 4 cm and a radius of 3 cm?

b. If the height and radius of a cylinder must be whole numbers whose sum is 10, how much should the height and radius be to get the cylinder with the largest surface area?

ON YOUR OWN

- Why do you think it's necessary to type an = at the beginning of each formula?
- Why might a person want to set up a spreadsheet to calculate the surface area of a cylinder instead of using a calculator or pencil and paper?

Section 11A Connect

In this section, you've used the dimensions of solids to find their surface areas. Now you'll answer a question that often faces package designers: If you know the surface area of a solid, how do you find the dimensions?

The Grapes of Wrap

Materials: Ruler

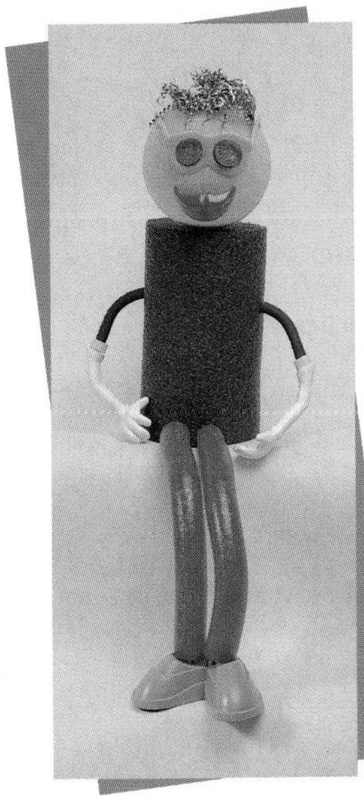

The Play-Brite Company has invented a new toy, known as a Squidge. The Squidge is a foam cylinder that can be decorated with different plastic legs, hands, mouths, eyes, and hair. You must design and decorate a package for the Squidge. Begin by drawing a net that meets the following conditions:

- It must fold together into a rectangular prism.
- It must have a surface area that is as close to 100 cm^2 as possible.

1. If your first try is too far below 100 cm^2, how could you increase the surface area? If it is too far above 100 cm^2, how could you decrease the surface area?

2. When you have a net that is between 90 cm^2 and 110 cm^2, cut it out. Label the lengths of each edge on each face.

3. Add designs and color to the package to make it as attractive as possible. Don't forget to show on the box why the Squidge is an ideal toy.

599

The Grapes of Wrap

The Point

In *The Grapes of Wrap* on page 579, students learned about designing packages for products. Now students will design and decorate a rectangular prism as a package for a new toy.

Materials

Metric ruler

Resources

Teaching Tool Transparency 16: Rulers

About the Page

- Discuss the number of sides in a package that has the shape of a rectangular prism.
- Remind students that their net must fold together into a box. There are no overlapping edges in this package.
- Ask students to determine the length of an edge if the package is shaped like a cube. 4 cm
- Discuss with students some of the things they could include in their design that would appeal to a consumer who might purchase the Squidge.

Ongoing Assessment

Check that students have designed an attractive package with a surface area between 90 cm^2 and 180 cm^2.

Extension

Have students work on the following problem. The Play-Brite Company is going to market the Squidge in two sizes. The small Squidge fits into the box with the 100 cm^2 surface area. The large size fits into a box that is 10 cm $\times$ 5 cm $\times$ 5 cm. Find the surface area of the larger box. 250 cm^2

Answers for Connect

1. To increase the surface area, increase the length of a measurement; To decrease the surface area, decrease the length of a measurement.

2–3. Answers may vary.

11A Review

Review Correlation

Item(s)	Lesson(s)
1–7	11-1
8–11	11-2,11-3
12	11-1

Test Prep

Test-Taking Tip

Suggest that students carefully examine all four figures and identify the characteristic which is unique to one of the figures. In this case, the figure in C has two congruent bases that are circles. The bases of all the other figures are polygons.

Answers for Review

3. Triangular prism; 6 vertices, 9 edges, 5 faces.
5. Cube or rectangular prism; 8 vertices, 12 edges, 6 faces.
6. Rectangular pyramid; 5 vertices, 8 edges, 5 faces.
7. A rectangular pyramid has one rectangular base, whereas a rectangular prism has two parallel rectangular bases of the same size.

Section 11A Review

REVIEW 11A

Classify each solid. If it is a polyhedron, tell how many vertices, edges, and faces it has.

1. 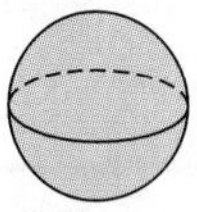
Sphere

2. 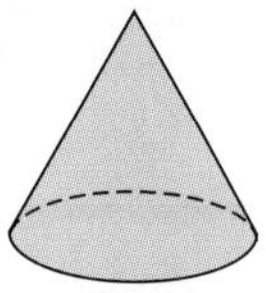
Cone

3. 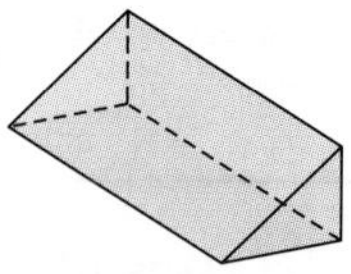

4. 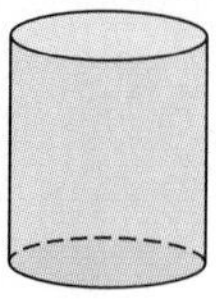
Cylinder

5. 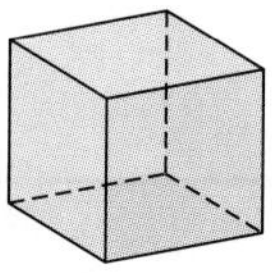

6. 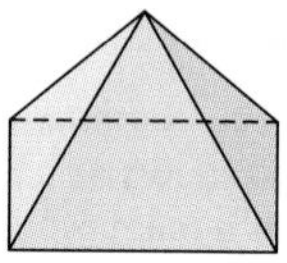

7. Journal Describe the difference between a rectangular pyramid and a rectangular prism.

Find the surface area of each figure.

8. 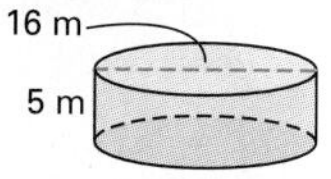

653.12 m^2

9. 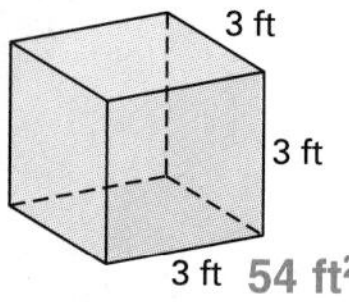

54 ft^2

10. 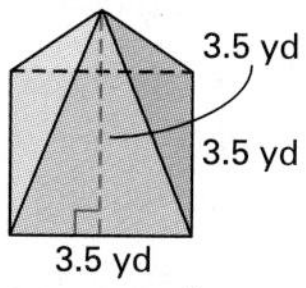

36.75 yd^2

11. Find the surface area of a rectangular prism that measures 20 cm by 40 cm by 60 cm. 8800 cm^2

Test Prep

In order for a shape to be a prism, it must have two congruent bases that are both polygons.

12. Which of the following is **not** a prism? C

Ⓐ 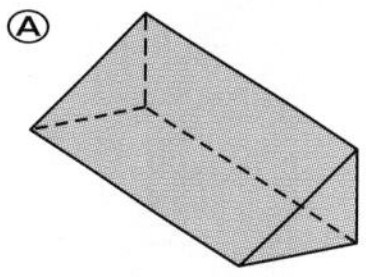
Ⓑ 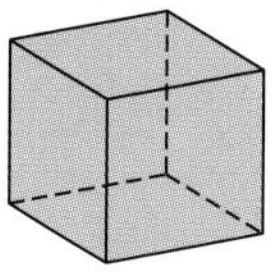
Ⓒ 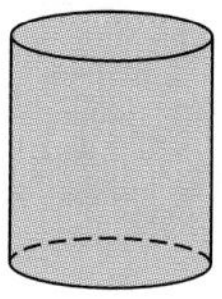
Ⓓ 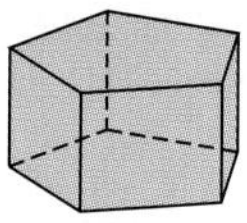

Resources

Practice Masters
Section 11A Review

Assessment Sourcebook
Quiz 11A

TestWorks
Test and Practice Software

PRACTICE

Name ______________________

Practice

Section 11A Review

Classify each solid. If it is a polyhedron, tell how many vertices, edges, and faces it has.

1. Triangular pyramid V: 4 E: 6 F: 4
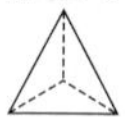

2. Rectangular prism V: 8 E: 12 F: 6
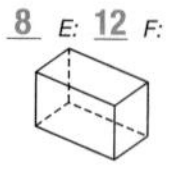

3. Sphere V: N/A E: N/A F: N/A

4. Triangular prism V: 6 E: 9 F: 5
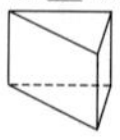

5. Cylinder V: N/A E: N/A F: N/A

6. Square pyramid V: 5 E: 8 F: 5
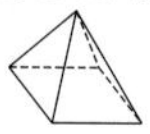

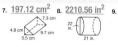

Find the surface area of each figure.

7. 197.12 cm^2
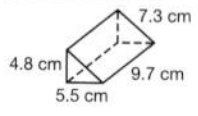

8. 2210.56 in^2
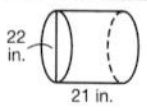

9. 429 ft^2
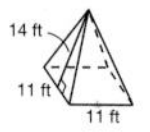

10. 722.2 mm^2
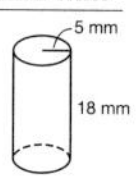

11. Find the surface area of a rectangular prism that measures 15 in. by 21 in. by 24 in. 2358 in^2

12. The symbol at the right is used to represent "clubs" in a deck of playing cards. Tell whether the symbol has line symmetry. If it does, draw all the lines of symmetry. *[Lesson 8-8]*
Yes

13. The distance from Berlin, Germany, to Rome, Italy, is about 734 miles. It is also 1181 kilometers. Using these measurements, find the number of kilometers in a mile. *[Lesson 10-6]* About 1.61 km

Section 11B

Volume

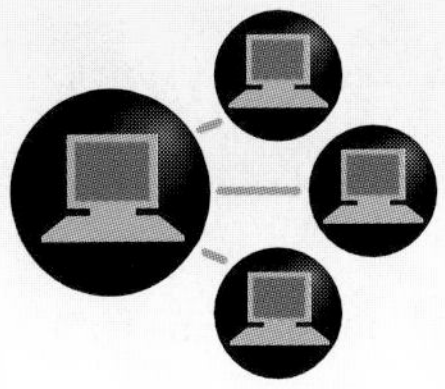

Visit www.teacher.mathsurf.com for links to lesson plans from teachers and other professionals, NCTM information, and other sites.

LESSON PLANNING GUIDE

Student Edition / Ancillaries*

LESSON		MATERIALS	VOCABULARY	DAILY	OTHER
	Section 11B Opener				
11-5	**Three-Dimensional Figures**	centimeter cubes		11-5	Teaching Tool Trans. 9 Lesson Enhancement Trans. 56
11-6	**Exploring Volume**	graph paper, dried beans, centimeter cubes, scissors, tape	volume, cubic units	11-6	Teaching Tool Trans. 2, 3 Lesson Enhancement Trans. 57 *Interactive CD-ROM Lesson* *WW Math*–Middle School
11-7	**Calculating Volume**	centimeter cubes		11-7	Technology Master 59 Ch. 11 Project Master
	Connect	ruler			Teaching Tool Trans. 16 Interdisc. Team Teaching 11B
	Review				Practice 11B; Quiz 11B; *TestWorks*
	Extend Key Ideas				
	Chapter 11 Summary and Review				
	Chapter 11 Assessment				Ch. 11 Tests Forms A–F *TestWorks*; Ch. 11 Letter Home
	Cumulative Review, Chapters 1–11				Cumulative Review, Ch. 1–11

* Daily Ancillaries include Practice, Reteaching, Problem Solving, Enrichment, and Daily Transparency. Teaching Tool Transparencies are in *Teacher's Toolkits*. Lesson Enhancement Transparencies are in *Overhead Transparency Package*.

SKILLS TRACE

LESSON	SKILL	FIRST INTRODUCED GR. 4	GR. 5	GR. 6	DEVELOP	PRACTICE/ APPLY	REVIEW
11-5	**Drawing solids.**			✗ p. 602	pp. 602–603	pp. 604–605	pp. 616, 638
11-6	**Finding volumes of rectangular prisms.**		✗		pp. 606–607	pp. 608–609	pp. 616, 638
11-7	**Using a formula to find volume.**		✗		pp. 610–612	pp. 613–614	pp. 616, 646

CONNECTED MATHEMATICS

The unit *Ruins of Montarek (Spatial Visualization)*, from the **Connected Mathematics** series, can be used with Section 11B.

INTERDISCIPLINARY TEAM TEACHING

Math and Art

(Worksheet pages 55–56: Teacher pages T55–T56)

In this lesson, students use solid geometry to explore technical drawings.

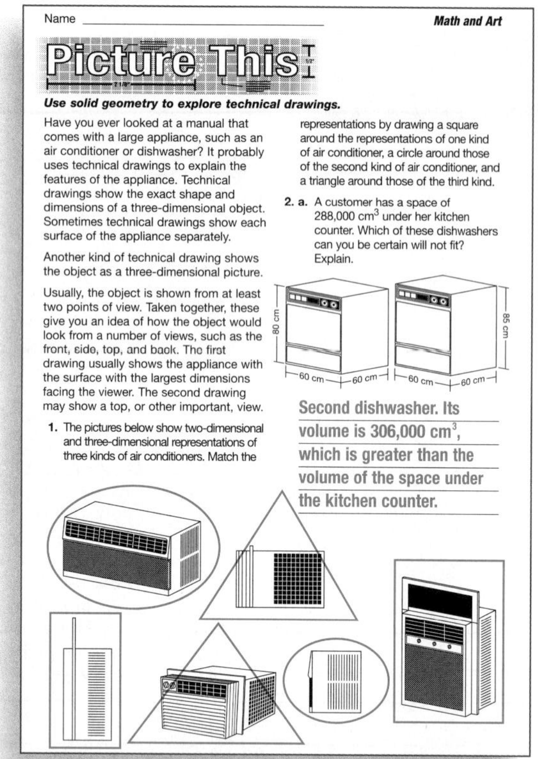
Name ______________________ **Math and Art**

Picture This

Use solid geometry to explore technical drawings.

Have you ever looked at a manual that comes with a large appliance, such as an air conditioner or dishwasher? It probably uses technical drawings to explain the features of the appliance. Technical drawings show the exact shape and dimensions of a three-dimensional object. Sometimes technical drawings show each surface of the appliance separately.

Another kind of technical drawing shows the object as a three-dimensional picture.

Usually, the object is shown from at least two points of view. Taken together, these give you an idea of how the object would look from a number of views, such as the front, side, top, and back. The first drawing usually shows the appliance with the surface with the largest dimensions facing the viewer. The second drawing may show a top, or other important, view.

1. The pictures below show two-dimensional and three-dimensional representations of three kinds of air conditioners. Match the representations by drawing a square around the representations of one kind of air conditioner, a circle around those of the second kind of air conditioner, and a triangle around those of the third kind.

2. a. A customer has a space of 288,000 cm^3 under her kitchen counter. Which of these dishwashers can you be certain will not fit? Explain.

Second dishwasher. Its volume is 306,000 cm^3, which is greater than the volume of the space under the kitchen counter.

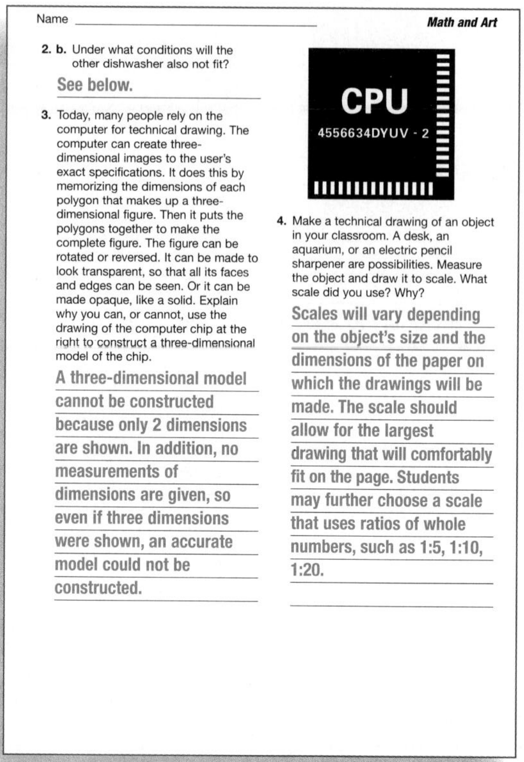
Name ______________________ **Math and Art**

2. b. Under what conditions will the other dishwasher also not fit?

See below.

3. Today, many people rely on the computer for technical drawing. The computer can create three-dimensional images to the user's exact specifications. It does this by memorizing the dimensions of each polygon that makes up a three-dimensional figure. Then it puts the polygons together to make the complete figure. The figure can be rotated or reversed. It can be made to look transparent, so that all its faces and edges can be seen. Or it can be made opaque, like a solid. Explain why you can, or cannot, use the drawing of the computer chip at the right to construct a three-dimensional model of the chip.

A three-dimensional model cannot be constructed because only 2 dimensions are shown. In addition, no measurements of dimensions are given, so even if three dimensions were shown, an accurate model could not be constructed.

4. Make a technical drawing of an object in your classroom. A desk, an aquarium, or an electric pencil sharpener are possibilities. Measure the object and draw it to scale. What scale did you use? Why?

Scales will vary depending on the object's size and the dimensions of the paper on which the drawings will be made. The scale should allow for the largest drawing that will comfortably fit on the page. Students may further choose a scale that uses ratios of whole numbers, such as 1:5, 1:10, 1:20.

Answers

2. b. If any of the dimensions is greater than the corresponding dimensions of the space under the kitchen counter.

BIBLIOGRAPHY

FOR TEACHERS

Geist, Sidney. *Brancusi; A Study of the Sculpture.* New York, NY: Grossman, 1968.

Kuriam, George Thomas. *The New Book of World Rankings.* New York, NY: Facts on File, 1990.

Nardo, Don. *Gravity: The Universal Force.* San Diego, CA: Lucent Books, 1990.

Smith, Carter. *The Pyramid Builders.* Englewood Cliffs, NJ: Silver Burdett Press, 1991.

Sterba, Gunther, ed. *The Aquarium Encyclopedia.* Cambridge, MA: MIT Press, 1983.

FOR STUDENTS

Banchoff, Thomas. *Beyond the Third Dimension: Geometry, Computer Graphics . . .* New York, NY: Scientific American Library, 1990.

Karemer, William J. *Strength Training for Young Athletes.* Champaign, IL: Human Kinetics Publishers, 1993.

Paxton, John R. and Eschmeyer, William N., eds. *Encyclopedia of Fishes.* San Diego, CA: Academic Press, 1995.

SECTION **11B**

Volume

▶ Science Link ▶ www.mathsurf.com/6/ch11/aquariums

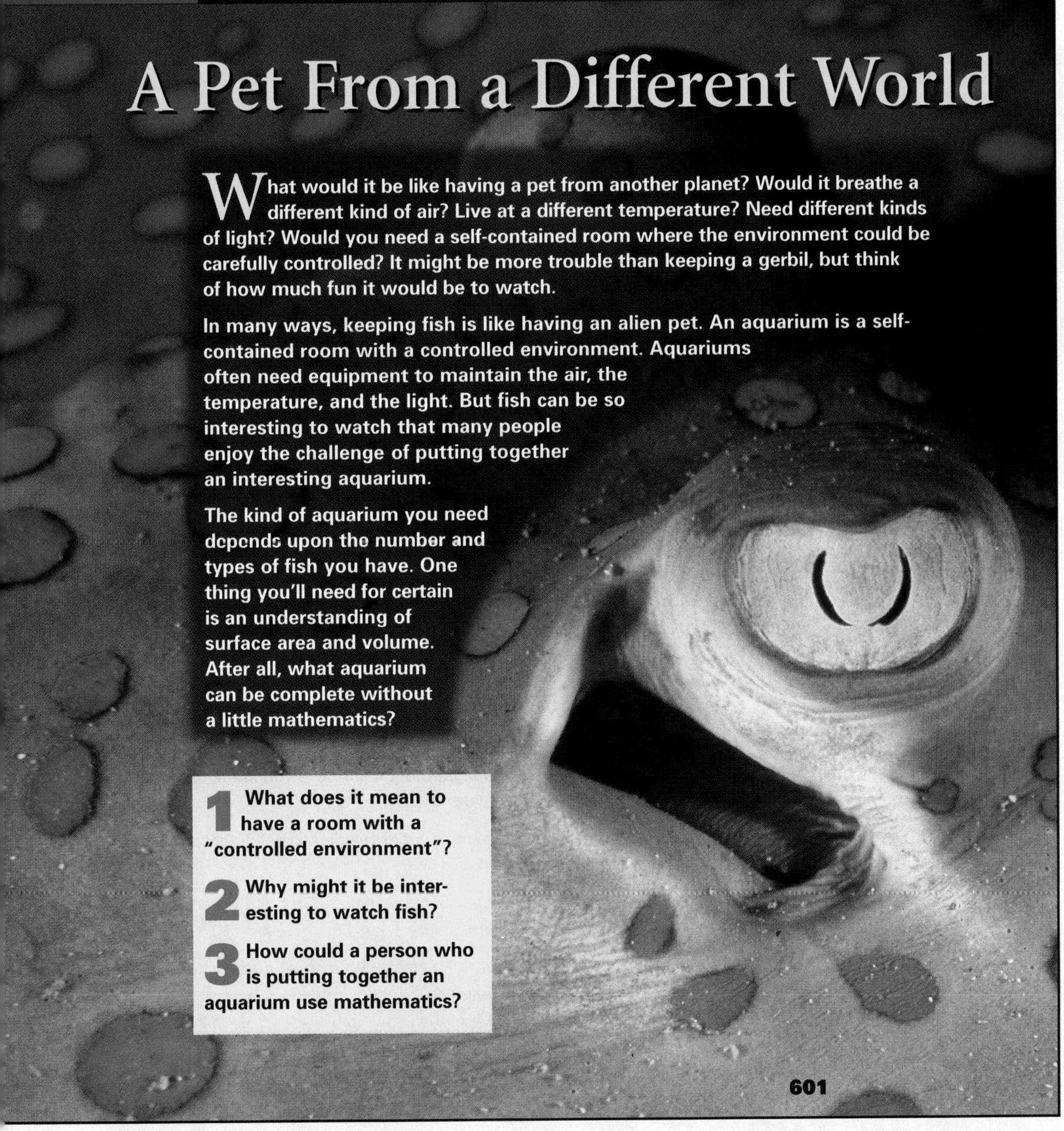

A Pet From a Different World

What would it be like having a pet from another planet? Would it breathe a different kind of air? Live at a different temperature? Need different kinds of light? Would you need a self-contained room where the environment could be carefully controlled? It might be more trouble than keeping a gerbil, but think of how much fun it would be to watch.

In many ways, keeping fish is like having an alien pet. An aquarium is a self-contained room with a controlled environment. Aquariums often need equipment to maintain the air, the temperature, and the light. But fish can be so interesting to watch that many people enjoy the challenge of putting together an interesting aquarium.

The kind of aquarium you need depends upon the number and types of fish you have. One thing you'll need for certain is an understanding of surface area and volume. After all, what aquarium can be complete without a little mathematics?

1 What does it mean to have a room with a "controlled environment"?

2 Why might it be interesting to watch fish?

3 How could a person who is putting together an aquarium use mathematics?

601

Where are we now?

In Section 11A, students identified solid figures and calculated the surface area of three-dimensional shapes.

They learned how to

- classify three-dimensional shapes.
- find the surface area of a polyhedron by using a net of the solid.
- use surface area formulas.
- find the surface area of a cylinder.

Where are we going?

In Section 11B, students will

- draw the front, side, and top views of a solid.
- calculate the volume of a rectangular prism.
- use the volume formula for rectangular prisms.

Theme: Aquariums

World Wide Web

If your class has access to the World Wide Web, you might want to use the information found at the Web site address given. The interdisciplinary link relates to topics discussed in this section.

About the Page

This page introduces the theme of the section, aquariums, and discusses the environment needed to maintain fish.

Ask ...

- What are some of the things you need to do to care for fish?
- How are different environments maintained in an aquarium?

Extension

The following activity does not require access to the World Wide Web.

Science

Have students select something that might be in an aquarium and draw or trace a picture of it. Create a "bulletin board" aquarium in your classroom.

Answers for Questions

1. Possible answer: The environment of the room, temperature, light, and air can be maintained the way you want it.
2. Possible answer: Fish can be relaxing to watch. One can learn more about them by watching them. Designing an aquarium by selecting what to put inside it can be an interesting hobby as well.
3. Possible answer: Mathematics can be used in determining measurements for the length, area, and volume of an aquarium, as well as the number of fish and the rate of water flow.

Connect

On page 615, students design a tank for tropical fish.

11-5 Lesson Organizer

Objective

- Draw the front, side, and top views of a solid.

Materials

- Explore: Centimeter cubes

NCTM Standards

- 1–4, 8, 12

Review

What geometric figure(s) do you see if you look down at each of the following objects from directly above?

1. A cube square
2. A soup can circle
3. A book rectangle

Available on Daily Transparency 11-5

1 Introduce

Explore

You may wish to use Teaching Tool Transparency 9: Isometric Dot Paper and Lesson Enhancement Transparency 56 with this lesson.

The Point

Students use centimeter cubes to model stacks of crates and then make drawings of the crates as seen from above.

Ongoing Assessment

Point out that the drawings of the crates show a corner view, rather than a front, side, or top view. Of course, this view would change if the viewer changed his or her location.

For Groups That Finish Early

Which two stacks have the same number of cubes? How many are in each stack? The first and fourth stacks both have 20 cubes.

11-5 Three-Dimensional Figures

You'll Learn ...

- to draw the front, side, and top views of a solid

... How It's Used

Technical artists make drawings of the front, side, and top views of objects when explaining how complex machines work.

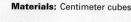

▶ Lesson Link In the last section, you learned to calculate surface areas of solids. Now you'll draw pictures of solids. ◀

Explore Three-Dimensional Figures

Something's Fishy!

Materials: Centimeter cubes

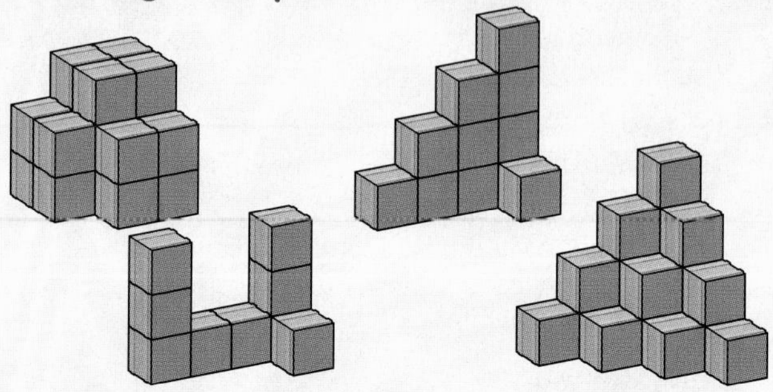

The stacks of crates pictured are stored in the Fish Farm warehouse. The manager records each stack by drawing what the crates look like from above and using numbers to show how many crates are in each stack.

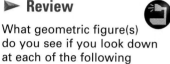

1. Build each stack of crates using centimeter cubes. Draw the crates as seen from above, as the manager did. Be sure to write in the number of crates for each square in your sketch.
2. Can you determine the number of cubes needed to build a stack from the manager's drawing? Explain.
3. Can you determine the number of cubes needed to build a stack from a picture of the stack? Explain.
4. Is it harder to draw a diagram of a stack with a small number of cubes, or a large number of cubes? Explain.

MEETING INDIVIDUAL NEEDS

Resources

- 11-5 Practice
- 11-5 Reteaching
- 11-5 Problem Solving
- 11-5 Enrichment
- 11-5 Daily Transparency
  - Problem of the Day
  - Review
  - Quick Quiz
- Teaching Tool Transparency 9
- Lesson Enhancement Transparency 56

Learning Modalities

Visual Have students make a bulletin board display showing a three-dimensional drawing of a building, as well as the front, side, and top views.

Kinesthetic Have students use cubes to make models of the solids shown in Exercises 5–12 on page 604.

Challenge

Have students select several real-world objects such as a television, a stove, or a sofa and then draw the front, side, and top views of each object.

Learn Three-Dimensional Figures

Recall that a solid is a three-dimensional figure. Solids are often drawn in perspective to show that they are three-dimensional.

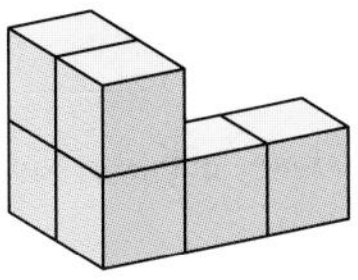

Solids can also be drawn using a flat view. Flat drawings show the solid from one view only. In order to record what the solid looks like, you usually need to show three views: front, side, and top.

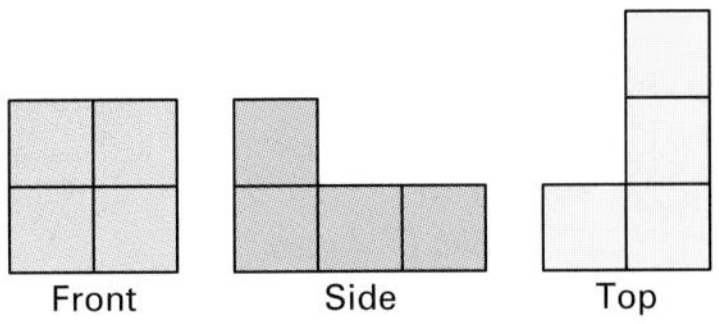

▶ Language Link

The flat drawings that show the front, side, and top views of a solid are also known as *orthographic projections.* A three-dimensional picture of a solid is an *isometric projection.*

Example 1

Draw front, side, and top views of the solid. There are no hidden cubes.

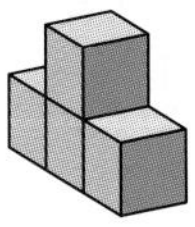

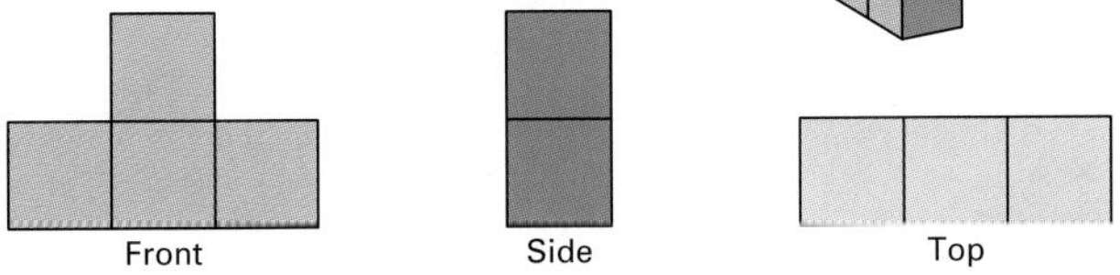

Try It

Draw front, side, and top views of the solid. There are no hidden cubes.

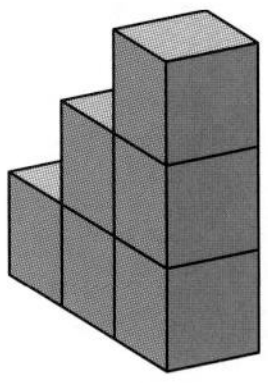

A solid also has other views, such as the back view and the bottom view. Because these views are mirror images of the front, side, and top views, they are not necessary when drawing a solid.

Check Your Understanding

1. Describe a solid with the same front, side, and top views.
2. Could you use the front, side, and top views of a solid to build it? Explain.

MATH EVERY DAY

▶ Problem of the Day

Complete the 400-year-old Chinese magic square, using all digits between 1 and 36.

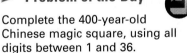

27	29			13	36
9	11	20		31	
		7		21	
14			30	12	
		15	17	26	19
1	24	33			10

27	29	2	4	13	36
9	11	20	22	31	18
32	25	7	3	21	23
14	16	34	30	12	5
28	6	15	17	26	19
1	24	33	35	8	10

The magic sum is 111.

Available on Daily Transparency 11-5

An Extension is provided in the transparency package.

Fact of the Day

U.S. commercial fishers caught more than 10,461,300,000 pounds of fish and seafood in 1994.

Estimation

Estimate each sum.

1. 207 + 99 300
2. 898 + 107 1000
3. 711 + 204 900
4. 689 + 489 1200

Answers for Explore

1.

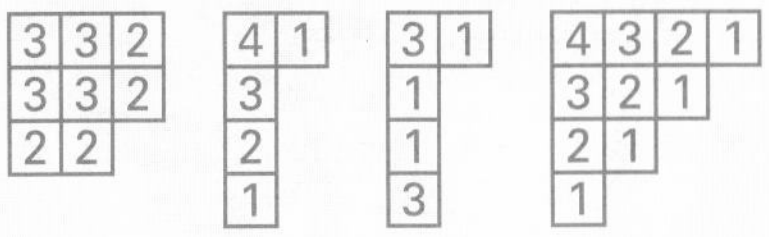

2. Yes; Add the stack numbers together.
3. Yes; As long as it is possible to determine which cubes must be stacked on top of other hidden cubes and then you can count the cubes.
4. Large number; There are more cubes to draw or count and there is a higher chance of some cubes being hidden.

2 Teach

Learn

Alternate Examples

1. Draw front, side, and top views of the solid. There are no hidden cubes.

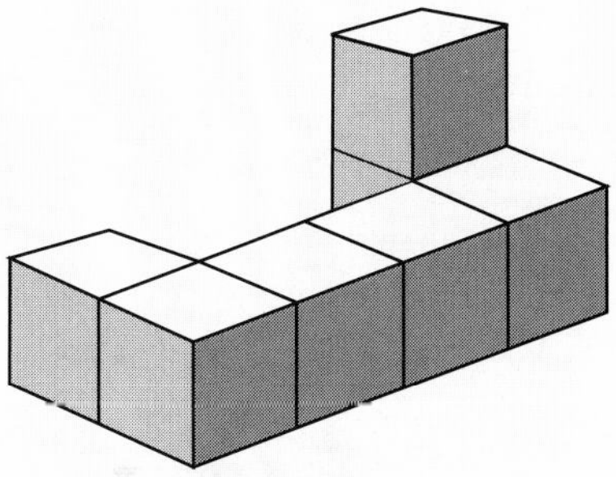

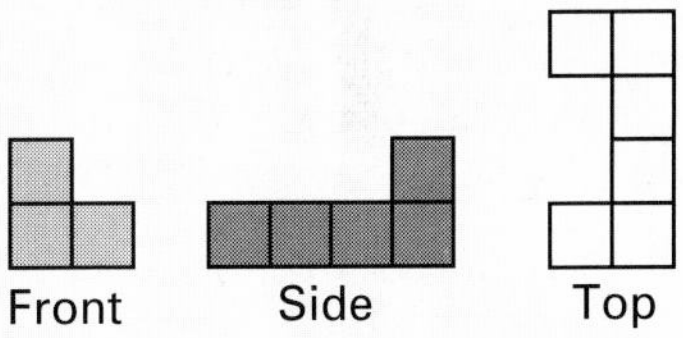

Answers for Try It

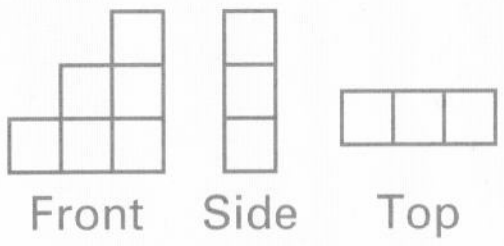

3 Practice and Assess

Check

Answers for Check Your Understanding

1. Possible answer: A stack of 8 cubes, 2 wide, 2 deep, and 2 high.
2. Sometimes; There may be cubes or gaps in the solid that you can't see from the front, side, and top views.

11-5 Exercises and Applications

Assignment Guide

- **Basic**
  1–4, 6–16 evens, 17,
  20–36 evens
- **Average**
  2–16 evens, 17–18,
  20–36 evens
- **Enriched**
  7–19, 21–35 odds

Exercise Notes

■ Exercises 5–12

Error Prevention Some students will give incorrect drawings because they are confused about what is considered the front and what is considered the side. Point out that the "front" is seen on the left and the "side" is seen on the right of the cubes in the three-dimensional drawings.

Exercise Answers

5.

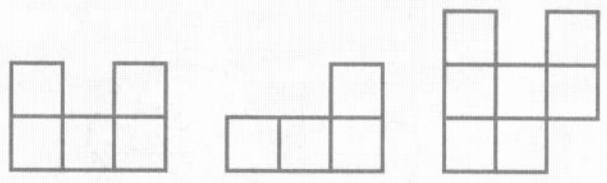

6.

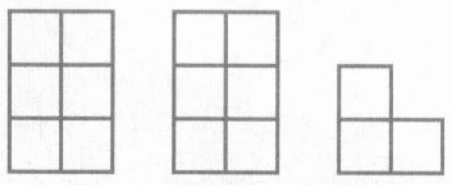

7–12. See page C5.

13. 36; Possible answer: For the number of cubes in the eighth solid of the pattern, you add $8 + 7 + 6 + 5 + 4 + 3 + 2 + 1$.

14. 22; The number of cubes increases by 3 for each solid and it began with one cube.

Reteaching

Activity

Materials: Centimeter cubes

- Work with a partner and use at least 20 centimeter cubes.
- Take turns building different configurations of cubes and then drawing the front, side, and top views of each solid.

11-5 Exercises and Applications

Practice and Apply

Getting Started State how many cubes are in each solid.

1. 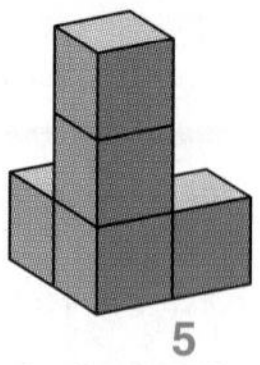 5

2. 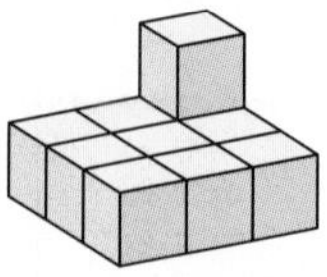 10

3. 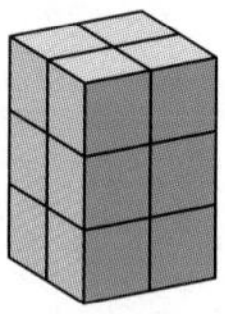 12

4.  6

Draw the front, side, and top views of each solid.

5. 

6. 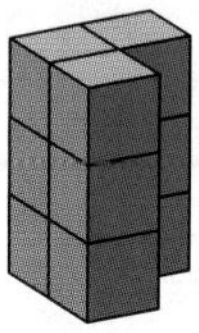

7. 

8. 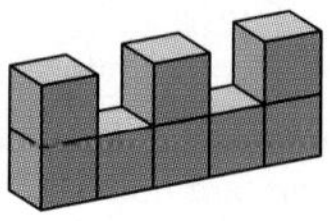

9. 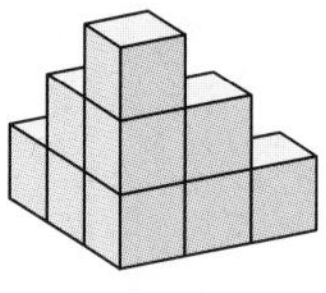

10. 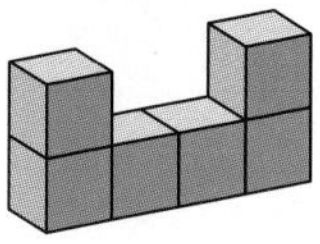

11. 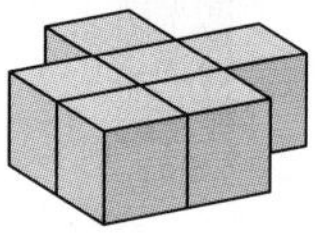

12. 

Patterns Describe each pattern. How many cubes are in the eighth solid of each pattern?

13.

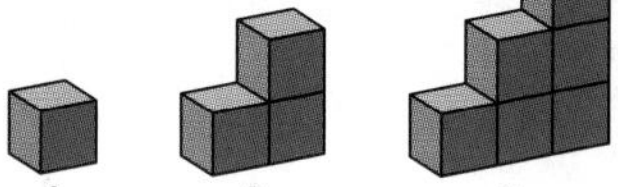

14. GPS

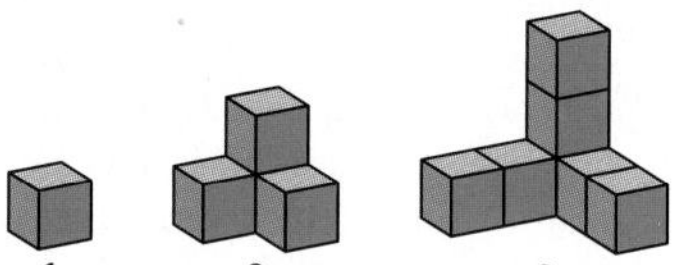

15. Problem Solving Each cube in the solid shown is 1.7 cm by 1.7 cm by 1.7 cm.

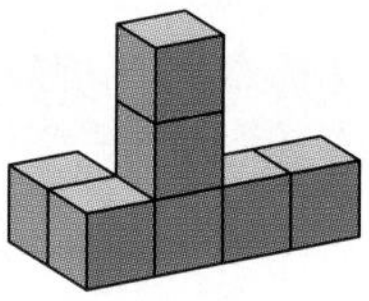

a. How many cubes are in the solid? 7

b. How tall is the solid at its highest point? 5.1 cm

c. How wide is the solid at its widest point? 6.8 cm

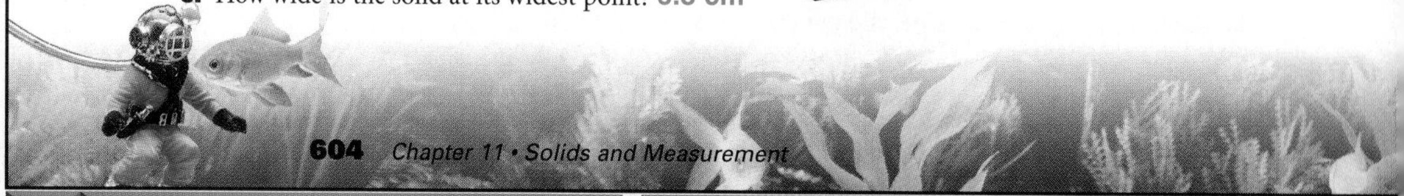

PRACTICE

Name ______________________

Practice 11-5

Three-Dimensional Figures

Draw the front, side, and top views of each solid. There are no hidden cubes.

1. 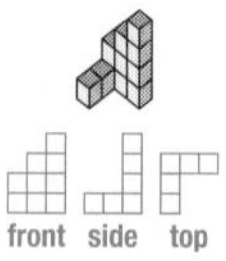

2. 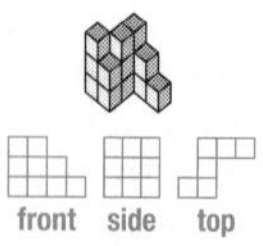

3. 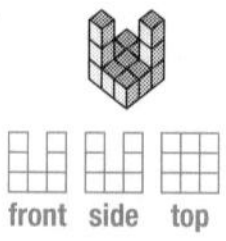

4. 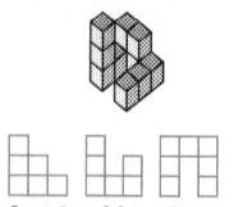

Describe each pattern. How many cubes are in the eighth solid of each pattern?

5. Possible answer: Each pattern is obtained by adding one cube in each of two directions and adding another layer; 120

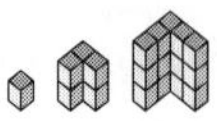

6. Possible answer: Each solid is obtained by adding one cube in each of five directions; 36

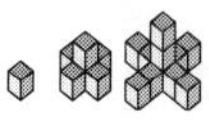

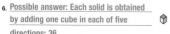

7. Each cube in the solid shown is 5 in. by 5 in. by 5 in.

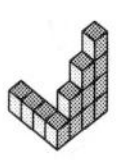

a. How many cubes are in the solid? 13

b. How tall is the solid at its highest points? 20 in.

c. How wide is the solid at its widest point? 20 in.

RETEACHING

Name ______________________

Alternative Lesson 11-5

Three-Dimensional Figures

Solids are often drawn in perspective to show that they are three-dimensional.

Solids can also be drawn using a flat view. Flat drawings show the solid from one view only. In order to record what the solid looks like, you usually need to show three views: front, side, and top.

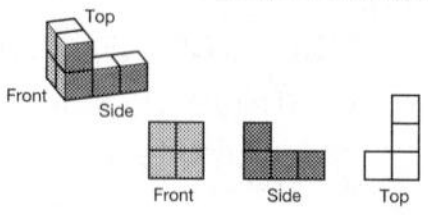

Example

Draw the front, side, and top views of the solid. There are no hidden cubes.

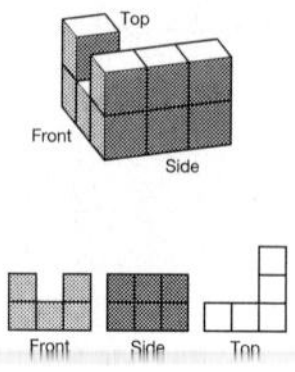

Look at the position of the cubes that make up the front view of the figure. There are two stacks of two cubes each and one stack of one cube. Draw squares to show each position.

Look at the position of the cubes that make up the side view of the figure. There are three stacks of two cubes each. Draw squares to show each position.

Look at the position of the cubes that make up the top view of the figure. There are four stacks of two cubes each and one stack of one cube. Draw squares to show each position.

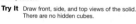

Try It Draw front, side, and top views of the solid. There are no hidden cubes.

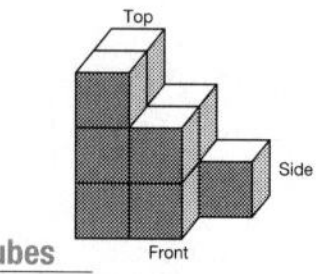

a. How many cubes make up the front view? 6 cubes

b. How many cubes make up the side view? 6 cubes

c. How many cubes make up the top view? 5 cubes

d. Draw the front view. e. Draw the side view. f. Draw the top view.

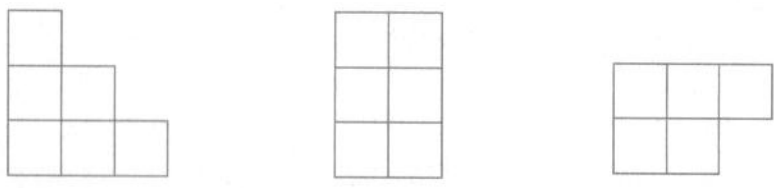

16. **Test Prep** How many cubes are in the tower? **C**

Ⓐ 6 Ⓑ 10

Ⓒ 14 Ⓓ 18

Problem Solving and Reasoning

17. Critical Thinking Tell if each set of views makes a prism. Explain.

a.

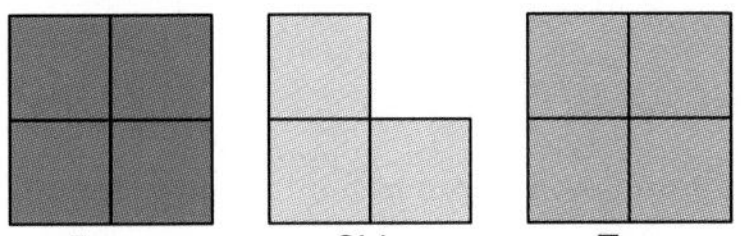

b.

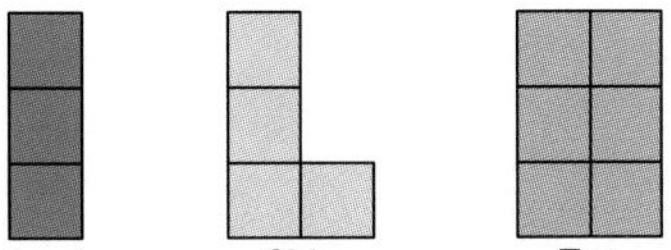

18. Critical Thinking Each solid is made up of 1-centimeter cubes. Find the surface area of each. Explain your reasoning.

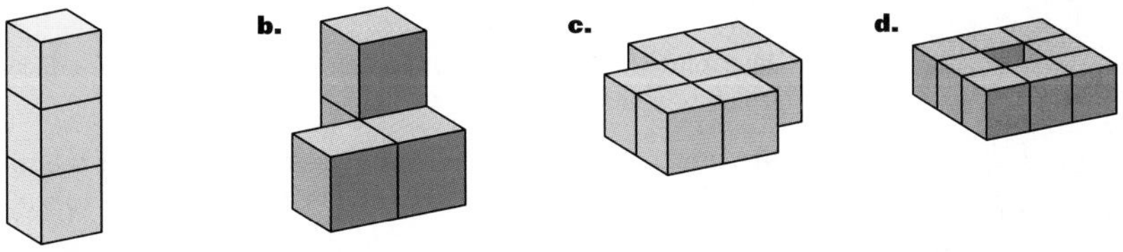

19. Communicate Suppose you have 24 cubes. Describe or draw the dimensions of three different rectangular prisms you can make with the cubes. Explain.

Mixed Review

Solve each proportion. *[Lesson 10-5]*

20. $\frac{4}{6} = \frac{8}{x}$ $x = 12$ **21.** $\frac{86}{f} = \frac{43}{24}$ $f = 48$ **22.** $\frac{5}{y} = \frac{42}{35}$ $y = 4.1\overline{6}$ **23.** $\frac{9}{21} = \frac{r}{7}$ $r = 3$ **24.** $\frac{p}{11} = \frac{33}{27}$ $p = 13.\overline{4}$

Convert each to a percent. *[Lesson 10-10]*

25. 1.56 156% **26.** 0.723 72.3% **27.** $\frac{11}{20}$ 55% **28.** 0.34 34% **29.** $\frac{7}{25}$ 28% **30.** $1\frac{3}{10}$ 130%

Convert each to a fraction or mixed number in lowest terms. *[Lesson 10-10]*

31. 67% $\frac{67}{100}$ **32.** 83.4% $\frac{417}{500}$ **33.** 250% $2\frac{1}{2}$ **34.** 99% $\frac{99}{100}$ **35.** 1% $\frac{1}{100}$ **36.** 0.6% $\frac{3}{500}$

PROBLEM SOLVING 11-5

Exercise Notes

■ Exercise 17a

The prism that is formed is a nonconvex prism. Tell students that they have probably seen many buildings or skyscrapers that are nonconvex prisms.

Exercise Answers

17. a. Yes; A prism with an L-shaped base.
 b. No; The top view is wider than the front view.

18. Possible answer: The area of each face of a cube is 1 cm^2. The surface area of the solid depends on how many cube faces are showing.
 a. 14 cm^2
 b. 18 cm^2
 c. 26 cm^2
 d. 32 cm^2

19. Possible answers: 1 by 2 by 12; 2 by 4 by 3; 1 by 3 by 8.

Alternate Assessment

Performance Have students make a drawing of a stack of several cubes and then draw the front, side, and top view of the stack.

Quick Quiz

Draw the front, side, and top views of the solid. There are no hidden cubes.

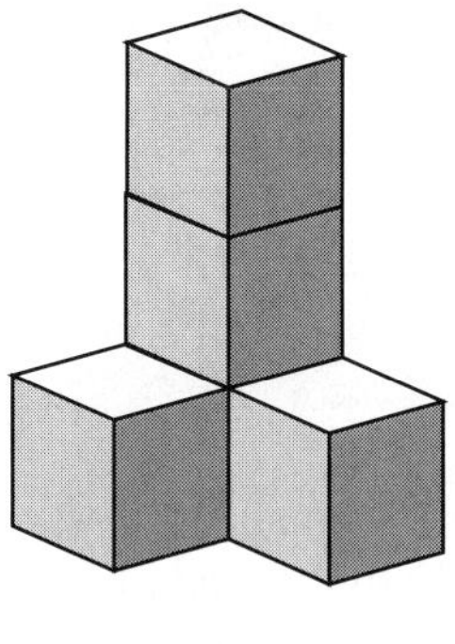

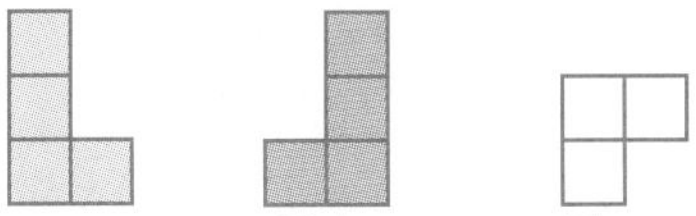

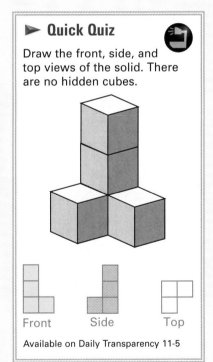

Available on Daily Transparency 11-5

PROBLEM SOLVING

Name ______________________

Guided Problem Solving 11-5

GPS PROBLEM 14, STUDENT PAGE 604

Describe the pattern.
How many cubes are in the eighth solid of the pattern?

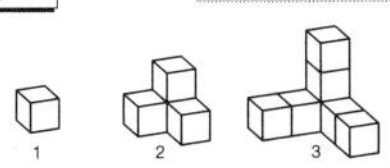

— Understand —

1. You are asked to find the number of cubes in which place in the pattern? Eighth.

— Plan —

2. Count the cubes in each figure in the pattern and use this data to complete the table.

Place	1	2	3	4	5	6	7	8
Number of Cubes	1	4	7	10	13	16	19	22

— Solve —

3. What is the rule for the pattern? Add 3.

4. Describe the pattern. Include how each figure in the pattern physically changes.
Possible answer: One cube is added to each of the three ends.

5. How many cubes are in the eighth solid of the pattern? 22 cubes.

— Look Back —

6. Continue the table to check your answer. What other strategy could you use to check your answer?
Possible answer: Draw a Diagram.

SOLVE ANOTHER PROBLEM

Describe the pattern.
How many cubes are in the tenth solid of the pattern?

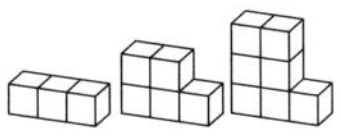

21 cubes; Two cubes added to top of two left stacks.

ENRICHMENT

Name ______________________

Extend Your Thinking 11-5

Visual Thinking

One of the simple figures in the row below is hidden in each of the figures in the lower part of the page.

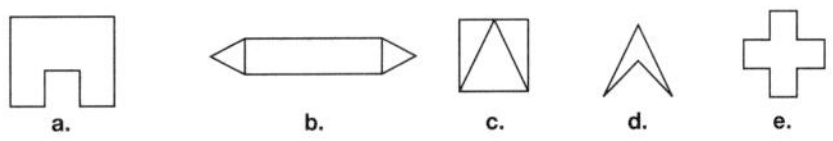

Write the letter of the simple figure that is a part of each figure.

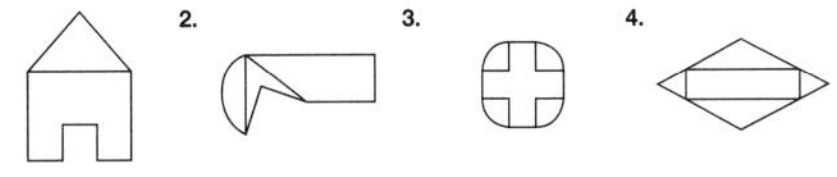

1. a 2. d 3. e 4. b

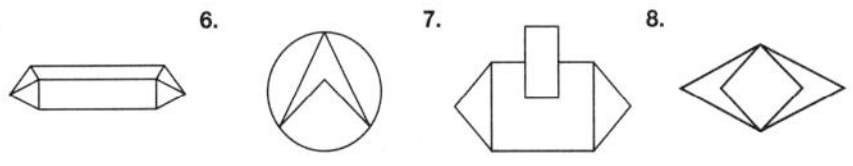

5. b 6. d 7. a 8. d

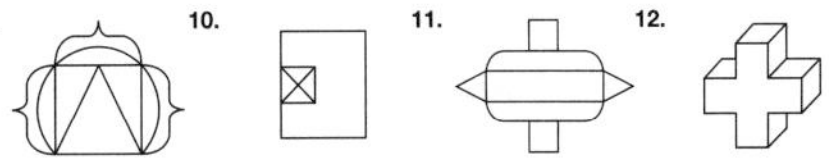

9. c 10. a 11. b 12. e

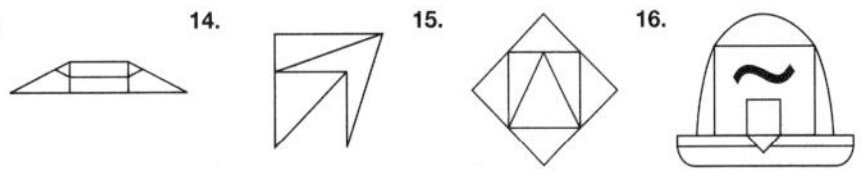

13. b 14. d 15. c 16. a

INTERACTIVE LESSON

11-6 Lesson Organizer

Objective

- Calculate the volume of a rectangular prism.

Vocabulary

- Volume, cubic units

Materials

- Explore: Graph paper, dried beans, centimeter cubes, scissors, tape

NCTM Standards

- 1–4, 12, 13

Review

Each figure is to be covered with a single layer of 1-inch cubes. How many cubes are needed?

1. 8-inch by 10-inch rectangle 80
2. 9-inch by 9-inch square 81
3. 1-foot by 2-foot rectangle 288

Available on Daily Transparency 11-6

1 Introduce

Explore

The Point
Students build two different open boxes. Then they determine how many beans and how many cubes it will take to fill the boxes.

Ongoing Assessment
Point out that the net for an open box has only 5 rectangles, not 6.

For Groups That Finish Early
Can you determine the number of cubes it takes to fill the boxes without actually filling them? Yes; Determine the number of cubes needed to cover the bottom and fill to the top. Then multiply the first number by the second.

Answers for Explore

1–2. Answers may vary.

3. 216; 300; The first box holds the least because the volume is less.

11-6 Exploring Volume

You'll Learn ...

- to calculate the volume of a rectangular prism

... How It's Used

Paramedics use volume to determine the amount of oxygen in an oxygen tank.

Vocabulary

volume

cubic units

▶ **Lesson Link** You've learned to sketch the different views of a solid. Now you'll find how many cubes it takes to fill the space inside a solid. ◀

Explore Volume

How Many Beans in a Box?

Materials: Graph paper, Dried beans, Centimeter cubes, Scissors, Tape

1. Using graph paper and tape, build an open box with a 6-by-6 cm base and a height of 6 cm. Build another open box with a 5-by-12 base and a height of 5. Do not make lids for the boxes.
2. Fill each box with beans. Record the number of beans that fit in each box.
3. Determine the number of centimeter cubes needed to fill each box. Which box holds the least? Explain.
4. Which material do you think most accurately measures the space inside each box? Which measures it least accurately? Explain.

Learn Exploring Volume

Recall that two-dimensional figures are measured by their *area.* You can find a figure's area by counting the number of *square units* it contains.

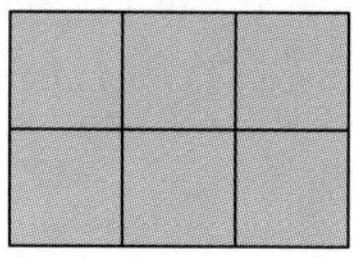

Area = 6 square units

Three-dimensional objects can be measured by their **volume** . The volume of an object is the number of **cubic units** it contains. You can find the volume of a rectangular prism by counting cubes.

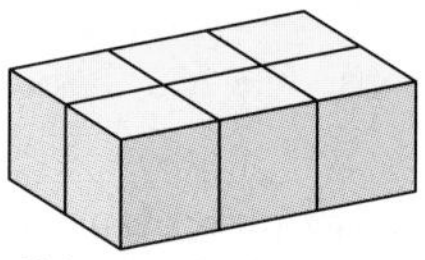

Volume = 6 cubic units

Recall that the exponent 2 means to multiply the base number by itself.

6^2 (read "6 *squared*") $= 6 \times 6 = 36$

The exponent 3 means to use the base number as a factor 3 times.

5^3 (read "5 *cubed*") $= 5 \times 5 \times 5 = 125$

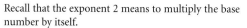

MEETING INDIVIDUAL NEEDS

Resources

- 11-6 Practice
- 11-6 Reteaching
- 11-6 Problem Solving
- 11-6 Enrichment
- 11-6 Daily Transparency
  - Problem of the Day
  - Review
  - Quick Quiz
- Teaching Tool Transparencies 2, 3
- Lesson Enhancement Transparency 57
- *Interactive CD-ROM Lesson*
- *Wide World of Mathematics* Middle School: Chunnel

Learning Modalities

Visual Have students make a bulletin board showing actual-size drawings of a cubic inch, a cubic centimeter, and a cubic foot.

Kinesthetic Have students use cubes and a variety of boxes to determine how many cubes are needed to fill the boxes.

English Language Development

Be sure that students understand that *cubic unit* is a general term for any cube. Point out that any convenient unit can be used, for example, a cubic inch, a cubic centimeter, a cubic yard, and so on.

Examples

1 Find the volume of the rectangular prism.

Each layer of the prism is 6 cubes by 2 cubes. This equals 6×2, or 12 cubes.

There are 4 layers in the prism. At 12 cubes per layer, this equals 4×12, or 48 cubes.

The volume is 48 cubic units. A shorthand way of writing this is 48 units^3.

2 Tropical Tanks received the shipment of cubical aquarium tanks shown. Each tank measures 1 m by 1 m by 1 m. Find the volume of the shipment.

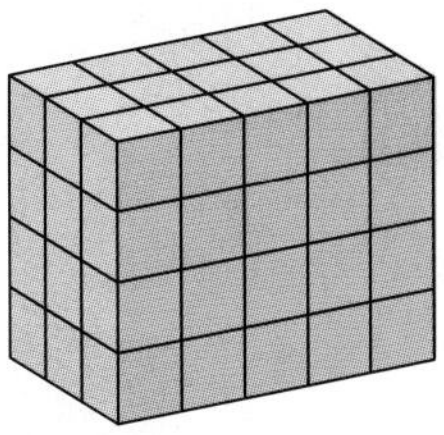

One layer is 5 m by 3 m. That's 5×3, or 15 m^2. There are 4 layers. At 15 m^2 per layer, this equals 15×4, or 60 m^3.

Try It

Find the volume of the prisms.

a.

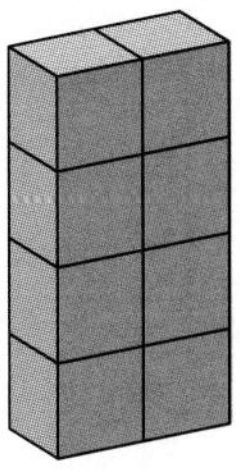

8 units^3

b.

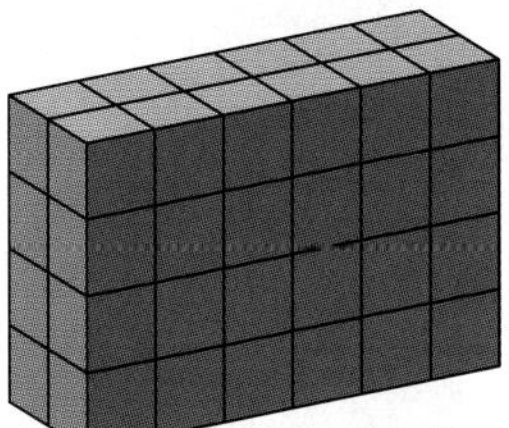

48 units^3

c.

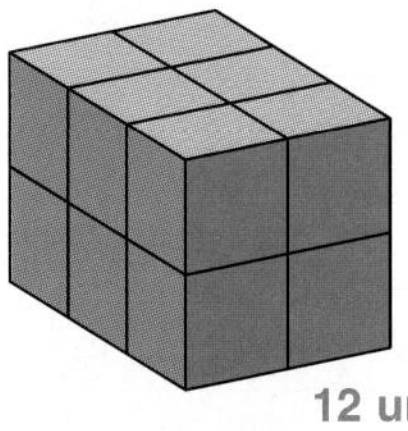

12 units^3

d.

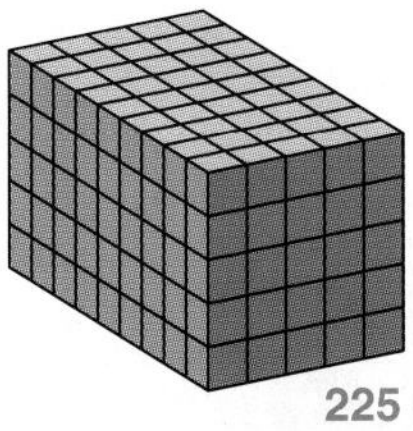

225 units^3

Check Your Understanding

1. Why is area measured in square units and volume measured in cubic units?

2. Is the volume of a solid the same as its surface area? Explain.

▶ Science Link

There are two types of aquarium tanks: glass and acrylic. Glass tanks are cheaper and harder to scratch. Acrylic tanks are lighter, harder to break, and don't distort images of the fish as much as glass tanks. Most pet store owners recommend glass tanks.

MATH EVERY DAY

▶ Problem of the Day

In 24 hours on a digital clock, how many times will at least two 2s occur? 80 times

Available on Daily Transparency 11-6

An Extension is provided in the transparency package.

Fact of the Day

In 1994, American farmers produced 31,816,000 tons of sugar cane and 32,008,000 tons of sugar beets.

Estimation

Estimate each product.

1. 2.7×9.3 27
2. 8.1×8.1 64
3. 7.12×9.89 70
4. 90.1×68.9 6300

Answers for Explore

4. The centimeter cubes measure more accurately because they are all the same size. Beans may vary in size.

2 Teach

Learn

You may wish to use Lesson Enhancement Transparency 57 with **Try It**.

Alternate Examples

1. Find the volume of the rectangular prism.

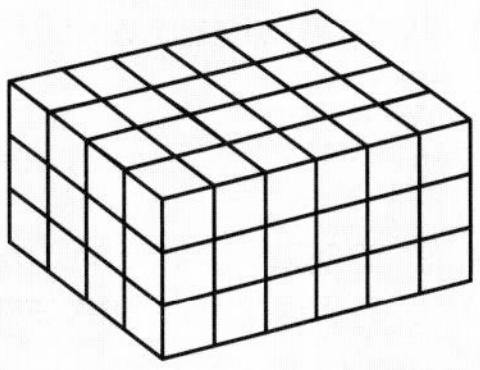

Each layer of the prism is 6 cubes by 4 cubes. This equals 6×4, or 24 cubes. There are 3 layers in the prism. At 24 cubes per layer, this equals 24×3, or 72 cubes.

The volume is 72 cubic units, or 72 units^3.

2. A shed is filled with cubical boxes as shown. The boxes measure 1 yd by 1 yd by 1 yd. Find the volume of the shed.

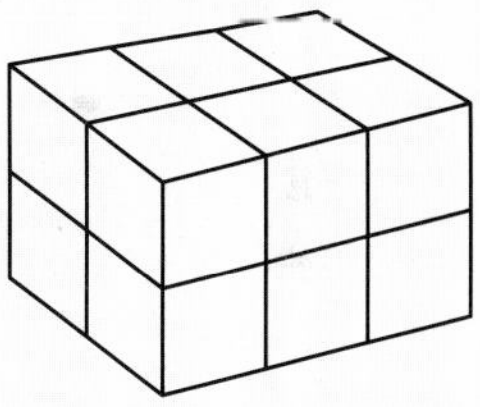

One layer is 3 yd by 2 yd. That is 3×2, or 6 yd^2. There are 2 layers. At 6 yd^2 per layer, this equals 6×2, or 12 yd^3.

The volume of the shed is 12 yd^3.

3 Practice and Assess

Check

Answers for Check Your Understanding

1. Possible answer: Square units are used for area because it is the product of two dimensions; Cubic units are used for volume because it is the product of three dimensions.
2. No; Volume is a measured in cubic units, but surface area is measured in square units.

11-6 Exercises and Applications

Assignment Guide

- Basic
  1–12, 14, 17–27 odds
- Average
  3–12, 14–15, 17–27 odds
- Enriched
  4–16, 18–28 evens

Exercise Notes

Exercise 11

Science Sugar comes from two main sources, sugar beets and sugar cane. Each source provides approximately half of the world's supply of sugar.

Exercise 12

Geography In terms of the volume of water held, the world's largest aquarium is the Living Seas Aquarium at Epcot Center, Florida. It opened in 1986 and it holds 6.25 million gallons.

11-6 Exercises and Applications

PRACTICE 11-6

Practice and Apply

Getting Started Find the volume of each solid.

1. 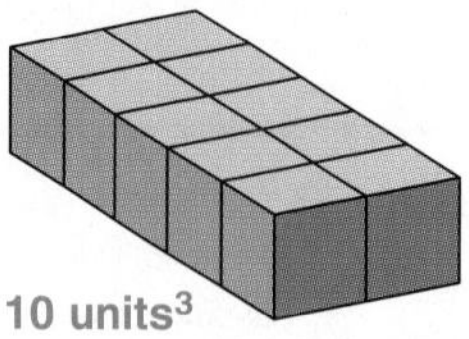
10 units^3

2. 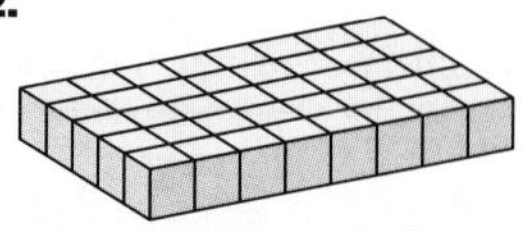
40 units^3

3. 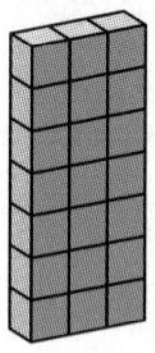
21 units^3

Find the volume of each solid.

4. 
80 units^3

5. 
360 units^3

6. 
12 units^3

7. 
64 units^3

8. 
280 units^3

9. 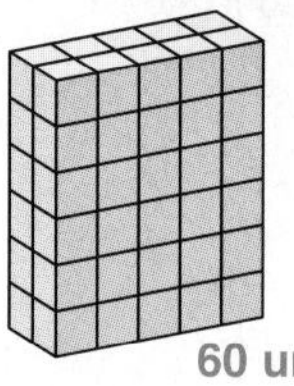
60 units^3

10. Geometry What is the volume of a rectangular prism that measures 8 cubes by 5 cubes by 4 cubes? 160 units^3

11. Consumer GPS When sugar cubes are produced, they are put into tightly packed boxes for purchasing. If the box of sugar cubes shown is 3 cubes high, how many sugar cubes are in the box? 126

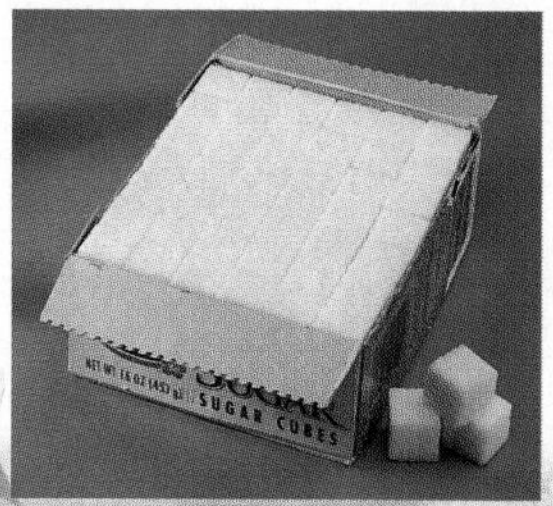

12. Test Prep Each cube in the aquarium shown measures 1 ft by 1 ft by 1 ft. What is the aquarium's volume? B

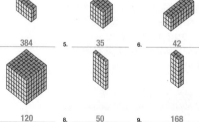

Ⓐ 1 ft^3

Ⓑ 24 ft^3

Ⓒ 26 ft^3

Ⓓ 52 ft^2

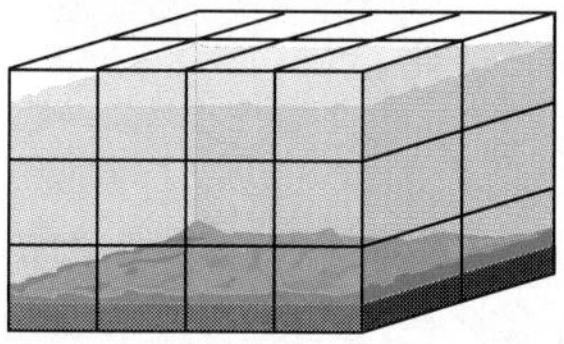
160 units^3

PRACTICE

Name ______________________

Practice 11-6

Exploring Volume

Find the volume of each solid.

1. 36 
2. 80 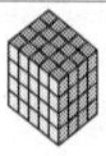
3. 81 
4. 384 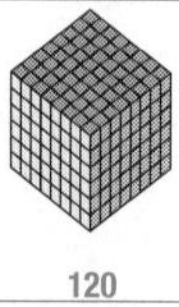
5. 35 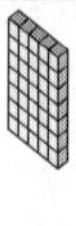
6. 42 
7. 120 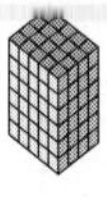
8. 50 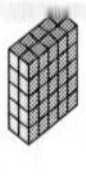
9. 168 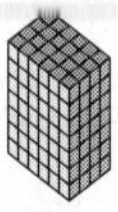
10. 27 
11. 120 
12. 210 
13. A farmer is loading bales of hay onto a wagon. The bales can fit 4 across, and there are 9 rows of bales from the front to the back of the truck. If each stack is to be 5 bales high, how many bales will fit in the wagon? 180 bales

RETEACHING

Name ______________________

Alternative Lesson 11-6

Exploring Volume

Three-dimensional objects can be measured by their volume. The **volume** of an object is the number of **cubic units** it contains. You can find the volume of a rectangular prism by counting cubes.

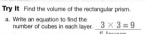

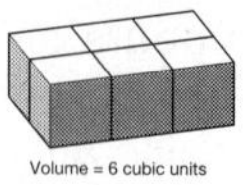
Volume = 6 cubic units

The exponent 3 means to use the base number as a factor 3 times.

5^3 (read "5 cubed") = 5 × 5 × 5 = 125

Example

Find the volume of the rectangular prism.

Each layer of the prism is 4 cubes by 5 cubes. This equals 4 × 5, or 20 cubes.

There are 3 layers in the prism. Multiply the number of layers by the number of cubes in each layer.

3 × 20 = 60 cubes

The volume of the prism is 60 cubic units, or 60 units^3

Try It Find the volume of the rectangular prism.

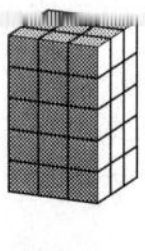

a. Write an equation to find the number of cubes in each layer. 3 × 3 = 9
b. How many layers are there? 5 layers.
c. Multiply to find the volume. 45 cubic units.

Find the volume of the rectangular prism.

d. Write an equation to find the number of cubes in each layer. 4 × 2 = 8
e. How many layers are there? 3 layers.
f. Multiply to find the volume. 24 cubic units.

Find the volume of each rectangular prism.

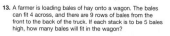

g. 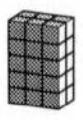
30 cubic units.

h. 
280 cubic units.

Reteaching

Activity

Materials: Cardboard boxes, cubes

- Work in groups of three or four.
- Use several small cardboard boxes and a large collection of cubes, all the same size.
- Use the cubes to determine how many cubes it would take to fill each box. Look for shortcuts.

13. Sonjay has 32 1-inch cubes and a box that is 5 in. by 4 in. by 2 in. Will all of Sonjay's blocks fit into the box? Yes

Problem Solving and Reasoning

14. **Critical Thinking** Each cube in each solid shown measures 1 cm by 1 cm by 1 cm. Order the solids from least to greatest according to their volumes. Would your list be different if you ordered the solids by surface areas? Explain. Volume: b, c, a; Surface area: b, a, c; The lists are different.

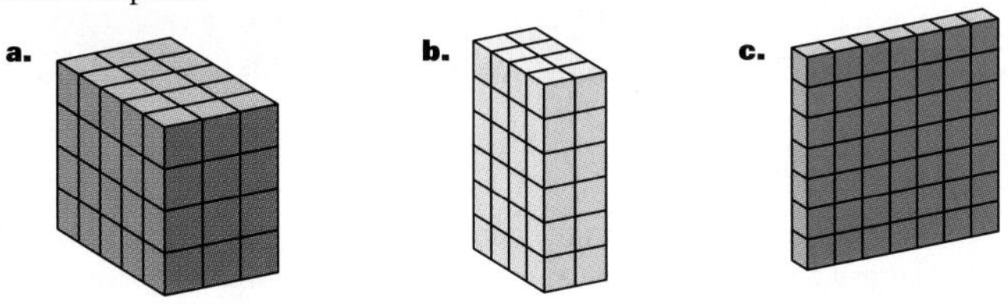

15. **Choose a Strategy** Raquel is selling cookies for a school fund-raiser. The Raisin Delight variety comes in square packages. Each shipment of Raisin Delights is made up of 12 square packages. How many different ways can the 12 packages be arranged to form a rectangular shipment? List the different ways.

Problem Solving STRATEGIES

- Look for a Pattern
- Make an Organized List
- Make a Table
- Guess and Check
- Work Backward
- Use Logical Reasoning
- Draw a Diagram
- Solve a Simpler Problem

16. **Critical Thinking** Use the views shown to find the volume of each solid.

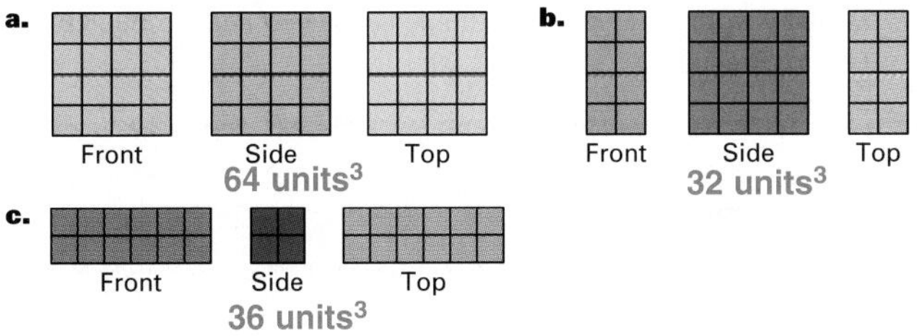

Mixed Review

Find the unit rate for each. *[Lesson 10-6]*

17. $\frac{9 \text{ mi}}{3 \text{ min}}$ 3 mi per min
18. $\frac{15 \text{ yd}^2}{5 \text{ rooms}}$ 3 yd² per room
19. $\frac{45 \text{ bananas}}{\$9}$ 5 bananas per dollar
20. $\frac{14 \text{ lb}}{4 \text{ sacks}}$ 3.5 lb per sack
21. $\frac{19 \text{ m}}{60 \text{ sec}}$ 0.316 m per sec
22. $\frac{28 \text{ elephants}}{27 \text{ mi}^2}$ 1.037 elephants per mi²
23. $\frac{9 \text{ worms}}{2 \text{ in}^2}$ 4.5 worms per in²
24. $\frac{4 \text{ dots}}{34 \text{ sec}}$ About 0.118 dot per sec

Estimate what percent of each figure is shaded. [Lesson 10-9]

25. About 20%
26. About 50%
27. About 20%
28. About 33%

PROBLEM SOLVING 11-6

Exercise Notes

Exercise 15

Error Prevention Some students will give more than four ways. For example, they might list *2 by 3 by 2* and *2 by 2 by 3* as two separate ways. Point out that both of these ways yield the same size of package.

Problem-Solving Tip You may wish to use Teaching Tool Transparencies 2 and 3: Guided Problem Solving, pages 1–2.

Exercise Answers

15. 4 ways; 1 by 1 by 12, 1 by 2 by 6, 1 by 3 by 4, and 2 by 3 by 2. Assume *l*, *w*, and *h* can be interchanged and the box has the same dimensions.

Alternate Assessment

Interview Show each student a drawing of a box with each dimension labeled in inches. Then have the student describe how he or she would determine the number of inch cubes needed to fill the box.

Quick Quiz

Find the volume of each solid.

1.

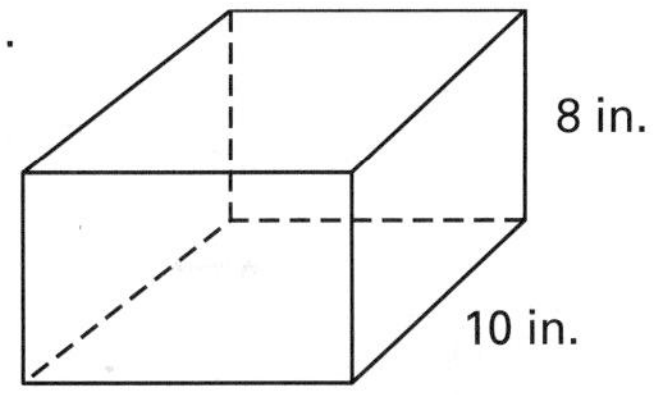

1040 in³

2.

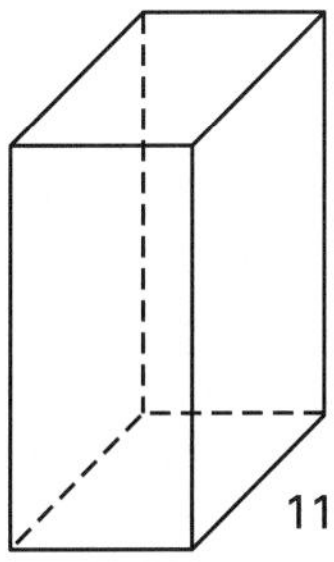

1155 mm³

Available on Daily Transparency 11-6

PROBLEM SOLVING

Name ____________

Guided Problem Solving 11-6

GPS PROBLEM 11, STUDENT PAGE 608

When sugar cubes are produced, they are put into tightly packed boxes for purchasing. If the box of sugar cubes shown is 3 cubes high, how many sugar cubes are in the box?

— Understand —

1. How many sugar cubes high is the box? 3 cubes.
2. What are you asked to find? Number of cubes in box.

— Plan —

3. How many cubes are in one row? 6 cubes.
4. How many cubes are in one column? 7 cubes.
5. How many cubes are in one layer? 42 cubes.

— Solve —

6. Complete the number sentence to find the number of sugar cubes in the box. 3 × 42 = 126
7. Write a sentence giving the number of cubes in the box. Possible answer: There are 126 sugar cubes in the box.

— Look Back —

8. Draw a diagram of each layer of sugar cubes. Make sure that the number of cubes matches your answer to Item 6. Possible answer:

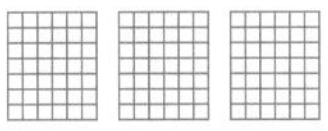

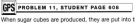

SOLVE ANOTHER PROBLEM

Centimeter cubes can be placed in tightly packed boxes. If the box of centimeter cubes shown is 4 cubes high, how many centimeter cubes are in the box?

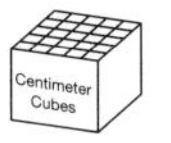

100 cubes.

ENRICHMENT

Name ____________

Extend Your Thinking 11-6

Decision Making

Ashley will be attending summer day camp during school vacation. Vacation starts June 1 and is over August 21. Ashley will attend camp for all but two weeks, when her family takes a vacation trip to the beach. She has narrowed her choices to the camps.

1. Which camp(s) has the lowest weekly cost? What is the weekly charge? You may want to sketch a calendar to help you.

Camp	Session 1	Session 2	Cost
Computer Camp	June 22–July 17	July 21–August 14	$150 per session
Middle Mania	June 1–June 26	June 30–July 24	$75 per session
Nature Camp	June 1–June 12	August 11–August 21	$100 per session
Whoop It Up	July 6–July 17	July 20–July 31	$70 per session
Drama Camp	enroll weekly open from June 1–August 21		$50 per week
Sport Camp	enroll weekly open from June 1–August 21		$35 per week

Middle Mania; $18.75 per week.

2. Which camp(s) has the highest weekly cost? What is the weekly charge?

Drama Camp and Nature Camp; $50 per week.

Ashley can attend any combination of camps, but she can only attend one session of each camp. Once she withdraws from a camp with a weekly enrollment, she can not return.

3. Plan a camp schedule for Ashley. Show the dates she will attend each camp. Be sure to allow for the two weeks at the beach? When the schedule is complete, find the cost for the summer. Possible answer: $375

Camp	Dates Attending	Length of camp	Cost
Sport	June 1–June 19	3 weeks	$105
Computer	June 22–July 17	1 session	$150
Whoop It Up	July 20–July 31	1 session	$70
Drama	Aug. 4–Aug. 7	1 week	$50
Vacation	August 10–August 21	2 weeks	N/A

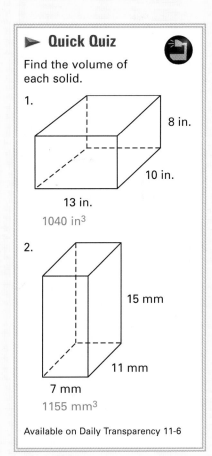

11-7 Lesson Organizer

Objective

- Use the volume formula for rectangular prisms.

Materials

- Explore: Centimeter cubes

NCTM Standards

- 1–4, 12, 13

Review

Find the unknown value in each equation.

1. $V = 12 \times 10 \times 9$ $V = 1080$
2. $100 = 5 \times 5 \times h$ $h = 4$
3. $240 = 8 \times 6 \times h$ $h = 5$

Available on Daily Transparency 11-7

1 Introduce

Explore

The Point
Students build a prism and determine how many centimeter cubes are needed to fill it. This helps them develop the formula for the volume of a rectangular prism.

Ongoing Assessment
Point out that the number of cubes needed for the first "story" of the prism is the same as the area of the base of the prism.

For Groups That Finish Early
How would using inch cubes instead of centimeter cubes affect the answers in Steps 1–3? The answers would be the same.

Answers for Explore

1. $4 \times 3 \times 1$
2. $4 \times 3 \times 2$
3. $4 \times 3 \times 3$
4. Multiply; In a rectangular prism, the volume is the product of the length, width, and height.

11-7 Calculating Volume

You'll Learn ...

- to use the volume formula for rectangular prisms

... How It's Used

Phlebotomists use volume to determine how much blood they have drawn from blood donors.

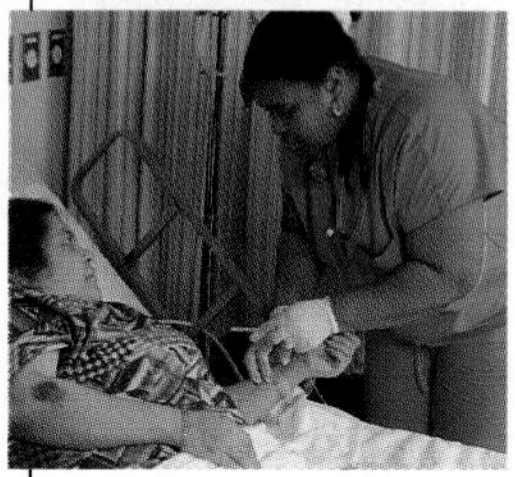

▶ Lesson Link You know how to find the volume of a prism by counting the number of cubes that fill the space inside. Now you'll find the volume using a formula. ◀

Explore Calculating Volume

Toy Stories

Materials: Centimeter cubes

1. Build a prism 4 cubes long, 3 cubes wide, and 1 cube high. Write an expression using multiplication for the total number of cubes needed.
2. Build a second 4-cube-by-3-cube "story" on top of the first. Write an expression using multiplication that gives the total number of cubes needed for the entire prism.
3. Add a third story and write an expression using multiplication for the total number of cubes needed for the entire prism.
4. If you know the length, width, and height of a prism, what is the fastest way to determine how many cubes you need to build the prism? Explain.

Learn Calculating Volume

The volume of a rectangular prism is measured by the number of cubic units that can fit inside it. One way to find the volume is to count the number of cubes inside the prism.

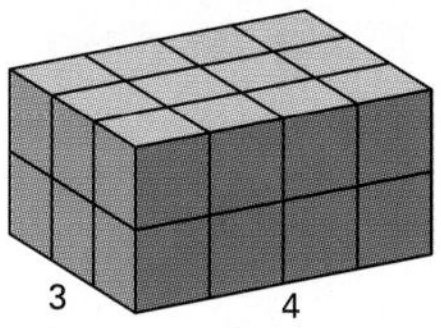

You can also use a formula. The volume of a rectangular prism is the product of the prism's length, width, and height.

Volume = length × width × height

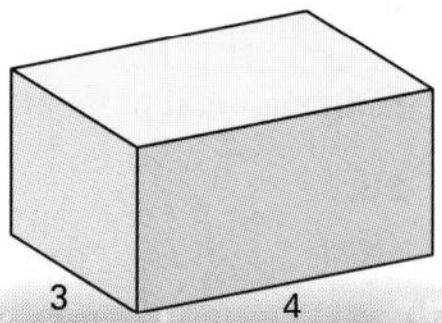

MEETING INDIVIDUAL NEEDS

Resources

- **11-7** Practice
- **11-7** Reteaching
- **11-7** Problem Solving
- **11-7** Enrichment
- **11-7** Daily Transparency
  - Problem of the Day
  - Review
  - Quick Quiz
- Technology Master 59
- Chapter 11 Project Master

Learning Modalities

Kinesthetic Have students measure several different boxes and then determine the volume.

Verbal Have students write a paragraph describing how they would find the volume of a box for which they know the length, width, and height.

Challenge

Have students discuss the following: Aldo found that a cube had a surface area of 216 square inches and a volume of 216 cubic inches. Is that possible? Explain. Yes; A 6 inch cube has 6 square faces, each having an area of 36 square inches for a total of 216 square inches. The volume is $6 \times 6 \times 6$, or 216 cubic inches.

Examples

1 Find the volume of the rectangular prism.

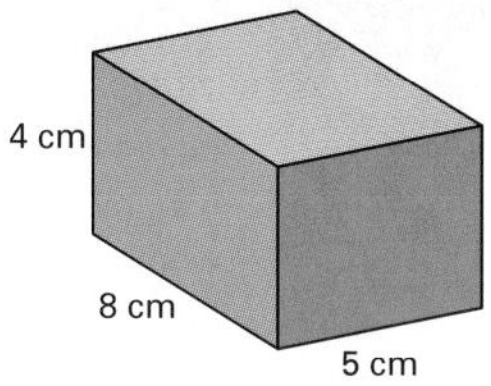

$V = l \times w \times h$ Write the formula.

$= 8 \times 5 \times 4$ Substitute known values.

$= 160$ Multiply.

The volume is 160 cm^3.

2 One gallon of water has a volume of 231 in^3. Find the volume of the tank in cubic inches and in gallons.

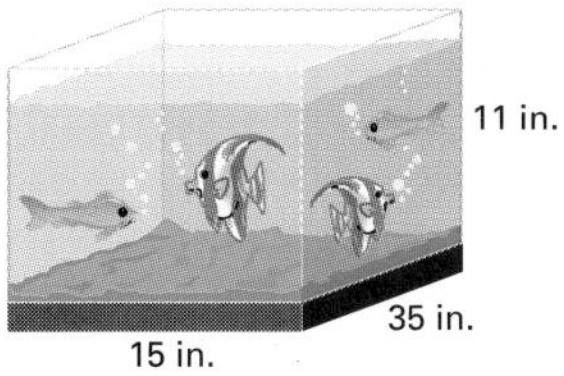

$V = l \times w \times h$ Write the formula.

$= 35 \times 15 \times 11$ Substitute known values.

$= 5775$ Multiply.

The volume is 5775 in^3.

Every 231 in^3 of water in the tank represents 1 gallon.

Therefore, the total number of gallons in the tank is $5775 \div 231 = 25$.

The tank has a volume of 25 gallons.

> **Science Link**
>
> The amount of space a fish needs varies from species to species. In general, saltwater fish require more space than freshwater fish of the same size.

If you know the volume of a rectangular prism and two of its dimensions, you can find the third dimension.

Example 3

Becky built an 8 ft by 6 ft sandbox for her best friend. She bought 48 ft^3 of sand for the box. How deep was the sand?

$V = l \times w \times h$ Write the formula.

$48 = 8 \times 6 \times h$ Substitute known values.

$48 = 48h$ Simplify. Think: What number times 48 equals 48?

$1 = h$ Use mental math.

The sand was 1 ft deep.

Try It

a. Find the volume of a rectangular prism measuring 7 in. by 5 in. by 3 in. 105 in^3

b. Find the length of a rectangular prism with a width of 15 in., a height of 8 in., and a volume of 2160 in^3. 18 in.

2 Teach

Learn

Alternate Examples

1. Find the volume of the rectangular prism.

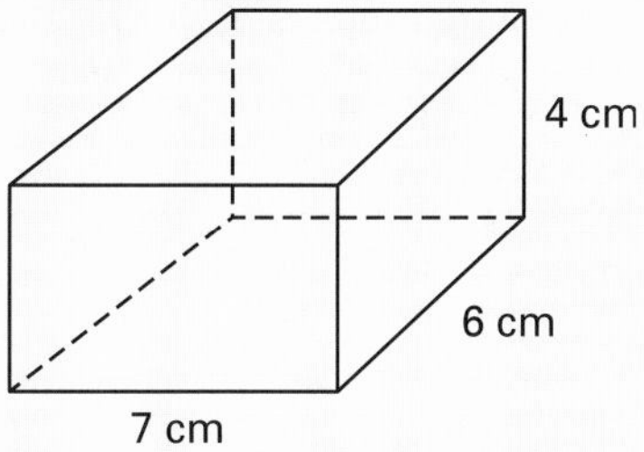

Use the formula, substitute known values, and multiply.

$V = l \times w \times h$

$= 7 \times 6 \times 4$

$= 168$

The volume is 168 cm^3.

2. One gallon of water has a volume of 231 in^3. Find the volume of the tank in gallons.

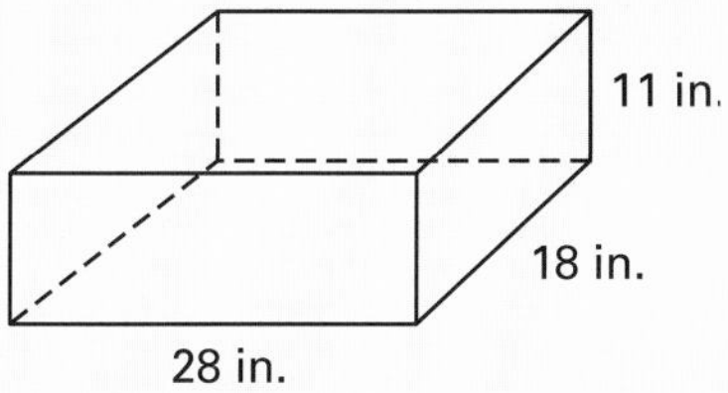

Use the formula, substitute known values, and multiply.

$V = l \times w \times h$

$= 28 \times 18 \times 11$

$= 5544$

The volume is 5544 in^3. Divide 5544 by 231 to find the number of gallons. $5544 \div 231 = 24$.

The tank has a volume of 24 gallons.

3. A rectangular reflecting pool is being filled with water. The pool is 10 ft by 6 ft. If 180 cubic feet of water are needed, how deep will the water be?

Use the formula and substitute known values. Then find the unknown value.

$V = l \times w \times h$

$180 = 10 \times 6 \times h$

$180 = 60h$

$3 = h$

The water will be 3 feet deep.

MATH EVERY DAY

Problem of the Day

The Vertical Assembly Building at Cape Canaveral, Florida, has the greatest volume in a single room. The building is 710 feet long. Its width is 25 feet less than half its length. Its height is 158 feet less than its length. Find the volume of the building. 129,333,600 ft^3 ($710 \times 330 \times 552$)

Available on Daily Transparency 11-7

An Extension is provided in the transparency package.

Fact of the Day

The Great Barrier Reef is a series of massive coral reefs extending for about 1250 miles. Swimmers and divers are attracted to the warm water and beauty of the reef.

Estimation

Estimate each sum.

1. $7.2 + 9.9$ 17
2. $3.3 + 8.4$ 11
3. $6.7 + 8.9 + 3.2$ 19
4. $4.19 + 6.78 + 1.29$ 12

WHAT DO YOU THINK?

Students see two ways of finding how many cubical blocks it will take to fill a box. One method involves counting blocks and using multiplication. The other involves using the volume formula. Students can decide which of the two correct methods is easier for them.

Answers for What Do You Think?

1. Yes; He multiplies the length, width, and height together.
2. Possible answer: Tyreka's method is easier to understand, but Larry's method is easier to do.

3 Practice and Assess

Check

Answers for Check Your Understanding

1. No; The simple formula is used only for finding the volume of rectangular prisms.
2. Possible answer: Use the Volume Formula.

WHAT DO YOU THINK?

A toy manufacturer makes 1 in. cubical building blocks. The blocks are packed in boxes measuring 12 in. by 6 in. by 4 in. Tyreka and Larry want to know how many blocks are in a box.

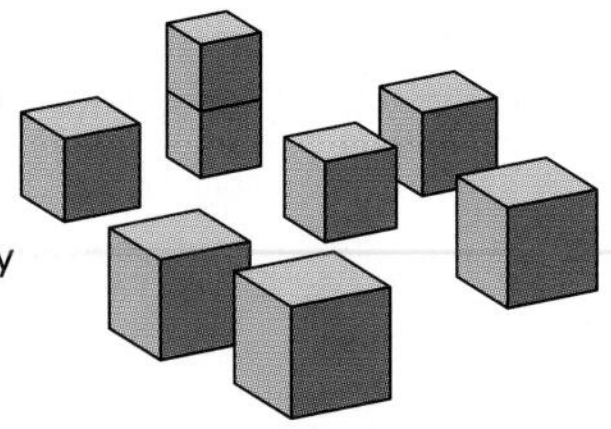

Tyreka thinks ...

I'll find the volume by counting the blocks and using multiplication.

The top layer has 6 rows with 12 blocks in each row. This equals 6×12, or 72 blocks.

There are 4 layers with 72 blocks in each layer. That equals 4×72, or 288 blocks.

There are 288 blocks in each box.

Larry thinks ...

I'll use the volume formula.

$V = l \times w \times h$

$V = 12 \times 6 \times 4 = 288$

There are 288 blocks in each box.

What do you think?

1. Tyreka says her method uses multiplication. Did Larry's method also involve multiplication? Explain.
2. Which method is the easier method to understand? Why?

Check Your Understanding

1. Can you use the formula $V = l \times w \times h$ to find the volume of any solid? Explain.
2. Describe an easy way to find the volume of a cube.

MEETING MIDDLE SCHOOL CLASSROOM NEEDS

Tips from Middle School Teachers

I like to give students as much experience as possible in filling boxes with cubes. Even though they sometimes joke about "playing with blocks," I know that this experience gives them a better understanding of volume.

Team Teaching

Work with the science teacher when discussing volume of rectangular prisms. Have students find the volume of various rectangular prisms that the science teacher uses for experiments or in the lab.

Geography Connection

The largest swimming pool in the world is in Casablanca, Morocco. It is 1574 feet long and 246 feet wide and is filled with seawater.

11-7 Exercises and Applications

Practice and Apply

Getting Started Find the volume of each solid.

1. 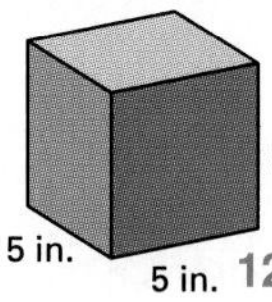

125 in^3

2. 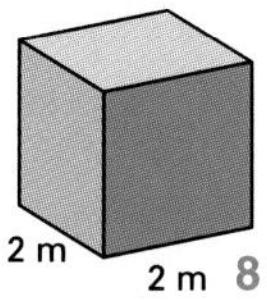

8 m^3

3. 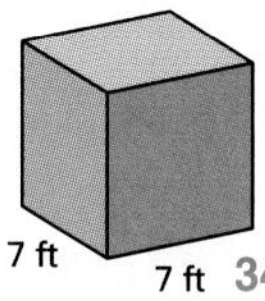

343 ft^3

Find the volume of each solid.

4. 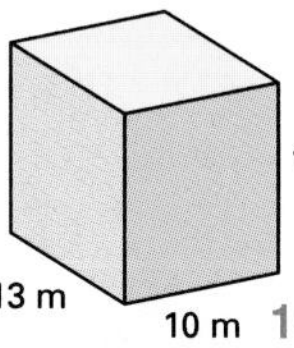

1430 m^3

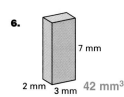

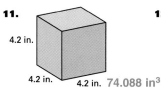

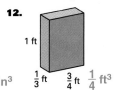

5. 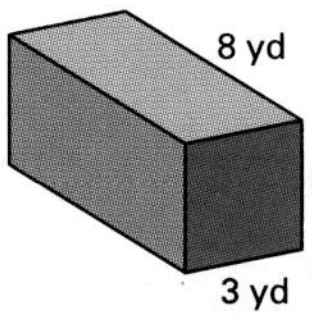

72 yd^3

6. 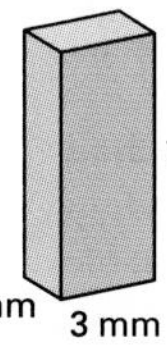

42 mm^3

7. 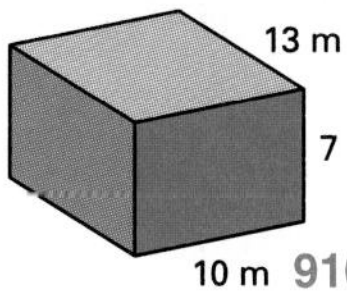

910 m^3

8. 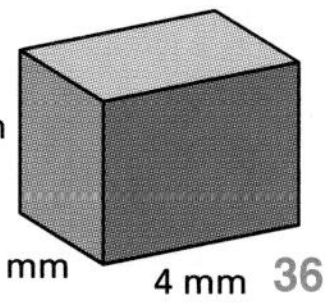

36 mm^3

9. 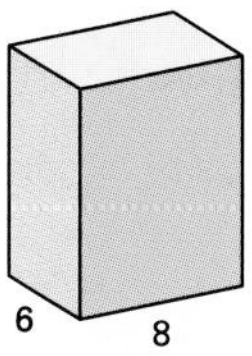

480 $units^3$

10. 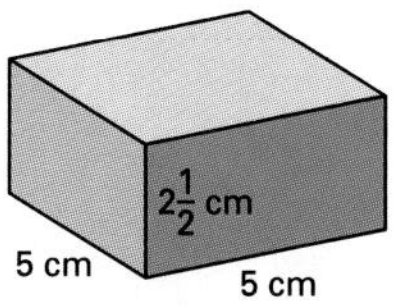

62.5 cm^3

11. 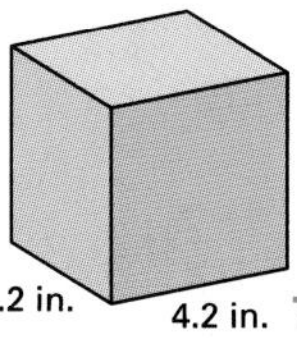

74.088 in^3

12. 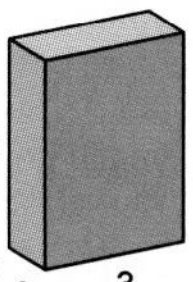

$\frac{1}{4}$ ft^3

13. Geography The Great Barrier Reef along the east coast of Australia is the world's largest coral reef. The coral reef tank at The Great Barrier Reef Aquarium in Townsville, Australia, is 38 meters long, 17 meters wide, and 4.5 meters deep. What is the volume of the tank? 2907 m^3

14. Number Sense The volume of an aquarium is 5000 cubic inches. If the width is 20 inches and the height is 10 inches, what is the length? 25 in.

PRACTICE 11-7

11-7 Exercises and Applications

Assignment Guide

- **Basic**
  1–17 odds, 19–23 odds
- **Average**
  3–23 odds
- **Enriched**
  8–14 evens, 15–18, 20–24 evens

Exercise Notes

Exercise 14

Science Plants are used in aquariums because they provide shelter and food for the fish. Fish breathe the oxygen given off by the plants, and plants take in the carbon dioxide the fish give off.

PRACTICE

Name ____________________

Practice 11-7

Calculating Volume

Find the volume of each solid.

1. 510 cm^3 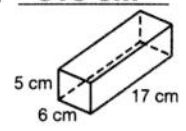

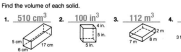

2. 100 in^3 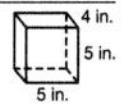

3. 112 m^3 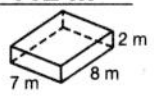

4. 105 ft^3 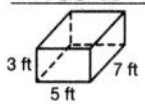

5. 300 cm^3 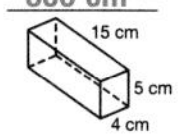

6. 512 in^3 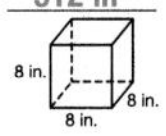

7. 768 m^3 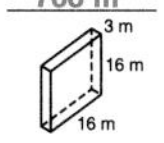

8. 72 yd^3 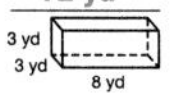

9. 6 cm^3 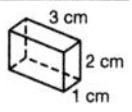

10. 98 ft^3 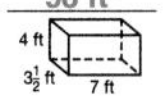

11. 1440 mm^3 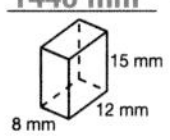

12. 500 in^3 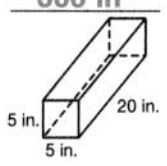

13. 71.68 m^3 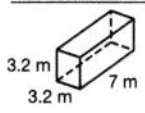

14. $7\frac{1}{2}$ ft^3 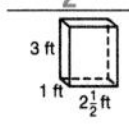

15. $112\frac{1}{2}$ in^3 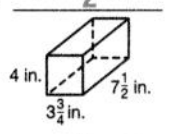

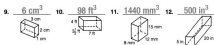

16. 248.93 cm^3 

17. 3024 mm^3 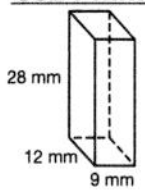

18. 1540 yd^3 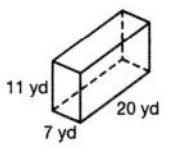

19. $50\frac{5}{8}$ in^3 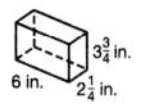

20. 1338.896 cm^3 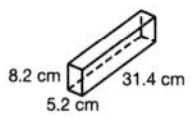

21. The Panama Canal has a length of 89,200 yd, a width of 37 yd, and a depth of 14 yd. Estimate the volume of water in the canal by assuming it has the shape of a rectangular prism. 46,205,600 yd^3

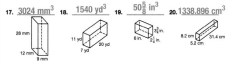

RETEACHING

Name ____________________

Alternative Lesson 11-7

Calculating Volume

You can use a formula to find the volume of a rectangular prism. The volume is the product of the prism's length, width, and height.

Volume = length × width × height

Example

Find the volume of the rectangular prism.

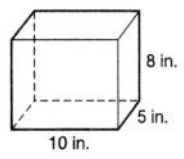

Find the measure of each dimension.
Length = 10 in. Width = 5 in. Height = 8 in.

Write the formula. $V = l \times w \times h$
Substitute the known values. $V = 10 \times 5 \times 8$
Multiply. $V = 400$

The volume of the prism is 400 cubic inches, or 400 in^3.

Try It Find the volume of the rectangular prism.

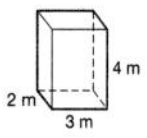

a. Write each measure.
Length 3 m   Width 2 m   Height 4 m

b. Substitute the values in the formula. $V =$ 3 × 2 × 4

c. Find the volume. 24 m^3

Find the volume of the rectangular prism.

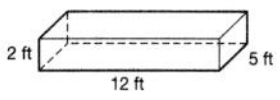

d. Write each measure.
Length 12 ft   Width 5 ft   Height 2 ft

e. Substitute the values in the formula. $V =$ 12 × 5 × 2

f. Find the volume. 120 ft^3

Find the volume of each rectangular prism.

g. 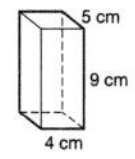

180 cm^3

h. 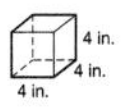

64 in^3

i. 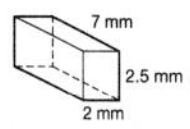

35 mm^3

Reteaching

Activity

Materials: Cardboard boxes

- Work in groups of three or four.
- Use several different cardboard boxes. Measure the length, width, and height in inches and in centimeters.
- Then use the volume formula to find the volume in both cubic inches and cubic centimeters.

Exercise Notes

■ Exercise 16

Science The goldfish is related to the carp. In its wild state, the goldfish is dull brown in color, but mutation produces a form in which all pigments are missing except red. This mutation is a form of albinism. Goldfish have been kept as pets for over 2000 years.

■ Exercise 17

Science The density of water varies with its temperature, and it is most dense at 4°C. Water is one of the few substances whose liquid form is denser than the solid (ice).

Project Progress

You may want to have students use Chapter 11 Project Master.

Alternate Assessment

Portfolio Have students choose several exercises that best exemplify the concepts of this lesson and add them to their portfolio.

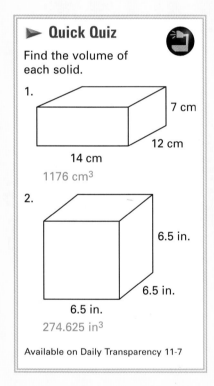

▶ Quick Quiz

Find the volume of each solid.

1.

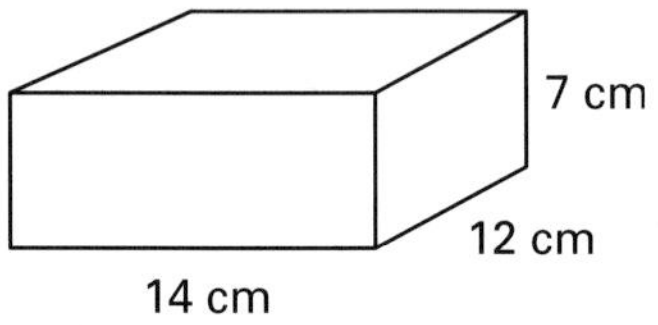

1176 cm^3

2.

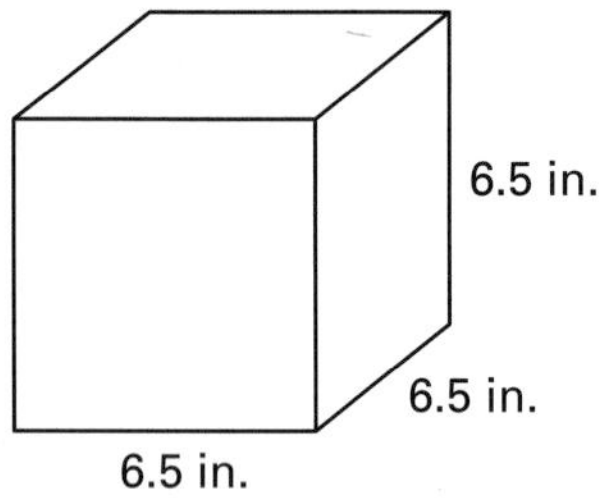

274.625 in^3

Available on Daily Transparency 11-7

15. **Test Prep** The length of a box is 28 inches. The width is 10 inches. What other information about the box do you need in order to find its volume? **B**

Ⓐ The weight　　Ⓑ The height

Ⓒ The contents　　Ⓓ The surface area

16. The size of a goldfish depends on the size of the pond or tank it is in. A small pond for a dozen 4-inch goldfish should be about 6 feet long, 4 feet wide, and 1.5 feet deep. What is the volume of this pond? **36 ft^3**

Problem Solving and Reasoning

17. **Critical Thinking** The volume of a gallon of water is about 231 cubic inches. If a 25-gallon aquarium is 32 inches long and 15 inches wide, how deep is it? Explain. **About 12 inches deep.**

GPS

18. **Critical Thinking** One area in Water-Play Park has a 15 ft by 20 ft pool that is 12 feet deep. The pool is filled at the start of summer at the rate of 1200 cubic feet of water per hour. How many hours does it take to fill the pool? Explain. **3 hr; (15 × 20 × 12) ÷ 1200**

Mixed Review

Find the missing side lengths for each pair of similar figures. *[Lesson 10-7]*

19.

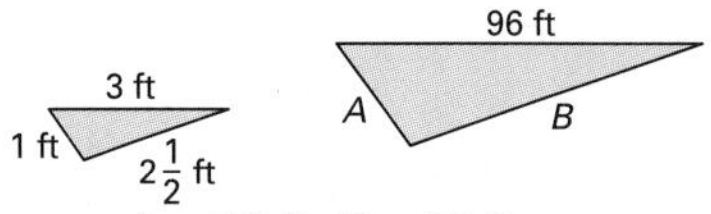

A = 32 ft, B = 80 ft

20.

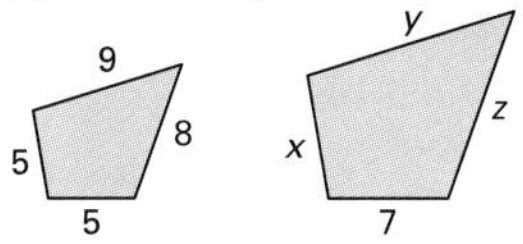

x = 7, y = 12.6, z = 11.2

For each figure, give the percent that is shaded. *[Lesson 10-8]*

21.

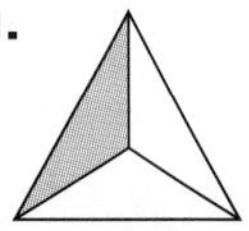

33.$\bar{3}$%

22.

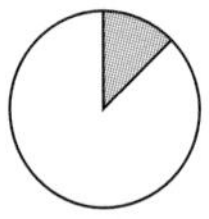

12.5%

23.

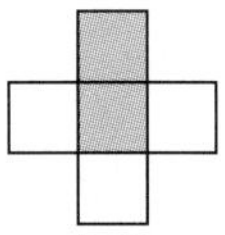

40%

24.

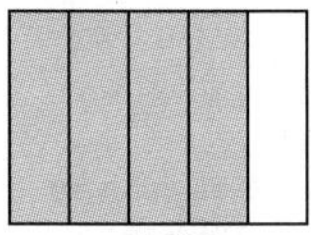

80%

Project Progress

Multiply the length, width, and height of your aquarium to find its volume. Find the volume of your classroom in cubic inches. Decide if your aquarium will fit comfortably in the classroom or if you will have to make adjustments.

Problem Solving
Understand
Plan
Solve
Look Back

PROBLEM SOLVING

Name ____________

Guided Problem Solving 11-7

GPS PROBLEM 17, STUDENT PAGE 614

The volume of a gallon of water is about 231 cubic inches. If a 25-gallon aquarium is 32 inches long and 15 inches wide, how deep is it? Explain.

— Understand —

1. What are you asked to find? **Depth (height) of an aquarium.**
2. What is the volume of a gallon of water? **231 cubic inches.**
3. Underline the dimensions of the aquarium that are given.

— Plan —

4. How can you find the volume of an aquarium that holds 25 gallons of water? **Multiply 25 and 231.**
5. What is the volume of the aquarium? **5775 cubic inches.**
6. What is the formula to find the volume of a rectangular prism? $V = l \times w \times h$
7. Substitute known values into the equation you wrote in Item 6. $5775 = 32 \times 15 \times h$

— Solve —

8. Multiply values in the equation. $5775 = 480 \times h$
9. Use mental math, or guess and check to find the depth of the aquarium to the nearest whole number. $h \approx 12$
10. How deep is the aquarium? Explain. **About 12 inches; $12 \times 32 \times 15 \approx 25 \times 231$.**

— Look Back —

11. Estimate to see if your answer is reasonable. **Possible answer: Since $10 \times 30 \times 20 = 30 \times 200$, the answer is reasonable.**

SOLVE ANOTHER PROBLEM

The volume of a gallon of water is about 231 cubic inches. If a 30-gallon aquarium is 25 inches long and 25 inches wide, how deep is it? Explain.

About 11 in.; $25 \times 25 \times 11 \approx 30 \times 231$

ENRICHMENT

Name ____________

Extend Your Thinking 11-7

Critical Thinking

You can use a formula to find the volume of a cylinder. As with prisms, the volume is measured in cubic units even though you cannot fill the cylinder with cubes.

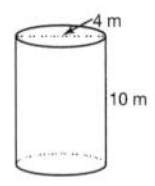

Volume of cylinder = area of base × height
= πr^2 × height

The volume of the cylinder above can be found by substituting the known values into the formula

Volume = πr^2 × height
= [3.14 × (2 × 2)] × 10
= [3.14 × 4] × 10
= [12.56] × 10
= 125.6 m^3

Use the formula to find the volume of each cylinder. Use 3.14 for π.

1.

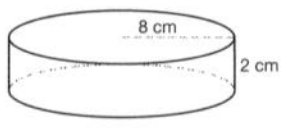

V = **401.92 cm^3**

2.

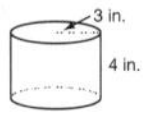

V = **113.04 in^3**

3.

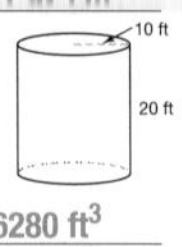

V = **6280 ft^3**

4.

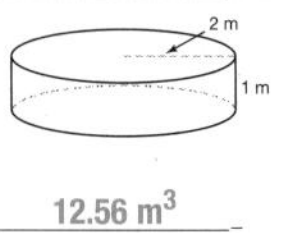

V = **12.56 m^3**

5.

V = **197.82 yd^3**

6.

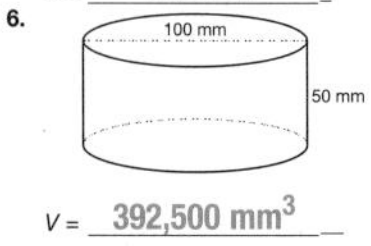

V = **392,500 mm^3**

7. How is the formula for the volume of a cylinder similar to the formula for the volume of the prism?
Possible answer: Both multiply the area of one base by the height of the figure.

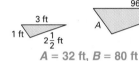

Section 11B Connect

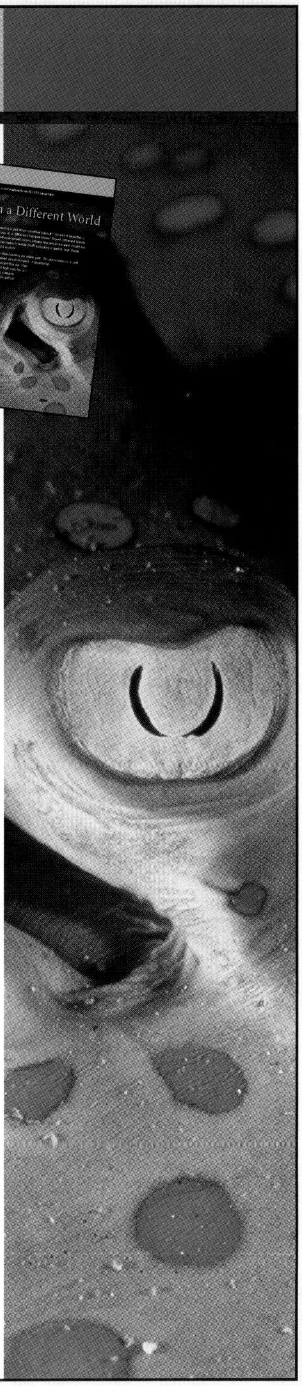

In this section, you've learned to find the volume of a rectangular prism given its dimensions. Now you'll determine what dimensions you should choose for an aquarium tank with a given volume.

A Pet from a Different World

Materials: Ruler

You've decided to build a 50 gal tank for tropical fish. A 50 gal tank has a volume of 11,550 in^3.

1. You want your tank to have a height of 22 in. Find a possible length and width for your tank. Make sure the length and width are reasonable.
2. Draw a net of your tank. (Remember, it's open-topped.)
3. You need to know how much glass to buy, so find the surface area of your tank, including the bottom.
4. Repeat Steps 1–3, finding a *different* possible length and width for your tank.
5. Would your two possible tanks cost the same amount to build? Explain.
6. Some aquarium owners use the rule "1 inch of fish per gallon of water." You've decided to stock your aquarium with the following species.

Species	Length (in.)
White Cloud Mountainfish	1
Zebra Danios	2
Red-Striped Rasboras	3
Cherry Barbs	$1\frac{1}{2}$

Choose the largest possible collection of fish for your aquarium. You should have at least 6 of each species. Explain how you determined how many of each species of fish should be in your collection.

Answers for Connect

1. 25 in. by 21 in.
2. 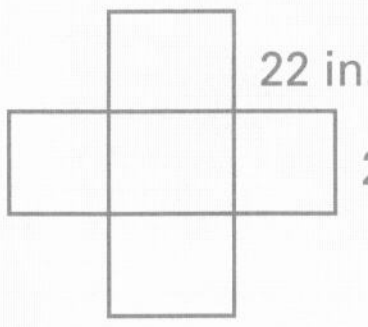

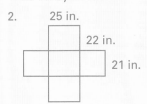

3. 2549 in^2
4. 15 in. by 35 in.
5. No; They will require different amounts of glass.
6. 11 White Cloud Mountainfish, 6 Zebra Danios, 6 Red-striped Rasboras, 6 Cherry Barbs; 45 gallons of water are required for 6 fish of each species. 5 additional White Cloud Mountainfish were added for the remaining 5 gallons of water.

A Pet from a Different World

The Point

In *A Pet From a Different World* on page 601, students learned about the controlled environment of an aquarium. Now students will determine the dimensions for an aquarium tank.

Materials

Ruler

Resources

Teaching Tool Transparency 16: Rulers

About the Page

- In the problem, students are given the volume and height and are asked to find the length and width. Discuss how using the inverse operation can help solve the problem.
- Ask students how many pieces of glass they will need for the aquarium. Five; Because the aquarium is open at the top.
- Remind students that the capacity of the tank is 50 gallons. Discuss what "1 inch of fish per gallon of water" means.

Ongoing Assessment

Check that students have determined two possible lengths and widths and have drawn an appropriate net. Check that they have determined the correct number of each species of fish for the tank.

Extension

Have students assume that they are stocking another 50 gallon tank aquarium with the same species of fish. This time they will need to have at least 4 of each species. Ask students to choose the least possible number of fish for their aquarium. Ask them to find the total number of fish they will have and the number of each species. 23 fish; 4 White Cloud Mountainfish, 5 Zebra Danios, 10 Red-striped Rasboras, 4 Cherry Barbs.

11B Review

Review Correlation

Item(s)	Lesson(s)
1–5	11-1
6–9	11-5
10	11-7

Test Prep

Test-Taking Tip

Students should review the suggestions for identifying unnecessary information. In this case, the depth of the fish tank is not needed to compute the surface area of the top.

Answers for Review

1. Rectangular prism; 8 vertices, 12 edges, 6 faces.
2. Triangular pyramid; 4 vertices, 6 edges, 4 faces.
3. Triangular prism; 6 vertices, 9 edges, 5 faces.

6.

Front Side Top

7.
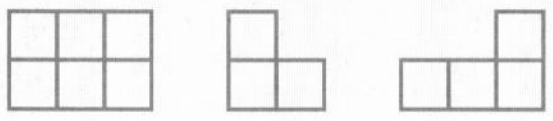
Front Side Top

8.
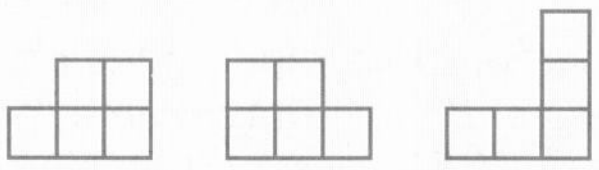
Front Side Top

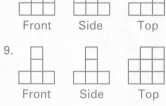

9.
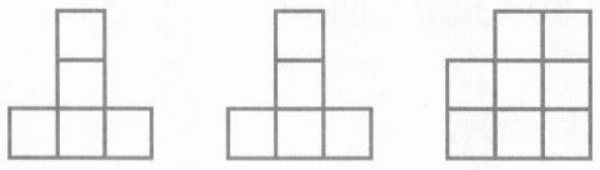
Front Side Top

REVIEW 11B

Section 11B Review

Geometry Classify each solid. If it is a polyhedron, tell how many vertices, edges, and faces it has.

1.
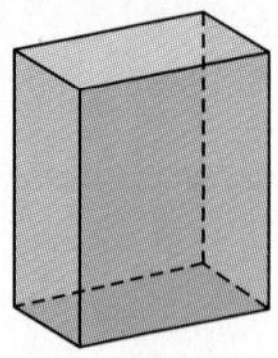

2.
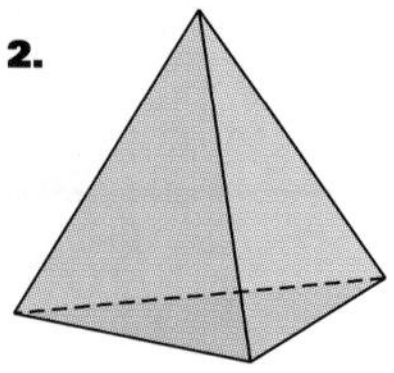

3.
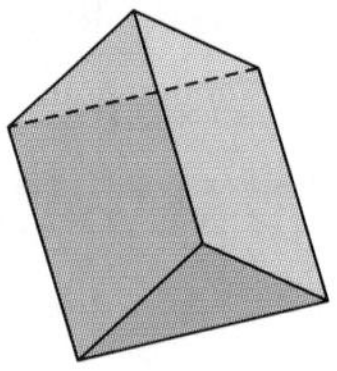

4.
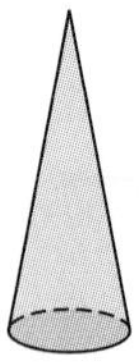
Cone

5. **Test Prep** Which of the following is **not** true of all polyhedrons? C

Ⓐ The volume is usually measured in cubic units.

Ⓑ All of the faces are flat.

Ⓒ There are two bases that are the same size and shape.

Ⓓ None of these.

Draw the front, side, and top views of each solid. There are no hidden cubes.

6.
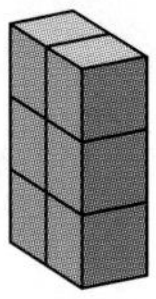

7.
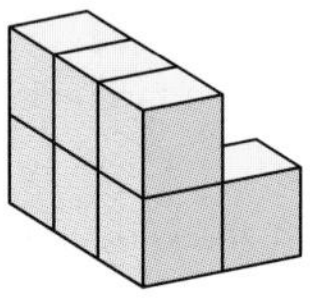

8.
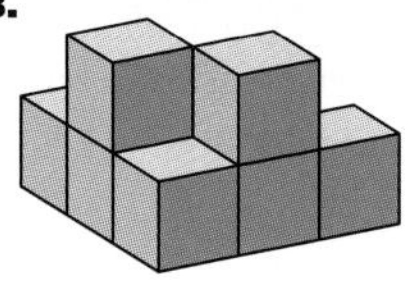

9.

Test Prep

You only need to multiply two numbers together to find the area of one side of a solid. If a problem asking for the area of one side of a solid gives you three numbers, at least one of the numbers is unnecessary information.

10. A good fish tank has a large surface at the top to provide the most oxygen possible. Which fish tank has the greatest area on top? A

Ⓐ 24 in. deep, 24 in. long, 14 in. wide

Ⓑ 32 in. deep, 23 in. long, 13 in. wide

Ⓒ 20 in. deep, 22 in. long, 12 in. wide

Ⓓ 22 in. deep, 26 in. long, 11 in. wide

Resources

Practice Masters
Section 11B Review

Assessment Sourcebook
Quiz 11B

TestWorks
Test and Practice Software

PRACTICE

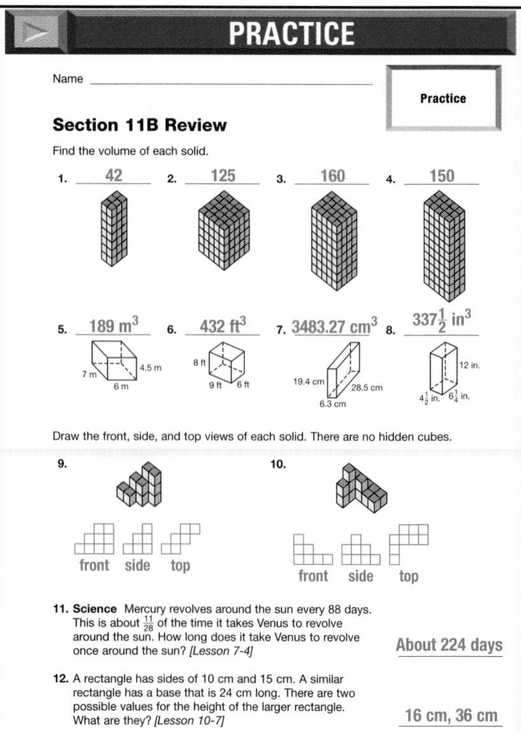

Name
Practice
Section 11B Review
Find the volume of each solid.
1. 42
2. 125
3. 160
4. 150
5. 189 m³
6. 432 ft³
7. 3483.27 cm³
8. 337½ in³
7 m
6 m
4.5 m
8 ft
9 ft
6 ft
19.4 cm
28.5 cm
6.3 cm
12 in.
4½ in.
6¼ in.
Draw the front, side, and top views of each solid. There are no hidden cubes.
9.
10.
front side top
front side top
11. Science Mercury revolves around the sun every 88 days. This is about 11/28 of the time it takes Venus to revolve around the sun. How long does it take Venus to revolve once around the sun? [Lesson 7-4]
About 224 days
12. A rectangle has sides of 10 cm and 15 cm. A similar rectangle has a base that is 24 cm long. There are two possible values for the height of the larger rectangle. What are they? [Lesson 10-7]
16 cm, 36 cm

Extend Key Ideas • Geometry

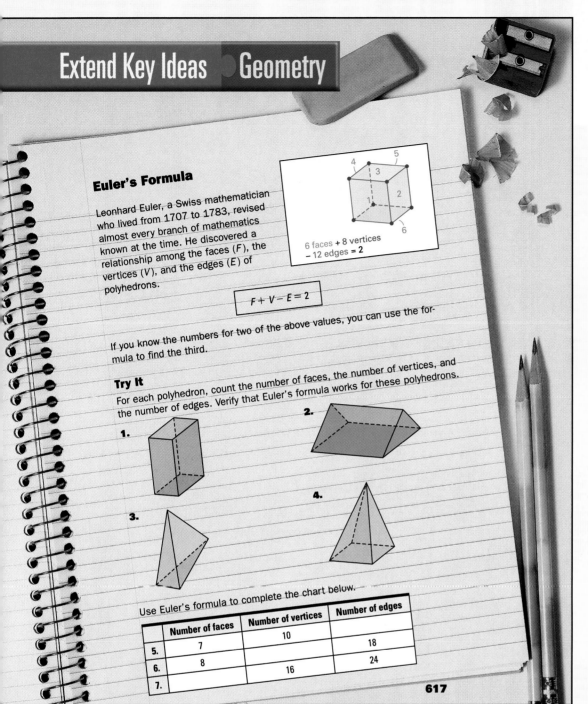

Euler's Formula

Leonhard Euler, a Swiss mathematician who lived from 1707 to 1783, revised almost every branch of mathematics known at the time. He discovered a relationship among the faces (F), the vertices (V), and the edges (E) of polyhedrons.

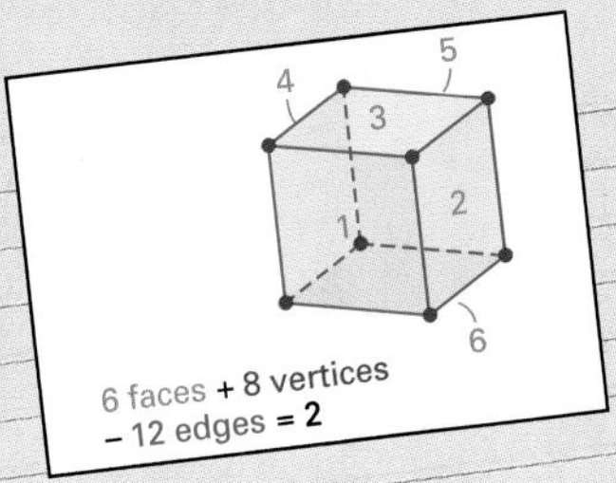

$$F + V - E = 2$$

If you know the numbers for two of the above values, you can use the formula to find the third.

Try It

For each polyhedron, count the number of faces, the number of vertices, and the number of edges. Verify that Euler's formula works for these polyhedrons.

1. 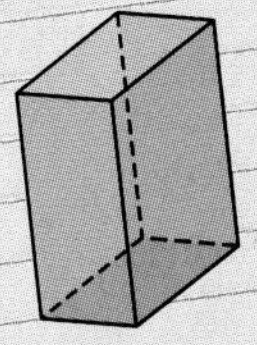

2. 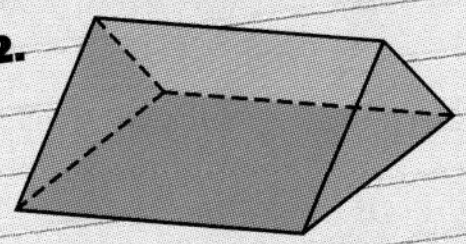

3. 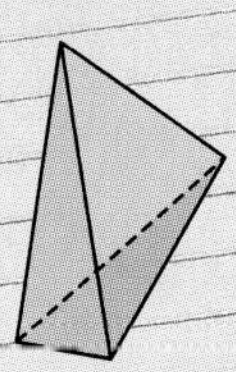

4. 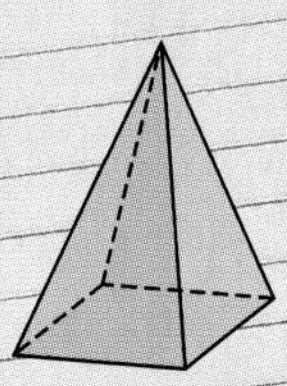

Use Euler's formula to complete the chart below.

	Number of faces	Number of vertices	Number of edges
5.	7	10	
6.	8		18
7.		16	24

617

Extend Key Ideas

Euler's Formula

The Point

Students verify Euler's Formula which states that for any polyhedron the number of faces added to the number of vertices, less the number of edges, equals 2.

About the Page

- Explain that edges are the lines that are drawn to define the solid, vertices are the corners, and each side is one face.
- Point out that drawings of three-dimensional solids usually include some dotted lines, and that portions of the figure are not visible but still have to be counted.

Ask …

- How many faces does the first polyhedron have? 6
- How many vertices does the first polyhedron have? 8
- How many edges does the first polyhedron have? 12
- Does Euler's Formula hold true for this polyhedron? Yes

Extension

Ask students to find out more about Euler's contributions to mathematics. Students should prepare a written or oral report to present to the class.

Answers for Try It

1. 6 faces, 8 vertices, 12 edges; $6 + 8 - 12 = 2$.
2. 5 faces, 6 vertices, 9 edges; $5 + 6 - 9 = 2$.
3. 4 faces, 4 vertices, 6 edges; $4 + 4 - 6 = 2$.
4. 5 faces, 5 vertices, 8 edges; $5 + 5 - 8 = 2$.
5. 15 edges
6. 12 vertices
7. 10 faces

Chapter 11 Summary and Review

Review Correlation

Item(s)	Lesson(s)
1–3	11-1
4–6	11-3, 11-4
7, 8	11-5
9–11	11-6, 11-7
12	11-4

For additional review, see page 672.

Answers for Review

1. Triangular prism; 5 faces, 9 edges, 6 vertices.
3. Rectangular pyramid; 5 faces, 8 edges, 5 vertices.

Chapter 11 Summary and Review

Graphic Organizer

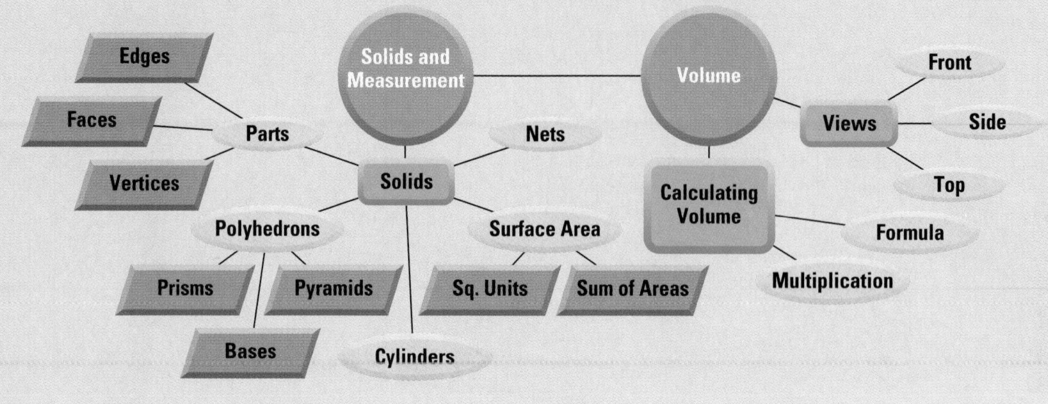

Section 11A Solids and Surface Area

Summary

- A **solid** is a three-dimensional figure with **faces, edges,** and vertices.
- A solid whose faces are polygons is a **polyhedron.** Some polyhedrons are **prisms** or **pyramids. Cylinders, cones,** and **spheres** are not polyhedrons.
- The **surface area (SA)** of a solid is the sum of the areas of all of its faces.
- A **net** is a flat pattern that can be folded into a solid. You can use a net or a formula to find the surface area of a solid.

Review

Classify each solid. If it is a polyhedron, state the number of faces, edges, and vertices.

1.

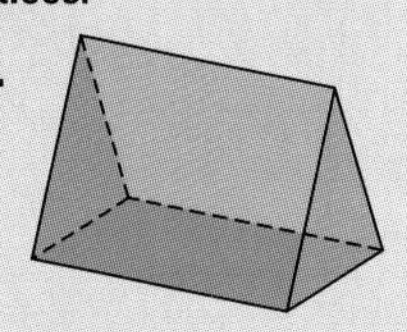

2.

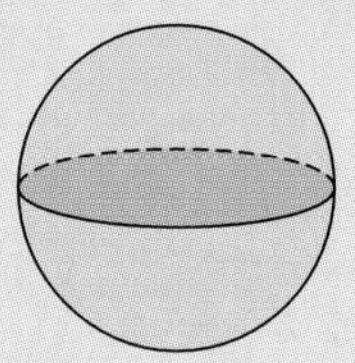

Sphere

3.

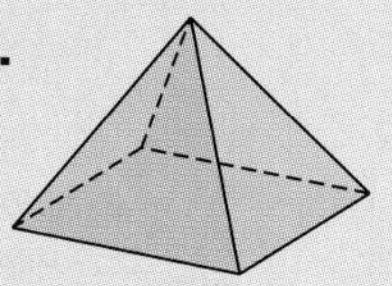

Resources

Practice Masters
Cumulative Review
Chapters 1–11

PRACTICE

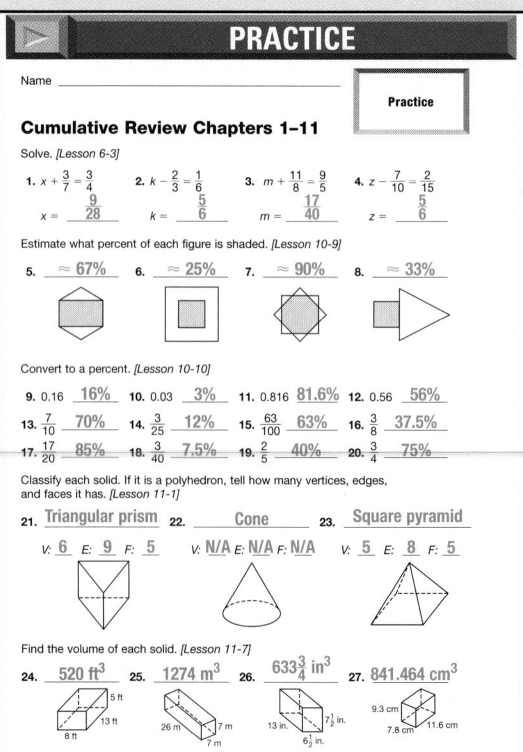
Name ______

Practice

Cumulative Review Chapters 1–11

Solve. *[Lesson 6-3]*

1. $x + \frac{3}{7} = \frac{3}{4}$ $x = \frac{9}{28}$
2. $k - \frac{2}{3} = \frac{1}{6}$ $k = \frac{5}{6}$
3. $m + \frac{11}{8} = \frac{9}{5}$ $m = \frac{17}{40}$
4. $z - \frac{7}{10} = \frac{2}{15}$ $z = \frac{5}{6}$

Estimate what percent of each figure is shaded. *[Lesson 10-9]*

5. ≈ 67% 6. ≈ 25% 7. ≈ 90% 8. ≈ 33%

Convert to a percent. *[Lesson 10-10]*

9. 0.16 16% 10. 0.03 3% 11. 0.816 81.6% 12. 0.56 56%
13. $\frac{7}{10}$ 70% 14. $\frac{3}{25}$ 12% 15. $\frac{63}{100}$ 63% 16. $\frac{3}{8}$ 37.5%
17. $\frac{17}{20}$ 85% 18. $\frac{3}{40}$ 7.5% 19. $\frac{2}{5}$ 40% 20. $\frac{3}{4}$ 75%

Classify each solid. If it is a polyhedron, tell how many vertices, edges, and faces it has. *[Lesson 11-1]*

21. Triangular prism V: 6 E: 9 F: 5
22. Cone V: N/A E: N/A F: N/A
23. Square pyramid V: 5 E: 8 F: 5

Find the volume of each solid. *[Lesson 11-7]*

24. 520 ft^3 (5 ft, 13 ft, 8 ft)
25. 1274 m^3 (26 m, 7 m, 7 m)
26. $633\frac{3}{4}$ in^3 (13 in., $7\frac{1}{2}$ in., $6\frac{1}{2}$ in.)
27. 841.464 cm^3 (9.3 cm, 7.8 cm, 11.6 cm)

Answers for Review

7.

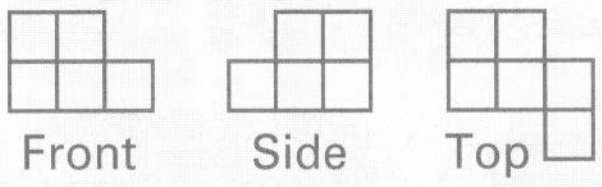

8.

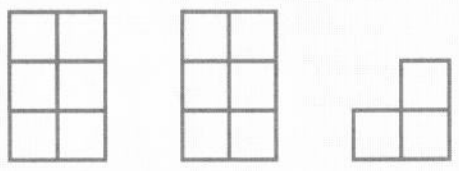

Section 11A Solids and Surface Area *continued*

Find the surface area of each solid.

4.

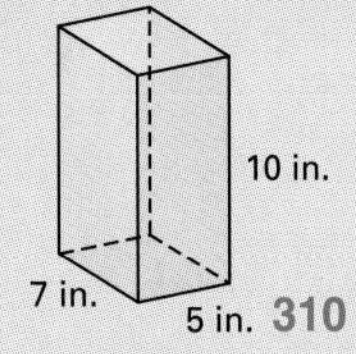

310 in^2

5.

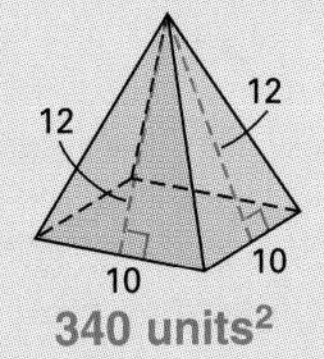

340 $units^2$

6.

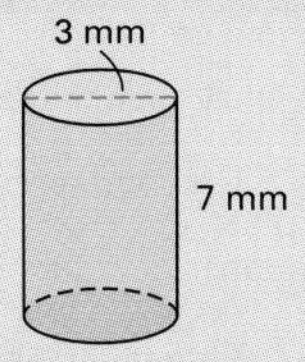

About 80.07 mm^2

Section 11B Volume

Summary

- A solid can be drawn with a front view, a side view, and a top view.
- The **volume** of a solid is the number of **cubic units** needed to fill it.
- If the cubes in a rectangular prism have been drawn in, you can find the volume by counting the number of cubes in one layer and multiplying that by the number of layers.
- You can find the volume of a rectangular prism using the formula $V = l \times w \times h$, where l is the length, w is the width, and h is the height.

Review

For each solid, draw the front view, the side view, and the top view.

7.

8.

Find the volume.

9.

80 $units^3$

10.

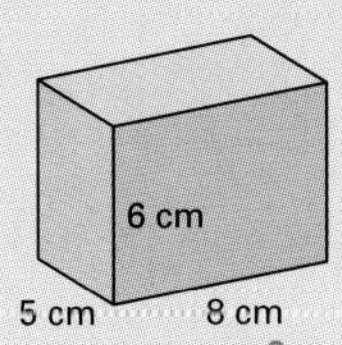

240 cm^3

11.

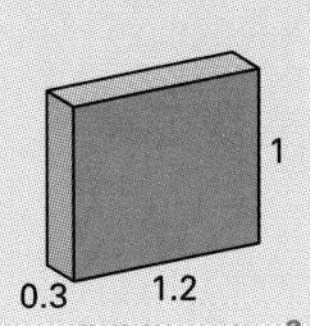

0.36 $units^3$

12. Prints Etc. uses tubes to mail posters to customers. Find the surface area of the tube shown. Use 3.14 for π. About 477.28 in^2

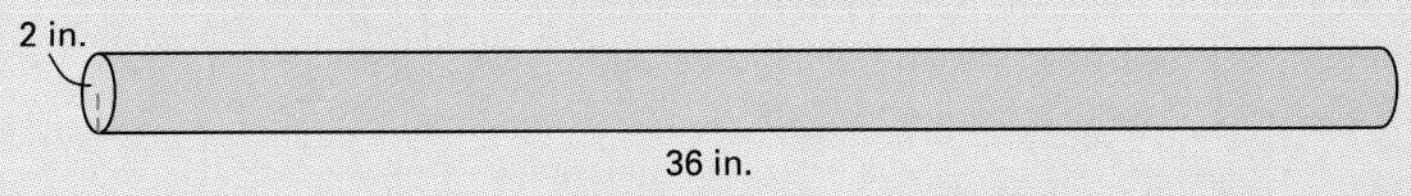

Chapter 11 Assessment

Assessment Correlation

Item(s)	Lesson(s)
1	11-1
2	11-6
3, 4	11-1
5	11-2
6, 7	11-1
8	11-4
9–11	11-3, 11-4
12–14	11-6, 11-7

Answers for Assessment

7. No; Yes; A cone has curved faces, whereas a polyhedron has faces that are polygons. A cube is a special rectangular prism where each of the six faces is a square.

8.

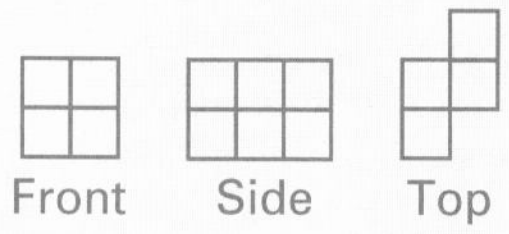

Answers for Performance Task

For the smaller prism, SA = 550 units^2 and V = 750 units^3; For the larger prism, SA = 2200 units^2 and V = 6000 units^3; The surface area is 2^2 or 4 times larger; The volume is 2^3 or 8 times larger.

Chapter 11 Assessment

Fill in each blank with the correct word.

1. A ____ is a solid whose faces are polygons. Polyhedron
2. The number of cubic units needed to fill a solid is the ____. Volume
3. An ____ is a line formed where two faces of a solid come together. Edge
4. A solid with one base where all the other faces are triangles is a ____. Pyramid
5. The ____ of a solid is the sum of the areas of the faces. Surface area
6. Like a pyramid, a ____ can be named by the shape of the base. Prism
7. Is a cone a polyhedron? Is a cube a polyhedron? Explain.
8. Draw the front, side, and top views of the solid. There are no hidden cubes.

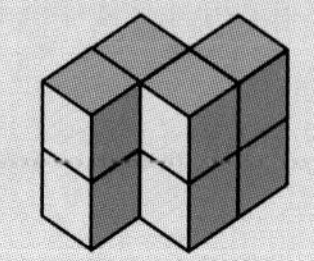

Find the surface area of each solid.

9.

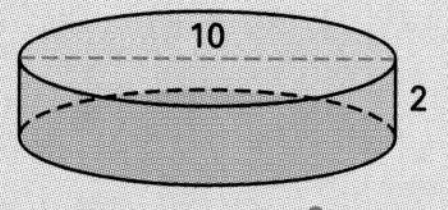

219.8 units^2

10.

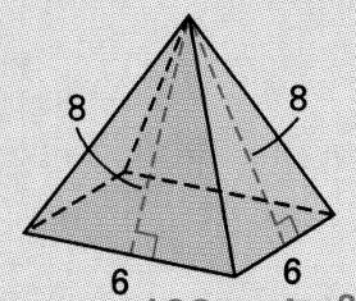

132 units^2

11.

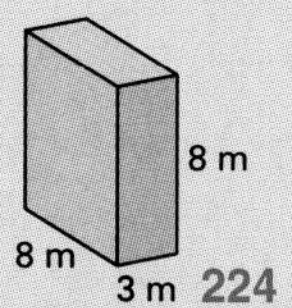

224 m^2

Find the volume of each solid.

12.

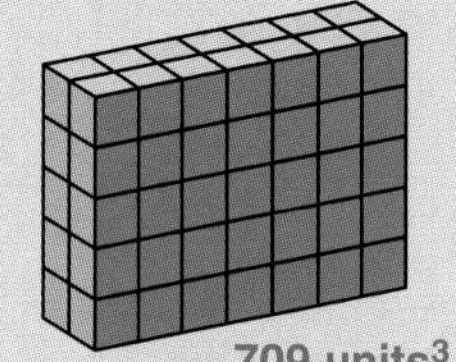

709 units^3

13.

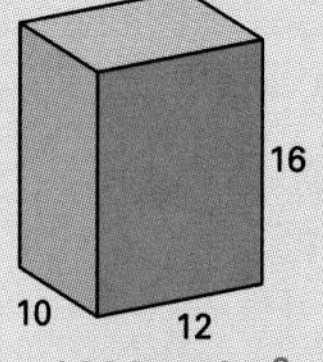

1920 units^3

14.

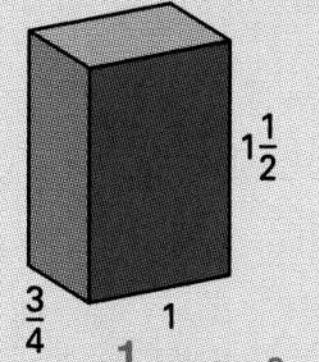

$1\frac{1}{8}$ units^3

Performance Task

Copy the sketch of a rectangular prism with a length of 10, a width of 5, and a height of 15. Find the surface area and volume of the prism. Then, draw a sketch of a rectangular prism with twice the length, twice the width, and twice the height of the first prism. Find the surface area and volume. Does doubling the length, width, and height of a solid double the surface area? Does it double the volume? Explain.

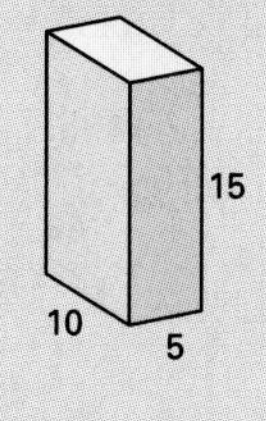

620 *Chapter 11 • Solids and Measurement*

Resources

Assessment Resources

Chapter 11 Tests
- Forms A and B (free response)
- Form C (multiple choice)
- Form D (performance assessment)
- Form E (mixed response)
- Form F (cumulative chapter test)

TestWorks
Test and Practice Software

Home and Community Connections
- Letter Home for Chapter 11 in English and Spanish

Cumulative Review Test Prep

Cumulative Review Chapters 1–11 Test Prep

Performance Assessment

Choose one problem.

The Mystery Quadrilateral

On a coordinate plane, connect these four points in order: (5,−3); (2, 7); (−4, 7); (−7, −3). Classify the shape. Find the shape's area, and explain how you found the area.

A Change of Data

Using a centimeter ruler, measure the diameter of four different coins (for example, a penny, a nickel, a dime, a half-dollar). Find the circumference for each coin. Display the data in a bar graph.

Round Pegs and Square Holes

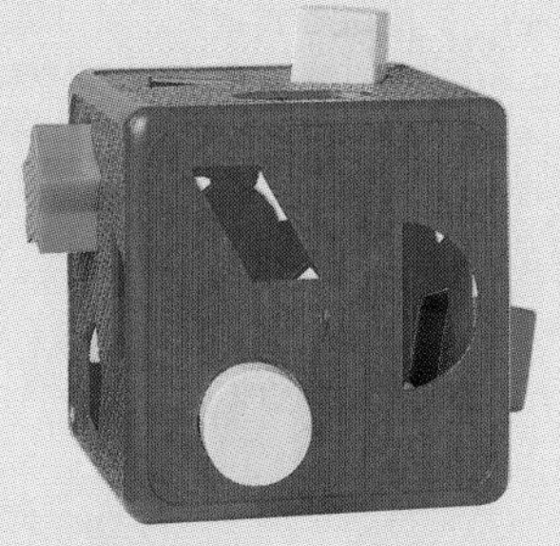

Draw a circle and a square. The length of the square should be the same as the diameter of the circle. Find the area of the circle and the square. What percent of the square's area is the circle's area? Repeat this for two more pairs of circles and squares. What patterns do you notice?

The One That Boasts the Most

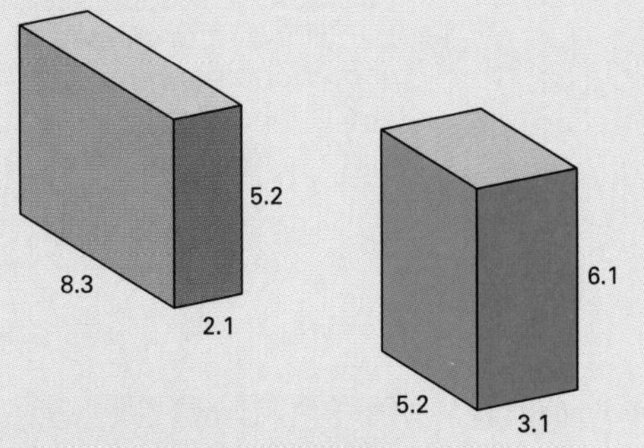

Calculate the surface area and volume for each of the two boxes. Which has more surface area? Which has the greater volume? Does the box with more surface area automatically have the greater volume? Explain.

About Performance Assessment

The Performance Assessment options ...

- provide teachers with an alternate means of assessing students.
- address different learning modalities.
- allow students to choose one problem.

Teachers may encourage students to choose the most challenging problem.

Learning Modalities
The Mystery Quadrilateral **Individual** Each student plots and connects points, classifies the resulting shape, and determines its area.
A Change of Data **Visual** Students summarize and display the results of measuring various coins in a bar graph.
Round Pegs and Square Holes **Logical** Students study a pattern to determine the relationship between the area of a square and a circle whose diameter is the same length as the side of the square.
The One That Boasts the Most **Verbal** Students may discuss the calculated surface area and volume for each of the two boxes and provide justification for the answers to the questions.

Answers for Assessment

- **The Mystery Quadrilateral**

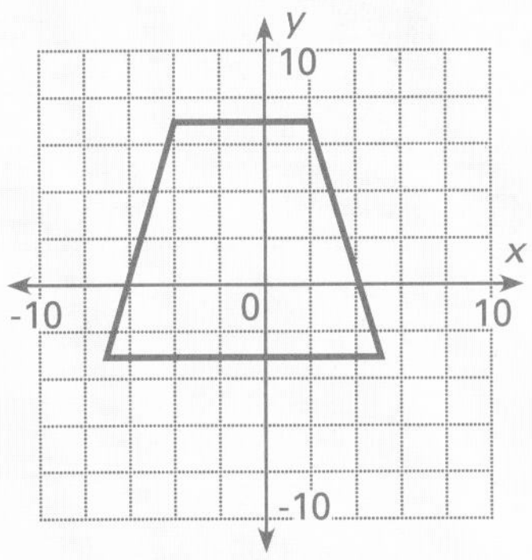

Trapezoid; 90 units^2; Split the trapezoid into a rectangle and two triangles, find the measurements using the grid; then add the areas of the polygons together to find the total area.

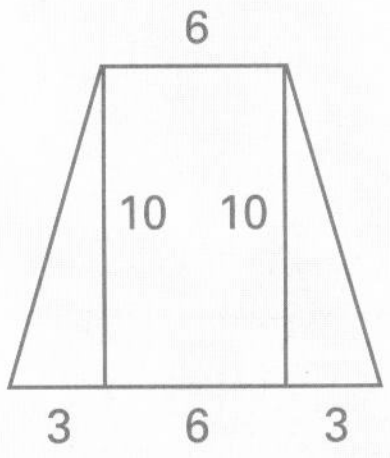

- **A Change of Data**

Possible answer:
Quarter: $d = 2.4$ cm; $C = 7.536$ cm

Dime: $d = 1.8$ cm; $C = 5.652$ cm

Nickel: $d = 2.1$ cm; $C = 6.594$ cm

Penny: $d = 1.9$ cm; $C = 5.966$ cm

- **Round Pegs and Square Holes**

The area of the circle is always about 78.5% of the area of the square.

- **The One That Boasts the Most**

The 8.3 by 2.1 by 5.2 box has more surface area and less volume; A greater surface area does not automatically mean a greater volume.

Chapter 12

▶ OVERVIEW

Probability

Section 12A

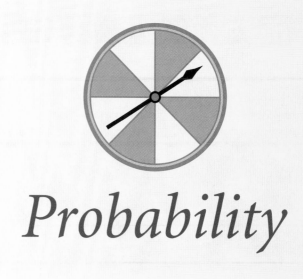

Introduction to Probability: Students learn to describe the chance of something happening.

12-1 Probability

12-2 Making Predictions

12-3 Geometric Models of Probability

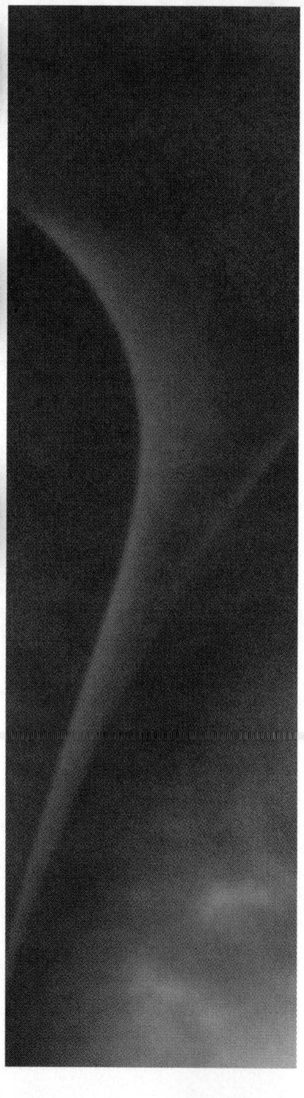

Section 12B

Fairness: Students learn to count the number of outcomes for a series of experiments and to find the probability of an event.

12-4 Tree Diagrams

12-5 Compound Events

12-6 Fairness and Unfairness

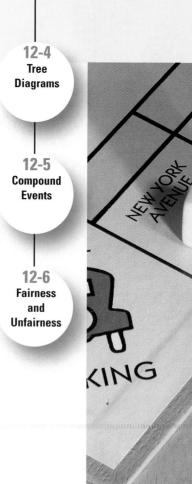

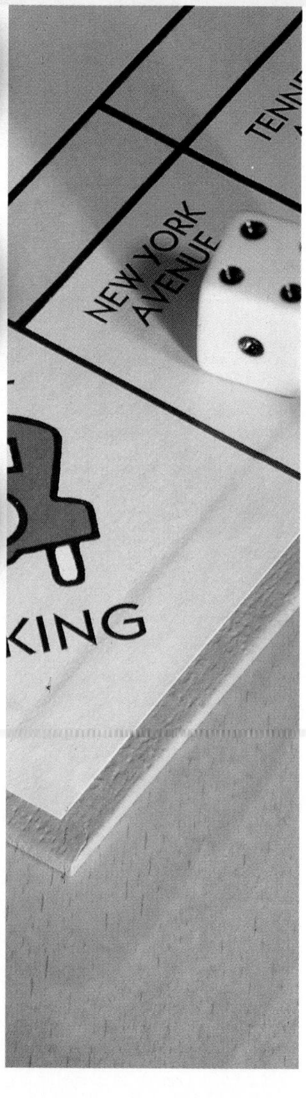

Meeting NCTM Standards

Curriculum Standards

Standard			pages
1	Problem Solving	Skills and Strategies	624, 629, 638, 645, 646, 653
		Applications	628–629, 632–633, 637–638, 639, 645–646, 649–650, 653–654, 655
		Exploration	626, 630, 635, 642, 647, 651
2	Communication	Oral	625, 627, 631, 637, *638*, 641, 644, 648, 652
		Written	*624*, 629, *633*, 638, *646*, 650, 654
		Cooperative Learning	*626*, *630*, *635*, *642*, *647*, *651*
3	Reasoning	Critical Thinking	629, 633, 646, 650, 654
4	Connections	Mathematical	See Standards 7, 11, 12 below.
		Interdisciplinary	Arts & Literature 622; Entertainment 622; Science 623, *625*, 628, *632*, *633*, 636, 637, 649; Social Studies 623; History 629; Consumer *645*; Industry 641, 646; Fine Arts *644*; Geography *625*, *649*
		Technology	634, 643
		Cultural	622
7	Computation and Estimation		*631*, 632, 640, *643*
11	Probability		626–657
12	Geometry		635–638, 656

Italic type indicates Teacher Edition reference.

Teaching Standards

Focus on Mathematical Connections

The acquisition of mathematical concepts means little if the content is learned in isolated ways. Teachers should

- represent mathematics as a network of interconnected concepts.
- emphasize connections between mathematics and other disciplines.

Assessment Standards

Focus on Inferences

Performance The Inferences Standard encourages teachers to use multiple sources of information when judging the level of students' understanding. Monitoring a student's progress as he or she completes a performance task may indicate areas of strength or weakness in understanding. In Chapter 12, students should

- understand the definition of terms.
- be able to make an organized list or tree diagram.

TECHNOLOGY

For the Teacher

- **Teacher Resource Planner CD-ROM**
  Use the teacher planning CD-ROM to view resources available for Chapter 12. You can prepare custom lesson plans or use the default lesson plans provided.
- **World Wide Web**
  Visit **www.teacher.mathsurf.com** for links to lesson plans from teachers and other professionals, NCTM information, and other sites.
- **TestWorks**
  TestWorks provides ready-made tests and can create custom tests and practice worksheets.

For the Parent

- **World Wide Web**
  Parents can use the Web site at **www.parent.mathsurf.com.**

For the Student

- **Interactive CD-ROM**
  Lesson 12-6 has an *Interactive CD-ROM Lesson*. The *Interactive CD-ROM Journal* and *Interactive CD-ROM Spreadsheet/Grapher Tool* are also used in Chapter 12.
- **Wide World of Mathematics**
  Lesson 12-2 Middle School: Hurricane Prediction
  Lesson 12-5 Middle School: Two-Sport Athlete
- **World Wide Web**
  Use with Chapter and Section Openers; Students can go online to the Scott Foresman-Addison Wesley Web site at **www.mathsurf.com/6/ch12** to collect information about chapter themes.
- **Jasper Woodbury Videodisc**
  Lesson 12-2: Rescue at Boone's Meadow

STANDARDIZED - TEST CORRELATION

SECTION 12A

LESSON	OBJECTIVE	ITBS Form M	CTBS 4th Ed.	CAT 5th Ed.	SAT 9th Ed.	MAT 7th Ed.	Your Form
12-1	• Find the probability of an event.	✘	✘	✘	✘	✘	
12-2	• Calculate probability from sample data.	✘	✘	✘	✘	✘	
12-3	• Calculate probability from geometric models.					✘	

SECTION 12B

LESSON	OBJECTIVE	ITBS Form M	CTBS 4th Ed.	CAT 5th Ed.	SAT 9th Ed.	MAT 7th Ed.	Your Form
12-4	• Make tree diagrams.						
12-5	• Find the probability of a compound event.						
12-6	• Tell if a game is fair.			✘		✘	

Key: ITBS - Iowa Test of Basic Skills; CTBS - Comprehensive Test of Basic Skills; CAT - California Achievement Test; SAT - Stanford Achievement Test; MAT - Metropolitan Achievement Test

ASSESSMENT PROGRAM

Traditional Assessment

QUICK QUIZZES	SECTION REVIEW	CHAPTER REVIEW	CHAPTER ASSESSMENT FREE RESPONSE	CHAPTER ASSESSMENT MULTIPLE CHOICE	CUMULATIVE REVIEW
TE: pp. 629, 633, 638, 646, 650, 654	SE: pp. 640, 656 *Quiz 12A, 12B	SE: pp. 658–659	SE: p. 660 *Ch. 12 Tests Forms A, B, E	*Ch. 12 Tests Forms C, E	SE: p. 661 *Ch. 12 Test Form F; Quarterly Test Ch. 1–12

Alternate Assessment

INTERVIEW	JOURNAL	ONGOING	PERFORMANCE	PORTFOLIO	PROJECT	SELF
TE: p. 638	SE: pp. 629, 638, 650, 654 TE: pp. 624, 633, 654	TE: pp. 626, 630, 635, 642, 647, 651	SE: pp. 660 TE: p. 646 *Ch. 12 Tests Forms D, E	TE: p. 629	SE: pp. 623, 638, 654 TE: p. 623	TE: p. 650

*Tests and quizzes are in *Assessment Sourcebook*. Test Form E is a mixed response test. Forms for Alternate Assessment are also available in *Assessment Sourcebook*.

TestWorks: Test and Practice Software

MIDDLE SCHOOL PACING CHART

REGULAR PACING

Day	5 classes per week
1	Chapter 12 Opener; Problem Solving Focus
2	Section **12A** Opener; Lesson **12-1**
3	Lesson **12-2;** Technology
4	Lesson **12-3**
5	**12A** Connect; **12A** Review
6	Section **12B** Opener; Lesson **12-4**
7	Lesson **12-5**
8	Lesson **12-6**
9	**12B** Connect; **12B** Review; Extend Key Ideas
10	Chapter 12 Summary and Review
11	Chapter 12 Assessment Cumulative Review, Chapters 1–12

BLOCK SCHEDULING OPTIONS

Block Scheduling for
Complete Course

Chapter 12 may be presented in

- five 90-minute blocks
- eight 75-minute blocks

Each block consists of a combination of

- Chapter and Section Openers
- Explores
- Lesson Development
- Problem Solving Focus
- Technology
- Extend Key Ideas
- Connect
- Review
- Assessment

For details, see *Block Scheduling Handbook.*

Block Scheduling for
Interdisciplinary Course

Each block integrates math with another subject area.

In Chapter 12, interdisciplinary topics include

- Disasters
- Games

Themes for Interdisciplinary Team Teaching 12A and 12B are

- Pi Bakery
- Scrabble®

For details, see *Block Scheduling Handbook.*

Block Scheduling for
Lab-Based Course

In each block, 30–40 minutes is devoted to lab activities including

- Explores in the Student Edition
- Connect pages in the Student Edition
- Technology options in the Student Edition
- Reteaching Activities in the Teacher Edition

For details, see *Block Scheduling Handbook.*

Block Scheduling for
Course with *Connected Mathematics*

In each block, investigations from **Connected Mathematics** replace or enhance the lessons in Chapter 12.

Connected Mathematics topics for Chapter 12 can be found in

- *How Likely Is It?*
- *Prime Time*

For details, see *Block Scheduling Handbook.*

INTERDISCIPLINARY BULLETIN BOARD

Set Up

Divide a bulletin board vertically into two sections. Label the left section *Female* and the right *Male.* Explain to the class that they will be designing clothes to be worn by females and males in a future time.

Procedure

- Have students decide for which sex they would like to design clothes and group them according to their preferences.
- Each group should assign members responsibility for designing three different tops or designing two different bottoms.
- Other group members should draw a basic tree diagram with room to show drawings of the six possible top and bottom combinations in the appropriate section on the board.
- Group members should draw the top and bottom combinations on the fashion tree.

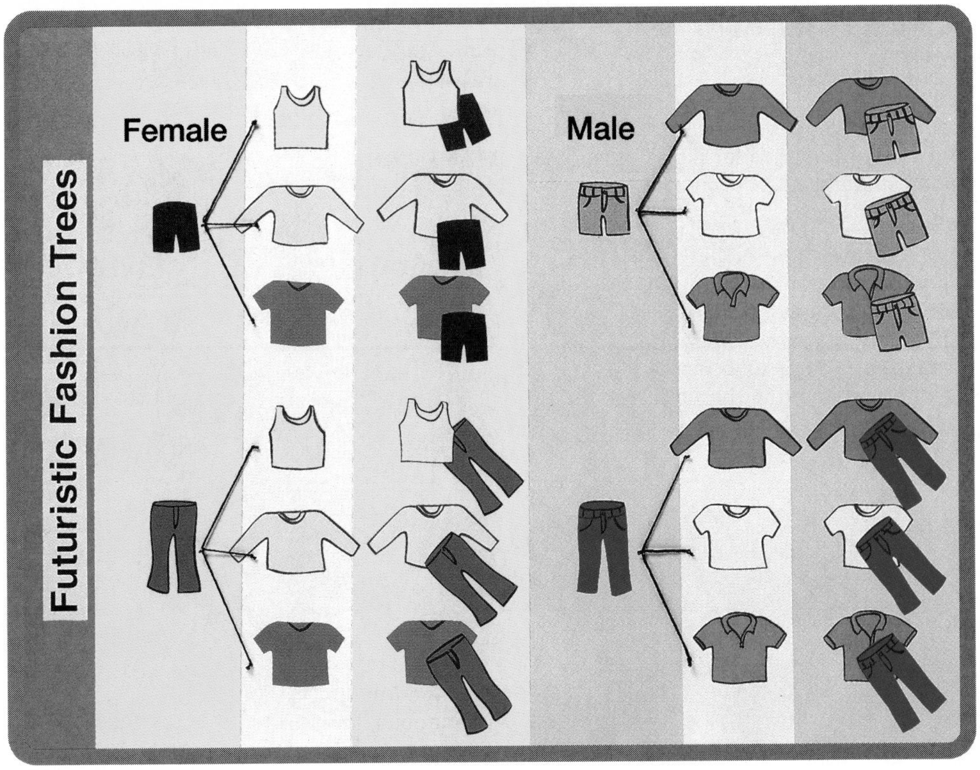

Chapter 12

The information on these pages shows how probability is used in real-life situations.

World Wide Web

If your class has access to the World Wide Web, you might want to use the information found at the Web site addresses given.

Extensions

The following activities do not require access to the World Wide Web.

People of the World
Have students play "rock-paper-scissors" and count the number of possible outcomes. Six possible outcomes: Rock-rock, rock-paper, rock-scissors, paper-paper, paper-scissors, and scissors-scissors.

Entertainment
Ask students to describe other board games that involve tossing number cubes, such as Parcheesi®. Point out that the chance of getting a double in Parcheesi is 1 in 6, or about 16.7%.

Arts & Literature
Talk about the meaning of the expression "50/50 chance" and elicit students' ideas about other events that have a 50/50 chance of occurring. Explain that a 50/50 chance means the two events are equally likely to occur.

Science
Suggest that students poll several different classrooms to determine how many students are left-handed.

Social Studies
Talk about sampling and why there is a margin of error in a poll. Have students investigate results of a poll given in a news magazine or newspaper to determine the margin of error stated in the poll.

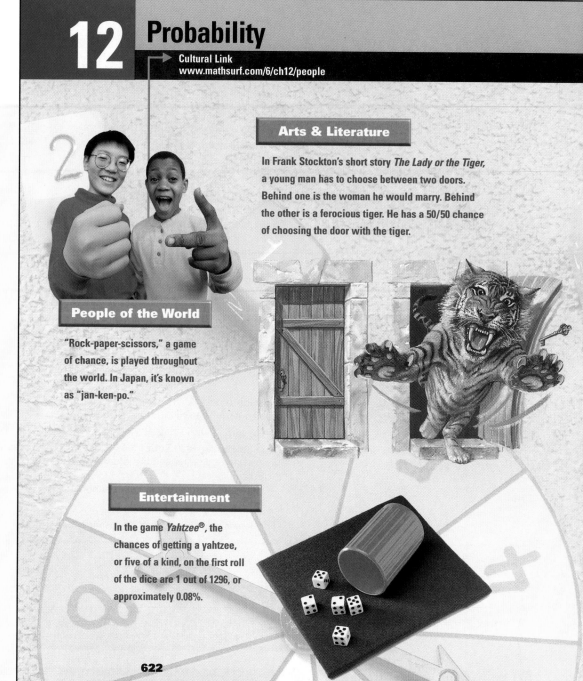

12 Probability

Cultural Link
www.mathsurf.com/6/ch12/people

People of the World

"Rock-paper-scissors," a game of chance, is played throughout the world. In Japan, it's known as "jan-ken-po."

Arts & Literature

In Frank Stockton's short story *The Lady or the Tiger,* a young man has to choose between two doors. Behind one is the woman he would marry. Behind the other is a ferocious tiger. He has a 50/50 chance of choosing the door with the tiger.

Entertainment

In the game *Yahtzee®*, the chances of getting a yahtzee, or five of a kind, on the first roll of the dice are 1 out of 1296, or approximately 0.08%.

622

TEACHER TALK

Meet Vera Holliday

Westlane Middle School
Indianapolis, Indiana

Approximately one week prior to beginning our unit on probability, my students are introduced to a simple game called "Something for Nothing." I prepare a bag of 90 yellow marbles and 10 blue marbles. For three days, I have each student pick a marble from the bag. The results are recorded on a tally form provided for them, and, after each student has drawn a marble, the marbles are collected and not returned to the bag. If they pick a blue marble from the bag, they receive a specified number of extra credit points. For the next three days, the same process is followed but this time students immediately return the marble to the bag before the next student picks a marble. I continue this game through the study of probability and use it as the basis for discussing the meaning of probability.

Science Link
www.mathsurf.com/6/ch12/science

Science

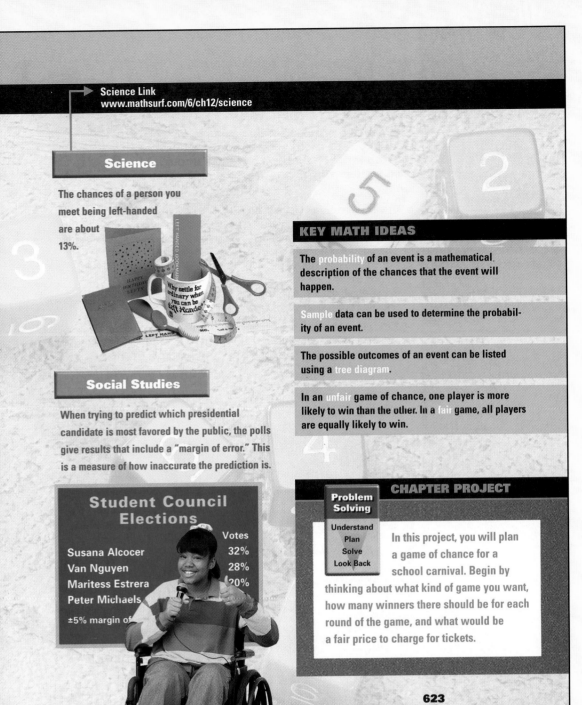

The chances of a person you meet being left-handed are about 13%.

Social Studies

When trying to predict which presidential candidate is most favored by the public, the polls give results that include a "margin of error." This is a measure of how inaccurate the prediction is.

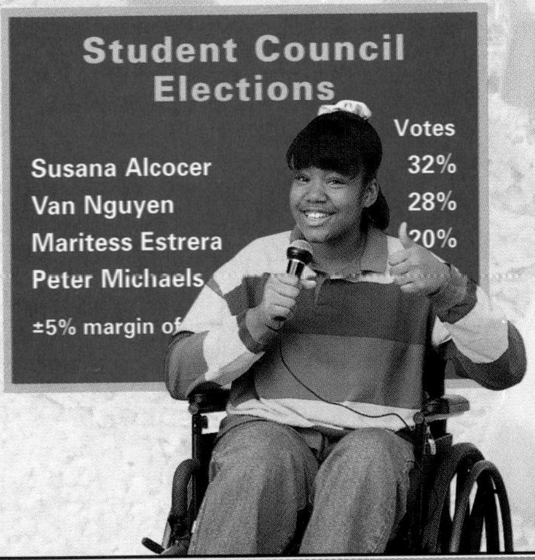

KEY MATH IDEAS

The **probability** of an event is a mathematical description of the chances that the event will happen.

Sample data can be used to determine the probability of an event.

The possible outcomes of an event can be listed using a **tree diagram**.

In an **unfair** game of chance, one player is more likely to win than the other. In a **fair** game, all players are equally likely to win.

CHAPTER PROJECT

Problem Solving
Understand
Plan
Solve
Look Back

In this project, you will plan a game of chance for a school carnival. Begin by thinking about what kind of game you want, how many winners there should be for each round of the game, and what would be a fair price to charge for tickets.

623

PROJECT ASSESSMENT

You may choose to use this project as a performance assessment for the chapter.

Performance Assessment Key

Level 4 Full Accomplishment

Level 3 Substantial Accomplishment

Level 2 Partial Accomplishment

Level 1 Little Accomplishment

Suggested Scoring Rubric

4	• Game of chance is challenging, creative, and mathematically correct. • Number of winners per round is realistic and a fair price is determined.
3	• Game of chance is creative and mathematically correct. • Number of winners per round is reasonable and a fair price is determined.
2	• Game reflects little element of chance. • Number of winners per round is not appropriate and the price is unreasonable.
1	• Game does not reflect any element of chance. • Number of winners per round is given little consideration and the price is unreasonable.

Chapter Project

Students devise a game of chance for a carnival, determining how many winners there should be and a fair price for a ticket.

Resources
Chapter 12 Project Master

Introduce the Project

- Ask students to describe games of chance they have played at carnivals, fun fairs, or similar events.
- Discuss how difficult the game should be for a person to win. Students should see that they need to find a compromise between making it so difficult that no one is interested and so easy that it will cost too much in prizes.
- Discuss where students might find information about games.

Project Progress

Section A, page 638 Students write instructions for each game. They also estimate playing time per game, number of players, and number of prizes needed.

Section B, page 654 Students make tickets for the games and indicate the probability of winning the game on the ticket.

Community Project

A community project for Chapter 12 is available in *Home and Community Connections.*

Cooperative Learning

You may want to use Teaching Tool Transparency 1: Cooperative Learning Checklist with **Explore** and other group activities in this chapter.

Problem Solving Focus

Checking for a Reasonable Answer

The Point
Students focus on using estimation to determine if their answer is reasonable.

Resources
Teaching Tool Transparency 18: Problem-Solving Guidelines

Interactive CD-ROM Journal

About the Page

Using the Problem-Solving Process
Once students have solved a problem, they need to determine if the solution they have found makes sense, fits the data, and is reasonable. Estimation can be used to check if an answer is reasonable. Discuss the following suggestions.

- Determine what the problem is asking.
- Review the solution process.
- Decide if your answer makes sense.

Ask ...
- How would you solve Problem 1? How can you estimate to see if your solution is correct? 31 × $150 × 10%; 30 × 150 × 0.1
- Which problem is easier to estimate, Problem 3 or Problem 4? Explain. Answers may vary.

Answers for Problems
1. Too low; $15 is only 10% of one booth rental.
2. Too low; Emilio's Pizzeria collected almost $9.00 for each pizza sold, so they donated almost $3.00 per pizza. They sold 59 pizzas, so the donation should be more than $150.00.
3. Close enough; $7758.76 ≈ $7800.
4. Too high; $\frac{1}{4}$ of $2469 is about $600.

Journal

Have students write an explanation of how they would use estimation in Problem 3 to check their answer.

Problem Solving
Understand
Plan
Solve
Look Back

Checking for a Reasonable Answer

When you have finished solving a problem, it may be helpful to look back to make sure your solution is reasonable. Estimation is a useful tool for determining if the answer is reasonable. If your estimate is very different from your answer, you may need to recheck your plan and your arithmetic.

Problem Solving Focus

Each of the problems below has an answer, but it is not exactly right. State if the answer is "too low," "too high," or "close enough," and explain why.

1. The Chelsea Flea Market raised money to help remodel the Chelsea Public Library. The market manager rented 31 booths at $150 a booth. She put aside 10% of the rental fee for clean-up expenses. How much did she plan to spend on clean-up? *$15*

2. Emilio's Pizzeria sold pizza for $1.10 a slice. Each pizza had 8 slices, and they sold 59 pizzas. Emilio's donated one-third of the money collected to the library. What was Emilio's donation? *$21.63*

3. The Flea Market raised a total of $10,345. Of that money, $2,586.24 went to cover the operating expenses of the Flea Market. The rest went to the library. How much went to the library? *$7800*

4. Martha's school is in the Chelsea neighborhood. The school rented a booth and sold $2469 worth of items. The school gave $\frac{1}{4}$ of the money to the library fund. How much did the school donate? *$1851.75*

624

Additional Problem

Roberto bought 78 T-shirts for $12 each and sold them for $18 each. He also bought 40 caps for $8 each and sold them for $10 each. He donated 12% of his profit to the chess club, which was raising money for a trip to a national tournament. How much did he donate to the chess club?

1. Rhonda estimated that Roberto donated $220 to the chess club. Is her estimate too high, too low, or close enough? How do you think she determined her estimate? Too high; She used the selling prices, not the profit.
2. Kele estimated that Roberto donated $50 to the chess club. Is his estimate too high, too low, or about right? Explain. About right; Check students' explanations.
3. Explain two different ways to estimate 12% of Roberto's profits. Possible answer: Round to 10% and multiply by 0.1 or round to $12\frac{1}{2}\% = \frac{1}{8}$ and divide by 8.

Section 12A

Introduction to Probability

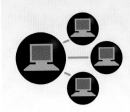

Visit www.teacher.mathsurf.com for links to lesson plans from teachers and other professionals, NCTM information, and other sites.

LESSON PLANNING GUIDE

Student Edition / Ancillaries*

LESSON		MATERIALS	VOCABULARY	DAILY	OTHER
	Chapter 12 Opener				Ch. 12 Project Master Ch. 12 Community Project Teaching Tool Trans. 1
	Problem Solving Focus				Teaching Tool Trans. 18 *Interactive CD-ROM Journal*
	Section 12A Opener				
12-1	Probability		experiment, outcome, event, probability	12-1	Lesson Enhancement Trans. 58 Technology Master 60
12-2	Making Predictions	bag with 2 cubes of one color, 6 cubes of a second color, 5 cubes of a third color	sample	12-2	Technology Master 61 *WW Math*–Middle School
	Technology	spreadsheet software			*Interactive CD-ROM Spreadsheet Grapher Tool*
12-3	Geometric Models of Probability	paper clips		12-3	Teaching Tool Trans. 2, 3 Lesson Enhancement Trans. 59 Technology Master 62 Ch. 12 Project Master
	Connect				Interdisc. Team Teaching 12A Lesson Enhancement Trans. 60
	Review				Practice 12A; Quiz 12A; *TestWorks*

* Daily Ancillaries include Practice, Reteaching, Problem Solving, Enrichment, and Daily Transparency. Teaching Tool Transparencies are in *Teacher's Toolkits*. Lesson Enhancement Transparencies are in *Overhead Transparency Package*.

SKILLS TRACE

LESSON	SKILL	FIRST INTRODUCED GR. 4	GR. 5	GR. 6	DEVELOP	PRACTICE/APPLY	REVIEW
12-1	Finding probabilities.		✗		pp. 626–627	pp. 628–629	pp. 640, 646, 658
12-2	Finding experimental probabilities.		✗		pp. 630–631	pp. 632–633	pp. 640, 650, 658
12-3	Using geometric models to calculate probabilities.			✗ p. 635	pp. 635–636	pp. 637–638	pp. 640, 650, 658

CONNECTED MATHEMATICS

Investigations 1–3 from the unit *How Likely Is It? (Probability)*, from the **Connected Mathematics** series, can be used with Section 12A.

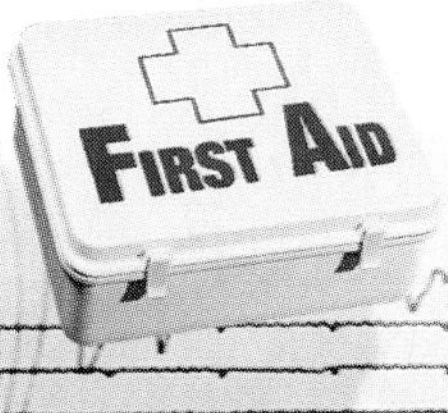

INTERDISCIPLINARY TEAM TEACHING

Math and Science/Technology

(Worksheet pages 57–58: Teacher pages T57–T58)

In this lesson, students use tree diagrams and the counting principle to help determine the identities of a fictitious band of burglars.

Name ______________________ ***Math and Science/Technology***

Who Robbed the Pi Bakery?

Use tree diagrams and the counting principle to help determine the identities of a fictitious band of burglars.

The Sweet Tooth Gang was at work again—or so it seemed to Detective Polly Gon at the Math City Police Department. It was a hot summer night when the alarm sounded at police headquarters. There was a burglary in progress at the huge warehouse of the Pi Bakery. Police raced to the scene, but the burglars had made their getaway with 314 Pi pies and a dozen big boxes containing $\frac{1}{2}$-gallon cartons of ice cream.

Police found one eyewitness at the scene, a security guard named Al Gebra, who was left tied up by the burglars. He gave Detective Gon the following description:

The burglars entered the store and overpowered Al at about 1:30 a.m. He saw three burglars, but he couldn't describe them fully. Al said some of the burglars had crew cuts and some had long hair, but he didn't know how many men had hair of each type. Al also noticed that one man was tall, one was of medium height, and the other was short.

Al said the burglars spent about 15 minutes carrying boxes of pies and ice cream out of the warehouse and putting them into the back of an old pick-up truck. As the burglars sped off in their truck, Al caught a glimpse of the license plate. He saw an LCM but could not make out the three numbers that followed.

This description is all that you and Detective Polly Gon have to go on. Use the information above and the illustrations below to answer the following questions.

1. The use of scientific evidence to solve a crime is called *forensics*. What kinds of clues left at the scene of a crime might be of use to detectives and forensic scientists?
   Answers will vary and could include the following: fingerprints, hair, blood, skin, fabric, footprints.

Name ______________________ ***Math and Science/Technology***

2. What clues were left behind by the burglars?
   See below.
3. Police know all six members of the Sweet Tooth Gang. Using Al Gebra's description of the burglars, police also know that two members of the gang were not involved in the burglary. Which two? How did the police know?
   See below.
4. Al Gebra saw men with crew cuts and long hair. One was tall, one was of medium height, and one was short. How many hair and height combinations are possible for the burglars? Show the possibilities with a tree diagram.
   Six combinations are possible. (See below.)
5. Al Gebra remembers that one man was tall and had a crew cut and another was short and had a crew cut. The third man had long hair. With this information Detective Polly Gon now knows the identities of the three burglars. Which ones are they? Explain your answer.
   See below.
6. At first, Detective Gon knows the three letters of the getaway truck's license plate, but none of the numbers. She figures she will have a lot of license plate numbers to check. How many combinations will she need to check? (Note: there are no zeroes on the plate and there are no repeated numbers.)
   She will need to check 504 plate numbers ($9 \times 8 \times 7$).
7. Al Gebra suddenly remembers that the first two numbers of the license plate were 9 and 2. How many license plates does Detective Gon have to check to find the gang's truck if the final numeral is not a zero or a repeat of any of the other numerals?
   Seven. The third number can only be 1, 3, 4, 5, 6, 7, or 8.
8. Detective Polly Gon runs a check of license plates and finds that the missing plate number is a prime number between 6 and 10. That plate is registered to Cal Culus. Detective Gon now has evidence that puts Cal Culus at the scene of the crime. What is Cal Culus' license plate number?
   The plate number is LCM 927. The only prime number between 6 and 10 is 7, so that must be the last number.
9. Forensic scientists and detectives have many tools to assist them in solving crimes. Do some research to find out about some of them. Pick one and report on how it was used in solving a real-life crime.
   Reports will vary. Students can report on any forensic tool as long as they show how it was used to solve an actual crime. The crime can be a famous one in the past or one that is recent.

Answers

2. The eyewitness managed to see their truck and part of the truck's license plate. He also saw the general body-types and hairstyles of the burglars. What they took also gave the police a clue.
3. P. Rob Ability because he has curly hair and Lynn E. R. Function because he is bald.
4. 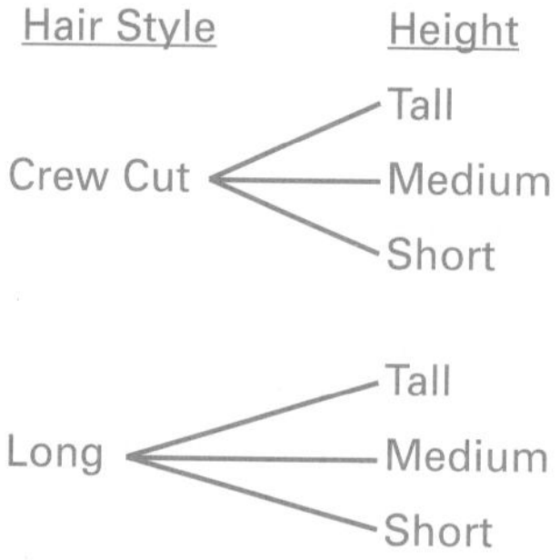

5. Cal Culus, E. Quation, and Des Imal. Cal Culus and E. Quation were the tall and the short men with crew cuts. In his original statement, Al said one man was of medium height and that there was a long-haired man involved. That can only be Des Imal.

BIBLIOGRAPHY

FOR TEACHERS

Krantz, Les. *Facts! That Matter: Everything You Need to Know About Everything.* Los Angeles, CA: Price Stern Sloan, 1993.

Nash, Jay Robert. *Darkest Hours: A Narrative Encyclopedia of Worldwide Disasters from Ancient Times to the Present.* Chicago, IL: Nelson-Hall, 1976.

Phillips, Richard. *Numbers: Facts, Figures, and Fiction.* New York, NY: Cambridge University Press, 1994.

FOR STUDENTS

Cornell, James. *The Great International Disaster Book.* New York, NY: Scribner, 1982.

Keller, David. *Great Disasters: The Most Shocking Moments in History.* New York, NY: Avon Books, 1990.

Nott, Valerie. *Great Disasters.* New York, NY: F. Watts, 1995.

Queen, Ellery. *The Ellery Queen Omnibus.* International Polygonics, 1988.

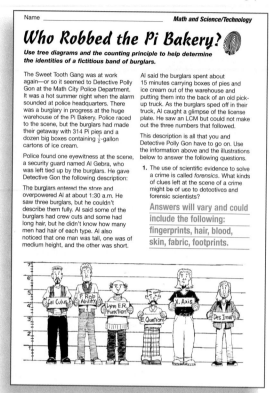

SECTION **12A**

Introduction to Probability

▶ Science Link ▶ Geography Link ▶ www.mathsurf.com/6/ch12/disasters

Decide if each statement about natural disasters is true or false.

1. *Four out of five fires are caused by nature. One out of five is caused by humans.*
2. *The center of a hurricane or tornado is known as the "eye." It's the most violent part of the storm.*
3. *Alaska, not California, is the state where the most earthquakes occur.*
4. *On the open ocean, the speed of a tsunami can reach 450 miles per hour.*

Force of Nature!

Natural disasters can be both expensive and deadly. Much of the loss of life and property can be prevented or avoided if the disaster can be anticipated. Scientists are constantly working to find better ways of predicting these disasters. Probability, a branch of mathematics, is one of their most useful tools.

1 **Why can't scientists predict disasters with 100% accuracy?**

2 **How do people use mathematics when trying to predict or prepare for disasters?**

625

Where are we now?

In Grade 5, students looked at different ways in which things can happen.

They learned how to

- predict outcomes from samples.
- predict outcomes from experiments.
- express probability as a fraction.

Where are we going?

In Grade 6, Section 12A, students will

- find the probability of an event.
- calculate probability from sample data.
- calculate probability from geometric models.

Theme: Disasters

World Wide Web

If your class has access to the World Wide Web, you might want to use the information found at the Web site address given. The interdisciplinary links relate to topics discussed in this section.

About the Page

This page introduces the theme of the section, disasters, and discusses how lives and money might be saved by accurately predicting natural disasters.

Ask ...

- What natural disasters can scientists predict with greater accuracy today?

Extensions

The following activities do not require access to the World Wide Web.

Science
A hurricane is a tropical cyclone with winds of 74 miles per hour or greater. Ask students to research major hurricanes and report on their location and impact.

Geography
Have students research major earthquakes and identify locations where they most frequently occur.

Answers for True/False Questions

1. False
2. False
3. True
4. True

Answers for Questions

1. Possible answer: Scientists may not have the technology necessary to make such accurate predictions.
2. Answers may vary.

Connect

On page 639, students will evaluate an emergency disaster plan.

12-1

Lesson Organizer

Objective

- Find the probability of an event.

Vocabulary

- Experiment, outcome, event, probability

NCTM Standards

- 1–4, 11

Review

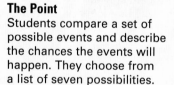

Write each fraction as a decimal and as a percent.

1. $\frac{1}{4}$ 0.25; 25%
2. $\frac{3}{5}$ 0.6; 60%

Write each fraction in lowest terms.

3. $\frac{8}{10}$ $\frac{4}{5}$
4. $\frac{6}{12}$ $\frac{1}{2}$

Available on Daily Transparency 12-1

1 Introduce

Explore

The Point
Students compare a set of possible events and describe the chances the events will happen. They choose from a list of seven possibilities.

Ongoing Assessment
Point out that some of the categories are less definite than others. For example, *impossible* and *for certain* leave little room for argument. But the other categories are open to interpretation.

For Groups That Finish Early
Give two other examples similar to those in **Explore**, one which is impossible and one which is certain. Possible answers: The daily high temperature will be 300°F. The Earth will rotate on its axis.

12-1 Probability

You'll Learn ...

- to find the probability of an event

... How It's Used

Safety inspectors use probability to determine the chances that a particular safety device will fail to work correctly.

Vocabulary

experiment
outcome
event
probability

▶ Lesson Link You have looked at different ways things can happen. Now you'll describe the chance of something happening. ◀

Explore Probability

What Are the Chances?

These words can describe the chances that something will happen.

impossible — rarely — probably not — even chance — possibly — probably — for certain

1. For each item, label where it belongs on the probability list.
   a. A quarter is tossed and it lands heads up.
   b. One of your parents wins the lottery.
   c. An earthquake will happen in your town in the next week.
   d. The sun will rise tomorrow morning.
   e. The President of the United States will visit your class today.
   f. There will be both boys and girls present in your next math class.
   g. Someone in the classroom owns a pet.
2. If you compared everyone's lists, do you think they would all be the same? Explain.
3. Why might a mathematician who studies chance have a difficult time using the chance line above?

Learn Probability

A probability **experiment** is a situation that can happen in more than one way. The **outcomes** of an experiment are the ways it can happen.

Outcomes: red, blue, green

Outcomes: 1, 2, 3, 4, 5, 6

Outcomes: heads, tails

MEETING INDIVIDUAL NEEDS

Resources

- **12-1** Practice
- **12-1** Reteaching
- **12-1** Problem Solving
- **12-1** Enrichment
- **12-1** Daily Transparency
  - Problem of the Day
  - Review
  - Quick Quiz

Lesson Enhancement Transparency 58

Technology Master 60

Learning Modalities

Visual Have students make a drawing of a spinner with several sections of different colors. Then have them label each section with the probability of landing in that section.

Verbal Have students think of a name of a city and write each letter in the name on a separate piece of paper. Then have them write a paragraph telling how to find the probability of picking at random each letter in the name.

Inclusion

Students who have visual problems might benefit from using a jar filled with marbles or other objects of distinct sizes and shapes to perform probability experiments. Once students understand the concepts, encourage them to answer the questions without using any materials.

Have students add new vocabulary to their reference book.

An **event** is the particular outcome that you're looking for. You can describe the **probability** that a particular event will happen by using a ratio.

$$P(\text{event}) = \frac{\text{number of ways the event can happen}}{\text{number of possible outcomes}}$$

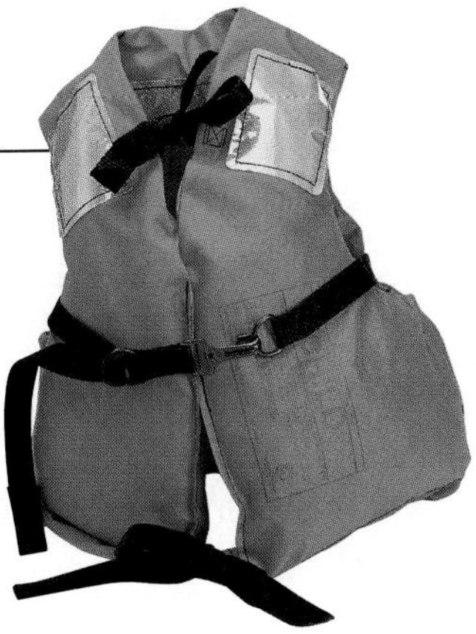

Example 1

An ocean liner has 8 lifeboats, numbered 1 through 8. In the event of an emergency, every passenger is randomly assigned to one of the 8 boats. What is the probability of being assigned to a boat whose number is less than 6?

Possible outcomes: 1, 2, 3, 4, 5, 6, 7, 8

Number of ways the event can occur: 5 (boat 1, 2, 3, 4, or 5)

$P(\text{less than } 6) = \frac{5}{8}$.

It is sometimes helpful to express a probability as a decimal or percent.

Example 2

What is the probability of rolling an even number on a number cube? Express your answer as a decimal and a percent.

Possible outcomes: 1, 2, 3, 4, 5, 6

Number of ways the event can occur: 3 (rolling a 2, a 4, or a 6)

$P(\text{even number}) = \frac{3}{6}$. As a decimal, this is 0.50. As a percent, 50%.

Try It

For each spinner, what is the probability of the pointer landing in a section that is:

a. Red? i. $\frac{3}{8}$ ii. 0

b. Blue or green? i. $\frac{1}{2}$ ii. $\frac{3}{5}$

i.

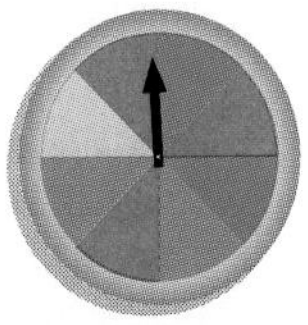

ii.

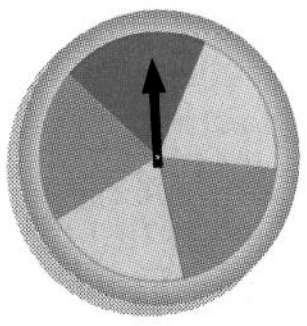

Check Your Understanding

1. Give an example of a situation with 4 outcomes.

2. If $P(\text{event}) = \frac{6}{6}$, what can you conclude about the event?

MATH EVERY DAY

Problem of the Day

How much string is needed to tie this box? Ignore the string needed for the knots.

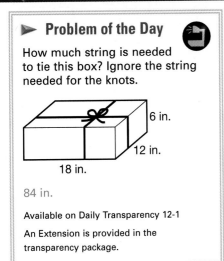

84 in.

Available on Daily Transparency 12-1

An Extension is provided in the transparency package.

Fact of the Day

Seismographs register more than 80,000 earthquakes each year. Most are so mild that they are not even noticed.

Mental Math

Find each product.

1. 20 × 90 1800
2. 80 × 80 6400
3. 700 × 900 630,000
4. 900 × 600 540,000

Answers for Explore

1. Possible answers:
   a. Even chance
   b. Rarely
   c. Rarely
   d. For certain
   e. Rarely
   f. Probably
   g. Probably
2. Possible answer: No; Some of the probabilities are subjective.
3. Possible answers: The chance line is non-specific. It doesn't record precise numerical data.

2 Teach

Learn

You may wish to use Lesson Enhancement Transparency 58 with **Try It**.

Alternate Examples

1. In a game show, a contestant can pick from five doors numbered 1 through 5. What is the probability that a contestant picked an even numbered door?

   Possible outcomes: 1, 2, 3, 4, 5

   Number of ways the event can occur: 2 (picking 2 or 4)

   $P(\text{even number}) = \frac{2}{5}$.

2. What is the probability of rolling a prime number on a standard number cube? Express your answer as a decimal and a percent.

   Possible outcomes: 1, 2, 3, 4, 5, 6

   Number of ways the event can occur: 3 (rolling a 2, 3, or 5)

   $P(\text{prime number}) = \frac{3}{6}$.

   As a decimal, this is 0.50. As a percent, 50%.

3 Practice and Assess

Check

Answers for Check Your Understanding

1. Possible answer: There are four students on a committee. One will be chosen to lead a meeting.
2. The event will definitely happen.

12-1 Exercises and Applications

Assignment Guide

- Basic
  1–22, 27, 29, 32–38 evens
- Average
  3–24, 27, 29–30, 32–38 evens
- Enriched
  9–31, 33–39 odds

Exercise Notes

Exercises 19–20

Error Prevention Some students may give wrong answers because they do not remember the distinction between vowels and consonants. Remind them that the vowels are *a, e, i, o, u*.

Exercise 22

Test Prep If students selected C, they did not carefully read the question. Instead they gave the probability of winning rather than not winning.

Exercise 24

Science Most earthquakes occur when rock on one side of a fault in the Earth's crust shifts with respect to the rock on the other side of the fault. The motion causes vibrations in the crust that travel through the rock as shock waves.

Reteaching

Activity

- Work with a partner.
- Each person should write his or her first and last name in large letters across the top of a sheet of paper.
- Exchange papers with your partner. Suppose that each letter in the name was placed in a container and one letter was chosen at random.
- Under each letter in his or her name write the probability of choosing that letter.
- Check your partner's work.

12-1 Exercises and Applications

Practice and Apply

Getting Started **Tell how many outcomes are possible for each experiment.**

1. Flipping a quarter. 2

2. Answering a true/false question. 2

3. Rolling a standard number cube. 6

4. Choosing a month at random. 12

A set of ten cards is labeled 1 through 10. Suppose you choose one card at random. Find the probability of each event.

5. $P(1)$ $\frac{1}{10}$ **6.** $P(\text{multiple of } 3)$ $\frac{3}{10}$ **7.** $P(\text{2-digit number})$ $\frac{1}{10}$ **8.** $P(6 \text{ or } 2)$ $\frac{1}{5}$

9. $P(12)$ 0 **10.** $P(\text{less than } 11)$ 1 **11.** $P(\text{odd number})$ $\frac{1}{2}$ **12.** $P(5)$ $\frac{1}{10}$

Suppose you roll a number cube. Find the probability of each event.

13. $P(6)$ $\frac{1}{6}$ GPS **14.** $P(\text{even number})$ $\frac{1}{2}$ **15.** $P(\text{less than } 6)$ $\frac{5}{6}$ **16.** $P(7)$ 0

There are 6 cards that spell out C H A N C E. Suppose you choose one card at random. Find the probability of each event.

17. $P(A)$ $\frac{1}{6}$ **18.** $P(C)$ $\frac{1}{3}$ **19.** $P(\text{vowel})$ $\frac{1}{3}$ **20.** $P(\text{consonant})$ $\frac{2}{3}$

21. Janice's board game uses 8 playing tokens, each a different color. If she places the 8 tokens in a bag so that she can't see them, what is the probability that she picks the blue token? The red token? Both are $\frac{1}{8}$

22. **Test Prep** The probability of getting a winning game piece in a contest is 3 in 5. What is the probability of **not** winning? B

Ⓐ $\frac{1}{5}$ Ⓑ $\frac{2}{5}$ Ⓒ $\frac{3}{5}$ Ⓓ $\frac{4}{5}$

23. At the Hamburger Hotline restaurant, each kid's meal comes with a dinosaur cup. The dinosaurs are Triceratops, Stegosaurus, Tyrannosaurus rex, Brontosaurus, and Parasaurolophus. What is the probability of getting the Tyrannosaurus rex cup? $\frac{1}{5}$

24. **Science** A group of scientists studying earthquakes plans to observe nine different devices that monitor seismic activity. If each scientist is assigned to a monitoring device at random, what is the probability that the first scientist will monitor either the laser reflector or creepmeter? $\frac{2}{9}$

25. **Logic** Suppose the probability of an event is $\frac{7}{13}$. Which is greater, the probability that the event will occur or the probability that it will *not* occur? Will occur

PRACTICE 12-1

PRACTICE

Name ______________

Practice 12-1

Probability

A set of 12 cards is labeled 1 through 12. Suppose you choose one card at random. Find the probability of each event.

1. $P(5)$ $\frac{1}{12}$ **2.** $P(\text{even number})$ $\frac{1}{2}$ **3.** $P(\text{multiple of } 5)$ $\frac{1}{6}$

4. $P(12)$ $\frac{1}{12}$ **5.** $P(\text{less than } 9)$ $\frac{2}{3}$ **6.** $P(\text{multiple of } 3)$ $\frac{1}{3}$

A set of 15 tiles is labeled 1 through 15. Suppose you choose one tile at random. Find the probability of each event.

7. $P(8)$ $\frac{1}{15}$ **8.** $P(7 \text{ or } 11)$ $\frac{2}{15}$ **9.** $P(\text{less than } 20)$ 1

10. $P(\text{odd number})$ $\frac{8}{15}$ **11.** $P(\text{multiple of } 3)$ $\frac{1}{3}$ **12.** $P(35)$ 0

Suppose you roll a number cube. Find the probability of each event.

13. $P(4)$ $\frac{1}{6}$ **14.** $P(8)$ 0 **15.** $P(2 \text{ or } 5)$ $\frac{1}{3}$

16. $P(\text{less than } 4)$ $\frac{1}{2}$ **17.** $P(\text{greater than } 5)$ $\frac{1}{6}$ **18.** $P(\text{multiple of } 5)$ $\frac{1}{6}$

There are 13 cards that spell out L I E C H T E N S T E I N. Suppose you choose one card. Find the probability of each event.

19. $P(L)$ $\frac{1}{13}$ **20.** $P(I)$ $\frac{2}{13}$ **21.** $P(E)$ $\frac{3}{13}$

22. $P(N)$ $\frac{2}{13}$ **23.** $P(\text{vowel})$ $\frac{5}{13}$ **24.** $P(\text{consonant})$ $\frac{8}{13}$

The bar graph shows the music preference of 28 students in Gregory's class. If a student is chosen at random, find the probability of each event.

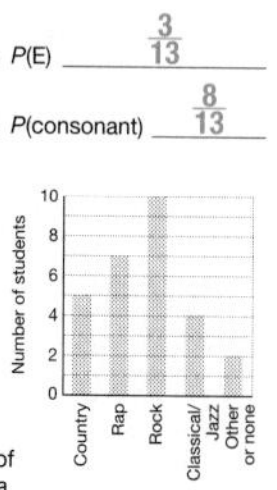

25. $P(\text{country})$ $\frac{5}{28}$ **26.** $P(\text{rock or rap})$ $\frac{17}{28}$

27. $P(\text{classical/jazz})$ $\frac{1}{7}$ **28.** $P(\text{country or rock})$ $\frac{15}{28}$

29. **Social Science** In 1992, there were 100 U.S. Senators, of whom 43 were Republicans. What is the probability that a Senator chosen at random from this group would be a Republican? Express your answer as a decimal and a percent. 0.43; 43%

RETEACHING

Name ______________

Alternative Lesson 12-1

Probability

A probability **experiment** is a situation that can happen in more than one way. The **outcomes** of an experiment are the ways it can happen. For example, there are 2 outcomes–a head or a tail–if you toss one coin.

An **event** is the particular outcome that you're looking for. You can describe the **probability** that a particular event will happen by using a ratio.

$$P(\text{event}) = \frac{\text{number of ways the event can happen}}{\text{number of possible outcomes}}$$

It is sometimes helpful to express a probability as a decimal or percent.

Example

Write the probability of spinning A. Then express your answer as a decimal and a percent.

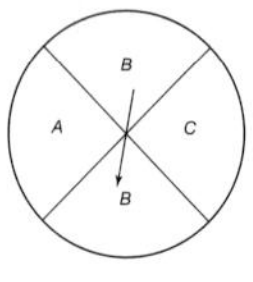

Each section on the spinner represents a different letter. All sections are the same size. Therefore, each outcome is equally likely to occur when you spin the spinner.

$P = \frac{1}{4}$ ← Number of ways the event can occur
← Possible outcomes: A, B, B, C

$\frac{1}{4} = 0.25$ or 25%

So, the probability of spinning A is $\frac{1}{4}$, 0.25, or 25%.

Try It Suppose you toss a six-sided number cube. You want to roll an odd number.

a. How many equally likely outcomes are there? 6

b. How many ways can the event occur? 3 ways

c. Write the probability of rolling an odd number as a fraction, a decimal, and a percent.
$\frac{3}{6}$ or $\frac{1}{2}$; 0.5; 50%

Write each probability. Express each answer as a decimal and a percent.

d. What is the probability of spinning B on the spinner in the example? $\frac{2}{4}$ or $\frac{1}{2}$, 0.5, 50%

e. A bag of buttons contains 4 red buttons, 4 blue buttons, 3 purple buttons, and 1 yellow button. What is the probability of picking a purple button without looking? $\frac{3}{12}$ or $\frac{1}{4}$, 0.25, 25%

26. History The first seismograph was built in the year 132 by the Chinese philosopher Zhang Heng. Eight bronze dragon heads were set around a large vessel above eight bronze toads. When an earthquake occurred, a ball fell out of a dragon's mouth and was caught by a toad. If the dragons were numbered 1 to 8, what was the probability that the ball would fall out of the mouth of a dragon with a prime number? $\frac{1}{2}$

The bar graph shows the eye color of the 32 students in Patty's class. If a student is chosen at random, find the probability of each event.

27. P(blue) $\frac{9}{32}$

28. P(brown or green) $\frac{21}{32}$

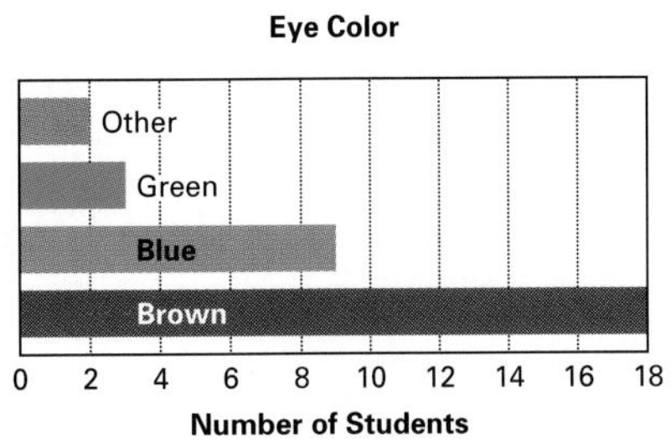

Problem Solving and Reasoning

29. Communicate Can the probability of an event be greater than 1? Less than 0? Explain.

30. Critical Thinking Is it more likely that you could roll a number cube twice and get a 3 and then a 5, or a 3 and then a 3? Explain.

31. Journal The probability of getting red on a spinner is 80%. What is the probability of not getting red? How are these two probabilities related?

Problem Solving TIP

Sometimes, acting a problem out can help you solve it.

Mixed Review

Classify each solid. *[Lesson 11-1]*

32. **33.** **34.** **35.**

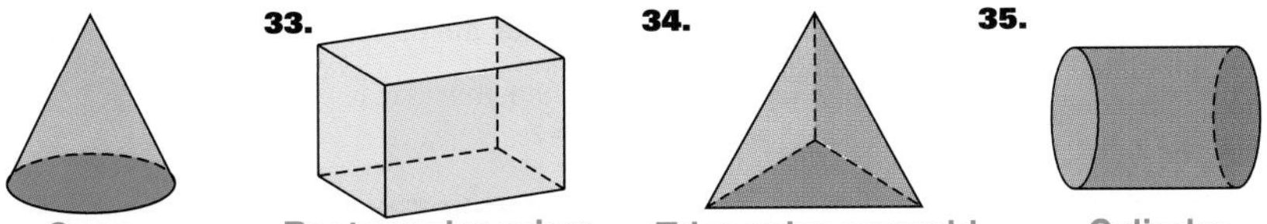

Cone | Rectangular prism | Triangular pyramid | Cylinder

Find the surface area for each solid. *[Lesson 11-2]*

36. **37.** **38.** **39.**

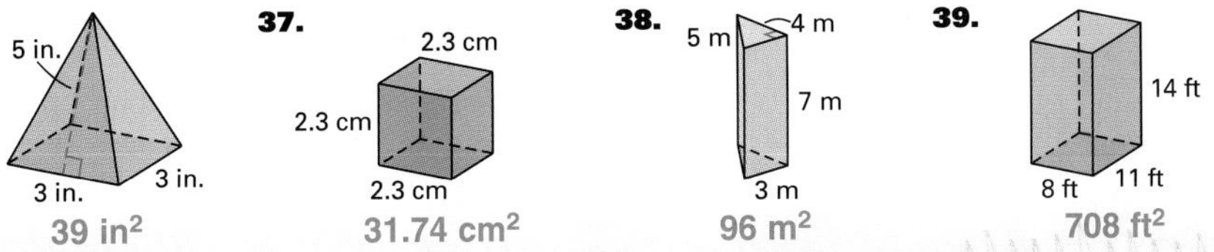

39 in² | 31.74 cm² | 96 m² | 708 ft²

Exercise Answers

29. No; No; $0 \leq \frac{\text{no. of ways an event can happen}}{\text{no. of possible outcomes}} \leq 1$.

30. Chances are the same; The probability is $\frac{1}{36}$ for each pair of rolls.

31. 20%; The sum of the probabilities is 100% or 1.

Alternate Assessment

Portfolio Have students pick out several exercises that best exemplify the concepts of this lesson and add them to their portfolio.

Quick Quiz

There are eight cards that spell out K E N T U C K Y. Suppose you pick one card at random. Find the probability of each event.

1. P(E) $\frac{1}{8}$
2. P(K) $\frac{1}{4}$
3. P(A) 0
4. P(vowel or consonant) 1

Available on Daily Transparency 12-1

PROBLEM SOLVING 12-1

PROBLEM SOLVING

Name ______

Guided Problem Solving 12-1

GPS PROBLEM 14, STUDENT PAGE 628

Suppose you roll a number cube. Find P(even number).

— Understand —

1. What does the problem ask you to find? The probability of rolling an even number.

— Plan —

2. How many numbers are on a number cube? 6 numbers.
3. How many possible outcomes are there when you roll a number cube? 6
4. What are the even numbers on a number cube? 2, 4, and 6
5. How many ways can you roll an even number? 3 ways.

— Solve —

6. Write the probability of rolling an even number. Which ratio will you use? a

   a. $P(\text{event}) = \frac{\text{number of ways event can happen}}{\text{number of possible outcomes}}$

   b. $P(\text{event}) = \frac{\text{number of possible outcomes}}{\text{number of ways event can happen}}$

7. Write the probability. $P(\text{even number}) = \frac{3}{6}$ or $\frac{1}{2}$

— Look Back —

7. Are all the possible outcomes equally likely? How do you know? Yes. Each has an equal chance of occurring.

SOLVE ANOTHER PROBLEM

Suppose you toss a twelve-sided number cube with numbers 1-12 on its faces. What is the probability of rolling a number which is a multiple of 5? $\frac{2}{12}$ or $\frac{1}{6}$

ENRICHMENT

Name ______

Extend Your Thinking 12-1

Critical Thinking

Use the words *impossible, probably not, even chance, probably,* and *certain* to help you describe the following events. Then find the probability.

1. Rolling a blue on a cube painted with 3 blue faces and 3 yellow faces. Even, $P(\text{blue}) = \frac{3}{6}$ or $\frac{1}{2}$
2. Drawing a 5 from a stack of cards numbered 0 through 10. Probably not, $P(\text{drawing 5}) = \frac{1}{11}$
3. Drawing a nickel from a purse containing 7 dimes and 3 nickels. Probably not, $P(\text{drawing a nickel}) = \frac{3}{10}$
4. Drawing a multiple of 10 if a number is chosen from the numbers 1 through 120. Probably not, $P(\text{multiple of 10}) = \frac{1}{12}$
5. Winning first or second prize in a drawing in which there are 3 prizes and 500 entries. Probably not, $P(\text{first or second prize}) = \frac{2}{500}$ or $\frac{1}{250}$
6. Spinning a yellow if the spinner has 12 equal regions, 10 of which are yellow. Probably, $P(\text{yellow}) = \frac{10}{12}$ or $\frac{5}{6}$
7. Drawing a dime or penny from a purse containing quarters and nickels. Impossible, $P(\text{dime or penny}) = 0$
8. Choosing at random a name starting with H from a page in the phone book beginning with Hardy and ending with Huffman. Certain, $P(\text{name starting with H}) = 1$
9. Drawing an S when picking a letter at random from letters in MISSISSIPPI. Probably not, $P(S) = \frac{4}{11}$
10. Drawing a multiple of 10 from a list of numbers starting with 5, counting by fives, through 150. Even, $P(S) = \frac{15}{30}$ or $\frac{1}{2}$

12-2 Lesson Organizer

Objective

- Calculate probability from sample data.

Vocabulary

- Sample

Materials

- Explore: A bag with 2 cubes of color 1, 6 cubes of color 2, 5 cubes of color 3

NCTM Standards

- 1–4, 11

Review

Write each expression as a fraction in lowest terms.

1. 8 out of 10 $\frac{4}{5}$
2. 15 out of 20 $\frac{3}{4}$
3. 50 out of 100 $\frac{1}{2}$
4. 24 out of 30 $\frac{4}{5}$

Available on Daily Transparency 12-2

1 Introduce

Explore

The Point
Students explore samples and predictions by drawing marbles of three different colors from a bag, recording the results, and using the results to determine the probability of picking marbles of each color.

Ongoing Assessment
Be sure students understand that they determine the probabilities in Step 4 by writing the number of times for each color over the total number of trials.

For Groups That Finish Early
If you repeat the process for 20 more trials, do you think the results will be same?

Answers for Explore
1–6. Answers may vary.

12-2 Making Predictions

You'll Learn ...

- to calculate probability from sample data

... How It's Used

Insurance sellers use probability from samples to determine how much to charge for a particular type of insurance.

Vocabulary

sample

▶ **Lesson Link** In the last lesson, you determined probability by counting the possible outcomes. Now you'll determine probability from data based on real-world situations. ◀

Explore Making Predictions

Gaze Into the Crystal Bag

Materials: A bag with 2 cubes of color 1, 6 cubes of color 2, 5 cubes of color 3

1. Choose a partner, and record what colors you are using for color 1, color 2, and color 3. Give your bag to another set of partners and ask them to remove three cubes from the bag. They should not tell you or show you which three have been removed.
2. Without looking in the bag, remove a cube at random and record what color it is. Put the cube back in the bag.

3. Repeat Step 2 until you have drawn from the bag 20 times.
4. Based on your data, determine the following probabilities:
   - **a.** P(drawing a color 1 cube)
   - **b.** P(drawing a color 2 cube)
   - **c.** P(drawing a color 3 cube)
5. Guess which three cubes were removed by the other students. After you have guessed, look inside the bag and check your answer.
6. Explain how you determined your guess in Step 5. Was your guess accurate? Why or why not?

Learn Making Predictions

Sometimes it is difficult to calculate the probability of an event because you don't know all the possible outcomes or you don't know how likely each outcome is. In these situations, you can sometimes collect data and predict the probability based on the data.

MEETING INDIVIDUAL NEEDS

Resources

- 12-2 Practice
- 12-2 Reteaching
- 12-2 Problem Solving
- 12-2 Enrichment
- 12-2 Daily Transparency
  - Problem of the Day
  - Review
  - Quick Quiz
- Technology Master 61
- *Wide World of Mathematics* Middle School: Hurricane Prediction

Learning Modalities

Verbal Have students describe how they could use past weather records to find the probability of snow occurring during a given month.

Individual Students may find that doing probability experiments and activities will help them develop more confidence in their intuitive feelings about probability and the ways they think about uncertainty in their world.

Challenge

Explain to students that the *complement* of an event is the probability that the event will not occur. If the probability that an event will occur is p, then the complement of that event is $1 - p$. Using Exercises 13–14, on page 633, have students find the probability of a tornado *not* occurring in May and the probability that a tornado does *not* occur during tornado season. $\frac{645}{826} \approx 0.78$, $\frac{157}{826} \approx 0.19$
Have students write and answer three problems dealing with finding the complement of an event.

A **sample** is a set of data that can be used to predict how a particular situation might happen. You can use sample data to determine probability.

Examples

1 At Paolo's Pizzeria, the manager wanted to know what kind of pizza slices customers order during the lunch hour. He collected the following data during one lunch shift. Based on this data, what is the probability that a lunch customer will order a cheese slice?

Pizza	Slices Ordered
Pepperoni	31
Veggie	13
Combination	10
Cheese	7

There were 61 slices ordered. Of the 61 slices, 7 were cheese. The manager can expect $\frac{7}{61}$ of the customers to order cheese.

2 Which of the three spinners was most likely the spinner that produced the sample data?

Data: red, blue, blue, red, red, red, red, red, red, blue

#1 #2 #3

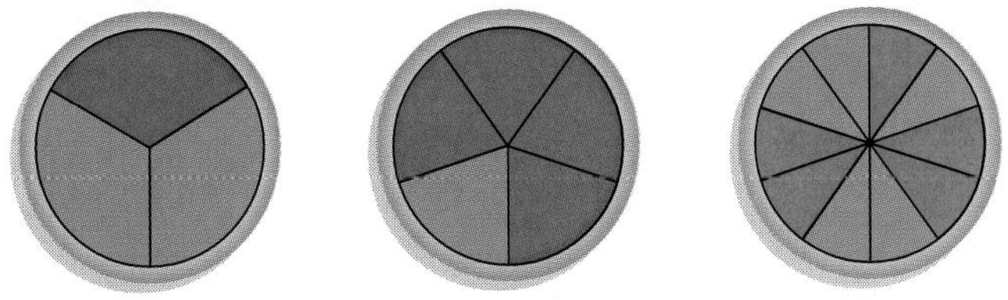

Red happened 7 out of 10 times, or $\frac{7}{10}$ of the time. On spinner #1, $\frac{1}{3}$ of the spinner is red. On spinner #2, $\frac{4}{5}$ are red. On spinner #3, $\frac{5}{10}$ are red. The fraction closest to $\frac{7}{10}$ is $\frac{4}{5}$. So, spinner #2 is the most likely spinner.

Remember

When comparing fractions, you can determine which fraction is larger by rewriting both as equal fractions with common denominators.

[Page 308]

Try It

Using Example 1, what are the chances a customer orders the following:

a. A veggie slice? $\frac{13}{61}$ **b.** A slice that's not a combination slice? $\frac{51}{61}$

Check Your Understanding

1. Is the probability calculated from sample data an estimate? Explain.

2. Why would it be a good idea to collect as large a set of sample data as possible before determining the probability of an event?

MATH EVERY DAY

Problem of the Day

Fold a piece of paper in half and then in half again. Punch holes as shown. Make a sketch of what the paper will look like when it is unfolded.

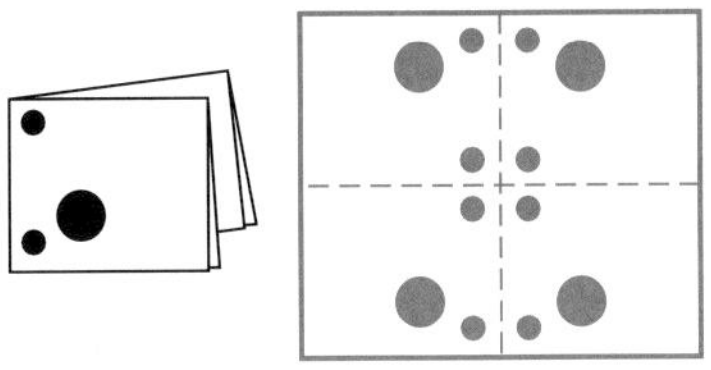

Available on Daily Transparency 12-2

An Extension is provided in the transparency package.

Fact of the Day

In August 1992, Andrew, the costliest hurricane to hit the United States, damaged about $20,000,000,000 worth of property.

Estimation

Estimate each sum.

1. 27 + 93 120
2. 81 + 81 160
3. 712 + 989 1700
4. 901 + 689 1600

2 Teach

Learn

Alternate Examples

1. The manager of a T-shirt shop recorded the sizes of shirts that were sold on one day. Based on this data, what is the probability that a customer will buy a large T-shirt?

T-shirt Size	Number Sold
Small	12
Medium	18
Large	20

There were 50 shirts sold. Of the 50 shirts, 20 were large. The manager can expect $\frac{20}{50}$ or $\frac{2}{5}$ of the customers to buy large T-shirts.

2. Which of the three spinners was most likely the spinner that produced the sample data?

Data: A, B, A, C, C, B, B, A, A, B, C, A

#1 #2 #3

The letter A resulted 5 out of 12 times, or $\frac{5}{12}$ of the time. On spinner #1, $\frac{1}{2}$ of the spinner is labeled A. On spinner #2, $\frac{3}{4}$ of the spinner is labeled A. On spinner #3, $\frac{1}{6}$ of the spinner is labeled A. The fraction closest to $\frac{5}{12}$ is $\frac{1}{2}$. So, spinner #1 is the most likely spinner.

3 Practice and Assess

Check

Answers for Check Your Understanding

1. Yes; Sample data represent only a partial number of outcomes.
2. When estimating probabilities, accuracy increases as the amount of data increases.

12-2 Exercises and Applications

Assignment Guide

- **Basic**
  1–13, 18–22 evens
- **Average**
  1, 3, 5–15, 18–22 evens
- **Enriched**
  1, 3, 5–7, 8–12 evens, 13–17, 19–21 odds

Exercise Notes

Exercise 1

Science A tsunami, sometimes called a tidal wave, is a fast-moving ocean wave caused by underwater earthquakes or volcanic eruptions. They occur mostly in the Pacific Ocean and often take a high toll in lives in affected coastal areas.

Exercise 12

Test Prep If students picked an answer other than D, they did not realize that D occurred 0 times, so $P(D) = 0$.

12-2 Exercises and Applications

Practice and Apply

Getting Started **Tell if you need sample data to determine the probability of each situation happening.**

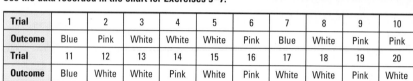

1. A tsunami striking Hawaii next year Yes

2. Meeting a person from Peru tomorrow Yes

3. Rolling a 2 on a number cube No

4. Choosing a red crayon out of a box No

Use the data recorded in the chart for Exercises 5–7.

Trial	1	2	3	4	5	6	7	8	9	10
Outcome	Blue	Pink	White	White	White	Pink	Blue	White	Pink	Pink
Trial	11	12	13	14	15	16	17	18	19	20
Outcome	Blue	White	White	Pink	White	Pink	White	White	Pink	White

5. How many different outcomes were there? 3

6. How many outcomes were blue? 3

7. What is the probability of the outcome being pink or white? $\frac{17}{20}$

Estimation **Ms. Shaw's 6th-grade class conducted an in-class survey.**

Question	Result
Are you male or female?	15 female, 17 male
Do you have an emergency kit at home?	21 yes, 11 no
Is the day of your birth an odd or even number?	20 even, 12 odd
Have you experienced a flood?	27 no, 5 yes

If there are 102 6th graders in the school, use the survey results to estimate the number of 6th graders in the school who:

8. Are girls 48

9. Have an emergency kit at home 67

10. Have an even birth date 64

11. Have experienced a flood 16

12. **Test Prep** The following data comes from a spinner: A, C, E, B, A, B, C, E, B, A, A. Based on the data, which of the following has the lowest probability? D

Ⓐ $P(A)$ Ⓑ $P(B)$ Ⓒ $P(C)$ Ⓓ $P(D)$

PRACTICE 12-2

Reteaching

Activity

Materials: Number cubes

- Work in groups of three or four.
- When a number cube is rolled, the probability for each number occurring is $\frac{1}{6}$.
- Have each person roll a number cube 25 times.
- Combine the results for all the people in the group.
- Compare the actual results to the probability for each number and see if the results are close to $\frac{1}{6}$ for each number.

PRACTICE

Name ______________________

Practice 12-2

Making Predictions

Use the data recorded in the chart for Exercises 1–3.

Trial	1	2	3	4	5	6	7	8
Outcome	square	circle	square	triangle	circle	square	square	circle

1. How many different outcomes were there? 3

2. How many times was the outcome a circle? 3

3. What is the probability of the outcome being a square? $\frac{1}{2}$

Use the data recorded in the chart for Exercises 4–6.

Trial	1	2	3	4	5	6	7	8
Outcome	blue	yellow	red	blue	green	red	yellow	blue

Trial	9	10	11	12	13	14	15
Outcome	blue	green	red	blue	blue	green	red

4. How many different outcomes were there? 4

5. How many times was the outcome red? 4

6. What is the probability of the outcome being yellow or green? $\frac{1}{3}$

One day, 40 members who came to an athletic club were asked to complete a survey.

Question	Result
Are you male or female?	28 male, 12 female
Are you under 26 years old?	24 yes, 16 no
Do you use weight machines?	32 yes, 8 no
Do you participate in aerobics classes?	14 yes, 26 no

If the athletic club has 870 members, use the survey results to estimate the number of members who:

7. are male ≈ 609

8. are 26 or older ≈ 348

9. use weight machines ≈ 696

10. take aerobics classes ≈ 305

RETEACHING

Name ______________________

Alternative Lesson 12-2

Making Predictions

Sometimes it is difficult to calculate the probability of an event because you don't know all the possible outcomes or you don't know how likely each outcome is. In these situations, you can sometimes collect data and predict the probability based on the data.

A **sample** is a set of data that can be used to predict how a particular situation might happen. You can use sample data to determine probability.

Example

The school cafeteria manager collected data to see what kind of snacks were chosen most often by the students. Based on this data, what is the probability that students will choose pretzels as a part of their lunch?

Type of snack	Number ordered
Potato	100
Corn	40
Tortilla	80
Cheese puffs	40
Barbecue	60
Pretzels	80

There were 400 bags of snacks chosen. Of the 400 bags, 80 bags were pretzels. So, the manager can expect $\frac{80}{400}$, or $\frac{1}{5}$, of the students to order pretzels.

Try It At Swann's Soda Shop, 7 students ordered vanilla shakes, 14 ordered chocolate shakes, and 9 ordered strawberry shakes.

a. How many students ordered shakes? 30 students.

b. How many ordered vanilla shakes? 7 students.

c. What is the probability the next student will order a vanilla shake? $\frac{7}{30}$

d. What is the probability the next student will *not* order a vanilla shake? $\frac{23}{30}$

Suppose you place cards showing the letters G A M E S into a sack.

e. How many cards are there? 5 cards.

f. How many cards show letters that are vowels? 2 cards.

g. What is the probability that, without looking, a student will draw a card showing a vowel? $\frac{2}{5}$

Problem Solving and Reasoning

Critical Thinking The chart shows the average number of tornadoes in the United States per month over 10 years.

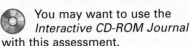

Month	Tornadoes	Month	Tornadoes	Month	Tornadoes	Month	Tornadoes
January	15	April	112	July	90	October	25
February	29	May	181	August	62	November	26
March	55	June	169	September	42	December	20

13. In what month is the probability of a tornado the greatest? If a tornado occurs, what is the probability that it occurs during that month? May; $\frac{181}{826} \approx 0.22$

14. Tornado season is from March through August. If a tornado occurs, what is the probability that it occurs during tornado season? $\frac{669}{826} \approx 0.81$

Critical Thinking Hurricane season in the United States is from June 1 to November 30. In an average season, there are ten tropical storms. Six are expected to reach hurricane strength and two of these are likely to strike the U.S. coast.

15. GPS Is the probability that a tropical storm will turn into a hurricane more than 50%? Yes

16. If a hurricane happens, what is the probability that the hurricane will hit the U.S. coast? $\frac{1}{3}$

17. In 1995, there were 19 tropical storms, of which 11 reached hurricane strength. Why was 1995 considered an unusual year?

Mixed Review

Tell which solid of each pair has the greater surface area. *[Lesson 11-3]*

18.

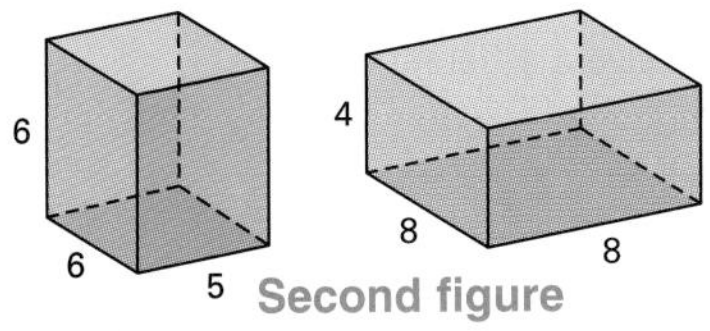

Second figure

19.

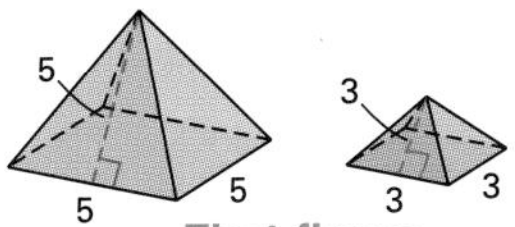

First figure

Find the surface area. Use 3.14 for π. *[Lesson 11-4]*

20.

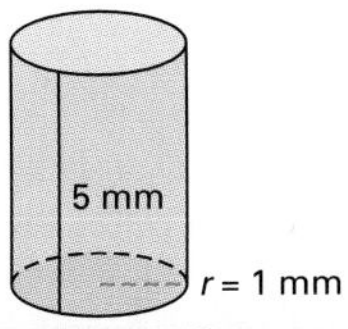

37.68 mm^2

21.

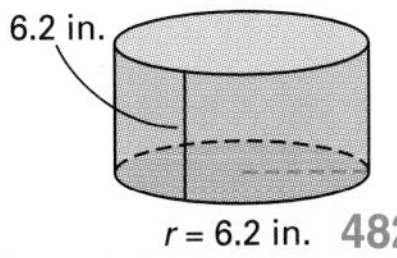

482.8 in^2

22.

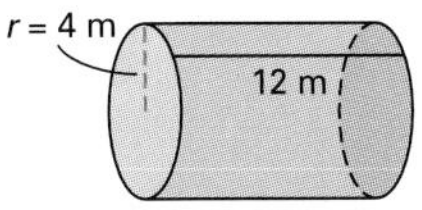

401.92 m^2

PROBLEM SOLVING 12-2

Exercise Notes

Exercise 13

Science Tornadoes occur worldwide, especially in the United States and Australia.

Exercise Answers

17. The number of tropical storms and the number of tropical storms that reached hurricane strength were considerably above average.

Alternate Assessment

You may want to use the *Interactive CD-ROM Journal* with this assessment.

Journal Have students describe how the owner of a store could use the concepts in this lesson to order inventory items. Have them include specific items and examples of numbers that might be reasonable.

Quick Quiz

The following chart shows the number of traffic accidents occurring on each day of the week over a period of one year.

Sun	M	T	W	Th	F	Sat
3	8	2	1	2	10	5

1. On what day is the probability of an accident highest? What is the probability? Friday; $\frac{10}{31}$
2. What is the probability of an accident occurring on Saturday or Sunday? $\frac{8}{31}$

Available on Daily Transparency 12-2

PROBLEM SOLVING

Name ______________________

Guided Problem Solving 12-2

GPS PROBLEM 15, STUDENT PAGE 633

Hurricane season in the United States is from June 1 to November 30. In an average season, there are ten tropical storms. Six are expected to reach hurricane strength and two of these are likely to strike the U.S. coast.

Is the probability that a tropical storm will turn into a hurricane more than 50%?

— Understand —

1. How many tropical storms are there in an average season? 10 storms.
2. How many of the tropical storms are expected to reach hurricane strength in an average season? 6 storms.

— Plan —

3. Describe the ratio you will use to show the probability that a tropical storm will turn into a hurricane. Number of tropical storms expected to reach hurricane strength: Number of tropical storms.
4. What will you compare the ratio to? The probability of 50%.

— Solve —

5. Find the probability that a tropical storm will turn into a hurricane. $\frac{6}{10}$ or $\frac{3}{5}$
6. Write the probability as a percent. 60%
7. Is the percentage less than, equal to, or greater than 50%? Greater than.

— Look Back —

8. How could you answer the question without changing the probability to a percent? 50% is equal to $\frac{1}{2}$. The probability is $\frac{3}{5}$. Since $\frac{3}{5} > \frac{1}{2}$, the probability of $\frac{3}{5}$ is greater than 50%.

SOLVE ANOTHER PROBLEM

Suppose 20 tropical storms are predicted. Twelve are expected to reach hurricane strength. What percentage will probably *not* become hurricanes? 40%

ENRICHMENT

Name ______________________

Extend Your Thinking 12-2

Decision Making

Sample size may influence the predictions you make.

Suppose your class is asked to choose the type of music to play during the noon hour over the PA system. As leader of the group, you appoint Jeff and Carla to survey students in the middle school to find what type of music they prefer.

Jeff surveyed 4 students. Of these students, 3 out of 4 students prefer country music and 1 student prefers rock music. So, Jeff reported: $P(\text{country music}) = \frac{3}{4}$ and $P(\text{rock music}) = \frac{1}{4}$.

Carla surveyed 35 students. Of these students, 10 students choose country music, 13 choose rock, 9 choose rhythm and blues, and 3 choose jazz. So Carla reported: $P(\text{country music}) = \frac{2}{7}$, $P(\text{rock music}) = \frac{13}{35}$, $P(\text{rhythm and blues}) = \frac{9}{35}$, and $P(\text{jazz}) = \frac{3}{35}$.

1. Which survey do you think is a more accurate reflection of the preferences of students in your school? Explain. Possible answer: Carla's survey, because the sample size is larger, its probability is likely to be closer to the actual probability.
2. What could you do to ensure a more accurate survey? Possible answer: Survey more students; make sure survey includes students from different grades, different classes, different groups within the school.
3. Which type of music would you recommend to be played during the lunch hour? Explain. Possible answer: A combination of rock, country, and rhythm and blues since Carla's survey indicates a strong preference for each of these musical categories.
4. Suppose the principal authorizes you to buy 100 CDs. About how many of each type would you buy based on Carla's survey? Possible answer: About 29 country, 37 rock, 26 rhythm and blues, and 8 jazz.

Technology

Using a Spreadsheet • Using Random Numbers

The Point

Students use the random number generator feature of the spreadsheet to simulate rolling two number cubes.

Materials

Spreadsheet software

Resources

Interactive CD-ROM Spreadsheet/Grapher Tool

About the Page

- The random number function generates a number greater than or equal to 0 but less than 1. This way, any desired set of numbers may be generated, using an appropriate formula.
- The ROUND function is used to eliminate the decimal portion of the number. For the number cubes, only the natural numbers 1–6 are needed. Some spreadsheets might use INT instead of ROUND.

Ask ...

- Why is there a +1 at the end of the formula? In order to generate numbers from 1–6, otherwise, the numbers generated would be from 0–5.
- There are 36 different possible outcomes when rolling two number cubes. How many ways can a 10 be rolled? What is the probability of rolling a 10? 3 ways; $\frac{3}{36} = \frac{1}{12}$, which is about 8.3%.

Answers for Try It

a. The probability should still be close to 8%.

b. Close to 2.8%.

On Your Own

For the second question, changing the number in front of *RAND changes the range of numbers generated.

Answers for On Your Own

- Spreadsheet; The spreadsheet can generate multiple rolls in a single moment.
- The range of the random numbers generated changes.

TECHNOLOGY

Using a Spreadsheet • Using Random Numbers

Problem: What are the chances of rolling two number cubes and getting a sum of 10?

You can use spreadsheets to quickly generate random data.

1 Enter the information into the spreadsheet as shown.

	A	B	C
1	Roll 1	Roll 2	Sum
2			

2 In cell A2, enter =ROUND((5*RAND(),0)+1). **Copy this formula into cell B2. Then copy the formula down to row 101. This will generate 100 random numbers from 1 to 6. (Your data may look different from the data shown here.)**

	A	B	C
1	Roll 1	Roll 2	Sum
2	3	5	
3	4	6	
4	6	3	
5	1	2	
6	2	1	
7	2	4	
8	3	5	
9	5	2	

3 In cell C2, enter the formula =(A2+B2). **Copy the formula down to row 101.**

4 Count the number of times 10 appears as the sum. This can easily be expressed as a ratio to 100, and as a percent.

Solution: Since the data is random, every spreadsheet can give a different answer. The answers should be close to 8%.

TRY IT

a. Repeat the experiment by recopying the formulas in row 2 down to row 101. How does your probability the second time compare to the first time?

b. Use the steps above to find the chances of getting a sum of 12.

ON YOUR OWN

- Can you roll two number cubes 100 times and record the results more quickly by hand or with a spreadsheet? Explain.
- Change the number in front of the "*RAND" to a different number, and copy the formula to row 101. How does this change the data?

634

Geometric Models of Probability

12-3

▶ Lesson Link You know how to determine probability from lists and from data. Now you will see how to determine probabilities that involve the areas of figures. ◀

You'll Learn ...

■ to calculate probability from geometric models

... How It's Used

The Coast Guard uses probability when describing the chances of locating a particular ship lost at sea.

Explore | Geometric Models

Materials: Paper clips

Betting on a Blizzard

The spinners below represent models of the chances of a blizzard occurring.

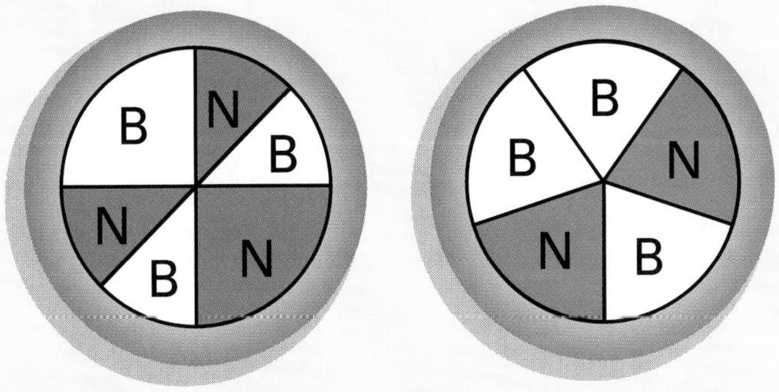

B = blizzard occurs **N = no blizzard occurs**

1. Trace each of the spinners onto a sheet of paper.
2. Unbend the end of a paper clip. Place the other end over the center of a spinner, and place your pencil point on the center of the spinner. Use the paper clip as the spinner pointer.
3. For each spinner, spin the pointer 20 times. Record the number of times a blizzard occurs, and the number of times it doesn't.
4. Which spinner is the least likely to have a blizzard? Explain.
5. Could you have determined which spinner would be most likely to have a blizzard without actually spinning the pointers? Explain.
6. Can two different spinners have the same chances of having a blizzard?

12-3 Lesson Organizer

Objective

- Calculate probability from geometric models.

Materials

- Explore: Paper clips

NCTM Standards

- 1–4, 11

▶ Review

Find the area of each circle.

1.

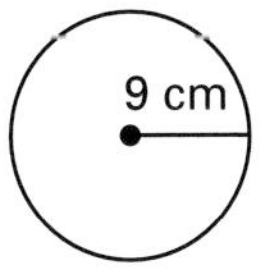

254.34 cm²

2.

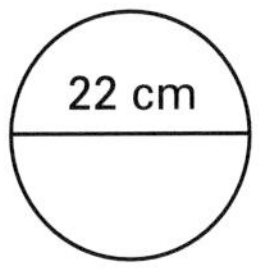

379.94 cm²

Available on Daily Transparency 12-3

1 Introduce

Explore

The Point

Students use spinners to find probabilities and then explore how to find the probabilities without actually spinning.

Ongoing Assessment

Check that students are recording the results for each spinner separately.

Answers for Explore

1–3. Answers may vary.

4. First spinner; It has less blizzard area.
5. Yes; The second spinner had more blizzard area.
6. Yes; If two spinners have the same amount of blizzard area, the chances will be the same.

MEETING INDIVIDUAL NEEDS

Resources

- **12-3** Practice
- **12-3** Reteaching
- **12-3** Problem Solving
- **12-3** Enrichment
- **12-3** Daily Transparency
  - Problem of the Day
  - Review
  - Quick Quiz
- Teaching Tool Transparencies 2, 3
- Lesson Enhancement Transparency 59
- Technology Master 62
- Chapter 12 Project Master

Learning Modalities

Visual Have students make a bulletin board display of various dart boards and label each dart board with the probability of hitting each area.

Kinesthetic Have students make the game board shown in Example 2 on page 636. Then have them toss a coin at least 100 times to see if the result is close to the probability given for the example.

Challenge

Draw the following diagram of a swimming pool located in a rectangular yard. Each curve is a semicircle. Have students find the probability that a parachutist landing somewhere in the yard will land in the pool. $\frac{157}{400}$

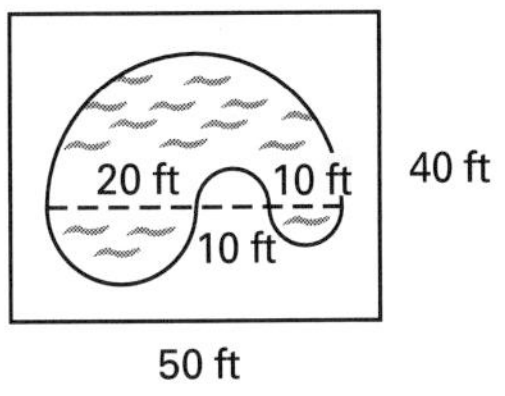

2 Teach

Learn

You may wish to use Lesson Enhancement Transparency 59 with **Examples** and **Try It**.

Alternate Examples

1. A glass window is made up of colored panes and clear panes. If a golf ball accidentally hits the window, what is the probability it will hit a colored pane? Colored panes are shown as shaded squares.

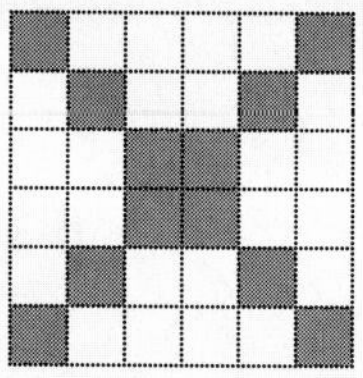

The total area is 36 square units. The shaded area is 12 square units.

The probability that the golf ball will hit the colored glass is $\frac{12}{36}$ or $\frac{1}{3}$.

2. If a number cube is dropped onto the game board at random, what is the probability that it will land in the circle?

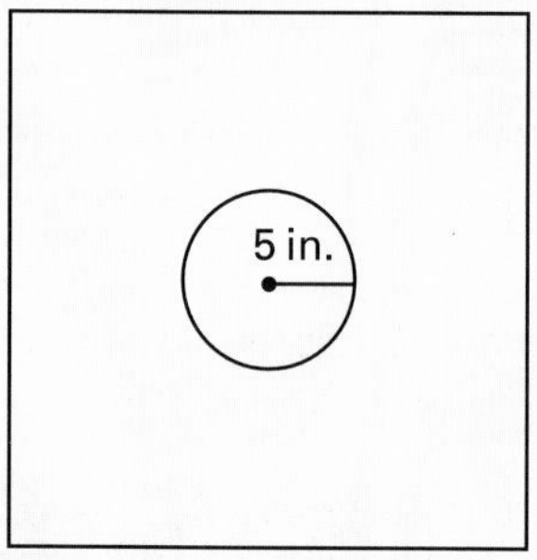

$P(\text{land in circle})$

$= \frac{\text{area of circle}}{\text{area of square}}$

$= \frac{3.14 \times 5 \times 5}{30 \times 30}$

$= \frac{78.5}{900} \approx 0.09$ or 9%

The probability that the number cube will land in the circle is approximately 9%.

▶ Science Link

Tornadoes are measured using the Fujita-Pearson Tornado Intensity Scale. An F0 tornado has a wind speed of 72 mi/hr and causes "light" damage. An F5 tornado has a wind speed of over 260 mi/hr and causes "unbelievable" damage.

Remember

The area of a circle is $\pi \times \text{radius}^2$. [Page 252]

Learn Geometric Models of Probability

Some events and outcomes are not single items that can be counted. For situations such as carnival games and dart boards, the probability of an event may depend upon the areas of portions of a figure. If you can determine each area within the figure, you can determine the probability of the situation.

Examples

1 A tornado has a very irregular path. When the funnel touches the ground, it might go straight, double back, or hop over places. If a tornado touches down in the area pictured, what is the probability that it will touch down in the shaded area?

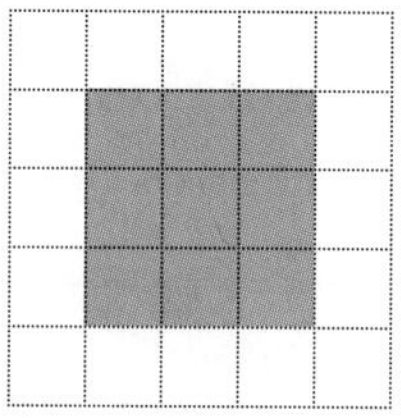

The total area is 25 square units. The shaded area is 9 square units.

The probability that the tornado will hit the shaded region is $\frac{9}{25}$.

2 If a coin is tossed onto the carnival game board at random, what is the probability that it will land in the circle?

$P(\text{land in circle}) = \frac{\text{area of circle}}{\text{area of rectangle}}$

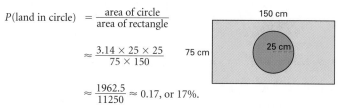

$\approx \frac{3.14 \times 25 \times 25}{75 \times 150}$

$\approx \frac{1962.5}{11250} \approx 0.17$, or 17%.

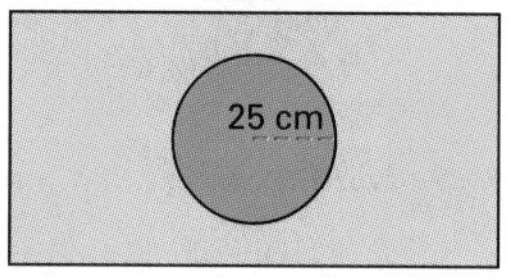

The probability that the coin will land in the circle is approximately 17%.

Try It

Find the probability of tossing a dart at the dart board and hitting the shaded region. 50%

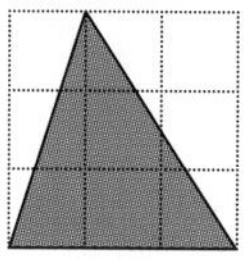

MATH EVERY DAY

▶ Problem of the Day

You throw a dart at each target. For which targets is the probability of hitting the shaded area equal to the probability of hitting the unshaded area?

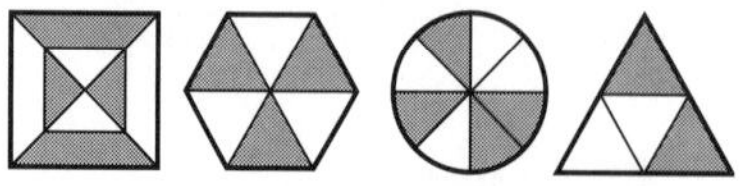

All of the targets. The probability is $\frac{1}{2}$ for all the targets.

Available on Daily Transparency 12-3

An Extension is provided in the transparency package.

Fact of the Day

A tornado can have winds up to 300 miles per hour. More than 1300 tornadoes hit the United States in 1992, killing 39 people.

Mental Math

Do these mentally.

1. $\frac{1}{2}$ of 20 10
2. $\frac{1}{3}$ of 24 8
3. $\frac{1}{4}$ of 100 25
4. $\frac{1}{5}$ of 50 10

Assignment Guide

- **Basic**
  1–9, 11, 17–21
- **Average**
  1–11, 13, 17–21
- **Enriched**
  4–13, 14–20 evens

Check Your Understanding

1. When calculating the probability of a geometric model, why is it important to know how to calculate the areas of figures?
2. One dart board has a bull's-eye of 20 square centimeters. Another dart board of the same size has two bull's-eyes, each with an area of 10 square centimeters. Which dart board would you choose to play? Why?

12-3 Exercises and Applications

Practice and Apply

Getting Started **Use the figure shown for Exercises 1–3.**

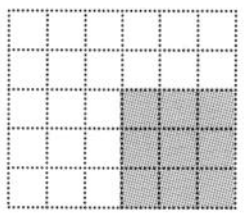

1. Find the area of the shaded square. 9 square units
2. Find the area of the rectangle. 30 square units
3. Find the probability that a token thrown at random will land on the shaded square. 30%

Suppose you drop a token on each shape in Exercises 4–7. Find the probability of the token landing on the shaded area. Write your answer as a percent.

4. 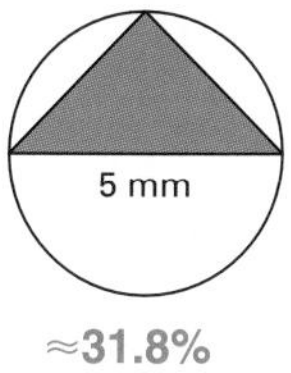

≈31.8%

5. 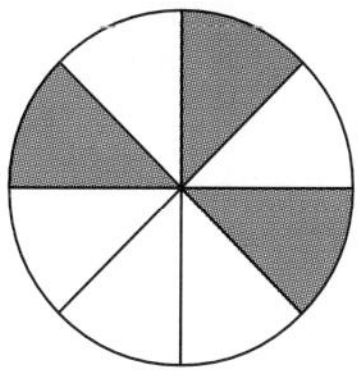
37.5%

6. 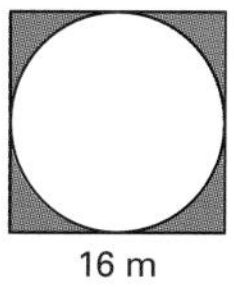

≈21.5%

7. 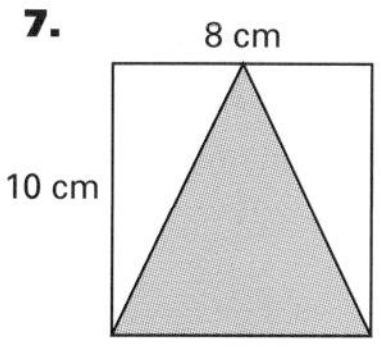

50%

8. **Science** Hurricanes blow in a spiral around a circular center known as the "eye." If a storm covers a circular area 400 miles wide and its eye is 20 miles wide, what is the probability of an object in a hurricane being in the eye of the hurricane? About 0.25%

GPS

9. **Test Prep** A parachutist is scheduled to land somewhere in the open field shown. Which is the best estimate of the probability that she will land within the grassy area? A

Ⓐ $\frac{1}{4}$ Ⓑ $\frac{1}{2}$ Ⓒ $\frac{3}{4}$

PRACTICE 12-3

3 Practice and Assess

Check

Answers for Check Your Understanding

1. Areas are used to determine the probabilities.
2. Possible answer: Either; The probability of hitting the bull's-eye is the same for both boards.

Exercise Notes

Exercises 6–7

Error Prevention If students have difficulty with these exercises, they may need to review earlier lessons on finding areas of geometric figures.

Exercise 8

Science The direction of the spiral of a hurricane is clockwise in the Southern Hemisphere and counterclockwise in the Northern Hemisphere. This phenomenon is called the Coriolis effect.

PRACTICE

Name ____________________

Practice 12-3

Geometric Models of Probability

Suppose you drop a token on each shape in Exercises 1–16. Find the probability of the token landing on the shaded area.

1. $\frac{14}{27}$ 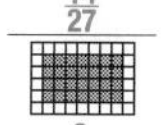
2. $\frac{1}{2}$ 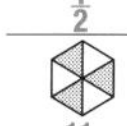
3. $\frac{4}{7}$ 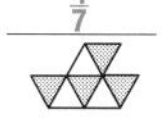
4. $\frac{1}{5}$ 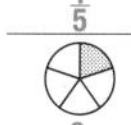
5. $\frac{3}{4}$ 
6. $\frac{11}{12}$ 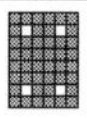
7. ≈ 0.54 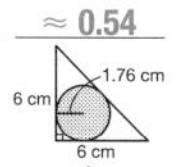

8. $\frac{3}{5}$ 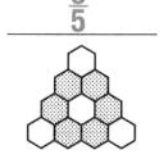
9. $\frac{5}{7}$ 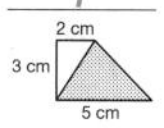

10. $\frac{1}{8}$ 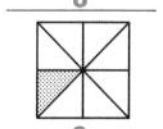
11. $\frac{1}{4}$ 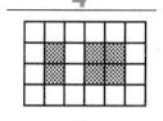
12. $\frac{4}{9}$ 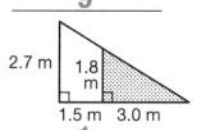

13. ≈ 0.79 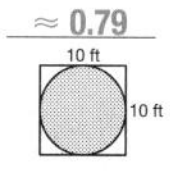

14. $\frac{2}{3}$ 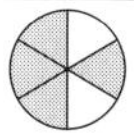
15. $\frac{3}{4}$ 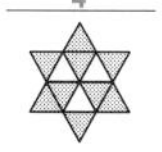
16. $\frac{1}{2}$ 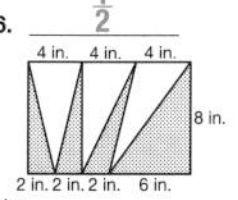

17. **Fine Arts** In 1934, Ben Nicholson used carved white boards to create a work of art resembling the drawing at the right. Suppose a speck of dust lands randomly on this work of art.

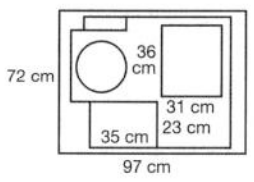

a. What is the probability that it lands in one of the smaller labeled rectangles?
About 0.275

b. The circle has a diameter of about 26 cm. What is the probability that the dust speck lands in the circle?
About 0.076

18. If you throw 500 darts at the hexagonal dart board shown, how many should you expect to land in the shaded area?
About 125 darts

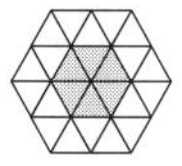

RETEACHING

Name ____________________

Alternative Lesson 12-3

Geometric Models of Probability

Some events and outcomes are not always single items that can be counted. For situations such as carnival games and dart boards, the probability of an event happening depends upon the areas of portions of a figure. If you can determine each area within the figure, you can determine the probability of the situation.

Example

A carnival game has a dart board with a pattern like the one at the right. What is the probability of hitting a shaded square?

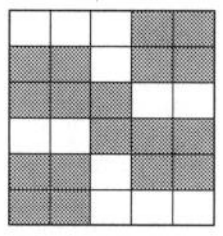

There are 30 square units in the rectangle. 18 of them are shaded. The probability of hitting a shaded square is $\frac{18}{30}$ or $\frac{3}{5}$.

Try It Use the game board to find each probability.

R	W	O	D
D	O	W	O
D	R	R	W
W	R	D	R

a. What is the probability of a marker landing on the letter *W*? $\frac{4}{16}$ or $\frac{1}{4}$

b. What is the probability of a marker landing on the letter *O*? $\frac{3}{16}$

c. What is the probability of a marker landing on the letter *R*? $\frac{5}{16}$

d. What is the probability of a marker landing on the letter *D*? $\frac{4}{16}$ or $\frac{1}{4}$

Suppose you drop a token on each shape. Find the probability of the token landing on the shaded area.

e. 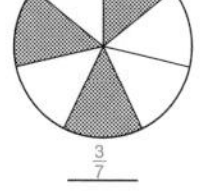
$\frac{3}{7}$

f. 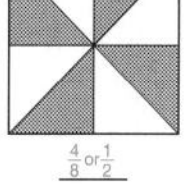
$\frac{4}{8}$ or $\frac{1}{2}$

g. 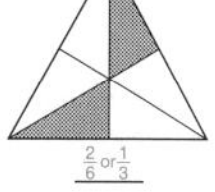
$\frac{2}{6}$ or $\frac{1}{3}$

A skydiver jumps out of a plane above an area represented by the map.

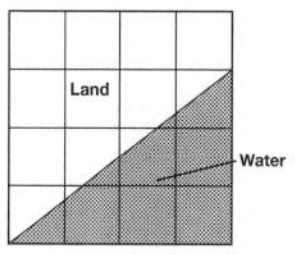

h. What is the probability the skydiver will land in water? $\frac{6}{16} = \frac{3}{8}$

i. What is the probability the skydiver will land on land? $\frac{10}{16} = \frac{5}{8}$

Reteaching

Activity

Materials: Graph paper

- Work in groups of three or four.
- Draw a rectangle on graph paper.
- Inside the rectangle color some of the squares to form a geometric pattern.
- Assume the pattern represents a game board on which a coin is dropped.
- Find the probability of the coin landing on one of the colored squares. Answers may vary.

Exercise Notes

■ Exercise 11

Problem-Solving Tip You may wish to use Teaching Tool Transparencies 2 and 3: Guided Problem Solving, pages 1–2.

Project Progress

You may want to have students use Chapter 12 Project Master.

Exercise Answers

11. 84 squares

12. Probability stays the same; The shaded area and the total area are proportional to the original areas.

13. Answers may vary.

14. 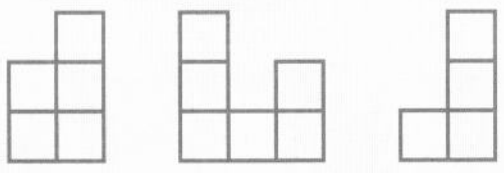

Front Side Top

15. 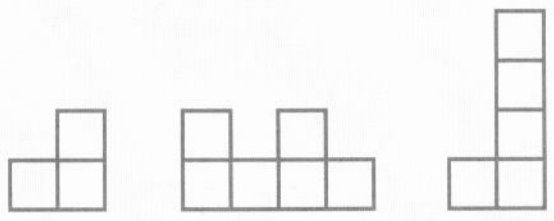

Front Side Top

16. 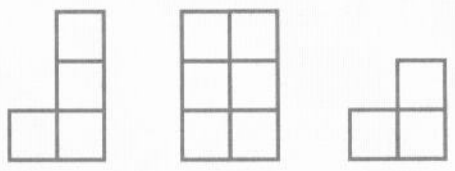

Front Side Top

17. 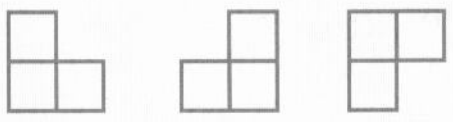

Front Side Top

Alternate Assessment

Interview Using a spinner with different colors, have students explain how to find the probability of landing on each color.

► Quick Quiz

What is the probability that a coin will land on the shaded area if it is randomly dropped?

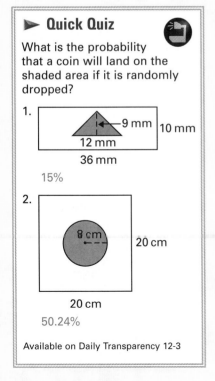

1. 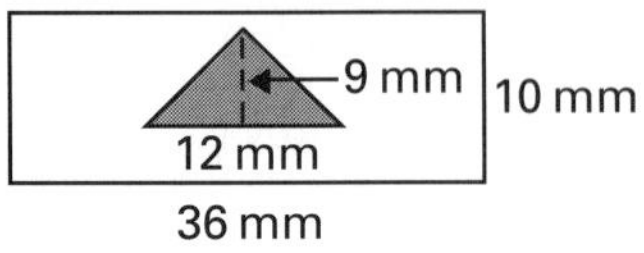

15%

2. 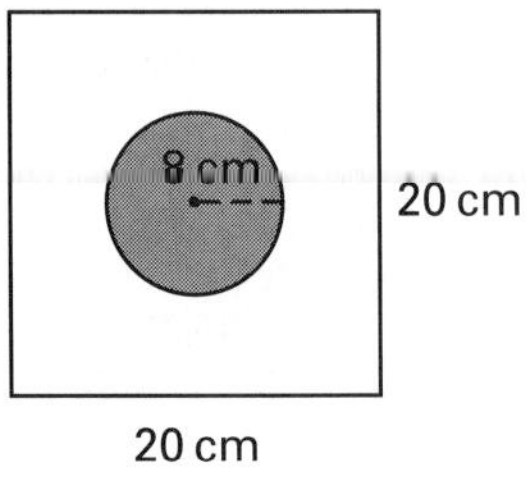

50.24%

Available on Daily Transparency 12-3

10. Chance If you throw 200 darts at the dart board shown, how many should you expect to land in the shaded area? 100

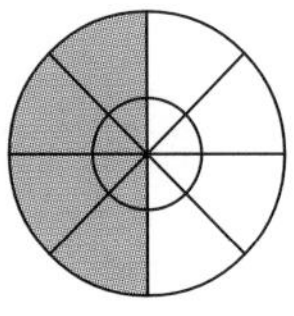

Problem Solving and Reasoning

11. Choose a Strategy On Jerome's game board, the probability of a coin randomly landing on a blue square is $\frac{1}{4}$, on a green square is $\frac{1}{3}$, and on a red square is $\frac{3}{14}$. What is the smallest number of squares that could be on Jerome's board?

12. Communicate In a geometric model of probability, if the entire model is reduced in size, what happens to the probability of randomly landing on the shaded area? Explain.

13. Journal Draw a dart board so that the probability of hitting the bull's-eye is $\frac{2}{3}$. Explain your drawing.

Problem Solving STRATEGIES

- Look for a Pattern
- Make an Organized List
- Make a Table
- Guess and Check
- Work Backward
- Use Logical Reasoning
- Draw a Diagram
- Solve a Simpler Problem

Mixed Review

Draw front, side, and top views for each figure. There are no hidden cubes. *[Lesson 11-5]*

14. 

15. 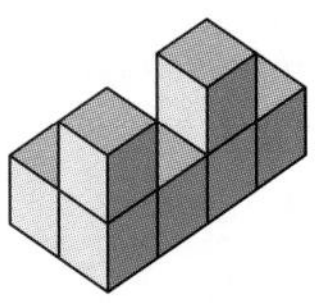

16. 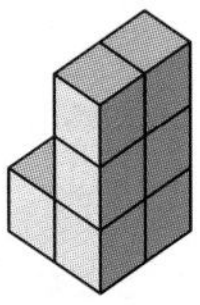

17. 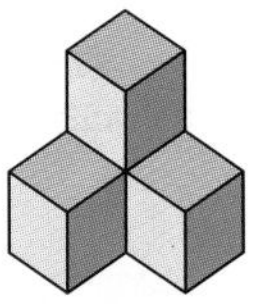

Find the volume. *[Lesson 11-6]*

18. 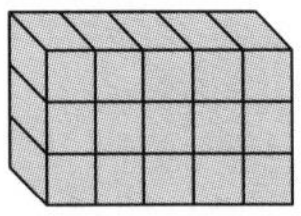

15 units^3

19. 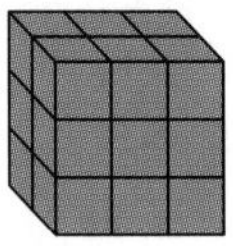

18 units^3

20. 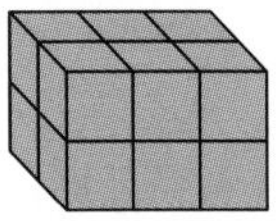

12 units^3

21. 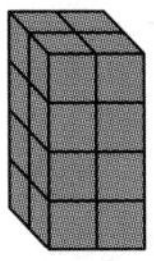

16 units^3

Project Progress

Write instructions for each game at your fun fair. Decide how long it takes to play one round of the game, and how many players and winners there will be for each round. Then figure out the number of prizes you will need to have to keep the game open during the entire fun fair.

Problem Solving
Understand
Plan
Solve
Look Back

PROBLEM SOLVING 12-3

PROBLEM SOLVING

Name ______________________

Guided Problem Solving 12-3

GPS PROBLEM 8, STUDENT PAGE 637

Hurricanes blow in a spiral around a circular center known as the "eye." If a storm covers a circular area 400 miles wide and its eye is 20 miles wide, what is the probability of an object in a hurricane being in the eye of the hurricane?

— Understand —

1. What is the width of the hurricane? 400 mi
2. What is the width of the hurricane's eye? 20 mi
3. What shape is the hurricane? The hurricane's eye? Both are circles.

— Plan —

4. Which ratio will you use to find the probability of an object being in the eye of the hurricane? a

   a. $\frac{\text{Area of the eye}}{\text{Area of the hurricane}}$ b. $\frac{\text{Area of the hurricane}}{\text{Area of the eye}}$

5. Which formula will you use to find the area of the hurricane and of its eye? c

   a. $A = Bh$ b. $A = s^2$ c. $A = \pi r^2$

— Solve —

6. What is the area of the hurricane? 125,600 mi^2
7. What is the area of the eye of the hurricane? 314 mi^2
8. What is the probability of an object being in the eye of the hurricane? $\frac{314}{125{,}600} = \frac{1}{400} = 0.25\%$

— Look Back —

9. How can you Solve a Simpler Problem to see if your answer is reasonable? Possible answer: Use 3 for π and estimate answer. The estimate and the actual answer are same.

SOLVE ANOTHER PROBLEM

What is the probability of an object being in the eye of a hurricane if the hurricane is 600 miles wide and its eye is 40 miles wide? $\frac{1256}{282{,}600} = \frac{1}{225} = 0.4\%$

ENRICHMENT

Name ______________________

Extend Your Thinking 12-3

Visual Thinking

Suppose you drop a token on each shape. Write the probability of the token landing in the shaded area as a percent.

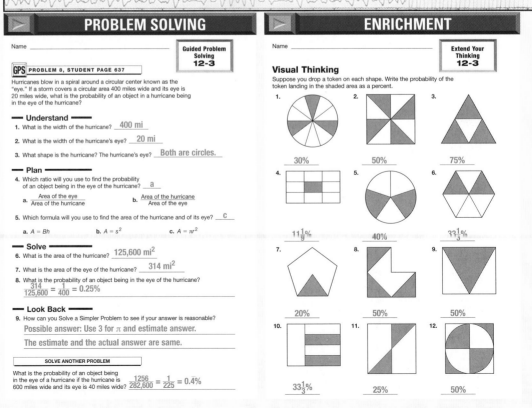

1. 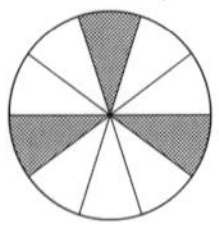
30%

2. 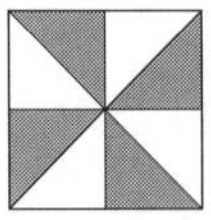
50%

3. 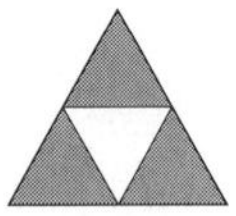
75%

4. 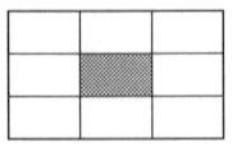
$11\frac{1}{9}\%$

5. 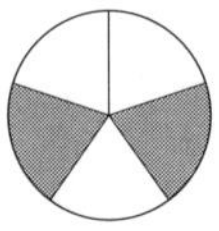
40%

6. 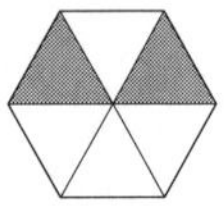
$33\frac{1}{3}\%$

7. 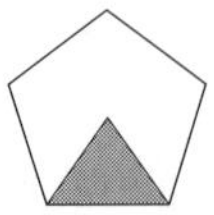
20%

8. 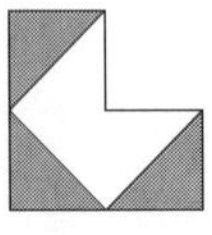
50%

9. 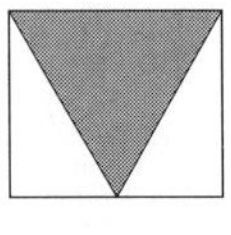
50%

10. 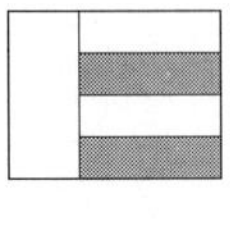
$33\frac{1}{3}\%$

11. 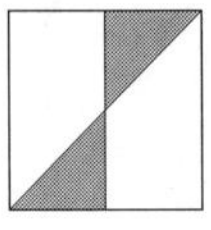
25%

12. 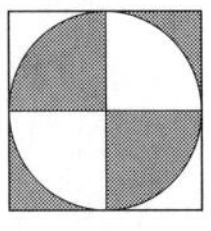
50%

Section 12A Connect

You have calculated probability in different situations. Now you will use these ideas to evaluate an emergency disaster plan.

Force of Nature! ...

The floor plan below details the Northrop City Branch Public Library.

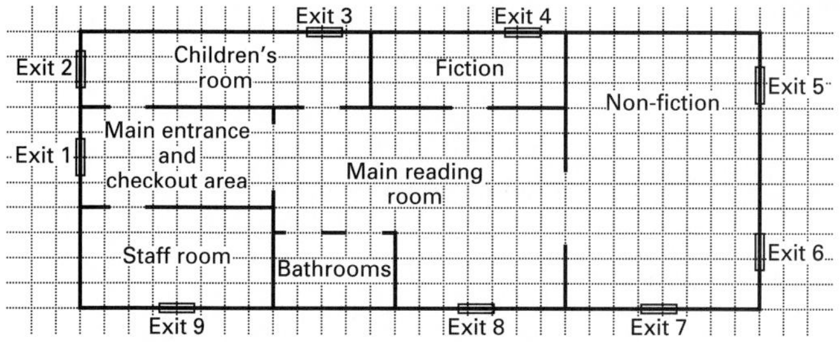

Time to evacuate patrons, in minutes, from 16 fire drills:

4	7	12	6	4	11	5	11
13	17	4	8	5	8	10	9

1. State the probability of each occurring and rank from least likely to most likely. Assume that it is equally likely that a fire will happen on any day.

- **a.** A fire will begin in the main reading room.
- **b.** A fire will begin in the children's room.
- **c.** A patron choosing an exit at random will choose Exit 3.
- **d.** A fire will occur on a Thursday.
- **e.** The patrons will evacuate the building in less than 5 minutes.
- **f.** The patrons will evacuate the building in 15 minutes or more.

2. Identify three different events like the ones above. The chances of the first event should be less than $\frac{1}{2}$, of the second should be exactly $\frac{1}{2}$, and of the third should be more than $\frac{1}{2}$.

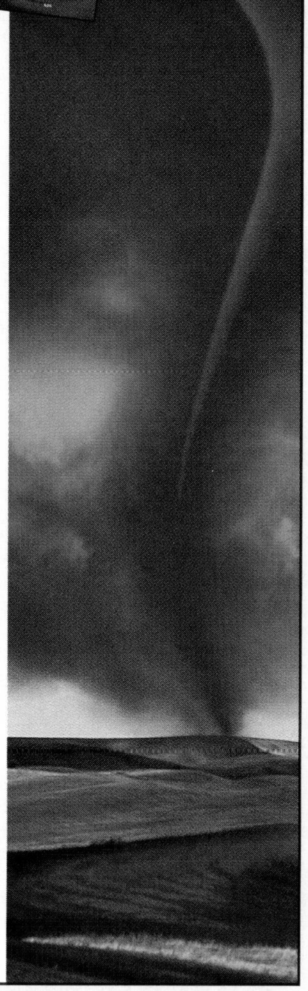

Force of Nature!

The Point

In *Force of Nature!* on page 625, students tested their knowledge about natural disasters. Now, they will evaluate an emergency disaster plan.

Resources

Lesson Enhancement Transparency 60

About the Page

- Review the map of the library with the students. Ask students to compare the various room sizes to help determine the likelihood of a fire occurring in a specific area.
- Count the number of exits with students.
- Ask students how many times patrons evacuated in under 5 minutes. Discuss how this information can be used as part of the ratio that will help them determine the probability.
- Discuss other factors that might influence the probability of a fire starting in a particular place.

Ongoing Assessment

Check that students have determined the correct probabilities and have correctly ordered the events from least likely to most likely.

Extension

Have students use the information given in the table to determine the probability that the library can be evacuated in ten minutes or less.

Answers for Connect

1. a. $\frac{81}{308}$
   b. $\frac{36}{308}$
   c. $\frac{1}{9}$
   d. $\frac{1}{7}$
   e. $\frac{3}{16}$
   f. $\frac{1}{16}$; The probability of each event occurring from least likely to most likely is f, c, b, d, e, a.
2. Answers may vary.

12A Review

Section 12A Review

A number cube is rolled. Find the probability of each event.

1. $P(1)$ $\frac{1}{6}$ **2.** $P(3 \text{ or } 4)$ $\frac{1}{3}$ **3.** $P(7)$ 0 **4.** $P(< 7)$ 1 **5.** $P(\text{not } 3)$ $\frac{5}{6}$

Use the spinner to find each probability.

6. $P(\text{red})$ $\frac{3}{8}$ **7.** $P(\text{not red})$ $\frac{5}{8}$

8. $P(\text{green})$ $\frac{1}{8}$ **9.** $P(\text{not yellow})$ $\frac{8}{8}$

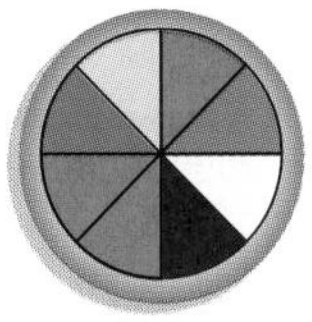

10. The probability of winning a game is $\frac{7}{9}$. If there are no ties or draws, what is the probability of losing the game? $\frac{2}{9}$

11. If $P(A) = \frac{3}{5}$, $P(B) = 0.52$, and $P(C) = 61\%$, which event has the greatest probability of occurring? C

12. Which probability is greater, 1 out of 10 or 15 out of 15,000? Explain.

13. Estimation On average, there are 100,000 thunderstorms in the United States every year. The probability that a thunderstorm will develop into a tornado is approximately $\frac{1}{100}$. About how many *tornadoes* are there every year? 1000

14. If 100 tokens were dropped on the figure shown, how many would you expect to hit the shaded region? About 33

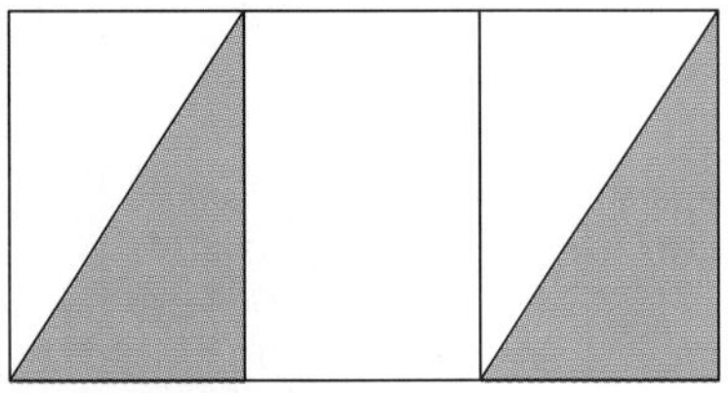

Test Prep

In order to determine the probability for one of two events happening, find the probability of each event and add the two probabilities together.

15. The probability of drawing a red marble out of a bag is $\frac{1}{5}$, for a green marble it is $\frac{1}{10}$, for a blue marble it is $\frac{3}{10}$, and for a yellow marble it is $\frac{2}{5}$. What are the chances of randomly drawing a marble that's either red or blue? B

Ⓐ $\frac{4}{10}$ Ⓑ $\frac{5}{10}$ Ⓒ $\frac{11}{20}$ Ⓓ $\frac{6}{10}$

REVIEW 12A

Review Correlation

Item(s)	Lesson(s)
1–10	12-1
11	12-2
12	12-1
13	12-2
14	12-3
15	12-2

Test Prep

Test-Taking Tip

Explain to students that it may be helpful to express all probabilities given in the problem in the same form. In this case, expressing probabilities in tenths may help students recognize that the red and blue marbles are actually half the marbles in the bag.

Answers for Review

12. 1 out of 10 is greater; 1 out of 10 is equal to 10%; 15 out of 15,000 is equal to 0.1%.

Resources

Practice Masters
Section 12A Review

Assessment Sourcebook
Quiz 12A

TestWorks
Test and Practice Software

PRACTICE

Name ____________________

Practice

Section 12A Review

A set of 8 tiles is numbered 1 through 8. Suppose you choose one tile at random. Find the probability of each event.

1. $P(5)$ $\frac{1}{8}$ **2.** $P(\text{odd number})$ $\frac{1}{2}$ **3.** $P(\text{multiple of } 3)$ $\frac{1}{4}$

4. $P(10)$ 0 **5.** $P(3 \text{ or } 5)$ $\frac{1}{4}$ **6.** $P(\text{prime number})$ $\frac{1}{2}$

Use the spinner to find each probability.

7. $P(A)$ $\frac{1}{2}$ **8.** $P(B)$ $\frac{1}{3}$

9. $P(C)$ $\frac{1}{6}$ **10.** $P(\text{consonant})$ $\frac{1}{2}$

11. $P(\text{not } C)$ $\frac{5}{6}$ **12.** $P(A \text{ or } C)$ $\frac{2}{3}$

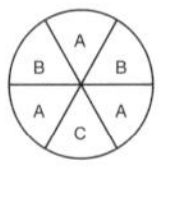

13. The probability that a Sloth Airlines flight will be on time is $\frac{2}{15}$. What is the probability that a flight will be late? $\frac{13}{15}$

14. If 160 tokens were dropped on the figure shown, how many would you expect to hit the shaded region? About 40

15. Which probability is greater, 13 out of 35 or 21 out of 57? Explain. $\frac{13}{35}$

Possible explanation: $\frac{13}{35} \approx 0.371$ and $\frac{21}{57} \approx 0.368$, so $\frac{13}{35} > \frac{21}{57}$.

16. In Detroit, Michigan, the average probability that it will rain on any given day is about $\frac{9}{25}$. About how many rainy days will there be in a 365-day year? About 131

17. If $P(X) = \frac{3}{20}$, $P(Y) = 18\%$, and $P(Z) = 0.2$, which event has the greatest probability of occurring? Z

18. Geography The shaded portion of the figure represents the percent of land used for crops in Ukraine. What percent of Ukraine's land is used for crops? *[Lesson 10-8]* 57%

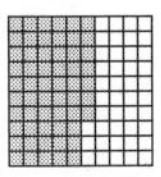

19. Measurement A carton measuring $5\frac{1}{2}$ in. by 6 in. by 7 in. holds exactly one gallon of liquid. How many cubic inches are in a gallon? *[Lesson 11-6]* 231 in^3

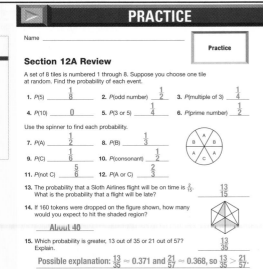

Section 12B

Fairness

Visit **www.teacher.mathsurf.com** for links to lesson plans from teachers and other professionals, NCTM information, and other sites.

LESSON PLANNING GUIDE

Student Edition / Ancillaries*

LESSON		MATERIALS	VOCABULARY	DAILY	OTHER
	Section 12B Opener				
12-4	**Tree Diagrams**		tree diagram	12-4	Teaching Tool Trans. 2, 3
12-5	**Compound Events**	number cubes	compound event	12-5	Technology Masters 63, 64 WW Math–Middle School
12-6	**Fairness and Unfairness**		fair, unfair	12-6	Ch. 12 Project Master *Interactive CD-ROM Lesson*
	Connect				Interdisc. Team Teaching 12B
	Review				Practice 12B; Quiz 12B; *TestWorks*
	Extend Key Ideas				
	Chapter 12 Summary and Review				
	Chapter 12 Assessment				Ch. 12 Tests Forms A–F *TestWorks*; Ch. 12 Letter Home
	Cumulative Review, Chapters 1–12				Cumulative Review Ch. 1–12 Quarterly Test Ch. 1–12

* Daily Ancillaries include Practice, Reteaching, Problem Solving, Enrichment, and Daily Transparency. Teaching Tool Transparencies are in *Teacher's Toolkits*. Lesson Enhancement Transparencies are in *Overhead Transparency Package*.

SKILLS TRACE

LESSON	SKILL	FIRST INTRODUCED GR. 4	GR. 5	GR. 6	DEVELOP	PRACTICE/ APPLY	REVIEW
12-4	**Making tree diagrams.**			✗ p. 642	pp. 642–644	pp. 645–646	pp. 654, 656, 659
12-5	**Finding probabilities of compound events.**			✗ p. 647	pp. 647–648	pp. 649–650	pp. 654, 656, 659
12-6	**Determining if a game is fair.**			✗ p. 651	pp. 651–652	pp. 653–654	pp. 656, 659

CONNECTED MATHEMATICS

Investigations 4–7 from the unit *How Likely Is It? (Probability)*, and Investigation 5 from the unit *Prime Time (Factors and Multiples)* from the **Connected Mathematics** series, can be used with Section 12B.

INTERDISCIPLINARY TEAM TEACHING

Math and Social Studies

(Worksheet pages 59–60: Teacher pages T59–T60)

In this lesson, students use theoretical and geometric probability to analyze aspects of Scrabble®.

Name ______________________ **_Math and Social Studies_**

SCRABBLING THE ODDS

Use theoretical and geometric probability to analyze aspects of Scrabble®.

Billions of rounds of Scrabble have been played since the game was invented by an out-of-work architect in the 1930s. Alfred E. Butts had plenty of time on his hands, so he decided to make up a board game. He wanted to create a game that would combine elements of anagrams and crossword puzzles and came up with something he called Criss Cross Words.

Butts wanted to give the letters of the alphabet used in the game different values. So he analyzed the English language to find out which letters appear most and least often. Butts assigned high values to letters that were infrequently used and lower values to letters that showed up more often in words.

At first, Butts produced Criss Cross Words by hand. He drew the boards himself, copied them as blueprints, then pasted them on checker boards. The letters of the tiles were also drawn by hand and glued to little squares of wood.

The Criss Cross game was very successful with Butts' friends. So he decided to submit his idea to a big game company, Parker Brothers. Parker Brothers rejected the game. But others had more faith in it. In 1948 a couple of Butts' friends decided to produce it using a small shop near their home in Connecticut. They made some minor changes to the game and gave it the catchy name, Scrabble. The game's popularity spread year by year. Eventually, another big game company, Milton Bradley, did buy the game. Today, it is the world's most popular word game.

The table shows the number of tiles for each letter.

Scrabble Letter Distribution

Letter	Tiles	Letter	Tiles
A	9	O	8
B	2	P	2
C	2	Q	1
D	4	R	6
E	12	S	4
F	2	T	6
G	3	U	4
H	2	V	2
I	9	W	2
J	1	X	1
K	1	Y	2
L	4	Z	1
M	2	BLANK	2
N	6		

1. Suppose you were asked to assign values to letters so that those letters that frequently occur in everyday written English get low values and that those that infrequently occur get high values. Name three letters that would get high values and three letters that would get low values. Explain your reasoning.
   See below.

Name ______________________ **_Math and Social Studies_**

2. a. At the beginning of a Scrabble game, each player draws 7 tiles. You turn over the first tile to see its letter. What letter is this most likely to be? What is the probability that you will draw that letter? Express this as a fraction and a percent.
   You have the greatest chance of drawing an E. The probability of drawing an E is $\frac{12}{100}$ or 12%.

   b. What letter, or letters, is this least likely to be? What is the probability that you will draw such a letter? Express this as a fraction and a percent.
   You have the least chance of drawing a J, K, Q, X or Z. The probability of drawing any one of them is $\frac{1}{100}$ or 1%.

3. The following sentence is from Abraham Lincoln's famous *Gettysburg Address*. Speaking of the soldiers who fought in the battle, Lincoln declared: "The world will little note, nor long remember what we say here, but it can never forget what they did here."

   a. How often do the letters D, H, R, T, W, and Y appear?
   D, 3; H, 6; R, 8; T, 10; W, 5; Y, 2

   b. What is the frequency of the appearance of each of these letters in the quote? Express as a fraction and percent.
   D, $\frac{3}{84}$, 3.6%; H, $\frac{6}{84}$, 7.1%; R, $\frac{8}{84}$, 9.5%; T, $\frac{10}{84}$, 11.9%; W, $\frac{5}{84}$, 6.0%; Y, $\frac{2}{84}$, 2.4%

   c. How do these frequencies compare to those for the same letters in a Scrabble game?
   See below.

   d. In this case, how is frequency related to probability?
   The probability of an event occurring is directly proportional to the frequency with which it can occur.

4. Look at the letters and the values you assigned to each in item 1. Have a competition with classmates to see who can form the word with the highest score using any number of these letters. Compare your word scores with those of classmates.
   Answers will vary.

Answers

1. Answers will vary but might include: low values, A, E, R, I, T; high values, J, Q, V, X, Z. The values are based on the ease or difficulty of using the letters in words.

3. c. D, more frequent but very close (3.6% rounded to the nearest % is 4%); H, T, and W appear much more frequently than their numbers in the Scrabble game; R is closer but still more frequent; Y is about the same frequency. The letters in the English language are used in the following order, from most to least: E, T, A, O, I, N, S, H, R, D, L, U, C, M, P, F, Y, W, G, B, V, K, J, X, Z, Q. The number on each tile letter in Scrabble does not necessarily correspond to these frequencies but is very close.

BIBLIOGRAPHY

FOR TEACHERS

Krantz, Les. *Facts! That Matter: Everything You Need to Know About Everything.* Los Angeles, CA: Price Stern Sloan, 1993.

Nash, Jay Robert. *Darkest Hours: A Narrative Encyclopedia of Worldwide Disasters from Ancient Times to the Present.* Chicago, IL: Nelson-Hall, 1976.

Phillips, Richard. *Numbers: Facts, Figures, and Fiction.* New York, NY: Cambridge University Press, 1994.

FOR STUDENTS

Archer, Jules. *Tornado!* New York, NY: Crestwood House, 1991.

Costello, Matthew J. *The Greatest Games of All Times.* New York, NY: J. Wiley, 1991.

Marschall, Ken. *Titanic: An Illustrated History.* New York, NY: Hyperion, 1992.

Sproul, Robert C. *Not a Chance: The Myth of Chance in Modern Science and Cosmology.* Grand Rapids, MI: Baker Books, 1994.

Section 12B

SECTION
12B Fairness

▶ Industry Link ▶ www.mathsurf.com/6/ch12/games

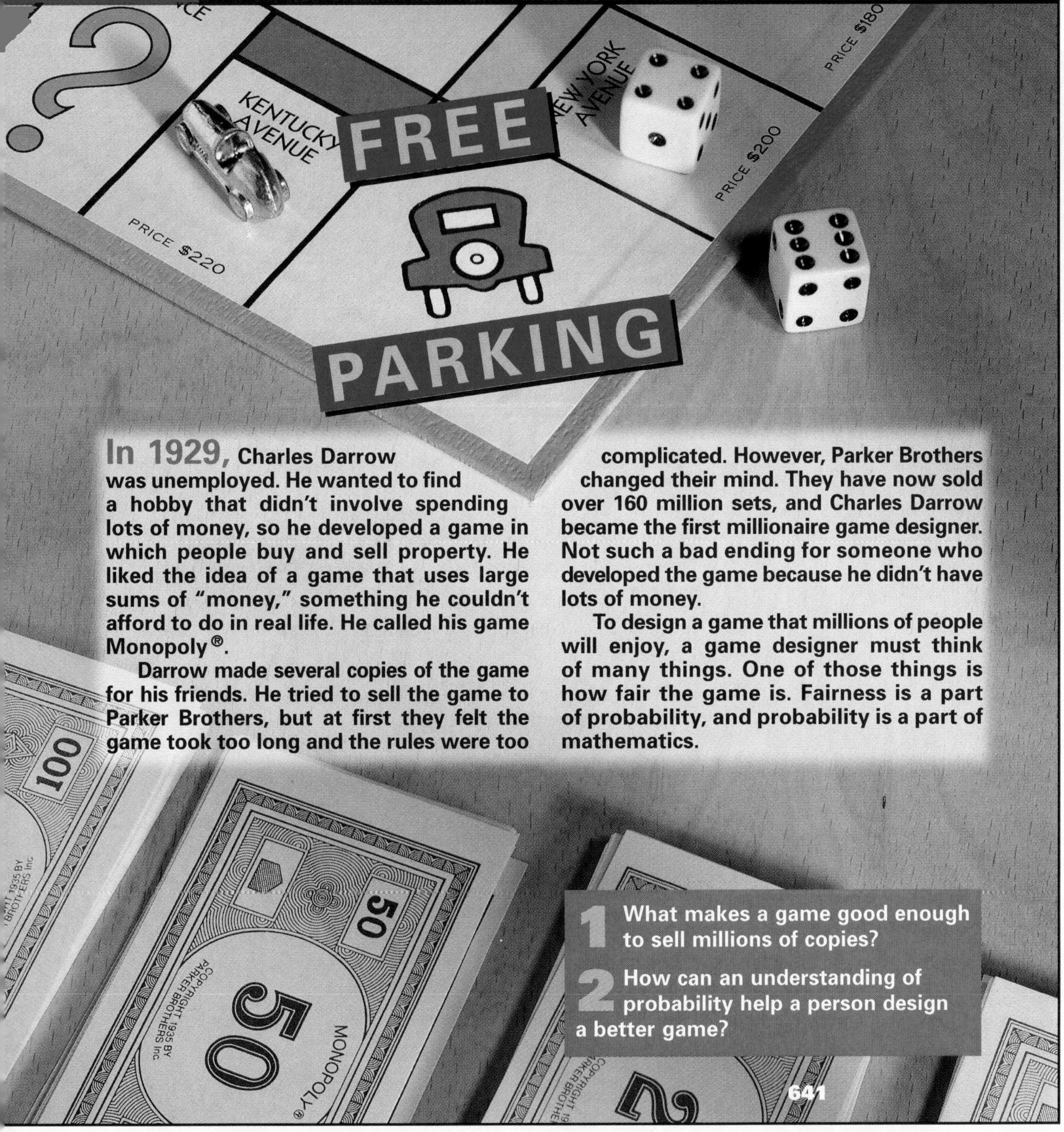

In 1929, Charles Darrow was unemployed. He wanted to find a hobby that didn't involve spending lots of money, so he developed a game in which people buy and sell property. He liked the idea of a game that uses large sums of "money," something he couldn't afford to do in real life. He called his game Monopoly®.

Darrow made several copies of the game for his friends. He tried to sell the game to Parker Brothers, but at first they felt the game took too long and the rules were too complicated. However, Parker Brothers changed their mind. They have now sold over 160 million sets, and Charles Darrow became the first millionaire game designer. Not such a bad ending for someone who developed the game because he didn't have lots of money.

To design a game that millions of people will enjoy, a game designer must think of many things. One of those things is how fair the game is. Fairness is a part of probability, and probability is a part of mathematics.

1 What makes a game good enough to sell millions of copies?

2 How can an understanding of probability help a person design a better game?

641

Where are we now?

In Section 12A, students learned how to count the number of outcomes for a single experiment.

They learned how to

- find the probability of an event.
- calculate probability from sample data.
- calculate probability from geometric models.

Where are we going?

In Section 12B, students will

- make tree diagrams.
- find the probability of a compound event.
- determine if a game is fair.

Theme: Games

World Wide Web

If your class has access to the World Wide Web, you might want to use the information found at the Web site address given. The interdisciplinary link relates to topics discussed in this section.

About the Page

This page introduces the theme of the section, games, and explains how Charles Darrow sold the game of Monopoly®.

Explain to students that in 1904, a woman named Lizzie Magie patented The Landlord's Game®. This game was further developed and revised by Charles Darrow, who sold the rights to his version of the game, now called Monopoly, to Parker Brothers. When Parker Brothers learned that Monopoly had been developed from The Landlord's Game, they acquired the rights to that game as well.

Ask ...

- What is your favorite game?
- What do you like about the game?
- Do you think the game is fair?
- Do you think you could design a game that people would buy?

Extension

The following activity does not require access to the World Wide Web.

Industry
Many new games are electronic or are played on the computer. Have students research the various methods the industry uses to sell a particular game.

Answers for Questions

1. Possible answers: If people like it; If it's fun and inexpensive.
2. Use probability to determine if the game is fair and easy or difficult to win.

Connect

On page 655, students will design two games of chance.

12-4 Lesson Organizer

Objective

- Make tree diagrams.

Vocabulary

- Tree diagram

NCTM Standards

- 1–4, 11

Review

1. Name the possible outcomes for picking a letter from the word *dog*. d, o, g
2. Name the possible outcomes for picking a letter from the word *cat*. c, a, t
3. Name the possible outcomes for first picking a letter from the word *dog* and then a letter from the word *cat*. dc, da, dt, oc, oa, ot, gc, ga, gt

Available on Daily Transparency 12-4

1 Introduce

Explore

The Point
Students explore multiple outcomes by examining diagrams for three different game boards that involve moving from one side to the other along several possible paths.

Ongoing Assessment
Be sure students understand that the chosen paths cannot involve backtracking.

For Groups That Finish Early
In Game 1, suppose one more path is inserted between the first two points. How many more possible paths does that add to the total number of paths from start to finish? Two

12-4 Tree Diagrams

You'll Learn ...

- to make tree diagrams

... How It's Used

Botanists use charts based on tree diagrams to determine all the possible offspring for two varieties of plants.

Vocabulary

tree diagram

▶ Lesson Link You have counted the number of outcomes for a single experiment. Now you will count the number of outcomes for a series of experiments. ◀

Explore Tree Diagrams

All Roads Lead to the Finish Line

The three sketches below are diagrams for three board games. In each game, players start on the left side and move to the right side. Players always move from left to right.

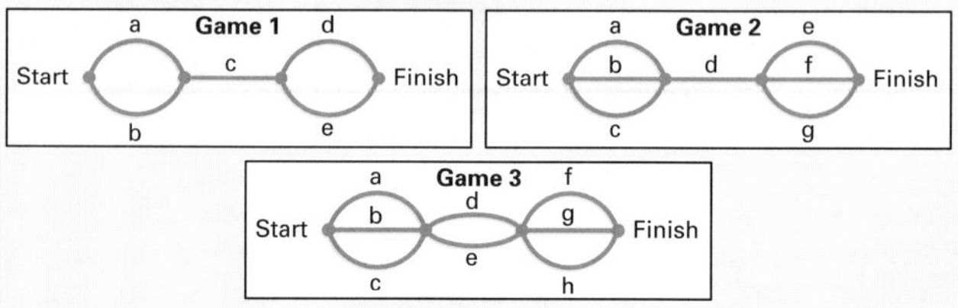

1. For each sketch, list all of the possible routes a player could take to get from start to finish. Use the letters next to each path to describe each route.
2. Can you be certain that you have found all possible routes for each game board? Explain.
3. Is it possible to move from start to finish using a set of paths that are not in alphabetical order? Explain.
4. Is it possible to determine the number of ways to go from start to finish without actually listing all of them? Explain.

Learn Tree Diagrams

It is often easy to list the outcomes for a single experiment. It can be more complicated to list the outcomes for a series of experiments. To list the outcomes for a series, you can use a **tree diagram**. This type of diagram shows one branch for each possible outcome.

MEETING INDIVIDUAL NEEDS

Resources

- **12-4** Practice
- **12-4** Reteaching
- **12-4** Problem Solving
- **12-4** Enrichment
- **12-4** Daily Transparency
  - Problem of the Day
  - Review
  - Quick Quiz

Teaching Tool Transparencies 2, 3

Learning Modalities

Visual Have students work together to make a tree diagram showing how many different possibilities there are for electing a president and vice-president from their class. Point out that it will require a very large diagram.

Logical Have students describe a mathematical method for solving the president and vice-president problem described above in the **Visual** learning modality.

Inclusion

Point out that a tree diagram has branches just like a real tree. You might want to show a tree diagram turned on its side to show the similarity to a tree.

Example 1

A sandwich shop has two choices for sandwiches (tuna or egg salad) and three for drinks (milk, juice, cider). If a "meal" is one sandwich and one drink, draw a tree diagram to show all of the possible meals.

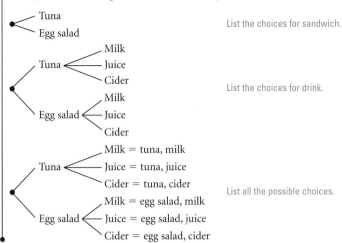

- Tuna
- Egg salad

List the choices for sandwich.

- Tuna
  - Milk
  - Juice
  - Cider
- Egg salad
  - Milk
  - Juice
  - Cider

List the choices for drink.

- Tuna
  - Milk = tuna, milk
  - Juice = tuna, juice
  - Cider = tuna, cider
- Egg salad
  - Milk = egg salad, milk
  - Juice = egg salad, juice
  - Cider = egg salad, cider

List all the possible choices.

You can use multiplication to find the *number* of possible outcomes. In the example above, there were 2 choices for sandwiches and 3 choices for drinks. All together, there were 2×3, or 6, possible combinations of choices.

Example 2

If you flip a penny, a nickel, and a dime, how many different ways can the three coins land?

There are two ways the penny can land: heads or tails. There are also two outcomes for the nickel, heads or tails, as well as for the dime. All together, there are $2 \times 2 \times 2$, or 8 possible outcomes.

Try It

a. Conway's Restaurant has three flavors of ice cream (chocolate, vanilla, and mint) and two toppings (hot fudge and butterscotch). Draw a tree diagram showing all the possible ice cream servings with one flavor of ice cream and one topping.

b. One spinner has the numbers 1, 2, 3, and 4 on it. Another spinner has the letters A, B, C, and D. If you spin both spinners, how many different outcomes are there? 16

DID YOU KNOW?

Computers use the idea of branches. At certain times, a computer's program will determine if a particular condition is true or false. If it is true, the program follows one branch, or set of instructions. If it's false, it follows a different branch.

MATH EVERY DAY

Problem of the Day

Markus had 4 sticks of clay. Each stick was shaped like a box. The end was 1 inch by 2 inches. The length of each was 4 inches long. He put all the clay together and rolled it into a cylinder that had a radius of 2 inches. What was the height of the cylinder? Round your answer to the nearest half-inch. $2\frac{1}{2}$ inches

Available on Daily Transparency 12-4

An Extension is provided in the transparency package.

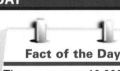

Fact of the Day

There are over 10,000 commercial radio stations in the United States. Of these stations, over 25% are devoted to the country-music format.

Estimation

Estimate each product.

1. 71×72 4900
2. 33×87 2700
3. 52×61 3000
4. 41×49 2000

Answers for Explore

1. Game 1: acd, ace, bcd, bce; Game 2: ade, adf, adg, bde, bdf, bdg, cde, cdf, cdg; Game 3: adf, adg, adh, aef, aeg, aeh, bdf, bdg, bdh, bef, beg, beh, cdf, cdg, cdh, cef, ceg, ceh.
2. Yes; Follow a pattern to check.
3. No; The routes are labeled in order from left to right in alphabetical order.
4. Yes; Multiply the number of choices at each stage by one another.

2 Teach

Learn

Alternate Examples

1. A store sells jackets in two colors: red or black. Three sizes are available: small, medium, and large. Draw a tree diagram to show all of the possible types of jackets.

   - Red
     - Small = red, small
     - Medium = red, medium
     - Large = red, large
   - Black
     - Small = black, small
     - Medium = black, medium
     - Large = black, large

2. One spinner has the letters X, Y, and Z. Another spinner has the numbers 6, 7, 8, and 9 on it. If you spin both spinners, how many different outcomes are there?

   There are three outcomes for the first spinner and four outcomes for the second spinner. All together there are 3×4, or 12 possible outcomes.

Answers for Try It

a. See page C5.

WHAT DO YOU THINK?

Students see two methods of finding how many boxed lunches they can make when given three choices for a main dish, two choices for a fruit, and two choices for a cookie. One involves using a tree diagram. The other involves using multiplication. Students can decide which of the two correct methods is easier for them.

Answers for What Do You Think?

1. Catherine's; You could use the tree diagram to see which combination you were missing.
2. No; If each lunch gets a bag of pretzels, you aren't making any more combinations.

3 Practice and Assess

Check

Answers for Check Your Understanding

1. A tree diagram lists each individual outcome.
2. No; It takes longer to draw a tree diagram than it does to look at the two sides of a coin and to see that either side can come up when flipped once.

WHAT DO YOU THINK?

Catherine and Van are preparing lunches for a field trip. Each lunch will have one main dish (chicken, roast beef sandwich, or pita sandwich), one fruit (banana or apple), and one cookie (chocolate chip or oatmeal raisin). They want to know how many different lunches they can make.

Catherine thinks . . .

I'll use a tree diagram.

There are 12 different possible lunches.

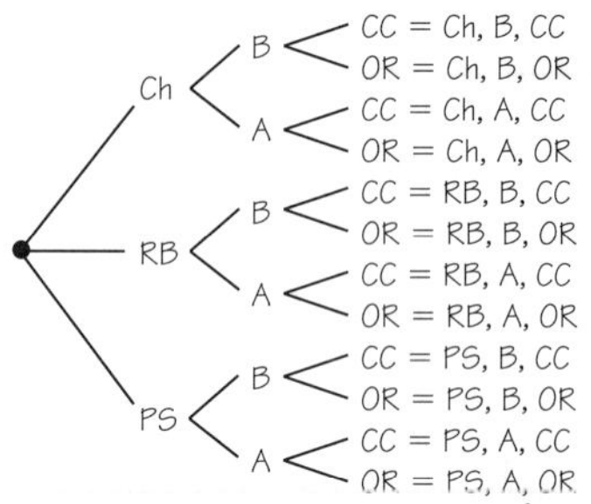

Van thinks . . .

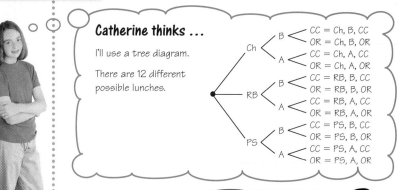

I'll use multiplication. There are 3 choices for a main dish, 2 for fruit, and 2 for a cookie. $3 \times 2 \times 2 = 12$.

There are 12 different possible lunches.

What do you think?

1. Which method would work better if Catherine and Van had 11 different lunches and were trying to determine which combination they hadn't made? Explain.
2. If every lunch also had one bag of pretzels, would this change the number of different lunches? Explain.

Check Your Understanding

1. What kind of information does a tree diagram give you?
2. Is a tree diagram helpful when determining the number of ways a single coin can be flipped once? Explain.

MEETING MIDDLE SCHOOL CLASSROOM NEEDS

Tips from Middle School Teachers

I find that students enjoy making tree diagrams. I have them make up their own problem situations for which a tree diagram is useful.

Team Teaching

Work with a nutrition or cooking instructor to present a tree diagram showing possible food combinations when choosing from the basic food groups.

Fine Arts Connection

Customarily the primary colors are considered to be red, orange, yellow, green, blue, and violet. Have students draw a tree diagram to find how many different art kits they could make if each art kit only two primary colors of paint. 30 kits Have students use multiplication to find the number of different art kits if three primary colors are in each kit. 120 kits

12-4 Exercises and Applications

Practice and Apply

1. **Getting Started** Follow these steps to draw a tree diagram showing the possible outcomes of rolling a number cube and flipping a coin.
   - **a.** Start the tree diagram by listing the outcomes of rolling a number cube.
   - **b.** Draw the branches and list the outcomes of flipping a coin.
   - **c.** List all of the possible outcomes.
   - **d.** How many outcomes are possible for rolling a number cube and flipping a coin?

For Exercises 2–4, draw a tree diagram showing all possible outcomes for each situation.

2. GPS The lunch choices of the day are bologna or peanut butter sandwich with either an apple, orange, or banana, and either juice or milk.

4. Each player gets two playing pieces for a board game: a cube (red, blue, green, or yellow) and a cylinder (1 in. high, 2 in. high, or 3 in. high).

6. If you spin both spinners at the same time, how many possible outcomes are there? 16

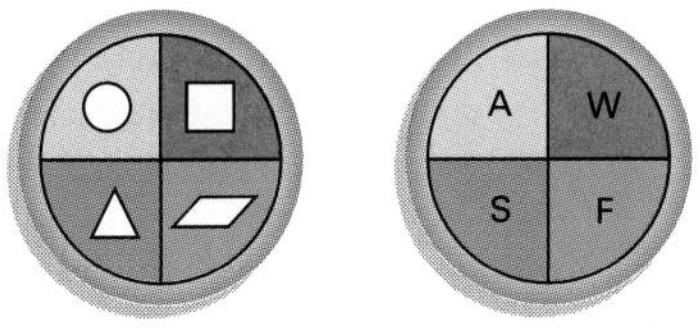

8. **Problem Solving** The Wild Outback Resort has 10 different board games, 5 different card games, and 6 different water games for their guests to play. Sam wants to borrow 1 of each type of game for the weekend. How many combinations of board, card, and water games are there? 300

3. A softball team has five pitchers and three catchers. Only one pitcher and one catcher are on the field at the same time.

5. **Test Prep** Mitzi has 3 sweaters, 8 blouses, 6 skirts, and 5 pairs of shoes. How many days can Mitzi wear a different outfit? D

   Ⓐ 22 Ⓑ 68 Ⓒ 512 Ⓓ 720

7. Prizes for first, second, and third place were wrapped in separate boxes. The labels identifying the prizes fell off.
   - **a.** How many ways can the labels be put on the boxes? 6
   - **b.** If one of the three labels is put on a box, what is the probability that it is the correct label? $\frac{1}{3}$

PRACTICE 12-4

FINISH

12-4 Exercises and Applications

Assignment Guide

- Basic
  1–7, 9, 11, 14–20 evens
- Average
  2–9, 11, 12, 14–20 evens
- Enriched
  2–13, 15–21 odds

Exercise Answers

1–4. See page C5.

PRACTICE

Name ______________________

Practice 12-4

Tree Diagrams

Possible answers:

For Exercises 1–4, draw a tree diagram for each situation.

1. A club is choosing a girl (Kathy, Linda, or Meg) and a boy (Warren or Xavier) to represents the club at a student council meeting.

   K — W = Kathy, Warren; X = Kathy, Xavier
   L — W = Linda, Warren; X = Linda, Xavier
   M — W = Meg, Warren; X = Meg, Xavier

2. You can have a cup or a bowl of soup. The flavors are split pea, minestrone, tomato, and cream of broccoli.

   C — SP = cup of split pea; M = cup of minestrone; T = cup of tomato; CB = cup of cream of broccoli
   B — SP = bowl of split pea; M = bowl of minestrone; T = bowl of tomato; CB = bowl of cream of broccoli

3. A coin is flipped three times in a row.

   H — H — H = heads, heads, heads; T = heads, heads, tails
   H — T — H = heads, tails, heads; T = heads, tails, tails
   T — H — H = tails, heads, heads; T = tails, heads, tails
   T — T — H = tails, tails, heads; T = tails, tails, tails

4. You are going horseback riding. You can choose one of 8 horses, and you may go to any one of 5 destinations. How many different ways can you make your selection? 40

5. If you spin both spinners at the same time, how many possible outcomes are there? 30

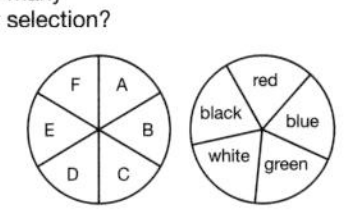

6. Gerald is taking a multiple-choice test in his Spanish class. The test has four questions, and each question has 5 possible answers.
   - **a.** How many different ways can Gerald complete his answer sheet? 625
   - **b.** Gerald forgot to study. If he guesses randomly, what is the probability that he will get the first problem right? $\frac{1}{5}$

RETEACHING

Name ______________________

Alternative Lesson 12-4

Tree Diagrams

It is often easy to list the outcomes for a single experiment. It can be more complicated to list the outcomes for a series of experiments. To list the outcomes for a series of experiments, you can use a **tree diagram.** A tree diagram shows one branch for each possible outcome.

Example

Janice has two skirts (one is red; the other is blue). She has three blouses (one is striped; one is plaid; one has polka dots). How many different outfits can she make?

List the choices for skirts.	List the choices for blouses.	List all possible choices.
Red	Striped	Red skirt, striped blouse
	Plaid	Red skirt, plaid blouse
	Polka dot	Red skirt, polka dot blouse
Blue	Striped	Blue skirt, striped blouse
	Plaid	Blue skirt, plaid blouse
	Polka dot	Blue skirt, polka dot blouse

Janice can make 6 different outfits.

Try It At a card shop, Ernie has his choice of birthday balloons (confetti, flowers, or bears) and his choice of ribbon colors (purple and green). Draw a tree diagram to show all of the possible combinations of balloons and ribbons.

List the choices for balloons.	List the choices for ribbons.	List all possible choices.
Confetti	Purple	Confetti balloon, purple ribbon
	Green	Confetti balloon, green ribbon
Flowers	Purple	Flower balloon, purple ribbon
	Green	Flower balloon, green ribbon
Bears	Purple	Bear balloon, purple ribbon
	Green	Bear balloon, green ribbon

Reteaching

Activity

- Work with a partner.
- One person names three different automobile colors.
- The other person names five different brands of automobiles.
- Together, make a tree diagram to show all the autos that could be purchased in one of the chosen colors and brands.

Exercise Notes

■ Exercise 12

Problem-Solving Tip You may wish to use Teaching Tool Transparencies 2 and 3: Guided Problem Solving, pages 1–2.

Exercise Answers

11. $\frac{1}{24}$; Use multiplication or draw a tree diagram.

12. a. 676; 1 choice for the first letter, 26 choices for the second letter, 26 choices for the third letter: $1 \times 26 \times 26$.

    b. Fewer; 1 choice for the first letter, 25 choices for the second letter, 24 choices for the third letter: $1 \times 25 \times 24 = 600$ possibilities

13. 12; 12; The number of branches stays the same, but the order in which the choices are listed is different.

Alternate Assessment

Performance Have students explain how they would solve the the following problem. Suppose that practice partners consisting of a bass player and a piano player are being formed. Arnelle and Jessica play bass and Jose, Dion, and Marie play piano. Find the number of different pairs of practice partners. 6; $2 \times 3 = 6$ possibilities

► Quick Quiz

1. Draw a tree diagram for the following situation: A coin is tossed and a letter is picked from the word CUBE.

heads — C = heads, C; U = heads, U; B = heads, B; E = heads, E

tails — C = tails, C; U = tails, U; B = tails, B; E = tails, E

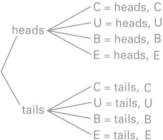

2. At a sweater store there are 6 colors, 3 sizes, and 2 styles of sweaters to choose from. How many different types of sweaters are possible? 36

Available on Daily Transparency 12-4

---

9. Industry A Texas license plate consists of "letter, letter, letter, number, number, letter." If all 26 letters of the alphabet and all 10 digits, 0–9, can be used, how many different license plates are possible? 45,697,600

10. The Wheel Shop sells five different brands of bikes. Each brand comes in three different models: 1-speed, 3-speed, or 10-speed. Each bike can also be red or blue. How many different kinds are there? 30

Problem Solving and Reasoning

11. Critical Thinking For his costume, Mike has to choose one wig and one scarf. The items he can choose are shown in the photo. What is the probability that Mike chooses the brown wig and the black scarf? Explain.

12. Choose a Strategy Each radio station in Kilkenney County has to have three call letters, with the first letter being K.

a. How many different radio stations can the county have? Explain.

b. If no two letters can be the same, are there more possibilities, or fewer possibilities? Explain.

Problem Solving STRATEGIES

- Look for a Pattern
- Make an Organized List
- Make a Table
- Guess and Check
- Work Backward
- Use Logical Reasoning
- Draw a Diagram
- Solve a Simpler Problem

13. Communicate Jessie is drawing a tree diagram to show possible combinations. She has red, orange, yellow, and green blocks. They come in three shapes: triangles, squares, and circles. How many branches will her tree diagram have if Jessie first lists the choices for color? If she first lists the choices for shape? Explain.

Problem Solving TIP

Draw a partial tree diagram. You will probably not need to finish the diagram in order to solve the problem.

Mixed Review

Find the volume. *[Lesson 11-7]*

14.

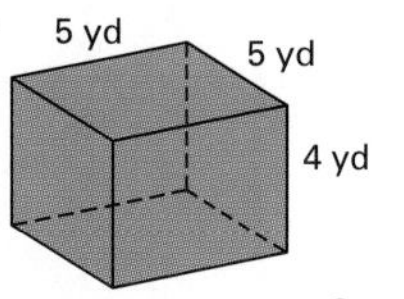

100 yd³

15.

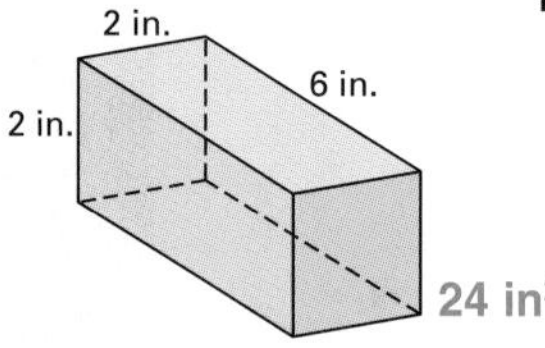

24 in²

16.

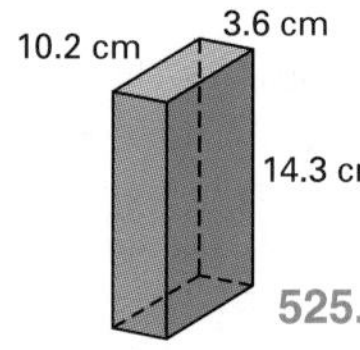

525.096 cm³

Suppose you roll a 10-sided die with faces numbered 1–10. Find the probability of each event. *[Lesson 12-1]*

17. $P(1, 6, \text{or } 9)$ $\frac{3}{10}$ **18.** $P(10)$ $\frac{1}{10}$ **19.** $P(5 \text{ or } 3)$ $\frac{1}{5}$ **20.** $P(12)$ 0 **21.** $P(\text{factor of } 10)$ $\frac{2}{5}$

PROBLEM SOLVING 12-4

PROBLEM SOLVING

Name ______

Guided Problem Solving 12-4

GPS PROBLEM 2, STUDENT PAGE 645

The lunch choices of the day are bologna or peanut butter sandwich with either an apple, orange, or banana, and either juice or milk. Draw a tree diagram showing all possible outcomes.

— Understand —

1. What are you asked to draw? A tree diagram.
2. What will you show on your drawing? All possible outcomes.

— Plan —

3. Which lunch choice will you list Possible answers:

a. first? Sandwiches b. second? Fruits c. third? Drinks

— Solve —

4. Make a tree diagram by listing your first lunch choice and drawing lines to your second and third choices. Then list all possible choices.

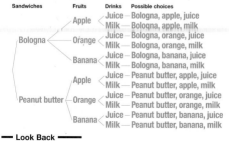

Sandwiches	Fruits	Drinks	Possible choices
Bologna	Apple	Juice	Bologna, apple, juice
		Milk	Bologna, apple, milk
	Orange	Juice	Bologna, orange, juice
		Milk	Bologna, orange, milk
	Banana	Juice	Bologna, banana, juice
		Milk	Bologna, banana, milk
Peanut butter	Apple	Juice	Peanut butter, apple, juice
		Milk	Peanut butter, apple, milk
	Orange	Juice	Peanut butter, orange, juice
		Milk	Peanut butter, orange, milk
	Banana	Juice	Peanut butter, banana, juice
		Milk	Peanut butter, banana, milk

— Look Back —

5. How can you check to see if your answer is reasonable? Multiply the number of outcomes: $2 \times 3 \times 2 = 12$.

SOLVE ANOTHER PROBLEM

How many possible choices would there be if soda was also available? You can draw a diagram on another sheet of paper to help you. 18

ENRICHMENT

Name ______

Extend Your Thinking 12-4

Patterns in Data

Complete this True-False quiz. Guess if you don't know the answers.

a. The oboe evolved from an outdoor instrument called the shawm.
b. The bassoon, a member of the oboe family, originally had only two keys.
c. The English horn, the bass of the oboe family, was once called an oboe da caccia.

1. Check your answers with the answer key at the bottom of the page. Record the number of questions answered correctly. Answers will vary.
2. What is the probability that you will guess the correct answer to any one item on the quiz? $\frac{1}{2}$
3. How many possible outcomes are there for guessing the correct answer to two questions? For three questions? You can draw a tree diagram on another sheet of paper to help you answer the questions. 2 questions: 4 outcomes; 3 questions: 8 outcomes.
4. What is the probability that you will guess the correct answers for

   a. two questions? $\frac{1}{4}$ b. for three questions? $\frac{1}{8}$
5. What pattern do you notice occurring in the probability as you add each additional question to the quiz? The denominator doubles. So, the probability of guessing all questions correctly decreases by one-half.
6. Predict the probability of guessing all the correct answers to a similar quiz that has

   a. 5 questions. $\frac{1}{32}$ b. 10 questions. $\frac{1}{1024}$
7. Try this quiz with sixteen friends. What fraction of them guessed the answers correctly? Is this fraction close to the probability of $\frac{1}{8}$? Explain. Possible answer: It will probably be close, but a larger sample is needed to be assured a prediction close to $\frac{1}{8}$.

Answer Key: a. True, b. False, it originally had 4 keys. c. False, the bassoon is the bass member of the family.

Compound Events

12-5

▶ Lesson Link You know how to find all of the possible outcomes for a series of experiments. Now you will find the probability of one of those outcomes. ◀

Explore Compound Events

Counting On a Way Out

Materials: Number cubes

In the game Monopoly®, you can get out of Jail if you roll a 7, an 11, or doubles (the same number on both number cubes).

1. Predict the number of times out of 100 rolls that you can roll a 7. Also, predict the number of 11's and the number of doubles.
2. Roll the cubes 25 times. For each roll, write down the sum of the numbers. Circle the sum if it was a double.
3. Share your data with three other groups.
4. Based on your collected data, determine the probability of getting just a 7, just an 11, or just doubles. Also, determine the probability for getting either a 7, an 11, or doubles.
5. Did your data match your prediction? Explain.
6. Why might it be a good idea to add the data from three other groups to your own data?

You'll Learn ...

■ to find the probability of a compound event

... How It's Used

State lottery designers use compound events when determining the chances for winning a lottery prize.

Vocabulary

compound event

Learn Compound Events

A single event is the outcome of a single experiment, such as tossing a coin and getting heads, or rolling a 6 on a number cube. A **compound event** is a combination of two or more single events, such as tossing a coin and getting heads *and* then rolling a 6 on a number cube.

$P(H) = \frac{1}{2}$ $P(6) = \frac{1}{6}$

and $P(H \text{ and } 6) = ?$

MEETING INDIVIDUAL NEEDS

Resources
12-5 Practice
12-5 Reteaching
12-5 Problem Solving
12-5 Enrichment
12-5 Daily Transparency
Problem of the Day
Review
Quick Quiz
Technology Masters 63, 64
Wide World of Mathematics Middle School: Two-Sport Athlete

Learning Modalities

Visual Have students make tree diagrams or charts to show all possible outcomes in Examples 1 and 2 on page 648.

Kinesthetic Refer students to Exercises 2–7 on page 649 and have them perform experiments to see if the results are similar to their answers.

English Language Development

Point out that a compound sentence is made of two or more simple sentences. In a similar way, a compound event is a combination of two or more single events.

12-5 Lesson Organizer

Objective

■ Find the probability of a compound event.

Vocabulary

■ Compound event

Materials

■ Explore: Number cubes

NCTM Standards

■ 1–4, 11

▶ Review

1. Name the ways in which two number cubes can be rolled to get a sum of 7. 3 and 4, 4 and 3, 1 and 6, 6 and 1, 2 and 5, 5 and 2
2. Name the ways in which two number cubes can be rolled to get a sum of 11. 5 and 6, 6 and 5

Available on Daily Transparency 12-5

1 Introduce

Explore

The Point

Students explore the probability of rolling a 7, 11, or doubles when two number cubes are tossed.

Ongoing Assessment

Remind students that they are finding probability based on data from experiments. Therefore, the data will vary from group to group.

Answers for Explore

1–5. Answers may vary. Data should yield probabilities close to the following:

$P(7) = \frac{1}{6}$;

$P(11) = \frac{1}{18}$;

$P(\text{doubles}) = \frac{1}{6}$;

$P(7 \text{ or } 11 \text{ or doubles}) = \frac{7}{18}$.

6. The more data you can base your prediction on, the better your prediction may be.

2 Teach

Learn

Alternate Examples

1. What is the probability of spinning a vowel on Spinner 1 and an even number on Spinner 2?

   Spinner 1 Spinner 2

   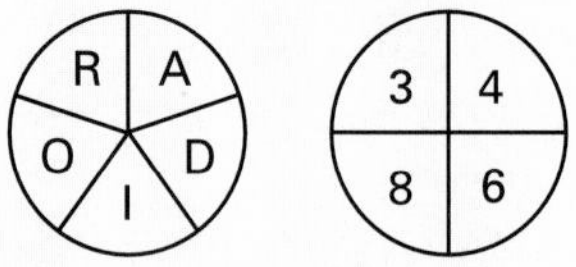

   There are 5 outcomes on the first spinner, and 4 on the second. There are 5 × 4 or 20 possible outcomes.

   There are 3 ways to get a vowel on the first spinner and 3 ways to get an even number on the second spinner. There are 3 × 3 or 9 ways to get a vowel and an even number.

   The probability of getting a vowel and an even number is $\frac{9}{20}$ or 45%.

2. What are the chances of rolling a number cube twice and getting 1 on each cube?

   There are 6 possible outcomes for each cube. There are 6 × 6 or 36 possible outcomes for two cubes. There is one way of getting 1 on each cube. There is 1 × 1 or 1 way to get a 1 on both cubes.

   The probability of getting 1 on each of two cubes is $\frac{1}{36}$ or about 3%.

3 Practice and Assess

Check

Answers for Check Your Understanding

1. Multiply the probability of the first event by the probability of the second event.
2. Answers may vary.

To find the probability for a compound event, first calculate the number of possible outcomes. Then, calculate the number of ways the compound event can happen. The probability is the ratio of these values.

Remember

To convert a fraction to a percent, you can use a proportion with the fraction as one ratio, and $\frac{x}{100}$ as the other.
[Page 559]

Examples

1 What is the probability of spinning a consonant (B, C, or D) on Spinner 1 and a prime number on Spinner 2?

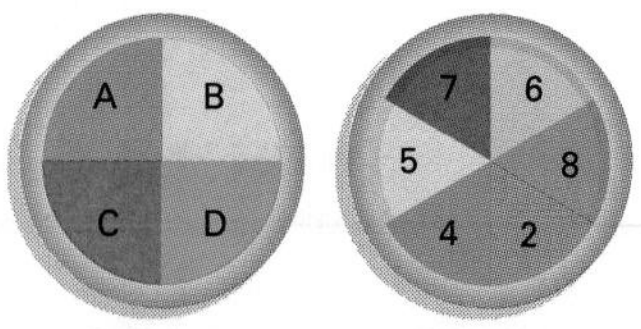

Spinner 1 Spinner 2

Recall that you can use multiplication to determine the number of possible outcomes. There are 4 outcomes on the first spinner, and 6 on the second. There are 4 × 6 or 24 possible outcomes.

There are 3 ways to get a consonant on the first spinner, and 3 ways to get a prime number on the second spinner. There are 3 × 3 or 9 ways to get a consonant and a prime number.

The probability of getting a consonant and a prime number is $\frac{9}{24}$, or 37.5%.

2 What are the chances of flipping three coins and getting all heads?

There are 2 outcomes for each of the three coins. There are 2 × 2 × 2 or 8 possible outcomes. There is 1 way of getting heads on each of the three coins. There is 1 × 1 × 1 or 1 way of getting three heads.

The probability of getting three heads is $\frac{1}{8}$, or 12.5%.

Try It

In Example 1, what is the probability of spinning a letter in the word "DAD" on Spinner 1 and an even number on Spinner 2? $\frac{1}{3}$

Check Your Understanding

1. How can multiplication help you find the probability of a compound event?
2. Give an example of a compound event in your life.

MATH EVERY DAY

Problem of the Day

The fastest growing tree is an Albizzia falcata planted on June 17, 1974 in Sabah, Malaysia. In 13 months it grew 35 ft 3 in. What was the average growth rate (in feet and inches) per month for that tree? Round your answer to the nearest half-inch.

2 ft $8\frac{1}{2}$ in. per month

Available on Daily Transparency 12-5

An Extension is provided in the transparency package.

Fact of the Day

Greeks and Romans used number cubes when they played board games more than 2300 years ago.

Mental Math

Find each product mentally.

1. 80 × 1000 80,000
2. 40 × 400 16,000
3. 700 × 700 490,000
4. 700 × 9000 6,300,000

12-5 Exercises and Applications

Practice and Apply

1. **Getting Started** Answer these questions to find the probability of rolling a number cube three times and getting a 4 each time.
   - **a.** How many outcomes are there for each roll? 6
   - **b.** How many possible outcomes are there? 216
   - **c.** How many ways can you get a 4 on each roll? 1
   - **d.** How many possible ways can you get three 4's? 1
   - **e.** What is the probability of getting a 4 each time? $\frac{1}{216}$

Three cards numbered 1, 4, and 7 are in a paper bag. Each time a card is drawn it is replaced. Find the probability of each event.

2. P(odd, then even) $\frac{2}{9}$
3. P(even, then even) $\frac{1}{9}$
4. P(odd, then odd) $\frac{4}{9}$
5. P(odd, even, odd) $\frac{4}{27}$
6. P(even, then odd) $\frac{2}{9}$
7. P(even, even, even) $\frac{1}{27}$
8. Use the menu shown to find the probability of a customer ordering an egg roll, sweet and sour pork, and juice. $\frac{1}{36}$

9. **Science** The probability of a newborn child being a girl is about $\frac{1}{2}$. What is the probability of all 5 children in a family being girls? About $\frac{1}{32}$ GPS

For Exercises 10–12, the spinner is spun twice.

10. Find the probability of spinning white both times. $\frac{1}{16}$
11. Find the probability of spinning white and then red. $\frac{2}{16}$
12. Find the probability of not spinning red either time. $\frac{4}{16}$
13. Two number cubes are tossed. What is the probability that the number on each cube is the same? Different? $\frac{1}{6}$, $\frac{5}{6}$
14. **Test Prep** Marcos rolls 2 eight-sided dice with each side numbered 1-8. What is the probability that he rolls a 7 and then a 1? D

    Ⓐ $\frac{1}{4}$ Ⓑ $\frac{1}{16}$ Ⓒ $\frac{1}{36}$ Ⓓ $\frac{1}{64}$

PRACTICE 12-5

PRACTICE

Name ____________________ Practice 12-5

Compound Events

Five cards numbered 1, 2, 3, 4, and 5 are in a paper bag. Each time a card is drawn it is replaced. Find the probability of each event.

1. P(even, then even) $\frac{4}{25}$
2. P(even, then odd) $\frac{6}{25}$
3. P(odd, then even) $\frac{6}{25}$
4. P(odd, then odd) $\frac{9}{25}$
5. P(odd, odd, odd) $\frac{27}{125}$
6. P(even, even, odd) $\frac{12}{125}$

For Exercises 7–10, the spinner is spun twice.

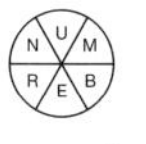

7. Find the probability of spinning N both times. $\frac{1}{36}$
8. Find the probability of spinning E then R. $\frac{1}{36}$
9. Find the probability of spinning a vowel then a consonant. $\frac{2}{9}$
10. Find the probability of not spinning B either time. $\frac{25}{36}$
11. Suppose you flip a coin and spin the spinner from Exercise 7. What is the probability that the coin lands heads and you spin M? $\frac{1}{12}$
12. Suppose you roll 5 number cubes while playing Yahtzee®. What is the probability of getting a number less than 5 on all of the number cubes? $\frac{32}{243}$
13. A Thai restaurant offers the curry special shown at the right. If a customer makes all choices randomly, what is the probability that she orders a yellow or green tofu curry with tea? $\frac{1}{12}$

    Curry Special $5.99
    Curried vegetables with your choice of beef, chicken, tofu, or shrimp.
    Choose yellow curry, green curry, or red curry.
    Drink included: tea or soda.

14. A standard deck of 52 playing cards includes 26 black cards (13 clubs and 13 spades) and 26 red cards (13 hearts and 13 diamonds). Suppose you draw a card, put it back, and then draw again. Find each probability.
    - **a.** P(black, then red) $\frac{1}{4}$
    - **b.** P(red, then spade) $\frac{1}{8}$
    - **c.** P(heart, then heart) $\frac{1}{16}$
15. The game of Scrabble® includes 100 lettered tiles. 42 of the tiles represent vowels. If you select a tile, put it back, and select again, what is the probability of getting a vowel both times? $\frac{441}{2500}$

RETEACHING

Name ____________________ Alternative Lesson 12-5

Compound Events

A single event is the outcome of a single experiment, such as tossing a coin and getting heads. A **compound event** is a combination of two or more single events, such as tossing a coin and getting heads *and* then rolling a 6 on a number cube.

To find the probability for a compound event, first calculate the number of possible outcomes. Then calculate the number of ways the compound event can happen. The probability is the ratio of these values.

Example

What is the probability of spinning an even number on Spinner 1 and an odd number on Spinner 2?

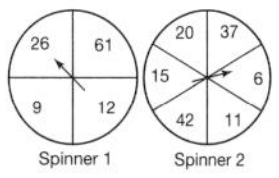

Spinner 1 Spinner 2

Find the number of possible outcomes for each spinner.

Spinner 1: 26, 61, 9, 12 → 4 outcomes
Spinner 2: 20, 37, 6, 11, 42, 15 → 6 outcomes

Multiply to find the total number of possible outcomes: 4×6, or 24 possible outcomes.

Determine the number of ways to get an even number for Spinner 1 and an odd number for Spinner 2.

Spinner 1, even number: 26, 12 → 2 ways
Spinner 2, odd number: 15, 37, 11 → 3 ways

Multiply to find the number of ways: $2 \times 3 = 6$.

So, the probability is $\frac{6}{24}$, or $\frac{1}{4}$.

Try It Find the probability of spinning a triangle on Spinner A and a pentagon on Spinner B.

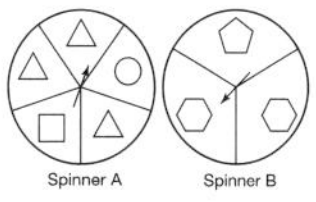
Spinner A Spinner B

- **a.** How many possible outcomes are there? $5 \times 3 = 15$; 15 outcomes.
- **b.** How many ways can you spin a triangle on Spinner A? 3 ways.
- **c.** How many ways can you spin a pentagon on Spinner B? 1 way.
- **d.** What is the probability of spinning a triangle and a pentagon? $\frac{3}{15}$, or $\frac{1}{5}$

Use Spinners A and B for the following exercises.

- **e.** Find the probability of spinning a circle on A and a hexagon on B. $\frac{2}{15}$
- **f.** Find the probability of spinning a triangle on A and a hexagon on B. $\frac{6}{15}$, or $\frac{2}{5}$
- **g.** Find the probability of spinning a square on A and a triangle on B. 0

12-5 Exercises and Applications

Assignment Guide

- **Basic** 1–14, 17, 20
- **Average** 3–17, 20, 21
- **Enriched** 5–22

Exercise Notes

Exercises 2–7

Error Prevention Some students will use addition instead of multiplication to find the possible outcomes. It might be helpful for them to draw tree diagrams to show all possible outcomes.

Exercise 9

Social Studies The ratio of males to females varies from country to country. According to the *Guinness Book of Records*, in 1990 there were 1,153 females for every 1000 males in the Ukraine. But in the United Arab Emirates there were only 493 females for every 1000 males.

Reteaching

Activity

Materials: Coins, number cubes

- Work in groups of three or four and predict the outcome for each of the following events.
- A coin is tossed 4 times and comes up heads each time. Answers may vary. $P(\text{4 heads}) = \frac{1}{2} \times \frac{1}{2} \times \frac{1}{2} \times \frac{1}{2} = \frac{1}{16}$
- A number cube is tossed 3 times and each time the result is 6. Answers may vary. $P(\text{3 sixes}) = \frac{1}{6} \times \frac{1}{6} \times \frac{1}{6} = \frac{1}{216}$
- After you have made your predictions, conduct an experiment and see how the results compare with your predictions.
- You should perform at least 100 trials for each experiment.

Exercise Answers

18. They are the same; The probability of each is $\frac{1}{16}$.

19. A tree diagram lists all the possible outcomes. The first set of branches lists the outcomes for the first event and the second set of branches lists them for the second event.

Alternate Assessment

Self Assessment Have students describe what they think is most difficult about finding the probability of a compound event.

Quick Quiz

The spinner is spun twice.

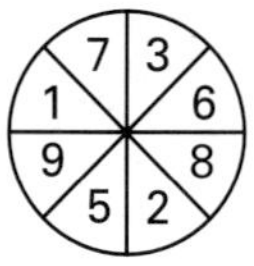

1. Find the probability of spinning an odd number each time. $\frac{25}{64}$
2. Find the probability of spinning an even number and then an odd number. $\frac{15}{64}$
3. Find the probability of spinning an even number each time. $\frac{9}{64}$

Available on Daily Transparency 12-5

---

15. Chance The probability of Josh winning the 50-yard dash at the school track meet is 0.6 and his probability of winning the hurdles is 0.7. Which pair of outcomes listed in the chart does Josh have the greatest chance of accomplishing? **Win, Win**

Dash	Hurdles
Win	Lose
Win	Win
Lose	Win
Lose	Lose

16. Suppose you have 26 cards, and each card has a different letter of the alphabet. Find each probability if you draw a card, put it back, and then draw another. The vowels are *A, E, I, O,* and *U.*

a. P(vowel and then consonant) $\frac{105}{676}$ **b.** P(vowel and then vowel) $\frac{25}{676}$

c. P(consonant and then consonant) $\frac{441}{676}$ **d.** P(X and then Y) $\frac{1}{676}$

Problem Solving and Reasoning

17. Critical Thinking Paul has 6 argyle socks, 8 green socks, and 4 brown socks in his drawer. While getting dressed, he picks out 1 sock at random, doesn't return it, and then picks out another. What is the probability that he picks an argyle sock on both tries? $\frac{5}{51}$

18. Communicate If you flip a coin 4 times, which is greater, P(3 heads and then 1 tail) or P(2 heads and then 2 tails)? Explain.

19. Journal How can a tree diagram help when finding the probability of a two-step event? Explain.

20. Critical Thinking Zack has two spinners with numbers on them. The probability of spinning a "7" on both spinners is $\frac{3}{20}$. If the probability of getting a "7" on the first spinner alone is $\frac{1}{4}$, what is the probability of getting a "7" on the second spinner alone? $\frac{3}{5}$

Mixed Review

21. Which of the three spinners is most likely to have produced the sample data? *[Lesson 12-2]* **#2**

Data:
green, green, yellow, yellow, yellow, yellow, green, green, yellow, green, yellow

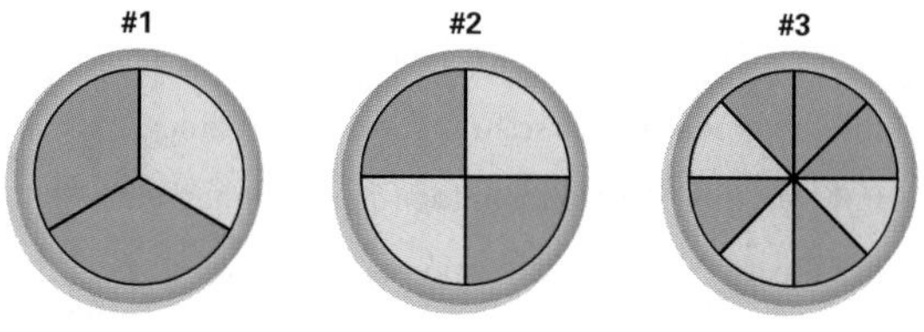

22. Suppose you drop a token on the rectangle shown. Find the probability of the token landing on the red area. *[Lesson 12-3]* $\frac{4}{15}$

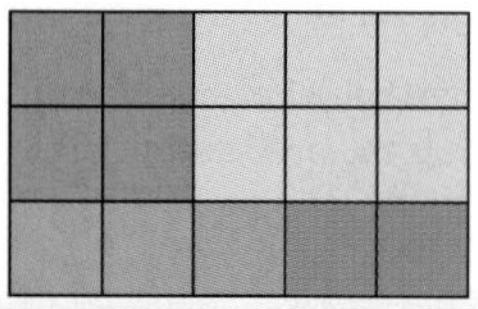

PROBLEM SOLVING 12-5

PROBLEM SOLVING

Name

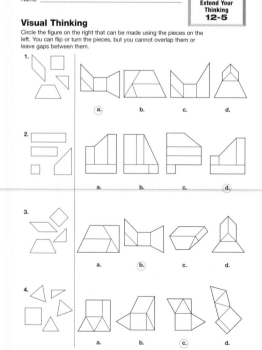

Guided Problem Solving 12-5

GPS PROBLEM 9, STUDENT PAGE 649

The probability of a newborn child being a girl is about $\frac{1}{2}$. What is the probability of all 5 children in a family being girls?

Understand

1. What is the probability of a newborn child being a girl? About $\frac{1}{2}$
2. What are you asked to find?
   The probability that all 5 children in a family are girls.

Plan

3. What is the outcome? a
   a. Gender of the child b. Number of children in family
4. How many possible outcomes are there for each event? 2
5. How many of the possible outcomes normally will be girls? 1
6. How many events are there? 5 events

Solve

7. Multiply to find the total number of possible outcomes for all events.
   2 × 2 × 2 × 2 × 2 = 32
8. Multiply to find the number of possible outcomes that result in the birth of a girl for all events.
   1 × 1 × 1 × 1 × 1 = 1
9. What is the probability of all 5 children in a family being girls as a ratio? $\frac{1}{32}$

Look Back

10. Since the probability given was *about* $\frac{1}{2}$, will your final answer be exact or approximate?
    Approximate; since the given probability is not precise.

SOLVE ANOTHER PROBLEM

What is the probability of all 4 children in a family being boys? $\frac{1}{16}$

ENRICHMENT

Name

Extend Your Thinking 12-5

Visual Thinking

Circle the figure on the right that can be made using the pieces on the left. You can flip or turn the pieces, but you cannot overlap them or leave gaps between them.

1.

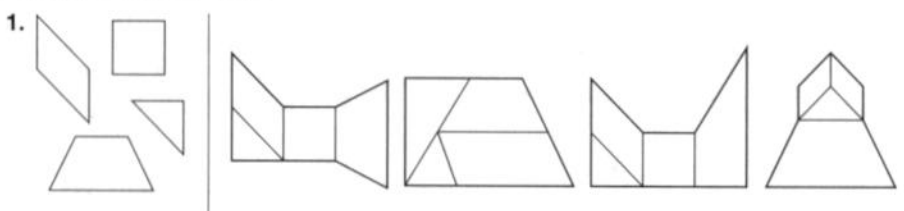

(a.) b. c. d.

2.

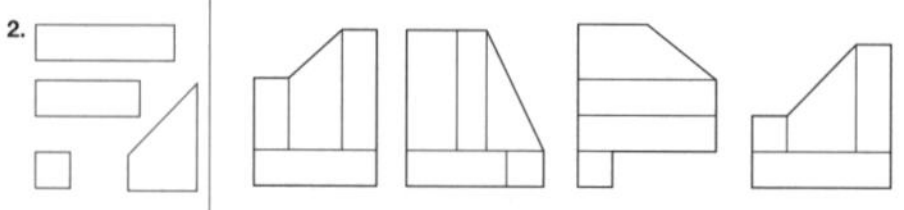

a. b. c. (d.)

3.

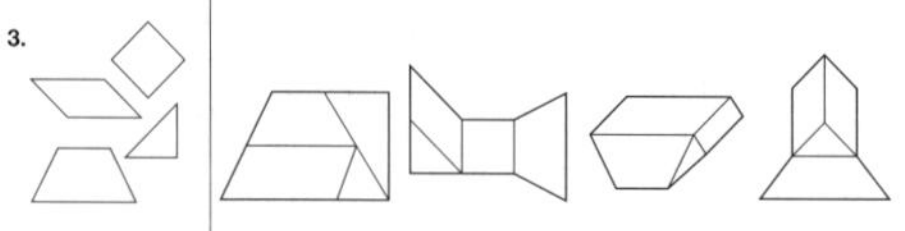

a. (b.) c. d.

4.

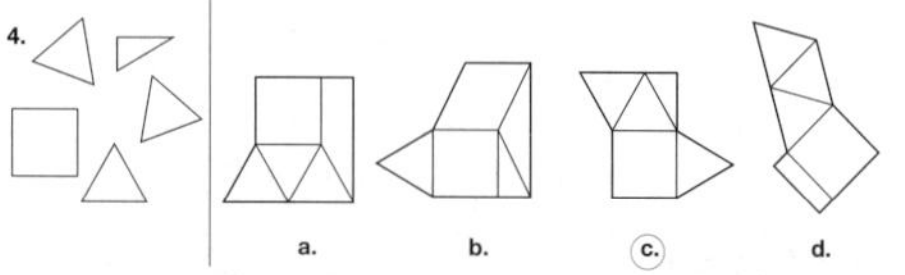

a. b. (c.) d.

Fairness and Unfairness

12-6

▶ **Lesson Link** You know how to find the probability of an event. Now you'll use probability to determine if a game is fair or unfair. ◀

You'll Learn ...

■ to tell if a game is fair

... How It's Used

Bowlers use fairness when determining game handicaps that will make games more even for less experienced players.

Vocabulary

fair

unfair

Explore Fairness and Unfairness

But That's Not Fair!

Get together in groups of three. One person will need to record the data.

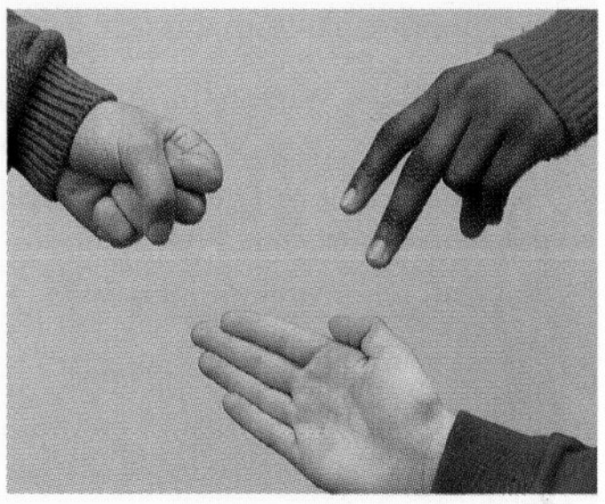

1. Decide who will be Player A, Player B, and Player C.

2. On the count of three, each person should form a hand into Rock, Paper, or Scissors. Player A gets a point if all three hands are the same. Player B gets a point if all three hands are different. Player C gets a point if two hands are the same and one is different.

3. Play the game 20 times, and record how many points each player gets. Based on your data, determine the chances of each player winning.

4. Play the game again 20 times, and record your results. From the new set of data, find the probability of each person winning. Was your second set of data the same as your first set, or different? Explain.

5. Does every player have an equal chance of winning the game? Explain.

Learn Fairness and Unfairness

A game is **fair** if each player has the same probability of winning. The game is **unfair** if one player has a greater probability of winning. You can determine if a game is fair or unfair by comparing the probabilities for winning.

MEETING INDIVIDUAL NEEDS

Resources
12-6 Practice
12-6 Reteaching
12-6 Problem Solving
12-6 Enrichment
12-6 Daily Transparency
Problem of the Day
Review
Quick Quiz
Chapter 12 Project Master
Interactive CD-ROM Lesson

Learning Modalities

Logical Students are asked to determine if the games in Exercises 2–5 on page 653 are fair or unfair. For those games that are unfair, have students change the rules to make the games fair.

Verbal Have students describe other games they have played besides the ones mentioned in the lesson. Then have them discuss if they think the games are fair or unfair.

Inclusion

Most students enjoy playing games. Give all students a chance to play some of the games described in the lesson. Students with disabilities may need extra attention. You may want to participate as a player in some of the games in order to assist any students who may have difficulty with the games. Students may also play in pairs so that they may assist one another.

INTERACTIVE LESSON

12-6 Lesson Organizer

Objective

■ Tell if a game is fair.

Vocabulary

■ Fair, unfair

NCTM Standards

■ 1–4, 11

▶ Review

1. If two coins are tossed, name all possible outcomes. Use H for heads and T for tails. HH, HT, TH, TT

2. If a letter is chosen at random from the alphabet, what is the probability that the letter will be a vowel (A, E, I, O, or U)? $\frac{5}{26}$

Available on Daily Transparency 12-6

1 Introduce

Explore

The Point

Students play the game called Rock, Paper, or Scissors for a total of 20 times and record the results to determine if the game is fair to all players.

Ongoing Assessment

Be sure students realize that if the game is fair, each player should win approximately the same number of times.

Answers for Explore

1–4. Answers may vary.

5. No; Player C has the greatest chance of winning.

$P(\text{A win}) = \frac{1}{9}$.

$P(\text{B win}) = \frac{2}{9}$.

$P(\text{C win}) = \frac{2}{3}$.

2 Teach

Learn

Alternate Examples

1. In a game, 3 coins are tossed. Player A wins if all coins match. Player B wins if exactly two coins match. Is the game fair?

   There are 2 outcomes for each coin. There are $2 \times 2 \times 2$ or 8 possible outcomes. Player A wins if all coins match (H-H-H) or (T-T-T). The probability of player A winning is $\frac{2}{8}$ or 25%. Player B wins if exactly two coins match (H-H-T), (H-T-H), (H-T-T), (T-H-H), (T-H-T), (T-T-H). The probability of player B winning is $\frac{6}{8}$ or 75%. The game is unfair.

2. In a game, each letter of the alphabet is written on a separate card. A card is drawn at random. If the letter is after the letter M, player A wins. Otherwise, player B wins. Is the game fair?

   There are 26 possible outcomes. There are 13 ways for player A to win (N, O, P, Q, R, S, T, U, V, W, X, Y, Z). The probability of player A winning is $\frac{13}{26}$, or 50%. There are also 13 ways for player B to win (A, B, C, D, E, F, G, H, I, J, K, L, M). The probability of player B winning is also $\frac{13}{26}$ or 50%. The game is fair.

3 Practice and Assess

Check

Answers for Check Your Understanding

Possible answers:

1. You may only be interested in playing the game if your chances of winning are equal to all other players.
2. The benefits of winning may be so great that it is worth the chance of losing in hopes of winning.

Remember

You can use multiplication to determine the total number of outcomes. You can use a tree diagram to list all of the possible outcomes.

[Pages 642–643]

Examples

1 In a game, two coins are flipped. If the coins match, Player A wins. If the coins don't match, Player B wins. Is the game fair?

There are 2 outcomes for each coin. There are 2×2 or 4 possible outcomes.

Player A wins if both coins are heads (H-H) or both are tails (T-T). The probability of Player A winning is $\frac{2}{4}$, or 50%.

Player B wins if the first coin is heads and the second tails (H-T) or if the first coin is tails and the second heads (T-H). The probability of Player B winning is $\frac{2}{4}$, or 50%. The game is fair.

2 In a game, each letter of the alphabet is written on a separate card. A card is drawn at random. If the letter is before the letter *M*, Player A wins. Otherwise, Player B wins. Is the game fair?

There are 26 possible outcomes. There are 12 ways for Player A to win (drawing an *A, B, C, D, E, F, G, H, I, J, K,* or *L*). The probability of Player A winning is $\frac{12}{26}$, or about 46%. There are 14 ways for Player B to win. The probability of Player B winning is $\frac{14}{26}$, or about 54%. The game is not fair.

Try It

a. Players A and B each write down a whole number less than 10. If one number is a factor of the other, Player A wins. If not, Player B wins. Is the game fair? No

b. Players A and B each write down a whole number. If the *difference* between the numbers is even, Player A wins. If not, Player B wins. Is the game fair? Yes

Check Your Understanding

1. Why is it important to consider whether or not a game is fair?

2. Why would anyone be willing to play a game that is unfair?

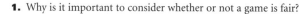

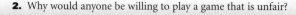

MATH EVERY DAY

Problem of the Day

Ruby Red, Buster Blue, Gracie Green, and Wilbur White were going to play miniature golf. The available colors of golf balls were blue, green, orange, red, white, and yellow. Each player takes one ball at random. Wilbur White went first. He drew a white ball and smiled. If Ruby Red draws next, what is the probability that she will draw a red ball? $\frac{1}{5}$

Available on Daily Transparency 12-6

An Extension is provided in the transparency package.

Fact of the Day

In football, the probability of scoring during the last two minutes of the game is greater than during any other two-minute interval of the game.

Mental Math

Find each sum mentally.

1. 8000 + 80 8080
2. 2000 + 20 + 2 2022
3. 50 + 5000 + 5 5055
4. 300 + 3 + 3000 + 30 3333

12-6 Exercises and Applications

Practice and Apply

1. **Getting Started** In a game, two number cubes are rolled. If the product of the resulting numbers is less than 18, Player A wins. Otherwise Player B wins. Follow these steps to determine if the game is fair.

a. Complete the chart to list the products of the numbers.

b. Find the probability for getting a product less than 18.

c. Find the probability for getting a product greater than or equal to 18.

d. Use the probabilities you found to determine if the game is fair.

First Roll (columns); Second Roll (rows)

	1	2	3	4	5	6
1	1	2	3	4	5	6
2	2				10	
3	3			12		
4	4					
5	5	10				
6	6					36

Problem Solving **For Exercises 2–5, determine if the game is fair. If it is *not*, tell which player has the higher probability of winning.**

2. A blue number cube is labeled −3, 3, 3, −5, 6, 6 and a red number cube is labeled −1, 2, 2, 4, 4, 6. Sheila wins if the number on the blue cube is greater than the number on the red cube. Manda wins if the number on the red cube is greater, or if both numbers are the same. Unfair; Manda

3. A nickel and a dime are tossed. The winner is determined as shown. Fair

GPS

Tim wins

Vern wins

Maggie wins

Urse wins

4. A number cube is tossed. Player 1 wins if the number is less than 3. Otherwise, Player 2 wins. Unfair; Player 2

5. Edna and Charity played a number game 20 times. Charity won 35% of the time. Edna won 65% of the time. Unfair; Edna

6. **Test Prep** The probabilities for each player winning a game are listed. Which group does not represent a fair game? A

Ⓐ $\frac{3}{12}, \frac{2}{4}$ Ⓑ $\frac{4}{8}, \frac{5}{10}$ Ⓒ $\frac{1}{3}, \frac{1}{3}, \frac{1}{3}$ Ⓓ $\frac{7}{14}, \frac{7}{14}$

PRACTICE 12-6

FINISH

PRACTICE

Name ____________________

Practice 12-6

Fairness and Unfairness

For Exercises 1–9, determine if the game is fair. If it is *not*, tell which player has the higher probability of winning.

1. A number cube is tossed. Evan wins if the number is even. Otherwise, Arnold wins. Fair

2. Tina and Jody use a computer to select two random numbers from 1 to 10. Tina wins if both numbers are prime or neither is prime. If one number is prime and the other is not, Jody wins. Not fair; Tina

3. Kim and Lance played a coin toss game 25 times. Kim won 60% of the games and Lance won 40%. Need more information

4. Two number cubes are tossed. If both numbers are even, Amy wins. If both numbers are odd, Brad wins. Otherwise, Cheryl wins. Not fair; Cheryl

5. A random number from 1 to 9 is selected. If the number is 5 or greater, Kelly wins. If it is less than 5, Hoang wins. Not fair; Kelly

6. Three coins are tossed. If there are more heads than tails, Beth wins. Otherwise, Dara wins. Fair

7. **Fine Arts** The color pairs on opposite sides of the spinner shown (such as blue and orange) are called *complementary colors.* The spinner is spun twice. If the two colors are the same or complementary, Steve wins. Otherwise, Anson wins.

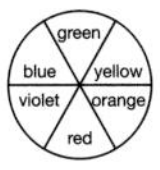

Not fair; Anson

8. The spinner in Exercise 7 is spun twice. If the two colors are the same or next to each other on the spinner, Kyle wins. Otherwise, Francis wins.

Fair

9. Carol, James, Nancy, and Tara played a card game 28 times. Tara made a bar graph to show how many times each player won. Can you be certain that the game was fair?

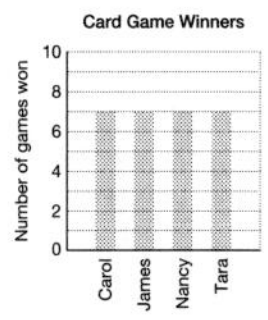

No

RETEACHING

Name ____________________

Alternative Lesson 12-6

Fairness and Unfairness

A game is **fair** if each player has the same probability of winning. The game is **unfair** if one player has a greater probability of winning. You can determine if a game is fair or unfair by comparing the probabilities for winning.

Example

In a game, 2 counters are tossed. One side of each counter is black and the other side is white. Player A wins if the colors are the same and Player B wins if the colors are different. Is the game fair?

There are 2 outcomes for each cube. Since there are two cubes, there are 2 × 2 or 4 possible outcomes.

Player A wins if both counters are black or if both are white. The probability of Player A winning is $\frac{2}{4}$, or $\frac{1}{2}$, or 50%, so the game is fair.

Try It There are 4 green buttons and 8 blue buttons in a bag. Player A wins if a green button is pulled out, Player B wins if a blue button is pulled out.

a. How many possible outcomes are there? 12 possible outcomes.

b. In how many ways can Player A win? 4 ways.

c. In how many ways can Player B win? 8 ways.

d. What is the probability of Player A winning? $\frac{4}{12}$, or $\frac{1}{3}$, or about 33%

e. What is the probability of Player B winning? $\frac{8}{12}$, or $\frac{2}{3}$, or about 67%

f. Is the game fair or unfair? Explain. Unfair, the probability of winning is not equal for each player.

Decide if each is a fair or unfair game. Explain.

g. A twelve-sided number cube is rolled. Player C wins if the number rolled is even. Player D wins is the number rolled is odd.
Fair; the probability of winning is 50% for each player.

h. Three coins are tossed. Player E wins if 1 head and 2 tails are tossed. Player F wins if 3 tails are tossed.
Unfair; the probability of winning is $\frac{3}{8}$ or 37.5% for Player E and $\frac{1}{8}$ or 12.5% for Player F.

12-6 Exercises and Applications

Assignment Guide

- Basic
  1, 3–8, 11
- Average
  2–9, 11
- Enriched
  3–12

Exercise Notes

Exercise 2

Error Prevention Some students will fail to realize that there are 36 possible ways in which the two number cubes can land. It will be helpful if they make a chart similar to the one suggested in Exercise 1.

Exercise Answers

1. a.

First Roll (columns); Second Roll (rows)

	1	2	3	4	5	6
1	1	2	3	4	5	6
2	2	4	6	8	10	12
3	3	6	9	12	15	18
4	4	8	12	16	20	24
5	5	10	15	20	25	30
6	6	12	18	24	30	36

b. $\frac{13}{18}$

c. $\frac{5}{18}$

d. The game is not fair.

Reteaching

Activity

Materials: Coins

- Work with a partner. Use 3 coins to play the following game.
- Toss 3 coins.
- Player A wins if two or more coins are heads. Otherwise, player B wins.
- Play the game for at least 50 trials to see if the game seems to be fair.
- Explain why you think the game is fair or unfair. The game is fair because there are 8 possible outcomes when 3 coins are tossed. Exactly 4 of the outcomes (HHH, HHT, HTH, THH) involve 2 or more heads.

Exercise Notes

■ Exercise 7

Error Prevention Some students say the game is unfair because the results are not equal for each possible outcome. Point out that there are 6 possible outcomes and 50 is not a multiple of 6. So it is impossible to get equal results for each outcome. Also, in real-life experiments, the results frequently vary slightly from the predicted outcome.

Project Progress

You may want to have students use Chapter 12 Project Master.

Exercise Answers

11. See page C6.

Alternate Assessment

You may want to use the *Interactive CD-ROM Journal* with this assessment.

Journal Have students write a paragraph describing how they would try to determine if a game is fair or unfair.

Quick Quiz

Decide if each game is fair. If it is not, tell which player has the higher probability of winning.

1. Two number cubes are tossed. If the sum of the numbers is 7 or less, player A wins. Otherwise, player B wins. Player A has the better chance.
2. A number is picked at random from the set consisting of 2, 3, 4, 5, 6, 7, 8, 9. Player A wins if the number is prime. Otherwise, player B wins. Fair.

Available on Daily Transparency 12-6

7. Daryn rolled a number cube 50 times and recorded how many times he got each number. His bar graph is shown. Is it possible that Daryn is using a fair cube?
Yes; The data from a fair cube doesn't always come out exactly evenly.

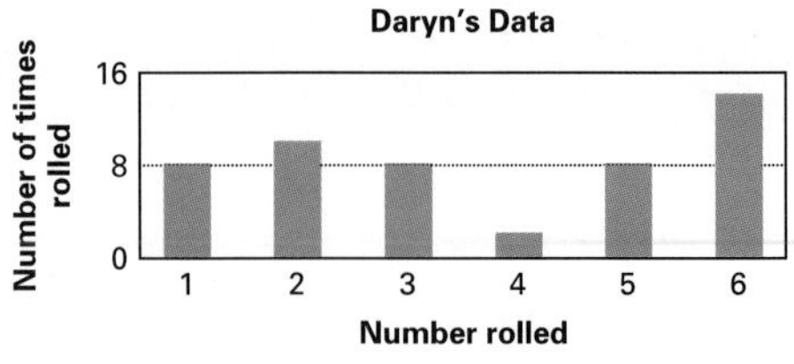

Problem Solving and Reasoning

8. Communicate In many games, the team or person that goes first is determined by flipping a coin. Heads goes first, tails goes second. Why do you think this is such a common method?
It's fair, and coins are easy to find.

9. Critical Thinking You and a friend toss a coin to decide who will go first for a game. Your friends says, "Heads I win. Tails you lose." Is this method fair or unfair? Explain. Unfair; Either way, you always lose.

10. Journal In a game, the probability that Player A wins is 40%. The probability that Player B wins is 40%. The probability that neither player wins is 20%. Is this game fair? Explain your reasoning. Yes; Both players have the same chance of winning.

Mixed Review

11. Draw a tree diagram showing the following. *[Lesson 12-4]*

a. The possible outcomes for tossing 3 coins.

b. The possible pizza combinations using 5 different toppings, 2 different cheeses, and 3 different crusts. Assume each pizza has one topping, one cheese, and one crust.

12. What is the probability of spinning a number less than 5 on Spinner 1 and an A on Spinner 2? *[Lesson 12-5]* $\frac{1}{8}$

Project Progress

Make tickets for each game. On the tickets, state the probability of winning the game. Explain the probability of winning, and make sure that each game is fair. Decide on prizes for the winners, and describe the prizes on the tickets. Schedule a time for your fun fair.

Problem Solving
Understand
Plan
Solve
Look Back

PROBLEM SOLVING 12-6

PROBLEM SOLVING

Name ______________________

Guided Problem Solving 12-6

GPS PROBLEM 3, STUDENT PAGE 653

Determine if the game is fair. If it is *not*, tell which player has the higher probability of winning.

A nickel and a dime are tossed. The winner is determined as shown.

Tim wins   Vern wins   Maggie wins   Urse wins

Understand

1. How many possible outcomes are there when the coins are tossed? 4
2. How many possible outcomes are the same? None.

Plan

3. What is the probability that Tim will win? $\frac{1}{4}$, or 25%
4. What is the probability that Maggie will win? $\frac{1}{4}$, or 25%
5. What is the probability that Vern will win? $\frac{1}{4}$, or 25%
6. What is the probability that Urse will win? $\frac{1}{4}$, or 25%

Solve

7. Is the game fair or unfair? Explain.
Fair; each player has an equal chance of winning.

Look Back

8. Both Tim's and Vern's coins show a head and a tail? How do they differ?
The heads and tails appear on different coins.

SOLVE ANOTHER PROBLEM

Suppose Tim, Vern, and Urse toss two nickels. Tim wins if two tails are tossed. Vern wins if two heads are tossed. Urse wins if a head and a tail are tossed. Is the game fair or unfair? Explain.
Unfair; P(2 tails) = $\frac{1}{4}$; P(2 heads) = $\frac{1}{4}$; P(1 head and 1 tail) = $\frac{1}{2}$.
Urse has a better chance of winning.

ENRICHMENT

Name ______________________

Extend Your Thinking 12-6

Critical Thinking

The class asked Joleen to set up a corner in the classroom filled with math games. Help her determine which of the following games are fair and which are unfair. If a game is unfair, tell what can be done to make it fair. Possible answers: Items 1-3

Game 1
Players take turns rolling two cubes numbered 1–6. Player A scores a point if the sum of the two numbers is even. Player B scores a point if the sum of the two numbers is odd. The first player to reach 10 points is the winner.

Fair; P(even sum) = $\frac{1}{2}$, P(odd sum) = $\frac{1}{2}$.

Game 2
Players take turns rolling two number cubes. Player A scores a point if the product of the two numbers is even. Player B scores a point if the product of the two numbers is odd. The first player to reach 10 points is the winner.

Unfair; P(even product) = $\frac{3}{4}$, P(odd product) = $\frac{1}{4}$. To make it fair, let one player score if product is less than 10 and other score if product is greater than 10.

Game 3
Players take turns rolling two number cubes. Player A scores a point if the difference between the numbers is even. Player B scores a point if the difference is odd. No one scores a point if the difference is 0. The first player to reach 10 points is the winner.

Unfair; P(even difference) = $\frac{1}{3}$; P(odd difference) = $\frac{1}{2}$; P(zero) = $\frac{1}{6}$; To make it fair, let Player A score if the difference is even or zero.

Help Joleen design another game to put in the math game corner. You can use number cubes, spinners, cards, and so on. Check students' answers.

Section 12B Connect

You learned how to find all possible outcomes by making tree diagrams, to calculate the probability of a compound event occurring, and to use probabilities to decide whether or not a game is fair. Now, you will use these ideas to design two games of chance.

Free Parking!

You will be designing two games of chance. When designing the games, you must follow these instructions:

1. Both games must be games of chance.
2. You can use any materials for either game, such as cards, number cubes, or spinners. You can use the same materials for both games, or a different set for each game.
3. One game should be a fair game. The other game should be an unfair game.
4. Each game should be accompanied by a set of rules clearly written, so that anyone could understand how to play the game.
5. Each game should have a written explanation of how you determined that the game was fair or unfair.

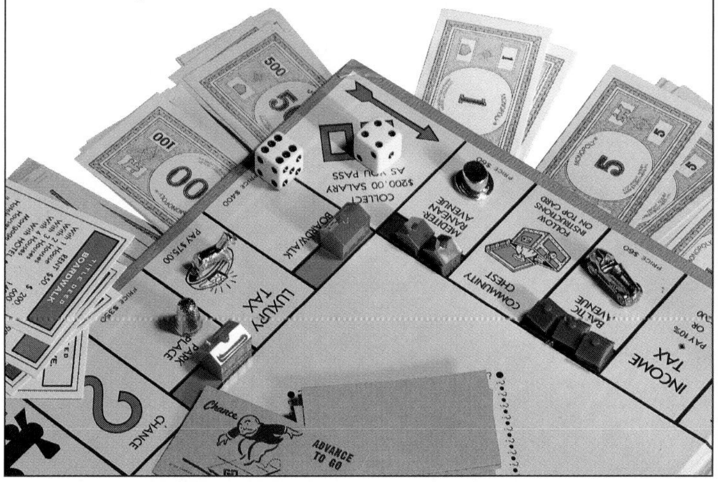

655

Free Parking

The Point

In *Free Parking* on page 641, students learned about the history of Monopoly. Now, they will use probability to design two games of chance.

About the Page

- Discuss the materials that are available for the students to use in designing their game.
- Explain to students that they need to keep in mind the number of players, the point of the game, how players take turns, how someone wins the game, and so on as they design their games and that all of this information should appear in the rules.
- Remind students that one of the games should be fair and the other should be unfair.

Ongoing Assessment

Check that students have designed appropriate games and written reasonable sets of rules.

Extension

Now that students have designed games, give them the opportunity to play some of the games. Divide students into groups of 4 and ask each group to play one of the games. Ask if they understand the rules of the game and if it is fair or unfair.

Answers for Connect

1–5. Answers may vary.

12B Review

Review Correlation

Item(s)	Lesson(s)
1	12-4, 12-5
2–4	12-5
5	12-4, 12-5
6–8	12-6

Test Prep

Test-Taking Tip

Sometimes, but not in this case, there will be more than one correct answer. Suggest that students consider all possible choices. In this case, B and C each offer a combination of choices.

Answers for Review

4. No; No matter where the circle is, the ratio of the nonshaded area to the total area is still the same.

6. Yes; $P(\text{A win}) = P(\text{B win}) = \frac{1}{2}$

7. No; $P(\text{A win}) = \frac{3}{8}$, $P(\text{B win}) = \frac{5}{8}$

Section 12B Review

1. Suppose you toss three coins.

a. How many possible outcomes are there? 8

b. What is the probability for each outcome happening? $\frac{1}{8}$

2. Laurel made 12 oatmeal cookies, 10 sugar cookies, and 15 chocolate chip cookies. Her brother took a cookie at random. What is the probability that he *didn't* take a chocolate chip cookie? $\frac{22}{37}$

3. There is one of four different prizes inside each box of Toastie Oaties. If you buy three boxes, what is the probability of getting the same prize in each box? $\frac{1}{64}$

4. Geometry Suppose you toss a quarter onto a 2-foot square that has a 1-foot diameter circular region shaded. Does the probability of the quarter landing outside the circular region depend on the location of the circle? Explain.

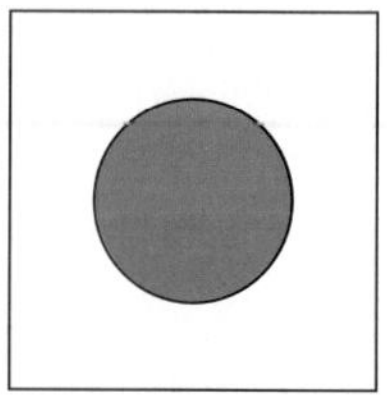

5. A locker combination has three numbers. Each number is a whole number from 1 to 35.

a. How many locker combinations are possible if the numbers can be repeated? 42,875

b. What is the probability that someone could choose the correct combination in one try? $\frac{1}{42{,}875}$

6. Two coins are tossed. Player A wins if they both land with the same side up. Player B wins if they land differently. Is the game fair? Explain.

7. One 8-sided die whose sides are numbered 1 through 8 is tossed. Player A wins if the number on top is less than 4. Player B wins if the number on top is greater than 3. Is the game fair? Explain.

Test Prep

In order for a game to be fair, all players must have an even chance of winning.

8. The following percentages list the chances of each player winning different 3-player games. Which game is fair? D

I. 20%, 30%, 40% **II.** 40%, 40%, 20% **III.** 50%, 50%, 0%

Ⓐ Only I Ⓑ II and III Ⓒ I, II, and III Ⓓ Not here

REVIEW 12B

Resources

Practice Masters
Section 12B Review

Assessment Sourcebook
Quiz 12B

TestWorks
Test and Practice Software

PRACTICE

Name ______________________ Practice

Section 12B Review

1. Suppose you roll three different-colored number cubes.
   a. How many outcomes are there? 216
   b. What is the probability for each outcome? $\frac{1}{216}$
2. A fast-food restaurant gives you one of 5 different drinking glasses with each meal. If you order 2 meals, what is the possibility that your drinking glasses will match? $\frac{1}{5}$
3. Eileen is making cupcakes. Each cupcake is made with either chocolate or vanilla cake and chocolate, vanilla, or mint frosting. Each cupcake also has either chopped nuts or colored sprinkles. How many different kinds of cupcakes can Eileen make? 12
4. Your uncle tells you that his license plate has 5 digits, and each digit is either 2, 4, or 6.
   a. How many different license plates can match this description? 243
   b. If you try to guess the license plate, what is the probability that you guess correctly? $\frac{1}{243}$
5. A random 2-digit number (10 to 99) is chosen. Anthony wins if the tens digit is greater than the units digit. Otherwise, Carlos, wins. Is the game fair? Explain.
   Yes. Possible explanation: Each player's probability of winning is $\frac{45}{90} = \frac{1}{2}$.
6. Two nickels and a dime are tossed. Candy wins if the value of the coins that come up heads is greater than the value of the coins that come up tails. Otherwise, Frederick wins. Is the game fair? Explain.
   No. Possible explanation: Candy's probability of winning is $\frac{3}{8}$ and Frederick's probability of winning is $\frac{5}{8}$.
7. The average daily minimum temperature for January is −14°F in Gulkana, Alaska, and 3°F in Minneapolis, Minnesota. How much warmer is the temperature in Minneapolis than in Gulkana? *[Lesson 9-3]* 17°F
8. A can of fancy mixed nuts has diameter 10.0 cm and height 9.3 cm. Find the surface area of the can. *[Lesson 11-4]* About 449.02 cm^2

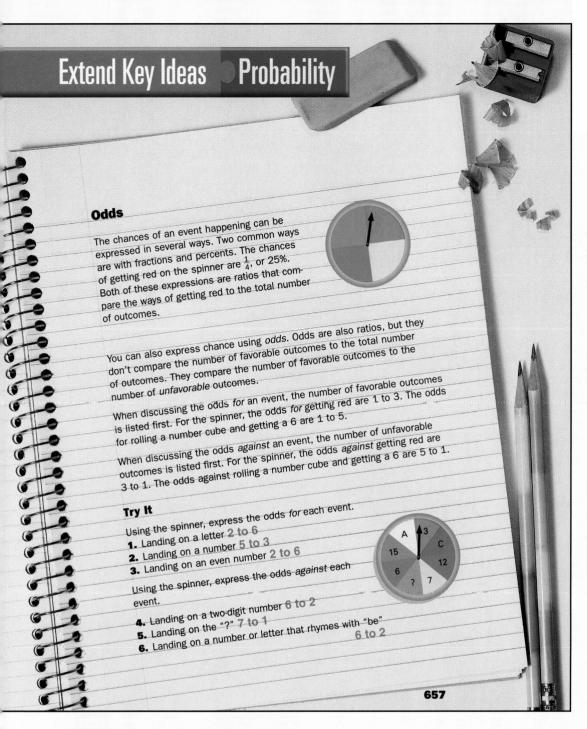

Extend Key Ideas ● Probability

Odds

The chances of an event happening can be expressed in several ways. Two common ways are with fractions and percents. The chances of getting red on the spinner are $\frac{1}{4}$, or 25%. Both of these expressions are ratios that compare the ways of getting red to the total number of outcomes.

You can also express chance using *odds*. Odds are also ratios, but they don't compare the number of favorable outcomes to the total number of outcomes. They compare the number of favorable outcomes to the number of *unfavorable* outcomes.

When discussing the odds *for* an event, the number of favorable outcomes is listed first. For the spinner, the odds *for* getting red are 1 to 3. The odds for rolling a number cube and getting a 6 are 1 to 5.

When discussing the odds *against* an event, the number of unfavorable outcomes is listed first. For the spinner, the odds *against* getting red are 3 to 1. The odds against rolling a number cube and getting a 6 are 5 to 1.

Try It

Using the spinner, express the odds *for* each event.

1. Landing on a letter 2 to 6
2. Landing on a number 5 to 3
3. Landing on an even number 2 to 6

Using the spinner, express the odds *against* each event.

4. Landing on a two-digit number 6 to 2
5. Landing on the "?" 7 to 1
6. Landing on a number or letter that rhymes with "be" 6 to 2

657

Extend Key Ideas

Odds

The Point

Students learn to express chance in terms of odds for an event and against an event occurring.

About the Page

- Odds and probability are two different ways of expressing the same thing.

Ask …

Why do you think that odds, rather than probabilities, are given for betting purposes ? Possible answer: Odds of 1 to 3 sound like you have a better chance of winning than saying that the likelihood of your winning is 1 in 4.

- If the odds in favor of an outcome are 3 to 5, what is the probability of that particular outcome? $\frac{3}{8}$
- If the probability of an outcome is $\frac{4}{7}$, what are the odds against that particular outcome? 3 to 4

Extension

Have students explain the rules of their favorite game and determine the odds of winning that game.

Chapter 12 Summary and Review

Review Correlation

Item(s)	Lesson(s)
1, 2	12-1
3, 4	12-2
5	12-3
6, 7	12-4
8–11	12-5
12,13	12-6

For additional review, see page 673.

Chapter 12 Summary and Review

Graphic Organizer

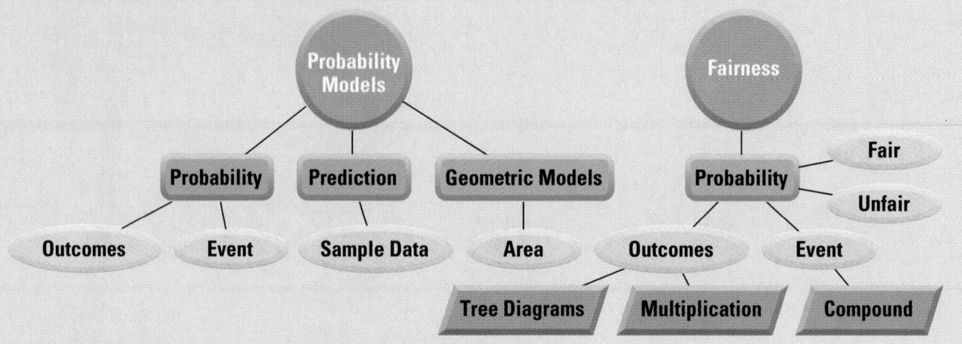

Section 12A Probability Models

Summary

- The **outcomes** of an **experiment** are all the results that can happen. The **probability** that an **event** or particular outcome will happen is a ratio.

  $P(\text{event}) = \dfrac{\text{number of ways an event can occur}}{\text{number of possible outcomes}}$

- When you don't know all the possible outcomes or the number of ways an event can occur, you can use **sample** data and make a prediction.
- When the chance of an event happening depends on the size of an area inside a figure, you can determine its probability using a ratio.

Review

1. Estimate the probability of having a birthday in a month that begins with a *J*. About $\frac{1}{4}$
2. If $P(\text{event}) = \frac{5}{6}$, what can you conclude about the event? It is likely to occur.
3. Jim is on call at work one day each week. What are his chances of being called to work on Tuesday, Wednesday, or Friday? $\frac{3}{7}$
4. Estimate the probability of hitting the shaded area with a dart. About $\frac{1}{4}$

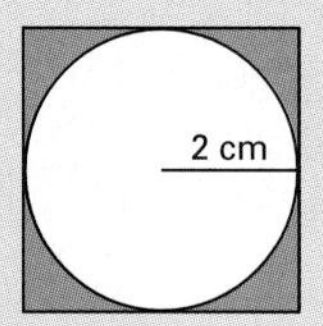

5. Nine businesses out of 27 surveyed on Main Street were closed more than 5 days because of a recent flood. Predict how many of the 48 businesses on the street were closed more than 5 days. 16

Resources

Practice Masters
Cumulative Review Chapters 1–12

Assessment Sourcebook
Quarterly Test Chapters 1–12

PRACTICE

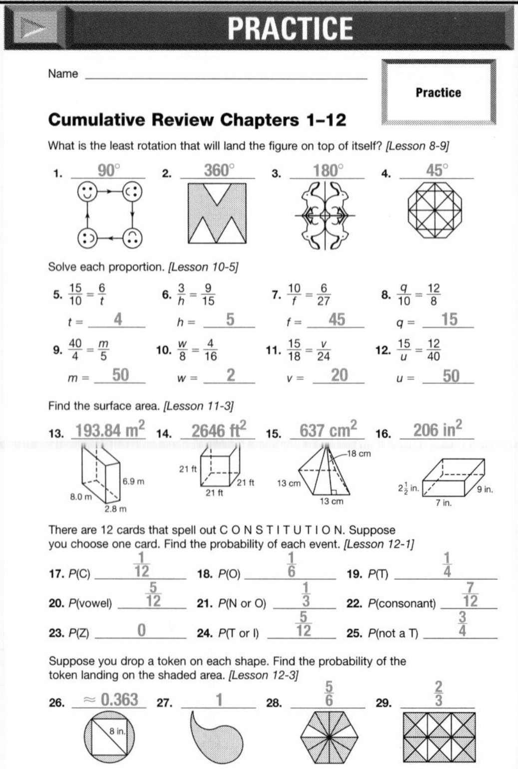
Name ______ Practice

Cumulative Review Chapters 1–12

What is the least rotation that will land the figure on top of itself? [Lesson 8-9]

1. 90° 2. 360° 3. 180° 4. 45°

Solve each proportion. [Lesson 10-5]

5. $\frac{15}{10} = \frac{6}{t}$ $t = 4$ 6. $\frac{3}{h} = \frac{9}{15}$ $h = 5$ 7. $\frac{10}{f} = \frac{6}{27}$ $f = 45$ 8. $\frac{q}{10} = \frac{12}{8}$ $q = 15$

9. $\frac{40}{4} = \frac{m}{5}$ $m = 50$ 10. $\frac{w}{8} = \frac{4}{16}$ $w = 2$ 11. $\frac{15}{18} = \frac{v}{24}$ $v = 20$ 12. $\frac{15}{u} = \frac{12}{40}$ $u = 50$

Find the surface area. [Lesson 11-3]

13. 193.84 m^2 14. 2646 ft^2 15. 637 cm^2 16. 206 in^2

There are 12 cards that spell out C O N S T I T U T I O N. Suppose you choose one card. Find the probability of each event. [Lesson 12-1]

17. P(C) $\frac{1}{12}$ 18. P(O) $\frac{1}{6}$ 19. P(T) $\frac{1}{4}$

20. P(vowel) $\frac{5}{12}$ 21. P(N or O) $\frac{1}{3}$ 22. P(consonant) $\frac{7}{12}$

23. P(Z) 0 24. P(T or I) $\frac{5}{12}$ 25. P(not a T) $\frac{3}{4}$

Suppose you drop a token on each shape. Find the probability of the token landing on the shaded area. [Lesson 12-3]

26. ≈ 0.363 27. 1 28. $\frac{5}{6}$ 29. $\frac{2}{3}$

Section 12B Fairness

Summary

- A **tree diagram** is used to list the outcomes of a series of experiments. You can also use multiplication to find the number of possible outcomes.
- You can find the probability of a **compound event** using a ratio:
  $\frac{\text{the number of ways a compound event can happen}}{\text{the number of possible outcomes}}$.
- A game is **fair** if each player has an equal probability of winning. Otherwise, it is **unfair.**

Review

6. Complete a tree diagram that shows how many different outfits can be worn if there are 2 kinds of shirts (T-shirts and sweatshirts), 4 types of pants (shorts, dress pants, jeans, and cutoffs), and 3 kinds of shoes (loafers, hiking boots, and sandals.) 24 outfits

7. Use multiplication to find the possible number of fishing-gear combinations that could be assembled using 5 poles, 3 kinds of spinners, 2 kinds of floaters, and a box of 6 hand-tied flies. 180

8. If you spin both of the spinners, how many possible outcomes are there? 8

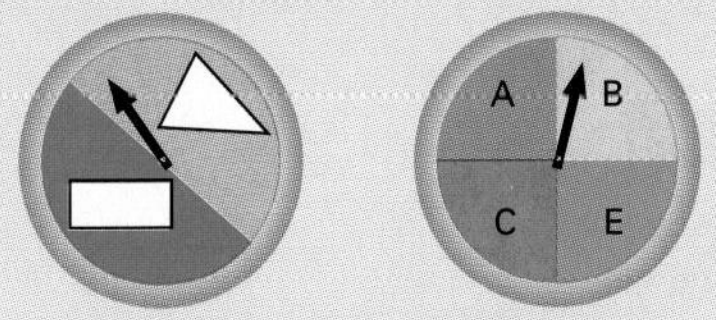

Spinner 1 Spinner 2

9. What is the probability of spinning a blue or red on Spinner 1 and a vowel on Spinner 2? $\frac{1}{3}$

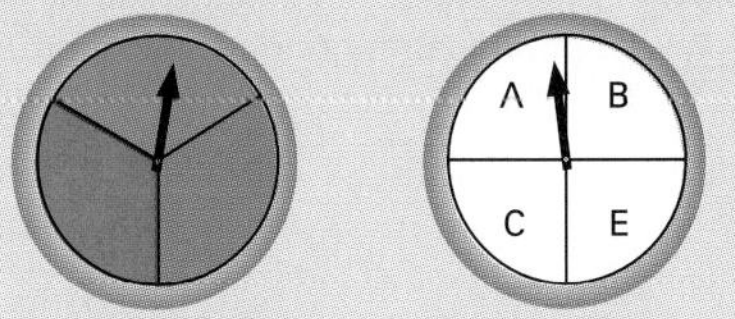

Spinner 1 Spinner 2

10. Jane rolls a six-sided number cube twice. What is the probability that she rolls a 3 and then a 1? $\frac{1}{36}$

11. What is the probability of flipping four coins and getting all tails? $\frac{1}{16}$

12.

5	10	15	20	25
30	35	40	45	50

In a card game, each card is labeled with one of the multiples of 5, from 5 to 50. Player A draws a card. If the number is 25 or less, Player A wins. Otherwise, Player B wins. Is the game fair? Explain.

13. Player A and Player B each roll a number cube. If the two numbers can be put together to make a 2-digit even number, Player A wins. Otherwise, Player B wins. Is the game fair? Explain.

Answers for Review

6. See page C6.
12. Yes; Each player has a 50% chance of winning.
13. No; Player A has a greater chance of winning.

Chapter 12 Assessment

Assessment Correlation

Item(s)	Lesson(s)
1, 2	12-1
3	12-5
4–6	12-2
7	12-4, 12-5
8	12-3
9	12-4
10	12-5

Answers for Assessment

6. Good; $\frac{320}{500} = 0.64 = 64\%$, $64\% > 51\%$.

Answer for Performance Task

The game is unfair as Players A and C each have a $\frac{1}{4}$ chance of getting a point, but Player B has a $\frac{4}{9}$ chance of scoring.

Chapter 12 Assessment

For questions 1–3, tell whether the statement is true or false. If it is false, change the words in bold to make it true.

1. The probability of an event = $\dfrac{\textbf{number of possible outcomes}}{\textbf{number of ways an event can happen}}$. False; $\dfrac{\text{number of ways an event can happen}}{\text{number of possible outcomes}}$

2. The **outcomes** of a situation are all the ways something can happen. True

3. A **compound event** lists the outcomes of a series of experiments. False; Tree diagram

4. One event has a probability of 65%, and one has a probability of $\frac{4}{5}$. Which is more likely to occur? The event with a probability of $\frac{4}{5}$.

5. An airline randomly assigns passengers to seats in rows 15 through 32. What are the chances of being assigned to a row number higher than 21? $\frac{11}{18}$

6. In an election poll, 320 out of 500 people said they would vote for a school bond issue. The bond issue needs 51% of the votes to pass. What are its chances of passing? Explain.

7. Two number cubes are tossed.

a. How many outcomes are there? 36

b. What is the probability that the number on each cube is a multiple of 3? $\frac{1}{9}$

8. If a button lands on the game board, what is the chance it will land on a shaded triangle? 50%

9. a. Name two methods of finding the number of possible kinds of sundaes that can be made with vanilla, chocolate, and strawberry ice creams; fudge, pineapple, raspberry, and cherry syrups; and toppings of peanuts, coconut, raisins, or candies. Tree diagram or multiplication

b. How many different sundaes can be made? 48

10. If you spin both spinners, what is the probability that the pointers will land on a circle and a triangle? $\frac{3}{8}$

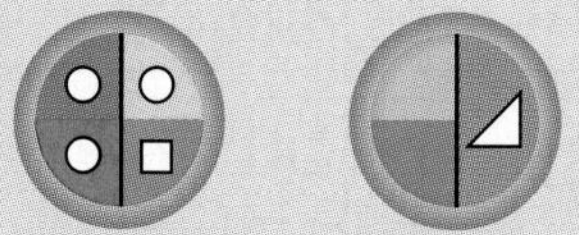

Spinner 1 Spinner 2

Performance Task

Roll two number cubes. If both numbers are prime, Player A gets a point. If both numbers are less than 5, Player B gets a point. If both numbers are even, Player C gets a point. Is the game fair or unfair? Explain.

Resources

Assessment Sourcebook

Chapter 12 Tests
- Forms A and B (free response)
- Form C (multiple choice)
- Form D (performance assessment)
- Form E (mixed response)
- Form F (cumulative chapter test)

TestWorks
Test and Practice Software

Home and Community Connections
- Letter Home for Chapter 12 in English and Spanish

Cumulative Review Chapters 1–12

Test Prep

Multiple Choice

Choose the best answer.

1. Divide 8.442 by 0.42. *[Lesson 3-11]* **C**

Ⓐ 0.021 Ⓑ 0.201

Ⓒ 20.1 Ⓓ 21

2. What conversion factor do you multiply by to convert from quarts to pints? *[Lesson 4-3]* **B**

Ⓐ 4 Ⓑ 2

Ⓒ $\frac{1}{2}$ Ⓓ $\frac{1}{4}$

3. Find the least common multiple of 36 and 54. *[Lesson 5-3]* **D**

Ⓐ 2 Ⓑ 9 Ⓒ 18 Ⓓ 108

4. Subtract: $4\frac{3}{8} - 3\frac{1}{2}$ *[Lesson 6-6]* **A**

Ⓐ $\frac{7}{8}$ Ⓑ $1\frac{1}{3}$

Ⓒ $1\frac{7}{8}$ Ⓓ $9\frac{7}{8}$

5. Multiply: $\frac{2}{3} \times 1\frac{5}{6}$ *[Lesson 7-3]* **A**

Ⓐ $1\frac{2}{9}$ Ⓑ $1\frac{4}{9}$

Ⓒ $2\frac{1}{3}$ Ⓓ None of these

6. Which description best fits the pair of lines? *[Lesson 8-1]* **D**

Ⓐ Parallel Ⓑ Perpendicular

Ⓒ Perpendicular and intersecting

Ⓓ Intersecting

7. If a figure with point $A($ 3, 4) is reflected over the x-axis, what is its image point? *[Lesson 8-8]* **C**

Ⓐ (3, 4) Ⓑ (3, −4)

Ⓒ (−3, 4) Ⓓ None of these

8. Find the product of -7×4. *[Lesson 9-4]* **D**

Ⓐ 28 Ⓑ 27 Ⓒ −27 Ⓓ −28

9. Which point does not lie on the graph of $y = -3x$? *[Lesson 9-7]* **B**

Ⓐ (10, −30) Ⓑ (−30, 10)

Ⓒ (−2, 6) Ⓓ (6, −18)

10. The sides of one triangle measure 3 ft, 5 ft, and 6 ft. The shortest side of a similar triangle measures 18 ft. What are the lengths of its other two sides? *[Lesson 10-7]* **B**

Ⓐ 30 ft, 48 ft Ⓑ 30 ft, 36 ft

Ⓒ 11 ft, 15 ft Ⓓ 6 ft, 10 ft

11. If Sandra saves 35% on the purchase of a $22 dress, how much does she save? *[Lesson 10-11]* **C**

Ⓐ $77.70 Ⓑ $14.30

Ⓒ $7.70 Ⓓ None of these

12. Find the surface area to the nearest tenth of a cylinder whose base has a radius of 4 cm and whose height is 2 cm. *[Lesson 11-4]* **B**

Ⓐ 196.5 cm^2 Ⓑ 150.7 cm^2

Ⓒ 50.2 cm^2 Ⓓ 25.1 cm^2

13. Find the volume of the box. *[Lesson 11-6]* **A**

Ⓐ 84 in^3

Ⓑ 66 in^3

Ⓒ 33 in^3

Ⓓ 84 in^2

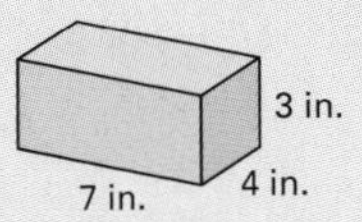

14. Eleven cards spell MATHEMATICS. What is the probability of picking an A card? *[Lesson 12-1]* **A**

Ⓐ $\frac{2}{11}$ Ⓑ $\frac{11}{2}$

Ⓒ $\frac{1}{5}$ Ⓓ None of these

Cumulative Review Test Prep

About Multiple-Choice Tests

The Cumulative Review found at the end of Chapters 2, 4, 6, 8, 10, and 12 can be used to prepare students for standardized tests.

Students sometimes do not perform as well on standardized tests as they do on other tests. There may be several reasons for this related to the format and content of the test.

- **Format**
Students may have limited experience with multiple-choice tests. For some questions, such tests are harder because having options may confuse the students.
- **Content**
A standardized test may cover a broader range of content than normally covered on a test, and the relative emphasis given to various strands may be different than given in class. Also, some questions may assess general aptitude or thinking skills and not include specific pieces of mathematical content.

It is important not to let the differences between standardized tests and other tests shake your students' confidence.

STUDENT RESOURCES

CONTENTS

Chapter 1 Review

Answers

1. $40
2. June
3. No, because the points do not lie near any straight line.
4. $11\frac{1}{2}$
5.

Score	Tally	Frequency
Under 70	II	2
70–79	卌 II	7
80–89	卌 I	6
90–100	卌	5

6.

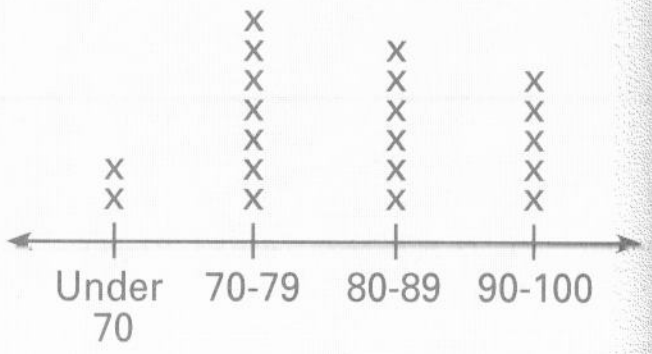

7.

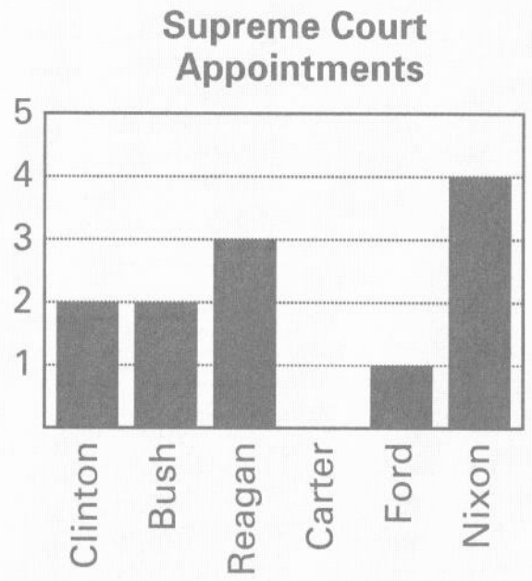

8.

Stem	Leaf
3	7 9
4	0 1 2 2 2 3 3 4 5 7 8
5	1 4 6

9. Median: 740.5; Mode: none; Mean: 790.7
10. The mean, because one outlier can dramatically change the total of the data, which will dramatically change the mean.

Chapter Review

Chapter 1 Review

1. How much was spent on clothes and entertainment?

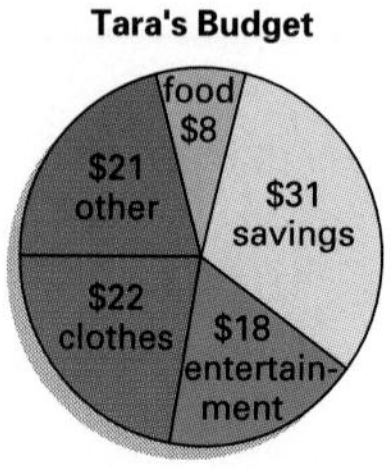

2. In which month did the sales of hot dogs increase the most when compared to the month before?

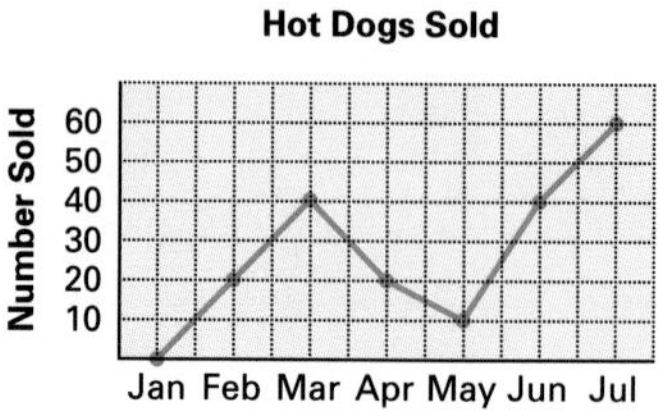

3. Does the scatterplot show a trend? Explain.

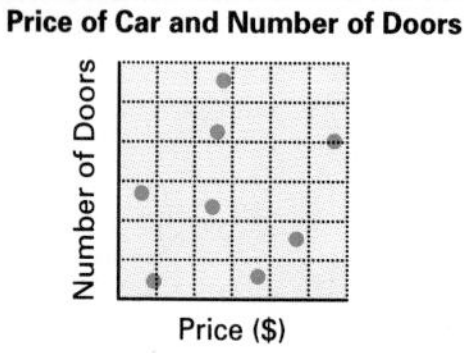

4. A pictograph's key shows that a symbol equals 10 bicycles. How many symbols would be needed to represent 115 bicycles?

Use the Science Test Scores data to answer Exercises 5 and 6.

5. Use tallies to make a frequency chart of test scores in these groups: under 70; 70–79; 80–89; 90–100.

6. Use the test score data to make a line plot.

Science Test Scores									
86	72	98	79	84	63	72	86	89	72
98	92	75	81	76	93	94	88	64	77

7. Make a bar graph using the number of Supreme Court Justices appointed by these Presidents: Clinton, 2; Bush, 2; Reagan, 3; Carter, 0; Ford, 1; and Nixon, 4.

8. Make a stem-and-leaf diagram for the following data: 43, 41, 56, 37, 42, 48, 45, 43, 51, 54, 39, 44, 42, 47, 42, 40.

9. Find the median, mode, and mean for these stolen-base records: Henderson, 1117; Brock, 938; Cobb, 892; Raines, 777; Collins, 743; Carey, 738; Wagner, 703; Morgan, 689; Wilson, 661; and Campaneris, 649.

10. For any data set, which of the three measures (mean, median, or mode) is most likely to be affected by an outlier? Explain.

Chapter 2 Review

1. Give the place value of 4 in 2,549,013.
2. Write 81,294,537 in word form.
3. Round 81,294,537 to the given place: **a.** Thousands **b.** Millions
4. Use > or < and compare 593,293 and 593,392.
5. Order from least to greatest: 3,192,536; 31,925,006; 3,492,426
6. Give the base and exponent of 13^6.
7. Write 6^5 in expanded form.
8. Write 3 squared in exponential notation.
9. Write each in standard form:
   a. 7^2 **b.** 8 cubed **c.** 12^1 **d.** 5 to the fourth power

Use mental math to solve each problem.

10. $170 + 30 + 64 + 36$
11. 8×303
12. 40×700
13. $54{,}000 \div 60$

Use estimation to solve each problem.

14. $592 - 128$
15. $4518 + 3179$
16. 47×712
17. $152 \times 9 \times 12$

Use the order of operations to solve each problem.

18. $7 \times 8 \div 2 + 3$
19. $(11 - 5)^2 \div 3 \times 7$

Find the next three numbers for each pattern.

20. 53, 49, 45, 41, 37, …
21. 24, 36, 35, 47, 46, …
22. State whether each phrase describes a constant or a variable.
    a. The number of quarters in a dollar
    b. The number of quarters in your pocket

Evaluate each expression for $x = 3$, 5, and 7.

23. $3x$
24. $x + 9$
25. Julio bought a roll of film with n pictures. He took 18 of them. Write an expression for the number of pictures left on the roll of film.
26. Is the equation $24 - x = 15$ true for $x = 9$? For $x = 11$?
27. Solve for x: **a.** $x + 6 = 27$ **b.** $\frac{x}{3} = 6$

CHAPTER 2 REVIEW

Chapter 2 Review

Answers

1. Ten thousands
2. Eighty-one million, two hundred ninety-four thousand, five hundred thirty-seven
3. a. 81,295,000
   b. 81,000,000
4. Possible answer: 593,293 < 593,392
5. 3,192,536; 3,492,426; 31,925,006
6. Base: 13; Exponent: 6
7. $6 \times 6 \times 6 \times 6 \times 6$
8. 3^2
9. a. 49 b. 512
   c. 12 d. 625
10. 300
11. 2424
12. 28,000
13. 900
14. 460
15. 7500
16. 35,000
17. 15,200
18. 31
19. 84
20. 33, 29, 25
21. 58, 57, 69
22. a. Constant
    b. Variable
23. 9, 15, 21
24. 12, 14, 16
25. $n - 18$
26. Yes; no
27. a. 21
    b. 18

CHAPTER REVIEW

Answers

1. a. 0.041
   b. 0.4
2. 1 cm; 1.4 cm
3. 0.693
4. 3.3, because 3.34 is 0.04 away from 3.3, but 0.06 away from 3.4.
5. 4.179 > 4.0182 > 4.018
6. 1.799×10^7
7. 100
8. 360
9. 96
10. 3
11. 430.33
12. 8.743
13. 29.93
14. 4
15. About 2.8
16. a. $h = 19.5$
    b. $x = 13.3$
17. 0.0368
18. 49,100
19. 0.83
20. 638,000
21. $k = 0.7$
22. $n = 4.5$

Chapter 3 Review

1. Show each number in decimal form.

a. 41 thousandths

b.

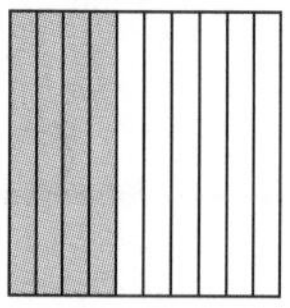

2. Give the fly's length to the nearest centimeter; the nearest tenth of a centimeter.

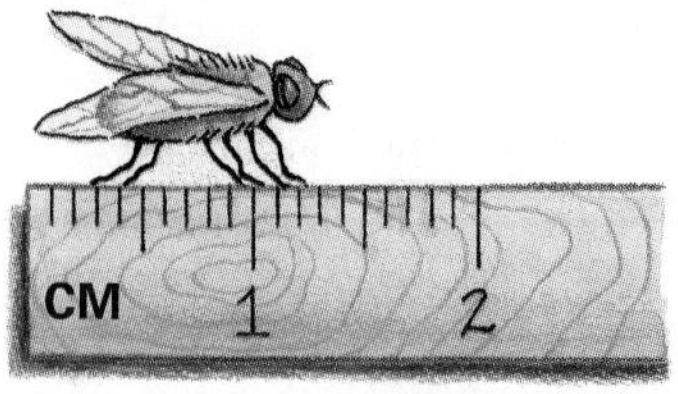

3. Round 0.6927 to the thousandths place.

4. On a ruler, is 3.34 closer to 3.3 or 3.4? Explain.

5. Use the < symbol to order the decimals from greatest to least: 4.018; 4.179; and 4.0182

6. The state of New York has a population of about 17,990,000. Write this number in scientific notation.

Estimate.

7. $29.21 + 72.4$ **8.** $451.8 - 93.507$ **9.** 15.9×6 **10.** $46.4 \div 15$

Simplify.

11. $8.4 + 421.93$ **12.** $11.03 - 2.287$ **13.** 7.3×4.1 **14.** $10.8 \div 2.7$

15. The star Arcturus is about 10.3 light-years from Earth. The star Vega is about 7.5 light-years from Earth. How many more light-years away from Earth is Arcturus?

16. Solve.

a. $h - 7.2 = 12.3$ **b.** $x + 6 = 19.3$

Simplify.

17. 3.68×0.01 **18.** $4.91 \times 10{,}000$ **19.** $83 \div 100$ **20.** $638 \div 0.001$

Solve.

21. $0.5k = 0.35$ **22.** $\frac{n}{0.9} = 5$

Chapter 4 Review

Find the perimeter of each figure.

1.

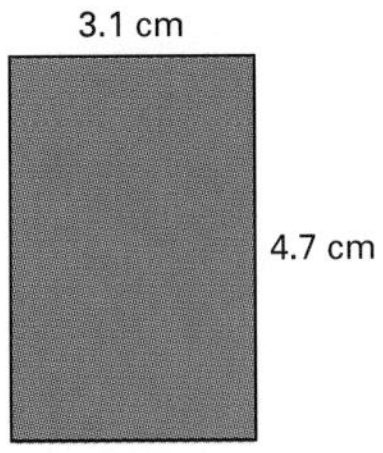

2.

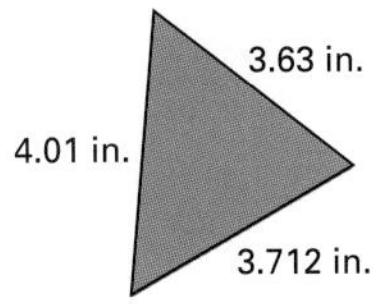

3.

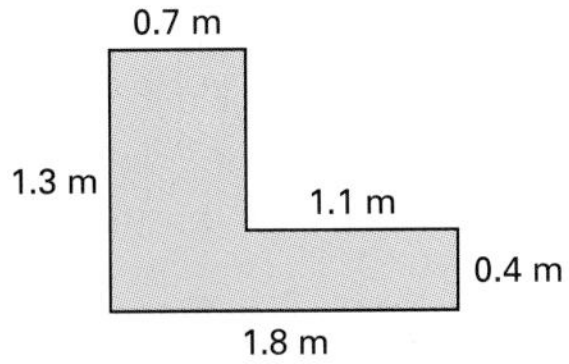

Use powers of 10 or conversion factors to find each measure.

4. 174 g = ☐ kg **5.** 60 in. = ☐ ft **6.** 6.5 lb = ☐ oz

7. 5 gal = ☐ qt **8.** 24.913 km = ☐ m **9.** 2.8 kg = ☐ g

10. A rectangular swimming pool is 25 m by 50 m. What is the perimeter of the pool in meters? In centimeters?

Find the area of each figure.

11.

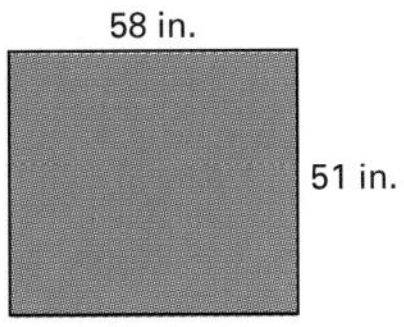

12.

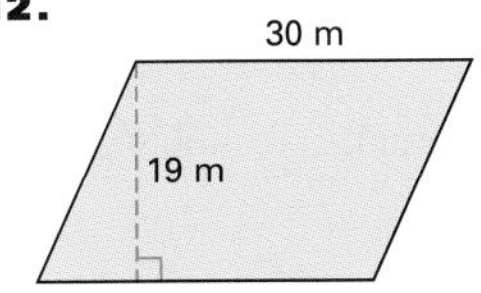

13.

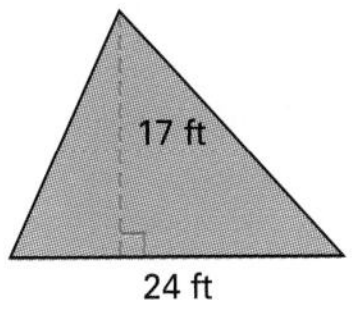

14. What is the area of a square with a side 12.5 m long?

15. What is the area of a rectangular desktop that is 2.5 ft long and 3 ft wide?

16. Find the base of a triangle whose height is 8.4 in. and area is 126 in^2.

17. The diameter of a circle is 12 mm.

a. Find the circumference. Use 3.14 for π.

b. Find its area.

18. Find the area of the irregular shape.

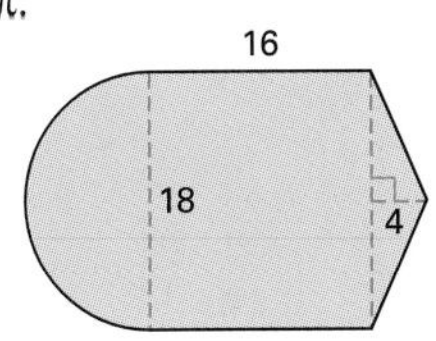

CHAPTER 4 REVIEW

Chapter 4 Review

Answers

1. 15.6 cm
2. 11.352 in.
3. 6.2 m
4. 0.174
5. 5
6. 104
7. 20
8. 24,913
9. 2800
10. 150 m; 15,000 cm
11. 2958 in^2
12. 570 m^2
13. 204 ft^2
14. 156.25 m^2
15. 7.5 ft^2
16. 30 in.
17. a. 37.68 mm
    b. 113.04 mm^2
18. 451.17 $units^2$

CHAPTER REVIEW

Answers

1. Divisible by 2 only
2. Divisible by 2, 3, 5, 6, and 10
3. Divisible by 2, 3, 5, 6, 9, and 10
4. Divisible by 2, 3, 5, 6, and 10
5. Composite: $2 \times 2 \times 19$
6. Prime
7. Composite: $3 \times 3 \times 3 \times 3 \times 3$
8. Composite: 5×17
9. 168
10. 105
11. $\frac{3}{7}$
12. $\frac{11}{24}$
13. 7 is the numerator; 12 is the denominator.
14. $\frac{3}{4}$
15. $\frac{3}{8}$
16. $\frac{2}{7}$
17. $\frac{7}{8}$
18. $8\frac{3}{5}$
19. $\frac{23}{6}$
20. $6\frac{1}{4}$
21. $\frac{51}{7}$
22. 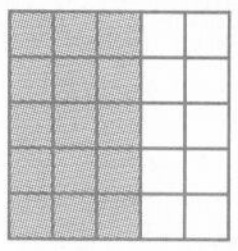

    Possible answer: $\frac{15}{25}$
23. $\frac{15}{4}$ in., $6\frac{1}{3}$ in., $\frac{15}{2}$ in., $7\frac{3}{4}$ in.
24. 0.875
25. $0.1\overline{6}$
26. 3.25
27. 2.8

Chapter 5 Review

Test each number for divisibility by 2, 3, 5, 6, 9, and 10.

1. 104 **2.** 660 **3.** 450 **4.** 1200

Label each number as prime or composite. If it is composite, find its prime factorization.

5. 76 **6.** 101 **7.** 243 **8.** 85

Find the least common multiple for each number pair.

9. 14, 24 **10.** 21, 35

What fraction does the shaded part of each model represent?

11.

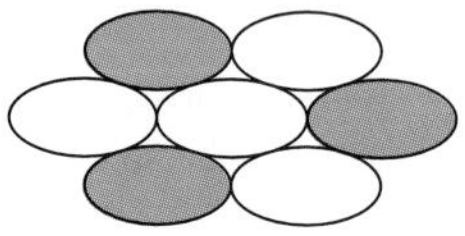

12.

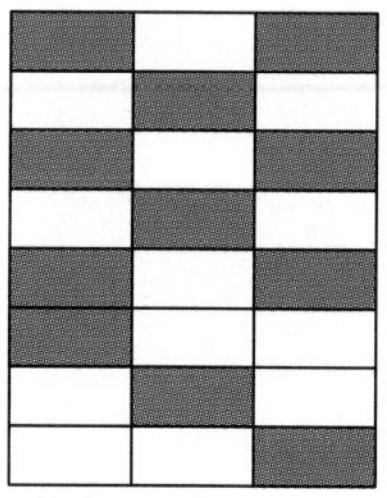

13. Identify the numerator and denominator in the fraction $\frac{7}{12}$.

Write each fraction in lowest terms.

14. $\frac{45}{60}$ **15.** $\frac{48}{128}$ **16.** $\frac{18}{63}$ **17.** $\frac{420}{480}$

Rewrite each as a mixed number or as an improper fraction.

18. $\frac{43}{5}$ **19.** $3\frac{5}{6}$ **20.** $\frac{25}{4}$ **21.** $7\frac{2}{7}$

22. Draw a model of the fraction $\frac{3}{5}$ and name an equivalent fraction.

23. Four drawings have heights of $6\frac{1}{3}$, $\frac{15}{2}$, $7\frac{3}{4}$, and $\frac{15}{4}$ inches. List their heights in order from shortest to tallest.

Rewrite each fraction as a decimal.

24. $\frac{7}{8}$ **25.** $\frac{1}{6}$ **26.** $\frac{13}{4}$ **27.** $\frac{14}{5}$

Chapter 6 Review

1. Write the equation this model represents.

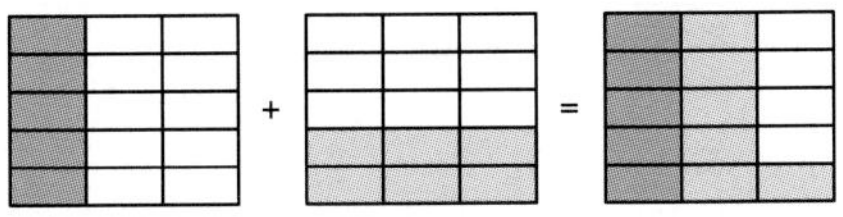

Find the least common multiple of each number pair.

2. 5, 8 **3.** 6, 24 **4.** 10, 14 **5.** 12, 27

Add or subtract. Write each answer in lowest terms.

6. $\frac{8}{9} - \frac{5}{9}$ **7.** $\frac{3}{8} + \frac{9}{8}$ **8.** $\frac{2}{11} + \frac{7}{11}$ **9.** $\frac{5}{6} - \frac{1}{6}$

10. $\frac{3}{19} + \frac{14}{19}$ **11.** $\frac{7}{16} - \frac{1}{4}$ **12.** $\frac{7}{8} + \frac{1}{3}$ **13.** $\frac{4}{7} - \frac{1}{2}$

14. $\frac{7}{9} + \frac{3}{4}$ **15.** $\frac{1}{6} + \frac{9}{10}$ **16.** $\frac{6}{7} - \frac{4}{5}$ **17.** $\frac{3}{4} - \frac{3}{5}$

Solve each equation.

18. $\frac{4}{15} + y = \frac{13}{15}$ **19.** $x - \frac{3}{10} = \frac{1}{5}$ **20.** $t + \frac{1}{4} = \frac{7}{8}$

Round each mixed number to the nearest whole number.

21. $7\frac{4}{5}$ **22.** $12\frac{1}{2}$ **23.** $23\frac{9}{19}$ **24.** $\frac{6}{11}$

Estimate each sum or difference.

25. $6\frac{3}{4} + 3\frac{1}{8}$ **26.** $11\frac{1}{5} - 5\frac{2}{7}$ **27.** $4\frac{7}{15} + 1\frac{2}{5}$ **28.** $8\frac{4}{5} - 2\frac{5}{11}$

29. Find the sum of $2\frac{7}{9}$ and $5\frac{1}{9}$. **30.** Find the difference between $12\frac{10}{13}$ and $4\frac{2}{13}$.

31. Elena wanted to tie a $37\frac{1}{2}$ in. ribbon on a gift. She had a $42\frac{1}{4}$ in. ribbon. How much would she need to trim off the ribbon in order to use it on the gift?

Simplify each expression.

32. $2\frac{3}{4} + 5\frac{1}{4}$ **33.** $7\frac{1}{8} + 4\frac{1}{3}$ **34.** $10\frac{7}{9} - 3\frac{2}{9}$ **35.** $5\frac{11}{16} - 4\frac{3}{16}$

36. $7\frac{4}{15} - 5\frac{1}{9}$ **37.** $8\frac{2}{5} + 7$ **38.** $6\frac{4}{5} - 2\frac{1}{3}$ **39.** $19 - 4\frac{7}{12}$

Answers

1. $\frac{1}{3} + \frac{2}{5} = \frac{11}{15}$
2. 40
3. 24
4. 70
5. 108
6. $\frac{1}{3}$
7. $\frac{3}{2}$
8. $\frac{9}{11}$
9. $\frac{2}{3}$
10. $\frac{17}{19}$
11. $\frac{3}{16}$
12. $\frac{29}{24}$
13. $\frac{1}{14}$
14. $\frac{55}{36}$
15. $\frac{16}{15}$
16. $\frac{2}{35}$
17. $\frac{3}{20}$
18. $y = \frac{3}{5}$
19. $x = \frac{1}{2}$
20. $t = \frac{5}{8}$
21. 8
22. 13
23. 23
24. 1
25. 10
26. 6
27. 6
28. 7
29. $7\frac{8}{9}$
30. $8\frac{8}{13}$
31. $4\frac{3}{4}$ in.
32. 8
33. $11\frac{11}{24}$
34. $7\frac{5}{9}$
35. $1\frac{1}{2}$
36. $2\frac{7}{45}$
37. $15\frac{2}{5}$
38. $4\frac{7}{15}$
39. $14\frac{5}{12}$

Chapter 7 Review

Answers

1. $3 \times \frac{3}{5} = 1\frac{4}{5}$
2. 28
3. 4
4. $\frac{12}{5}$
5. $\frac{9}{56}$
6. $\frac{4}{9}$
7. $\frac{3}{40}$
8. $\frac{5}{36}$
9. $\frac{184}{65}$
10. $\frac{72}{32}$
11. 9
12. $\frac{5}{12}$ mi
13. Yes, because a mixed number is always greater than 1.
14. $5 \times \frac{4}{5} = 4$
15. $\frac{11}{4}$
16. $\frac{1}{5}$
17. $\frac{16}{3}$
18. $\frac{5}{18}$
19. $\frac{25}{42}$
20. $\frac{5}{2}$
21. $\frac{5}{36}$
22. $\frac{1}{32}$
23. $\frac{1}{24}$
24. $\frac{5}{21}$
25. No
26. No
27. Yes
28. $x = \frac{5}{4}$
29. $t = 1$
30. $j = \frac{2}{7}$
31. $h = \frac{7}{8}$

Chapter 7 Review

1. Write the problem the model represents.

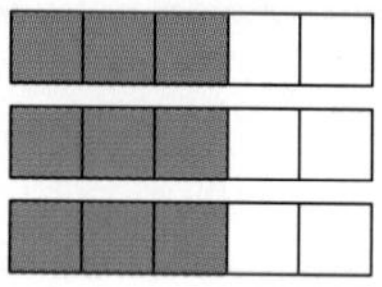

Estimate.

2. $3\frac{1}{2} \times 7\frac{1}{8}$

3. $15\frac{5}{7} \div 3\frac{3}{4}$

Simplify.

4. $\frac{2}{5} \times 6$ **5.** $\frac{3}{7} \times \frac{3}{8}$ **6.** $\frac{2}{3} \times \frac{2}{3}$ **7.** $\frac{3}{10} \times \frac{1}{4}$

8. $\frac{1}{6} \times \frac{5}{6}$ **9.** $4\frac{3}{5} \times \frac{8}{13}$ **10.** $1\frac{1}{4} \times 1\frac{7}{8}$ **11.** $2\frac{7}{10} \times 3\frac{1}{3}$

12. The distance between Joaquin's house and the store is $1\frac{1}{4}$ miles. If he walks $\frac{1}{3}$ of the way to the store, how far has he walked?

13. Is the product of two mixed numbers always larger than either number? Explain.

14. Write the equation that the model represents.

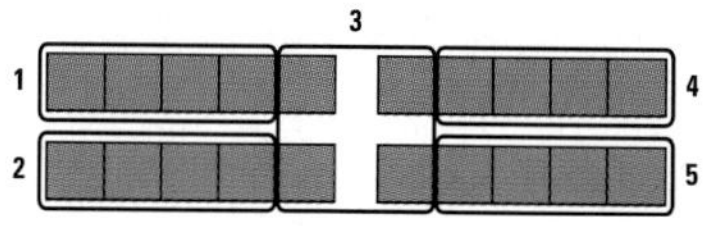

State the reciprocal.

15. $\frac{4}{11}$ **16.** 5

Simplify.

17. $4 \div \frac{3}{4}$ **18.** $\frac{1}{3} \div \frac{6}{5}$ **19.** $\frac{10}{7} \div \frac{12}{5}$ **20.** $\frac{5}{8} \div \frac{1}{4}$

21. $\frac{5}{9} \div 4$ **22.** $\frac{1}{4} \div 8$ **23.** $\frac{3}{12} \div 6$ **24.** $\frac{5}{6} \div 3\frac{1}{2}$

For each equation, state if the given value will make the equation true.

25. $\frac{3}{4}u = \frac{3}{10}; u = \frac{3}{5}$ **26.** $t \div \frac{1}{4} = \frac{5}{3}; t = \frac{20}{3}$ **27.** $\frac{5}{6}r = \frac{25}{36}; r = \frac{5}{6}$

Solve.

28. $\frac{2}{3}x = \frac{5}{6}$ **29.** $\frac{3}{4}t = \frac{15}{20}$ **30.** $\frac{4}{5}j = \frac{8}{35}$ **31.** $\frac{3}{10}h = \frac{21}{80}$

Chapter 8 Review

1. Draw and label a segment with end points *C* and *D*.

2. Draw and label an acute angle through points *A*, *B*, and *C* with *B* as the vertex.

3. Which angle sum has the same number of degrees as a right angle, two complementary angles or two supplementary angles?

4. Draw and label:

a. Two rays that are perpendicular

b. *AB*

5. Classify the triangle whose angles measure 73°, 24°, and 83°.

6. What kind of triangle has two sides with length 4 cm and one side with length 5 cm?

7. Which quadrilaterals have two pairs of parallel sides?

8. Explain why all squares are rectangles, but not all rectangles are squares.

Tell whether each transformation is a reflection, translation, or rotation.

9.

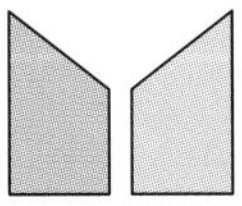

10.

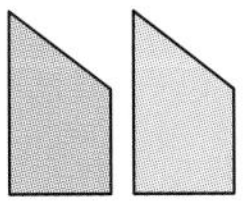

11.

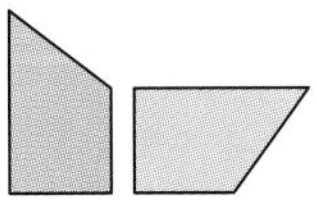

12. Are the figures in Exercises 9–11 congruent? Explain.

13. Trace the figure and draw its reflection over the line.

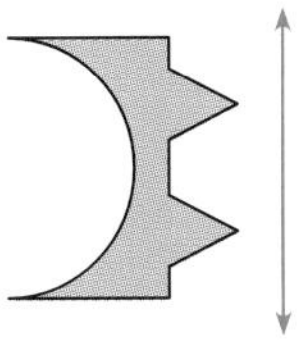

14. Tell whether the figure has line symmetry. If it does, draw its line(s) of symmetry.

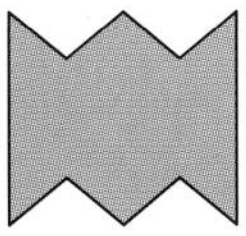

15. Give the number of degrees and the direction the figure has been rotated.

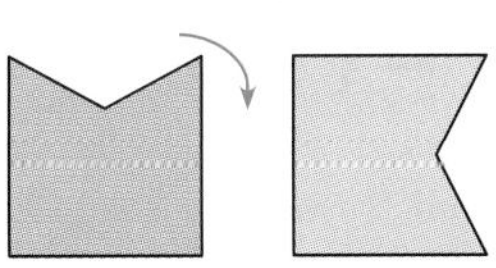

16. What is the least rotation that will land the rectangle on top of itself?

17. If a figure has rotational symmetry, can it also have line symmetry? Explain.

18. Do all parallelograms tessellate? If not, what type of parallelograms tessellate?

Chapter 8 Review

Answers

1. Possible answer:

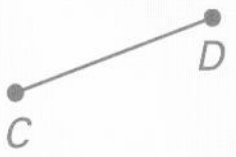

2. Possible answer:

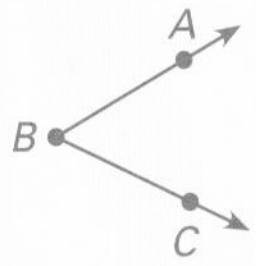

3. Two complementary angles

4. Possible answers:

a.

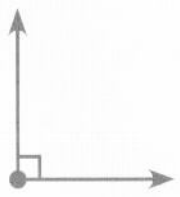

b.

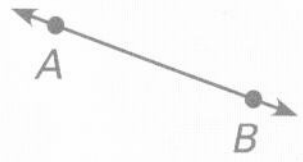

5. Acute triangle
6. Isosceles triangle
7. Parallelograms
8. All squares have 4 right angles and 4 congruent sides, but not all rectangles have 4 congruent sides.
9. Reflection
10. Translation
11. Rotation
12. Yes, since the size and shape of the polygon remains unchanged in each case.
13.

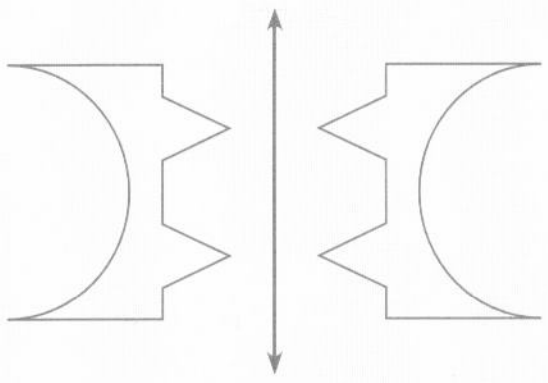

14. Yes

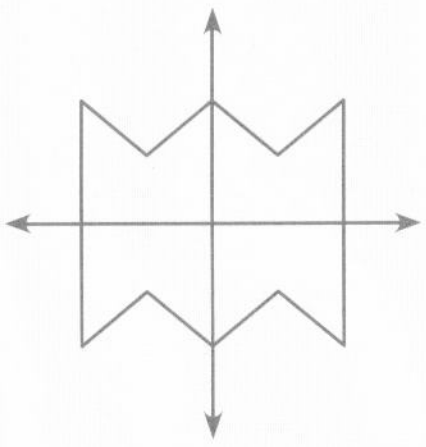

15. 90° clockwise
16. 180°
17. Yes; Example: A square
18. Yes

Answers

1. 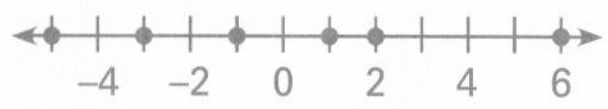

2. −5
3. Negative
4. Positive
5. 3 − 4 = −1
6. 2 − 7 = −5
7. −12
8. −4
9. 7
10. −15
11. 7
12. −5
13. 0
14. −40
15. 36
16. −21
17. −6
18. 5
19. (2, −7)
20. III
21. a. (3, 0)
    b. (0, −3)
22. 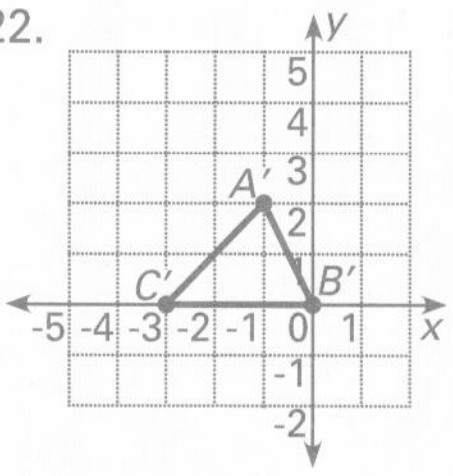

    A(−1, 2), B(0, 0), C(−3, 0)
23. Q′(5, 1), R′(5, 3), S′(1, 3), T′(1, 1)
24. a. 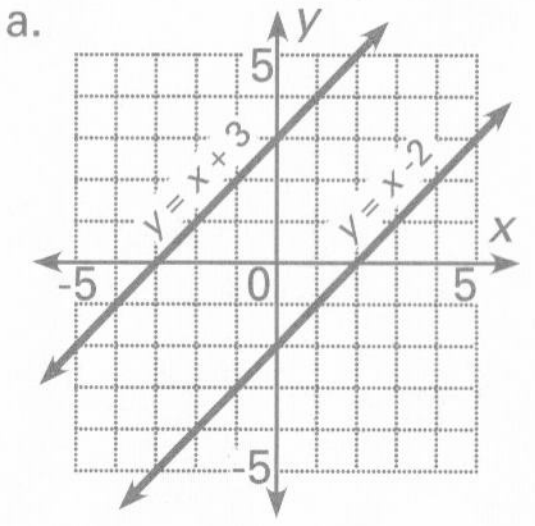

    b. Because the lines are parallel, if one line is moved up or down and right or left it will coincide with the other line.

Chapter 9 Review

1. Locate the integers −3, 2, −5, 6, 1, and −1 on a number line.

2. What is the closest integer to the right of $-5\frac{2}{3}$ on a number line?

3. Is the product of one positive and one negative number a positive or negative value?

4. Is the quotient of two negative numbers positive or negative?

Write the equation that is shown by each model.

5. 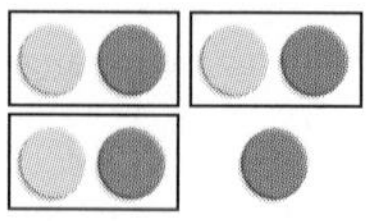

6. 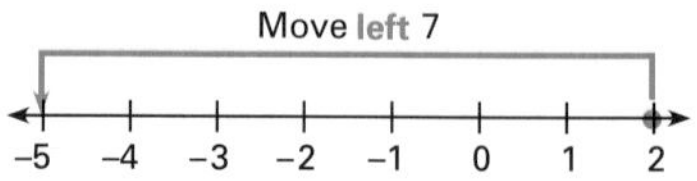

Simplify.

7. −3 + (−9) **8.** 2 + (−6) **9.** −4 + 11

10. −7 − 8 **11.** 5 − (−2) **12.** −6 − (−1)

13. −7 − (−7) **14.** 8 × (−5) **15.** −4 × (−9)

16. −7 × 3 **17.** −24 ÷ 4 **18.** −45 ÷ (−9)

19. Name the ordered pair for the point 2 units to the right of the origin and 7 units down.

20. Name the quadrant where the point (−1, −4) is located.

21. Name a point the same *distance* from the origin as (0, 3) and located:

a. On the x-axis **b.** On the y-axis

22. Create $A'B'C'$ by translating the triangle ABC 3 units to the left and 2 units down. Give the coordinates of A', B', and C'.

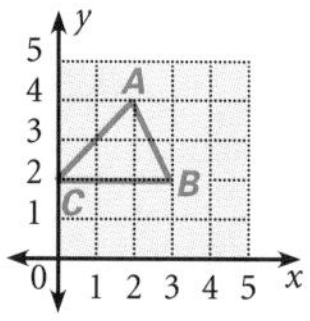

23. Rectangle $QRST$ has coordinates $Q(-5, 1)$, $R(-5, 3)$, $S(-1, 3)$, and $T(-1, 1)$. If $QRST$ is reflected across the y-axis, name the coordinates of Q', R', S', and T'.

24. a. Graph the equations $y = x - 2$ and $y = x + 3$ on the same coordinate grid.

b. Explain why one of the graphs is a translation of the other.

Chapter 10 Review

1. Show three ways to write the ratio of four lemons to seven limes.

2. Write the ratio $\frac{35}{60}$ in lowest terms.

3. Each bag contains 8 red marbles and 11 blue marbles. If there are 4 bags, what is the ratio in lowest terms:

a. Of red marbles to blue marbles?

b. Of blue marbles to red marbles?

c. Of red marbles to total marbles?

d. Of bags to marbles?

4. According to the graph, what is the ratio of fiction books to nonfiction books? Of fiction books to total books?

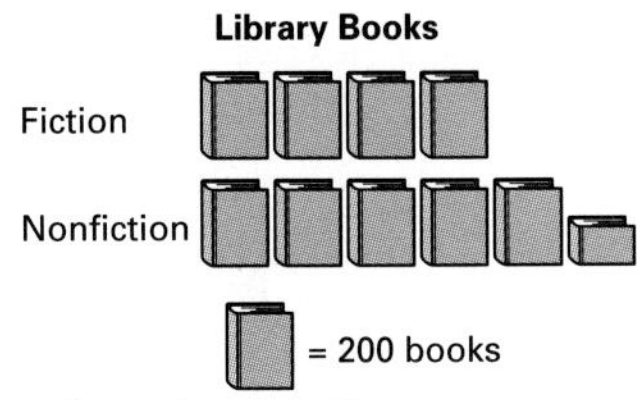

5. Which of the following ratios is *not* equal to the ratio 8 to 24?

Ⓐ $\frac{5}{15}$ Ⓑ $\frac{30}{10}$ Ⓒ 7:21 Ⓓ $\frac{1}{3}$

6. Which of the following is not a rate?

Ⓐ $\frac{5\text{ ft}}{4\text{ sec}}$ Ⓑ $\frac{4\text{ ft}}{1\text{ sec}}$ Ⓒ $\frac{4\text{ sec}}{5\text{ ft}}$ Ⓓ $\frac{4\text{ sec}}{5\text{ sec}}$

7. Use a table to find four equal rates that describe boiling 2 gallons of water in 4 minutes.

8. What is the unit rate of a car's travel time if the car travels 240 miles in 5 hours?

9. Can the ratios $\frac{5\text{ mi}}{8\text{ s}}$ and $\frac{35\text{ s}}{56\text{ mi}}$ form a proportion? Explain.

10. Solve for a: $\frac{6}{15} = \frac{4}{a}$.

11. Apples cost $1.20 per pound. How much do 40 oz of apples cost?

12. Explain why the two triangles are similar.

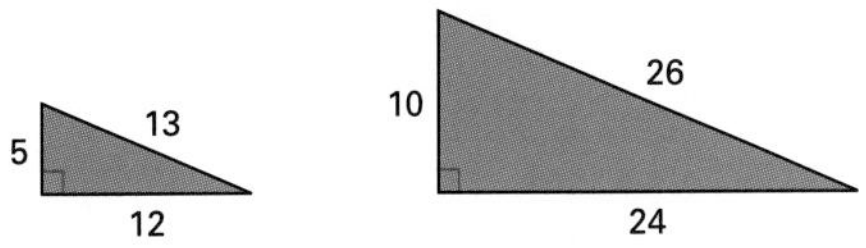

Write each percent as a ratio of a number to 100, as a fraction in lowest terms, and as a decimal.

13. 60% **14.** 12% **15.** 45% **16.** 52%

17. In Denver, Colorado, in 1990, 23% of the population was Latino. If the total population was 467,610, about how many Latino people lived in Denver?

Answers

1. 4 to 7, 4:7, $\frac{4}{7}$
2. $\frac{7}{12}$
3. a. $\frac{8}{11}$ b. $\frac{11}{8}$ c. $\frac{8}{19}$ d. $\frac{1}{19}$
4. $\frac{8}{11}$; $\frac{8}{19}$
5. B
6. D
7. Possible answer: $\frac{0.5\text{ gal}}{1\text{ min}} = \frac{1\text{ gal}}{2\text{ min}} = \frac{3\text{ gal}}{6\text{ min}} = \frac{4\text{ gal}}{8\text{ min}}$
8. 48 mi/hr
9. No, because the units are reversed.
10. $a = 10$
11. $3.00
12. Each side on the larger one is twice as long as the corresponding side on the smaller one.
13. 60:100, $\frac{3}{5}$, 0.6
14. $\frac{12}{100}$, $\frac{3}{25}$; 0.12
15. $\frac{45}{100}$, $\frac{9}{20}$, 0.45
16. $\frac{52}{100}$, $\frac{13}{25}$, 0.52
17. 107,550

Chapter 11 Review

Answers

1. Sphere
2. Triangular prism; 5 faces, 9 edges, 6 vertices
3. Cone
4. 192 m^2
5. 326.56 ft^2
6. 214 cm^2
7. 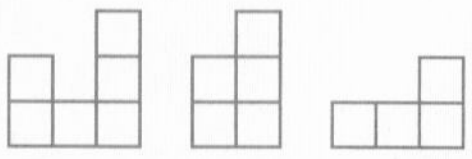

8. 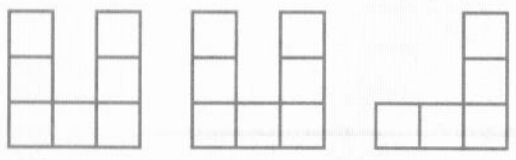

9. 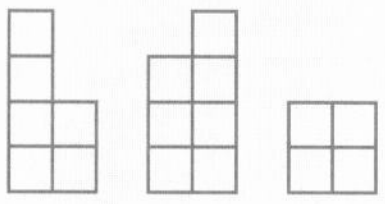

10. 280 $units^3$
11. 1232 ft^3
12. 216 cm^3
13. 87.92 $in.^2$

Chapter 11 Review

Classify each solid. If it is a polyhedron, state the number of faces, edges, and vertices.

1. 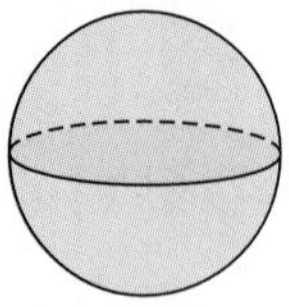

2. 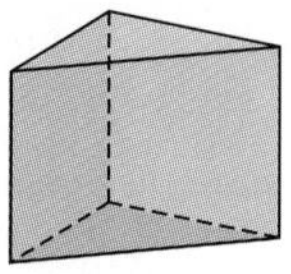

3. 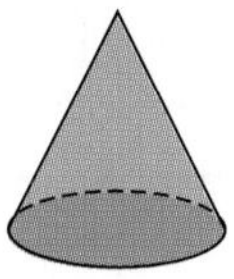

Find the surface area of each figure. Use 3.14 for π.

4. 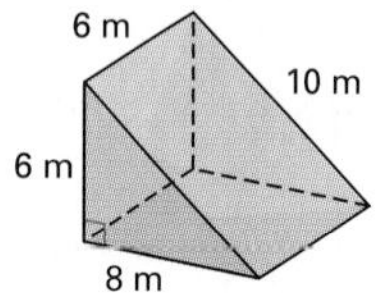

5. 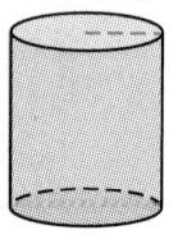

6. 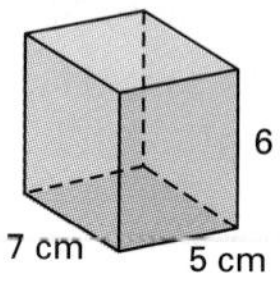

For each solid, draw the front view, the side view, and the top view.

7. 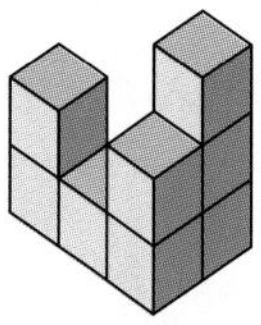

8. 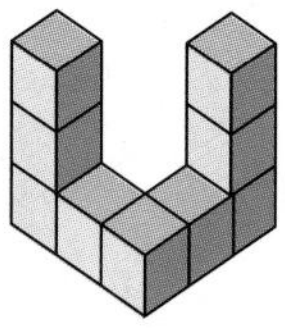

9. 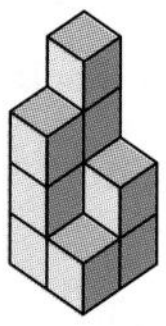

Find each volume.

10. 

11. 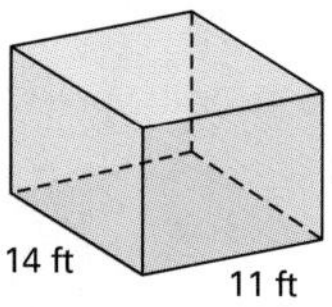

12. 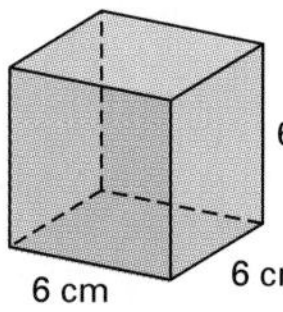

13. The Veggie Soup Co. sells its soup in cans like the one pictured. Find the surface area of the can. Use 3.14 for π.

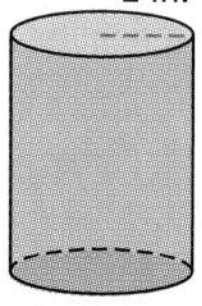

Chapter 12 Review

1. Estimate the probability of choosing a person at random whose birthday falls on a Monday next year.

2. If $P(\text{event}) = \frac{2}{3}$, what is the probability that the event will not occur?

3. Michiko bought 12 eggs. Three of them were brown. One was spotted. The rest were white. If she chooses an egg at random, what are the chances she will choose a white or brown egg?

4. In one neighborhood, 30 out of 45 people surveyed said they read at least one book each week. Predict how many of the 600 people in the neighborhood read at least one book each week.

5. A spinner has 6 equal sections labeled A, B, C, D, E, and F.

a. What is the probability of landing in the "B" section?

b. What is the probability of *not* landing in "B" section?

6. Estimate the probability of hitting the shaded area with a dart.

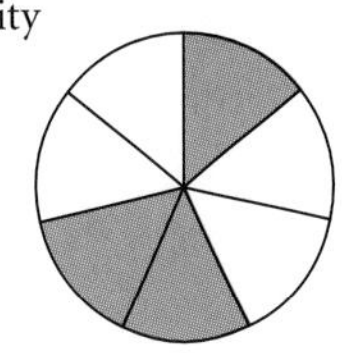

7. Complete a tree diagram that shows how many different kinds of lunches can be made if there are 4 kinds of sandwiches (tuna, peanut butter, turkey, and cheese); 2 kinds of snacks (chips and fruit); and 3 kinds of drinks (milk, juice, and soda.)

8. Use multiplication to find the possible number of stereo systems that could be assembled using one each of 3 tuners, 5 compact disc players, 4 cassette players, and 3 amplifiers.

9. If you spin both of the spinners, how many possible outcomes are there?

10. What is the probability of spinning A or B on Spinner 1 and an odd number on Spinner 2?

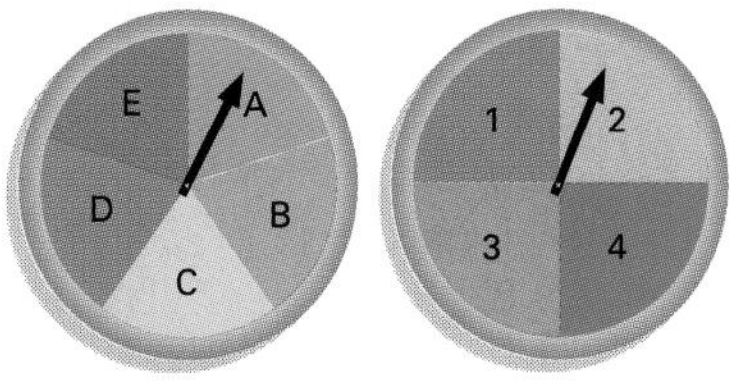

11. Emily rolls one six-sided number cube twice. What is the probability that she rolls an even number and then a 5?

12. What is the probability of flipping three coins and getting all heads?

13. Player A and Player B each roll a number cube. If the sum of the two numbers is greater than 5, Player A wins. Otherwise, Player B wins. Is the game fair? Explain.

Chapter 12 Review

Answers

1. $\frac{1}{7}$
2. $\frac{1}{3}$
3. $\frac{11}{12}$
4. 400
5. a. $\frac{1}{6}$
   b. $\frac{5}{6}$
6. $\frac{3}{7}$
7. See below left for tree diagram.
8. 180
9. 12
10. $\frac{1}{5}$
11. $\frac{1}{12}$
12. $\frac{1}{8}$
13. No. Player A's chance of winning is $\frac{13}{18}$, and Player B's chance is $\frac{5}{18}$.

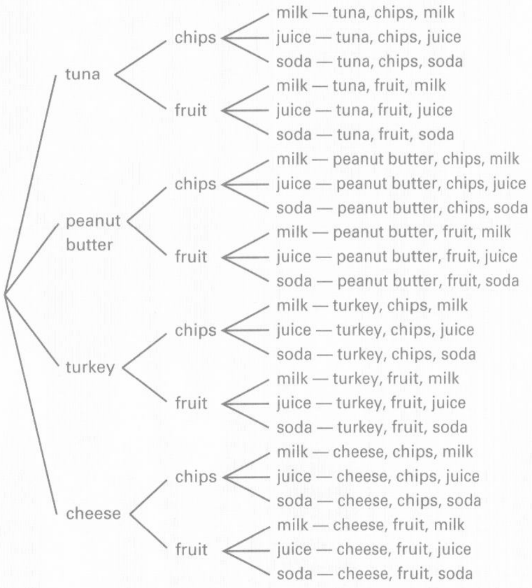

24 different kinds of lunches

Geometric Formulas

TABLES

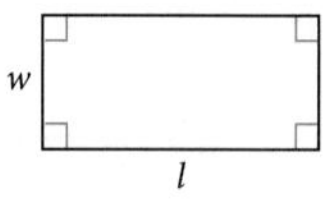 **Rectangle** Area: $A = lw$ Perimeter: $p = 2l + 2w$	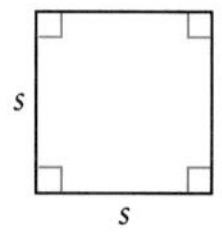 **Square** Area: $A = s^2$ Perimeter: $p = 4s$	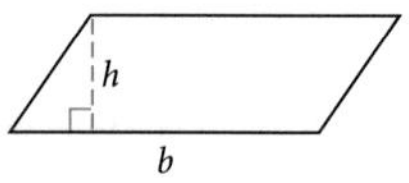 **Parallelogram** Area: $A = bh$
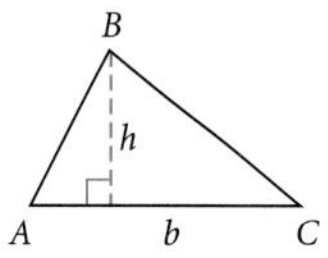 **Triangle** Area: $A = \frac{1}{2}bh$ $m\angle A + m\angle B + m\angle C = 180°$	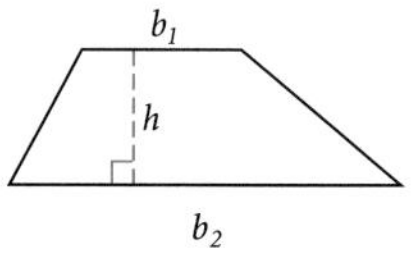 **Trapezoid** Area: $A = \frac{1}{2}h(b_1 + b_2)$	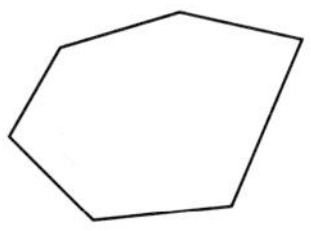 **Polygon** Sum of angle measures for n-sided polygon: $S = (n - 2)180°$ Perimeter: sum of measures of all sides
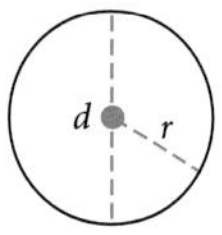 **Circle** Area: $A = \pi r^2$ Circumference: $C = \pi d = 2\pi r$	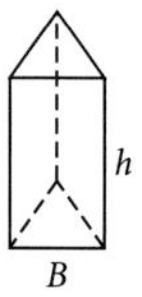 **Prism** Volume: $V = Bh$ Surface Area: $SA = ph + 2B$	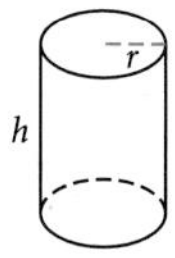 **Cylinder** Volume: $V = \pi r^2 h$ Surface Area: $SA = 2\pi rh + 2\pi r^2$

Measurement Conversion Factors

Metric Measures of Length
1000 meters (m) = 1 kilometer (km)
100 centimeters (cm) = 1 m
10 decimeters (dm) = 1 m
1000 millimeters (mm) = 1 m
10 cm = 1 decimeter (dm)
10 mm = 1 cm

Customary Measures of Length
12 inches (in.) = 1 foot (ft)
3 ft = 1 yard (yd)
36 in. = 1 yd
5280 ft = 1 mile (mi)
1760 yd = 1 mi
6076 ft = 1 nautical mile

Area
100 square millimeters (mm^2) = 1 square centimeter (cm^2)
10,000 cm^2 = 1 square meter (m^2)
10,000 m^2 = 1 hectare (ha)

Area
144 square inches (in^2) = 1 square foot (ft^2)
9 ft^2 = 1 square yard (yd^2)
43,560 sq ft^2 = 1 acre (A)

Volume
1000 cubic millimeters (mm^3) = 1 cubic centimeter (cm^3)
1000 cm^3 = 1 cubic decimeter (dm^3)
1,000,000 cm^3 = 1 cubic meter (m^3)

Volume
1728 cubic inches (cu in.) = 1 cubic foot (cu ft)
27 cu ft = 1 cubic yard (cu yard)

Capacity
1000 milliliters (mL) = 1 liter (L)
1000 L = 1 kiloliter (kL)

Capacity
8 fluid ounces (fl oz) = 1 cup (c)
2 c = 1 pint (pt)
2 pt = 1 quart (qt)
4 qt = 1 gallon (gal)

Mass
1000 kilograms (kg) = 1 metric ton (t)
1000 grams (g) = 1 kg
1000 milligrams (mg) = 1 g

Weight
16 ounces (oz) = 1 pound (lb)
2000 lb = 1 ton (T)

Temperatures in Degrees Celsius (°C)
0°C = freezing point of water
37°C = normal body temperature
100°C = boiling point of water

Temperatures in Degrees Fahrenheit (°F)
32°F = freezing point of water
98.6°F = normal body temperature
212°F = boiling point of water

Time
60 seconds (sec) = 1 minute (min)
60 min = 1 hour (hr)
24 hr = 1 day

TABLES

Symbols

TABLES

$+$	plus or positive
$-$	minus or negative
$\cdot$	times
$\times$	times
$\div$	divided by
$\pm$	positive or negative
$=$	is equal to
$\neq$	is not equal to
$<$	is less than
$>$	is greater than
$\leq$	is less than or equal to
$\geq$	is greater than or equal to
$\approx$	is approximately equal to
%	percent
$a:b$	the ratio of a to b, or $\frac{a}{b}$
$\cong$	is congruent to
$\sim$	is similar to
$^\circ$	degree(s)
$\overleftrightarrow{AB}$	line containing points A and B
$\overline{AB}$	line segment with endpoints A and B
$\overrightarrow{AB}$	ray with endpoint A and containing B
$\llcorner$	right angle
$\perp$	is perpendicular to
$\parallel$	is parallel to
AB	length of $\overline{AB}$; distance between A and B
$\triangle ABC$	triangle with vertices A, B, and C
$\angle ABC$	angle with sides $\overrightarrow{BA}$ and $\overrightarrow{BC}$
$\angle B$	angle with vertex B
$m\angle ABC$	measure of angle ABC
$'$	prime
a^n	the nth power of a
$\lvert x \rvert$	absolute value of x
$\sqrt{x}$	principal square root of x
π	pi (approximately 3.1416)
(a, b)	ordered pair with x-coordinate a and y-coordinate b
$P(A)$	the probability of event A
$n!$	n factorial

Glossary

acute angle An angle smaller than a right angle. [p. 413]

acute triangle A triangle with three acute angles. [p. 424]

addend A number added to one or more others.

addition An operation that gives the total number when two or more numbers are put together.

algebra A branch of mathematics in which arithmetic relations are explored using letter symbols to represent numbers.

algebraic expression An expression that contains at least one variable. Example: $n - 7$.

angle Two rays with the same endpoint. [p. 412]

area The amount of surface a figure covers. [p. 229]

Associative Property The fact that changing the grouping of addends or factors does not change the sum or product. Example: $(5 + 3) + 7 = 15$ and $5 + (3 + 7) = 15$. [p. 87]

average See mean.

axes See x-axis and y-axis.

bar graph A graph using vertical or horizontal bars to display numerical information. [p. 7]

base [of an exponent] A number multiplied by itself the number of times shown by an exponent. Example: $6^2 = 6 \times 6$, where 6 is the base and 2 is the exponent. [p. 78]; [of a figure] On a two-dimensional figure, the distance across the bottom. [p. 230] On a prism, one of the two parallel and congruent faces. [p. 580]

binary number system A base-2 place value system. [p. 201]

bisect Dividing a geometric figure into two equal parts. [p. 459]

box-and-whisker plot A graph showing the shape of a data set. [p. 57]

capacity The volume of a figure, given in terms of liquid measure.

center The point at the exact middle of a circle.

centi- A prefix meaning $\frac{1}{100}$. [p. 216]

circle See examples below. [p. 246]

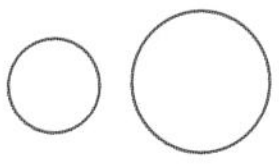

circle graph A round graph that uses different-sized wedges to show how portions of a set of data compare with the whole set. [p. 8]

circumference The perimeter of a circle. [p. 246]

clockwise The direction of rotation when the top of a figure turns to the right. [p. 448]

clustering An estimation method where numbers that are approximately equal are treated as if they were equal. Example: $26 + 24 + 23$ is about $25 + 25 + 25$, or 3×25. [p. 91]

common denominator A denominator that is the same in two fractions. [p. 309]

common factor A number that is a factor of two different numbers. Example: 4 is a common factor of 8 and 12.

common multiple A number that is a multiple of each of two given numbers. Example: 44 is a common multiple of 2 and 11. [p. 281]

Commutative Property The fact that changing the order of addends or factors does not change the sum or product. Example: $4 \times 7 = 28$ and $7 \times 4 = 28$. [p. 87]

compatible numbers Pairs of numbers that can be computed easily. Example: 30 + 70. [p. 86]

compensation Choosing numbers close to the numbers in a problem, and then adjusting the answer to compensate for the numbers chosen. [p. 87]

complementary angles Two angles whose measures add up to 90°. [p. 417]

composite number A whole number greater than 1 that is not prime. [p. 276]

compound event A combination of two or more single events. Example: getting heads on a coin toss and then rolling 4 with a number cube. [p. 647]

cone See example below. [p. 581]

congruent Having the same size and shape. [p. 444]

constant A quantity that does not change. [p. 111]

GLOSSARY

677

conversion factor The number of measurement units that another unit is equal to. Example: to convert inches to feet, divide by the conversion factor 12 (12 inches = 1 foot). [p. 222]

coordinate One of the numbers in an ordered pair. [p. 489]

coordinate plane A set of lines used to locate points in a plane. [p. 489]

counterclockwise The direction of rotation when the top of a figure turns to the left. [p. 448]

cross product For two ratios, the product of the top value from one and the bottom value from the other. [p. 530]

cube A prism whose faces are all squares of the same size. [p. 581]

cubed Raised to the power of 3. Example: 2 cubed = $2^3 = 8$. [p. 79]

cubic unit A unit measuring volume, consisting of a cube with edges one unit long. [p. 606]

customary system (of measurement) The measurement system often used in the United States, using inches, feet, miles, ounces, pounds, quarts, gallons, etc.

cylinder See example below. [p. 581]

deca- A prefix meaning 10. Example: the decameter = 10 meters. [p. 217]

decagon A polygon with 10 sides. [p. 433]

deci- A prefix meaning $\frac{1}{10}$. Example: the decimeter = 0.1 meter. [p. 217]

decimal system A base-10 place value system.

degree A unit of angle measure, $\frac{1}{360}$ of a complete circle. [p. 417]

denominator The bottom number in a fraction, telling how many parts the whole is divided into. [p. 289]

diameter A line connecting two points on a circle and passing through the circle's center. [p. 246]

difference The result of subtracting one number from another. [p. 114]

digit The symbols used to write the numerals 0, 1, 2, 3, 4, 5, 6, 7, 8, and 9.

Distributive Property The fact that numbers can be broken into smaller numbers for calculating. Example: $(32 \times 5) = (30 + 2) \times 5 = (30 \times 5) + (2 \times 5) = 160$. [p. 87]

dividend A number being divided by another number. Example: in $5 \div 3$, 5 is the dividend. [p. 185]

divisible Can be divided by another number without leaving a remainder. Example: 18 is divisible by 6. [p. 271]

division An operation that tells how many equal sets or how many in each equal set.

divisor A number that another number is being divided by. Example: in $4 \div 9$, 9 is the divisor. [p. 185]

dodecagon A polygon with 12 sides. [p. 433]

edge The line where two faces of a solid come together. [p. 580]

endpoint A point at the end of a segment or ray. [p. 409]

equality A mathematical relation of being exactly the same.

equation A mathematical sentence stating that two expressions are equal. Example: $14 = 2x$. [p. 119]

equilateral triangle A triangle with three sides of the same length. [p. 428]

equivalent fractions Two fractions naming the same amount. [p. 289]

estimate An approximation for the result of a calculation.

Euler's formula A formula about edges, faces, and vertices of polyhedrons stating: $E = F + V - 2$. [p. 617]

evaluate To find the number that an algebraic expression names.

even number A whole number that has 0, 2, 4, 6, or 8 in the ones place.

event The particular outcome one is looking at in a probability experiment. [p. 627]

expanded form A way of writing an exponential number showing all of the factors individually. Example: $9 \times 9 \times 9$. [p. 79]

experiment A situation that can turn out in more than one way. [p. 626]

exponent A raised number telling how many times another number, the base, is being multiplied by itself. Example: $9^3 = 9 \times 9 \times 9$, where 3 is the exponent and 9 is the base. [p. 78]

exponential notation A way of writing repeated multiplication of a number using exponents. Example: 9^3. [p. 78]

expression A mathematical phrase containing variables, constants, and operation symbols. Example: $12 - x$. [p. 111]

face A flat surface on a solid. [p. 580]

factor A number that divides another number without remainder. Example: 6 is a factor of 42. [p. 78]

GLOSSARY

678

factor tree A diagram showing how a composite number breaks down into its prime factors. [p. 276]

fair game A game in which each player has the same probability of winning. [p. 651]

flip See *reflection.*

foot A unit in the customary system of measurement equal to 12 inches. [p. 221]

formula A rule showing relationships among quantities. Example: $A = bh$.

fraction A number describing part of a whole when the whole is cut into equal pieces. [p. 288]

frequency chart A table listing each value that appears in a data set followed by the number of times it appears. [p. 25]

front-end estimation An estimation method where only the first digit of each number is used for computation, and the result is adjusted based on the remaining digits. [p. 91]

gallon A unit in the customary system of measurement equal to 4 quarts. [p. 221]

geometry A branch of mathematics in which the relations between points, lines, figures, and solids are explored.

gram The basic unit of mass in the metric system. [p. 215]

graph A diagram that shows information in an organized way.

greatest common factor (GCF) The greatest whole number that divides two whole numbers. Example: 16 is the GCF of 32 and 48. [p. 295]

hecto- A prefix meaning 100. Example: the hectometer = 100 meters. [p. 217]

height The distance along a figure that is perpendicular to the base. [p. 230]

heptagon A polygon with 7 sides. [p. 433]

hexagon A polygon with 6 sides. [p. 433]

horizontal axis The horizontal line of the two lines on which a graph is built. [p. 29]

improper fraction A fraction whose numerator is greater than or equal to its denominator. Example: $\frac{22}{7}$. [p. 298]

inch A unit of length in the customary measurement system. [p. 221]

inequality A statement that two expressions are not equal. Example: $7 > 5$.

integers The set of positive whole numbers, their opposites, and 0: ... −3, −2, −1, 0, 1, 2, 3, ... [p. 469]

intersect To cross through the same point. [p. 409]

interval One of the equal-sized divisions on a bar graph scale. [p. 29]

isosceles triangle A triangle with exactly two sides of the same length. [p. 428]

kilo- A prefix meaning 1000. [p. 216]

least common denominator (LCD) The least common multiple (LCM) of two denominators. Example: 30 is the LCD of $\frac{1}{6}$ and $\frac{1}{15}$. [p. 330]

least common multiple (LCM) The smallest multiple common to two numbers. Example: 60 is the LCM of 10 and 12. [p. 281]

like denominators Denominators that are the same in two fractions. [p. 325]

line A one-dimensional figure that extends forever in both directions. [p. 409]

line graph A graph in which a line shows changes in data, often over time. [p. 8]

line of symmetry The imaginary "mirror" in line symmetry.

line plot A plot that shows the shape of a data set by stacking ×'s above each value on a number line. [p. 26]

line symmetry The ability of a figure to be folded into congruent halves. [p. 444]

liter The basic unit of volume in the metric system. [p. 215]

lowest terms The name for a fractional amount where the numerator and denominator have a greatest common factor of 1. [p. 294]

mass The amount of matter that something contains.

mean The sum of the values in a data set divided by the number of values. [p. 47]

median The middle value in a data set when the values are listed from lowest to highest. [p. 42]

mental math Performing calculations in your mind, without using pencil and paper or a calculator.

meter The basic unit of length in the metric system. [p. 215]

metric system (of measurement) A system of measurements used to describe how long, heavy, or big something is. [p. 215]

mile A unit in the customary system of measurement equal to 5280 feet. [p. 221]

milli- A prefix meaning $\frac{1}{1000}$. [p. 216]

mixed number A number combining a whole number with a fraction. Example: $2\frac{7}{8}$. [p. 298]

mode One of the values appearing most often in a data set. [p. 42]

GLOSSARY

679

GLOSSARY

multiple The product of a given number and any whole number. [p. 281]

multiplication An operation that combines two numbers, called factors, to give one number, called the product.

negative numbers Numbers less than 0. [p. 469]

net A flat pattern that can be folded into a solid. [p. 581]

nonagon A polygon with 9 sides. [p. 433]

number line A line that shows numbers in order.

number-word form A way of writing a number using digits and words. Example: 45 trillion. [p. 67]

numeral A symbol for a number.

numerator The top number in a fraction, telling how many parts of the whole are being named. [p. 289]

obtuse angle An angle greater than a right angle but smaller than a straight angle. [p. 413]

obtuse triangle A triangle with an obtuse angle. [p. 424]

octagon A polygon with 8 sides. [p. 433]

odd number A whole number that has 1, 3, 5, 7, or 9 in the ones place.

odds A ratio expressing the chances of an event happening that compares the number of favorable to unfavorable outcomes. [p. 657]

operation A mathematical procedure. Examples: addition, subtraction, multiplication, division.

opposite The integer on the opposite side of zero from a given number, but at the same distance from zero. Example: 7 and –7 are opposites of each other. [p. 472]

order of operations The rules telling what order to do operations in: (1) simplify inside parentheses, (2) simplify exponents, (3) multiply and divide from left to right, and (4) add and subtract from left to right. [p. 99]

ordered pair A pair of numbers, such as (3, –7), used to locate a point on a coordinate plane. [p. 489]

origin The point (0, 0), where the *x*- and *y*-axes of a coordinate plane intersect. [p. 489]

ounce A unit of weight in the customary measurement system. [p. 221]

outcome One of the ways an experiment can turn out. [p. 626]

outlier A number very different from the other numbers in a data set. [p. 51]

parallel Two lines, segments, or rays that do not cross, no matter how far they extend. [p. 409]

parallelogram A four-sided figure whose opposite sides are parallel and of the same length. [p. 234]

pentagon A polygon with 5 sides. [p. 433]

percent A ratio comparing a part to a whole using the number 100. The percent is the number of hundredths that the part is equal to. [p. 550]

perimeter The distance around the outside of a figure. [p. 210]

perpendicular Two lines are perpendicular if they cross at right angles. [p. 409]

pi (π) For any circle, the ratio of the circumference divided by the diameter. Pi equals 3.14159265... . [p. 247]

pictograph A graph using symbols to represent data. [p. 7]

place value The multiple of ten telling how much a digit represents. Example: in 374, the 7 is in the tens place. [p. 66]

polygon A closed figure made of line segments. [p. 432]

polyhedron A solid consisting entirely of flat faces. [p. 580]

positive numbers Numbers greater than 0. [p. 469]

pound A unit in the customary system of measurement equal to 16 ounces. [p. 221]

power An exponent. [p. 79]

prime factorization The set of primes whose product is a given composite. Example: $70 = 2 \times 5 \times 7$. [p. 276]

prime number A whole number greater than 1 with exactly two whole positive factors: 1 and itself. Examples: 2, 3, 5, 7, 11, ... [p. 276]

prism A polyhedron that has two faces congruent and parallel. See examples below. [p. 580]

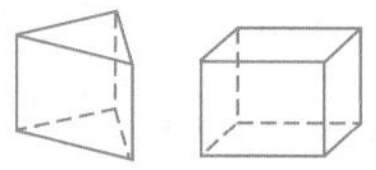

probability A ratio of the number of ways an event can happen to the total number of possible outcomes. [p. 627]

product The result of multiplying numbers. [p. 114]

proportion A pair of equal ratios. [p. 531]

protractor A tool that measures angles. [p. 417]

pyramid A solid with one base and whose other sides are all triangles. See examples below. [p. 581]

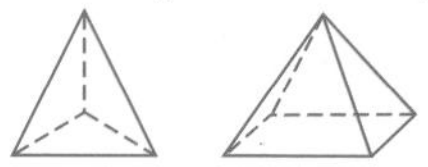

680

quadrants The four regions into which the two axes of a coordinate grid divide the plane. [p. 489]

quadrilateral A polygon with 4 sides. [p. 433]

quart A unit of volume in the customary measurement system. [p. 221]

quotient The result of dividing one number by another. [p. 114]

radius A line from the center of a circle to any point on the circle. [p. 246]

range The difference between the highest and lowest values in a data set. [p. 30]

rate A ratio in which two quantities with different units of measure are compared. Example: 18 dollars per 2 hours. [p. 523]

ratio A comparison of two quantities, often written as a fraction. [p. 515]

ray A part of a line that has one endpoint and extends forever in the other direction. [p. 409]

reciprocal A fraction whose numerator and denominator have been switched. [p. 383]

rectangle A parallelogram with opposite sides the same length and all angles measuring 90°.[p. 437]

reflection The mirror image of a figure that has been "flipped" over a line. [p. 444]

regular polygon A polygon whose sides and angles all have the same measure. [p. 433]

remainder The number less than the divisor that remains after the division process is completed.

repeating decimal A decimal number that repeats a pattern of digits continuously on the right. Example: 6.141414 ... . [p. 304]

rhombus A parallelogram with all sides the same length. [p. 437]

right angle An angle like the corner of an index card. It measures 90°. [pp. 230, 413]

right triangle A triangle with a right angle. [p. 424]

rotation The image of a figure that has been "turned," as if on a wheel. [p. 448]

rotational symmetry The ability of a figure to be rotated less than a full circle and exactly match its original image. [p. 449]

rounding Adjusting a number to make it more convenient to use, according to a given place value. Example: 2571 rounded to the nearest hundred is 2600. [p. 71]

sample A set of data used to predict how a particular situation might happen. [p. 631]

scale The "ruler" that measures the heights of the bars in a bar graph. [p. 29]

scalene triangle A triangle with no sides of equal length. [p. 428]

scatterplot A graph showing paired data values. [p. 17]

scientific notation Writing a number as the product of a decimal and a power of 10. Example: $350 = 3.50 \times 10^2$. [p. 153]

segment Part of a line, with two endpoints. [p. 409]

side Each of the rays forming an angle. [p. 412]

similar Figures having the same shape but possibly different sizes. [p. 543]

slide See *translation*.

solid A three-dimensional figure. [p. 580]

sphere See example below. [p. 582]

square A quadrilateral with all sides the same length and all angles measuring 90°. [p. 437]

square centimeter The area of a square with 1-centimeter sides. [p. 229]

square inch The area of a square with 1-inch sides. [p. 229]

square root The length of one side of a square with an area equal to a given number. [p. 261]

squared Raised to the power of 2. Example: 3 squared = $3^2 = 9$. [p. 79]

standard form A way of writing a number using digits. Example: 45,000,000,000,000. [p. 67]

stem-and-leaf diagram A graph showing the shape of a data set by breaking each value into a "stem" part and a "leaf" part. [p. 35]

straight angle An angle formed by two rays pointing in opposite directions. [p. 413]

subtraction An operation that tells the difference between two numbers, or how many are left when some are taken away.

sum The result of adding numbers. [p. 114]

supplementary angles Two angles whose measures add up to 180°. [p. 417]

surface area (SA) The sum of the areas of each face of a polyhedron. [p. 584]

symmetry See *line symmetry* and *rotational symmetry*.

T-table A table showing corresponding *x*- and *y*-values for an equation. [p. 499]

tally marks Marks used to organize a large set of data. Each mark indicates one time a value appears in the data set. [p. 25]

GLOSSARY

681

terminating decimal A decimal number that ends on the right. [p. 304]

tessellation A pattern of congruent shapes covering a surface without gaps or overlaps. [p. 454]

translation The image of a figure that has been slid to a new position without flipping or turning. [p. 453]

trapezoid A quadrilateral with exactly two sides parallel. [p. 437]

tree diagram A branching, tree-like diagram showing all possible outcomes of a situation. [p. 642]

trend A relationship between two sets of data that shows up as a pattern in a scatterplot. [p. 18]

triangle A closed figure made from three line segments. [p. 424]

turn See *rotation.*

unfair game A game in which not all players have the same probability of winning. [p. 651]

unit One of something. An amount or quantity used as a standard of measurement.

unit fraction A fraction with a numerator of 1.

unit rate A rate in which the second number in the comparison is one unit. Example: 25 gallons per minute. [p. 524]

unlike denominators Denominators that are different in two fractions. [p. 329]

variable A quantity that can change or vary, often represented with a letter. [p. 111]

Venn diagram A diagram that uses regions to show relationships between sets of things. [p. 315]

vertex The common endpoint of two rays forming an angle. Plural: vertices. [p. 412]

vertical axis The vertical line of the two lines on which a graph is built. [p. 29]

volume The number of cubic units an object contains. [p. 606]

weight A measure of the force that gravity exerts on a body.

whole number Any number in the set {0, 1, 2, 3, 4, ... }.

word form A way of writing a number using only words. Example: forty-five trillion. [p. 67]

***x*-axis** The horizontal axis on a coordinate plane. [p. 489]

***x*-coordinate** The first number in an ordered pair, locating a point on the *x*-axis of a coordinate plane. [p. 489]

***y*-axis** The vertical axis on a coordinate plane. [p. 489]

***y*-coordinate** The second number in an ordered pair, locating a point on the *y*-axis of a coordinate plane. [p. 489]

yard A unit in the customary system of measurement equal to 3 feet. [p. 221]

zero pair A number and its opposite. Example: 7 + (–7).

GLOSSARY

682

Selected Answers

Chapter 1

1-1 Try It (Example 2)

a. 200 m **b.** 800

1-1 Try It (Example 4)

a. 1993 **b.** Interactive TV

1-1 Exercises & Applications

1. Pictograph **3.** Circle graph **5.** 11–50 m; 51–100 m **7.** 3 **9.** $37 **11.** Medical, clothes; other, transportation; housing **13.** 64,000,000 sq mi **17.** 6 million **21.** 5106 **23.** 8022 **25.** 90 **27.** 806 **29.** 694 **31.** 630 **33.** 433 **35.** 790 **37.** 1000 **39.** 1586 **41.** 600 **43.** 1056

1-2 Try It

a. Possible answer: It looks like Crispies sells almost as much cereal as Crunchies, but there is $9 million difference. **b.** Possible answer: It looks like Pete's Pizza pays twice as much as Prize Pizza, but they only pay 50 cents more.

1-2 Exercises & Applications

3. 30 yr; 70 yr **5.** B **7.** Twice; $1\frac{1}{2}$ **9.** Mouse: 300; robin: 600 **11.** 2 million **15.** Two hundred four **17.** Nine hundred thirteen **19.** Eight thousand nine hundred twelve **21.** One thousand forty-five **23.** 614 **25.** 772 **27.** 71 **29.** 306

1-3 Try It

a. (80, 40) **b.** (100, 45) **c.** (125, 32) **d.** (160, 22) **e.** (200, 20)

1-3 Exercises & Applications

1. a. 15 right, 600 up **b.** 600 lb, 15 ft **3. a.** 20 right, 3000 up **b.** 3000 lb, 20 ft **5.** No trend **7.** A **11.** 24; 51 **15.** 6606 **17.** 8900 **19.** 4329 **21.** 1888

Section 1A Review

3. 3 million **5.** Yes **7.** The daily garbage per person increases.

1-4 Try It (Example 1)

a.

History	Frequency
Test Scores	
Under 60	1
60–69	3
70–79	4
80–89	7
90–100	5

b. 7; 4

1-4 Try It (Example 2)

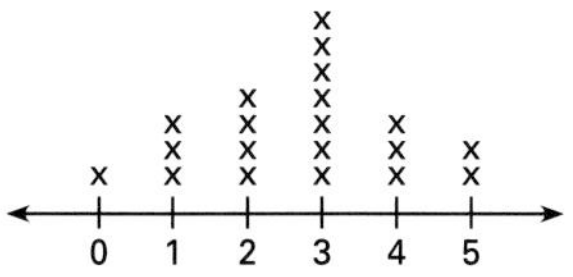

The line plot shows that 3 is the most common number of phone calls, 0 is the least common, and 1 and 4 appear with the same frequency.

1-4 Exercises & Applications

1.

a.		**b.**		**c.**	
1	IIII	13	I	1500	I
2	I	17	I	2000	II
3	III	18	I	2500	I
4	III	19	II	3500	I
5	I	20	IIII	4000	II
6	I	21	II	5000	I
7	I	22	II	6000	I
10	I	23	I	6500	I

3.

Shoes in Closet

Shoes	Frequency
2	5
4	6
6	9
8	13
10	16
12	18

11. Two hundred seventeen **13.** Six hundred sixteen **23.** 25 **25.** 21 **27.** 11 **29.** 19 **31.** 24 R2 or 24.7

1-5 Try It

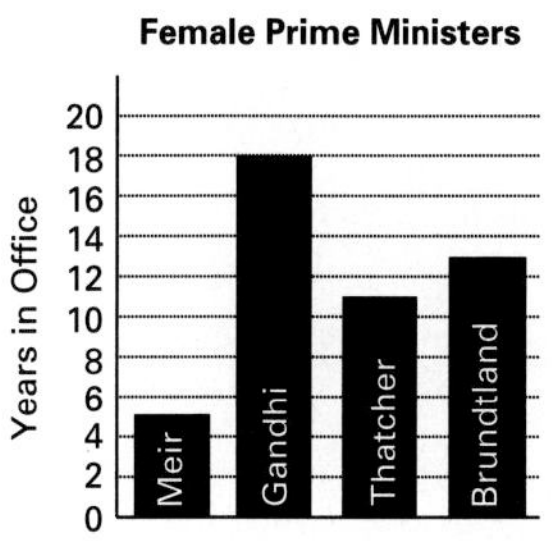

1-5 Exercises & Applications

1. a. Range 13, interval 2
b. Range 90, interval 25
3.

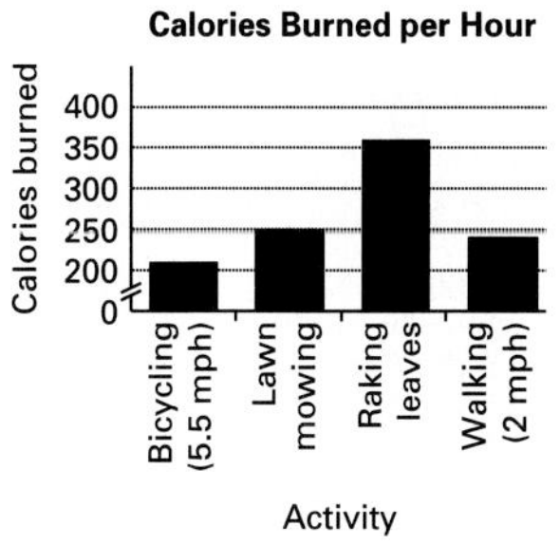

5. a. The first graph has range 40, interval 20. The second has range 40, interval 10. **7.** 8587 **9.** 718,530 **11.** 32,717 **13.** 3594 **15.** 153,885 **17.** 13,991

1-6 Try It

Stem	Leaf
9	0 3 3 5 7
10	0 1 5 8 8
11	3 4 5 8
12	4 6 8 8
13	0 0 3 3 6
14	1 1 2 3 4 6 8

SELECTED ANSWERS

683

1-6 Exercises & Applications

1. a.

Stem	Leaf
1	8 9 0 9
2	7 9
3	8 2 6
4	2 0 7 2

b.

Stem	Leaf
1	0 8 9 9
2	7 9
3	2 6 8
4	0 2 2 7

5. 52 **7.** A **11.** There will be more leaves in the 5 stem. **13.** 1152 **15.** 1360 **17.** 193 **19.** 158

Section 1B Review

1.

No. of Elections Lost	Frequency
1	13
2	3
3	2

3.

Stem	Leaf
1	5 5 7 8 9
2	2 3 3 3 3 4
3	2 2

1-7 Try It

a. 108 **b.** No mode

1-7 Exercises & Applications

1. a. Median \$4, mode \$10 **b.** Median 19, modes 12 and 54 **c.** Median 86, mode 82 **d.** Median 306, no mode **3.** 36 **5.** Median 12, mode 10 **7.** Median 11, mode 13 **9.** Median 21, modes 13 and 31 **11.** Median 10, no mode **13.** Median, mode 28 **21.** 2204 **23.** 8918 **25.** 5436 **27.** 32,760 **29.** 48,256 **31.** 517,176 **33.** 95,207 **35.** Basketball **37.** 15 pairs

1-8 Try It

a. \$14.39 **b.** 1.5

1-8 Exercises & Applications

1. \$5 **3.** 5 **5.** 11.81 seconds **7.** 3.63 **9.** D **13.** It doesn't change. **15.** 51 R4 or ≈ 51.57 **17.** 88 R5 or 88.625 **19.** 40 R2 or ≈ 40.15 **21.** 49 **23.** 11 **25.** 23 **27.** 3

1-9 Try It

With the outlier: Median 21, no mode, mean 28; Without the outlier: Median 19, no mode, mean 18.29

1-9 Exercises & Applications

1. 56 **3.** 0 **5.** 3 **7.** 70 **9. a.** With the outlier: Mean 287.4, median 287, mode 287; Without the outlier: Mean 286.25, median 286.5, modes 287. **11. a.** Mean 74.8, median 82, mode 82 **b.** Mean 69.64, median 82, mode 82 **13.** 1687 **15.** 34 R1 or 34.11 **17.** 83,210 **19.** 30 R14 or ≈ 30.47 **21.** 5

Section 1C Review

1. Mean 4.81, median 5, modes 5 and 1 **3.** Mean 15.07, median 12, modes 10 and 25 **5.** The mean **7.** C

Chapter 1 Summary & Review

1. 80 blue jackets **2.** 270 mi

3.

Box of Souvenirs	Tally Marks	Frequency
Flags	𝍸	5
White House models	III	3
Posters	IIII	4
Uncle Sam hats	I	1

4.

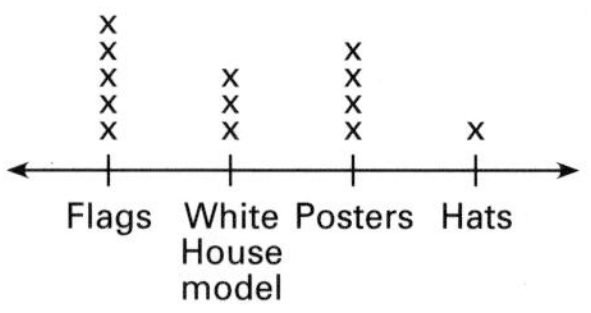

5.

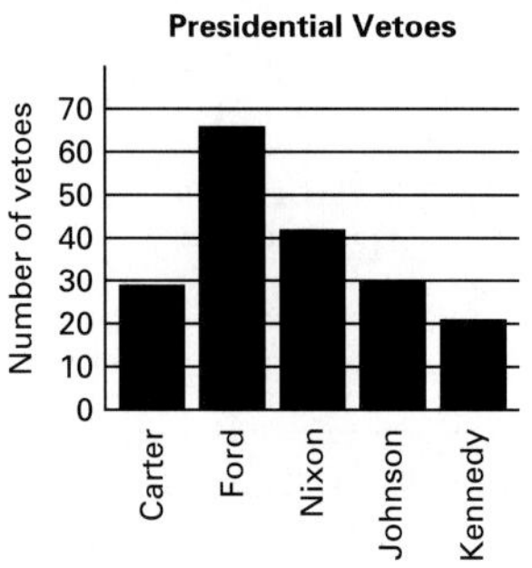

6. Stems will be 0 through 9. Leaves will be 2, 4, 6, and 8 for the row opposite the zero stem and leaves of 0, 2, 4, 6, and 8 for each row opposite the 1 through 9 stems. **7.** Median, 563; Mode, 521; Mean, 591.91 or ≈ 592 **8.** The mean

Chapter 2

2-1 Try It

a. Ten-millions **b.** Nineteen million, eight hundred eighty-eight thousand, eight hundred **c.** 5,020,000,000,300

2-1 Exercises & Applications

1. Ones **3.** Ten-thousands **5.** Millions **7.** Thousands **9.** Thirty million, eighty thousand, seven hundred five **11.** Eight thousand, two hundred thirty-five **13.** Seven thousand, ninety-eight **15.** Fifty-six million, fifty-six thousand, five hundred sixty **17.** 93 million **19.** 888 million **21.** 2 billion, 791 million **23.** 52,000,000 **25.** 560,000,000 **27.** 9000 **29.** 321,000 **31.** 42,006,000 **33.** 9,020,000,000,030 **35.** 81,500 **37.** Thousand **39.** Billion **45.** D **47.** 3,666,200,000 **49.** 14 **51.** 1.9

2-2 Try It

a. 70,000 **b.** 74,000 **c.** 74,000

2-2 Exercises & Applications

1. a. 4 **b.** Less than 5 **c.** Leave it the same because the next digit is less than 5. **d.** 1,370,000 **3.** 90,000 **5.** 740 **7.** 3,900,000 **9.** 23,000 **11.** Two billion, seven hundred fifty-eight million, five hundred thirty thousand, nine hundred twenty-eight **13.** B **17.** 9 buses

2-3 Try It

a. 98,419; 138,417; 146,416 **b.** 190,000 < 198,000

2-3 Exercises & Applications

1. > **3.** < **5.** < **7.** < **9.** 5678; 5687; 5768 **11.** 20,002; 20,200;

22,000 **13.** 10 hundred; 10 million; 1 trillion **15.** 6 hundred; 62 thousand; 29 billion **17.** D **19.** The diameter at the equator is greater. **21.** Calcutta, Rio de Janeiro, Buenos Aires **23.** 268,356,000 > 261,931,000 **29.** 29,297

2-4 Try It

a. 12^4 **b.** $5 \times 5 \times 5 \times 5 \times 5 \times 5 \times 5$ **c.** 81 **d.** 161,051

2-4 Exercises & Applications

1. a. 4 **b.** 7 **c.** 4; 7 **d.** 4^7 **3.** 9^5 **5.** 79^2 **7.** $7^2 \times 3^2$ **9.** 36^1 **11.** 25×25 **13.** $200 \times 200 \times 200 \times 200$ **15.** $7 \times 7 \times 7 \times 7 \times 7 \times 7 \times 7$ **17.** $3 \times 3 \times 3 \times 3$ **19.** $5 \times 5 \times 5 \times 5 \times 5 \times 5 \times 5 \times 5$ **21.** $9 \times 9 \times 9 \times 9 \times 9 \times 9 \times 9 \times 9$ **23.** 125 **25.** 243 **27.** 1 **29.** 256 **31.** 729 **33.** 8^6: base 8, exponent 6, 262,144; 3^5: base 3, exponent 5, 243. **35.** > **37.** < **39. b.** 2^{50} cells **41.** 6

Section 2A Review

1. 16; 20 **3.** 100,000; 100,000 **5.** 81; 100 **7. a.** 864°F **9.** 7,000; 17,000; 19,000; 19,000; 20,000; 23,000; 29,000 **11.** = **13.** < **15.** > **19.** C

2-5 Try It

a. 1,200,000 **b.** 300 **c.** 183 **d.** 347 **e.** 1300 **f.** 351 **g.** 174 **h.** 714

2-5 Exercises & Applications

1. a. 240 **b.** 24,000 **c.** 2,400,000 **d.** 24,000,000 **e.** 70 **f.** 70 **g.** 7 **h.** 7 **3.** 565 **5.** 1100 **7.** 40 **9.** 147 **11.** 50 **13.** 900 **15.** 124 **17.** 693 **19.** 534 **21.** 3500 **23.** 35,000 **25.** 7,200,000 **27.** 290 **29.** 2858 **31.** 166 **33.** 200 **35.** 336 **37.** 525 **39.** 50 **41.** 174 **43.** 777 **45.** $105 **47.** 50 yards **51.** $2.20; No **53.** 335,728,642 **57.** Three million, ninety-three thousand, two **59.** 73,259 **61.** 2,674,445 **63.** 61,236 **65.** 2,146,337

2-6 Try It

a. 1600 **b.** 2000 **c.** 900

2-6 Exercises & Applications

1. a. ≈ 740; ≈ 740 **b.** ≈ 1200; ≈ 1200 **c.** ≈ 72,000; ≈ 73,000 **d.** ≈ 1000; ≈ 990 **3–21.** Possible answers are given: **3.** ≈ 3000 **5.** ≈ 500 **7.** ≈ 325 **9.** ≈ 3,300,000 **11.** ≈ 1000 **13.** ≈ 600,000 **15.** ≈ 18,000 **17.** ≈ 70 **19.** ≈ 19,000,000 **21.** ≈ 250 **23.** ≈ 120 in. **25.** ≈ 99,000,000; ≈ 98,400,000 **27.** D **31.** 7,000,000 **33.** 400,000,000 **35.** $695.86 **37.** $16,402.44

2-7 Try It (Examples 1–2)

a. 24,000 **b.** 200

2-7 Try It (Examples 3–4)

a. 600 **b.** 7

2-7 Exercises & Applications

Possible answers: **1. a.** 2400 **b.** 400 **c.** 35,000 **d.** 30 **e.** 7 **f.** 300 **g.** 1000 **h.** 120,000 **3.** 56,000,000 **5.** 25,000 **7.** 1700 **9.** 20 **11.** 15,000 **13.** 4000 **15.** 100 **17.** 350,000 **19.** 6 **21.** 14,000 **23.** 40 **25.** 560 **27.** 50 **29.** 300 **31.** 2 **33.** 100,000 **35.** Under **37.** 60,000 **39.** C **43.** < **45.** < **47.** < **49.** 10; 356; 383; 1009; 1023 **51.** 12,140 **53.** 18,240 **55.** 252 **57.** 3120 **59.** 144 **61.** 2142

2-8 Try It

a. 25 **b.** 1 **c.** 3 **d.** 48

2-8 Exercises & Applications

1. a. Multiplication **b.** Addition **c.** Division **d.** Simplify exponents **e.** Subtraction **f.** Multiplication **g.** Subtraction **h.** Subtraction **3.** 56 **5.** 8 **7.** 48 **9.** 27 **11.** 0 **13.** 120 **15.** 27 **17.** 300 **19.** 10 **21.** 0 **23.** 5 **25.** 20 **27.** 33 **29.** 1 **31.** 66 **33.** 8200 **35.** 190 **37.** $20 \times (15 - 2) = 260$ **39.** $2 \times (6^2 - 8) = 56$ **41.** $(12 + 10) \div 11 = 2$ **43.** $(5 + 4) \div 3 = 3$ **45.** B **47.** $(4 \times 7 - 2 + 1.96) \div 2 = 13.98$ **51.** 100,000 **53.** 4096 **55.** 38,416 **57.** $2^7 = 128$ **59.** 62,103 **61.** 1,921,899,992

2-9 Try It

a. 30 **b.** 10

2-9 Exercises & Applications

1. a. Add **b.** Add **c.** Subtract **d.** Subtract **e.** Subtract **f.** Subtract **g.** Subtract **h.** Add **3.** Add 3 **5.** Add 13 **7.** Subtract 1 **9.** Add 11 **11.** Subtract 29 **13.** Subtract 8 **15.** Add 15 **17.** Add 58 **19.** 271, 266, 260 **21.** 76, 70, 64 **23.** 1010, 1028, 1049 **25.** 10, 9, 11 **27.** 125, 180, 245 **29.** 1131, 1135, 1139 **31.** 332, 348, 301 **33.** $22 **35.** 550 **41.** 166 **43.** 1661 **45.** 205 **47.** 6 **49.** $121.68 **51.** $185,295.50 **53.** $23.80 **55.** $1453.32

Section 2B Review

1. 60,000 **3.** 879 **5.** 4000 **7–17.** Possible answers: **7.** 30,000 **9.** 300 **11.** 17,000 **13.** 30 **15.** 23,000 **17.** 1600 **19.** C **21.** D **23.** E **25.** B

2-10 Try It

a. 21, 28, 35 **b.** 12, 11, 10 **c.** 20, 15, 12 **d.** 26, 27, 28

2-10 Exercises & Applications

1. a. Constant **b.** Variable **c.** Variable **d.** Constant **e.** Variable **f.** Variable **3.** 9, 10, 11 **5.** 12, 18, 24 **7.** 14, 15, 16 **9.** 16, 24, 32 **11.** 17, 18, 19 **13.** 18, 13, 9 **15.** 17, 15, 11 **17.** 15, 9, 5 **19.** 6, 8, 12 **21.** 3, 5, 9 **23.** 6, 10, 18 **25.** 9, 25, 81 **27.** 28, 14, 8 **29.** 6, 12, 21 **31.** 10, 20, 35 **33.** 8, 16, 28 **35.** 29, 31, 34 **37.** 14, 16, 19 **39.** Number of stars: 13, 26, 39, 52, $13w$ **41.** A **43. a.** ii **b.** i **c.** iii **45.** 7000 **47.** 35,000 **49.** 6400 **51.** 64, 8, 384 **53.** 24, 30

2-11 Try It

a. $c + 8$ **b.** $\frac{n}{9}$ **c.** $r + 5$ **d.** $7x$

2-11 Exercises & Applications

1. A **3.** F **5.** $10q$ **7.** $6d$ **9.** $s - 3$ **11.** $20v$ **13.** $y - 3$ **15.** $n - 5$ **17.** $n - 4$ **19.** $\frac{x}{8}$ **21.** $4 + s$

SELECTED ANSWERS

SELECTED ANSWERS

685

23. $t - 146$ degrees **25.** $22{,}278 - m$ square miles **29. a.** $x + x + x + x$ or $4x$ **b.** $x + 2 + x + 2 + x + 2 + x + 2$ or $4x + 8$ **c.** $x + 3 + x + 3 + x + 3 + x + 3$ or $4x + 12$ **31.** ≈ 800 **33.** $\approx 250{,}000$ **35.** ≈ 2 **37.** ≈ 3 **39.** 122 **41.** 319 **43.** 78 **45.** 4332

2-12 Try It

a. No **b.** No **c.** Yes

2-12 Exercises & Applications

1. a. True **b.** False **c.** False **d.** True **e.** False **f.** False **g.** True **h.** False **i.** True **j.** True **3.** No **5.** Yes **7.** Yes **9.** No **11.** Yes **13.** No **15.** No **17.** Yes **19.** Yes **21.** $\frac{12}{p} = 3$ **23.** $1600 + x = 3212$ **25.** $84 + d = 88$ **27.** $75 - b = 26$ **29.** No **33.** $555 \div 111 = 5$ **35.** $1536 \div 48 = 32$ **37.** $546 \div 13 = 42$ **39.** $1978 \div 86 = 23$ **41.** $8 \times 8 = 64$ **43.** $4 \times 8 = 32$ **45.** $63 \times 56 = 3528$ **47.** $87 \times 12 = 1044$ **49.** 13; 14; 15 **51.** 36; 18; 12 **53.** 6; 12; 18 **55.** 30; 15; 10 **57.** 8; 9; 10

2-13 Try It

a. $a = 15$ **b.** $b = 63$ **c.** $c = 22$ **d.** $d = 48$

2-13 Exercises & Applications

1. Less **3.** Less **5.** Less **7.** Greater **9.** Greater **11.** 2 **13.** 8 **15.** 8 **17.** 10 **19.** 22; 26; 31; 43 **21.** $j = 1.2$ **23.** $k = 6$ **25.** $v = 6$ **27.** $n = 8$ **29.** $z = 80$ **31.** $g = 5$ **33.** $k = 9$ **35.** $r = 168$ **37.** B **39.** 1000 ft/hr **41.** 1038 m **43.** It must decrease by 2. **45.** $200 - 151 = 49$ **47.** $43 + 10 = 53$ **49.** $159{,}000 + 21{,}000 = 180{,}000$

Section 2C Review

1. Constant **3.** $\frac{d}{4}$ **5.** $16m$ **7.** $\frac{d}{17}$ **9.** ≈ 9000 **11.** ≈ 60 **13.** 17 **15.** 220 **17.** 4 **19.** 12 **21.** No **23.** $x = 22$ **25.** $x = 5$ **27.** 5000 ft **29.** D

Chapter 2 Summary & Review

1. Thousands **2.** Twenty-nine million, one hundred fifty-eight thousand, six hundred forty-seven **3. a.** 29,160,000 **b.** 29,000,000 **4.** $129{,}058{,}647 < 129{,}186{,}000$ **5.** 4,067,338; 4,567,238; 40,098,001 **6.** Base 5, exponent 9 **7.** $7 \times 7 \times 7$ **8.** 8^2 **9. a.** 16 **b.** 8 **c.** 10,000 **d.** 9 **e.** 121 **10.** 400 **11.** 1224 **12.** 900,000 **13.** 700 **14. a.** 300 **b.** 11,000 **15. a.** 5 **b.** 750 **16.** 9 **17.** 351 **18.** 29, 22, 15 **19.** 126, 141, 156 **20.** 12, 18, 24 **21.** 4, 3, 2 **22.** $\frac{m}{11}$ **23.** Yes; No **24. a.** $x = 61$ **b.** $x = 116$

Cumulative Review Chapters 1–2

1. C **2.** B **3.** D **4.** B **5.** A **6.** B **7.** D **8.** A **9.** D **10.** C **11.** A **12.** C **13.** B **14.** D **15.** C

Chapter 3

3-1 Try It

a. 0.81 **b.** 0.4

c.

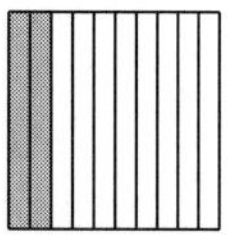

d.

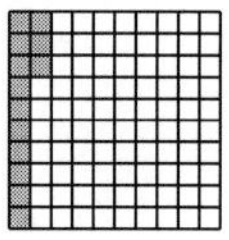

e. Three and fifty-one thousandths **f.** One hundred seventy-one thousandths **g.** Forty-seven hundredths **h.** Eight and one tenth **i.** 0.09 **j.** 2.101

3-1 Exercises & Applications

1. a. 0.6 **b.** 0.43 **c.** 0.312 **d.** 0.9 **e.** 0.097 **f.** 0.08 **3.** 0.78 **5.** 2.45

7.

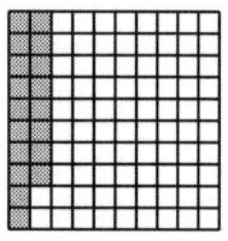

9.

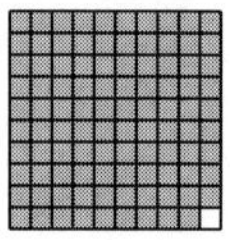

13. 1.067 **15.** 0.08 **17.** 0.2 **19.** 0.015 **21.** Sixty-seven hundredths **23.** Eight and six hundred eleven thousandths **25.** Twelve and six thousandths **27.** Ten and forty-eight hundredths **29.** B **31.** Possible answer: 3.608 **33.** Infinitely many **37.** 11; 8; 5 **39.** 1; 8; 11 **41.** 17; 15; 1 **43.** 416 **45.** 3 **47.** 356 **49.** 2

3-2 Try It (Examples 1–2)

a. 0.8 **b.** 7.05 **c.** 3.462 **d.** 1.9 cm

3-2 Try It (Example 3)

a. 3 cm; 2.5 cm **b.** 13 cm; 13.1 cm

3-2 Exercises & Applications

1. a. 1 **b.** 3 **c.** 3 **d.** 0 **e.** 1 **f.** 2 **3.** 5.8 **5.** 0.472 **7.** 4.3 **9.** 0.100 **11.** 33.5 **13.** 16.13 **15.** 7.30 **17.** 88 **19.** 7.3 **21.** 8.2 **23.** 0.7893 **25.** 60 **27.** 1000 cm **29.** 2 cm; 2.2 cm **31.** 5 cm; 5.4 cm **33.** 3 cm; 2.5 cm **35.** 6 cm; 55 mm **43.** $12 + k$

3-3 Try It (Examples 1–2)

a. $>$ **b.** $>$ **c.** $>$ **d.** $<$

3-3 Try It (Example 3)

1.009, 1.08, 1.6, 1.725, 1.74

3-3 Exercises & Applications

1. a. 0.280 **b.** 1.4500 **c.** 1.670 **d.** 0.3000 **3.** $=$ **5.** $>$ **7.** $=$ **9.** $<$ **11.** $<$ **13.** $<$ **15.** $<$ **17.** $<$ **19.** 0.675 **21.** 27.939, 27.946, 27.948 **23.** 1.23, 1.5, 2.64 **25.** 2.84, 2.96, 3.02 **27.** 3.107, 30.17, 31.07, 31.7, 310.7 **29.** A **31.** Angela and Temeca **33.** Possible answer: 8.743 **37.** True **39.** False

3-4 Try It

a. 30,000 **b.** 90,620,000,000 **c.** 5.2×10^4 **d.** 1.74×10^9

3-4 Exercises & Applications

1. a. 4 **b.** 5 **c.** 3 **3.** 75,000 **5.** 200,000 **7.** 8,890,000 **9.** 2,459,000,000,000 **11.** 445,600,000,000 **13.** 6,900,000,000 **15.** 370,000 **17.** 57,000,000 **19.** 50,000; 100,000 **21.** 5×10^3 **23.** 1.6×10^5 **25.** 7.9×10^9 **27.** 5.1×10^7 **29.** 6×10^{12} **31.** 5×10^2 **33.** 1.2×10^7 **35.** D **39.** 3.65 **41.** Median: 7; modes: 5, 7, 8 **43.** 10 **45.** 12

SELECTED ANSWERS

686

Section 3A Review

1. 0.7 **3.** 26.5 **5.** 2 cm **7.** 0.1 **9.** 2.42 **11.** 7.0 **13. a.** KB: 1000; MB: 1,000,000; GB: 1,000,000,000 **b.** 2.4×10^9 **15.** 120,000,000 **17.** 560,000 **19.** 4.5×10^{10} **21.** 6.78×10^6 **23.** 6×10^7 **25.** 5.69×10^4 **27.** A

3-5 Try It

a. $34 **b.** 35 **c.** 630 **d.** 8

3-5 Exercises & Applications

1. a. 50 **b.** 25 **c.** 10 **d.** 5
3–33. Possible answers given.
3. $2 **5.** 5 **7.** 9 **9.** 300 **11.** $240 **13.** 6 **15.** 43 **17.** 73 **19.** 164 **21.** 1800 **23.** $2 **25.** 6 **27.** 8100 **29.** 900 **31.** 11 **33.** 5 **35.** About $700 **37.** Yes **39.** About 3 km **45.** 65.625 **47.** 0.32 **49.** 0.789 **51.** 0.05

3-6 Try It

a. 8.617 **b.** 3.957 **c.** 7.573 **d.** 2.85

3-6 Exercises & Applications

1. a. i **b.** ii **c.** i **3.** 46.906 **5.** 8.4 **7.** $11.25 **9.** 25.904 **11.** 66.2284 **13.** 0.061 **15.** $10.01 **17.** 14.38 **19.** 442.1822 **21.** 41.69 **23.** 4.947 **25.** 15.678 **27.** 42.63 **29.** $76.57 **31.** 104.67 **33.** D **43.** 5.998 **45.** 35 **47.** 0.2

3-7 Try It

a. $x = 10.1$ **b.** $n = 10.6$ **c.** $j = 5.1$ **d.** $p = 2.2$

3-7 Exercises & Applications

1. a. True **b.** False **c.** True **d.** False **3.** $d = 0.4$ **5.** $x = 8.1$ **7.** $u = \$2.37$ **9.** $w = 28.2$ **11.** $a = 1.22$ **13.** $c = 0.02$ **15.** $f = \$3.25$ **17.** $i = 87.7$ **19.** $m = 0.088$ **21.** $w = 2.32$ **23.** $z = 60$ **25.** $t = 0.67$ **27.** $g =$ 12.1 cm **29.** A **31.** $26.49 + $18.50 = s; s = $44.99 **37.** 0.123, 0.672, 1.784

Section 3B Review

1. 2.7 cm **3.** 3.3 cm **5.** 2.5 **7.** 0.88 **9.** 0.03 **11.** 28.4 **13.** 5.161 **15.** 13.776 cm **17.** $x = 24.05$ **19.** $n = 17.5$

3-8 Try It

a. 4.8 **b.** 4.2 **c.** 117.756 **d.** 62

3-8 Exercises & Applications

1. a. i **b.** ii **c.** i **3.** 34.12 **5.** 24.032 **7.** 872.83 **9.** 357.8 **11.** 52.2 **13.** 872.3 **15.** $603.05 **17.** 12.865 **19.** 80.7 **21.** 3850 **23.** $2539 **25.** $6 **27.** C **29.** Yes **33.** 34,790,001; 34,890,000; 34,891,000 **35.** 5540 **37.** 14,200 **39.** 928,000 **41.** 1,932,000

3-9 Try It

a. 9.44 **b.** 146.72 **c.** 0.0369 **d.** 56.77 **e.** 0.21 **f.** 0.6

3-9 Exercises & Applications

1. a. i **b.** i **c.** ii **3.** 0.9591 **5.** 8.19541 **7.** 4238.01 **9.** 0.068 **11.** 0.0065 **13.** 0.00425 **15.** 38.86 **17.** 23.22 **19.** 0.546 **21.** 54.288 **23.** 0.7496 **25.** 0.775 **27.** 4.232 **29.** $2; $2.12 **31.** $<$ **33.** $=$ **35.** C **41.** 7 **43.** 29 **45.** 2 **47.** 143 **49.** 3 **51.** 3 **53.** 10 **55.** 40

3-10 Try It

a. 19.3 **b.** 0.89 **c.** 0.1085 **d.** 0.262 **e.** 0.003012 **f.** 4.5

3-10 Exercises & Applications

1. a. i **b.** i **c.** i **3.** 5.87 **5.** 0.994 **7.** 0.0258 **9.** 1.548 **11.** 3.254 **13.** 0.013 **15.** 0.084 **17.** 1.24 **19.** 49.75 **21.** 22.476 **23.** 18.96 **25.** 0.407 **27.** 0.67 **29.** 9.4 **31.** 137.667 mi **37.** 73, 78, 79 **39.** 23, 17, 10 **41.** 33, 30, 27 **43.** 52.07 **45.** 0.007 **47.** 3.53 **49.** 6.999

3-11 Exercises & Applications

1. a. ii **b.** ii **c.** i **3.** 2.8 **5.** 0.4 **7.** 4.79 **9.** 1.09 **11.** 8 **13.** 0.07 **15.** 6.1 **17.** 9.87 **19.** 1.94 **21.** 42 **23.** 3.7 **25.** 0.6 **27.** 500 **29.** 14.74 mi per day **31.** A **33.** 21,900 **37.** $15 \times 15 \times 15$ **49.** $e = 8.1$ **51.** $g = 1.2$ **53.** $j = 1.3$

3-12 Try It

a. $j = 0.7$ **b.** $w = 6$ **c.** $t = 5.5$ **d.** $f = 0.49$

3-12 Exercises & Applications

1. a. 1000 **b.** 100 **c.** 0.1 **d.** 0.1 **3.** $e = 0.63$ **5.** $r = 50$ **7.** $w = 0.02$ **9.** $s = 114.49$ **11.** $u = 45$ **13.** $q =$ 12.5 **15.** $h = 6$ **17.** $n = 0.07$ **19.** $v = 10.8$ **21.** $k = 0.08$ **23.** $j = 0.14$ **25.** $u = 0.02$ **27.** $8.3d = 83$; 10 days **29.** $\frac{t}{9} =$ 0.08; 0.72 kg **31.** $465 - x = 165.3$; 299.7 kg **33.** 36 **37.** Greek pasta salad **39.** 8.7 **41.** 21.8 **43.** 54.06

Section 3C Review

1. 5,600,000 **3.** 400,000,000 **5.** 122,000 **7.** 16,000,000,000 **9.** 23.5 **11.** 250 **13.** 20.6 **15.** 60.02 **17.** 2.04 **19.** 310.75 **21.** 3.6 **23.** 2.793 **25.** 10.78 km **27.** $u = 142.2$ **29.** $n = 50$ **31.** $s = 24.31$ **33.** $v = 830$ **35.** $0.36 **37.** B

Chapter 3 Summary & Review

1. a. 0.25 **b.** 0.7 **2. a.** 5.6 **b.** 0.8 **3. a.** $>$ **b.** $<$ **4. a.** 71,600 **b.** 395,000 **5.** $\approx$ 700; 729.36 **6.** $\approx$ 270; 262.277 **7.** 65.92 **8.** $4.4 < 4.876$ **9.** 6.4 mm **10. a.** $t = 4.6$ **b.** $k = 13.5$ **11.** $\approx$ 120; 128.8 **12.** $\approx$ 12; 13.25 **13.** $\approx$ 1; 0.893 **14.** $\approx$ 2; 2.2 **15.** 0.04533 **16.** 751 **17.** 0.367 **18.** 3.1

Chapter 4

4-1 Try It

a. 27 **b.** 46

4-1 Exercises & Applications

1. 180 cm **3.** 100 in. **5.** 8 cm **7.** 16 in. **9.** $a = 9$ in.; $b = 3$ in. **11.** $f = 12$ mm; $g = 26$ mm **13.** A **19.** 90 milliseconds **21.** 5.6×10^4

SELECTED ANSWERS

687

23. 2×10^{12} **25.** 1.6×10^3 **27.** 9.456×10^7

4-2 Try It (Example 1)

a. km **b.** cm **c.** kg **d.** L

4-2 Try It (Examples 2–3)

a. 7360 **b.** 8 **c.** 0.325

4-2 Exercises & Applications

1. 1 kilometer **3.** 1 meter **5.** 1 centimeter **7.** Kilogram **9.** Kilometer **11.** Gram **13.** 0.09 **15.** 100 **17.** 0.00788 **19.** 4.2 **21.** 0.005 **23.** 131 **25.** 267,000 **27.** 42,900 **31.** B **33.** 480 mm; 48 cm; 0.48 m **35.** 562 cm **37.** 103 **39.** 45,000,000,000 **41.** 45,612 **43.** 0.55 **45.** 0.067 **47.** 0.4 **49.** 0.02 **51.** 0.008

4-3 Try It (Example 1)

a. Miles **b.** Pounds **c.** Quarts

4-3 Try It (Examples 2–3)

a. 28 **b.** 4 **c.** 10,560

4-3 Exercises & Applications

1. 3 ft **3.** 8 ft **5.** 5 ft **7.** 21 **9.** 12 **11.** 32 **13.** 36 **15.** 384 **17.** 21,120 **19.** 7040 **21.** 72 in.; 6 ft **23.** 24 oz **25.** D **31.** 60 points; A and D **33.** B and C **35.** 1.06, 1.34, 1.36, 1.66 **37.** 0.0349, 0.56, 0.678, 0.982 **39.** 66.3, 67.1, 67.4, 67.5, 68.3

Section 4A Review

1. 35.6 cm **3.** 3120 cm **5.** 32,000 cm **7.** 42,240 ft **9.** 60 ft **11.** 8000 **13.** 38,000,000 **15.** 29 **17.** A

4-4 Try It (Example 2)

a. 14 in^2 **b.** 12 cm^2 **c.** 28 ft^2

4-4 Try It (Examples 3–4)

a. 20 in^2 **b.** 54 cm^2 **c.** 28 yd^2

4-4 Exercises & Applications

1. 25 **3.** 24 **5.** 24 cm **7.** 27 ft^2 **9.** 1.2 km^2 **11.** 132 mm^2 **13.** C **15.** 4 cm^2 **17.** 1 cm^2 **19.** 720 in^2 **21.** C **23.** **a.** 12,800 ft^2 **25.** $60,000 **27.** The mean **29.** 70 **31.** 28 **33.** 5 **35.** 143

4-5 Try It

a. 18 **b.** 198 mm^2

4-5 Exercises & Applications

1. 35 **3.** 24 **5.** 44 cm^2 **7.** 5.52 km^2 **9.** 0.07 in^2 **11.** 7500 m^2 **13.** 84 yd^2 **15.** 266.07 cm^2 **17.** 1,000,000 km^2 **19.** 50,830 mi^2 **21.** 14.57 m^2 **25.** **a.** 2.36 m^2 **b.** 384 in^2 **c.** 132 mm^2 **d.** 456 mm^2 **27.** 81 **29.** 144 **31.** 64 **33.** 1 **35.** 2,097,152 **37.** 5,764,801 **39.** 1.913 **41.** 232.47 **43.** 6.8

4-6 Try It

a. 6 **b.** 4.75 yd^2 **c.** 1.75 in^2

4-6 Exercises & Applications

1. 15 **3.** 6 **5.** 45 cm^2 **7.** 2,466,000 km^2 **9.** 1581 yd^2 **11.** 260 **13.** 27 in^2 **15.** 31.5 in^2 **17.** 1440 **21.** 52 **23.** 6^5 **25.** 7^4 **27.** 10^4 **29.** $3^4 \times 8$

Section 4B Review

1. 48 in^2 **3.** 0.935 yd^2 **5.** Yes **7.** 96 **9.** 3.2 **11.** 48 in. **13.** 110 mm

4-7 Try It

a. 37.68 cm **b.** 23.9 ft **c.** 18.84 ft **d.** 25.16 cm

4-7 Exercises & Applications

1. True **3.** False **5.** 43.96 cm **7.** 37.68 mm **9.** 9 **11.** 7.5 yd; 15 yd **13.** 5.5 m; 34.54 m **15.** 9.3 **17.** 6.28 cm **19.** 0.83 m **23.** 42 **25.** 11,658 **27.** $3 \times 3 \times 3 \times 3 \times 3$ **29.** $9 \times 9 \times 9 \times 9 \times 9 \times 9$ **31.** $12 \times 12 \times 12 \times 12 \times 12$ **33.** $6 \times 6 \times 6$ **35.** $13 \times 13 \times 13 \times 13 \times 13 \times 13 \times 13 \times 13 \times 13 \times 13 \times 13$ **37.** 900 **39.** 10 **41.** 200 **43.** $6

4-8 Try It

a. 1133.54 cm^2 **b.** 3.14 in^2

4-8 Exercises & Applications

1. True **3.** False **5.** 803.84 yd^2 **7.** 12.56 ft^2 **9.** 128.6144 ft^2 **11.** 907.46 ft^2 **13.** 7850 mm^2 **15.** 1.1304 mi^2 **17.** 1.3 km; 5.4 km^2 **19.** 0.5 mm; 0.8 mm^2 **21.** 0.2 mi; 0.1 mi^2 **23.** 2.9 m; 25.8 m^2 **25.** 1.32665 yd^2 **27.** C **29.** A **31.** 144 ft^2 **33.** **a.** C, B, D, A **35.** No **37.** 75 **39.** 240 **41.** 1600 **43.** 800,000

4-9 Exercises & Applications

1. Rectangle, semicircle **3.** Semicircle, rectangle **5.** 34.8125 **7.** 450 ft^2 **9.** $\approx$ 31.8 cm^2 **11.** 412,090.5 mi^2 **15.** 289.56 ft^2 **17.** 21 **19.** 134 **21.** 24 **23.** 6 **25.** 7 **27.** 8.02 **29.** 162.5 **31.** 5.3

Section 4C Review

1. 12,000 **3.** 9.2 **5.** A: 43.2 mm^2; P: 28 mm **7.** A: 0.5024 km^2; C: 2.512 km **9.** A: 153.86 in^2; C: 43.96 in. **11.** A: 119.065 $units^2$; P: 42.71 units **13.** The perimeter of the square

Chapter 4 Summary & Review

1. 33.6 **2.** 4.14 **3.** 2.407 **4.** 5300 **5.** 73 **6.** 48 **7.** 14 **8.** 11,726 **9.** 0.432 **10.** $18.\overline{3}$ ft **11.** 19,200 ft^2 **12.** 1200 cm^2 **13.** 75 ft^2 **14.** 56.25 mm^2 **15.** 21 ft^2 **16.** 30 ft **17.** **a.** 9.42 yd **b.** 7.065 yd^2 **18.** 167.13 sq. units

Cumulative Review Chapters 1–4

1. B **2.** A **3.** C **4.** B **5.** D **6.** B **7.** C **8.** A **9.** B **10.** D **11.** A **12.** A

Chapter 5

5-1 Try It

a. 3 **b.** 5 **c.** 2, 3, 6, 9 **d.** 3, 5 **e.** 2, 3, 5, 6, 9, 10

5-1 Exercises & Applications

1. **a.** 2 **b.** 2 **c.** 5 **d.** 2, 5, 10 **e.** 5 **f.** 2, 5, 10 **3.** 5 **5.** 3, 9 **7.** 2, 5, 10

SELECTED ANSWERS

688

9. 2, 3, 6 **11.** 2, 3, 5, 6, 9, 10 **13.** 2, 3, 5, 6, 9, 10 **15.** 2 **17.** 3, 5, 9 **19.** 2 **21.** 2, 3, 6 **23.** 2, 3, 5, 6, 10 **25.** 2, 3, 6 **27.** 3, 5 **29.** 5 **31.** 2, 3, 6 **33.** Yes **35.** No **37.** No **39.** Yes **41.** Yes **43.** Yes **45.** No **47.** Yes **49.** No **51.** No **53.** Yes **55.** Yes **57. a.** No **b.** No **c.** No **d.** Yes **e.** Yes **59.** No **61. a.** 2, 5, 10 **b.** 2, 5, 10 **c.** 2, 5, 10 **73.** 16 **75.** 4.86 **77.** 6.8 **79.** 13.6

5-2 Try It

a. $2^2 \times 3$ **b.** $2^2 \times 5$ **c.** $2^2 \times 3^2$ **d.** $3^2 \times 5$ **e.** $2 \times 3 \times 5 \times 7$

5-2 Exercises & Applications

1. a. 5×3 **b.** 11×3 **c.** 7×2 **d.** 7×3 **e.** 2×3 **f.** 5×7 **3.** Prime **5.** Composite **7.** Composite **9.** 5^2 **11.** 5×19 **13.** 5^3 **15.** 2×3 **17.** $2^3 \times 11$ **19.** $2^3 \times 3^2$ **21.** $2^2 \times 3^2 \times 19$ **23.** $2^2 \times 3 \times 5$ **25.** $3 \times 5 \times 7$ **27.** $2^4 \times 3$ **29.** 5×17 **31.** 2×3^4 **33.** $3 \times 5 \times 11$ **35.** $2^2 \times 3^2 \times 13$ **37.** $2 \times 3 \times 7$ **39.** Composite **41.** 101, 103, 107, 109 **43.** 41, 43, 47, 53, 59, 61, 67, 71, 73, 79 **49.** 5,700,000 **51.** 5,890,000,000 **53.** 1.2 **55.** 0.25 **57.** 0.25 **59.** 0.5

5-3 Try It (Examples 1–2)

a. 35 **b.** 30 **c.** 20 **d.** 45

5-3 Try It (Example 3)

a. 18 **b.** 8 **c.** 100 **d.** 60 **e.** 55 **f.** 30 **g.** 54 **h.** 1297

5-3 Exercises & Applications

1. a. 3, 6, 9, 12, 15 **b.** 10, 20, 30, 40, 50 **c.** 11, 22, 33, 44, 55 **d.** 8, 16, 24, 32, 40 **e.** 4, 8, 12, 16, 20 **f.** 5, 10, 15, 20, 25 **3.** 5, 10, 15 **5.** 60, 120, 180 **7.** 42, 84, 126 **9.** 8, 16, 24 **11.** 16, 32, 48 **13.** 28, 56, 84 **15.** 33 **17.** 65 **19.** 10 **21.** 12 **23.** 42 **25.** 42 **27.** 20 **29.** 14 **31.** 15 **33.** Every 60 minutes **35.** D **37.** Every 12 days **39.** March 2 **41.** 150 **43.** > **45.** > **47.** 2000

Section 5A Review

1. No **3.** Yes **5.** No **7.** Yes **9.** Yes **11.** Yes **13.** $2^2 \times 19$ **15.** 2×11 **17.** $2^2 \times 3$ **19.** $2 \times 3 \times 19$ **21.** 73 is prime **23.** 3^4 **25.** 2, 4, 6, 8, 10, 12, 14 **27.** 7, 14, 21, 28, 35, 42, 49 **29.** 0, 0, 0, 0, 0, 0, 0 **31.** 6 **33.** 18 **35.** 20 **37.** 1998, 2000, 2002, 2004 **39.** 585

5-4 Try It

a. $\frac{6}{11}$ are red; $\frac{5}{11}$ are not. **b.** $\frac{7}{8}$; $\frac{14}{16}$

5-4 Exercises & Applications

1. a. $\frac{1}{2}$ **b.** $\frac{1}{4}$ **c.** $\frac{5}{8}$ **d.** $\frac{3}{4}$ **3–19.** Possible equivalent fractions: **3.** $\frac{14}{18}$ **5.** $\frac{24}{34}$ **7.** $\frac{4}{6}$ **9.** $\frac{1}{2}$ **11.** $\frac{2}{5}$ **13.** $\frac{6}{16}$ **15.** $\frac{12}{16}$ **17.** $\frac{4}{8}$ **19.** $\frac{18}{20}$ **21.** $\frac{2}{9}$ **23.** B **25.** $\frac{6}{7}$ **27.** $\frac{8}{28}$ or $\frac{2}{7}$ **29.** $\frac{10}{16}$ in. or $\frac{5}{8}$ in. **31.** a, b **33.** 101.9 **35.** 48.3 **37.** 9 **39.** $n = 100$ **41.** $h = 2$

5-5 Try It

Possible answers for a–c: **a.** $\frac{3}{5}$, $\frac{12}{20}$ **b.** $\frac{4}{5}$, $\frac{24}{30}$ **c.** $\frac{1}{3}$, $\frac{14}{42}$ **d.** 5 **e.** 2 **f.** 9 **g.** $\frac{4}{5}$ **h.** $\frac{3}{4}$ **i.** $\frac{2}{3}$

5-5 Exercises & Applications

1. a. Yes **b.** No **c.** Yes **d.** Yes **e.** No **f.** Yes **3–13.** Possible answers given. **3.** $\frac{2}{6}$, $\frac{1}{3}$ **5.** $\frac{2}{12}$, $\frac{3}{18}$ **7.** $\frac{3}{7}$, $\frac{18}{42}$ **9.** $\frac{2}{5}$, $\frac{20}{50}$ **11.** $\frac{1}{3}$, $\frac{22}{66}$ **13.** $\frac{8}{18}$, $\frac{20}{45}$ **15.** $\frac{1}{5}$ **17.** $\frac{1}{3}$ **19.** $\frac{4}{5}$ **21.** $\frac{3}{5}$ **23.** $\frac{1}{6}$ **25.** $\frac{2}{3}$ **27.** $\frac{1}{4}$ **29.** $\frac{1}{6}$ **31.** $\frac{1}{6}$ **33.** 5 **35.** 2 **37.** 1 **39.** 8 **41.** 10 **43.** 4 **45.** 9 **47.** 4 **49.** 3 **51.** C **59.** 25 kg **61.** Flyweight and Cruiserweight; 40 kg

5-6 Try It

a. $4\frac{2}{3}$ **b.** $2\frac{8}{9}$ **c.** $8\frac{3}{4}$ **d.** $\frac{11}{6}$ **e.** $\frac{33}{8}$ **f.** $\frac{13}{5}$

5-6 Exercises & Applications

1. a. Proper **b.** Improper **c.** Improper **d.** Proper **e.** Improper **f.** Improper **3.** $\frac{14}{5}$ **5.** $\frac{10}{3}$ **7.** $\frac{14}{4}$ **9.** $\frac{14}{5}$ **11.** $\frac{31}{10}$ **13.** $\frac{33}{12}$ **15.** $2\frac{4}{5}$ **17.** $5\frac{1}{2}$ **19.** $2\frac{7}{8}$ **21.** $9\frac{9}{10}$ **23.** $100\frac{5}{8}$ **25.** $2\frac{7}{11}$ **27.** $\frac{31}{8}$ **29.** Yes **31.** 12 **39.** 10,560 **41.** 9 **43.** 26,400 **45.** 30

5-7 Try It

a. $\frac{4}{5}$ **b.** $\frac{6}{25}$ **c.** $\frac{3}{8}$ **d.** 0.2; Terminates **e.** 0.65; Terminates **f.** $0.\overline{36}$; Repeats

5-7 Exercises & Applications

1. a. $\frac{3}{10}$ **b.** $\frac{7}{10}$ **c.** $\frac{11}{100}$ **d.** $\frac{37}{100}$ **e.** $\frac{121}{1000}$ **f.** $\frac{333}{1000}$ **3.** $0.\overline{14}$ **5.** $1.\overline{345}$ **7.** $0.\overline{18}$; Repeats **9.** 0.45; Terminates **11.** 0.28; Terminates **13.** $0.\overline{6}$; Repeats **15.** 2.5; Terminates **17.** 1.25; Terminates **19.** 0.72; Terminates **21.** 0.75; Terminates **23.** 0.5; Terminates **25.** $\frac{2}{5}$ **27.** $\frac{11}{25}$ **29.** $\frac{67}{100}$ **31.** $\frac{7}{20}$ **33.** $\frac{13}{25}$ **35.** $\frac{24}{125}$ **37.** $\frac{7}{10}$ **39.** $\frac{16}{125}$ **41.** $\frac{22}{25}$ **43.** $\frac{1}{8}$ in., $\frac{1}{4}$ in., $\frac{3}{8}$ in., $\frac{1}{2}$ in., $\frac{5}{8}$ in., $\frac{3}{4}$ in., $\frac{7}{8}$ in. **45.** D **47.** $0.\overline{02}$; $0.\overline{37}$ **51.** 600 **53.** 2040 **55.** 15,000 **57.** 102

5-8 Try It

a. $\frac{7}{16}$ **b.** $\frac{5}{6}$ **c.** $\frac{8}{11}$

5-8 Exercises & Applications

1. a. < **b.** > **c.** < **d.** > **e.** < **f.** < **3.** 24; > **5.** 6; < **7.** 4; = **9.** 132; < **11.** 33; < **13.** 2; = **15.** $\frac{4}{8} < \frac{7}{9} < \frac{5}{6}$ **17.** $\frac{3}{11} < \frac{11}{11} < \frac{11}{3}$ **19.** $\frac{4}{7} < \frac{4}{6} < \frac{4}{5}$ **21.** $\frac{2}{7} < \frac{3}{8} < \frac{3}{5}$ **23.** $\frac{2}{33} < \frac{3}{22} < \frac{10}{11}$ **25.** $\frac{1}{6} < \frac{7}{36} < \frac{13}{4}$ **27.** $\frac{7}{8}$, $\frac{10}{16}$, $\frac{3}{8}$, $\frac{10}{32}$, $\frac{1}{4}$, $\frac{2}{16}$ **29.** Renaldo **35.** 0; 4; 6 **37.** 198; 110; 90 **39.** 35; 63; 77 **41.** 8; 4; 2

SELECTED ANSWERS

689

SELECTED ANSWERS

Section 5B Review

1. Yes; 3^3 **3.** No; 2^5 **5.** Yes; $2^4 \times 3$ **7.** $\frac{1}{2}$; numerator 1; denominator 2 **9.** $\frac{3}{8}$; numerator 3; denominator 8 **11.** $\frac{3}{4}$; 0.75 **13.** $\frac{1}{3}$; $0.\overline{3}$ **15.** $\frac{1}{2}$; 0.5 **17.** $3\frac{2}{10} = 3\frac{1}{5}$ **19.** $\frac{39}{5}$ **21.** $8\frac{2}{5}$ **23.** Beverly; Tom and Maye

Chapter 5 Summary & Review

1. 2, 3, 6, and 9 **2.** 2 **3.** 2, 3, 5, 6, and 10 **4.** 3 and 5 **5.** Composite **6.** Prime **7.** Composite **8.** Composite **9.** 108 **10.** 126 **11.** $\frac{5}{8}$ **12.** $\frac{4}{6}$ or $\frac{2}{3}$ **13.** The numerator is 11, the denominator is 3. **14.** $\frac{2}{3}$ **15.** $\frac{1}{8}$ **16.** $\frac{1}{6}$ **17.** $\frac{4}{5}$ **18.** $4\frac{1}{4}$ **19.** $\frac{43}{5}$ **20.** $6\frac{5}{7}$ **21.** $\frac{26}{9}$ **22.** $\frac{7}{8}$ in., $1\frac{1}{4}$ in., $2\frac{3}{4}$ in., $\frac{7}{2}$ in. **23.** $0.\overline{6}$ **24.** 5.5 **25.** 0.375 **26.** 1.4 **27.** $\frac{1}{20}$ **28.** $3\frac{4}{5}$ **29.** $\frac{5}{8}$ **30.** $2\frac{23}{1000}$

Chapter 6

6-1 Try It

a. $\frac{7}{10}$ **b.** $\frac{2}{7}$ **c.** $\frac{17}{2}$ **d.** 0

6-1 Exercises & Applications

1. a. Yes **b.** Yes **c.** No **d.** No **e.** Yes **3.** $\frac{1}{10}$ **5.** 2 **7.** $\frac{1}{3}$ **9.** $\frac{1}{2}$ **11.** $\frac{1}{6}$ **13.** $\frac{4}{9}$ **15.** $\frac{6}{13}$ **17.** = **19.** > **21.** < **23.** > **25.** > **27.** $\frac{7}{13}$ **29.** $\frac{4}{17}$ **31.** $\frac{9}{20}$ **33.** $\frac{3}{10}$ **39.** 16 **41.** 31 **43.** 33, 40, 48

6-2 Try It (Example 1)

a. $\frac{5}{6}$ **b.** $\frac{1}{2}$ **c.** $\frac{17}{20}$ **d.** $\frac{1}{10}$

6-2 Try It (Examples 2–3)

a. $\frac{1}{4}$ **b.** $\frac{2}{3}$ **c.** $\frac{7}{10}$ **d.** $\frac{13}{18}$

6-2 Exercises & Applications

1. Possible answers: **a.** 6 **b.** 18 **c.** 8 **d.** 77 **e.** 24 **3.** $\frac{1}{4}$ **5.** $\frac{1}{6}$ **7.** $\frac{5}{4}$ **9.** $\frac{27}{28}$ **11.** $\frac{17}{30}$ **13.** $\frac{21}{20}$ **15.** $\frac{4}{25}$ **17.** 4, 7 **19.** 15, 4 **21.** 4, 3 **23.** $\frac{37}{7}$ weeks **25.** $\frac{23}{42}$ **27.** $\frac{11}{12}$ **29.** $\frac{1}{2}, \frac{7}{12}, \frac{2}{3}$ **31.** 49 **33.** $4h$

6-3 Try It

a. $\frac{2}{3}$ **b.** $\frac{8}{3}$ **c.** 1

6-3 Exercises & Applications

1. a. 1 **b.** $\frac{2}{7}$ **c.** $\frac{5}{9}$ **d.** $\frac{6}{5}$ **3.** $\frac{3}{10}$ **5.** $\frac{7}{8}$ **7.** 4 **9.** $\frac{25}{7}$ **11.** $\frac{1}{6}$ **13.** $\frac{22}{9}$ **15.** $\frac{2}{11}$ **17.** $\frac{1}{3}$ **19–25.** Possible answers given. **19.** $\frac{3}{4} - \frac{1}{4} = \frac{1}{2}$ **21.** $\frac{1}{6} + \frac{5}{12} = \frac{7}{12}$ **23.** $\frac{90}{81} - \frac{1}{3} = \frac{14}{18}$ **25.** $\frac{2}{12} + \frac{7}{10} = \frac{13}{15}$ **27.** $\frac{7}{15}$ **29.** $\frac{7}{12}$ lb **31.** A **33.** $\frac{1}{2}$ yard **37.** 60 **39.** No **41.** Yes

Section 6A Review

1. $\frac{8}{11}$ **3.** $\frac{1}{2}$ **5.** $\frac{27}{20}$ **7.** $\frac{5}{12}$ **9.** $\frac{2}{9}$ **11.** $\frac{19}{20}$ **15.** $\frac{7}{20}$ **17.** $\frac{1}{4}$ **19.** $\frac{3}{4}$ **21.** $\frac{2}{3}$ **23.** $\frac{3}{8}$

6-4 Try It

a. 6 **b.** 2 **c.** 4 **d.** 16 **e.** 8

6-4 Exercises & Applications

1. 0 **3.** 1 **5.** 1 **7.** 4 **9.** 5 **11.** 26 **13.** 34 **15.** 8 **17.** 7 **19.** 2 **21.** 18 **23.** 9 **25.** 7 **27.** 8 **29.** 5 **31.** 26 **33.** 15 **35.** 19 **37.** 7 **39.** $20\frac{5}{8}$ ft **41.** $4\frac{1}{2}$ **43.** 7 inches **47.** 5 **49.** 16 in^2 **51.** 21 **53.** 32 **55.** 8 **57.** 22 **59.** 6 **61.** 5

6-5 Try It

a. $8\frac{3}{4}$ **b.** $4\frac{3}{4}$ **c.** $6\frac{1}{2}$ **d.** $7\frac{5}{12}$

6-5 Exercises & Applications

1. $11\frac{2}{3}$ **3.** $6\frac{1}{2}$ **5.** $9\frac{2}{3}$ **7.** $62\frac{3}{4}$ **9.** 11 **11.** $5\frac{17}{24}$ **13.** $6\frac{4}{5}$ **15.** $15\frac{8}{9}$ **17.** $13\frac{1}{9}$ **19.** $14\frac{1}{10}$ **21.** $21\frac{16}{21}$ **23.** 8 **25.** $41\frac{7}{9}$ **27.** $52\frac{1}{12}$ **29.** $38\frac{1}{4}$ ft **31.** $10\frac{3}{4}$ millions of dollars **33.** $15\frac{53}{60}$ millions of dollars **35.** A: $1\frac{2}{3}$ m^2; B: 3 m^2 **37.** 9.42 ft; 62.8 in.; 113.04 in. **39.** 427,000 **41.** 1,124,000 **43.** 9,000,000,000 **45.** 666,300,000,000

6-6 Try It

a. $3\frac{2}{5}$ **b.** $4\frac{5}{6}$ **c.** $2\frac{4}{9}$

6-6 Exercises & Applications

1. $2\frac{3}{4}$ **3.** $2\frac{1}{2}$ **5.** $1\frac{1}{4}$ **7.** $\frac{1}{2}$ **9.** $\frac{2}{3}$ **11.** $1\frac{1}{24}$ **13.** $8\frac{1}{8}$ **15.** $3\frac{1}{5}$ **17.** $4\frac{11}{20}$ **19.** $\frac{3}{4}$ **21.** $3\frac{3}{5}$ **23.** $6\frac{13}{28}$ **25.** $1\frac{1}{5}$ ft **27.** C **29.** $2\frac{1}{4}$ hr **35.** 54.2325 **37.** 3.4×10^5 **39.** 5×10^6 **41.** 6.2×10^6

Section 6B Review

1. $1\frac{3}{5}$ **3.** $\frac{17}{45}$ **5.** $3\frac{5}{9}$ **7.** $111\frac{11}{24}$ **9.** 7 **11.** $4\frac{2}{3}$ **13.** $\frac{1}{18}$ **15.** $3\frac{1}{4}$ **17.** $\frac{1}{21}$ **19.** 6 hours **21.** D

Chapter 6 Summary & Review

1. $\frac{1}{5} + \frac{3}{5} = \frac{4}{5}$ **2.** 12 **3.** 28 **4.** 30 **5.** 63 **6.** $\frac{2}{7}$ **7.** $\frac{11}{15}$ **8.** 1 **9.** $\frac{1}{5}$ **10.** $1\frac{1}{4}$ **11.** $\frac{1}{14}$ **12.** $1\frac{1}{6}$ **13.** $\frac{2}{15}$ **14.** $\frac{15}{22}$ **15.** $\frac{41}{42}$ **16.** $\frac{5}{24}$ **17.** $\frac{7}{72}$ **18.** $\frac{9}{13}$ **19.** $\frac{3}{4}$ **20.** $\frac{7}{10}$ **21.** 3 **22.** 5 **23.** 2 **24.** 79 **25.** 1 **26.** 14 **27.** 20 **28.** 2 **29.** 2 **30.** 3 **31.** $2\frac{3}{4}$ in. **32.** $5\frac{4}{5}$ **33.** $13\frac{2}{3}$ **34.** $4\frac{3}{4}$ **35.** $\frac{7}{17}$ **36.** $8\frac{73}{88}$ **37.** $13\frac{3}{7}$ **38.** $2\frac{1}{6}$ **39.** $16\frac{7}{9}$ **40.** $9\frac{2}{3}$ **41.** $2\frac{5}{6}$ **42.** $28\frac{6}{7}$ **43.** 14 **44.** $10\frac{1}{2}$ m **45.** $28\frac{7}{8}$ yd

690

Cumulative Review Chapters 1–6

1. A **2.** C **3.** C **4.** D **5.** B **6.** A **7.** D **8.** D **9.** C **10.** C **11.** B **12.** C

Chapter 7

7-1 Try It

a. 15 **b.** 3 **c.** 3 **d.** 1

7-1 Exercises & Applications

1. 5 **3.** 6 **5.** 9 **7.** 15 **9.** 50 **11.** 12 **13.** 72 **15.** 60 **17.** 35 **19.** 28 **21.** 12 **23.** 40 **25.** 30 **27.** 20 **29.** 6 **31.** A **33.** No **35.** 3 **39.** 800 **41.** 97.6 **43.** 0.453 **45.** No **47.** No **49.** Yes **51.** Yes **53.** No **55.** Yes

7-2 Try It

a. $2\frac{2}{3}$ **b.** $5\frac{1}{4}$ **c.** 8 **d.** 25

7-2 Exercises & Applications

1. $3 \times \frac{3}{5}$ **3.** $4 \times \frac{2}{3}$ **5.** $\frac{2}{3}$ **7.** $\frac{3}{5}$ **9.** $6\frac{2}{3}$ **11.** 2 **13.** $1\frac{1}{2}$ **15.** $6\frac{3}{5}$ **17.** $2\frac{2}{9}$ **19.** $5\frac{2}{5}$ **21.** $4\frac{3}{4}$ **23.** $12\frac{5}{6}$ **25.** $9\frac{3}{5}$ **27.** 27 **31.** $2\frac{1}{4}$ lb rice and $1\frac{1}{2}$ lb sugar **33.** 28 years **37.** 98 **39.** 8 **41.** 17 **43.** $3^2 \times 7$ **45.** 17 **47.** 3×19

7-3 Try It

a. $\frac{12}{35}$ **b.** $1\frac{1}{3}$ **c.** $2\frac{8}{21}$ **d.** $\frac{2}{45}$

7-3 Exercises & Applications

1. $\frac{2}{3} \times \frac{2}{4} = \frac{4}{12}$ **3.** $\frac{5}{6} \times \frac{3}{10} = \frac{15}{60}$ **5.** $\frac{2}{7}$ **7.** $\frac{21}{40}$ **9.** $3\frac{59}{105}$ **11.** $\frac{78}{187}$ **13.** $8\frac{3}{10}$ **15.** $\frac{13}{60}$ **17.** $1\frac{146}{169}$ **19.** $1\frac{5}{14}$ **21.** $\frac{11}{42}$ **23.** $\frac{3}{64}$ **25.** $\frac{36}{121}$ **27.** $2\frac{32}{49}$ **29.** $6\frac{1}{4}$ ft **31.** $\frac{1}{8}$ cup sugar, $\frac{1}{8}$ cup flour, and $\frac{7}{8}$ cup water **37.** 126,720 **39.** 190,080 **41.** 63,360 **43.** 6 **45.** 8 **47.** 35 **49.** 72 **51.** 29 **53.** 9

Section 7A Review

1. 3 **3.** 30 **5.** 2 **7.** 11 **9.** 3 oz wax; $19\frac{1}{2}$ tbs oil; 9 tbs water; $\frac{3}{4}$ tsp borax **11.** Yes **13.** $1\frac{2}{3}$ **15.** D

7-4 Try It

a. $6\frac{2}{3}$ **b.** $1\frac{3}{4}$ **c.** $2\frac{6}{17}$ **d.** 5

7-4 Exercises & Applications

1. $\frac{7}{5}$ **3.** $\frac{9}{2}$ **5.** 4 **7.** 9 **9.** $3\frac{1}{2}$ **11.** $11\frac{1}{4}$ **13.** $1\frac{3}{29}$ **15.** $1\frac{7}{23}$ **17.** $3\frac{3}{10}$ **19.** 40 **21.** $3\frac{9}{13}$ **23.** $\frac{9}{32}$ **25.** $10\frac{1}{2}$ **27.** $1\frac{9}{13}$ **29.** $\frac{9}{34}$ **31.** B **33.** 30 **35. a.** About $3\frac{1}{2}$ **b.** 2 **c.** About 11 **37.** No **39.** 896 **41.** 400 **43.** 160

7-5 Try It

a. $1\frac{7}{25}$ **b.** $1\frac{1}{2}$ **c.** $\frac{1}{10}$ **d.** $\frac{1}{25}$

7-5 Exercises & Applications

1. $\frac{2}{3} \div \frac{1}{6} = 4$ **3.** $\frac{1}{3} \div \frac{2}{12} = 2$ **5.** $\frac{2}{5}$ **7.** 7 **9.** $1\frac{1}{4}$ **11.** $\frac{20}{189}$ **13.** $\frac{2}{31}$ **15.** $\frac{5}{16}$ **17.** 10 **19.** 8 **21.** $\frac{4}{25}$ **23.** $\frac{19}{41}$ **25.** 7 **27.** B **29. a.** 9 **b.** 108 **35.** $r = 8$ cm; $d = 16$ cm **37.** $r = 4$ mm; $d = 8$ mm **39.** $\frac{6}{10}$ **41.** $\frac{2}{8}$

7-6 Try It (Example 2)

a. 6 **b.** $\frac{5}{4}$ **c.** 12

7-6 Try It (Example 4)

a. 2 **b.** $\frac{7}{2}$ **c.** $1\frac{1}{2}$

7-6 Exercises & Applications

1. Yes **3.** No **5.** $\frac{24}{133}$ **7.** 15 **9.** $\frac{3}{4}$ **11.** 2 **13.** $125\frac{1}{45}$ **15.** $2\frac{13}{25}$ **17.** 68 **19.** $1\frac{1}{3}$ **21.** $1\frac{1}{4}$ **23.** $6\frac{6}{7}$ **33. a.** 256 **b.** 7000 **c.** 240 **d.** 5760 Possible answers for 35–39: **35.** $\frac{9}{24}, \frac{6}{16}$ **37.** $\frac{1}{2}, \frac{2}{4}$ **39.** $\frac{22}{28}, \frac{33}{42}$ **41.** 3 **43.** 1

Section 7B Review

1. 8 **3.** $7\frac{1}{2}$ **5.** $2\frac{4}{7}$ **7.** $4\frac{17}{22}$ **9.** 50 **11.** 13 **13.** 4 **15.** $v = 32$ **17.** $x = 2$ **19.** $p = \frac{2}{5}$ **21.** $u = 1\frac{3}{5}$ **25.** 3 gallons **27.** A

Chapter 7 Summary & Review

1. $2 \times \frac{5}{7} = \frac{10}{7}$ **2.** ≈ 14 **3.** ≈ 5 **4.** $\frac{3}{32}$ **5.** $\frac{1}{81}$ **6.** $\frac{4}{15}$ **7.** $\frac{12}{49}$ **8.** 25 **9.** 2 **10.** $11\frac{1}{4}$ **11.** $10\frac{5}{9}$ **12.** $1\frac{1}{4}$ cups **13.** No **14.** $4 \div \frac{2}{3} = 6$ **15.** $\frac{8}{5}$ **16.** $\frac{1}{3}$ **17.** $4\frac{1}{2}$ **18.** $\frac{5}{6}$ **19.** $\frac{9}{35}$ **20.** $\frac{8}{35}$ **21.** $\frac{3}{28}$ **22.** $\frac{4}{63}$ **23.** $\frac{1}{40}$ **24.** $\frac{7}{22}$ **25.** Yes **26.** Yes **27.** No **28.** No **29.** $x = \frac{3}{2}$ **30.** $m = \frac{3}{4}$ **31.** $w = \frac{7}{30}$ **32.** $q = \frac{7}{3}$ **33.** 10 pieces

Chapter 8

8-1 Exercises & Applications

1. Ray **3.** Ray **5.** Line **13.** Parallel **15.** Parallel **17.** Intersecting **19.** Perpendicular **31.** $1\frac{2}{3}$ **33.** $2\frac{1}{3}$ **35.** $3\frac{1}{2}$ **37.** $1\frac{4}{5}$ **39.** $1\frac{1}{2}$ **41.** $2\frac{2}{5}$ **43.** 1 **45.** $1\frac{3}{5}$ **47.** $1\frac{1}{4}$ **49.** $1\frac{2}{3}$ **51.** 1

8-2 Try It

a. Straight **b.** Right **c.** Obtuse **d.** Acute

8-2 Exercises & Applications

1. *I* **3.** *B* **5.** Obtuse **7.** Acute **9.** Acute **11.** Right **13.** $\angle ABC$, $\angle CBA$, $\angle B$ **15.** $\angle GHI$, $\angle IHG$, $\angle H$ **21.** Obtuse **23.** Straight **25.** Acute **29.** 6 **31.** Acute **33.** $\frac{33}{5}$ **35.** $\frac{7}{2}$ **37.** $\frac{119}{11}$ **39.** $\frac{39}{4}$ **41.** $\frac{13}{6}$ **43.** $\frac{27}{7}$ **45.** $1\frac{19}{36}$ **47.** $1\frac{1}{3}$ **49.** $\frac{3}{8}$ **51.** $\frac{1}{2}$ **53.** $\frac{9}{11}$

SELECTED ANSWERS

691

8-3 Exercises & Applications

1. Greater than **3.** Less than **5.** 72° **7.** 135° **9.** 180° **11.** 55° **15.** Obtuse **17.** Obtuse **19.** 11° **21.** 87° **23.** 128° **25.** 90° **29.** B **33.** 0.5 **35.** 0.25 **37.** $0.\overline{3}$ **39.** $0.\overline{4}$ **41.** $0.\overline{54}$ **43.** 1.0 **45.** $\frac{1}{24}$ **47.** $1\frac{25}{66}$ **49.** $\frac{5}{72}$ **51.** $\frac{9}{10}$

Section 8A Review

1. Parallel **3.** Nonintersecting **5.** Right **7.** Obtuse **9.** 37°; C = 53°; S = 143° **11.** 75°; C = 15°; S = 105° **13.** A

8-4 Try It

a. 39°; Right **b.** 122°; Obtuse

8-4 Exercises & Applications

1. 40° **3.** 80° **5.** 100° **7.** Acute **9.** Obtuse **11.** Right **13.** Obtuse **15.** Acute **17.** Right **19.** 66°, 56°, 58° **21.** 43°, 112°, 25° **23.** 77°, 45°, 58° **25.** 79°, 60°, 41° **27.** 31° **29.** 5° **31.** 90° **33.** Yes; Acute **35.** Yes; Obtuse **37.** 30°, 43°, 107° **41.** 28° **43.** $\frac{39}{50}$ **45.** $\frac{9}{10}$ **47.** $\frac{18}{25}$ **49.** $\frac{69}{500}$ **51.** $\frac{3}{8}$ **53.** $\frac{999}{1000}$ **55.** 5 **57.** 16 **59.** 5 **61.** 5

8-5 Try It

a. Yes **b.** No **c.** No

8-5 Exercises & Applications

1. 4 m **3.** 20 ft **5.** 9 yd **7.** Scalene **9.** Isosceles **11.** Equilateral **13.** Scalene **15.** Scalene **17.** Equilateral **19.** Yes **21.** Yes **23.** No **25.** Yes **27.** Scalene **29.** No **31.** Right scalene **33.** Obtuse scalene **35.** Yes **37.** Right scalene triangles **39.** $>$ **41.** $=$ **43.** $11\frac{4}{15}$ **45.** $23\frac{1}{2}$ **47.** $11\frac{17}{35}$ **49.** $7\frac{23}{35}$

8-6 Try It

a. Regular quadrilateral **b.** Irregular triangle **c.** Irregular pentagon

8-6 Exercises & Applications

1. Not closed **3.** Not closed **5.** Regular pentagon **7.** Irregular hexagon **9.** Regular quadrilateral **11.** Regular octagon **19.** Octagon **21.** Pentagon **23.** Triangle **25.** Quadrilateral **27.** 8 **29.** 40 in. **33.** $\frac{4}{5}, \frac{7}{8}, \frac{8}{9}$ **35.** $\frac{6}{9}, \frac{6}{6}, \frac{9}{6}$ **37.** $\frac{1}{4}, \frac{1}{3}, \frac{1}{2}$ **39.** $\frac{6}{7}, \frac{9}{8}, \frac{7}{6}$ **41.** $1\frac{27}{35}$ **43.** $\frac{1}{8}$ **45.** $3\frac{11}{56}$ **47.** $6\frac{4}{9}$ **49.** $4\frac{9}{28}$

8-7 Try It

a. False **b.** True **c.** Trapezoid, quadrilateral

8-7 Exercises & Applications

1. 2 **3.** 2 **5.** False **7.** True **23.** A **25.** Yes **31.** $>$ **33.** $>$ **35.** $=$ **37.** $<$ **39.** $=$ **41.** $>$ **43.** 29.4 **45.** 226.8 **47.** 48.23 **49.** 0.4

Section 8B Review

1. ∠*JAH*, ∠*HAJ*, ∠*A* **3.** ∠*IPK*, ∠*KPI*, ∠*P* **5.** 24° **7.** 135° **9.** 128° **11.** Scalene; 57° **13.** Scalene; 18° **19.** Rhombus, parallelogram, irregular quadrilateral, polygon **21.** Trapezoid, irregular quadrilateral, polygon

8-8 Try It

a. No **b.** Yes **c.** Yes

8-8 Exercises & Applications

1.

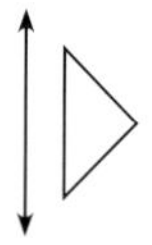

3.

5. Not symmetric **7.** Not symmetric **9.** Yes **11.** Yes **13.** Yes **17.** 2 **19.** Octagon **23.** $\frac{2}{3}$, 0.75, $\frac{7}{9}$ **25.** 1.1, $\frac{7}{6}$, 1.167 **27.** $\frac{1}{3}$, 1.3, $\frac{3}{1}$ **29.** 0.25, $\frac{2}{5}$, 2.5 **31.** 30.528 **33.** 4.3792 **35.** 17.29 **37.** 3.96

8-9 Try It

a. 90° counterclockwise **b.** 270° clockwise **c.** 2

8-9 Exercises & Application

1.

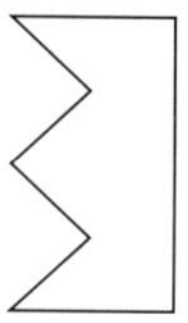

3.

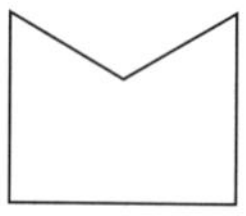

5. 360° **7.** 180° **13.** 45° **15.** 180° **17.** 90° **19.** 72° **25.** 3.55 **27.** 0.13 **29.** 0.06 **31.** 2.37 **33.** 18.2 **35.** 2.69 **37.** 14.2 **39.** 7

8-10 Try It

Yes

8-10 Exercises & Applications

1. No **3.** Yes **7.** Yes **9.** No **11.** No **13.** Yes **15.** Hexagon **17.** Yes **21.** 28 cm **23.** 26 mm **25.** 3100 **27.** 56 **29.** 0.106

Section 8C Review

7. Obtuse, 110°, 40°, 30° **9.** Acute, 65°, 65°, 50° **11.** Regular octagon; Yes; 16 **13.** Irregular triangle; No **15.** Yes **17.** No **19.** 104° **21.** 81° **23.** 90° **25.** C

Chapter 8 Summary & Review

1.

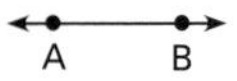

2.

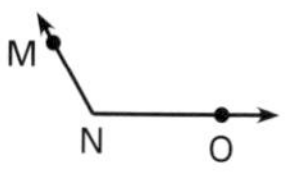

3. a.

b.

4. Acute triangle **5.** All rectangles are parallelograms because their opposite sides have the same

692

lengths and are parallel. But some parallelograms do not have all 90° angles, which rectangles must have. **6.** Translation **7.** Reflection **8.** Rotation **9.** Yes. The figures have the same size and shape.
10.

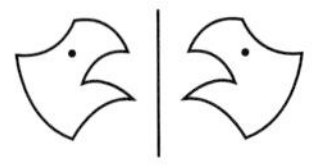

11. Symmetric

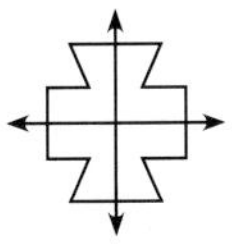

12. 90° clockwise

Cumulative Review Chapters 1–8

1. B **2.** A **3.** B **4.** C **5.** A **6.** A **7.** D **8.** C **9.** A **10.** B **11.** C **12.** B **13.** C **14.** D **15.** A

Chapter 9

9-1 Try It

a. 4° **b.** −6° **c.** −10, −3, 0, 1, 7, 10

9-1 Exercises & Applications

1. Yes **3.** Yes **5.** Yes
7–11.

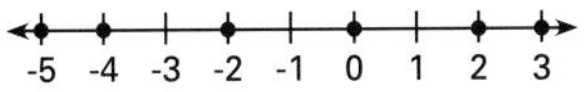

13. > **15.** < **17.** > **19.** > **21.** > **23.** 3, 2, −4, −5 **25.** 13, −16, −56, −78 **27.** 16, 12, 0, −10 **29.** 19, 17, 16, −18 **31.** −114 **33.** 62 **35.** −7 **37.** −213, −211, −107, −76, −52 **39.** −12, 22 **41.** −20, −15, −5, −4, −3, −2, −1 **47.** 14 **49.** 1 **51.** 44 **53.** 180 **55.** Intersecting **57.** Perpendicular **59.** Perpendicular **61.** Intersecting

9-2 Try It

a. 10 **b.** −8 **c.** 1 **d.** 0 **e.** 7 **f.** 6 **g.** 3 **h.** −3

9-2 Exercises & Applications

1. 8 + (−5) = 3 **3.** 3 + (−1) = 2 **5.** −12 **7.** 40 **9.** 1589 **11.** Negative **13.** Positive **15.** Zero **17.** Negative **19.** Negative **21.** −12 **23.** −2 **25.** 6 **27.** −12 **29.** −17 **31.** 1 **33.** 2 **35.** −6 **37.** 13 **39.** −14 **41.** 9 **43.** −1 **45.** −31 **47.** −14 **49.** 0 **51.** Opposite of 211 **55.** B **57.** Yes **59.** $34\frac{1}{2}$ **61.** 1 **63.** $6\frac{2}{3}$ **65.** 50 **67.** Right **69.** Acute

9-3 Try It (Examples 1–2)

a. −2 **b.** −8 **c.** 4 **d.** −1

9-3 Try It (Example 3)

a. 17 **b.** 5 **c.** 26 **d.** −11

9-3 Exercises & Applications

1. −2 − 4 = −6 **3.** −4 − 2 = −6 **5.** −5 − (−2) = −3 **7.** −9 **9.** 9 **11.** 12 **13.** 2 **15.** −11 **17.** 19 **19.** −20 **21.** −11 **23.** −8 **25.** 13 **27.** −5 **29.** 20 **31.** −13 **33.** 22 **35.** 11 **37.** 30,300 ft **39.** 16 feet **41.** 65° **43.** **b.** 33 and 26 **45.** 116° **47.** 87° **49.** $4\frac{3}{5}$ **51.** $2\frac{3}{40}$

9-4 Try It

a. −36 **b.** 90 **c.** 60 **d.** −10 **e.** −4 **f.** 3 **g.** −5 **h.** 3

9-4 Exercises & Applications

1. Negative **3.** Negative **5.** Negative **7.** 9 **9.** 100 **11.** −12 **13.** 18 **15.** −20 **17.** −48 **19.** −32 **21.** −2 **23.** −4 **25.** −7 **27.** −20 **29.** −2 **31.** −7 **33.** −8 **35.** 3 **37.** −12; 2; 0; −4; −2; −4, −3, 12 **39.** −2; −3; 0; 3, 3; 3, 2; 9, 3, 3 **43.** His actual average is −3. **45.** $4\frac{2}{3}$ **47.** $9\frac{1}{3}$ **49.** 28 **51.** $2\frac{1}{22}$ **53.** 73 **55.** 11

Section 9A Review

1. −63 **3.** −1 **5.** −4 **7.** 2 **9.** −9 **11.** −42 **13.** −1 **15.** −2 **17.** −6 **19.** 10 **21.** −40 **23.** 24 **25.** −23 **27.** Lost 12 yards **29.** −4°C **31.** D

9-5 Try It

a. *A*(2, 1); *B*(3, −4); *C*(0, 5); *D*(−1, 2); *E*(4, 0); *F*(1, −3); *G*(2, −3)
b.

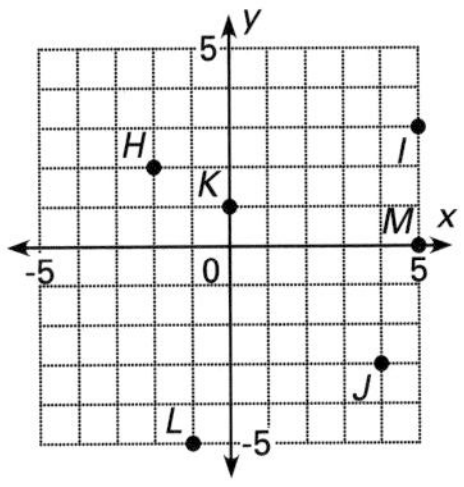

9-5 Exercises & Applications

1. I **3.** III **5.** (−5, 4) **7.** (−3, −2) **9.** I **11.** IV **13.** IV **25.** Start at the origin. Go left 35 units and down 18 units. **27.** Start at the origin. Go right 4 units and up 10 units. **29.** Start at the origin. Go right 88 units and down 23 units. **31.** **a.** 1 (300, 100); 2 (400, 300); 3 (0, 400)
33. **a.**

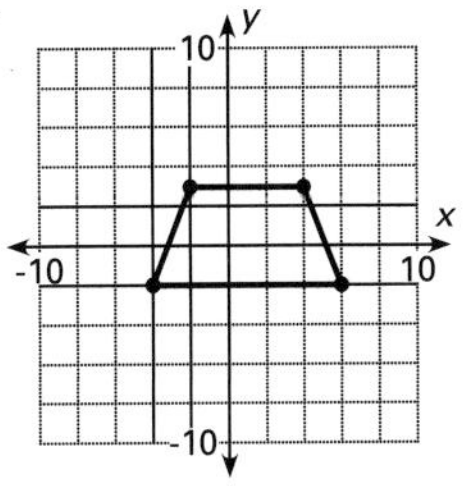

b. Trapezoid, quadrilateral, irregular polygon **35.** (10, 8) **37.** $\frac{147}{256}$ **39.** $2\frac{13}{144}$ **41.** Yes **43.** Yes

9-6 Try It (Example 1)

L'(1, −2); *M'*(2, 0); *N'*(6, −3)

9-6 Try It (Example 2)

X'(−1, −1); *Y'*(−3, 4); *Z'*(−5, 1)

9-6 Exercises & Applications

1. (4, 6) **3.** (7, 4) **5.** (−3, 6) **7.** *P'*(5, 3) **9.** *P'*(3, 5) **11.** *P'*(2, 2)

SELECTED ANSWERS

SELECTED ANSWERS

693

13.

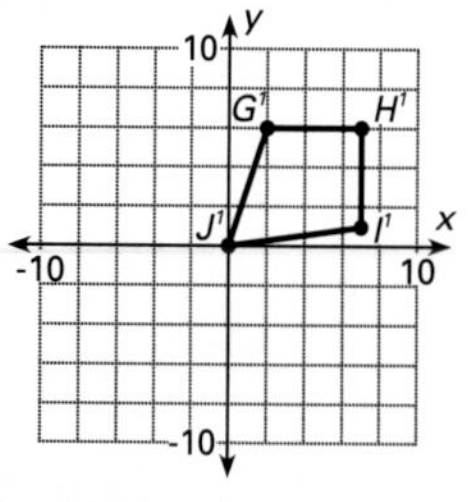

17. c. $R'(2, 3)$, $S'(4, 5)$, $T'(7, 1)$ **19.** 6 right and 8 up **21.** $A'(2, 3)$, $B'(-1, 3)$, $C'(-1, 3)$, $D'(2, -3)$ **25.** $p = 4\frac{2}{5}$ **27.** $e = \frac{9}{8}$ **29.** Irregular heptagon or polygon **31.** Irregular quadrilateral

9-7 Try It

a.

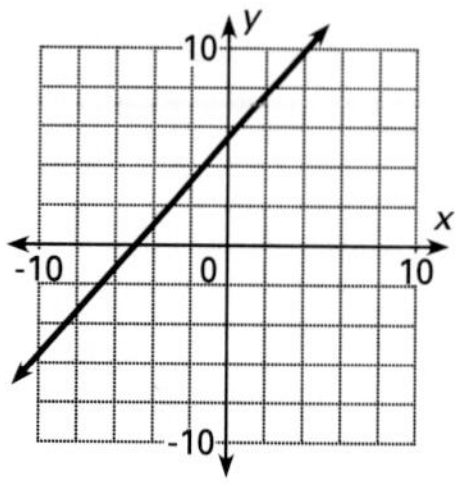

b.

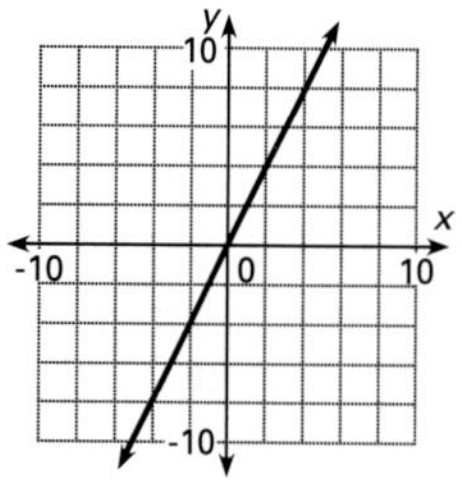

c.

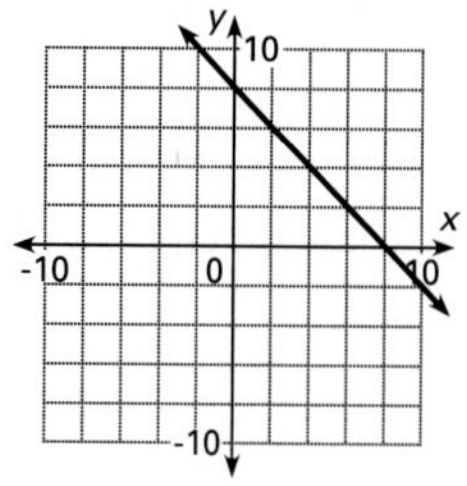

d.

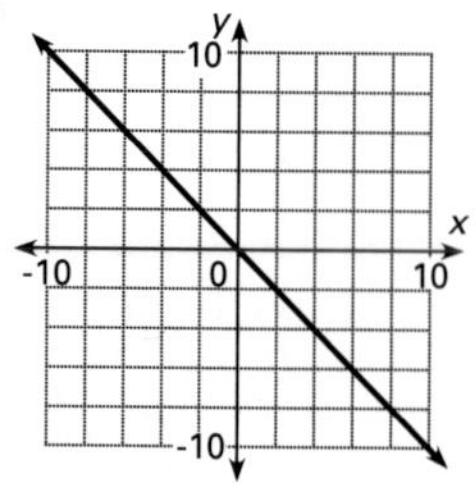

9-7 Exercises & Applications

1. a–d.

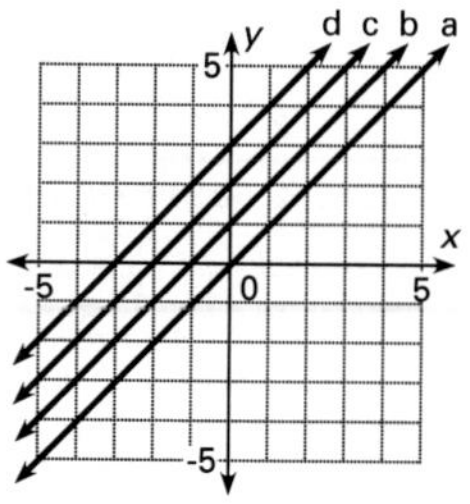

The lines are parallel.

Possible answers for 3–5:

3.

x	y
-2	25
-1	26
0	27
1	28
2	29

5.

x	y
-2	100
-1	50
0	0
1	-50
2	-100

7.

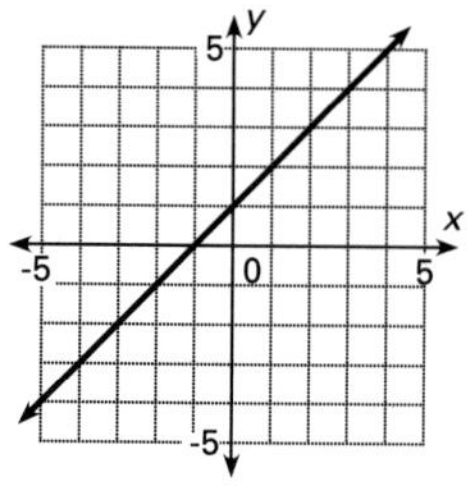

19.

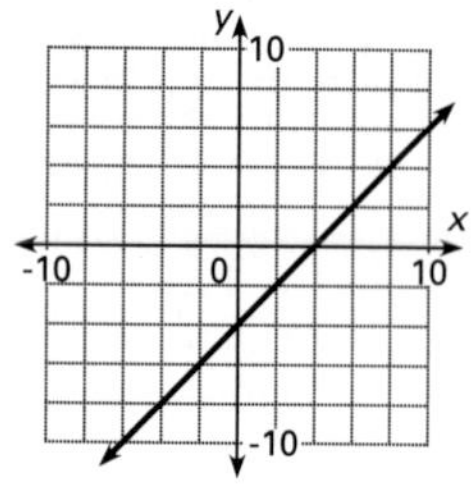

27. 43 **29.** −7 **31.** −2 **39.** 864 **41.** 36 **43.** 9

Section 9B Review

1. 8 **3.** −12 **5.** −10 **7.** 35 **9.** 5 **11.** $A(-3, 2)$, $B(2, 1)$, $C(-2, -2)$, $D(1, -1)$ **13.** $(-2, 1)$ **15.** $(4, 4)$ **17.**

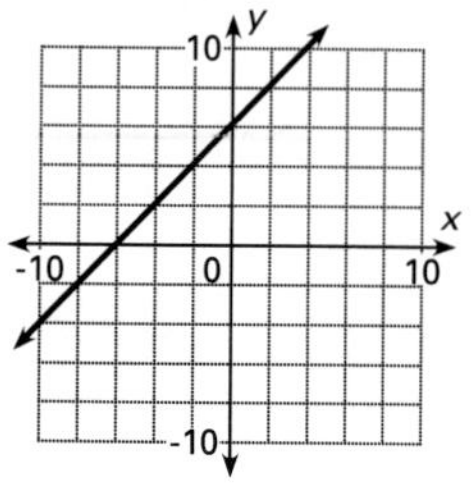

19.

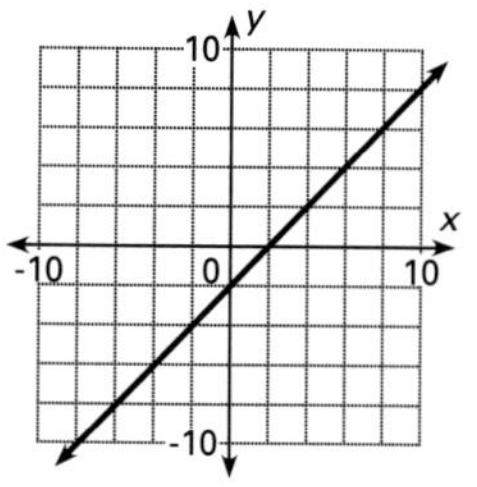

21. (2, 2), (2, 4), (4, 2), (4, 4) **23.** A

Chapter 9 Summary & Review

1.

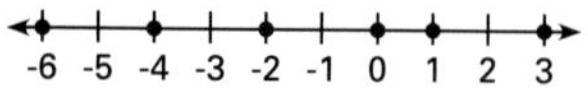

2. −3 **3.** Negative **4.** Positive **5.** $4 + (-5) = -1$ or $4 - 5 = -1$ **6.** $2 + (-4) = -2$ or $2 - 4 = -2$ **7.** 4 **8.** −6 **9.** 2 **10.** 0 **11.** −6 **12.** −10 **13.** 0 **14.** 28 **15.** −21

SELECTED ANSWERS

694

16. 36 **17.** −8 **18.** 3 **19.** (−6, −5) **20.** Quadrant II **21. a.** (5, 0) **b.** (0, 5) or (0, −5) **22.** $R'(-4, -2)$, $S'(-3, -4)$, $T'(-2, -2)$ **23.** $A'(0, 2)$; $B'(3, 2)$; $C'(3, 0)$; $D'(0, 0)$

24. a.

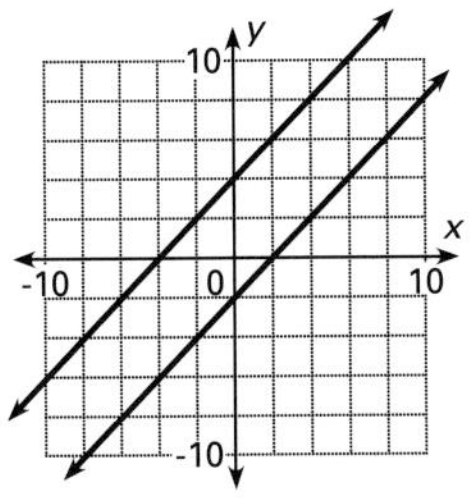

b. Each point on the upper line has been translated down 3 units to create the lower line.

Chapter 10

10-1 Try It

a. 2:5 **b.** 1:2

10-1 Exercises & Applications

1. Yes **3.** Yes **5.** No **7.** 3:2 **9.** 2:3 **11. a.** 20:9 **b.** 9:29 **13.** 3:8; $\frac{3}{8}$; 3 to 8 **15.** 1:7; $\frac{1}{7}$; 1 to 7 **17.** 24:49 **19.** Turtles **21.** Turtles to dogs **23.** You can't tell **25.** Yes **27.** No **29.** 9 in. **31.** 2 km

10-2 Try It

Possible answers: **a.** 10:18; 15:27 **b.** $\frac{6}{16}$; $\frac{9}{24}$ **c.** 3 to 5; 6 to 10 **d.** 2:26; 3:39 **e.** 24:8; 3:1

10-2 Exercises & Applications

1. Yes **3.** Yes **5.** No Possible answers for 7–17: **7.** 8 to 10; 12 to 15 **9.** 6:4; 3:2 **11.** $\frac{2}{3}$; $\frac{16}{24}$ **13.** $\frac{1}{2}$; $\frac{2}{4}$ **15.** $\frac{2}{16}$; $\frac{3}{24}$ **17.** $\frac{6}{8}$; $\frac{12}{16}$ **19.** Yes **21.** Yes **25.** A Possible answers for 27: **27.** 14:20; 28:40; 21:30 **29.** Men: 8, 12; Women: 5; 20 **31.** 19 **33.** 180° **35.** 360° **37.** 20 unit^2 **39.** 36 cm^2 **41.** 15.75 m^2

10-3 Try It

Possible answers: About 0.44 mi in 1 min; 18 miles in 41 min; About 7 mi in 16 min; 72 mi in 164 min

10-3 Exercises & Applications

1. Yes **3.** No **5.** Yes **7.** No Possible answers for 9–11: **9.** 7 mi/hr, 21 mi/3 hr **11.** $\frac{15 \text{ j.j.}}{20 \text{ sec}}$, $\frac{3 \text{ j.j.}}{4 \text{ sec}}$ Possible answer for 13: **13.** An ostrich runs 5 miles in 10 minutes. **15.** About 25 mi **17.** Orange **19.** D **21.** $2\frac{1}{2}$ hours **25.** Yes **27.** No **29.** 2.4 m^2 **31.** 0.12 cm^2 **31.** 120,000 mi^2

Section 10A Review

1. 23:30 **3.** Possible answer: $\frac{3 \text{ red}}{5 \text{ blue}}$, $\frac{3 \text{ red}}{4 \text{ green}}$, $\frac{3 \text{ red}}{7 \text{ red or green}}$, $\frac{1 \text{ red}}{3 \text{ blue or green}}$, $\frac{1 \text{ red}}{4 \text{ total}}$ **5.** Possible answers: 3:8, 12:32, 15:40 **7.** 1:3 **9.** Possible answer: $\frac{3 \text{ blue stones}}{28 \text{ stones}}$ **11.** D

10-4 Try It

a. Yes **b.** No **c.** No **d.** Yes

10-4 Exercises & Applications

1. a. II **b.** III **c.** I **d.** IV **3.** No **5.** No **7.** No **9.** No **11.** No **13.** Yes **15.** b **17.** c **19.** Yes **21.** D **23.** Ms. Lee and Mrs. Nieto **25.** You use multiplication to see if the cross products are equal. **27.** $3 \times 2 = 6$, but $8 \times 2 \neq 9.5$. **29.** 55, 31, −13, −55 **31.** −9, −17, −31, −53 **33.** 44, 41, −14, −41 **35.** 133, 0, −100, −178 **37.** 4.2 **39.** $r = 4.4$ yd; $d = 8.8$ yd

10-5 Try It

a. 9 **b.** 10 **c.** 1.5 **d.** 7.2

10-5 Exercises & Applications

1. $9x = 36$ **3.** $44j = 275$ **5.** $16s = 56$ **7.** 12 **9.** 25 **11.** 16.5 **13.** 0.96 **15.** 6 **17.** 3 **19.** $2.\overline{6}$ **21.** 3.6 **23.** 154 **25.** $23.\overline{3}$ **27.** 12 **29.** $5\frac{1}{3}$ ft **31.** A **33.** 6 **35.** Greater than **37.** −18 **39.** −6 **41.** 12.56 cm^2 **43.** 153.86 cm^2

10-6 Try It

a. 3600 ft/min **b.** $2.80

10-6 Exercises & Applications

1. 3 **3.** 7 **5.** 8 **7.** 2 houses/mi **9.** $5\frac{1}{6}$ holes/in^2 **11.** 0.6 waves/sec **13.** 3 slices/person **15.** $\frac{1}{3}$ m/hr **17.** 0.5 cup/serving **19.** 1.5 turtles/mi^2 **21.** 7.5 m/sec **23.** 252 mi **25.** 2.2 points **27.** 9 drips **29.** 1.2 apples **31.** $\frac{70 \text{ apples}}{6 \text{ baskets}} = \frac{x}{3}$ baskets; $x = 35$ apples **33.** 3 pounds for 72¢ **35.** $0.58\overline{3}$ ft, or $\frac{7}{12}$ ft **41.** −17 **43.** 14 **45.** 4 **47.** 13 **49.** 34 **51.** 33.25 in^2 **53.** 154 mm^2

10-7 Try It

6

10-7 Exercises & Applications

1. Congruent **3.** Neither **5.** $A = B = C = 1$ mm **7.** $A = C = 0.625$ yd, $B = 0.5$ yd **9.** 12.5 m **11. a.** 1000 mi; 675 mi; 1667.5 mi **b.** Yes **13.** 25 ft or 64 ft **15.** No; Yes **17.** −21 **19.** 16 **21.** −70 **23.** 26 **25.** 12 **27.** Yes **29.** No **31.** Yes **33.** Yes **35.** Yes **37.** Yes

Section 10B Review

1. Possible answers: $\frac{5 \text{ cm}}{2 \text{ sec}}$, $\frac{2.5 \text{ cm}}{1 \text{ sec}}$, $\frac{10 \text{ cm}}{4 \text{ sec}}$ **3.** $0.65/min **5.** 0.6 commercials/min **7.** 50.4 **9.** $0.30 **11.** 5 **13.** $A = 4.\overline{6}$, $B = 3$, $C = 7$ **15.** B

10-8 Try It

a. 25% **b.** 75%

10-8 Exercises & Applications

1. Greater **3.** Less **5.** Less **7.** 50% **9.** 25% **11.** 50% **13.** 74% **15.** About 12%; About 88% **17.** India, Myanmar, Other **19.** 25% **21. a.** 89% **b.** No **23.** Yes **25.** Yes **33.** 5^2 **35.** 5×19 **37.** 5^3 **39.** 2×3 **41.** $2^3 \times 11$ **43.** $2^3 \times 3^2$

SELECTED ANSWERS

695

10-9 Try It

a. 20% **b.** 70%

10-9 Exercises & Applications

1. 50% **3.** 40% **5.** 25% **7.** 70% **9.** 33% **11.** 25% **13.** 10% **15.** 50% **17.** 75% **19.** 60% **21.** 1% **23.** 7% **25.** C **27.** 33% **29.** $\frac{7}{200}$ **31.** 66% are not **37.** 6 **39.** 12 **41.** 10 **43.** 30 **45.** 42 **47.** 6

10-10 Try It

a. $\frac{83}{100}$; 0.83 **b.** $\frac{7}{100}$; 0.07 **c.** 37.5%

10-10 Exercises & Applications

1. 0.37 **3.** 1.0 **5.** 0.1 **7.** 2.34 **9.** 0.673 **11.** 0.8887 **13.** $\frac{14}{25}$ **15.** $\frac{3}{4}$ **17.** $1\frac{1}{2}$ **19.** $\frac{89}{100}$ **21.** $\frac{9}{10}$ **23.** $2\frac{17}{50}$ **25.** 84% **27.** 4% **29.** 110% **31.** 85% **33.** 53% **35.** 30% **37.** 56% **39.** 48% **41.** 75% **43.** 67.5% **45.** 33.3% **47.** 38% **49.** 40%, $\frac{2}{5}$, 0.4 **51.** 50%, $\frac{4}{8}$, 0.5 **53.** $66.\overline{6}$% **55.** C **57.** $\frac{27}{200}$

10-11 Try It (Example 2)

a. 611 **b.** 133

10-11 Try It (Example 3)

a. 70 **b.** 50,000

10-11 Exercises & Applications

1. 50 **3.** 2 **5.** 22.1 **7.** 18.48 **9.** 104.94 **11.** 54.3 **13.** 22.44 **15.** 0.376 **17.** 15.2 **19.** ≈ $2.75 **21.** 6.12 **23.** 8.51 **25.** 250 **27.** 200 **29.** 88 **31.** 176 **33.** 20 or more **35.** $36,720 **37.** 249 **39.** $90.00 **41.** Probably Gloria **43.** About 62 points **47.** $\frac{1}{5}$ **49.** $\frac{1}{3}$ **51.** $\frac{4}{5}$ **53.** $\frac{3}{5}$ **55.** $\frac{1}{6}$ **57.** $\frac{2}{3}$ **59.** $1\frac{1}{5}$ **61.** $3\frac{1}{3}$ **63.** $2\frac{2}{7}$ **65.** $\frac{47}{4}$ **67.** $8\frac{1}{8}$ **69.** $\frac{119}{12}$

Section 10C Review

1. a. 3:4 **b.** $\frac{3}{4}$; 0.75 lettuce/carrot **c.** ≈ 57.14% **3.** Yes **5.** Yes **7.** 4 **9.** 10 **11.** 1200 **13.** A and $C = 0.2$ in.; $B = 0.3$ in. **15.** 28.86 **17.** 17.52 **19.** Possible answers: **a.** 85% **b.** 60% **21.** 95%; 60%

Chapter 10 Summary & Review

1. 6:11, 6 to 11, $\frac{6}{11}$ **2.** $\frac{3}{4}$ **3. a.** 10 to 1 **b.** 1 to 10 **c.** 5 to 1 **d.** 2 to 1 **4.** 3 to 4; 3 to 7 **5.** A **6.** B **7.** No **8.** 15 **9.** $4.32 **10.** Possible answer: The ratios of all the matching sides are equal. The angle measures are equal. **11.** $\frac{35}{100}$, $\frac{7}{20}$, 0.35 **12.** $\frac{20}{100}$, $\frac{1}{5}$, 0.2 **13.** $\frac{8}{100}$, $\frac{2}{25}$, 0.08 **14.** $\frac{75}{100}$, $\frac{3}{4}$, 0.75 **15.** ≈ 4,680,998 people **16.** Possible answer: $\frac{6}{4}$, $\frac{12}{8}$, $\frac{18}{12}$, $\frac{24}{16}$ **17.** $\frac{1.5 \text{ min}}{1 \text{ mi}}$

Cumulative Review Chapters 1–10

1. D **2.** B **3.** A **4.** C **5.** C **6.** B **7.** D **8.** A **9.** B **10.** C **11.** A **12.** D **13.** C **14.** A

Chapter 11

11-1 Exercises & Applications

1. Triangles and squares or rectangles **3.** Squares or rectangles **5.** Sphere **7.** Triangular prism; 6 vertices, 9 edges, 5 faces **9.** Cylinder **11.** Cone **17.** Rectangular prisms **19.** Spheres **25.** No; No; No **27.** 100 to 10 **29.** 2.5 **31.** 0.75 **33.** 0.83

11-2 Try It

a. 6 faces: All rectangles **b.** 272 units^2

11-2 Exercises & Applications

1. 12 units^2 **3.** 18 units^2 **5.** 24 cm^2; Cube or rectangular prism **7.** 60 units^2; Triangular prism **9.** 6 faces: All rectangles; 310 ft^2 **13.** 5 faces: 2 triangles, 3 rectangles; 112.4 in^2 **15.** D **19.** Sometimes; No
Possible answers for 21–25: **21.** 3:12, 2:8 **23.** 14 to 18, 21 to 27 **25.** 6:16, 9:24 **27.** $\frac{1}{6}$, $\frac{5}{6}$, 6.7 **29.** $\frac{1}{3}$, $\frac{3}{3}$, 3.3

11-3 Try It

a. 358 units^2 **b.** 96 units^2 **c.** 380 units^2

11-3 Exercises & Applications

1. 6 cm^2 **3.** 96 m^2 **5.** 48 ft^2 **7.** 268 units^2 **9.** 34.56 mm^2 **11.** 109.8 cm^2 **13.** 13.5 cm^2 **15.** C **17.** 1128 in^2 **19.** Yes **21.** No **23.** $\frac{1}{6}$ **25.** $\frac{13}{28}$ **27.** $\frac{10}{63}$

11-4 Exercises & Applications

1. 15.7 cm **3.** 6.28 ft **5.** 61.23 m^2 **7.** 17.27 in^2 **9.** 150.72 ft^2 **11.** 747.32 units^2 **13.** 266.9 units^2 **15. a.** 42.39 in^2 **b.** 56.52 in^2 **17.** C **19.** 37.68 in^2 **21.** No **23.** No **25.** No **27.** Yes **29.** No **31.** 124 **33.** 18.72 **35.** 13.5 **37.** 18.48

Section 11A Review

1. Sphere **3.** Triangular prism; 6 vertices, 9 edges, 5 faces **5.** Cube or rectangular prism; 8 vertices, 12 edges, 6 faces **9.** 54 ft^2 **11.** 8800 cm^2

11-5 Try It

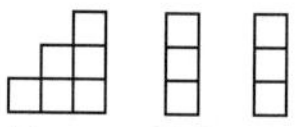

11-5 Exercises & Applications

1. 5 **3.** 12 **13.** 36 **15. a.** 7 **b.** 5.1 cm **c.** 6.8 cm **17. a.** No **b.** No **21.** $f = 48$ **23.** $r = 3$ **25.** 156% **27.** 55% **29.** 28% **31.** $\frac{67}{100}$ **33.** $2\frac{1}{2}$ **35.** $\frac{1}{100}$

11-6 Try It

a. 8 units^3 **b.** 48 units^3 **c.** 16 units^3 **d.** 225 units^3

SELECTED ANSWERS

696

11-6 Exercises & Applications

1. 10 units^3 **3.** 21 units^3 **5.** 360 units^3 **7.** 64 units^3 **9.** 60 units^3 **11.** 60 **13.** Yes **15.** 4 ways **17.** 3 mi per min **19.** 5 bananas per dollar **21.** $0.3\overline{16}$ m per sec **23.** 4.5 worms per in^2 **25.** About 20% **27.** About 20%

11-7 Try It

a. 105 in^2 **b.** 18 in.

11-7 Exercises & Applications

1. 125 in^3 **3.** 343 ft^3 **5.** 72 yd^3 **7.** 910 m^3 **9.** 480 units^3 **11.** 74.088 in^3 **13.** 2907 m^3 **15.** B **17.** About 12 inches deep **19.** $A = 32$ ft, $B = 64$ ft **21.** $33.\overline{3}\%$ **23.** 40%

Section 11B Review

1. Rectangular prism; 8 vertices, 12 edges, 6 faces **3.** Triangular prism; 6 vertices, 9 edges, 5 faces **5.** $16.39

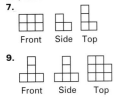

7.

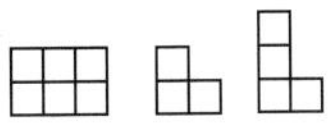

Front Side Top

9.

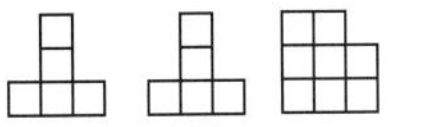

Front Side Top

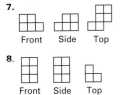

Chapter 11 Summary & Review

1. Triangular prism; 5 faces, 9 edges, 6 vertices. **2.** Sphere **3.** Rectangular pyramid; 5 faces, 8 edges, 5 vertices. **4.** 310 in^2 **5.** 340 units^2 **6.** 80.07 mm^2

7.

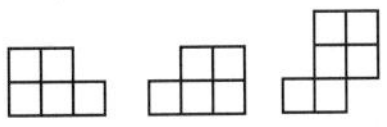

Front Side Top

8.

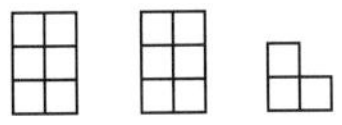

Front Side Top

9. 80 units^3 **10.** 240 cm^3 **11.** 0.36 units^3 **12.** 477.28 in^2

Chapter 12

12-1 Try It

a. i. $\frac{3}{8}$ **ii.** 0 **b. i.** $\frac{1}{2}$ **ii.** $\frac{3}{5}$

12-1 Exercises & Applications

1. 2 **3.** 6 **5.** $\frac{1}{10}$ **7.** $\frac{1}{10}$ **9.** 0 **11.** $\frac{1}{2}$ **13.** $\frac{1}{6}$ **15.** $\frac{5}{6}$ **17.** $\frac{1}{6}$ **19.** $\frac{1}{3}$ **21.** Both are $\frac{1}{8}$ **23.** $\frac{1}{5}$ **25.** Will occur **27.** $\frac{9}{32}$ **29.** No; No **33.** Rectangular prism **35.** Cylinder **37.** 31.74 cm^2 **39.** 708 ft^2

12-2 Try It

a. $\frac{13}{61}$ **b.** $\frac{51}{61}$

12-2 Exercises & Applications

1. Yes **3.** No **5.** 3 **7.** $\frac{17}{20}$ **9.** 67 **11.** 16 **13.** May; $\frac{181}{826} \approx 0.22$ **15.** Yes **17.** The numbers are considerably above average. **19.** First figure **21.** 482.8 in^2

12-3 Try It

50%

12-3 Exercises & Applications

1. 9 square units **3.** 30% **5.** 25% **7.** 37.5% **9.** 50% **11.** A **21.** 18 units^3 **23.** 16 units^3

Section 12A Review

1. $\frac{1}{6}$ **3.** 0 **5.** $\frac{5}{6}$ **7.** $\frac{5}{8}$ **9.** 1 **11.** C **13.** 1000 **15.** B

12-4 Try It

a. Possibilities are: chocolate, hot fudge; chocolate, butterscotch; vanilla, hot fudge; vanilla butterscotch; mint, hot fudge; mint, butterscotch. **b.** 16

12-4 Exercises & Applications

1. 12 outcomes **5.** D **7. a.** 6 **b.** $\frac{1}{3}$ **9.** 45,697,600 **13.** 12; 12 **15.** 24 in^2 **17.** $\frac{3}{10}$ **19.** $\frac{1}{5}$ **21.** $\frac{2}{5}$

12-5 Try It

$\frac{1}{3}$

12-5 Exercises & Applications

1. a. 6 **b.** 216 **c.** 1 **d.** 1 **e.** $\frac{1}{216}$ **3.** $\frac{1}{9}$ **5.** $\frac{4}{27}$ **7.** $\frac{1}{27}$ **9.** About $\frac{1}{32}$ **11.** $\frac{1}{16}$ **13.** $P(\text{same}) = \frac{1}{6}$; $P(\text{different}) = \frac{5}{6}$ **15.** Winning both the 50-yard dash and the hurdles. **17.** $\frac{5}{51}$ **21.** #2

12-6 Try It

a. No; If Player A always chooses 1, Player A will always win. If the numbers are chosen at random, Player B has a greater chance of winning. **b.** Yes

12-6 Exercises & Applications

1. b. $\frac{13}{18}$ **c.** $\frac{5}{18}$ **d.** No; Player A has a greater chance of winning. **3.** Fair **5.** Unfair; Edna **7.** Yes; He got each number about the same amount of times. **9.** Unfair

Section 12B Review

1. a. 8 **b.** $\frac{1}{8}$ **3.** $\frac{1}{16}$ **5. a.** 42,875 **b.** $\frac{1}{42{,}875}$ **7.** No; $P(\text{A win}) = \frac{3}{8}$, $P(\text{B win}) = \frac{5}{8}$

Chapter 12 Summary & Review

1. About $\frac{1}{4}$ **2.** It is likely to occur. **3.** $\frac{3}{7}$ **4.** 16 **5.** About $\frac{1}{4}$ **6.** 24 outfits **7.** 180 **8.** 8 **9.** $\frac{1}{3}$ **10.** $\frac{1}{36}$ **11.** $\frac{1}{16}$ **12.** Yes **13.** No

Cumulative Review Chapters 1–12

1. C **2.** B **3.** D **4.** A **5.** A **6.** D **7.** C **8.** D **9.** B **10.** B **11.** C **12.** B **13.** A **14.** A

SELECTED ANSWERS

697

Photographs

Cover/Spine: Uniphoto Picture Agency, Inc.

Front Matter **iii** GHP Studio* **iii (background)** John Banagan/The Image Bank **v-xvi T** GHP Studio* **xviii L** Cheryl Fenton* **xviii R** George Hunter/Tony Stone Images **xix T** Parker/Boon Productions and Dorey Sparre Photography* **xix B** Ken Karp,* Dennis Geaney* & Parker/Boon Productions and Dorey Sparre Photography* **xxii** Jean-Marc Giboux/Liaison International **xxiii** Pictor/Uniphoto Picture Agency **xxiv** Ken Karp* **xxv** Fridmar Damm/Leo de Wys Inc. **xxvi** John Lund/Tony Stone Images **xxvii** Robie Price* **xxviii** Mark C. Burnett/Stock, Boston

Chapter 1 **2–3 (background)** Ralph Mercer/Tony Stone Images **2 TR (frame)** John Michael/International Stock Photo **2 TR (inset)** Christopher Liu/China Stock **2 BR** NASA/Stock, Boston **2 BL** Robie Price* **3** ZEFA/The Stock Market **4 B** Soames Summerhays/Photo Researchers **4 T** Ed R. Degginger/Photo Researchers **5** Robie Price* **6** Douglas Faulkner/Photo Researchers **8** Blake/Reuters/Corbis-Bettmann **10** Damien Lovegrove/SPL/Photo Researchers **11 L** Marc Chamberlain/Tony Stone Images **11 R** Geoffrey Nilsen Photography* **12** Jeff Rotman **14** W. Gregory Brown/Animals, Animals **15** Bob Daemmrich/Stock, Boston **16** Pete Saloutos/The Stock Market **17** David Hall/Photo Researchers **18 T** David Madison/Bruce Coleman Inc. **18 B** Dr. Nigel Smith/Earth Scenes **19 T** Paul Humann/Jeff Rotman Photography **19 B** Geoffrey Nilsen Photography* **20** Lee F. Snyder/Photo Researchers **21** Robie Price* **23 L** Joseph Nettis/Stock, Boston **23 R** Jon Feingersh/The Stock Market **24** Ron Chapple/FPG International **26 R** UPI/Corbis-Bettmann **26 L** Portrait by Ellis Sawyer/FPG International **28** from HERBLOCK: A CARTOONIST'S LIFE (Macmillan Publishing, 1993) **29** Owen Franken/Stock, Boston **31 BLC** Popperfoto/Archive Photos **31 BR** Ron Thomas/Reuters/Corbis-Bettmann **31 BRC** Mark Reinstein/FPG International **31 T** Worldsat International Inc./SPL/Photo Researchers **31 BL** FPG International **32** Robert Frerck/Tony Stone Images **33** Geoffrey Nilsen Photography* **34 R** Win McNamee/Reuters/Corbis-Bettmann **34 L** Jeffrey Sylvester/FPG International **35** AFP/Archive Photos **36 L** Dennis Geaney* **36 R** Parker/Boon Productions and Dorey Sparre Photography* **37** Corbis-Bettmann **38** Archive Photos **39** Jon Feingersh/The Stock Market **40 B** © 89 Mug Shots/The Stock Market **40 T** Geoffrey Nilsen Photography* **41 T** Geoffrey Nilsen Photography* **41 B** Geoffrey Nilsen Photography* **41 (inset)** Mississippi Valley State University **42** Shelley Gazin/The Image Works **43** Bill Reitzel **45** Kevin Lamarque/Reuters/Corbis-Bettmann **46 TL** Berenguier & Jerrican/Photo Researchers **46 TR** Robie Price* **46 B** Geoffrey Nilsen Photography* **47** Paul Souders/Allsport **48 T** Dennis Geaney* **48 B** Al Bello/Allsport **49** Gail Shumway/FPG International **51** Tim DeFrisco/Allsport **52** Otto Rogge/The Stock Market **53** Robie Price* **54** Brad Mangin/Duomo **55 BL** National Baseball Hall of Fame © Topps **55 TL** Geoffrey Nilsen Photography* **55 TR** Geoffrey Nilsen Photography* **55 BR** Geoffrey Nilsen Photography* **56** Popperfoto/Archive Photos **57** Geoffrey Nilsen Photography* **61 T** Stewart L. Craig, Jr./Bruce Coleman Inc. **61 C** Robie Price* **61 B** Geoffrey Nilsen Photography*

Chapter 2 **62–63 (background)** Comstock **62 TL** Erich Lessing/Art Resource, NY **62 TR** David Frazier/Science Source/Photo Researchers **62 B** Cheryl Fenton* **63 T** Robert Fried/Stock, Boston **63 B** Cheryl Fenton* **64 T** Mark Gamba/The Stock Market **64 B** John Terence Turner/FPG International **65 T** Rob Lewine/The Stock Market **65 B** NASA **66 T** Alan Carey/The Image Works **68** Frank Rossotto/The Stock Market **69 L** NASA/Science Source/Photo Researchers **69 R** NASA/Lunar & Planetary Inst. **70** Robert Houser/Comstock **72 L** Lunar & Planetary Inst. **72 R** NASA/ESA/Tom Stack & Associates **73** Robie Price* **74** Tim Flach/Tony Stone Images **75** Lunar & Planetary Institute **77** Sovfoto/Eastfoto **78** Gabe Palmer/Mugshots/The Stock Market **79 T** NASA/JPL/TSADO/Tom Stack & Associates **79 B** NASA **80 L** Parker/Boon Productions and Dorey Sparre Photography* **80 R** Dennis Geaney* **81** NASA/JPL/TSADO/Tom Stack & Associates **82** NIBSC/SPL/Photo Researchers **82 (inset)** CNRI/SPL/Photo Researchers **83 T** Rob Lewine/The Stock Market **83 B** NASA **84** NASA/Mark Marten/Photo Researchers **86 L** Mike Malyszko/FPG International **87** Underwood Collection/Corbis-Bettmann **88** Geoffrey Nilsen Photography* **89** Carl Yarbrough/Uniphoto Picture Agency **90 L** Billy Hustace/Tony Stone Images **90 R** Geoffrey Nilsen Photography* **93** Geoffrey Nilsen Photography* **94 L** John Coletti/Tony Stone Images **94 R** Geoffrey Nilsen Photography* **95** Bob Daemmrich/The Image Works **96 R** Fujifotos **97 T** Geoffrey Nilsen Photography* **97 C** Robie Price* **98 L** Lawrence Migdale/Stock, Boston **98 R** Hewlett Packard **100** Robie Price* **101** Geoffrey Nilsen Photography* **102 TL** Stephen Frisch/Stock, Boston **102 TR** Robie Price* **102 B** Gregory Sams/SPL/Photo Researchers **104 L** Ken Karp* **104 R** Parker/Boon Productions and Dorey Sparre Photography* **105** Anne Dowie* **106** IFA-Bildesteam/Uniphoto Picture Agency **107 L** Geoffrey Nilsen Photography* **108** Anne Dowie* **109** Barry E. Parker/Bruce Coleman Inc. **110 L** Jon Feingersh/Stock, Boston **110 R** Steve Starr/Stock, Boston **113** Martin Rogers/Stock, Boston **114 L** Anne Dowie* **114 R** Robie Price* **115** Topham/The Image Works **116** Eric A. Wessman/Stock, Boston **117** ©1986 Carmen Lomas Garza, photo by Wolfgang Dietze **118** Jeff Lepore/Photo Researchers **119** Mark Gamba/The Stock Market **120** Navaswan/FPG International **122** Lawrence Migdale/Photo Researchers **123** Brian Parker/Tom Stack & Associates **125** Monteath C./Hedgehog House N. Zeal./Explorer/Photo Researchers **127** Barry E. Parker/Bruce Coleman Inc. **127 TL** Peter David/Photo Researchers **127 BL** Richard Pasley/Stock, Boston **128** Thomas Kitchin/Tom Stack & Associates **129** Geoffrey Nilsen Photography*

Chapter 3 **134–135 (background)** Superstock **134 L** Steven E. Sutton/Duomo **134 TR** J. P. Courau/DDB Stock Photo **134 BR** Stuart Cohen/Comstock **135 T** Cheryl Fenton* **135 B** Kimimasa Mayama/UPI/Corbis-Bettmann **136 T** Anne Dowie* **136 B** Jane Burton/Bruce Coleman Inc. **137** Robie Price* **137 (insets)** Stephen Cooper/Tony Stone Images **138** Doug Wechsler/Earth Scenes **139** G. C. Kelley/Photo Researchers **140** Andrew Syred/SPL/Photo Researchers **141** Popperfoto/Archive Photos **142 L** Gabe Palmer/Mugshots/The Stock Market **142 R** Robie Price* **143 L** Ray Coleman/Photo Researchers **143 R** John Fennell/Bruce Coleman Inc. **144 T** Geoffrey Nilsen Photography* **144 C** Geoffrey Nilsen Photography* **144 B** Rod Planck/Tony Stone Images **145 L** Geoffrey Nilsen Photography* **145 R** Parker/Boon Productions and Dorey Sparre Photography* **146 L** Gilbert S. Grant/Photo Researchers **146 R** John Gerlach/Animals, Animals **148** David Madison **149** Jan C. Taylor/Bruce Coleman Inc. **150 L** Ken Karp* **150 R** Dennis Geaney* **151 L** James H. Carmichael, Jr. /Photo Researchers **151 R** L. West /National Audubon Society/Photo Researchers **152** Bob Llewellyn/Uniphoto Picture Agency **153** ATC Productions 1993/The Stock Market **155 T** Astrid & Hanns-Frieder Michler/SPL/Photo Researchers **155 B** Kim Taylor/Bruce Coleman Inc. **156** Geoffrey Nilsen Photography* **157 L** James Carmichael/Bruce Coleman Inc. **157 R** Robie Price* **158 TL** Buddy Mays/FPG International **158 TR** Buddy Mays/FPG International **158 B** David Parker/SPL/Photo Researchers **159** Robie Price* **160** Martin Rogers/Tony Stone Images **161** Geoffrey Nilsen Photography* **162** Geoffrey Nilsen Photography* **163** Robie Price* **164** Jeff Albertson/Stock, Boston **165** Anne Dowie* **166 L** Ken Karp* **166 R** Dennis Geaney* **167** Jeff Greenberg/The Image Works **168 T** Anne Dowie* **169** Robie Price* **170** Robie Price* **171** Robie Price* **172 T** Geoffrey Nilsen Photography* **172 B** Robie Price* **173** Robie Price* **174** Geoffrey Nilsen Photography* **175** Western History Department/Denver Public Library **176** Terry Qing/FPG International **177** Antman Archive/The Image Works **178** Corbis-Bettmann **180** Ron Cronin **181** Bill Stormont/The Stock Market **184 T** Geoffrey Nilsen Photography* **184 B** Robie Price* **185** Geoffrey Nilsen Photography* **187** Jon Feingersh/The Stock Market **188** McLaughlin Historical File 1/FPG International **189** Doug Pensinger/Allsport **190** Laima Driskis/Stock, Boston **192 L** Parker/Boon Productions and Dorey Sparre Photography* **192 R** Ken Karp* **194** Western History Department/Denver Public Library **195** Shaw McCutcheon/Bruce Coleman Inc. **196** Western History Department/Denver Public Library **197** Richard Price/FPG International **199** Western History Department/Denver Public Library **200** Alan Carey/The Image Works **201** Geoffrey Nilsen Photography* **205 T** Uniphoto Picture Agency **205 CL** Geoffrey Nilsen Photography* **205 TCR** Roy Morsch/The Stock Market **205 BL** Bob Daemmrich/Stock, Boston **205 BCR** Lawrence Migdale/Stock, Boston

Chapter 4 **206–207 (background)** Marc Romanelli/The Image Bank **206 T** Matthew Borkoski/Stock, Boston **206 L** Louis S. Glanzman/National Geographic Image Collection **206 B** Anne Dowie* **207 TL** Michael Macor/San Francisco Chronicle **207 TR** Richard Martin/Agency Vandystadt/Allsport **207 BL** Prim & Ray Manley/Superstock **207 BR** NASA **208 T** Jack Zehrt/FPG International **208 (background)** NASA/SPL/Photo Researchers **208 BL** NASA **208 BC** NASA/The Image Works **208 BR** Owen Franken/Stock, Boston **209** John Elk/Stock, Boston **210** Robie Price* **211** Michael Thompson/Comstock **212 L** Parker/Boon Productions and Dorey Sparre Photography* **212 R** Dennis Geaney* **213** Robie Price* **214** Jerry Wachter/Photo Researchers **215** Donald Carroll/The Image Bank **216** Chuck Place/The Image Bank **217** Andy Snyder/San Francisco Zoo **218 T** Robie Price* **218 C** Robie Price* **218 B** Steve Dunwell/The Image Bank

219 T Telegraph Colour Library/FPG International **219 B** Norman O. Tomalin/Bruce Coleman Inc. **220** Robie Price* **221** Geoffrey Nilsen Photography* **222** Robie Price* **223 T** Anne Dowie* **223 B** Robie Price* **224** Susan Kuklin/Photo Researchers **225 CL** Yellow Dog Prods./The Image Bank **225 R** John Elk/Stock, Boston **225 BL** Ted Russell/The Image Bank **227 (foregound)** Cheryl Fenton* **227** Kunio Owaki/The Stock Market **228** Julie Houck/Stock, Boston **230** Robie Price **231** NMAA, Smithsonian Institution/Art Resource, NY **233** Comstock **236** Geoffrey Nilsen Photography* **237** Anne Dowie* **239 L** Ken Karp* **239 R** Ken Karp* **241** Robie Price* **243 (foreground)** Cheryl Fenton* **243** Kunio Owaki/The Stock Market **246** Pictor/Uniphoto Picture Agency **247 BL** Robie Price* **247 BR** Robie Price* **248 TR** Arthur Tilley/FPG International **248 BL** Cheryl Fenton* **248 BR** David Sams/Stock, Boston **249 R** FPG International **250** Walter Iooss/The Image Bank **251 BL** Cheryl Fenton* **251 BR** Cheryl Fenton* **252 L** Georg Gerster/Comstock **253** James Carmichael/The Image Bank **254** James Blank/The Stock Market **256 L** Dennis Geaney* **256 R** Parker/Boon Productions and Dorey Sparre Photography* **257 TL** Mark Antman/The Image Works **257 TLC** Cheryl Fenton* **257 TRC** Cheryl Fenton* **257 TR** Andrea Pistolesi/The Image Bank **257 BL** Cheryl Fenton* **257 BR** Cheryl Fenton* **259 TL** Corbis-Bettmann **259 CL** Corbis-Bettmann **261** Geoffrey Nilsen Photography*

Chapter 5 **266–267 (background)** Pierre-Yves Goavec/The Image Bank **266 L** Geoffrey Nilsen Photography* **266 R** Kevin Schafer/Tony Stone Images **267 T** Cheryl Fenton* **267 B** Ellen Beach/Bruce Coleman Inc. **268** Robie Price* **69** NASA **270** Dennis O'Clair/Tony Stone Images **272** Peggy and Ronald Barnett/The Stock Market **274 T** FPG International **274 BL** George Hunter/Tony Stone Images **274 BR** ET Archive/Superstock **275** RLC Trust/Superstock **277 L** Ken Karp* **277 R** Parker/Boon Productions and Dorey Sparre Photography* **279** M. Fischer/Art Resource, NY **280** Pekka Parviainen/SPL/Photo Researchers **281** The Cartoon Bank, Inc. **282 T** Pat Lanza Field/Bruce Coleman Inc. **282 B** Superstock **283** Robie Price* **284** Anne Dowie* **285** NASA **286** Photri/The Stock Market **287** Cheryl Fenton* **288** Robie Price* **289** Cheryl Fenton* **290** Cheryl Fenton* **292** Geoffrey Nilsen Photography* **293** Anne Dowie* **296** Cheryl Fenton* **297** AKG/Superstock **298** Anne Dowie* **300** Robie Price* **301** Anne Dowie* **302** Lee Snider/The Image Works **303** Geoffrey Nilsen Photography* **304 B** Superstock **304 T** M. Greenlar/The Image Works **305** Cheryl Fenton* **308 T** Anne Dowie* **308 B** Cheryl Fenton* **309** Cheryl Fenton* **310** Parker/Boon Productions and Dorey Sparre Photography* **312 L** V. Rouse/Southern Card & Novelty, Inc. **312 R** Rindy Nyberg/Southern Card & Novelty, Inc. **313** Cheryl Fenton* **314** Robie Price* **315** Geoffrey Nilsen Photography* **319** Larry Gatz/The Image Bank

Chapter 6 **320–321 (background)** John Elk/Stock, Boston **320 L** Snowdon/Hoyer/Focus/Woodfin Camp & Associates **320 TR** Robie Price* **320 BR** Jane Grushow/Grant Heilman Photography **321 T** Townsend P. Dickinson/Comstock **321 B** Tom Till/Tony Stone Images **322 T** Hans Pfletschinger/Peter Arnold, Inc. **322 BL** Myron J. Dorf/The Stock Market **322 BR** Cheryl Fenton* **324** Geoffrey Nilsen Photography* **325** AP/Wide World Photos **327** Pictos/Uniphoto Picture Agency **328** Anne Dowie* **329** Robie Price* **330** Anne Dowie* **331** David Scharf **332** Geoffrey Nilsen Photography* **333** Texas Instruments **334** Dave Watts/Tom Stack & Associates **335 L** SIU/Peter Arnold, Inc. **335 R** Robie Price* **337** Jay Freis/The Image Bank **338** Larry Mulvehill/Photo Researchers **340** Michael Tamborrino/FPG International **341** Tom Dietrich/Tony Stone Images **342** Kevin Horan/Tony Stone Images **343** Owen Franken/Stock, Boston **344** Tom Till/DRK Photo **346** Peter Beck/The Stock Market **347** Library of Congress/Superstock **348 L** Thomas Dimock/The Stock Market **348** R Lori Adamski Peek/Tony Stone Images **349** MacTavish/Comstock **350** Robie Price* **351 L** Bob Burch/Bruce Coleman Inc. **351 R** Culver Pictures **352** Parker/Boon Productions and Dorey Sparre Photography* **353** Anne Dowie* **355** Tom Dietrich/Tony Stone Images **356** UPI/Corbis-Bettmann **357** Geoffrey Nilsen Photography*

Chapter 7 **362–363 (background)** Geoffrey Nilsen Photography* **362 TL** Dimitri Messinis/Agence France/Corbis-Bettmann **362 TR** Michele Burgess/The Stock Market **362 BL** Bill Bachmann/The Image Works **362 BR** Ken Cole/Earth Scenes **363 T** David Woodfall/Tony Stone Images **363 BL** Culver Pictures **363 BR** Draeger/Culver Pictures **364** Bruce M. Herman/Photo Researchers **365** Lawrence Migdale/Stock, Boston **365 (background)** Jeff Schultz/AlaskaStock **366** Grant Heilman Photography **367** R. Dahlquist/Superstock **368** George F. Godfrey/Earth Scenes **369 L** Archive Photos **369 R** Kunio Owaki/The Stock Market **370** M. Timothy O'Keefe/Bruce Coleman Inc. **371** Robert A. Tyrrell **372 L** Dennis Geaney* **372 R** Ken Karp* **373** Geoffrey Nilsen Photography* **374 L** Renee Stockdale/Animals, Animals **374 R** Karl & Kay Ammann/Bruce Coleman Inc. **375** David Hundley/The Stock Market **376** James Carmichael/Bruce Coleman Inc. **377** James H. Robinson/Photo Researchers **378** Robie Price* **379** Lawrence Migdale/Stock, Boston **379 (background)** Jeff Schultz/AlaskaStock **380** Akos Szilvasi/Stock, Boston **381** Steve Liss/People Weekly **381 (inset)** Stanley Tretick/People Weekly **382** Dean Siracusa/FPG International **383** Larry Brownstein/Rainbow **384** Parker/Boon Productions and Dorey Sparre Photography* **385** Kwok Leung Paul Lau/Liaison International **386** Robie Price* **387** John Eastcott/The Image Works **388 L** Culver Pictures **388 R** Simon Bruty/Allsport **389** Robie Price* **390** Geoffrey Nilsen Photography* **391** Texas Instruments **392** Stephen Frisch/Stock, Boston **393** Cheryl Fenton* **395** Geoffrey Nilsen Photography* **396** Bob Daemmrich/Stock, Boston **397 R** Steve Liss/People Weekly **397 L** The MIT Museum **398** Jack Daniels/Tony Stone Images **399** Geoffrey Nilsen Photography **403 TL** Cheryl Fenton* **403 TR** Bruce Wilson/Tony Stone Images **403 BL** Henry Ausloos/Animals, Animals **403 BR** David Madison

Chapter 8 **404–405 (background)** Bruce Hands/Comstock **404 T** Derek Berwin/The Image Bank **404 C** Art Resource, NY **404 B** Corbis-Bettmann **405 T** John David Fleck/Liaison International **405 BL** William Johnson/Stock, Boston **405 BR** Kim Taylor/Bruce Coleman Inc. **406 T** Cheryl Fenton* **406 BL** Robie Price* **406 BC** Robie Price* **406 BR** Robie Price* **407** Cheryl Fenton* **408** Steven H. Begleiter/Uniphoto Picture Agency **409** Cheryl Fenton* **410** Cheryl Fenton* **411** Bob Llewellyn/Uniphoto Picture Agency **412 L** Bob Daemmrich/The Image Works **412 R** Cheryl Fenton* **416** Ilene Perlman/Stock, Boston **418 T** Pascal Rondeau/Allsport USA **418 C** Ken Karp* **418 B** Parker/Boon Productions and Dorey Sparre Photography* **419** Cheryl Fenton* **421** Cheryl Fenton* **423** Cheryl Fenton* **424** Bard Wrisley/Liaison International **425** Cheryl Fenton* **427** Cheryl Fenton* **428** Pierre Boulat/Woodfin Camp & Associates **430** Cheryl Fenton* **431** Jenny Thomas* **432** Comstock **433** Cheryl Fenton* **434 L** Eduardo Garcia/FPG International **434 CL** Peter Menzel/Stock, Boston **434 CR** Archive Photos **434 R** S. Vidler/Superstock. **435 T** Dave B. Fleetham/Tom Stack & Associates **435 BL** Cheryl Fenton* **435 BC** Cheryl Fenton* **435 BR** Cheryl Fenton* **436** Bill Gallery/Stock, Boston **438** Archive Photos **441** Cheryl Fenton* **443** Adam Woolfitt/Woodfin Camp & Associates **444** Art Wolfe/Tony Stone Images **445** ©1994, Asian Art Museum of San Francisco **446 TL** Chris Arend/Tony Stone Images **446 TLC** Barry L. Runk/Grant Heilman Photography **446 TCR** Carl Zeiss/Bruce Coleman Inc. **446 TR** Noble Stock/International Stock Photo **446 B** Robert Fried/Stock, Boston **447** Wolfgang Kaehler/Liaison International **448** Bill Lyons/Liaison International **450 T** Richard Pasley/Liaison International **450 C** Parker/Boon Productions and Dorey Sparre Photography* **450 B** Parker/Boon Productions and Dorey Sparre Photography* **451** ©1994, Asian Art Museum of San Francisco **452** Will & Deni McIntyre/Tony Stone Images **453** Robie Price* **454** Barry Brukoff/Woodfin Camp & Associates **455 T** Sylvain Grandadam/Tony Stone Images **455 CL** A.K.G. Berlin/Superstock **455 CC** Cheryl Fenton* **455 CR** Wolfgang Kaehler/Liaison International **455 B** Bruce Hands/Comstock **456 T** Arvind Garg/Liaison International **456 B** Oddo & Sinibaldi/The Stock Market **457** Adam Woolfitt/Woodfin Camp & Associates **459** Geoffrey Nilsen Photography **462** Henryk T. Kaiser/Uniphoto Picture Agency

Chapter 9 **464–465 (background)** Gary & Vivian Chapman/The Image Bank **464 T** Bonnie Schiffman **464 B** Joe McBride/Tony Stone Images **465 T** John Lawrence/Tony Stone Images **465 B** Robie Price* **466** Cheryl Fenton* **467** Cheryl Fenton* **468 TL** James Elness/Comstock **468 TC** Parker/Boon Productions and Dorey Sparre Photography* **468 TR** Ken Karp* **468 BL** Parker/Boon Productions and Dorey Sparre Photography* **468 BC** Parker/Boon Productions and Dorey Sparre Photography* **468 BR** Dennis Geaney* **469 L** Charles Thatcher/Tony Stone Images **469 R** Glyn Kirk/Tony Stone Images **470** Chris & Donna McLaughlin/The Stock Market **471** Telegraph Colour Library/FPG International **472** Lambert/Archive Photos **473** Michael Collier/Stock, Boston **474** Ken Chernus/FPG International **475** Ken Karp* **476** Bob Daemmrich/The Image Works **477** Lawrence Migdale/Tony Stone Images **478** Ken Karp* **479** Comstock **481** John Eastcott-Yva Momatiuk/Stock, Boston **484** Don Smetzer/Tony Stone Images **485 L** Laurance B. Aluppy/FPG International **485 R** Cheryl Fenton* **487** Cheryl Fenton* **488** Bruce Silverstein/FPG International **493** Telegraph Colour Library/FPG International **494** Robert DiGiacomo/Comstock **496** Robie Price* **498** Ted Horowitz/The Stock Market

500 Parker/Boon Productions and Dorey Sparre Photography* **501** Ken Karp* **502** Jeffry Myers/Stock, Boston **503** Cheryl Fenton* **505** Geoffrey Nilsen Photography* **509 L** Andrew Unangst/The Image Bank **509 R** Gary S. Chapman/The Image Bank

Chapter 10 **510–511 (background)** Harald Sund/The Image Bank **510 TL** Steve Vidler/Superstock **510 C** Superstock **510 B** Chris Arend/AlaskaStock **511 B** Superstock **511 T** Cheryl Fenton* **512 T** C. M. Fitch/Superstock **512 BL** Patricia J.Bruno/Positive Images **512 BR** Margaret Hensel/Positive Images **513** Superstock **514** Bill Bachmann/Stock, Boston **515 T** Cheryl Fenton* **515 B** Ken Karp* **516 T** Gary Irving/Tony Stone Images **516 B** Cheryl Fenton* **518** Ken Karp* **519** Robie Price* **520** Parker/Boon Productions and Dorey Sparre Photography* **522** Stan Osolinski/Tony Stone Images **523 TL** Ken Karp* **523 TR** Cary S.Wolinsky/Stock, Boston **523 B** Jack Daniels/Tony Stone Images **525** Kent Knudson/Stock, Boston **527** Superstock **528** Cheryl Fenton* **529** Scott Barrow/Superstock **530** Cary Wolinsky/Stock, Boston **531** Christian Michaels/FPG International **532** Jonathan Wright/Bruce Coleman Inc. **534 T** Liaison International **534 BL** Ken Karp* **534 BR** Rafael Macia/Photo Researchers **535** Russell D.Curtis/Photo Researchers **536 L** Mike Nazzaschi/Stock, Boston **536 R** S. L. Craig, Jr./ Bruce Coleman Inc. **537** Jack S. Grove/Tom Stack & Associates **538** Superstock **539** Paul Harris/Tony Stone Images **540** Dennis Geaney* **541** Robert Frerck/Tony Stone Images **542** Robie Price* **543** John Eastcott-Yva Momatiuk/Stock, Boston **545 L** Superstock **545 R** FPG International **547 L** Jerry Jacka Photography **547 CL** Jerry Jacka Photography **547 C** Ron Sanford/Tony Stone Images **547 CR** Chris Arend/AlaskaStock **547 R** Scott Barrow/Superstock **548** Jeff Gnass/The Stock Market **549 (background)** Art Wolfe/Tony Stone Images **549 T** Nancy Adams/Tom Stack & Associates **549 C** David M. Dennis/Tom Stack & Associates **549 BL** Roy Toft/Tom Stack & Associates **549 BR** Gregory G.Dimijian/Photo Researchers **550 L** Superstock **550 C** Ken Karp* **550 R** Ken Karp* **554** Spencer Grant/FPG International **555** Robie Price* **556 L** Fritz Prenzel/Animals, Animals **556 R** John Cancalosi/Stock, Boston **558** Superstock **559** Jeff Lepore/Photo Researchers **560 T** P. Curto/U.P./ Bruce Coleman Inc. **560 C** Parker/Boon Productions and Dorey Sparre Photography* **560 B** Parker/Boon Productions and Dorey Sparre Photography* **562** David Austen/Stock, Boston **563** Keith Wood/Tony Stone Images **564** Philippe Plailly/Eurelios/SPL/Photo Researchers **565** Ken Karp* **566 T** Cheryl Fenton* **566 B** Robert A. Tyrell **569 CR** Stuart Westmorland/Tony Stone Images **569 BL** Art Wolfe/Tony Stone Images **569 TR** Art Wolfe/ Tony Stone Images **569 BC** Rodolpho Machado/ Nexus/DDB Stock Photo **569 BR** Gail Shumway/ FPG International **571** Geoffrey Nilsen Photography*

Chapter 11 **576–577 (background)** Geoffrey Nilsen Photography* **576 TL** Mark Segal/Tony Stone Images **576 TR** Christie's Image, London/Superstock **576 BL** Geoffrey Nilsen Photography* **576 BR** Ken Karp* **577 T** Superstock **577 B** Sylvain Grandadam/Tony Stone Images **578 T** B. Cavedo/Superstock **578 B** Ken Karp* **579** Geoffrey Nilsen Photography* **580** Richard Pasley/Stock, Boston **581 L** Corbis-Bettmann **581 C** Cheryl Fenton* **581 R** C. G. Maxwell/National Audubon Society/Photo Researchers **583 L** Joseph Nettis/Stock, Boston **583 R** National Gallery of Art, photo by Philip A. Charles **584** John Blaustein/Liaison International **585** Geoffrey Nilsen Photography* **586** Cheryl Fenton* **587** Geoffrey Nilsen Photography* **588** Superstock **592** Alan Carey/The Image Works **593** Robie Price* **595 L** Ken Karp* **595 R** Dennis Geaney* **596** Geoffrey Nilsen Photography* **599 L** Cheryl Fenton* **599 R** Geoffrey Nilsen Photography* **601** Mike Severns/Tony Stone Images **602** Alfred Pasieka/SPL/Photo Researchers **606** Frank Siteman/Tony Stone Images **607** Jane Burton/Bruce Coleman Inc. **608** Cheryl Fenton* **610** Michael Fisher/Custom Medical Stock **611** Robie Price* **612** Parker/Boon Productions and Dorey Sparre Photography* **613** Jeff Hunter/The Image Bank **614** Jeff Rotman/Tony Stone Images **615 L** Jeffrey Sylvester/FPG International **615 R** Mike Severns/Tony Stone Images **617** Geoffrey Nilsen Photography* **621 T** Robie Price* **621 B** Cheryl Fenton*

Chapter 12 **622–623 (background)** Cheryl Fenton* **622 T** Ken Karp* **622 B** Cheryl Fenton* **623 T** Cheryl Fenton* **623 B** Ken Karp* **624 T** Cheryl Fenton* **624 B** Rafael Macia/Photo Researchers **625** Paul & Lindamarie Ambrose/FPG International **626** Chuck Keeler/Tony Stone Images **627** Ken Karp* **628** Cheryl Fenton* **629** ChinaStock **630 L** John Coletti/Stock, Boston **630 R** Ken Karp* **631** George B. Fry III* **632** Warren Bolster/Tony Stone Images **633** NASA/GSFC/Science Source/Photo Researchers **635** Philippe Brylak/Liaison International **636** Howard Bluestein/Photo Researchers **639** Paul & Lindamarie Ambrose/FPG International **640** Ralph H. Wetmore II/Tony Stone Images **641** Cheryl Fenton* **642** Louis Bencze/Tony Stone Images **644 L** Dennis Geaney* **644 R** Ken Karp* **645** Cheryl Fenton* **646 T** Bob Daemmrich/Stock, Boston **646 B** Robie Price* **647** Ken Karp* **649** Cheryl Fenton* **650** George B. Fry III* **651 L** Ken Karp* **651 R** Michael Stuckey/Comstock **654** Ken Karp* **655** Cheryl Fenton* **656** Robie Price* **657** Geoffrey Nilsen Photography* **659** Cheryl Fenton*

*Photographs provided expressly for Scott Foresman-Addison Wesley.

Illustrations

Jenny Ahrens: **407a, 409g, 410o, 412a, 419n** Christine Benjamin: **142b, 205a, 223b, 518b, 664b** Ken Bowser: **538c, 584a** Barbara Friedman: **160a, 191a** Cynthia Gamo: **118a** Joe Heiner Studio: all icons and borders Barbara Hoopes Ambler: **622b** Marlene Howerton: **345d** Dave Jonason: **597a** Jane McCreary: **515b, 517a** Patrick Merewether: **273a, 524a** Karen Minot: **319d, 285a** Andrew Muonio: **23c, 61e, 70a, 225a, 255c** Bill Pasini: **179d, 183d, 186a, 235l, 258d, 439a, 545i, 554e, 557b, 565b, 567a** Matt Perry: **421a, 532b, 545j, 545k** Precision Graphics: All illustrative artwork throughout: all generated electronically Bill Rieser: **284a, 292a, 297b, 301a, 319b, 591d** Rob Schuster: **9a, 22a, 22d, 24a, 29b, 42a, 44a, 66a, 76a, 96b, 116a, 120b, 148a, 168b, 195a, 198b, 238d, 241b, 244e, 260i, 278a, 291e, 299a, 320c, 320d, 349a, 354a, 357a, 366a, 372e, 379a, 379b, 380a, 385b, 386a, 429a, 441a, 465a, 470b, 480e, 484a, 485a, 508c, 514a, 519e, 521a, 527c, 552b, 582q,r,s, 589c, 590a, 597i, 621a, 633f, 649b, 652b** Bob Ting: **492a, 503a, 509b, 571a** Joe Van Der Bos: **73c, 240l, 243a, 258b** Tom Ward: **7a, 16b, 37a, 38a, 74a, 92a** Sarah Woodward: **323a** Rose Zgodzinski: **525m, 563a, 592a**

Chapter 7

Page 371

7-2 Answers for Explore

1. a. $\frac{4}{5}$;

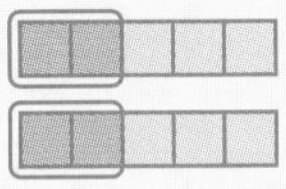

b. $3\frac{1}{2}$;

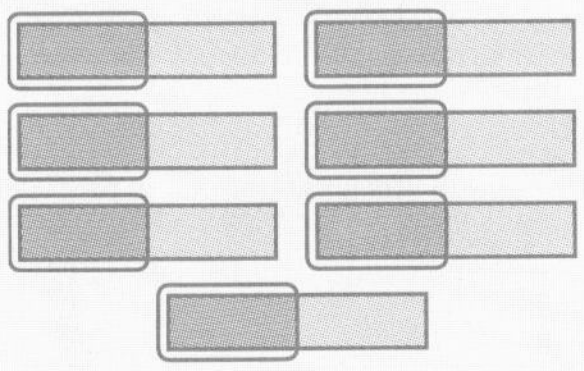

c. $3\frac{1}{3}$;

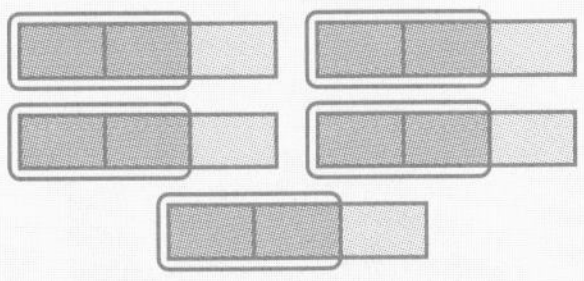

d. $2\frac{2}{9}$;

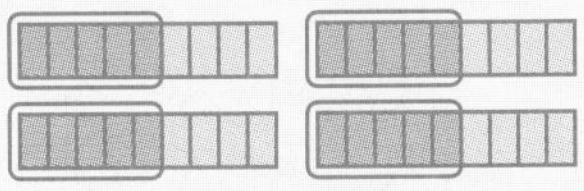

e. $2\frac{2}{5}$;

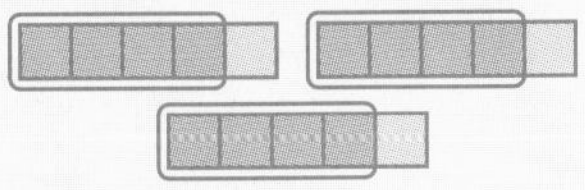

f. $\frac{2}{7}$;

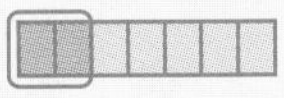

g. 6;

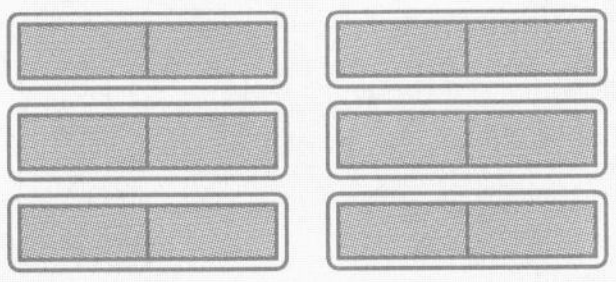

h. 1;

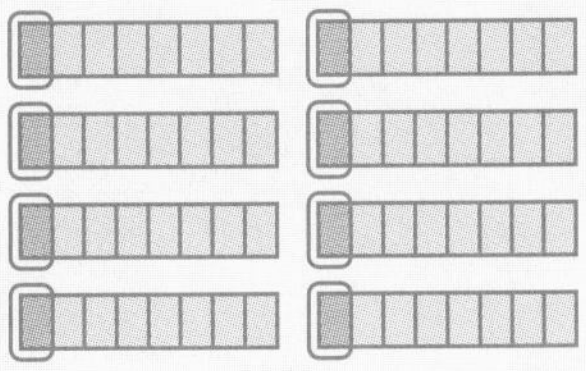

Page 376

7-3 Answers for Explore

1. a. $\frac{1}{6}$;

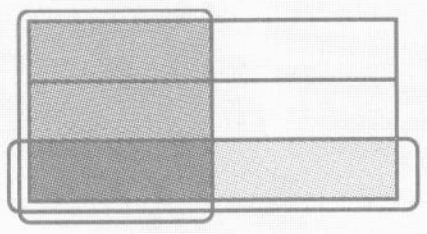

b. $\frac{2}{20}$ or $\frac{1}{10}$;

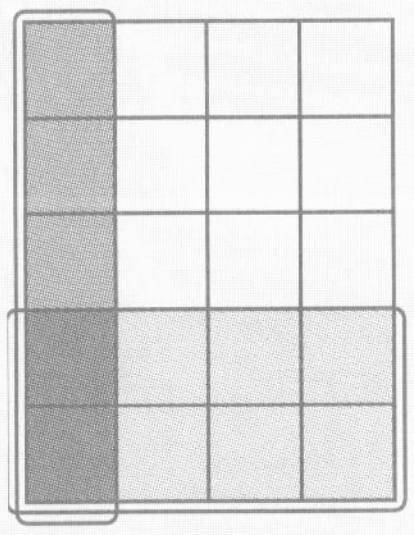

c. $\frac{10}{18}$ or $\frac{5}{9}$;

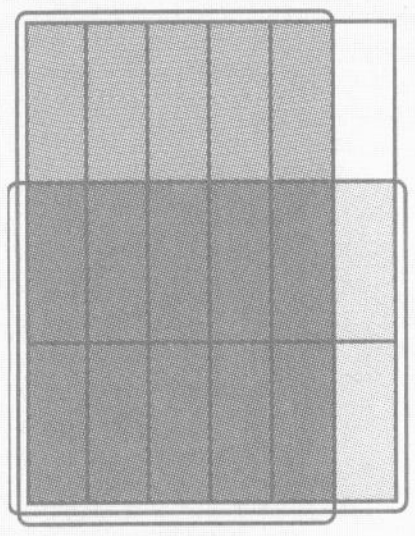

d. $\frac{4}{49}$;

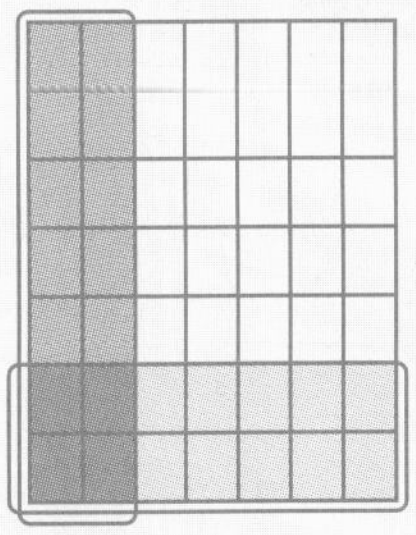

e. $\frac{3}{25}$;

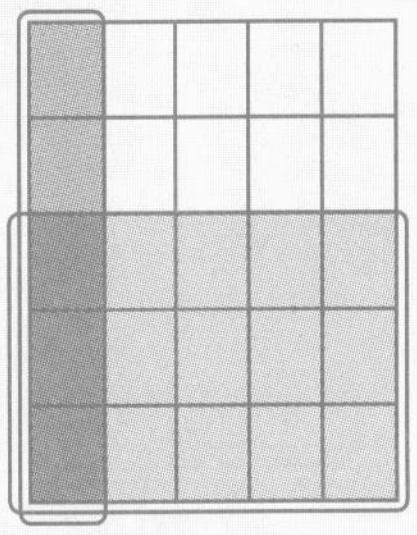

f. $\frac{5}{16}$;

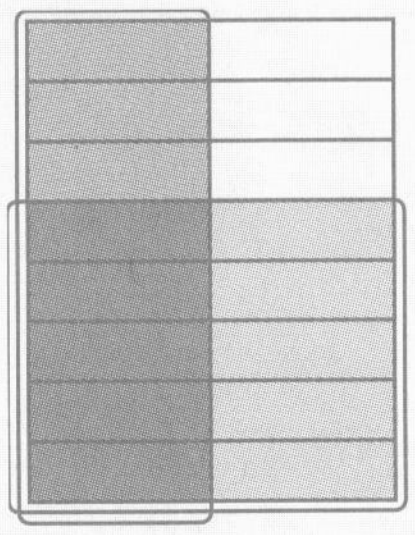

Chapter 8

Page 451

8-9 Exercise Answers

9.

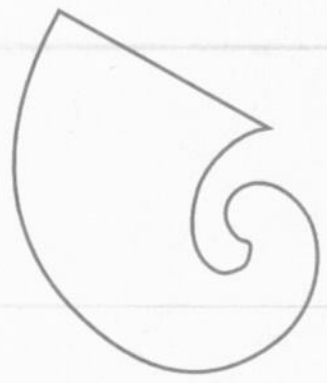

10.

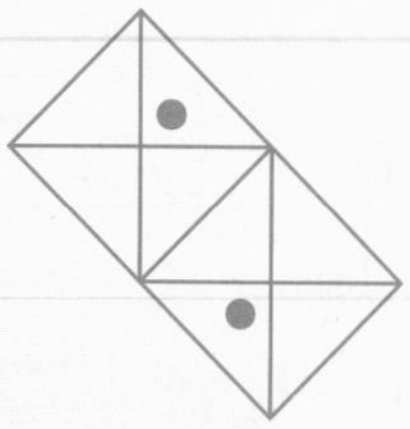

11.

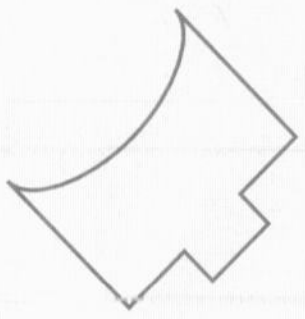

12.

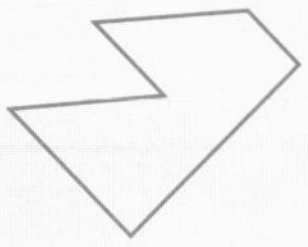

Page 458

Answers for 8C Review

17. No

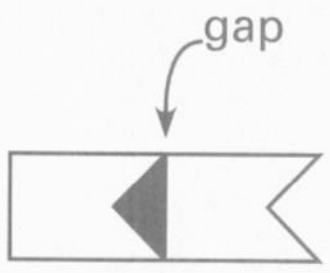

18. Yes

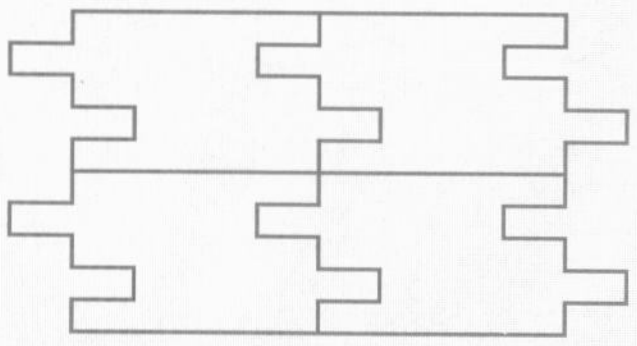

Chapter 9

Page 469

9-1 Answers for Explore

3.

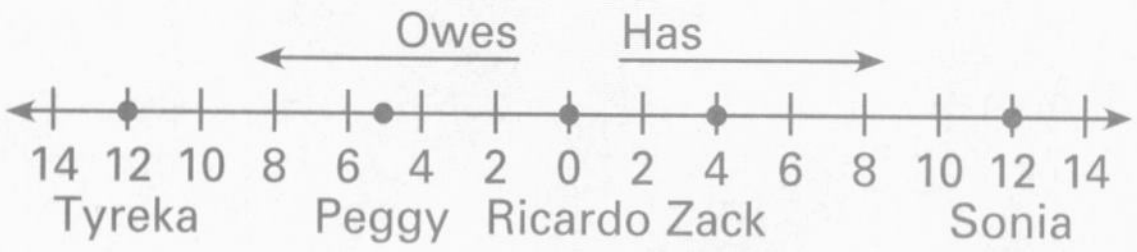

Page 482

9-4 Answers for Explore

2.

	A	B	C	D	E	F	G	H	I	J
1		-4	-3	-2	-1	0	1	2	3	4
2	-4	16	12	8	4	0	-4	-8	-12	-16
3	-3	12	9	6	3	0	-3	-6	-9	-12
4	-2	8	6	4	2	0	-2	-4	-6	-8
5	-1	4	3	2	1	0	-1	-2	-3	-4
0	0	0	0	0	0	0	0	0	0	0
7	1	-4	-3	-2	-1	0	1	2	3	4
8	2	-8	-6	-4	-2	0	2	4	6	8
9	3	-12	-9	-6	-3	0	3	6	9	12
10	4	-16	-12	-8	-4	0	4	8	12	16

Page 489

9-5 Answers for Try It

a. $A(2, 1)$; $B(3, {}^{-}4)$, $C(0, 5)$, $D({}^{-}1, 2)$, $E(4, 0)$, $F(1, {}^{-}3)$, $G({}^{-}2, {}^{-}3)$.

b.

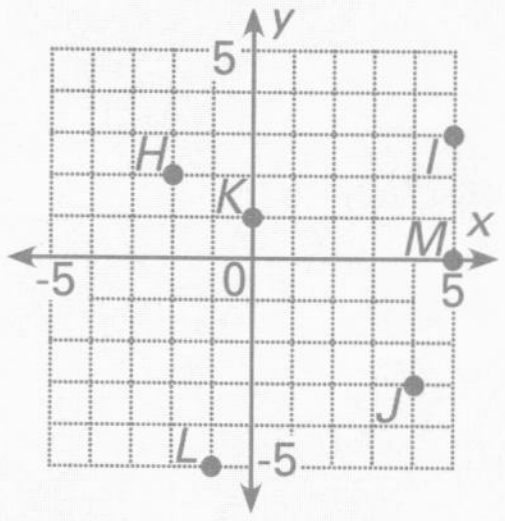

Page 496

9-6 Exercise Answers

13.

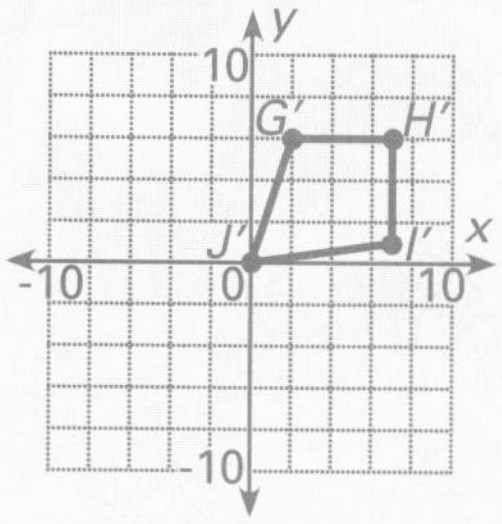

14.

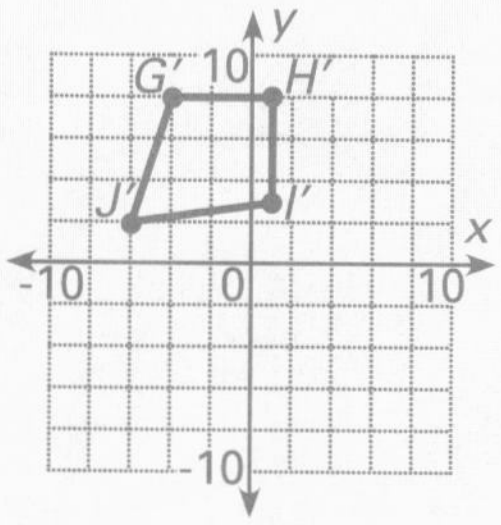

15.

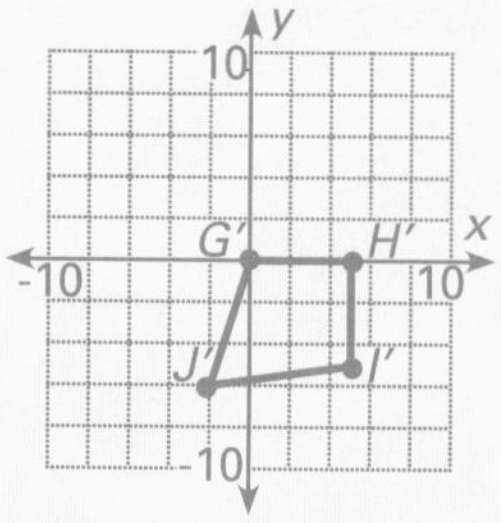

16.

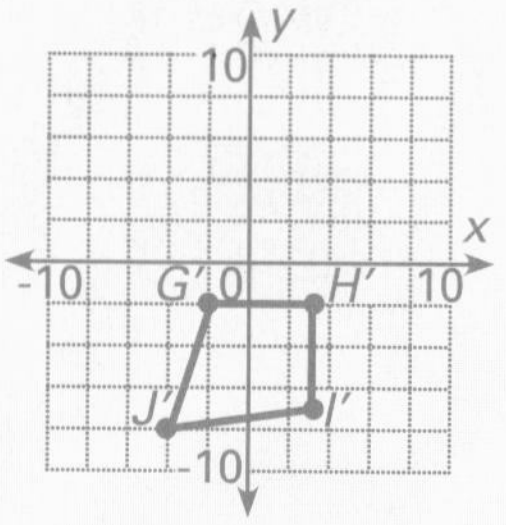

17. a.

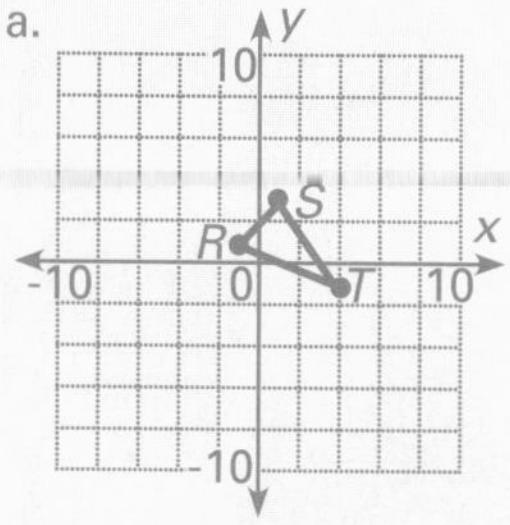

b.

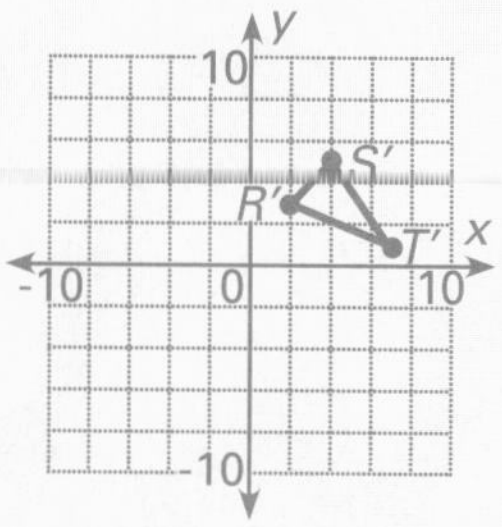

Answers continue on next page.

ADDITIONAL ANSWERS

19. a.

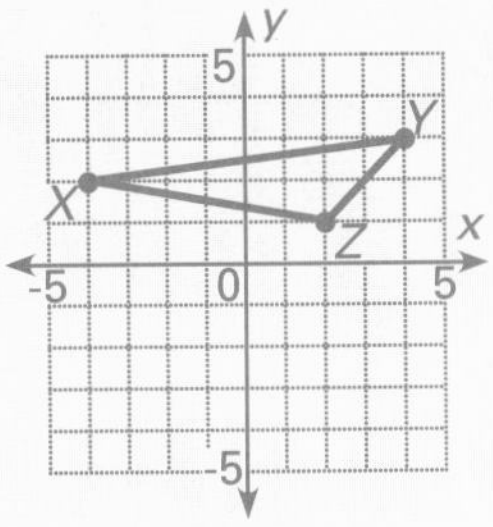

b.

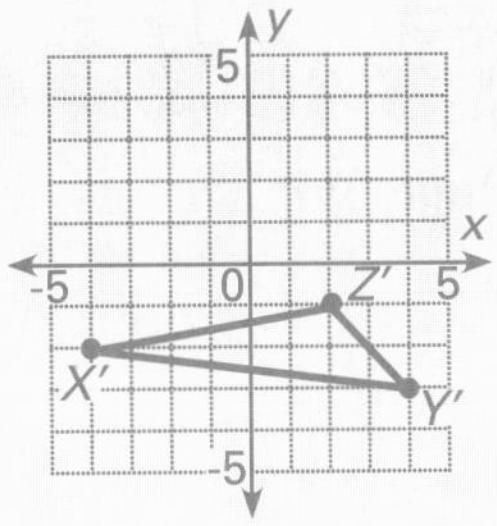

Page 499

9-7 Answers for Try It

a.

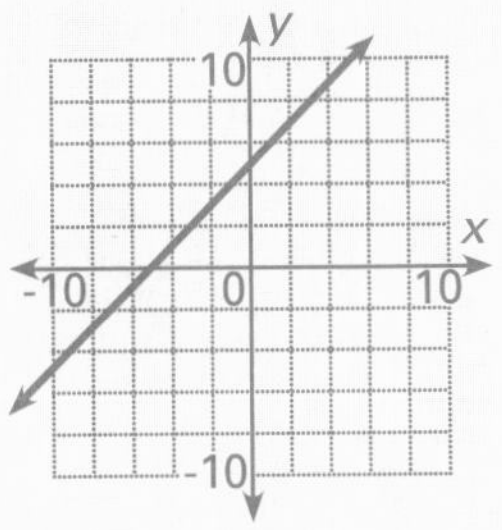

b.

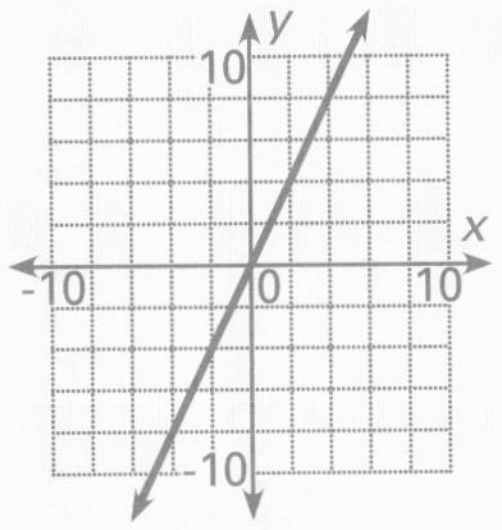

c.

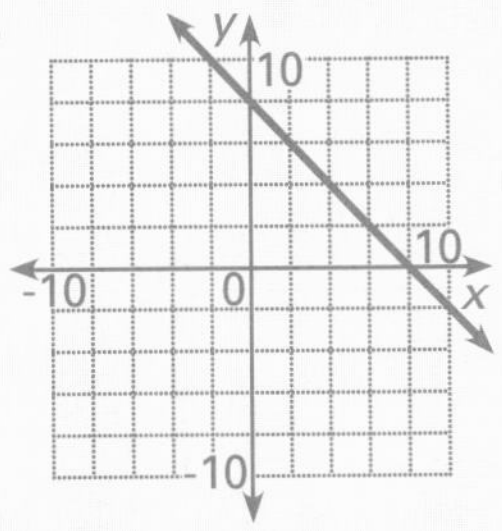

d.

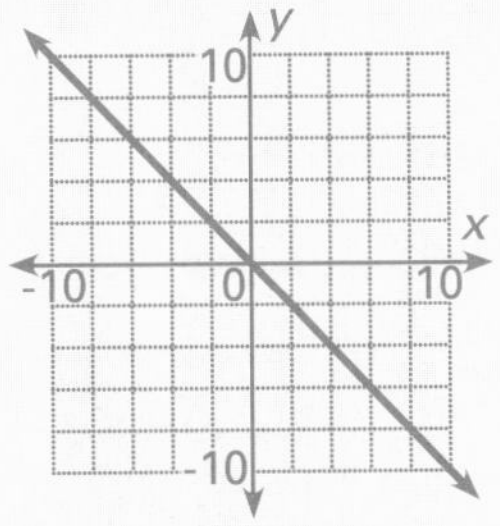

Pages 501–502

9-7 Exercise Answers

Possible answers for 2–6:

2.

x	y
-2	-55
-1	-54
0	-53
1	-52
2	-51

3.

x	y
-2	25
-1	26
0	27
1	28
2	29

4.

x	y
-2	-108
-1	-107
0	-106
1	-105
2	-104

5.

x	y
-2	100
-1	50
0	0
1	-50
2	-100

6.

x	y
-2	-24
-1	-12
0	0
1	12
2	24

7.

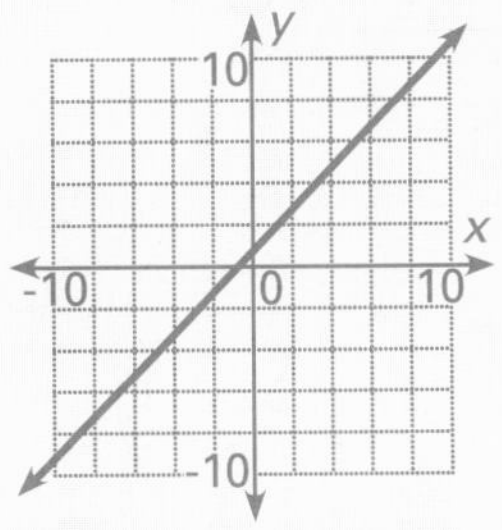

8.

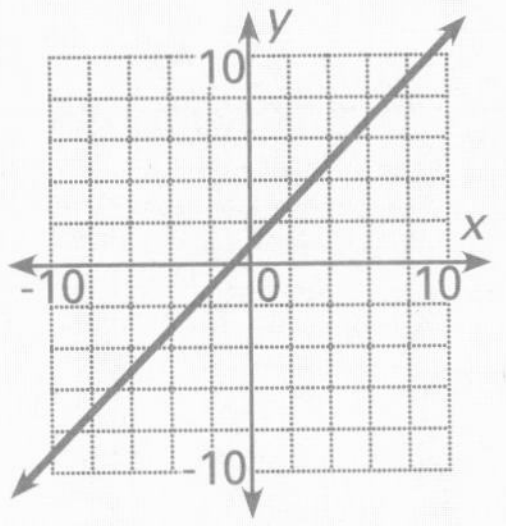

9.

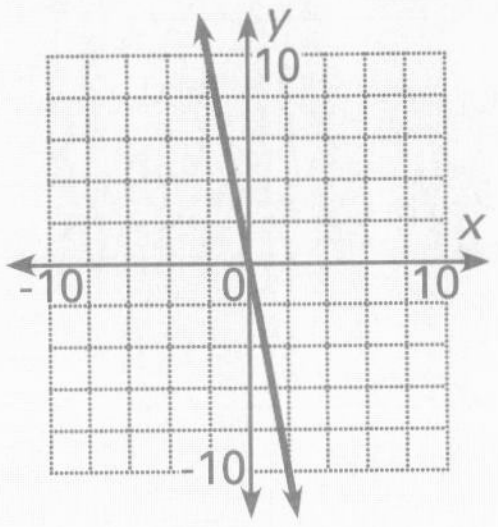

10.

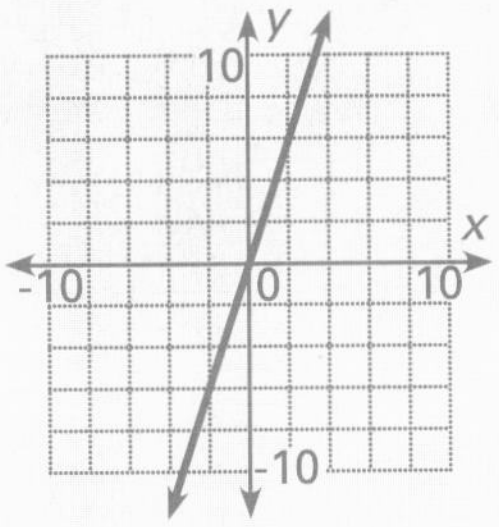

11.

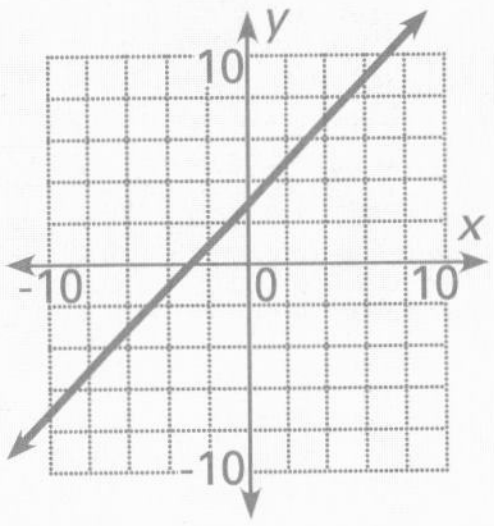

12.

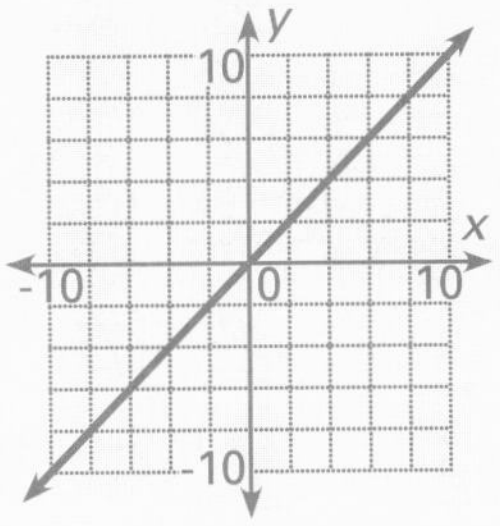

13.

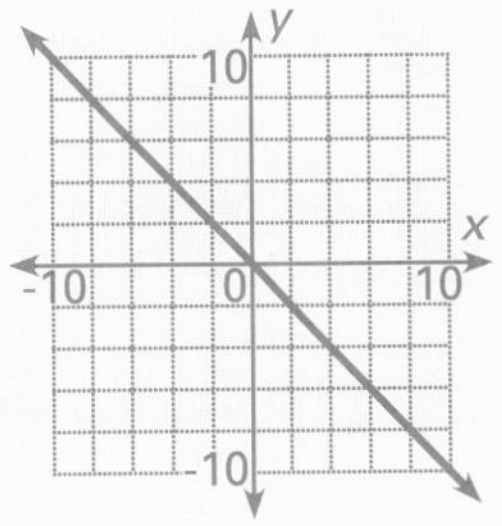

14.

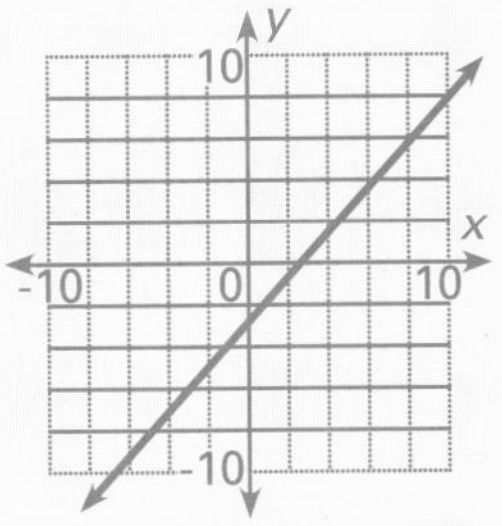

15.

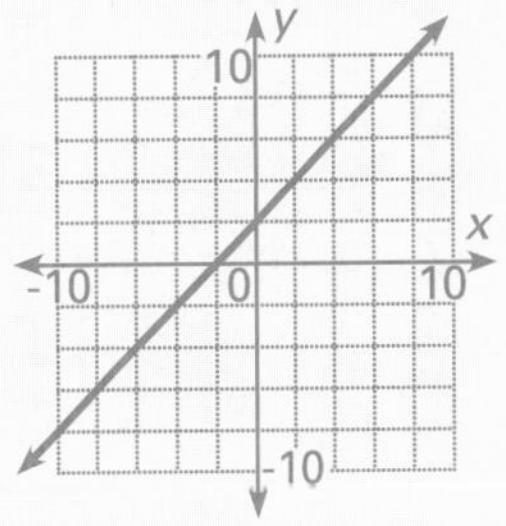

16.

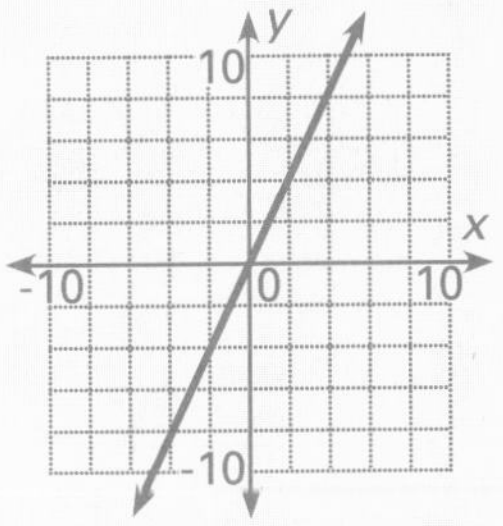

17.

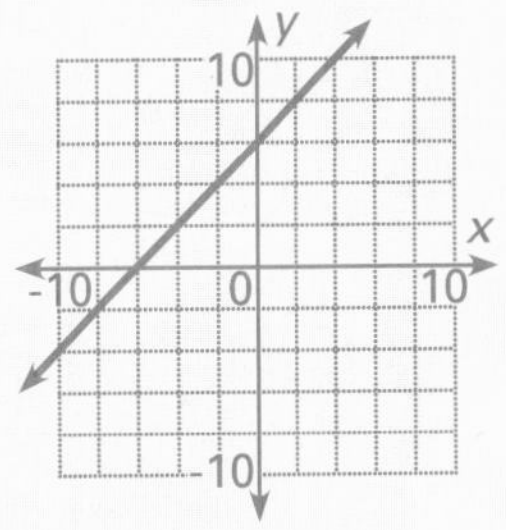

18.

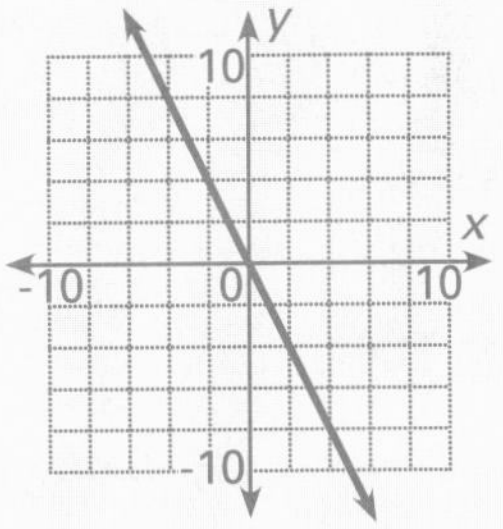

19.

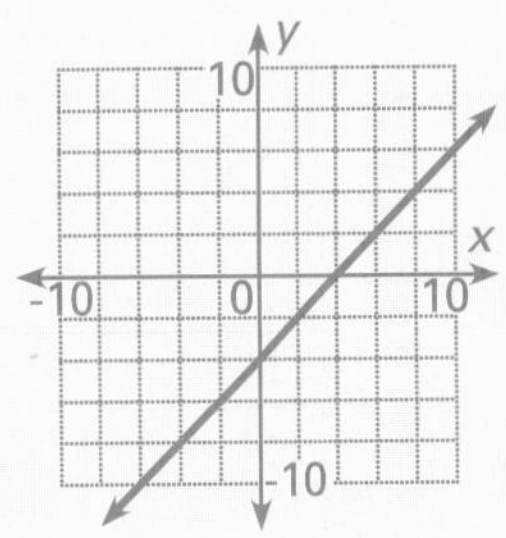

20.

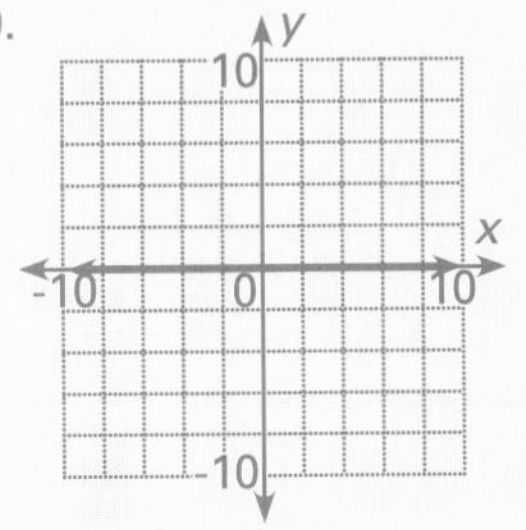

21.

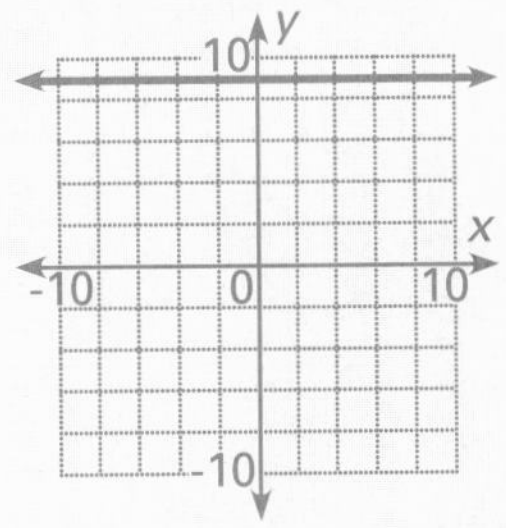

22.

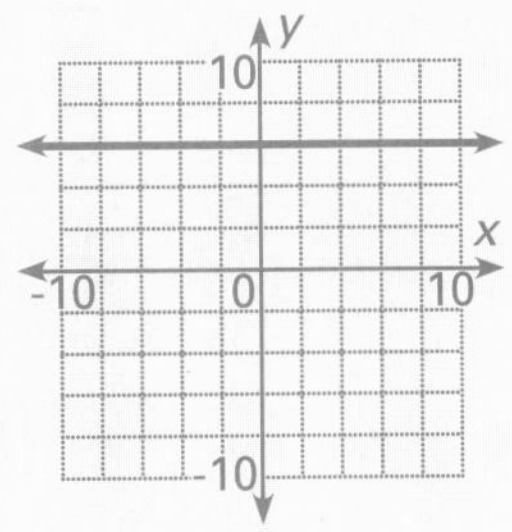

Answers continue on next page.

23.
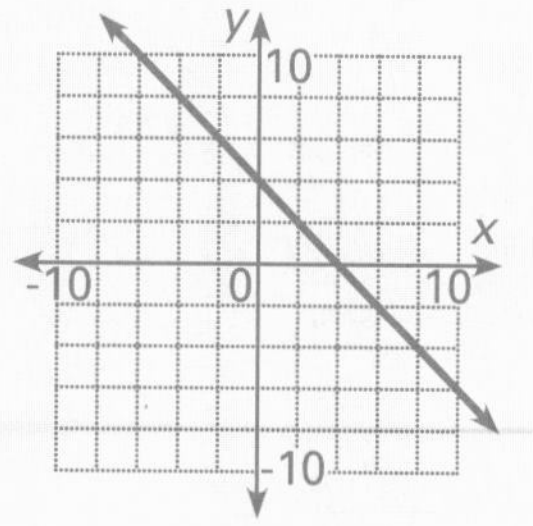

24.
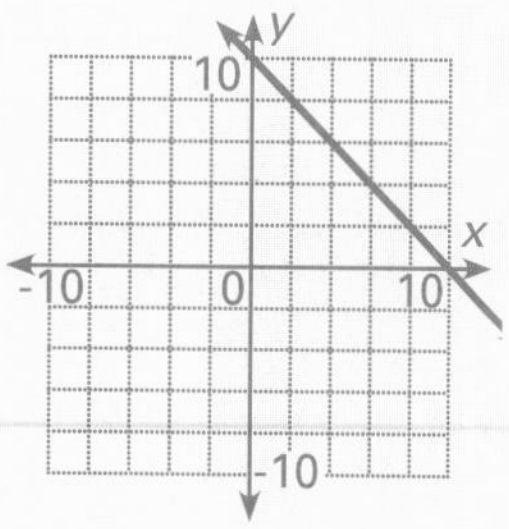

25.
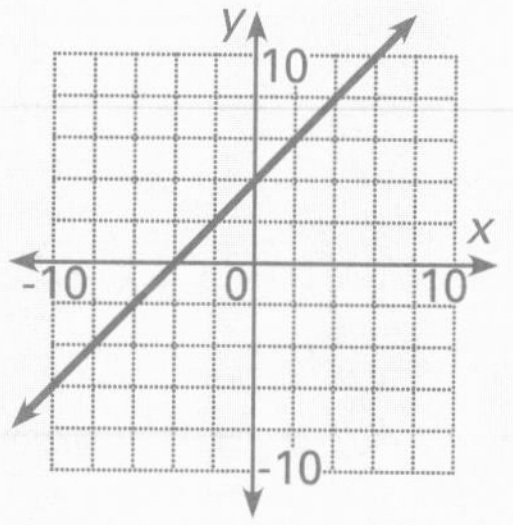

26.
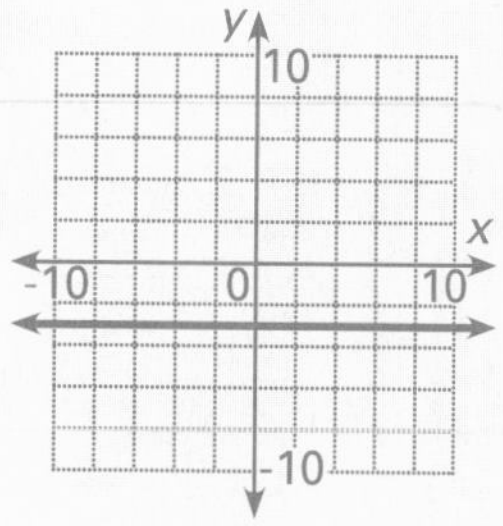

32.
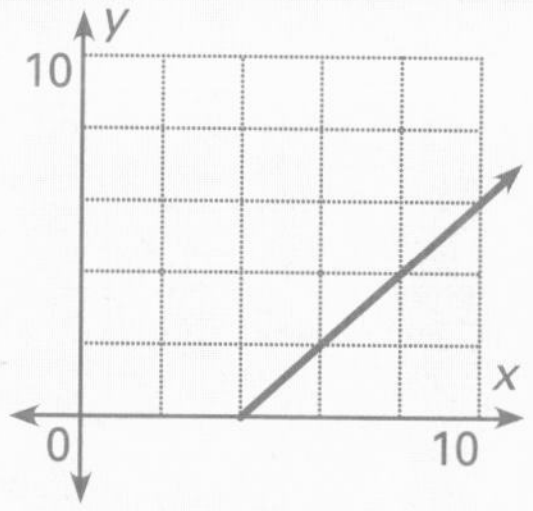

33.
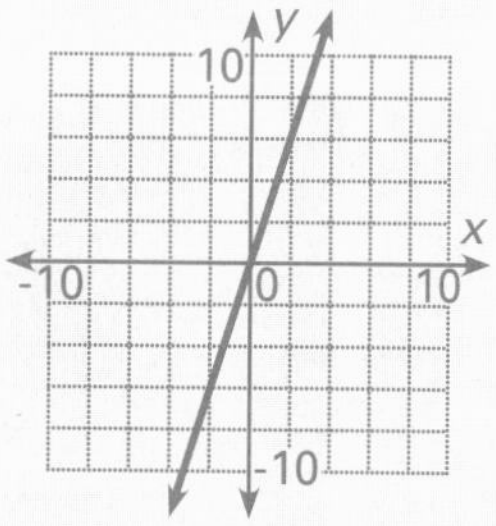

45.
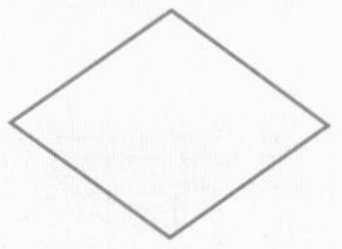

46.
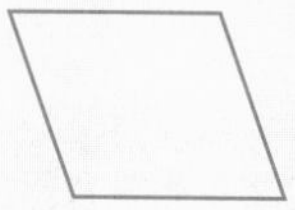

47.
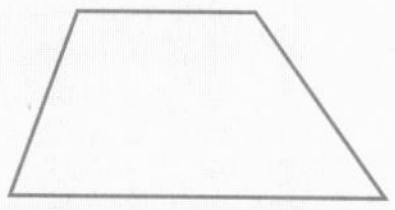

48.

49. Parallelogram, quadrilateral, irregular polygon.
50. Trapezoid, quadrilateral, irregular polygon.
51. Rhombus, parallelogram, quadrilateral, irregular polygon.
52. Square, rectangle, parallelogram, rhombus, quadrilateral, regular polygon.

Page 504

Answers for 9B Review

19.
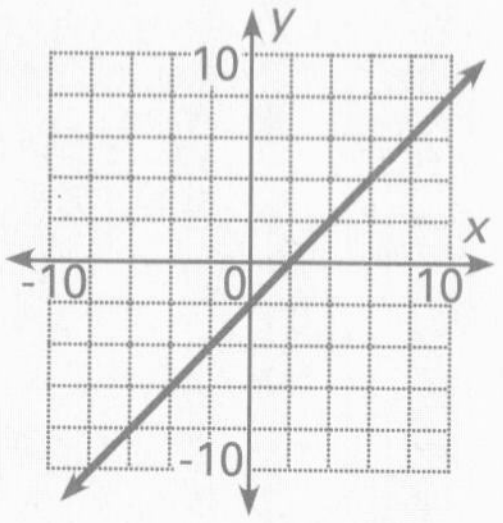

20.
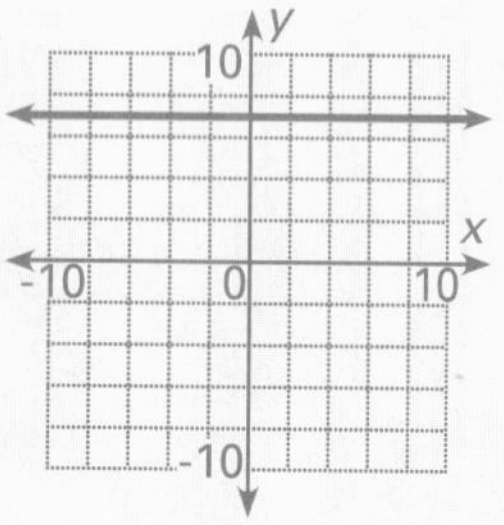

21. (2, 2), (2, 4), (4, 2), (4, 4)

22.
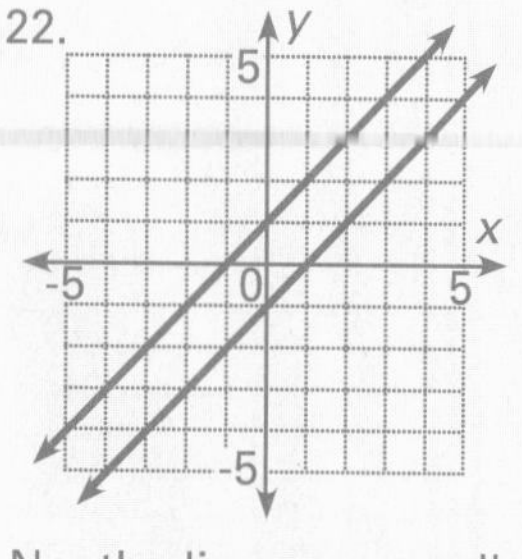

No, the lines are parallel.

Chapter 10

Page 557

10-9 Exercise Answers

33.
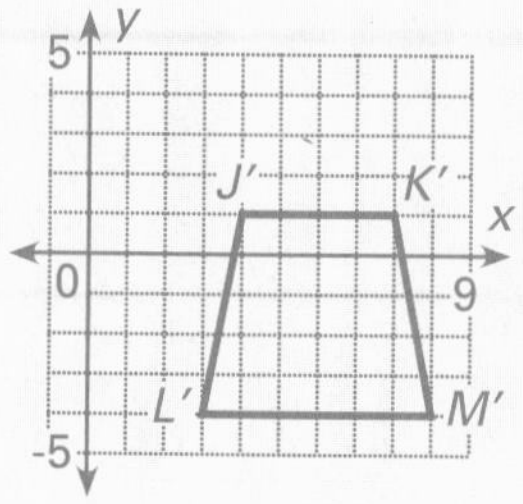

34.
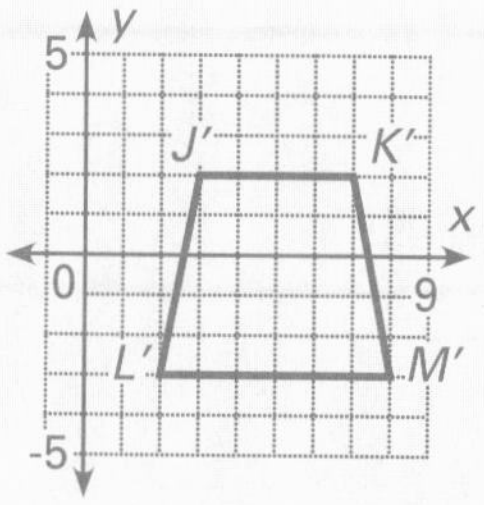

35.
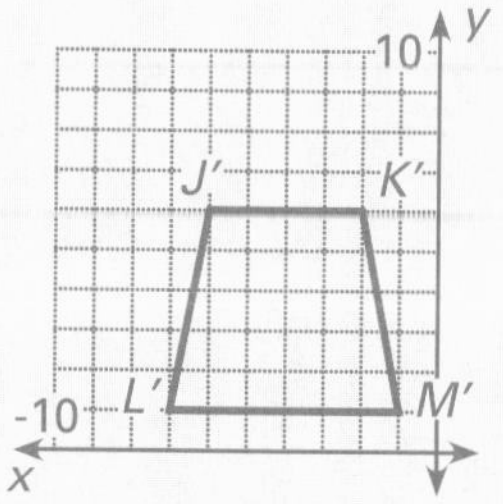

36.
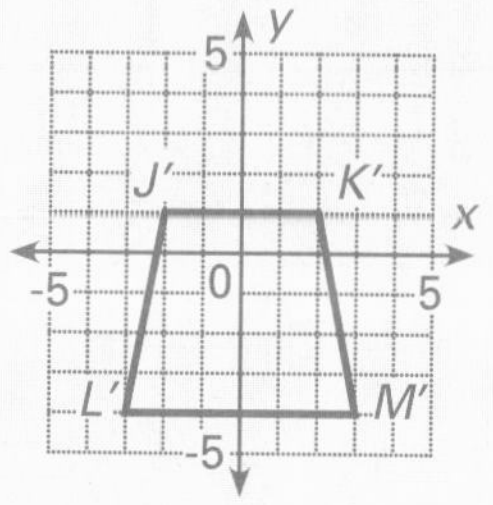

Page 559

10-10 Answers for Explore

3. a.
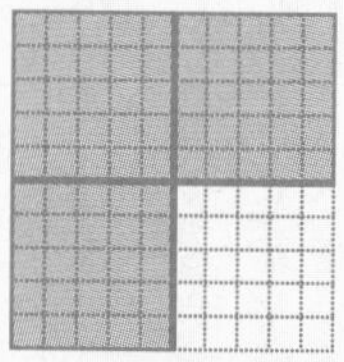

b.
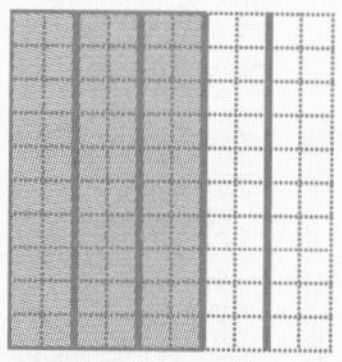

c.
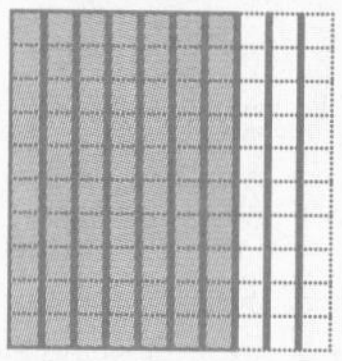

d.
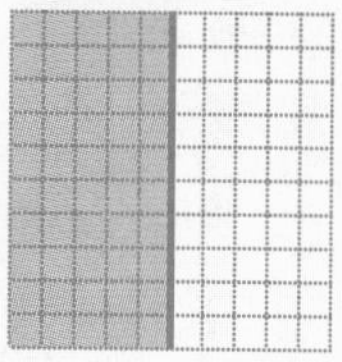

Page 562

10-10 Exercise Answers

63.
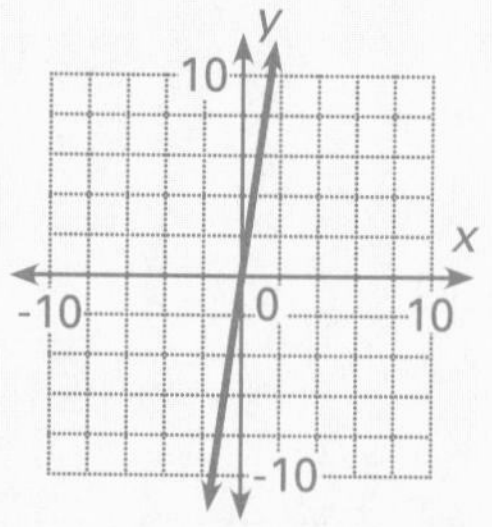

64.
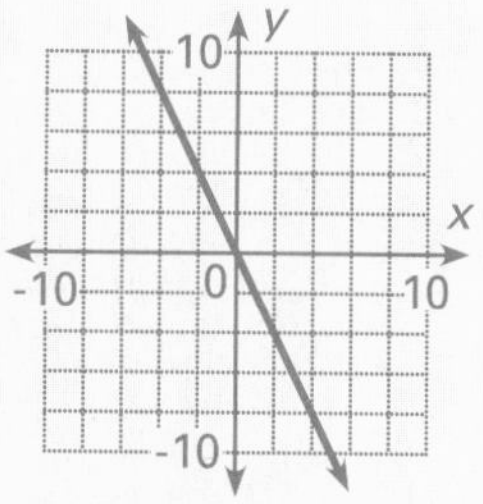

65.
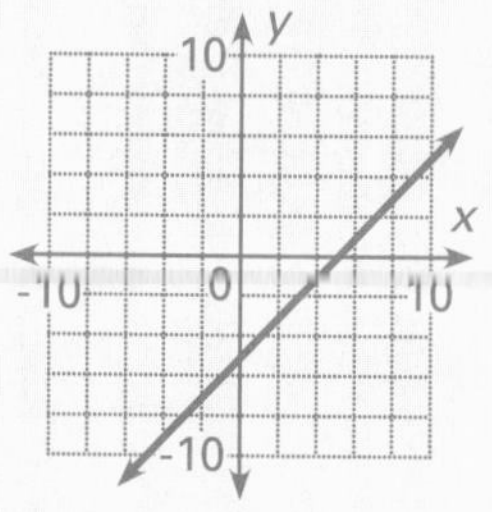

Chapter 11

Page 582

11-1 Exercise Answers

13.

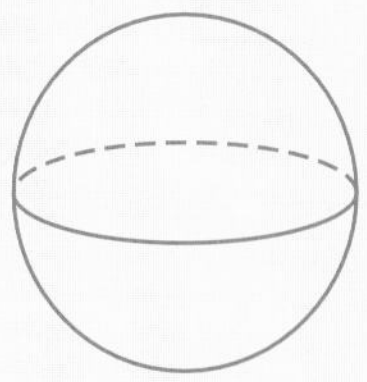

14.

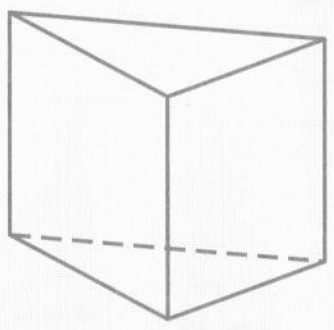

15.

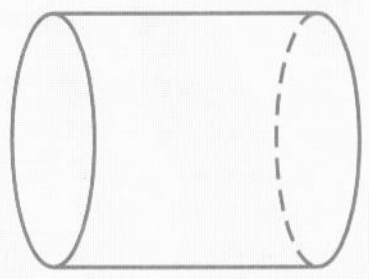

16.

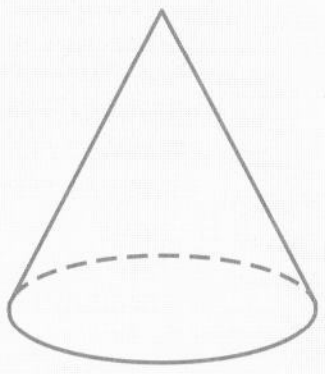

Page 604

11-5 Exercise Answers

7.

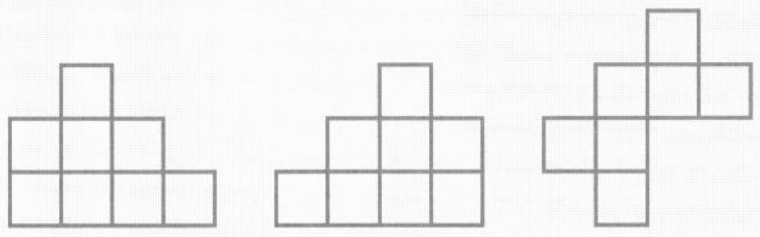

Front Side Top

8.

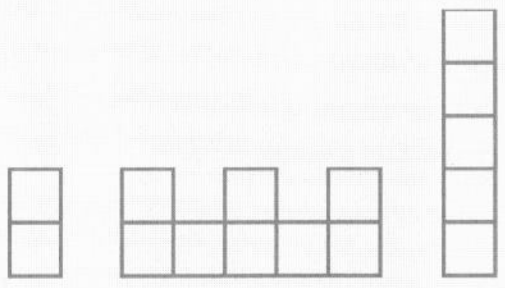

Front Side Top

9.

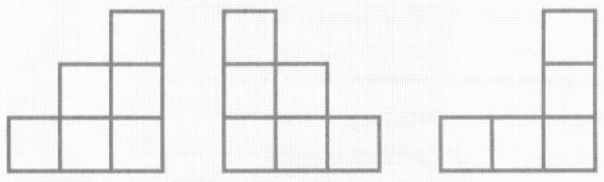

Front Side Top

10.

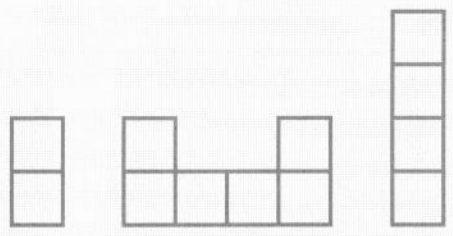

Front Side Top

11.

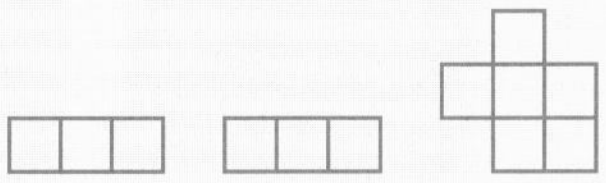

Front Side Top

12.

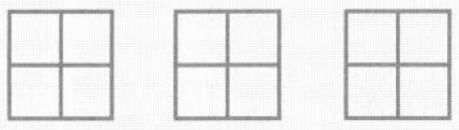

Front Side Top

Chapter 12

Page 643

12-4 Answers for Try It

a.
- Chocolate
  - Hot fudge = chocolate, hot fudge
  - Butterscotch = chocolate, butterscotch
- Vanilla
  - Hot fudge = vanilla, hot fudge
  - Butterscotch = vanilla, butterscotch
- Mint
  - Hot fudge = mint, hot fudge
  - Butterscotch = mint, butterscotch

Page 645

12-4 Exercise Answers

1. a–c.
- 1
  - Heads = roll 1, flip heads
  - Tails = roll 1, flip tails
- 2
  - Heads = roll 2, flip heads
  - Tails = roll 2, flip tails
- 3
  - Heads = roll 3, flip heads
  - Tails = roll 3, flip tails
- 4
  - Heads = roll 4, flip heads
  - Tails = roll 4, flip tails
- 5
  - Heads = roll 5, flip heads
  - Tails = roll 5, flip tails
- 6
  - Heads = roll 6, flip heads
  - Tails = roll 6, flip tails

d. 12 ways

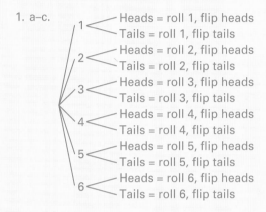

2.
- Bologna
  - Apple
    - Juice = bologna, apple, juice
    - Milk = bologna, apple, milk
  - Orange
    - Juice = bologna, orange, juice
    - Milk = bologna, orange, milk
  - Banana
    - Juice = bologna, banana, juice
    - Milk = bologna, banana, milk
- Peanut Butter
  - Apple
    - Juice = peanut butter, apple, juice
    - Milk = peanut butter, apple, milk
  - Orange
    - Juice = peanut butter, orange, juice
    - Milk = peanut butter, orange, milk
  - Banana
    - Juice = peanut butter, banana, juice
    - Milk = peanut butter, banana, milk

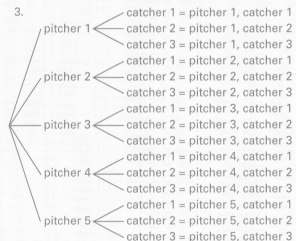

3.
- pitcher 1
  - catcher 1 = pitcher 1, catcher 1
  - catcher 2 = pitcher 1, catcher 2
  - catcher 3 = pitcher 1, catcher 3
- pitcher 2
  - catcher 1 = pitcher 2, catcher 1
  - catcher 2 = pitcher 2, catcher 2
  - catcher 3 = pitcher 2, catcher 3
- pitcher 3
  - catcher 1 = pitcher 3, catcher 1
  - catcher 2 = pitcher 3, catcher 2
  - catcher 3 = pitcher 3, catcher 3
- pitcher 4
  - catcher 1 = pitcher 4, catcher 1
  - catcher 2 = pitcher 4, catcher 2
  - catcher 3 = pitcher 4, catcher 3
- pitcher 5
  - catcher 1 = pitcher 5, catcher 1
  - catcher 2 = pitcher 5, catcher 2
  - catcher 3 = pitcher 5, catcher 3

Answers continue on next page.

4.

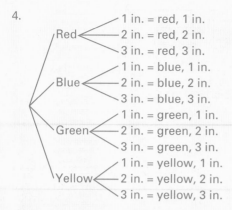

- Red
  - 1 in. = red, 1 in.
  - 2 in. = red, 2 in.
  - 3 in. = red, 3 in.
- Blue
  - 1 in. = blue, 1 in.
  - 2 in. = blue, 2 in.
  - 3 in. = blue, 3 in.
- Green
  - 1 in. = green, 1 in.
  - 2 in. = green, 2 in.
  - 3 in. = green, 3 in.
- Yellow
  - 1 in. = yellow, 1 in.
  - 2 in. = yellow, 2 in.
  - 3 in. = yellow, 3 in.

Page 654

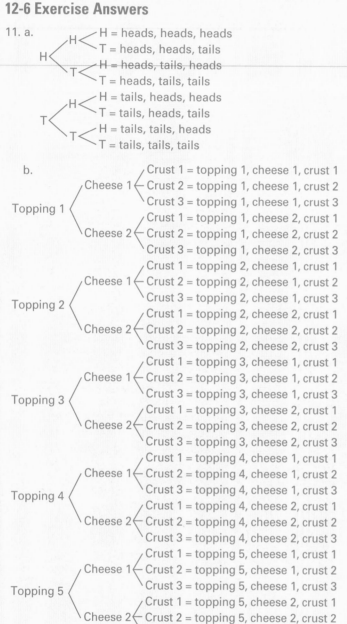

12-6 Exercise Answers

11. a.

- H
  - H
    - H = heads, heads, heads
    - T = heads, heads, tails
  - T
    - H = heads, tails, heads
    - T = heads, tails, tails
- T
  - H
    - H = tails, heads, heads
    - T = tails, heads, tails
  - T
    - H = tails, tails, heads
    - T = tails, tails, tails

b.

- Topping 1
  - Cheese 1
    - Crust 1 = topping 1, cheese 1, crust 1
    - Crust 2 = topping 1, cheese 1, crust 2
    - Crust 3 = topping 1, cheese 1, crust 3
  - Cheese 2
    - Crust 1 = topping 1, cheese 2, crust 1
    - Crust 2 = topping 1, cheese 2, crust 2
    - Crust 3 = topping 1, cheese 2, crust 3
- Topping 2
  - Cheese 1
    - Crust 1 = topping 2, cheese 1, crust 1
    - Crust 2 = topping 2, cheese 1, crust 2
    - Crust 3 = topping 2, cheese 1, crust 3
  - Cheese 2
    - Crust 1 = topping 2, cheese 2, crust 1
    - Crust 2 = topping 2, cheese 2, crust 2
    - Crust 3 = topping 2, cheese 2, crust 3
- Topping 3
  - Cheese 1
    - Crust 1 = topping 3, cheese 1, crust 1
    - Crust 2 = topping 3, cheese 1, crust 2
    - Crust 3 = topping 3, cheese 1, crust 3
  - Cheese 2
    - Crust 1 = topping 3, cheese 2, crust 1
    - Crust 2 = topping 3, cheese 2, crust 2
    - Crust 3 = topping 3, cheese 2, crust 3
- Topping 4
  - Cheese 1
    - Crust 1 = topping 4, cheese 1, crust 1
    - Crust 2 = topping 4, cheese 1, crust 2
    - Crust 3 = topping 4, cheese 1, crust 3
  - Cheese 2
    - Crust 1 = topping 4, cheese 2, crust 1
    - Crust 2 = topping 4, cheese 2, crust 2
    - Crust 3 = topping 4, cheese 2, crust 3
- Topping 5
  - Cheese 1
    - Crust 1 = topping 5, cheese 1, crust 1
    - Crust 2 = topping 5, cheese 1, crust 2
    - Crust 3 = topping 5, cheese 1, crust 3
  - Cheese 2
    - Crust 1 = topping 5, cheese 2, crust 1
    - Crust 2 = topping 5, cheese 2, crust 2
    - Crust 3 = topping 5, cheese 2, crust 3

Page 659

Answers for Review

6.

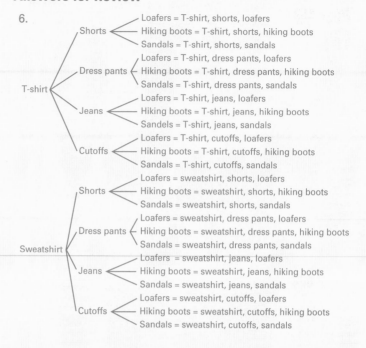

- T-shirt
  - Shorts
    - Loafers = T-shirt, shorts, loafers
    - Hiking boots = T-shirt, shorts, hiking boots
    - Sandals = T-shirt, shorts, sandals
  - Dress pants
    - Loafers = T-shirt, dress pants, loafers
    - Hiking boots = T-shirt, dress pants, hiking boots
    - Sandals = T-shirt, dress pants, sandals
  - Jeans
    - Loafers = T-shirt, jeans, loafers
    - Hiking boots = T-shirt, jeans, hiking boots
    - Sandels = T-shirt, jeans, sandals
  - Cutoffs
    - Loafers = T-shirt, cutoffs, loafers
    - Hiking boots = T-shirt, cutoffs, hiking boots
    - Sandals = T-shirt, cutoffs, sandals
- Sweatshirt
  - Shorts
    - Loafers = sweatshirt, shorts, loafers
    - Hiking boots = sweatshirt, shorts, hiking boots
    - Sandals = sweatshirt, shorts, sandals
  - Dress pants
    - Loafers = sweatshirt, dress pants, loafers
    - Hiking boots = sweatshirt, dress pants, hiking boots
    - Sandals = sweatshirt, dress pants, sandals
  - Jeans
    - Loafers = sweatshirt, jeans, loafers
    - Hiking boots = sweatshirt, jeans, hiking boots
    - Sandals = sweatshirt, jeans, sandals
  - Cutoffs
    - Loafers = sweatshirt, cutoffs, loafers
    - Hiking boots = sweatshirt, cutoffs, hiking boots
    - Sandals = sweatshirt, cutoffs, sandals

D

E

F

INDEX

INDEX